The restaurants included in
The Good Food Guide
are the very best in the UK.

Distributed by Combined Book Services Ltd
Unit D, Paddock Wood Distribution Centre, Paddock Wood, Tonbridge, Kent, TN12 6UU

Data management and export by AMA DataSet Ltd, Preston
Printed and bound in Italy by L.E.G.O. S.p.A.

A catalogue record for this book is available from the British Library
ISBN: 978 0 95379 837 7

Maps designed and produced by Cosmographics Ltd, cosmographics.co.uk
Mapping contains Ordnance Survey data © Crown copyright and database right 2018
UK digital database © Cosmographics Ltd, 2018. Greater London map and North and South London maps © Cosmographics Ltd, 2018. West, Central and East London map data © Cosmographics Ltd, 2018 used with kind permission of VisitBritain.

Consultant Editor: Elizabeth Carter
Editor: Amber Dalton
Content Producer: Ria Martin

The Good Food Guide makes every effort to be as accurate and up to date as possible. All inspections are anonymous, and main entries have been contacted separately for details. As we are an annual publication, we have strict guidelines for fact checking information ahead of going to press, so some restaurants were removed if they failed to provide the information we required. The editors' decision on inclusion and scores in *The Good Food Guide* is final, and we will not enter into any discussion on the matter with individual restaurants.

The publisher cannot be held responsible for any errors or omissions or for changes in the details given in this guide. Restaurants may close, change chefs or adjust their opening times and prices during the Guide's lifetime, and readers should always check with the restaurant at the time of booking.

We would like to extend special thanks to the following people: Iain Barker, Jackie Bates, Ruth Coombs, Alan Grimwade, Joanne Murray, Alan Rainford, Mark Taylor, Steve Trayler, Rochelle Venables, Ashleigh Vinall, Stuart Walton, Lisa Whitehouse and Blanche Williams. And thanks in particular to all of our hard-working inspectors.

thegoodfoodguide.co.uk

Contents

Introduction

Elizabeth Carter, consultant editor

To eat out in the UK today is to be overwhelmed by choice. This 68th edition of *The Good Food Guide* is stuffed with more brilliant new entries than I've seen in my 12 years as Consultant Editor. Whether these restaurants turn out to be forerunners of lasting change, only time will tell. But it's undeniable – we've come a long way since *The Good Food Guide* first appeared on the nation's bookshelves in 1951.

And I'm pleased to note that these new restaurants are spread right across the country. Picking the standouts is very difficult: in Nottingham, the brilliant Alex Bond, a protégé of Sat Bains, is demonstrating enormous skill every day at Alchemilla, quite an achievement given that the restaurant is in a fairly workaday part of the city. Impressive, too, is the Moorcock in West Yorkshire, where Alisdair Brooke-Taylor has converted an old boozer – right on top of a remote moor – that is already creating a buzz across the country.

A proliferation of exciting and diverse new entries means London continues to live up to its reputation as one of the world's most energetic and creative cities for eating out. In Shoreditch, Tomos Parry's hot-ticket Brat has given the former Kitty Fisher's chef more room to expand on his wood-fired obsession. Cornerstone, a seafood-focused venture from the gifted Tom Brown, has been a smash hit in seriously on-the-up Hackney Wick, an area ripe for restaurant gentrification. And Sam Herlihy and James Ramsden's Magpie joins Nieves Barragán's Sabor as one of several modern new openings that are helping to transform the Regent Street area.

Meet the new nines

The wide geographical spread of our Top 50 restaurants list (now in its twelfth iteration) is another reason to be cheerful. This year, two chefs whose careers we have been following closely since they won our *Chef to Watch* award have stood out. Both have redefined our ideas of good food and good restaurants. Indeed, Gareth Ward's promotion to a score of nine is something to shout about. The Ynyshir chef's original and extraordinary cooking demands to be considered among the very best. Every bit as confident and brilliant is Casamia's Peter Sánchez-Iglesias, our *Chef of the Year* in 2018, whose wonderfully light touch and meticulous craftsmanship add up to culinary excellence. The enormously talented Claude Bosi completes an impressive trio, regaining the nine he held at Hibiscus – his modern French cooking has helped make Bibendum a serious contender on the international food scene.

'This 68th edition of *The Good Food Guide* is stuffed with more brilliant new entries than I've seen in my 12 years as consultant editor'

And a new 10

Absent from the Guide for two years, and sorely missed, Clare Smyth is back with a smash hit. At Core in London's Notting Hill she has found a stage on which to show off her brilliantly artistic, deeply memorable creations, and we are delighted to welcome her back with another perfect 10 – a score she held previously at Restaurant Gordon Ramsay – joining Nathan Outlaw and Simon Rogan in that rather élite club.

The bigger picture

This is not the full story, though. You only have to glance at the headlines to see that 2018 has had its complications. Times are tough for restaurants: higher property rates, rents and increased labour and food costs have forced some operators to restructure their businesses or simply give up altogether (this year, the team at *The Good Food Guide* has logged a higher than usual number of closures). Chain restaurants are trimming branches and examining dated concepts, paving the way for highly affordable independents such as Bristol's Flour & Ash, which specialises in lovingly made pizza, or fresh pasta joints including Pasta Ripiena, Manchester's Pasta Factory and London's Pastaio or Padella.

Just as single-dish restaurants are attracting so much positive attention, the current crop of vegan restaurants has left diners wanting. Although more than a quarter of evening meals in the UK are vegan or vegetarian, some chefs have been slow to catch on to demand for plant-based dishes. What we need are more places like Gauthier Soho where chef Alexis Gauthier (a vegan convert), offers high-gloss modern French tasting menus in vegan and non-vegan versions. Or Tom Oldroyd who, with his meat-free Mondays, has set aside one day a week to offer dishes for vegans (and vegetarians) at his tiny self-named restaurant in Islington. Then there's Bristol's Box-E, which runs ticketed vegan takeovers in its harbourside shipping container, and The Olive Tree in Bath with its Vegan Seven menu.

Vegetarians are starting to get a lot more love, too. At the top end, places such as L'Enclume and Pollen Street Social have long offered good choice via dedicated tasting menus. Now, more affordable places are offering imaginative multi-course meat-free menus – among this year's new entries, The Small Holding in Kent and Liverpool's Röski stand out.

Waste not, want not

UK restaurants produce almost 200,000 tonnes of food waste each year, according to research by the Waste and Resources Action Programme (WRAP). Chefs with an eye on the bottom line try to avoid it, waste being neither good for restaurant budgets nor for the environment.

In Brighton, Douglas McMaster's Silo, with its 'reuse, reduce, share, repeat' mission statement, claims to be the country's first zero waste restaurant, and others are starting to follow suit. At Spring in Somerset House, Skye Gyngell has developed a pre-theatre

'The Guide's perennial strength is the integrity of its expert, anonymous inspections, coupled with continuous feedback from you, the reader'

'Scratch Menu' using kitchen scraps, vegetable trimmings, leftover cheese or yesterday's bread to craft dishes from ingredients that might otherwise be wasted. It's a similar story at Angela's in Margate, where what little isn't used in the kitchens is turned into compost for a community gardening project. I believe we'll see more restaurants showing a willingness to transform 'waste' into lovely things to eat.

Goodbye to all that

While 2018 has brought restaurant trends that we can all get behind, there are some aspects of dining out that are, frankly, baffling. Take incomprehensible dish descriptions, those pretentious lists of ingredients devoid of prepositions, participles or conjunctions that you have to ask waiting staff to explain: 'beef, sprouts, coffee' only invites puzzlement and a battalion of questions. Join us in calling for a ban on these inscrutable menus.

Keep in touch

The Guide's perennial strength is the integrity of its expert, anonymous inspections, coupled - inseparably - with continuous feedback from you, the reader. As each year brings new ideas, fresh thinking, and some great food, to discover it all we at *The Good Food Guide* need help from you to point us in the right direction. Be sure to tell us about your eating out experiences, both good and bad. If a restaurant does not have a clear recommendation from both our inspectors and readers, it will not go in - or stay in - the Guide. Working on this edition has shown me there is plenty to rejoice in, so please share your dining experiences with us at thegoodfoodguide.co.uk.

The chain gang

This year, we've chosen to take a different approach to how we inspect and review the (relatively few) chain restaurants that make it into the Guide. For restaurant groups in London with three or more sites, whose offering is broadly similar from branch to branch, we are now writing just one main review. We have, however, taken care to point out key differences between the sites: after all, the better restaurant groups are not in the business of churning out cookie cutter clones.

2018 was not a good year for chain restaurants. Many well-known names have fallen victim to the so-called 'casual dining crunch' that has decimated the midmarket. The press has been full of stories of those that have been forced to restructure and close branches to weather the perfect storm of rising interest rates, rents, high inflation and staff costs. It's heartening to note, then, that many of the restaurant groups we include in this year's guide are actually expanding and opening larger, more ambitious sites than ever.

It's not usually taken as a compliment to be described as a 'chain' but we'd argue that chains, groups, collections - call them what you will - have their strengths. The best of the bunch offer consistency, reliability, rock-solid staff training and a family-friendly approach that many independents would do well to emulate.

The Top 50

The UK's best restaurants

1. Restaurant Nathan Outlaw, Cornwall (10)
2. L'Enclume, Cumbria (10)
3. Core by Clare Smyth (10) *New*
4. Restaurant Sat Bains, Notts (9)
5. Ynyshir, Powys (9)
6. Claude Bosi at Bibendum, London (9)
7. Restaurant Gordon Ramsay, London (9)
8. Casamia, Bristol (9)
9. Pollen Street Social, London (9)
10. The Fat Duck, Berkshire (8)
11. Moor Hall, Lancashire (8)
12. Restaurant Andrew Fairlie, Tayside (8)
13. Adam Reid at The French, Manchester (8)
14. Bohemia, Jersey (8)
15. Le Champignon Sauvage, Glos (8)
16. Restaurant Story, London (8)
17. André Garrett at Cliveden, Berkshire (8)
18. The Ledbury, London (8)
19. Fraiche, Merseyside (8)
20. Roganic, London (8) *New*
21. Midsummer House, Cambridgeshire (8)
22. Alain Ducasse at the Dorchester, London (8)
23. The Peat Inn, Fife (8)
24. Marcus, London (8)
25. Dinner by Heston Blumenthal, London (8)
26. The Kitchin, Edinburgh (7)
27. Forest Side, Cumbria (7)
28. A. Wong, London (7) *New*
29. Orwells, Oxfordshire (7)
30. Sketch, Lecture Room & Library, London (7)
31. Hedone, London (7)
32. The Ritz, London (7)
33. Castle Terrace, Edinburgh (7)
34. The Three Chimneys, Isle of Skye (7)
35. The Waterside Inn, Berkshire (7)
36. Simon Radley at the Chester Grosvenor, Cheshire (7) *New*
37. Restaurant James Sommerin, Glamorgan (7)
38. Whatley Manor, The Dining Room, Wiltshire (7)
39. Matt Worswick at the Latymer, Surrey (7) *New*
40. The Raby Hunt, Co Durham (7)
41. The Greenhouse, London (7)
42. The Sportsman, Kent (7)
43. Restaurant Martin Wishart, Edinburgh (7)
44. Artichoke, Buckinghamshire (7)
45. Lake Road Kitchen, Cumbria (7) *New*
46. Adam's, Birmingham (7)
47. Morston Hall, Norfolk (7) *New*
48. Le Gavroche, London (7)
49. The Whitebrook, Monmouthshire (7)
50. Hambleton Hall, Leicestershire and Rutland (7)

Editors' Awards

The editors of *The Good Food Guide* are delighted to recognise the following restaurants and chefs for their talent and commitment to excellence.

Chef of the Year
Gareth Ward
Ynyshir, Powys

Chef to Watch
Alex Bond
Alchemilla, Nottingham

Restaurant of the Year
A. Wong
Victoria, London

Best New Entry, UK
The Moorcock
Sowerby Bridge, West Yorkshire

Best New Entry, London
Cornerstone
Hackney Wick, London

Best for Sustainability
Angela's
Margate, Kent

Best Local Restaurants

We asked our readers to nominate their favourite neighbourhood restaurants, places that give a warm welcome and share a passion for local produce, plus a commitment to the community. *The Good Food Guide* judges visited the finalists before selecting a winner in each region, plus an overall UK winner.

OVERALL WINNER
East England
The Old Bank, Snettisham, Norfolk

REGIONAL WINNERS
Wales
Hare & Hounds, Aberthin, Glamorgan

Scotland
Forage & Chatter, Edinburgh

Northern Ireland
Hadskis, Belfast

Midlands
Harborne Kitchen, Harborne, West Midlands

North East England
The Feathers Inn, Hedley on the Hill, Northumberland

North West England
Joseph Benjamin, Chester, Cheshire

South East England
Pulpo Negro, Alresford, Hampshire

South West England
The Three Tuns, Great Bedwyn, Wiltshire

London
Home SW15, Putney

How to use *The Good Food Guide*

In our opinion, the restaurants included in *The Good Food Guide* are the very best in the UK; this means that simply getting an entry is an accomplishment to be proud of, and a Score 1 or above is a significant achievement.

The Good Food Guide is completely rewritten every year and compiled from scratch. Our research list is based on the huge volume of feedback we receive from readers, which, together with anonymous inspections by our experts, ensures that every entry is assessed afresh. Please keep the reports coming in: visit thegoodfoodguide.co.uk for details.

Scoring

We add and reject many restaurants when we compile each guide. There are always subjective aspects to ratings systems, but our inspectors are equipped with extensive scoring guidelines to ensure that restaurant bench-marking around the UK is accurate. As we take into account reader feedback on each restaurant, any given review is based on several meals.

'New chef' in place of a score indicates that the restaurant has had a recent change of chef and we have been unable to score it reliably; we particularly welcome reports on these restaurants.

Local Gem

These entries highlight a range of brilliant neighbourhood venues, bringing you a wide choice at great value for money. Simple cafés, bistros and pubs, these are the places that sit happily on your doorstep, delivering good, freshly cooked food.

Readers Recommend

These are direct quotes from our reader feedback and highlight places that have caught the attention of our loyal followers. Reports are particularly welcome on these entries also.

Vegetarian and vegan

While many restaurants offer individual dishes suitable for non-meat eaters, those marked 'V menu' (vegetarian) and 'Vg menu' (vegan) in the 'Details' section of the entry offer dedicated menus.

The Good Food Guide scoring system

1 Capable cooking with simple food combinations and clear flavours, but some inconsistencies.

2 Decent cooking, displaying good technical skills and interesting combinations and flavours. Occasional inconsistencies.

3 Good cooking, showing sound technical skills and using quality ingredients.

4 Dedicated, focused approach to cooking; good classical skills and high-quality ingredients.

5 Exact cooking techniques and a degree of ambition; showing balance and depth of flavour in dishes.

6 Exemplary cooking skills, innovative ideas, impeccable ingredients and an element of excitement.

7 High level of ambition and individuality, attention to the smallest detail, accurate and vibrant dishes.

8 A kitchen cooking close to or at the top of its game. Highly individual with impressive artistry. There is little room for disappointment here.

9 Cooking that has reached a pinnacle of achievement, making it a hugely memorable experience for the diner.

10 Just perfect dishes, showing faultless technique at every service; extremely rare, and the highest accolade the Guide can give.

Symbols

We contact restaurants that we're considering for inclusion ahead of publication to check key information about opening times and facilities. They are also invited to participate in the £5 voucher scheme. The symbols against each entry are based on the information given to us by each restaurant.

£XX The average price of a three-course dinner, excluding wine.

£30 It is possible to have three courses, excluding wine, at the restaurant for less than £30.

The restaurant is participating in our £5 voucher scheme. See vouchers for terms and conditions.

The restaurant has a wine list that our experts consider to be outstanding, either for an in-depth focus on a particular region, attractive margins on fine wines, or strong selections by the glass.

Accommodation is available.

London explained

London is split into six regions. Restaurants within each region are listed alphabetically. Each main entry and local gem entry has a map reference. Here are the areas covered in each region.

CENTRAL

Aldwych, Bloomsbury, Covent Garden, Fitzrovia, Holborn, Hyde Park, Marylebone, Mayfair, Pimlico, Soho, Victoria, Westminster

NORTH

Archway, Camden, Euston, Finsbury Park, Golders Green, Hampstead, Highbury, Islington, Kensal Green, King's Cross, Newington Green, Primrose Hill, Stoke Newington, Swiss Cottage

EAST

Bethnal Green, Canary Wharf, City, Clerkenwell, Dalston, Farringdon, Hackney, Hoxton, Haggerston, Leytonstone, Moorgate, Old Street, Shoreditch, Spitalfields, Tower Hill, Whitechapel

SOUTH

Balham, Battersea, Bermondsey, Blackheath, Borough, Brixton, Camberwell, Clapham, Deptford, East Dulwich, Elephant & Castle, Forest Hill, Greenwich, Herne Hill, Peckham, Putney, South Bank, Southwark, Stockwell, Vauxhall, Wandsworth, Wimbledon

WEST

Belgravia, Chelsea, Chiswick, Ealing, Earl's Court, Fulham, Hammersmith, Kensington, Knightsbridge, Notting Hill, Olympia, Parsons Green, Shepherd's Bush, South Kensington

GREATER

Barnes, Croydon, East Sheen, Harrow-on-the-Hill, Kew, Richmond, South Woodford, Southall, Surbiton, Twickenham, Walthamstow, Wanstead

LONDON

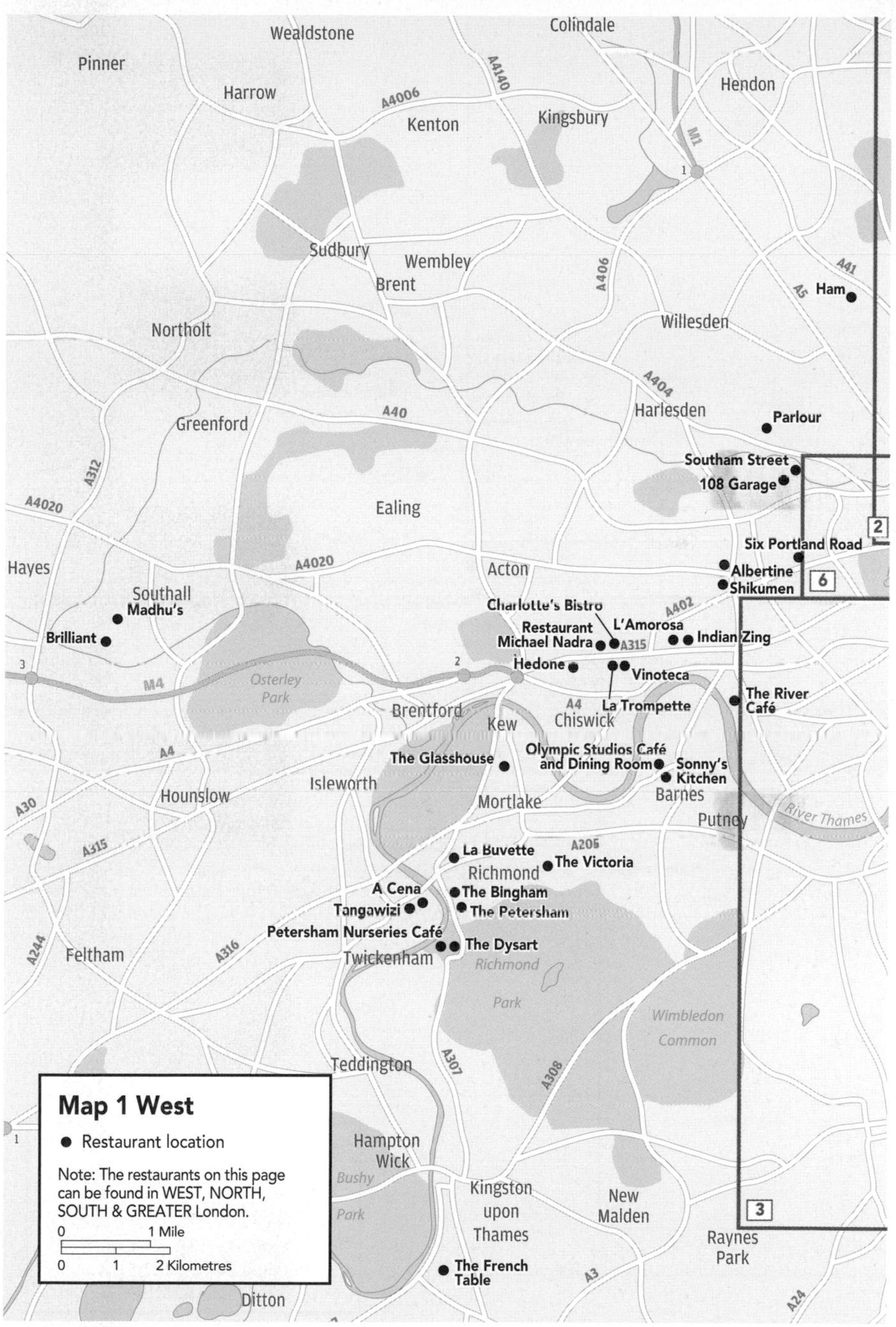
Wealdstone
Colindale
Pinner
Harrow
A4006
A4140
Kenton
Kingsbury
Hendon
M1
Sudbury
Wembley
Brent
A406
A41
A5
Ham
Northolt
Willesden
A404
Harlesden
A40
Greenford
Parlour
Southam Street
108 Garage
A312
A4020
Ealing
2
Six Portland Road
Hayes
A4020
Acton
Albertine
Shikumen
6
Southall
Madhu's
Charlotte's Bistro
A402
Restaurant
Michael Nadra
L'Amorosa
A315
Indian Zing
Brilliant
Hedone
M4
Osterley
Park
Vinoteca
A4
La Trompette
The River
Café
Brentford
Kew
Chiswick
A4
The Glasshouse
Olympic Studios Café
and Dining Room
Sonny's
Kitchen
Hounslow
Isleworth
Barnes
A30
Mortlake
Putney
River Thames
A315
A205
La Buvette
The Victoria
Richmond
A Cena
The Bingham
Tangawizi
The Petersham
Petersham Nurseries Café
The Dysart
A244
Feltham
A316
Twickenham
Richmond
Park
Wimbledon
Common
Teddington
A307
A308
Map 1 West
Restaurant location
Note: The restaurants on this page can be found in WEST, NORTH, SOUTH & GREATER London.
0
1 Mile
0
1
2 Kilometres
Hampton
Wick
Bushy
Park
Kingston
upon
Thames
New
Malden
3
Raynes
Park
The French
Table
A3
A24
Ditton

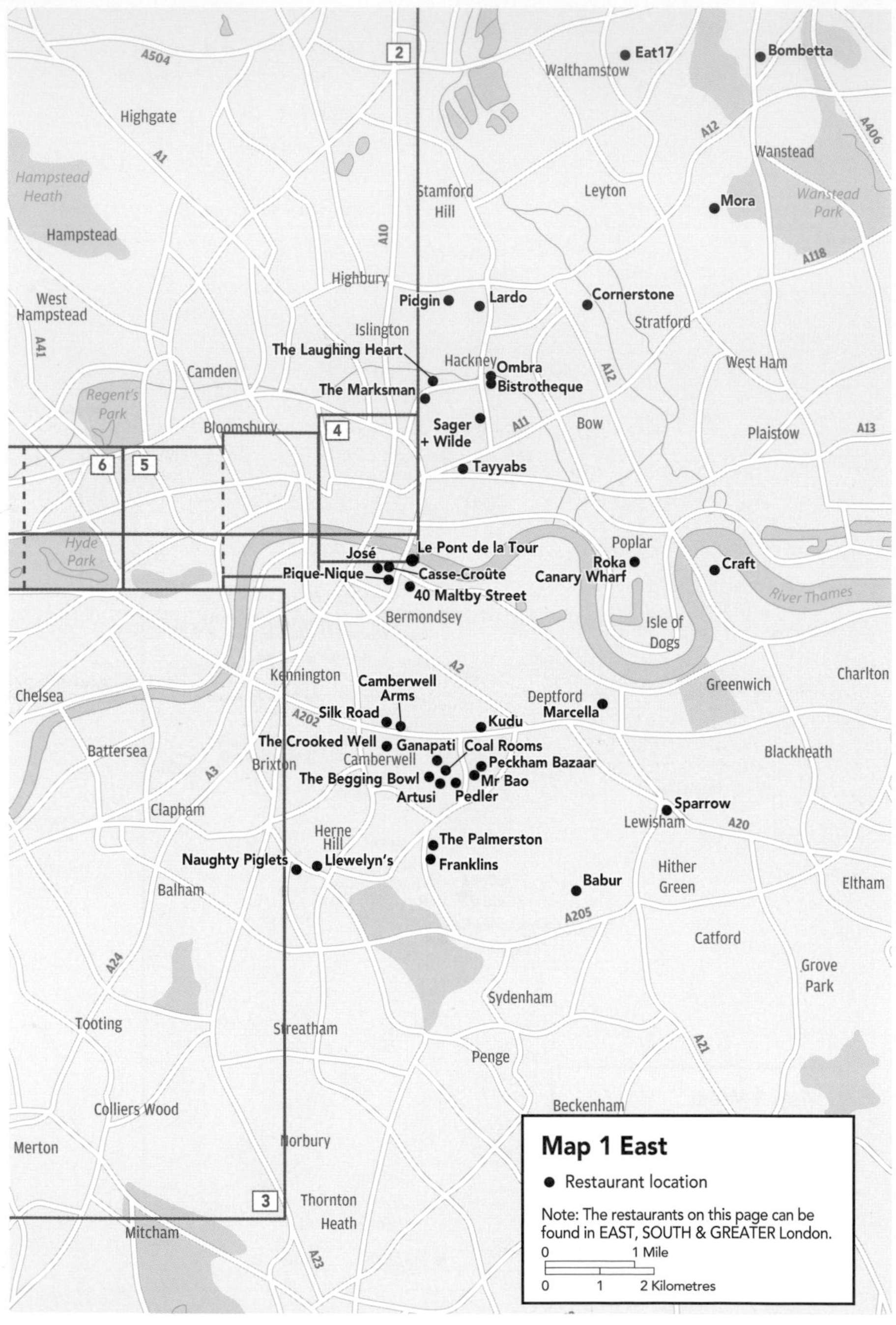

Map 1 East
Restaurant location
Note: The restaurants on this page can be found in EAST, SOUTH & GREATER London.
0 1 Mile
0 1 2 Kilometres
Eat17
Bombetta
Walthamstow
Highgate
Wanstead
Hampstead Heath
Stamford Hill
Leyton
Mora
Wanstead Park
Hampstead
Highbury
West Hampstead
Pidgin
Lardo
Cornerstone
Stratford
Islington
The Laughing Heart
Camden
Hackney
Ombra
Bistrotheque
West Ham
The Marksman
Regent's Park
Sager + Wilde
Bow
Plaistow
Bloomsbury
Tayyabs
Hyde Park
Poplar
José
Le Pont de la Tour
Roka
Craft
Pique-Nique
Casse-Croûte
Canary Wharf
40 Maltby Street
River Thames
Bermondsey
Isle of Dogs
Kennington
Camberwell Arms
Charlton
Chelsea
Greenwich
Deptford
Silk Road
Marcella
Kudu
The Crooked Well
Ganapati
Coal Rooms
Battersea
Camberwell
Peckham Bazaar
Blackheath
Brixton
The Begging Bowl
Mr Bao
Artusi
Pedler
Sparrow
Clapham
Lewisham
Herne Hill
The Palmerston
Naughty Piglets
Llewelyn's
Franklins
Hither Green
Balham
Babur
Eltham
Catford
Grove Park
Sydenham
Tooting
Streatham
Penge
Colliers Wood
Beckenham
Merton
Norbury
Thornton Heath
Mitcham
A504
A1
A10
A12
A406
A118
A41
A11
A13
A2
A202
A3
A20
A205
A24
A21
A23
2
4
5
6
3

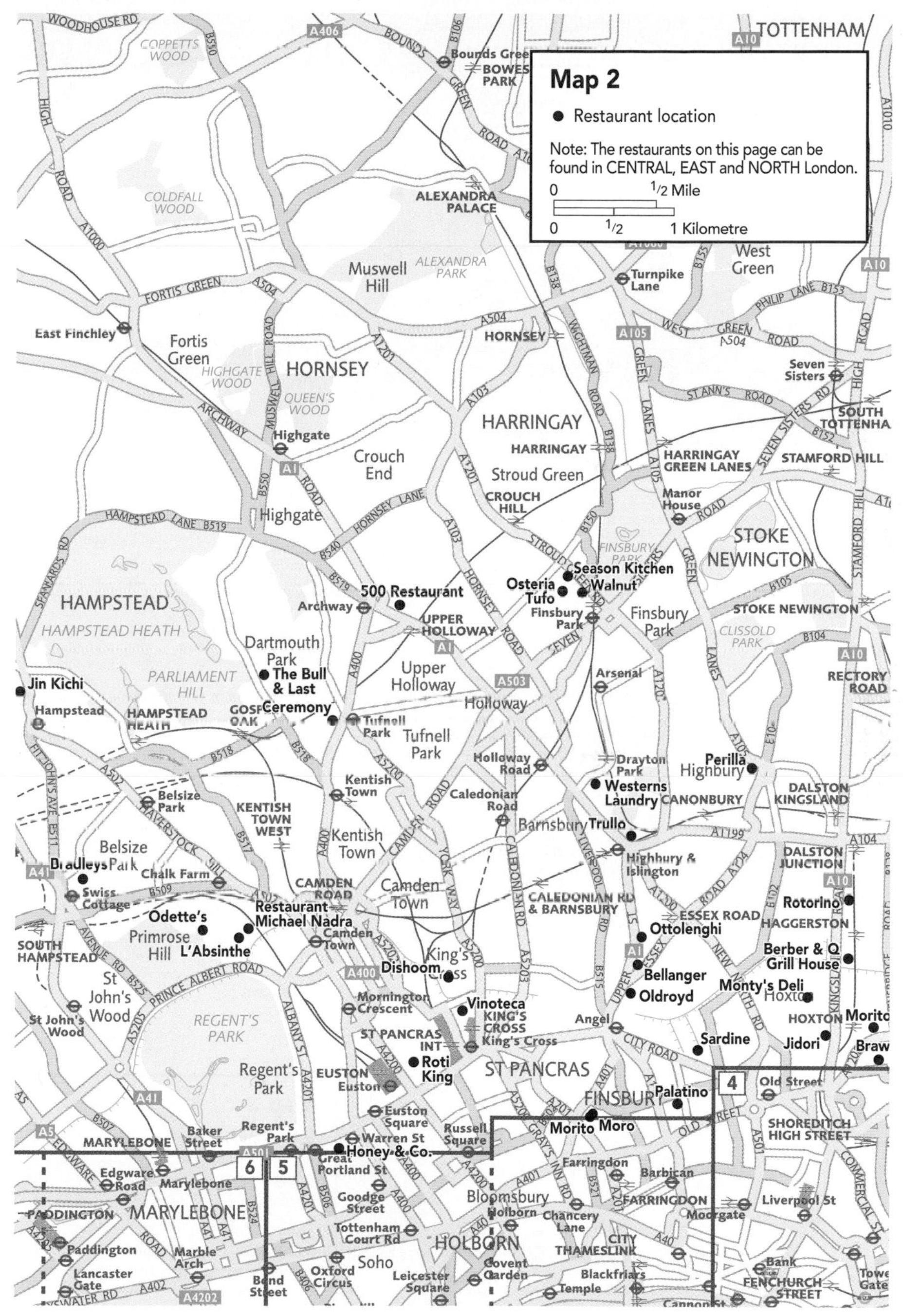
Map 2
Restaurant location
Note: The restaurants on this page can be found in CENTRAL, EAST and NORTH London.
0
1/2 Mile
0
1/2
1 Kilometre
TOTTENHAM
Bounds Green
BOWES PARK
ALEXANDRA PALACE
Muswell Hill
ALEXANDRA PARK
COPPETTS WOOD
COLDFALL WOOD
Turnpike Lane
West Green
East Finchley
Fortis Green
HIGHGATE WOOD
HORNSEY
QUEEN'S WOOD
HARRINGAY
Seven Sisters
SOUTH TOTTENHAM
Highgate
Crouch End
Stroud Green
CROUCH HILL
HARRINGAY GREEN LANES
STAMFORD HILL
Manor House
STOKE NEWINGTON
FINSBURY PARK
Season Kitchen
Osteria Tufo
Walnut
Finsbury Park
STOKE NEWINGTON
CLISSOLD PARK
500 Restaurant
Archway
UPPER HOLLOWAY
HAMPSTEAD
HAMPSTEAD HEATH
PARLIAMENT HILL
Dartmouth Park
The Bull & Last
Upper Holloway
Holloway
Arsenal
RECTORY ROAD
Jin Kichi
Hampstead
HAMPSTEAD HEATH
GOSPEL OAK
Ceremony
Tufnell Park
Tufnell Park
Holloway Road
Drayton Park
Perilla
Highbury
Westerns Laundry
CANONBURY
DALSTON KINGSLAND
Belsize Park
KENTISH TOWN WEST
Kentish Town
Kentish Town
Caledonian Road
Barnsbury
Trullo
Belsize Park
Bradleys
Chalk Farm
Swiss Cottage
CAMDEN ROAD
Camden Town
Highbury & Islington
DALSTON JUNCTION
CALEDONIAN RD & BARNSBURY
ESSEX ROAD
Rotorino
HAGGERSTON
Odette's
Restaurant Michael Nadra
Primrose Hill
L'Absinthe
SOUTH HAMPSTEAD
Camden Town
Ottolenghi
Berber & Q Grill House
Dishoom
King's Cross
Bellanger
Oldroyd
Monty's Deli
Hoxton
St John's Wood
St John's Wood
REGENT'S PARK
Mornington Crescent
Vinoteca
KING'S CROSS
Angel
HOXTON
Morito
ST PANCRAS INT
King's Cross
Sardine
Jidori
Braw
Regent's Park
EUSTON
Euston
Roti King
ST PANCRAS
FINSBURY
Palatino
4
Old Street
Euston Square
Morito
Moro
SHOREDITCH HIGH STREET
Baker Street
MARYLEBONE
Regent's Park
Warren St
Honey & Co.
Russell Square
6
5
Great Portland St
Edgware Road
Marylebone
Farringdon
Barbican
Goodge Street
Bloomsbury
Holborn
FARRINGDON
Liverpool St
PADDINGTON
MARYLEBONE
Chancery Lane
Moorgate
Tottenham Court Rd
HOLBORN
CITY THAMESLINK
Paddington
Marble Arch
Soho
Lancaster Gate
Bond Street
Oxford Circus
Leicester Square
Covent Garden
Blackfriars
Temple
Bank
FENCHURCH STREET
Tower Gateway

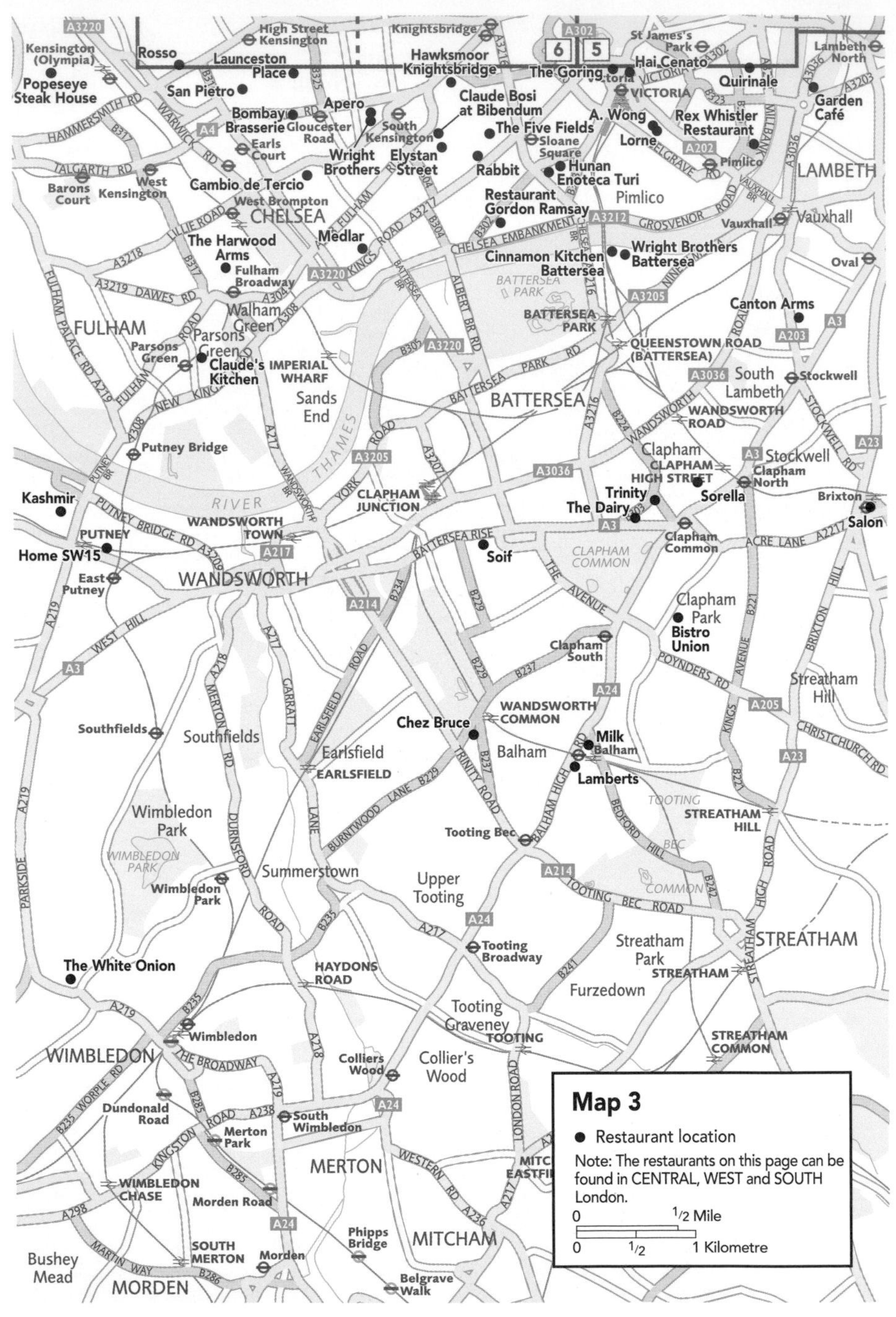
Map 3
● Restaurant location
Note: The restaurants on this page can be found in CENTRAL, WEST and SOUTH London.
0 1/2 Mile
0 1/2 1 Kilometre
Rosso
Launceston Place
San Pietro
Popeseye Steak House
Bombay Brasserie
Apero
Hawksmoor Knightsbridge
Claude Bosi at Bibendum
The Five Fields
Wright Brothers
Elystan Street
Rabbit
The Goring
Hai Cenato
Quirinale
A. Wong
Lorne
Rex Whistler Restaurant
Hunan
Enoteca Turi
Restaurant Gordon Ramsay
Cambio de Tercio
Medlar
The Harwood Arms
Cinnamon Kitchen Battersea
Wright Brothers Battersea
Canton Arms
Garden Café
Claude's Kitchen
Kashmir
Home SW15
Trinity
The Dairy
Sorella
Salon
Soif
Bistro Union
Chez Bruce
Milk
Lamberts
The White Onion
Kensington (Olympia)
High Street Kensington
Knightsbridge
St James's Park
Lambeth North
Gloucester Road
South Kensington
Earls Court
Sloane Square
Victoria
Pimlico
Vauxhall
Oval
West Kensington
Barons Court
West Brompton
CHELSEA
LAMBETH
Fulham Broadway
Walham Green
FULHAM
Parsons Green
IMPERIAL WHARF
Sands End
BATTERSEA PARK
QUEENSTOWN ROAD (BATTERSEA)
BATTERSEA
South Lambeth
Stockwell
WANDSWORTH ROAD
Clapham
CLAPHAM HIGH STREET
Clapham North
Brixton
RIVER THAMES
Putney Bridge
PUTNEY
CLAPHAM JUNCTION
WANDSWORTH TOWN
WANDSWORTH
East Putney
CLAPHAM COMMON
Clapham Common
Clapham Park
Clapham South
Streatham Hill
WANDSWORTH COMMON
Balham
Southfields
Earlsfield
EARLSFIELD
Wimbledon Park
TOOTING BEC COMMON
STREATHAM HILL
Tooting Bec
Summerstown
Upper Tooting
Tooting Broadway
STREATHAM
Streatham Park
Furzedown
HAYDONS ROAD
Tooting Graveney
TOOTING
STREATHAM COMMON
Wimbledon
WIMBLEDON
Colliers Wood
Collier's Wood
Dundonald Road
South Wimbledon
Merton Park
MERTON
WIMBLEDON CHASE
Morden Road
MITCHAM EASTFIELDS
SOUTH MERTON
Morden
Phipps Bridge
MITCHAM
Belgrave Walk
Bushey Mead
MORDEN

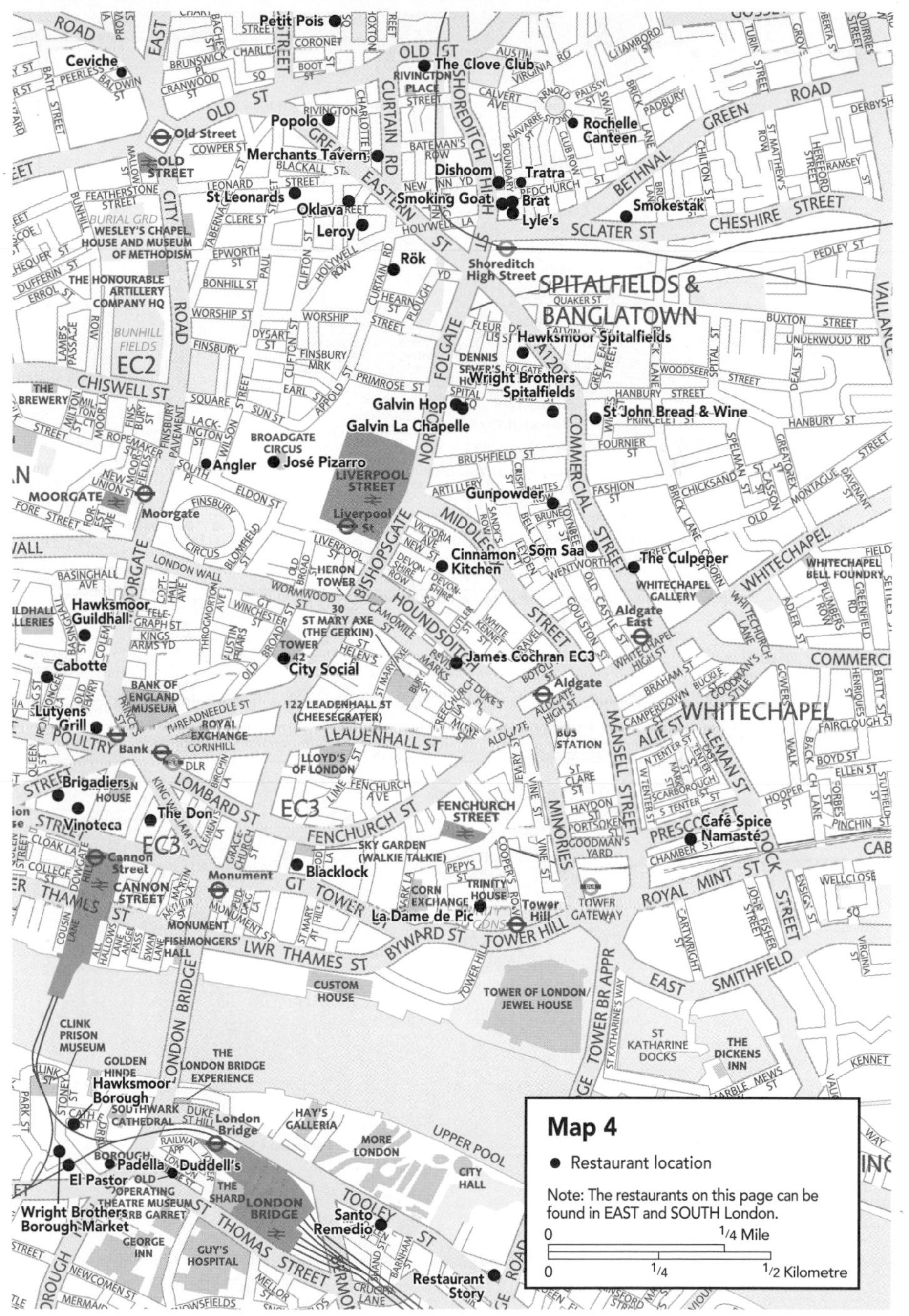
Petit Pois
Ceviche
The Clove Club
Rochelle Canteen
Popolo
Merchants Tavern
Dishoom
Tratra
Smoking Goat
Brat
Lyle's
St Leonards
Oklava
Leroy
Smokestak
Rök
SPITALFIELDS & BANGLATOWN
Hawksmoor Spitalfields
Wright Brothers Spitalfields
Galvin Hop
Galvin La Chapelle
St John Bread & Wine
Angler
José Pizarro
Gunpowder
Cinnamon Kitchen
Som Saa
The Culpeper
Hawksmoor Guildhall
Cabotte
James Cochran EC3
City Social
WHITECHAPEL
Lutyens Grill
Brigadiers
Vinoteca
The Don
Café Spice Namasté
Blacklock
La Dame de Pic
Hawksmoor Borough
Padella
Duddell's
El Pastor
Wright Brothers Borough Market
Santo Remedio
Restaurant Story
EC2
EC3
Map 4
Restaurant location
Note: The restaurants on this page can be found in EAST and SOUTH London.
0
1/4 Mile
0
1/4
1/2 Kilometre

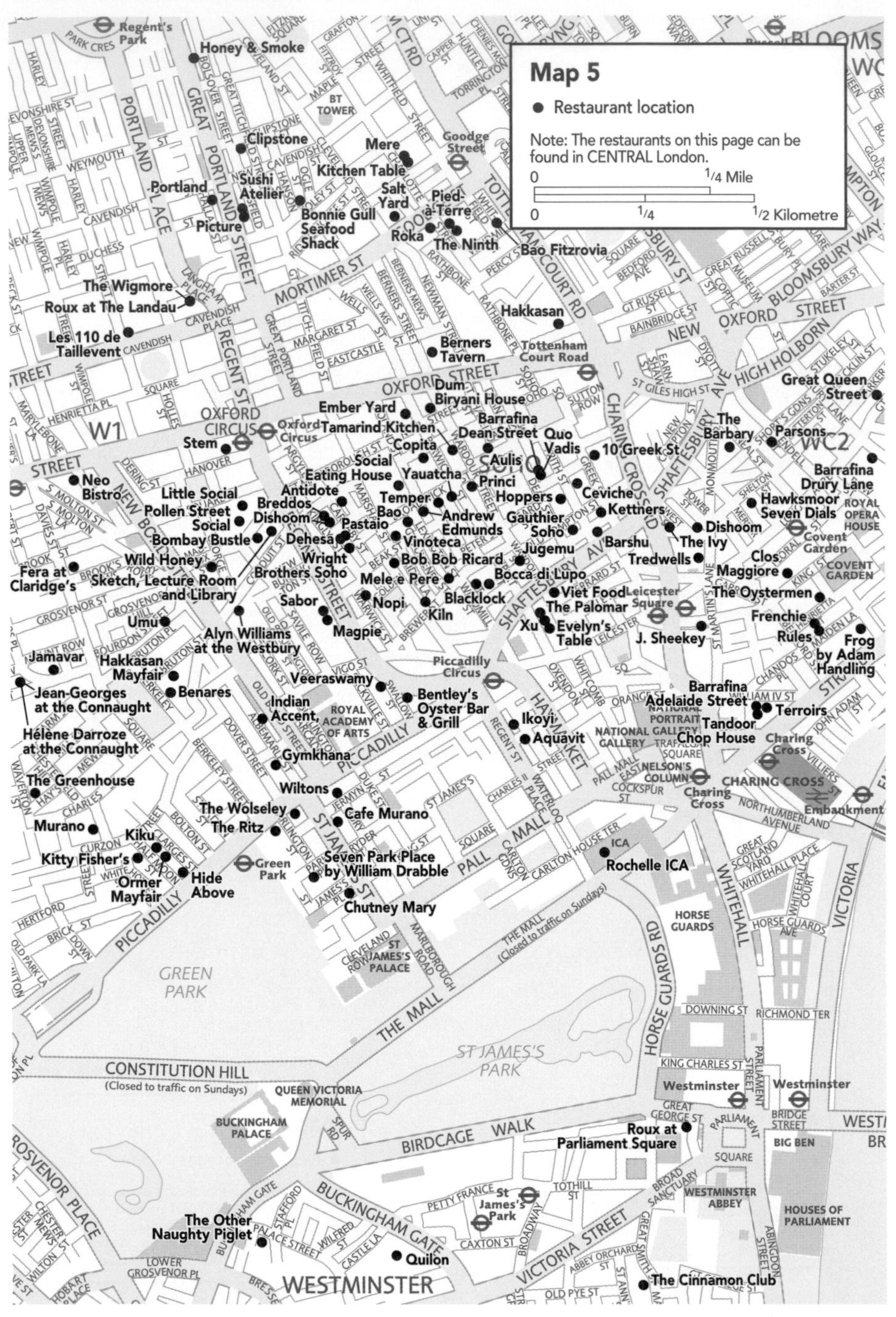
Map 5
Restaurant location
Note: The restaurants on this page can be found in CENTRAL London.
0
1/4 Mile
0
1/4
1/2 Kilometre
Honey & Smoke
Clipstone
Mere
Kitchen Table
Portland
Sushi Atelier
Salt Yard
Pied-à-Terre
Bonnie Gull Seafood Shack
Roka
The Ninth
Picture
Bao Fitzrovia
The Wigmore
Roux at The Landau
Les 110 de Taillevent
Hakkasan
Berners Tavern
Dum Biryani House
Ember Yard
Tamarind Kitchen
Barrafina Dean Street
Quo Vadis
Copita
Aulis
10 Greek St
Stem
Social Eating House
Yauatcha
Princi
Neo Bistro
Antidote
Temper
Hoppers
Ceviche
Little Social
Breddos
Bao
Andrew Edmunds
Kettners
Pollen Street Social
Dishoom
Pastaio
Gauthier Soho
Bombay Bustle
Dehesa
Vinoteca
Barshu
Jugemu
The Ivy
Wild Honey
Wright Brothers Soho
Bob Bob Ricard
Tredwells
Fera at Claridge's
Sketch, Lecture Room and Library
Mele e Pere
Bocca di Lupo
Viet Food
Sabor
Nopi
Blacklock
The Palomar
Umu
Kiln
Xu
Evelyn's Table
J. Sheekey
Alyn Williams at the Westbury
Magpie
Jamavar
Hakkasan Mayfair
Veeraswamy
Jean-Georges at the Connaught
Benares
Bentley's Oyster Bar & Grill
Indian Accent
Hélène Darroze at the Connaught
Ikoyi
Aquavit
Gymkhana
The Greenhouse
Wiltons
The Wolseley
Cafe Murano
Murano
The Ritz
Kiku
Kitty Fisher's
Seven Park Place by William Drabble
Ormer Mayfair
Hide Above
Chutney Mary
Rochelle ICA
Great Queen Street
The Barbary
Parsons
Barrafina Drury Lane
Hawksmoor Seven Dials
Dishoom
Clos Maggiore
The Oystermen
Frenchie
Rules
Frog by Adam Handling
Barrafina Adelaide Street
Terroirs
Tandoor Chop House
Roux at Parliament Square
The Other Naughty Piglet
Quilon
The Cinnamon Club
Regent's Park
Goodge Street
Tottenham Court Road
Oxford Circus
OXFORD CIRCUS
W1
SOHO
WC2
Leicester Square
Covent Garden
COVENT GARDEN
ROYAL OPERA HOUSE
Piccadilly Circus
ROYAL ACADEMY OF ARTS
NATIONAL PORTRAIT GALLERY
NATIONAL GALLERY
NELSON'S COLUMN
Charing Cross
CHARING CROSS
Embankment
Green Park
GREEN PARK
ST JAMES'S PALACE
ICA
HORSE GUARDS
ST JAMES'S PARK
CONSTITUTION HILL
(Closed to traffic on Sundays)
THE MALL
(Closed to traffic on Sundays)
QUEEN VICTORIA MEMORIAL
BUCKINGHAM PALACE
BIRDCAGE WALK
St James's Park
Westminster
BIG BEN
WESTMINSTER ABBEY
HOUSES OF PARLIAMENT
WESTMINSTER
BT TOWER
OXFORD STREET
NEW OXFORD STREET
HIGH HOLBORN
BLOOMSBURY WAY
PICCADILLY
REGENT ST
GREAT PORTLAND STREET
PORTLAND PLACE
CHARING CROSS RD
SHAFTESBURY AV
TOTTENHAM COURT RD
HAYMARKET
PALL MALL
WHITEHALL
VICTORIA STREET
BUCKINGHAM GATE
GROSVENOR PLACE
HORSE GUARDS RD
MORTIMER ST
DOWNING ST
RICHMOND TER
KING CHARLES ST
PARLIAMENT STREET
NORTHUMBERLAND AVENUE

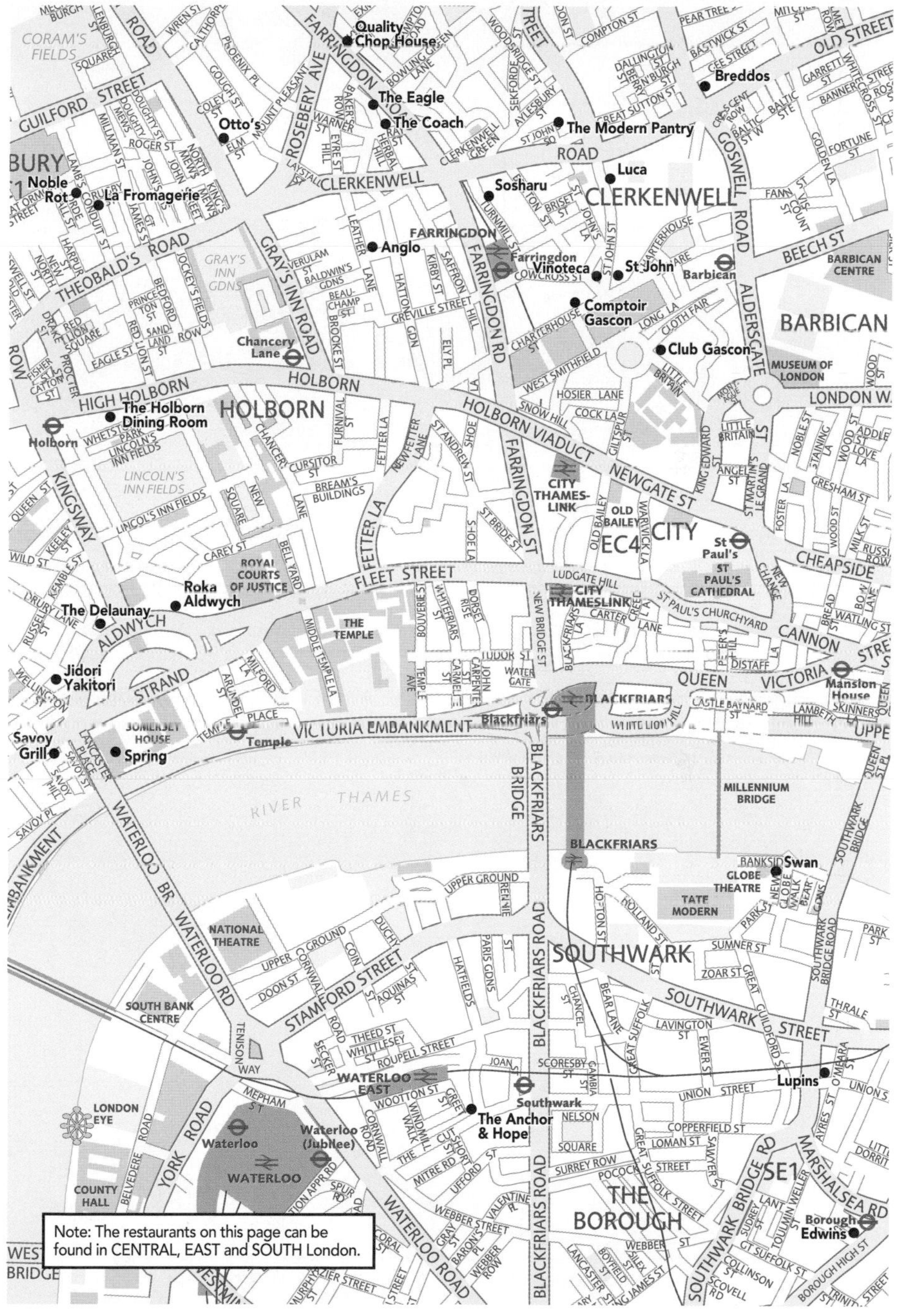
Quality Chop House
The Eagle
The Coach
Breddos
The Modern Pantry
Otto's
Luca
Sosharu
CLERKENWELL
Noble Rot
La Fromagerie
Anglo
FARRINGDON
Farringdon
Vinoteca
St John
Barbican
Comptoir Gascon
Club Gascon
BARBICAN
BARBICAN CENTRE
MUSEUM OF LONDON
Chancery Lane
HOLBORN
The Holborn Dining Room
Holborn
LINCOLN'S INN FIELDS
GRAY'S INN GDNS
CORAM'S FIELDS
CITY THAMESLINK
OLD BAILEY
EC4
CITY
St Paul's
ST PAUL'S CATHEDRAL
ROYAL COURTS OF JUSTICE
Roka Aldwych
The Delaunay
THE TEMPLE
Jidori Yakitori
Savoy Grill
SOMERSET HOUSE
Spring
Temple
Blackfriars
BLACKFRIARS
Mansion House
RIVER THAMES
MILLENNIUM BRIDGE
Swan
GLOBE THEATRE
TATE MODERN
NATIONAL THEATRE
SOUTH BANK CENTRE
SOUTHWARK
WATERLOO EAST
Southwark
The Anchor & Hope
Lupins
LONDON EYE
Waterloo
Waterloo (Jubilee)
WATERLOO
COUNTY HALL
THE BOROUGH
SE1
Borough
Edwins
Note: The restaurants on this page can be found in CENTRAL, EAST and SOUTH London.

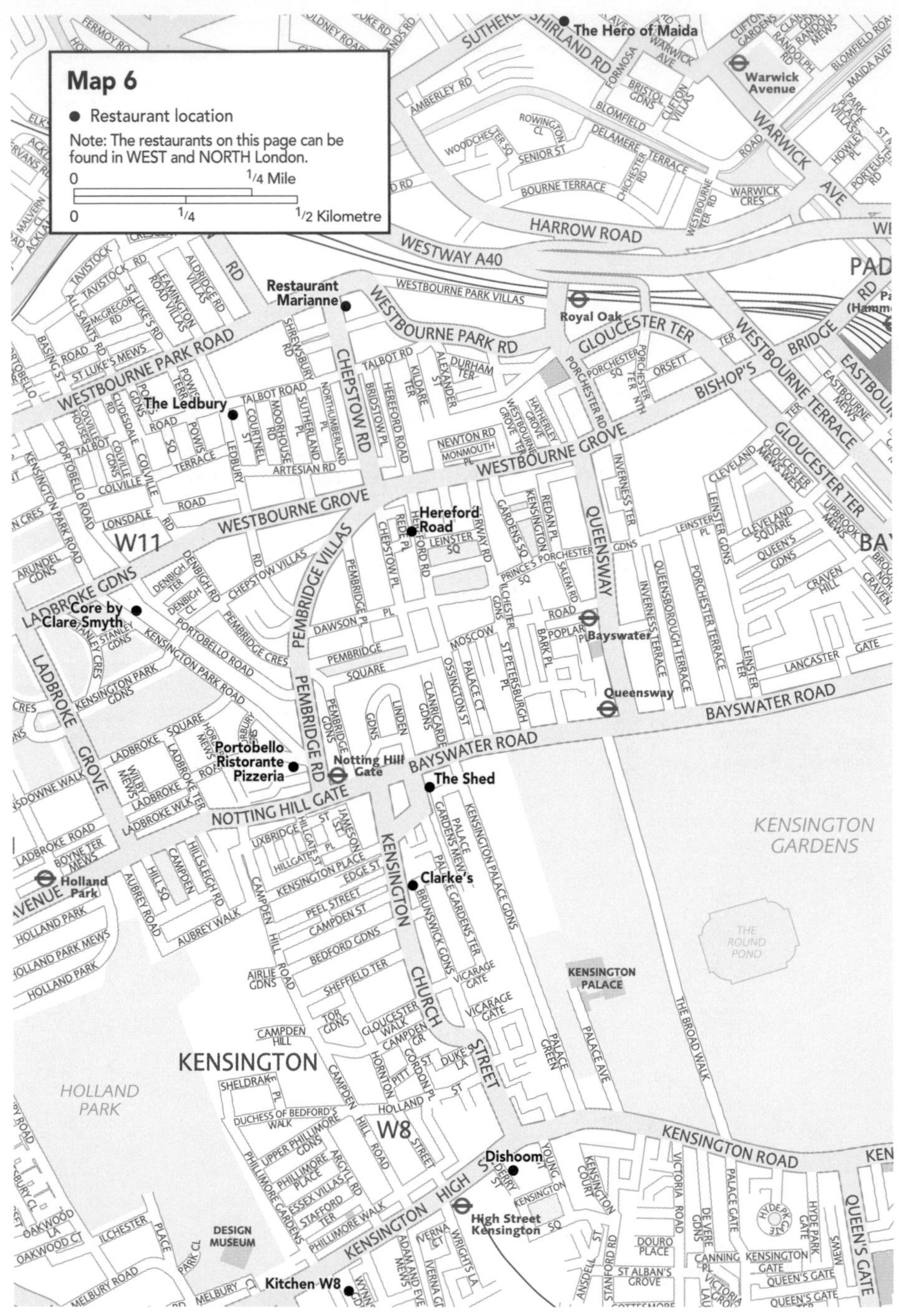
Map 6
Restaurant location
Note: The restaurants on this page can be found in WEST and NORTH London.
0
1/4 Mile
0
1/4
1/2 Kilometre
The Hero of Maida
Warwick Avenue
Restaurant Marianne
Royal Oak
The Ledbury
Hereford Road
Core by Clare Smyth
Bayswater
Queensway
Portobello Ristorante Pizzeria
Notting Hill Gate
The Shed
Clarke's
Holland Park
Dishoom
High Street Kensington
Kitchen W8
W11
W8
KENSINGTON
HOLLAND PARK
KENSINGTON GARDENS
THE ROUND POND
KENSINGTON PALACE
DESIGN MUSEUM
HARROW ROAD
WESTWAY A40
WESTBOURNE PARK ROAD
WESTBOURNE PARK VILLAS
WESTBOURNE GROVE
WESTBOURNE TERRACE
GLOUCESTER TER
BISHOP'S BRIDGE RD
QUEENSWAY
BAYSWATER ROAD
NOTTING HILL GATE
PEMBRIDGE VILLAS
PEMBRIDGE RD
CHEPSTOW RD
LADBROKE GROVE
LADBROKE GDNS
KENSINGTON PARK ROAD
PORTOBELLO ROAD
KENSINGTON CHURCH STREET
KENSINGTON HIGH ST
KENSINGTON ROAD
KENSINGTON PALACE GDNS
THE BROAD WALK
WARWICK AVE
SHIRLAND RD
QUEEN'S GATE

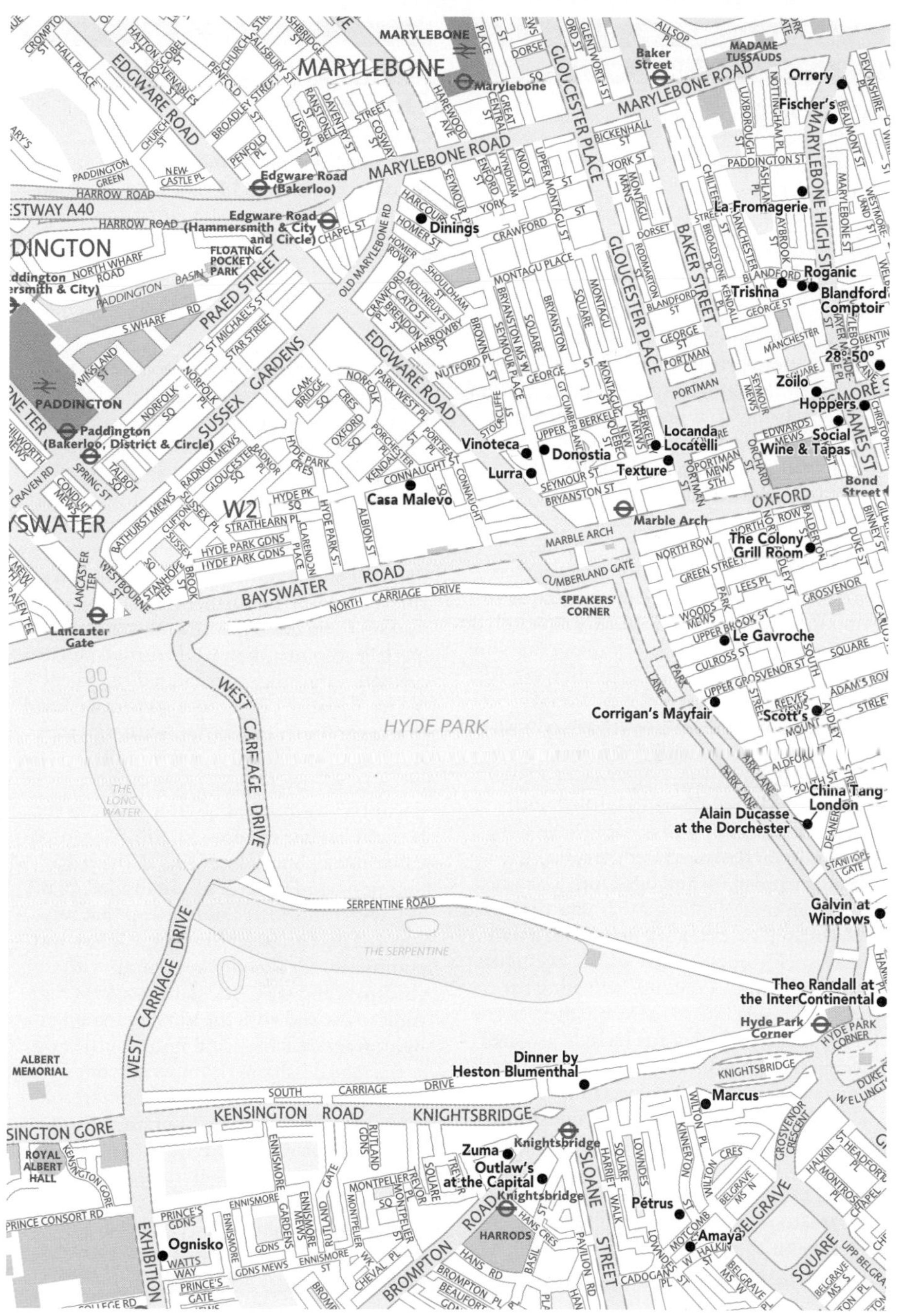
MARYLEBONE
MARYLEBONE
Marylebone
Baker Street
MADAME TUSSAUDS
MARYLEBONE ROAD
EDGWARE ROAD
Edgware Road (Bakerloo)
Edgware Road (Hammersmith & City and Circle)
PRAED STREET
SUSSEX GARDENS
PADDINGTON
Paddington (Bakerloo, District & Circle)
W2
BAYSWATER ROAD
Lancaster Gate
GLOUCESTER PLACE
BAKER STREET
MARYLEBONE HIGH ST
OXFORD
Bond Street
Marble Arch
SPEAKERS' CORNER
HYDE PARK
THE LONG WATER
WEST CARRIAGE DRIVE
SERPENTINE ROAD
THE SERPENTINE
PARK LANE
Hyde Park Corner
HYDE PARK CORNER
ALBERT MEMORIAL
ROYAL ALBERT HALL
KENSINGTON ROAD
KNIGHTSBRIDGE
Knightsbridge
HARRODS
BROMPTON ROAD
SLOANE STREET
BELGRAVE SQUARE
Orrery
Fischer's
La Fromagerie
Dinings
Roganic
Trishna
Blandford Comptoir
28°-50°
Zoilo
Hoppers
Social Wine & Tapas
Vinoteca
Donostia
Locanda Locatelli
Lurra
Texture
Casa Malevo
The Colony Grill Room
Le Gavroche
Corrigan's Mayfair
Scott's
China Tang London
Alain Ducasse at the Dorchester
Galvin at Windows
Theo Randall at the InterContinental
Dinner by Heston Blumenthal
Marcus
Zuma
Outlaw's at the Capital
Pétrus
Amaya
Ognisko

★ RESTAURANT OF THE YEAR ★

★ TOP 50 ★

A. Wong

Cooking score: 7
⊖ Victoria, map 3
Chinese | £60
70-71 Wilton Road, Victoria, SW1V 1DE
Tel no: (020) 7828 8931
awong.co.uk

Discreetly set in a row of shops and eating places a short hop from Victoria station, its dark exterior partially hidden by potted trees, this game-changing Chinese restaurant seems deliberately low-key. Inside, it's unfussily done out in cream, dark grey and wood and dominated by an open kitchen. This is a sharp operation, confirmed by efficient and charming service, and backed up by excellent management that keep things running smoothly. It is here that Andrew Wong has redefined the notion of Chinese cooking in London – he has planted the cuisine solidly in this century with a revelatory menu that's an intelligent selection from different regions. Based on excellent ingredients, Wong's nuanced cooking shows great variety with the best dishes having a where-did-that-come-from quality: a dainty, crisp-coated Zhou dynasty-style crab claw snack filled with diced, cured scallop and wasabi; Xi'an City 'lamb burger' flavoured with sesame, coriander and chilli and piled into a steamed bun; from central China a rich, multi-layered slow-braised Ibérico pork belly with a dark, glossy, sticky sauce; seared wagyu beef with mint, chilli and lemongrass reflecting the flavours found close to the Vietnamese border. Luscious crossover desserts include poached meringue with fruit textures – a brilliant amalgam of coconut, passion fruit, lychee, mango and brittle sugar. Lunchtime dim sum is worth noting, too. The fastidious food-friendly wine list is known for its quality.

Chef/s: Andrew Wong. **Closed:** Sun, Christmas, 31 Dec. **Meals:** main courses £12 to £18. Tasting menu £75. **Details:** 60 seats. 8 seats outside. Bar. Wheelchairs.

★ TOP 50 ★

Alain Ducasse at the Dorchester

Cooking score: 8
⊖ Hyde Park Corner, map 6
Modern French | £110
The Dorchester Hotel, 53 Park Lane, Mayfair, W1K 1QA
Tel no: (020) 7629 8866
alainducasse-dorchester.com

A discreet entrance off the Dorchester's Promenade leads into a large, light and elegant room, where cosseting surrounds are tailor-made for Park Lane and for cooking that relies on top ingredients and meticulous craftsmanship. And in Jean-Philippe Blondet, Alain Ducasse has a chef who interprets his style with confidence – classic techniques and flavour combinations, rather than novelty, rule here. Look no further than a long-standing Ducasse signature lobster dish, its 'perfect accompaniment' of truffled chicken quenelles and silky pasta pulled together by a 'heavenly sauce', an intense sauté gourmand. Praise continues to pour in, with reports singling out a fine fillet of turbot, its sweetness offset by earthy, intense beetroot, or a flavourful halibut with oyster and seaweed. Delight has been expressed, too, for a good-value 'lunch-hour menu' that delivered a prosaic-sounding dish of soft-boiled quail's egg with cauliflower and saffron that was deemed 'exceptional'. Elsewhere, there was enthusiasm for a tender veal rump with chickpeas and sage. Standards are kept high right to the end with the kitchen sending out a light, fragrant lemon and mint soufflé as well as the famed baba au rhum, with your choice of aged rum. There are lots of extra treats thrown in, of course, and a premier-league sommelier providing advice on a wine list that ticks the boxes for serious intent and quality at Mayfair prices.

Chef/s: Jean-Philippe Blondet. **Closed:** Sun, Mon, 26 to 30 Dec, first week Jan, Easter, 3 weeks Aug. **Meals:** £100 (3 courses) to £120 (4 courses). Set L

£70. Tasting menu £150 (7 courses). Seasonal menu £190 to £290. **Details:** 82 seats. V menu. Bar. Wheelchairs. Music. Parking. Children over 10 yrs.

Alyn Williams at the Westbury

Cooking score: 6
⊖ Oxford Circus, map 5
Anglo-French | £70
The Westbury Hotel, 37 Conduit Street, Mayfair, W1S 2YF
Tel no: (020) 7183 6426
alynwilliams.com

Since 2011, this spacious Mayfair hotel dining room has been a showcase for Alyn Williams' inimitable talent in an area that's not exactly short on high-end dining addresses. Not a chef to seek the limelight, every ounce of Williams' accumulated skill and devotion to his craft is channelled into dishes that are immaculately conceived, fastidiously constructed and hugely enjoyable. The cooking may have its roots in classical French cuisine but the style is modern British, using first-rate produce whether you're eating from the carte, seven-course tasting menu (with a fabulous vegetarian version), or terrific value three-course lunch. King crab makes for an impressive opening, served with celeriac, lovage and hazelnuts. After that, there could be faultless poached halibut with Champagne velouté, or the much-praised 55-day aged pork with langoustines, braised endive and hen of the woods mushrooms. Desserts show the same degree of balance and impressive technique – the flavours of blood orange and kaffir lime, say, with chocolate crisp. Attentive staff pitch the tone just right. The wine list opens at £35, but heads north pretty rapidly; the beer selection is an interesting alternative.
Chef/s: Alyn Williams. **Closed:** Sun, Mon, first 2 weeks Jan, last 2 weeks Aug. **Meals:** set L £30 (3 courses). Set D £70 (3 courses). Tasting menu £90. **Details:** 45 seats. V menu. Bar. Wheelchairs. Music. Parking.

Andrew Edmunds

Cooking score: 2
⊖ Oxford Circus, Piccadilly Circus, map 5
Modern European | £40
46 Lexington Street, Soho, W1F 0LP
Tel no: (020) 7437 5708
andrewedmunds.com

'I've not been here since the mid-90s and I'm pleased to say very little has changed... the same buzz, the same sort of bistro food, and the same timeless appeal – long live old Soho,' declared one diner who revelled in the continuing lure of this veteran bistro (est. 1986). Spread over two tightly packed floors, complete with flickering candles in wine bottles, there's a contented hum to this 18th-century townhouse, partly helped along by the excellent wines available at fair prices. The menu's squiggly handwriting reveals a seasonal output, where simplicity rules. Get off the mark with sourdough bread and butter, before a first course of tender squid in a tomatoey stew with fennel and aïoli, or a salad of crunchy chicory and confit pig's cheek. Roast turbot is cooked just-so, and braised duck leg with carrots provides unctuous satisfaction. The proof of the pudding is in a 'rightly wobbly' toasted almond panna cotta. That wine list opens at £19.50.
Chef/s: Chris Gillard. **Closed:** 24 to 30 Dec. **Meals:** main courses £14 to £27. **Details:** 60 seats.

Antidote

Cooking score: 3
⊖ Oxford Circus, map 5
Modern European | £32
12A Newburgh Street, Soho, W1F 7RR
Tel no: (020) 7287 8488
antidotewinebar.com

Gently nudging the French bistro into the modern age, Antidote is an airy restaurant and wine bar off Carnaby Street. No stale baguette or rough rouge here, it stakes its reputation on its bread (Hedone Bakery) and wine (natural, mainly French and guest-starring some of the industry's great names). Perch in the street-level bar à vins over glasses of red, white and orange with snacks of ham and red pepper arancini or lonza affumicata (smoked pork loin). Or book a table in the white-walled, wooden-floored first-floor dining room (or pavement tables) to explore the weekly changing European menu. Regulars know they're on to a good thing: raw sea bass, pickled grapes, cucumber and nori mayo, hake with chicken skin aïoli and wild mushrooms and the £12 *plat du jour*, such as bavette and bitter leaves, punch well above their price point. Finish with cheese (and what's left in the bottle).

Chef/s: Daniel Whalan. **Closed:** Sun, bank hols. **Meals:** main courses £11 to £20. **Details:** 45 seats. 20 seats outside. Bar. Music.

Aquavit

Cooking score: 3
⊖ Piccadilly Circus, map 5
Nordic | £45
St James's Market, 1 Carlton Street, Mayfair, SW1Y 4QQ
Tel no: (020) 7024 9848
aquavitrestaurants.com

St James's Market is a gleaming development of dining options all kitted out in their West End best, among which Aquavit brings a blast of bracing Nordic style. From an original New York template, it's an all-day venue decorated with artisan tapestries hanging on blond wood walls and staff in black designer attire. The most exciting section of the menu remains the smörgåsbord, small plates that should be liberally ordered amid reviving tots of savoury-perfumed aquavit. Dooncastle oysters with elderflower, shallots and dill, the incomparable matjes herrings, and blood pudding with lingonberries and bacon are replete with sharply pointed seasonings and delicate textures. The main-menu items go more mainstream, as in a starter of crab and fennel on rye brioche, or mains of whole boned trout with almonds and capers, or Swedish meatballs with pickled cucumber. A sweet Norwegian omelette filled with sea buckthorn and vanilla makes a change from crème brûlée. As well as the speciality aquavits, there are some well-chosen wines and inspired cocktails.

Chef/s: Henrik Ritzén and Harry Saddy. **Meals:** main courses £18 to £29. Set L £20 (2 courses) to £24. **Details:** 114 seats. 20 seats outside. Bar. Wheelchairs. Music.

★ NEW ENTRY ★

Aulis

Cooking score: 6
map 5
Modern British | £195
St Annes Court, Soho, W1F 0BN
Tel no: (020) 3948 9665
aulis.london

'There's a lot to like,' commented one seasoned inspector impressed by the faultless hospitality at the latest incarnation of Aulis, Simon Rogan's eight-seat development kitchen. In a space almost entirely devoid of ornament, guests are seated at a counter while two chefs prepare, cook, serve and talk their way through a surprise multi-course tasting menu. Designed to give a unique insight into the creative process at Rogan's L'Enclume and Roganic (see entries), dishes are produced in quantities that allow for refinement and experimentation. A series of small bites may include silky oyster custard topped with Exmoor caviar, and raw beef in a sheet of fermented kohlrabi with pungent wild garlic capers, with the lightest brioche to follow, accompanied by a luxuriously intense mushroom and truffle dip. As you'd expect from the Rogan stable, vegetables prepared every which way – confit, puréed, roasted, fermented, crisped – are allowed to shine. Monkfish roasted with hispi cabbage might pave the way for superb aged beef fillet with purées of celeriac and nasturtium, finished with an intense, glossy, meaty sauce. Intriguing desserts explore combinations of fruit, cream and herbs. Though no bargain, wine, soft drinks and service are included in the £195 price tag so expect some good-quality, well-matched selections. Given the no-frills setting, it's not the full-on, captivating experience of L'Enclume but your hosts are generous with their time, their knowledge and their pours.

Chef/s: Simon Rogan. **Closed:** Sun, Mon, 23 Dec to 8 Jan. **Meals:** tasting menu £195 (12 to 15 courses). **Details:** 8 seats. Music. Pre-payment only.

Bao Fitzrovia

Cooking score: 2
⊖ Tottenham Court Road, map 5
Taiwanese | £35
31 Windmill Street, Fitzrovia, W1T 2JN
Tel no: (020) 3011 1632
baolondon.com

Competition is fierce in the streets of Fitzrovia, but this sleek, two-tier corner spot just off Tottenham Court Road, more than holds its own. It's struck such a chord with its many fans that it's best to book to avoid joining the inevitable queue. Street-level seats are arranged around a central bar; downstairs is darker but table seating gives a view of the open kitchen. Light, fluffy bao (steamed buns) are at the centre of the tick-box menu (making ordering a quick process) – black cod or the classic braised pork bao (with fermented greens, coriander and crushed peanuts) are favourites. There are other options such as Taiwanese fried chicken chop with soy-cured egg, and a couple of ice cream-based desserts – our advice: wolf down another bao instead. To drink, try the (sweet) peanut milk, interesting cocktails or something from the brief wine list.

Chef/s: Erchen Chang and Shing Tat Chung. **Closed:** Sun. **Meals:** bao £4 to £5. Xiao chi £5 to £9. **Details:** 40 seats. Music.

Bao Soho

Cooking score: 2
⊖ Oxford Circus, map 5
Taiwanese | £35
53 Lexington Street, Soho, W1F 9AS
baolondon.com

Be prepared to queue at this, the original Bao, although the mix of counter seating and tables ensures a quick turnover. There is slightly less choice than at the Fitzrovia branch (see entry).

Chef/s: Erchen Chang. **Closed:** Sun. **Meals:** bao £4 to £5. Xiao chi £3 to £6. Set L £15. **Details:** 24 seats. Music.

The Barbary

Cooking score: 4
⊖ Covent Garden, map 5
North African | £30
16 Neal's Yard, Covent Garden, WC2H 9DP
thebarbary.co.uk

Judging by the success of this Mediterranean and North African hybrid, the folk behind The Palomar (see entry) clearly know a thing or two about running restaurants. It's a small space, essentially a bar built around a kitchen – perch on stools and watch the chefs at work cooking over open flames. Each dish comes with grilled or smokey notes and bold, punchy flavours are the norm, whether in small plates of Jaffa-style cauliflower (deep fried and topped with tomato, lemon and coriander) or in a stew of chargrilled octopus and chickpeas. There's delight, too, in tender lamb cutlets, brightly flavoured baba ghnoush and piping hot chargrilled naan bread teamed with dips of zhug (hot, garlicky) and harissa – though the Jerusalem bagel has many fans. If you like lemon, garlic, coriander, chilli and yoghurt, then you're in the right place. Kanafeh, a cheese pastry drenched in sugar syrup, is the perfect way to finish. Israeli and Lebanese wines feature on the short list which opens at £35.

Chef/s: Daniel Alt. **Meals:** main courses £8 to £20. **Details:** 24 seats. V menu. Children over 8 yrs.

Bread: all you knead

No longer a mere meal-time accessory, the staff of life is starting to be venerated as a course in its own right. Here are a few of our favourites.

In Devon, **Coombeshead**'s sourdough is intense, dense and full of nutty, sweet-acidic flavour: best-in-class. Meanwhile at **Ballintaggart Farm** in Perthshire the 'outstanding' bread draws rave reviews alongside acclaim for the accompanying butter and Scottish rapeseed oil.

The Beach House celebrates its gorgeous location on Oxwich Bay, south Wales by putting laverbread in the centre of its hot mini loaves.

At **Spring** in London's Somerset House Skye Gyngell's deliciously nutty rye bread starts proceedings. Nearby at **Barbary** hot, blistered, chargrilled naan is teamed with zhug, harissa and pickled chilli.

Also in Covent Garden, **Tandoor Chop House** serves bone-marrow butter naan straight off the grill, meanwhile, at **Roti King,** near Euston, flaky, buttery flatbreads are the main draw and are cooked to order in the open kitchen. Be prepared to queue.

And lest we forget one of the early pioneers, Mikael Jonsson continues to bake some of the country's best sourdough at **Hedone** in Chiswick.

Barrafina Adelaide Street

Cooking score: 4
⊖ Charing Cross, map 5
Spanish | £40
10 Adelaide Street, Covent Garden, WC2N 4HZ
barrafina.co.uk

One sip of fino, a few slivers of ruby jamón Ibérico, that's all it takes for the Hart brothers' tapas bars to transport you to that little place you know in Barcelona. The restaurants are tiny and they're known for queues, so go early. Note: seating is at bar stools around the counter (though there's private dining at both Covent Garden branches) and the policy is not to seat incomplete groups. The specials board and placemat menu together offer a vast range of croquetas (the cuttlefish ones are magnificent), tortillas, grilled meats, cured meats and fresh seafood (the £18.80-a-pop carabineros are on proud display). Much is prepared en el minuto: our beetroot, orange and fennel salad was sliced and dressed to order; our runny-centred artichoke tortilla individually cooked. For 'postres', flan would have been perfect without its 'crumble' topping. Enjoy fantastic sherries and Spanish wines, many by the glass. Barrafina King's Cross is slated to open late 2018.

Chef/s: Angel Zapata Martin. **Closed:** 25 and 26 Dec, 1 Jan, bank hols. **Meals:** tapas £3 to £19. **Details:** 29 seats.

Barrafina Dean Street

Cooking score: 5
⊖ Tottenham Court Road, map 5
Spanish | £50
26-27 Dean Street, Soho, W1D 3LL
barrafina.co.uk

The Hart brothers relocated their original Soho tapas bar to a new space within their Dean Street restaurant, Quo Vadis (see entry), in 2016. Be prepared to queue. For main entry, see Adelaide Street branch.

Chef/s: Angel Zapata Martin and Juanjo Carillo. **Closed:** bank hols. **Meals:** tapas £3 to £19. **Details:** 26 seats. 12 seats outside.

Barrafina Drury Lane

Cooking score: 4
⊖ Covent Garden, map 5
Spanish | £40
43 Drury Lane, Covent Garden, WC2B 5AJ
barrafina.co.uk

One of two Covent Garden Barrafinas, the Drury Lane site benefits from a covered terrace and private dining room. The significantly revitalised menu includes the house signature arroz negro. For main entry, see Adelaide Street branch.

Chef/s: Angel Zapata Martin. **Closed:** 25 and 26 Dec, 22 Apr, 6 May, 27 May, 26 Aug. **Meals:** tapas £3 to £22. **Details:** 23 seats. 12 seats outside.

Barshu

Cooking score: 4
⊖ Leicester Square, map 5
Chinese | £35
28 Frith Street, Soho, W1D 5LF
Tel no: (020) 7287 8822
barshurestaurant.co.uk
£5 OFF

On a busy Soho corner, Barshu gives a taste of the fiery flavours of Szechuan cooking. The region's spicy pepper and liberal use of chillies bring a 'satisfying tingle' to much of the menu – boiled sea bass with sizzling chilli oil, for example, or 'fragrant chicken in a pile of chillies'. There's an authenticity and a refreshing honesty when it comes to dish descriptions: 'fragrant and hot pig's intestines', 'numbing and hot dried beef'. Get going with sweet-and-sour spare ribs or preserved duck egg with green peppers, or one of their 'herbal' soups (duck with dry bamboo shoots, say). Abalone arrives whole or sliced as sashimi, gong bao chicken with peanuts is a perennial favourite, and among a host of porcine options might be pork meatballs with sweet potato noodles. Finish on a sweet note with black sesame mousse cake. Drink Tsingtao beer, or wines from £23.90.

Chef/s: Mr Zheng. **Closed:** 24 and 25 Dec. **Meals:** main courses £10 to £58. **Details:** 80 seats. Wheelchairs. Music.

You butter believe it

Just when you think you know what butter is, along comes a chef to reinvent it for you. There's no doubt it's having a moment in the UK's restaurants. Here are our inspectors' favourites.

Butter with coarse salt and charred leek ash at **Kitty Fisher's** in Mayfair, London.

Whipped parsley butter in a pool of chive oil at Liverpool's **Röski**.

Smoked bone-marrow butter at **James Cochran EC3**, Aldgate, London.

Funky, homemade wild ferment sour culture butter at **Lake Road Kitchen** in Ambleside, Cumbria.

Whipped, light-as-air brown butter at **Magpie** in London's Mayfair.

Lamb-fat butter (partnering seaweed sourdough) at **Perilla**, in Newington Green, north London.

Melted seafood butter at **Kudu** in Peckham, south London.

Caramelised butter at **Wine & Brine** in Moira, Co Armagh.

Benares

Cooking score: 5
⊖ Green Park, map 5
Indian | £60
12a Berkeley Square, Mayfair, W1J 6BS
Tel no: (020) 7629 8886
benaresrestaurant.com

Atul Kochhar's Mayfair flagship occupies a windowless first-floor room done out in cream and chocolate tones with a beautiful flower-strewn pond at its entrance. The effect is classy, sophisticated and luxurious, a perfect backdrop to the kitchen's inspired forays into the world of modern Indian cuisine. Readers have singled out the pan-seared octopus with cumin-spiced new potatoes for praise, although Kochhar's adroit fusion of Asian spicing and considered European technique also yields such delights as tamarind-glazed tandoori quail with textures of beetroot, or chargrilled Scottish salmon partnered by spiced vermicelli, crab croquette and moilee sauce. Vegetables and breads show the same level of creativity, while crossover desserts include a must-have chocolate and cherry lava cake with fragrant rose bhapa doi (baked yoghurt). With a chef's table, offbeat Asian-themed cocktails and a sharing menu of regional street food in the adjoining bar, Benares is clearly in expansive mood. Added to that, the cooking is complemented by a substantial list of spice-friendly wines complete with a superior Coravin selection by the glass.

Chef/s: Atul Kochhar. **Meals:** main courses £26 to £38. Set L and early D £29 (2 courses) to £35. Tasting menu £98 (6 courses). **Details:** 85 seats. V menu. Bar. Wheelchairs. Music. Children over 7 yrs after 7.30pm.

Bentley's Oyster Bar & Grill

Cooking score: 4
⊖ Piccadilly Circus, map 5
Seafood | £60
11-15 Swallow Street, Mayfair, W1B 4DG
Tel no: (020) 7734 4756
bentleys.org

At the sign of the oyster, on the little connecting street between Regent Street and Piccadilly, you'll find a venerable West End seafood institution. Oysters fed the Victorian poor, before their increasing rarity turned them into a rich folks' delicacy, but there is an agreeable all-in-together feel to the panelled ground-floor room here, where a narrow gangway extends between counter seats and banquettes. Bivalves of varied provenance find their way here, some baked with garlic, some Rockefellered, others Vietnamesed, leading neatly on to fish and seafood specialities that explore the range of the day's catch. Spiced crab and mussel broth might light the way to a main-course showstopper of Dover sole, turbot or the royally laden fish pie. A handful of meats are offered too, and desserts are agreeably light, in the manner of vanilla panna cotta with rhubarb, orange and gingerbread. Appetising wines by the glass lead off a stylistically classified list of excellent choices with prices to match the Mayfair location.

Chef/s: Richard Corrigan and Michael Lynch. **Closed:** bank hols. **Meals:** main courses £20 to £31. **Details:** 130 seats. 60 seats outside. Bar. Music.

Berners Tavern

Cooking score: 5
⊖ Tottenham Court Road, map 5
Modern British | £60
10 Berners Street, Fitzrovia, W1T 3NP
Tel no: (020) 7908 7979
bernerstavern.com

Its walls crowded with a broad assortment of pictures, under look-at-me chandeliers, the Tavern occupies part of the ground floor of the London Edition hotel, another Jason

Atherton refuge in central London, and undoubtedly one of the glitzier ones. Phil Carmichael oversees the rigorous all-day-every-day repertoire, which keeps the place as busy as a city A&E department, and there is a pleasing flexibility. A couple dropping in during Christmas week decided to settle on fish and chips with mushy peas twice, and then a splendid flamed Alaska. Traditional pork pie is sliced from a trolley and dressed with piccalilli, pickled veg and mustard, after which roast cod and crispy squid in tomato consommé might enter the lists, or a bowl of wildly rich mac and cheese, optionally value-added with wine-braised beef blade. American-style finishings take in blueberry pancakes with honey banana, or vanilla waffles and raspberries got up in whipped cream and grated chocolate. Wines run from French country varietals at £9.50 a glass to mature clarets for those throwing caution to the wind.

Chef/s: Phil Carmichael. **Meals:** main courses £19 to £39. Set L £25 (2 courses) to £30. **Details:** 130 seats. Bar. Wheelchairs. Music.

Blacklock

Cooking score: 2
⊖ Piccadilly Circus, map 5
British | £25

24 Great Windmill Street, Soho, W1D 7LG
Tel no: (020) 3441 6996
theblacklock.com

Down the stairs, beneath a boutique, in a former brothel – so far, so Soho – lies the original Blacklock: there's a City branch too (see entry). It's a millennial chop house, delivering groaning plates of red meat (see the 'all in' chop selection and the Sunday roast) without the big bills and spendy wines of yore. Instead, there are wood-fired cuts of pork, beef and lamb (no chicken or 'blah' veggie option) from 'skinny' to Flintstone-esque, sold per chop or by weight, with a short wine list of 'on-tap' pours from £4.50. The clued-up carnivore will note the name of Cornish butcher Philip Warren and specialist cuts such as lamb T-bone, pork tomahawk and bone-in sirloin. Add sides of sticky onion and gravy and 10-hour roasted sweet potato or a new-style Caesar of charred baby gem and anchovy for a killer feast. Should the one pudding – cheesecake – not appeal, summon the cocktail trolley.

Chef/s: Waldek Dural. **Closed:** 25 and 26 Dec. **Meals:** main courses £12 to £18. Set L and D £20. **Details:** 70 seats. Music.

Blandford Comptoir

Cooking score: 3
⊖ Baker Street, Bond Street, map 6
Mediterranean | £38

1 Blandford Street, Marylebone, W1U 3DA
Tel no: (020) 7935 4626
blandford-comptoir.co.uk

On a street well stocked with places to eat there's a lot of competition for Xavier Rousset's tiny wine bar. But the light, modern space holds its own with a welcoming look, drawing in drinkers with a wine enthusiasts' list and diners with a simple menu of Mediterranean dishes designed to complement the wines. Squeeze around the tight-packed tables to share plates of Italian charcuterie, half a dozen Sicilian red prawns, whole suckling pork belly or côte de boeuf, or you could anchor yourself on a bar stool and have a whole roasted quail with polenta and cime di rapa all to yourself. No one could fault the enthusiasm of the sommelier for a wine list that's in danger of hogging the limelight. Not only is it packed with little-known gems and quality drinking but it is also noted for the attention it pays to the £25 to £45 range. This is more than your average wine bar.

Chef/s: Ben Mellor. **Closed:** 24 to 26 Dec, 1 and 2 Jan. **Meals:** main courses £16 to £24. Set L £20 (2 courses). **Details:** 40 seats. 11 seats outside. Music.

Bob Bob Ricard

Cooking score: 3
⊖ Piccadilly Circus, map 5
Anglo-French/Russian | £55
1 Upper James Street, Soho, W1F 9DF
Tel no: (020) 3145 1000
bobbobricard.com

The 'Press for Champagne' button is the first clue: Bob Bob Ricard is a place where one can really go to town. Opulent, extravagant, OTT, this all-booth Soho spot has achieved near legendary status in the space of just a decade. The culinary 'theme' is Anglo-French and Russian 'comfort food for a special occasion', which new kitchen signing Eric Chavot translates into such camera-ready dishes as steak or salmon tartare (with optional caviar), baked oysters 'Brezhnev' with black truffle, and a glossy beef wellington for two. BBR isn't aimed at oligarchs, however: us serfs can take advantage of new 'off-peak' pricing (lunch is up to 20 per cent cheaper than dinner). At inspection, truffle potato vareniki, gluey and bland, were the only hiccup; fillet of sole with lobster and Champagne velouté was near perfect, and rich sour cherry soufflé had a delicious sharp edge. Fine wines are surprisingly accessible; there's even Château d'Yquem by the glass. A second branch is slated to open in the City in late 2018.

Chef/s: Eric Chavot. **Meals:** main courses £20 to £46. **Details:** 130 seats. V menu. Wheelchairs. Music. Children over 12 yrs.

Bocca di Lupo

Cooking score: 2
⊖ Piccadilly Circus, map 5
Italian | £50
12 Archer Street, Soho, W1D 7BB
Tel no: (020) 7734 2223
boccadilupo.com

Perch at the long marble bar if you want a slice of the action at this jam-packed Soho Italian, or aim for the small dining area at the back. Either way, expect regional dishes arranged in sections such as 'raw and cured', 'stewing pot or frying pan'. Sharing is the way to go, so head to Sardinia for smoked ricotta with peas grilled in their pods, detour to Lazio for 'fossil fish' (sea bream charred in a 'sarcophagus of salt') or travel to Tuscany for some properly dressed tagliata. Seasonal pastas might include trofie with potato, green beans and wild garlic pesto, while gelati come from Bocca's sibling Gelupo (opposite). Despite the din and the cramped interiors, readers confirm that the place is running as smoothly as ever, helped along by staff who are eager to please. Bocca's wine list picks up on the regional theme, with some terrific stuff by the glass or carafe.

Chef/s: Jake Simpson. **Closed:** 25 Dec, 1 Jan. **Meals:** main courses £12 to £29. **Details:** 77 seats. Wheelchairs.

★ NEW ENTRY ★

Bombay Bustle

Cooking score: 3
⊖ Oxford Circus, map 5
Indian | £38
29 Maddox Street, Mayfair, W1S 2PA
Tel no: (020) 7290 4470
bombaybustle.com

Nothing evokes the melting pot of Mumbai's culinary heritage like the content of the city's thousands of tiffin tins, distributed daily from home kitchens to office workers thanks to a network of dabbawalas. Bringing the diverse tastes and bustle of Mumbai to Mayfair, this laid-back sibling of nearby Jamavar (see entry) keeps things slick with Art Deco-style surroundings, inspired by the city's first-class train carriages, yet is an altogether modern affair. The menu of eclectic dishes kicks off with more than a dozen sharing plates, of which the rich, beautifully spiced rarah keema pao (goat mince) with pillow-soft buns is a must-try. Move on to tandoori dishes, curries, dhals, dosas and biryanis plus a plethora of breads. A variety of tiffin boxes suits lunch-break crowds. Echoing the dabbawalas' efficiency, service is brisk, and pricing democratic. Spice-friendly wines take second billing to some imaginative cocktails.

Chef/s: Bhaskar Banerjee. **Meals:** main courses £16 to £23.

Bonnie Gull Seafood Shack

Cooking score: 3
⊖ Oxford Circus, Goodge Street, map 5
Seafood | £40
21a Foley Street, Fitzrovia, W1W 6DS
Tel no: (020) 7436 0921
bonniegull.com

It's worth seeking out this tiny, New England-style restaurant in the back streets of Fitzrovia. The bright, nautical-themed interior and emphatic piscatorial name spell out the kitchen's intentions: fish and seafood from British waters form the backbone of a menu that changes daily according to the market. Global influences are glimpsed in snacks of tempura oysters or starters of grilled Cornish sardines teamed with ajo blanco and pickled lemon. At main-course stage there could be whole brill in a raisin, caper and beurre blanc sauce, or lemon sole with anchovy butter and samphire – it's all very lively, simple and unfussy, letting the freshness of the fish and its straightforward treatment speak for itself. Cauliflower cheese gratin and skinny fries with rosemary salt make perfect accompaniments, and to finish there could be buttermilk mousse. Fish-friendly European wines start at £24. There's a second branch on Bateman Street in Soho, W1D 3AN.

Chef/s: Christian Edwardson and James Erasmus. **Meals:** main courses £12 to £27. **Details:** 28 seats. 10 seats outside. Music.

★ NEW ENTRY ★

Breddos

Cooking score: 1
⊖ Oxford Circus, map 5
Mexican | £25
26 Kingly Street, Soho, W1B 5QD
Tel no: (020) 3890 8545
breddostacos.com

Starting out life as a small shack in a Hackney car park, Breddos has settled into two permanent addresses, first in Clerkenwell (see entry) and now in Soho. The inspiration comes from the small taquerias that pepper the roadside in the Americas, and be warned: it fills up fast. Fans perch on bar stools or hunker down at a table, tucking into a feisty guacamole with 'a good kick of chilli' and tortilla chips, before one of the signature tacos – Baja-style deep-fried fish, say, or masa-coated fried chicken with habanero mayonnaise, or a vegetarian version with Bermondsey Frier cheese and king oyster mushrooms. A larger 'La Familia' plate arrives piled high with rare chargrilled onglet and spring greens. To drink: check out the Margaritas and canned beers.

Chef/s: Adrian Hernandez Farina. **Closed:** 25 Dec. **Meals:** main courses £9 to £14. Tacos £6 to £7. **Details:** 77 seats. 6 seats outside. Bar. Wheelchairs. Music.

Café Murano

Cooking score: 4
⊖ Green Park, map 5
Italian | £35
33 St James's Street, Mayfair, SW1A 1HD
Tel no: (020) 3371 5559
cafemurano.co.uk

It's more easy-going than Murano (see entry), but Angela Hartnett's cafe offshoot isn't simply a dressed-down clone of the original. Low lights set the mood in the long dining room, which offers the option of gregarious lunches at round tables, cosy diners à deux, or flying solo at the bar. Hartnett's chefs know how to interpret her distinctive style, particularly when it comes to homemade pasta, risottos and gnocchi (the latter paired with guanciale, baby spinach and peas). Salads such as asparagus with hazelnut pangrattato come bursting with seasonal vigour, while meats bring a rustic note (as in lamb steak with freekeh, mint and goat's curd). Occasional misfires aren't unknown (a one-dimensional dish of cod and lentils, for example), and service can lapse into forgetfulness. On the upside, the regional Italian wine list promises well-priced drinking by the glass or carafe.

Chef/s: Sam Williams and Adam Jay. **Closed:** 25 and 26 Dec. **Meals:** main courses £18 to £32. **Details:** 86 seats. 4 seats outside. Music.

Casa Malevo

Cooking score: 2
⊖ Marble Arch, map 6
Argentinian | £40
23 Connaught Street, Marylebone, W2 2AY
Tel no: (020) 7402 1988
casamalevo.com

The charcoal grill is the star at this slice of Argentina, where red leather chairs and banquettes set the tone, and black-and-white photos on bare-brick walls are reminders of the home country. Empanadas are the perfect opener; lacquered and plump, they come in beef, chicken and vegetarian versions (sweetcorn, pumpkin and mozzarella). Lamb sweetbreads with grilled mushrooms and pea purée make a gutsy starter, while Provoleta cheese with roasted peppers, tomatoes and oregano is a comfort classic. Lustrous prime cuts of meat are cut to order, so anyone wanting to beef up their 300 grams of bife ancho (ribeye steak) or vacío (flank steak) can do just that. The grill also offers up lamb chops (with anchovy salsa verde), lomo, and bife de chorizo, and for non-meat eaters there's pan-fried sea bass with tomato ceviche or pumpkin and goat's cheese ravioli. The wine list acknowledges the rest of the world while highlighting big Argentinian reds.

Chef/s: Jan Suchanek. **Meals:** main courses £15 to £30. **Details:** 37 seats. 6 seats outside. Music.

Les 110 de Taillevent

Cooking score: 4
⊖ Oxford Circus, map 5
French | £50
16 Cavendish Square, Marylebone, W1G 9DD
Tel no: (020) 3141 6016
les-110-taillevent-london.com

The '110' (or 'les cent dix', rather) refers not to how many metres this upmarket Parisian export is from Oxford Street (that would be around 300) but to the number of wines it lists by the glass. The concept's clever: for every dish, there's a choice of four wines by the glass, each in a different price bracket. Take the Comté-crusted beef fillet with artichokes, garlic and parsley – we're on serious bistro turf here – one might choose a modest Côtes du Luberon at £7 for a small glass or an aristocratic Pessac-Léognan at £79 for the same measure. The influence of its Paris siblings is keenly felt in the quietly luxurious surrounds of the former Coutts building. The menu's a gentle update of old-school French, where pig trotter croquette, potato salad and quail's egg and a spelt lobster risotto meet main courses of stuffed rabbit saddle or lamb navarin. Finish with fromage.

Chef/s: Raphael Grima. **Closed:** Sun. **Meals:** main courses £24 to £38. Set L £23 (2 courses) to £28. Tasting menu £59. **Details:** 76 seats. 16 seats outside. Bar. Wheelchairs. Music. Parking.

LOCAL GEM

Ceviche

⊖ Tottenham Court Road, map 5
Peruvian | £25
17 Frith Street, Soho, W1D 4RG
Tel no: (020) 7292 2040
cevicheuk.com

Whether you grab a stool in the colourful bar or push on to the more roomy dining room, you'll find this homage to Lima's bohemian neighbourhood of Barranco alive with the flavours and aromas of Peru. That might be a pisco sour to get you going, or vibrant platefuls of the signature ceviche, but there's also sticky duck wings, and prime cuts cooked on the grill (lamb rump with huacatay herbs and spicy potato purée). The concise wine list has a good showing from South America.

Local Gem

These entries highlight a range of neighbourhood venues, delivering good, freshly cooked food at great value for money.

China Tang London

Cooking score: 2
⊖ Hyde Park Corner, map 6
Chinese | £70
The Dorchester Hotel, 53 Park Lane, Mayfair, W1K 1QA
Tel no: (020) 7629 9988
chinatanglondon.co.uk

Sir David Tang, who established China Tang in the Dorchester's basement over a decade ago, died in 2017, but the breathtakingly glamorous Cantonese restaurant lives on. Amid the exquisite bar decor of floral motifs and framed vintage photographs, cocktails of the old school make a fitting prelude to the Art Deco magnificence of the dining room, which displays traditional and contemporary Chinese artefacts collected by the late founder. Chef Fong looks after the gastronomic side of proceedings, with immaculate dim sum selections added to a set of fixed-price menus that take in precisely rendered familiar dishes such as stir-fried beef in black pepper sauce and sea bass steamed with soy and chilli, as well as a lengthy carte featuring hot-plate lamb with leeks, and a ritzy (dorchestery?) version of Peking duck that has caviar inveigled into it. Vegetarian and gluten-free menus come as a pleasant surprise, the whopping markups on the wine list less so. Glasses begin at £9.

Chef/s: Chun Chong Fong. **Closed:** 24 and 25 Dec. **Meals:** main courses £15 to £68. Set L £35 (4 courses) to £60. Set D £78 (5 courses) to £138. **Details:** 140 seats. V menu. Vg menu. Bar. Wheelchairs. No children under 10 yrs after 8pm.

Chutney Mary

Cooking score: 5
⊖ Green Park, map 5
Indian | £70
73 St James's Street, Mayfair, SW1A 1PH
Tel no: (020) 7629 6688
chutneymary.com

A vision of Indian plush that seems perfectly at ease in Mayfair, Chutney Mary is all about classy opulence – from the moment an impeccably garbed doorman ushers you into the super-smart premises. Pause for crossover cocktails in the Pukka Bar, before heading to the lavishly upholstered dining room with its towering floral arrangements, mirrored ceilings, decorative panels and soft, flattering lighting. The kitchen matches the setting with food of remarkable quality and precision, spiced to perfection and presented with real élan. Much of the repertoire is familiar (tandoori lamb cutlets, dhal makhani, home-style chicken curry), but the menu also offers a selection of contemporary-style small plates ranging from lobster chilli fry to tokri chaat (a straw potato basket filled with street-food favourites, yoghurt and chutneys). Don't ignore the Malabar fish curry or the achar gosht – a house special of on-the-bone goat powerfully infused with pickling spices. Weekend brunch, touting everything from lamb sliders in pau bread to curried eggs with parathas, is a winner. Spice-tolerant wines start at £35.

Chef/s: Manav Tuli. **Closed:** Sun. **Meals:** main courses £19 to £33. Set L £30 (2 courses) to £34. **Details:** 119 seats. V menu.

The Cinnamon Club

Cooking score: 5
⊖ Westminster, map 5
Indian | £75
30-32 Great Smith Street, Westminster, SW1P 3BU
Tel no: (020) 7222 2555
cinnamonclub.com

There's still something enjoyably surreal about this smart Westminster establishment, where new-wave Indian food is eaten in an expansive mezzanine library amid the book stacks. A skylight lets a little sunshine in on the magic, and the menus do the rest, speaking a language of Subcontinental innovation, of which Vivek Singh was among the prime movers. Tandoori octopus with chutney-dressed potato and fennel salad in a tomato and lemon dressing, or pigeon, pumpkin and peanuts with raita, are forward-thinking starters, and if mains don't offer some reassuring classics, such as the rogan josh of Romney Marsh lamb saddle, or chicken korma under a crumble of garlic naan, there's also seared sea bass on spiced red lentils with puffed buckwheat. A side of sangri beans with raisins and fenugreek should complete the deal, although desserts are pretty hot too, when gulab jamun and yuzu tart with iced double cream is on hand. Small glasses (from £5.50) and half-litre carafes (from £22) offer a flexible way into a compendious list of elegant wines chosen with the challenging flavours of the menu in mind.

Chef/s: Vivek Singh and Rakesh Nair. **Meals:** main courses £20 to £40. Set L £28 (2 courses) to £32. Tasting menu £95 (6 courses). **Details:** 250 seats. V menu. Bar. Music.

Clipstone

Cooking score: 5
⊖ Great Portland Street, map 5
Modern European | £35
5 Clipstone Street, Fitzrovia, W1W 6BB
Tel no: (020) 7637 0871
clipstonerestaurant.co.uk

Clipstone is the kind of modern bistro Paris is already good at and London is beginning to do well. Its kitchen has a strong vision, matched by a clever two-pronged wine menu that features a thoughtfully compiled standard list (by glass, carafe and bottle) and a 'single bottle list' of specials. The weekday set lunch is a good option. It includes Clipstone's stellar Paris-Brest, though you'll need to fork out extra for sides and snacks such as the appetite-whetting house pickles. The full menu (Clipstone has switched from a sharing concept to à la carte) offers inventive, vibrant pairings, for example halibut crudo emboldened by cherry, almonds and preserved lemon, or Cornish hake with white asparagus, kohlrabi, gooseberry and yuzu butter. Portions are on a small scale, as is the charming corner spot itself. It's certainly attractive, although the tiled surfaces are easier on the eye than the ear.

Chef/s: Stuart Andrew. **Closed:** Sun, 2 weeks Christmas. **Meals:** main courses £19 to £27. Set L £24 (2 courses) to £27. **Details:** 39 seats. 18 seats outside. Music.

Clos Maggiore

Cooking score: 3
⊖ Covent Garden, map 5
French | £45
33 King Street, Covent Garden, WC2E 8JD
Tel no: (020) 7379 9696
closmaggiore.com

A reputation as a romantic hot spot is well deserved – the conservatory dining room looking positively magical on a summer's evening when the glass is opened up. The maximum effect depends on securing a table in a prime position, the weather coöperating, and, of course, your companion. The elegant setting and refined French-Mediterranean-inspired cooking is reason enough to head for this little corner of Covent Garden, and candles and real fires keep the magic alive year round. An octopus salad with lime zest and basil comes with a pig's trotter croquette in a typical first course, while a main of roast rack of lamb for two comes with chargrilled belly, pipérade and garden herb pesto. Finish with a classic Paris-Brest. Given that prices are 'Covent Garden high', the Monday-to-Thursday pre-theatre menu is worthy of a mention. The stellar wine list traverses the world and, thanks to the Coravin system, includes some fine vintages by the glass.

Chef/s: Marcellin Marc. **Closed:** 24 and 25 Dec. **Meals:** main courses £22 to £30. Set L £25 (2 courses) to £30. Set D £29 (2 courses) to £35. Sun L £38. Tasting menu £65 (5 courses). **Details:** 66 seats. V menu. Music. Children over 3 yrs.

The Colony Grill Room

Cooking score: 3
⊖ Bond Street, map 6
North American | £40
The Beaumont, 8 Balderton Street, Brown Hart Gardens, Mayfair, W1K 6TF
Tel no: (020) 7499 9499
colonygrillroom.com

Having conquered London with their grand European cafés and brasseries (see entries for The Wolseley, The Delaunay, Fischer's et al), Chris Corbin and Jeremy King looked across the pond for inspiration when devising The Colony Grill Room at The Beaumont (the duo's first hotel venture). Monochrome prints of movie stars, red leather banquettes and Art Deco murals provide the glamorous backdrop for a bullish repertoire that runs from breakfast and brunch to an all-day menu dominated by American and British flag wavers. Stateside diner classics such as club salads, lobster rolls, buttermilk fried chicken and Cajun-spiced swordfish are pitched alongside dressed crab, shepherd's pie, kedgeree and roast pork belly, although it's back to the USA for desserts such as red velvet cake, key lime pie, knickerbocker glory and bananas Foster (assembled tableside with theatrical brio). To drink, smoothies and cocktails give way to an illuminating list of wines from the Old and New Worlds.
Chef/s: Christian Turner. **Meals:** main courses £12 to £50. **Details:** 100 seats. V menu. Bar. Wheelchairs. Parking.

Copita

Cooking score: 3
⊖ Oxford Circus, map 5
Spanish | £35
27 d'Arblay Street, Soho, W1F 8EP
Tel no: (020) 7287 7797
copita.co.uk

In sync with the beating heart of Soho, this laid-back tapas bar offers the option of grazing alfresco or perching on high stools close to the busy kitchen. Artisan Spanish hams, charcuterie, cheeses and breads are traditional to a fault, but the daily changing menu quickly moves into less orthodox territory. Plates of green asparagus with chestnut butter and kale, black ink croquetas, 'quick-cured' salmon with gazpacho and fennel or empanadillas de sobrasada with curried yoghurt appear alongside more familiar offerings. By any standards, these are not your usual tapas. Likewise, desserts might include a spiced pear crumble with salted toffee as well as crema catalana and churros. The word 'copita' translates as 'little glass', and that's your cue to dip into the knowledgeably assembled list of fine sherries, cavas and competitively priced Spanish regional wines. Just about everything is available in those titular receptacles, which makes exploration of the viticultural possibilities even more satisfying.
Chef/s: Ngamedy Khouma. **Closed:** Sun, Christmas, New Year, bank hols. **Meals:** tapas £3 to £13. **Details:** 38 seats. 6 seats outside. Bar. Music.

Corrigan's Mayfair

Cooking score: 5
⊖ Marble Arch, map 6
British | £85
28 Upper Grosvenor Street, Mayfair, W1K 7EH
Tel no: (020) 7499 9943
corrigansmayfair.com

'It was refreshing to eat in a place without the affliction of the Instagram food photographer,' enthused one visitor to Richard Corrigan's hospitable Mayfair restaurant that remains a sanctuary from the frenetic pace of modern London and its over-sharing social media enthusiasts. This effortlessly classy – almost club-like – space has taken on a new lease of life with the appointment of Aidan McGee as head chef. The culinary approach has always been to showcase British and Irish produce and McGee does just that, hitting exactly the right notes with a menu that encompasses classics yet is replete with bright ideas. Lobster bisque, whole Dover sole meunière or 38-day dry-aged Hereford rib of beef (for two) are old-school crowd-pleasers, but there's also courgette flower with Yorkshire burrata, aubergine and basil, a fine piece of brill served with squid linguine, fennel and grapefruit, and a sensational blood orange soufflé matched with frozen sheep's yoghurt. Given the high prices on the carte, it's no surprise that the list of thoroughbred wines takes no prisoners; bottles start at £40.

Chef/s: Aidan McGee. **Closed:** 25 and 26 Dec, 1 Jan, Mother's Day, Father's Day, bank hols. **Meals:** main courses £19 to £44. Set L £28 (2 courses) to £34. Sun L £49. Tasting menu £85. **Details:** 85 seats. Bar. Wheelchairs. Music.

Dehesa

Cooking score: 2
⊖ Oxford Circus, map 5
Spanish/Italian | £25
25 Ganton Street, Soho, W1F 9BP
Tel no: (020) 7494 4170
saltyardgroup.co.uk

Named after a woodland area of Spain where the Ibérico pig doth roam, Dehesa is part of the Salt Yard group, which, for the uninitiated, means pin-sharp small plates with Spanish and Italian leanings. The corner spot is rammed much of the time, spilling on to the pavement for a bit of alfresco Soho. Given the name, jamón Ibérico seems the perfect place to start, or cast your net wider with Spanish or Italian charcuterie and cheese plates. Tuck into smoked haddock croquetas with a slick of dill emulsion, pan-roasted hake with calçot onions or squid ink fumet, and remember you can always order more. Corn-fed chicken is cooked a la plancha (with Puy lentils and wild garlic), chorizo picante arrives with celeriac and homemade focaccia, and vegetarian options include chargrilled asparagus with cured egg yolk. Finish with a classy tiramisu. The wine list sticks to the Spanish-Italian theme.

Chef/s: William Breese. **Closed:** 25 Dec, 2 Jan. **Meals:** tapas £5 to £12. Set L £15 (2 dishes). **Details:** 42 seats. 28 seats outside.

The Delaunay

Cooking score: 3
⊖ Temple, map 5
Modern European | £38
55 Aldwych, Covent Garden, WC2B 4BB
Tel no: (020) 7499 8558
thedelaunay.com

One could while away some very pleasant hours ensconced in The Delaunay, the 'buzzy' restaurant from the Corbin and King stable, watching the day unfold. It might begin with a business-friendly breakfast of viennoiserie, kale smoothies, eggs every which way and the reader-recommended kedgeree with the morning papers, in the style of the 'grand café'. An all-day menu smoothes the transition into lunch, when one can find everything from Dorset crab and pink grapefruit cocktail, to chopped salads, currywurst, lobster rolls and pleasingly old-school beef stroganoff. Thursdays bring wild boar shoulder, one of the reliable 'Tagesteller' (daily dishes). It's an exhaustive offering, geared to both the high-rolling and penny-wise. There's no commitment to the full afternoon tea, for example: one can take just a slice of flawless dobos (multi-layered chocolate sponge) or a 'käse rarebit'. Supper is served until late, allowing for the aftershow set to make their way in for cocktails, serious wines, fancy ice cream coupes and the signature steak tartare.

Chef/s: Malachi O'Gallagher. **Closed:** 25 Dec. **Meals:** main courses £15 to £35. **Details:** 175 seats. V menu. Bar. Wheelchairs.

Dinings

Cooking score: 3
⊖ Marylebone, map 6
Japanese | £50
22 Harcourt Street, Marylebone, W1H 4HH
Tel no: (020) 7723 0666
dinings.co.uk

The Lilliputian ground-floor space of this converted Marylebone townhouse is given over to classic sushi and saké. In the basement, defiantly ungarnished with the slightest hint of decoration, you'll find a cross-section of

Japanese izakaya menu staples and more obviously Western bites, figured as 'tapas'. Fish and seafood from the Cornish day boats, supplemented by Scottish salmon and Japanese wagyu beef, are the heart of the operation. The results? A dining experience that can oscillate from fried Padrón peppers with garlic chips to chargrilled shiitakes with truffled salsa and ponzu jelly, and then back from wagyu donburi, and lobster and tomato miso soup, to crab with jalapeño mayonnaise. One visitor felt that, but for its tepid serving temperature, the grilled duck breast could have been 'the best I have ever had'. Lunch deals include fixed-price sushi and sashimi platters of up to 15 pieces with soup.
Chef/s: Masaki Sugisaki. **Meals:** tapas £7 to £40. Sushi and sashimi £5 to £9. **Details:** 28 seats. Music.

Dishoom Carnaby

Cooking score: 2
⊖ Oxford Circus, map 5
Indian | £30
22 Kingly Street, Soho, W1B 5QP
Tel no: (020) 7420 9322
dishoom.com

There's a 1960s vibe to this branch of the groovy Indian chain sited just off Carnaby Street. The house special is sali boti, a Parsi lamb curry with straw potatoes. For main entry, see Shoreditch branch, east London.
Chef/s: Naved Nasir. **Closed:** 25 and 26 Dec, 24 Jul. **Meals:** mains from £7 to £22. **Details:** 198 seats. 25 seats outside. Vg menu. Wheelchairs. Music.

Dishoom Covent Garden

Cooking score: 2
⊖ Leicester Square, Covent Garden, map 5
Indian | £30
12 Upper St Martin's Lane, Covent Garden, WC2H 9FB
Tel no: (020) 7420 9320
dishoom.com

The original Dishoom, in shopping and dining complex St Martin's Courtyard off Long Acre. For main entry, see Shoreditch branch, east London.
Chef/s: Naved Nasir. **Closed:** 25 and 26 Dec, 1 and 2 Jan. **Meals:** main courses £6 to £18. **Details:** 140 seats. 18 seats outside. Vg menu. Bar. Wheelchairs. Music.

Donostia

Cooking score: 3
⊖ Marble Arch, map 6
Spanish | £30
10 Seymour Place, Marylebone, W1H 7ND
Tel no: (020) 3620 1845
donostia.co.uk

A haven of authentic Basque gastronomy secreted away from the West End's hurly-burly, this new-wave tapas bar references the foodie hub of San Sebastián (aka Donostia) – although its pure-white, wood and marble-hued interiors are a touch more formal than those of its rustic Spanish cousins. Platters of top-drawer charcuterie and regional cheeses are the headline acts, closely followed by a brigade of small plates – perhaps crab pintxos, salt cod pil-pil on pipérade or 'cider house' peppers. Alternatively, trade up to bigger servings of monkfish with black rice or veal fillet with ratte potatoes and mustard dressing. Sharing feasts run to whole turbot and dry-aged 14-year Galician Blond beef, while desserts are in the classic mould of Santiago tart. To drink, natural Basque cider is poured from a great height, the G&Ts are big boys, and there's also a spirited assortment of Spanish regional wines. Younger sibling Lurra is across the road (see entry).
Chef/s: Francisco Ignacio Rivera Tellado. **Meals:** tapas £10 to £20. Set L £15 (2 courses) to £20. **Details:** 40 seats. 12 seats outside. Music.

Vegetarian and vegan

While many restaurants offer individual dishes suitable for non-meat eaters, those marked 'V menu' (vegetarian) and 'Vg menu' (vegan) offer separate menus.

LOCAL GEM

Dum Biryani House

⊖ Tottenham Court Road, map 5
Indian | £27
187b Wardour Street, Soho, W1F 8ZB
Tel no: (020) 3638 0974
dumlondon.com

The name refers to the traditional cooking of this famous South Indian dish: kept on 'dum' means a biryani is steamed on a low heat for a few hours until the rice and meat are cooked together to perfection. Aside from the biryanis – lamb shank, chicken or seasonal vegetables – there are other dishes from the Andhra Pradesh region of India including warming lamb and lentil curry, perhaps accompanied by a paratha and side of beetroot raita. Drink spiced cocktails, beer or lassi, or choose from the short wine list.

Ember Yard

Cooking score: 3
⊖ Tottenham Court Road, map 5
Modern European | £30
60 Berwick Street, Soho, W1F 8SU
Tel no: (020) 7439 8057
emberyard.co.uk

A Basque-style grill is the mainstay of the kitchen at compact Ember Yard, where single-species sustainable charcoal and wood from Kent add their own smokey flavours to Spanish- and Italian-inspired small plates, built for sharing. There are classic dishes, such as haddock croquetas, served here with samphire and roasted garlic aïoli, or jamón Ibérico presa, as well as more modish offerings: mackerel escabèche with brown crab emulsion, say, or white asparagus risotto with wild garlic and smoked egg yolk. Hot-smoked Gloucester Old Spot pork belly, glistening from its glaze of cider and smoked apple, might serve two or a few, and on Sundays there's the option of a fixed-price 'feast' with bottomless Prosecco or house wine. Finish with cinnamon churros. It's all served in the dark wood ground-floor restaurant and basement bar, and there's good drinking to be had, too, with creative cocktails, a range of sherries, and well-chosen wines from £23.

Chef/s: Szymon Mackowiak. **Closed:** 25 Dec, 1 Jan. **Meals:** tapas £8 to £11. Set L £20. **Details:** 106 seats. 8 seats outside.

★ NEW ENTRY ★

Evelyn's Table

Cooking score: 3
⊖ Piccadilly Circus, map 5
Modern European | £45
The Blue Posts, 28 Rupert Street, Soho, W1D 6DJ
theblueposts.co.uk

Evelyn's Table, the latest addition to the Palomar and Barbary stable (see entries), is what's fashionably dubbed a 'micro-restaurant' beneath the renovated Blue Posts pub in Chinatown. Excitement mounts as one descends the stairs: this chic, evenings-only hideaway will surprise even those who know Soho inside out. Luke Robinson cooks to an audience of 11 at the counter (and four at tables) so be sure to book. Seafood comes in daily from Cornwall and is sparkling and fresh, though, in the case of perfectly cooked Dover sole with monk's beard, chanterelles and smoked eel, a little overstyled. The small plates menu has a Mediterranean flavour that encompasses pasta (duck cappelletti in broth), tempura-style vegetables (perhaps artichokes or samphire), seafood and a couple of meat dishes. Cooking is sometimes attention seeking rather than attention grabbing but is smartly bookended by Hedone bread, La Fromagerie cheese and exemplary tarte tatin. Service is friendly, wine-pricing too.

Chef/s: Luke Robinson. **Closed:** 25 to 26 Dec. **Meals:** mains £10 to £23. **Details:** 15 seats. Bar. Music.

Fera at Claridges

Cooking score: 7
⊖ Bond Street, map 5
Modern British | £85
49 Brook Street, Mayfair, W1K 4HR
Tel no: (020) 7107 8888
feraatclaridges.co.uk

Glide through the black-and-white chequered foyer of this opulent Mayfair hotel to reach the light, spacious Art Deco-themed restaurant, which soothes visitors with its mood of calming serenity. Subtle sage green, cream and gold hues and lots of glass (in mirrors and ceiling panels) complement the varnished wood of well-spaced tables. The cooking here combines modern juxtapositions with classical technique, used to good effect in a quartet of excellent snacks – among them rabbit with lovage, and Berkswell cheese with onion ash – and a vivacious opener of Portland crab with golden beetroot, tarragon and sea greens. Matt Starling's adventurous ideas are enhanced on the plate by fine presentation and interesting variations of flavour and texture, as seen in a fine piece of brill with chervil root and black tea, or Scottish red deer with blackcurrant, January king cabbage and hen of the woods. Terse dish descriptions give little away, as in a dessert of 'Jerusalem artichoke, toffee apple and salted caramel', though the results are no less satisfying. Supremely capable and courteous staff ensure seamless service, among them a sommelier who makes apposite, sensible suggestions from a carefully selected, inspiring wine list.

Chef/s: Matt Starling. **Meals:** main courses £30 to £46. Set L £42. Tasting menu £85 to £110. **Details:** 90 seats. V menu. Bar. Wheelchairs. Children over 5 yrs.

Fischer's

Cooking score: 2
⊖ Baker Street, Regent's Park, map 6
Austrian | £40
50 Marylebone High Street, Marylebone, W1U 5HN
Tel no: (020) 7466 5501
fischers.co.uk

Evoking the city of schnitzels and Sachertorte as surely as that *Third Man* zither tune, Messrs Corbin & King's vision of old Vienna is a well-padded amalgam of polished wood, picture-lined walls and leather trim with a giant clock at one end of the smart dining room. Starting with breakfasts of buttermilk pancakes, rösti or Kassler ham with a fried egg, the Fischer's kitchen delivers one reassuring hit after another – from chicken soup with spätzle or Bismarck herrings on rye sourdough via numerous würsten (sausages), braised beef (tafelspitz) and grilled veal chops to strudels and ice cream coupes. Elsewhere, Vienna's indulgent konditorei tradition is duly celebrated with a cavalcade of tarts, cakes, florentines and chocolate dobos (a multi-layered sponge). To drink, coffee and hot chocolate (preferably with a separate jug of hot full-cream milk) are obligatory, although it also pays to explore the fascinating list of wines from Mittel European vineyards.

Chef/s: Maciej Banaş. **Closed:** 25 Dec. **Meals:** main courses £14 to £38. **Details:** 98 seats. 4 seats outside. V menu. Wheelchairs.

Frenchie

Cooking score: 5
⊖ Leicester Square, Covent Garden, map 5
Modern French | £45
16 Henrietta Steet, Covent Garden, WC2E 8QH
Tel no: (020) 7836 4422
frenchiecoventgarden.com

Although Covent Garden boasts many places to eat, they are geared very much to tourists, so Gregory Marchand's Parisian spin-off is a welcoming beacon of hospitality. Alongside its bright, contemporary look and mix of seating – at the bar, at one of the close-packed tables or overlooking the kitchen downstairs – Frenchie delivers good service and a short menu of food you really want to eat. The bacon scone (with maple syrup and Cornish clotted cream) is close to achieving cult status, but relish, too, the sparkling fresh simplicities of sea bream tartare with kohlrabi, wild rice, apple and vadouvan (Indian spice blend) or creamy, citrussy burrata with black pepper lavosh (crispbread). It's all such good quality, with mains producing lamb ragù with pappardelle, Kalamata olives, confit lemon and Espelette peppers or hake à la grenobloise with lemon and broccoletti. Desserts follow the same path, perhaps a perfect lemon and passion fruit tart with speculoos ice cream. Drinks run from interesting cocktails to a rather pricey wine list of mainly artisanal producers available by the glass, carafe or bottle.

Chef/s: Gregory Marchand. **Closed:** 25 and 26 Dec, 31 Dec, 1 Jan. **Meals:** main courses £18 to £29. Set L £27 (2 courses) to £30. Tasting menu £58 (5 courses). **Details:** 72 seats. Wheelchairs. Music.

★ NEW ENTRY ★

Frog by Adam Handling

Cooking score: 4
⊖ Covent Garden, map 5
Modern British | £65

34-35 Southampton Street, Covent Garden, WC2E 7HF
Tel no: (020) 7199 8370
frogbyadamhandling.com

Competition might be fierce in restaurant heavy Covent Garden, but readers rate the Adam Handling's 'creative, exciting and tasty' food. This is new British cuisine, so while a simple dish of asparagus, wild garlic and Spenwood cheese will hammer home seasonality, a terrific paring of tuna and beef tartare enlivened with kimchi reveals a kitchen that draws on European and Far Eastern flavours. A lively piece of hake, topped with white crabmeat and given heft by a lingering, sweet-sour shellfish broth, continues this subtle fusion theme. In more traditional fashion, a lamb wellington delivers layer after layer of flavour, from the quality of the meat, to the little shepherd's pie of shoulder ragù, to a side dish of delicious risotto-style barley. Crispy chicken butter with sourdough is a similar delight. Don't be fooled by the unclothed tables and open-to-view kitchen: the Adam Handling experience comes at a price. So it is a shame when the kitchen swings and misses at dessert stage. Better, perhaps, to look to the cocktail menu instead. The well-curated wine list stays on top of emerging trends.

Chef/s: Adam Handling and Steven Kerr. **Closed:** Sun, 25 and 26 Dec. **Meals:** main courses £19 to £35. Set L £30 (2 courses) to £35. Set D £45 (2 courses) to £55. Tasting menu £65 (5 courses) to £95. **Details:** 60 seats. V menu. Bar. Wheelchairs. Music.

LOCAL GEM

La Fromagerie Bloomsbury

⊖ Russell Square, Holborn, map 5
Modern European | £30

52 Lamb's Conduit Street, Bloomsbury, WC1N 3LL
Tel no: (020) 7242 1044
lafromagerie.co.uk

'Is Lamb's Conduit Street the foodiest street in London?' asked a reader, noting that this mini offshoot of La Fromagerie in Marylebone (see entry) is a perfect fit. Open from breakfast to dinner, it combines a pared-back food shop, tiny cheese room and tightly packed café (with a larger, secondary dining room in the basement). The menu offers cheesy things on toast, boards of cheese and charcuterie, Secret Smokehouse smoked salmon, and the likes of spinach, feta, caramelised onion and dill tart, or a full-flavoured twice-baked cheese soufflé. Desserts are designed to work with morning coffee or afternoon tea. To drink, there are cocktails and a clutch of European wines.

LOCAL GEM

La Fromagerie Marylebone

⊖ Baker Street, Bond Street, map 6
Modern European | £25
2-6 Moxon Street, Marylebone, W1U 4EW
Tel no: (020) 7935 0341
lafromagerie.co.uk

This much-loved Marylebone haunt is an urban-minded cheese shop, deli and café rolled into one. Open from breakfast through to high tea (later on Mondays and Fridays), the menu showcases produce sold on the premises, from charcuterie and cheese plates to salads, soups – perhaps broccoli, courgette and basil – and small plates, such as roast peppers, grilled aubergine and romanesco. In addition, there could be organic chicken pie or Yorkshire lamb stew. You can't book, and though it's more of a café than a restaurant proper, many loyal fans have been won by the honest, good-value dishes. European wines from £22.30.

Galvin at Windows

Cooking score: 4
⊖ Hyde Park Corner, Green Park, map 6
French | £82
Hilton Hotel, 22 Park Lane, Mayfair, W1K 1BE
Tel no: (020) 7208 4021
galvinatwindows.com

A lift whizzes you up to the 28th floor of the Hilton on Park Lane where the spacious dining room with its floor-to-ceiling windows and clever tiered layout is designed to optimise the magnificent views across London. It's a full-dress experience with crisp table linen, comfortable padded chairs, muted colour scheme and ranks of clued-up staff – with prices to match. The cooking may not surprise or intrigue, but you're unlikely to be disappointed by Joo Won's interpretation of contemporary French cuisine. A passion for first-class, seasonal ingredients underpins the whole enterprise: a winter lunch brought beetroot-cured Loch Fyne salmon layered over brown crab mousseline and celeriac rémoulade, fillet of halibut with pomme purée, seafood blanquette and parsley, and a loin of Balmoral venison, venison pie, chanterelles, quince chutney and grand-veneur sauce. A 'properly made' mango and passion fruit soufflé provided the final flourish. Good by-the-glass options open the wide-ranging, classy wine list that could soon see your bill head north.

Chef/s: Joo Won. **Meals:** set L £32 (2 courses) to £38. Alc D £65 (2 courses) to £82. Sun L £55. Tasting menu £119. **Details:** 109 seats. Bar. Wheelchairs. Parking.

Gauthier Soho

Cooking score: 6
⊖ Leicester Square, map 5
Modern French | £50
21 Romilly Street, Soho, W1D 5AF
Tel no: (020) 7494 3111
gauthiersoho.co.uk

Ringing the bell to get into this Regency townhouse makes you feel as if you are entering a private dining club. The light, high-ceilinged rooms are more elegant than grand, with simple furnishings, comfortable seating and well-spaced, white-clothed tables. A range of menus, including a seasonal, fixed-price carte, five-course lunch and eight-course 'Goût du Jour' – these last two with vegan versions – hint at the aspirations of the kitchen. Alexis Gauthier is a keen advocate of British produce, so the spring menu, for example, may open with wild garlic velouté with sautéed shiitake, Scottish mushroom royale and a light tempura of fresh herbs. Elsewhere, accurate timing has made the most of Atlantic cod served with new season's peas and broad beans and a classic fish velouté, and of Black Angus fillet partnered by a fricassée of beans and asparagus. Among desserts, chocolate genoise with crunchy chocolate and strawberry (mousse and sorbet) is highly rated. While visitors are unanimous in their praise of the food, service divides opinion; some have felt 'let down', others say it's a 'very

well-oiled machine'. France is obviously the first love of the wine list whose authoritative selection includes impressive bottles and producers.
Chef/s: Alexis Gauthier and Gerrard Virolle. **Closed:** Sun, Mon. **Meals:** set L £30. Set D £50. Tasting menu £45 (5 courses) to £75. **Details:** 80 seats. Vg menu.

★ TOP 50 ★

Le Gavroche

Cooking score: 7
⊖ Marble Arch, map 6
French | £150
43 Upper Brook Street, Mayfair, W1K 7QR
Tel no: (020) 7408 0881
le-gavroche.co.uk

There are two views of Le Gavroche: you either fail to see the need for its lavish formalities and classical French cuisine, or you rejoice in them as testimony to how things were once, and still can be, done. The service, which brings new meaning to bending over backwards, establishes a mood that the green basement room with its sentimental pictures and enveloping upholstery reinforces. And Michel Roux Jr can reliably be expected to undertake a perambulation of the tables at some point, signing books and menus with unflagging courtesy. The Menu Exceptionnel is an eight-course taster whose opening, the rich dairy bomb that is the soufflé suissesse, still delights aficionados. Next might come carpaccio of Belted Galloway in horseradished array, softly roasted scallops with charred leeks in vermouth, and a marination of stone bass in orange with endive and hazelnuts. Exemplary meat dishes could take the form of glazed pig's cheek in rosemary jus, or venison in juniper with stuffed red cabbage. The closing turn may be Calvados-soaked baba, or pistachio and chocolate cake with rum-spiced dried fruits and bitter chocolate sorbet. There's also a traditional three-course format, among whose dishes are many that have been going strong since it all began here in 1967. Wines are a matchless selection of Francocentric classics, opening at £50, and swiftly disappearing into the firmament.
Chef/s: Rachel Humphrey and Michel Roux Jr. **Closed:** Sun, Mon, 2 weeks late Dec. **Meals:** main courses £29 to £77. Set L £70. Tasting menu £175 (8 courses) to £275. **Details:** 80 seats. V menu. Bar.

Great Queen Street

Cooking score: 3
⊖ Covent Garden, map 5
Modern European | £29
32 Great Queen Street, Covent Garden, WC2B 5AA
Tel no: (020) 7242 0622
greatqueenstreetrestaurant.co.uk

With The Anchor & Hope and Oxford's Magdalen Arms as stablemates (see entries), it should come as no surprise that this theatreland evergreen is doggedly unfussy, fast-paced, gregarious, invariably packed and dedicated to the provision of big-hearted, seasonally inspired food. The daily menu moves tantalisingly from plates of Welsh rock oysters and bowls of gazpacho to bountiful sharing feasts such as rolled veal flank with risotto milanese or a mammoth suet-crusted pie packed with rare-breed chicken, fennel and bacon, and every dish screams 'eat me'. Offal gets star billing in dishes of lamb's sweetbreads with pea purée or a warm salad of duck heart, liver, chorizo and sherry vinegar, and if that wasn't enough, hot chocolate pudding with hazelnut ice cream should seal the deal. Speedy 'worker's lunches' live up to their billing and the wine list is a celebration of Old World viticulture, with magnums reinforcing the sharing ethos.
Chef/s: Sam Hutchins. **Closed:** Christmas, bank hols. **Meals:** main courses £15 to £28. Set L £20 (2 courses) to £22. **Details:** 70 seats. 8 seats outside.

★ TOP 50 ★

The Greenhouse

Cooking score: 7
⊖ Green Park, map 5
Modern European | £100
27a Hay's Mews, Mayfair, W1J 5NY
Tel no: (020) 7499 3331
greenhouserestaurant.co.uk
£5 OFF

A long-standing safe haven in Mayfair, reached by means of a plant-lined decked walkway, The Greenhouse has always been a name to reckon with. The dining room is stylish yet understated, airy yet never glaring, public but with enough space for privacy, and the service responds smoothly to the mood at table. While there is no striving for innovation or fashion, the food is modern and beautifully presented, and meals have a spare luxury about them. Arnaud Bignon offers a menu that gives little away: 'Veal sweetbread, pineapple, black sesame, ginger' may tell you the ingredients, but nothing about how they are put together. But the prosaic descriptions only add to the sense of adventure and that dish, as well as smoked eel with beetroot, dill and pumpernickel, has proven to be a punchy, exciting start. Visitors have also spoken well of Galloway beef served with chestnut mushrooms, bone marrow, spring onion and yuzu, and of Rhug Estate organic lamb teamed with aubergine, redolent with the flavours of sesame salt, harissa and soya. Desserts play on interesting combinations, as in a pineapple soufflé with coriander and yellow chilli. Ancillaries – appetisers, petits fours, bread and so on – are determinedly good if not downright clever. The same could be said of the wine list, a substantial 3,000-bin tome; make the most of the sommelier's impressive knowledge to choose something by the glass or bottle.

Chef/s: Arnaud Bignon. **Closed:** Sun, 23 to 4 Jan. **Meals:** main courses £55 to £75. Set L £45 (3 courses). Set D £100 (3 courses). Tasting menu £125 (6 courses) to £145. **Details:** 50 seats. V menu. Vg menu. Wheelchairs.

Gymkhana

Cooking score: 5
⊖ Piccadilly Circus, Green Park, map 5
Indian | £65
42 Albemarle Street, Mayfair, W1S 4JH
Tel no: (020) 3011 5900
gymkhanalondon.com

Mayfair is becoming a prime spot for first-rate Indian cuisine, and this relaxed, colonial-style restaurant from the Sethi family, also owners of Trishna in Marylebone and two branches of Hoppers (see entries), is no exception. The menu mixes the contemporary with the traditional to outstanding effect, the latter appearing in the shape of a genuine tandoor and familiar-sounding dishes such as rogan josh, but these are merely starting points for a kitchen that provides authentic modern Indian cooking. Tandoori masala lamb chops are served medium-rare, paneer tikka on a sweetcorn chaat, and a biryani of tender, flavourful muntjac is mildly spicy, its crisp, light pastry top cracked open at table. Meals are rounded out with snacky starters such as aloo tikka chaat, Punjabi samosa and kid goat methi keema, and side dishes of broccoli and butternut squash and Rajasthani bhindi (okra), as well as the usual rice and breads. To finish, try coconut and cardamom crème brûlée. The extensive wine list gives due consideration to the food.

Chef/s: Sid Ahuja. **Closed:** Sun, Christmas, bank hols. **Meals:** main courses £12 to £45. Tasting menu £75 (6 courses). **Details:** 173 seats. Bar. Music.

Hai Cenato

Cooking score: 2
⊖ Victoria, map 3
Italian | £35
Cardinal Place, 2 Sir Simon Milton Square, Victoria, SW1E 5DJ
Tel no: (020) 3816 9320
haicenato.co.uk

'Set at the base of yet another lookey-likey glass monolith, this time near Victoria Station . . . it feels like a restaurant waiting to become a chain.' So ran the notes of one visitor to this ostensibly New York-style Italian restaurant from the Jason Atherton group. There is a laudable emphasis on English producers – the menu is peppered with the likes of Cobble Lane salami, Wye Valley asparagus and Cumbrian pork chop. Excellent small plates might include a generous portion of sea bass crudo, a citrus dressing providing 'the perfect foil', or grilled octopus, beautifully soft and served with creamy polenta – though it really didn't need the huge pile of rocket dumped on top. Come here, too, for pasta dishes and grills of steaks, lamb rump and whole fish, as well as sourdough pizzas ranging from margherita to fennel sausage and prosciutto. The set two-course lunch/pre-theatre menu is good value, and the predominantly Italian wine list starts at £23.

Chef/s: Frankie Van Loo. **Closed:** 25 Dec, 2 Jan. **Meals:** main courses £10 to £28. Set L and early D £16 (2 courses) to £20. **Details:** 100 seats. 24 seats outside. Bar. Wheelchairs. Music.

Hakkasan

Cooking score: 5
⊖ Tottenham Court Road, map 5
Chinese | £65
8 Hanway Place, Fitzrovia, W1T 1HD
Tel no: (020) 7927 7000
hakkasan.com

Over the past two decades, Hakkasan has extended its tentacles sinuously around the globe, embracing North America, the Emirates, India and China in its cosmopolitan reach. The Hanway Place branch was its first London incarnation, and it remains a singular venue, approached via an Alice-like descent into a nether world of crepuscular lighting and oak lattice screens. Lunchtime and Sunday dim sum are the populist end of the operation, offering duck and bean dumplings, scallop shumai, and baked venison puffs, among much else. Otherwise, it's an opulent journey into contemporary Chinese cuisine, with tasting menus that showcase the likes of sweet-and-sour pomegranate pork, sea bass with truffles and shimejis, and three-mushroom stir-fry with gai lan (Chinese kale) and macadamias. Structurally dazzling desserts include a Jivara chocolate bomb crunchy with praline, or the tropical version of baked Alaska with passion fruit, coconut and pineapple. Coravin-dispensed wines head up a list that's big on pedigree, starting at £29, with premium sakés and appetising cocktails to boot.

Chef/s: Goh Wee Boon. **Closed:** 24 and 25 Dec. **Meals:** main courses £20 to £60. Set L £38. Set D £38 to £128. **Details:** 200 seats. V menu.

Hakkasan Mayfair

Cooking score: 4
⊖ Green Park, Bond Street, map 5
Chinese | £80
17 Bruton Street, Mayfair, W1J 6QB
Tel no: (020) 7907 1888
hakkasan.com

The second manifestation of Hakkasan in central London, the Mayfair branch is a little way from Berkeley Square, a comfortably heeled environ that fits it like a glove. Upwards of 200 lucky souls can be accommodated here, some in the ground-floor restaurant and bar, others in the more intimate, wood-screened ambience of the room downstairs. The menus are identical to those served at Hanway Place (see entry), with fixed-price Signature tasting deals encompassing the likes of golden-fried soft-shell crab spiked with red chilli, cod glazed in rice vinegar, and forays outside the Chinese heartlands for chicken satay and Mongolian lamb chop. The dim sum remain a strong draw for those on the value trail, but if money is no obstacle, the upper reaches of the Signature menus take in Peking duck in Prunier caviar, steamed har gau dumplings with gold leaf, and a glass of Louis Roederer to start. Drinking is a matter of classed-growth wines and premium spirit brands, as well as some dazzling cocktails.

Chef/s: Tong Chee Hwee. **Meals:** main courses £20 to £60. Set L £38. Set D £38 to £128. **Details:** 220 seats. V menu.

Hawksmoor Seven Dials

Cooking score: 4
⊖ Covent Garden, map 5
British | £60
11 Langley Street, Covent Garden, WC2H 9JG
Tel no: (020) 7420 9390
thehawksmoor.com

The handsome Covent Garden branch of the steakhouse group, housed in a former brewery, is particularly versatile: it offers its full menu in the bar, Sunday roasts and pre- and post-theatre menus. For main entry, see Knightsbridge branch, west London.

Chef/s: Karol Poniewaz. **Closed:** 25 and 26 Dec, 1 Jan. **Meals:** main courses £12 to £55. Set L and early D £25 (2 courses) to £28. Sun L £21. **Details:** 142 seats. Bar. Wheelchairs. Music.

Hélène Darroze at The Connaught

Cooking score: 5
⊖ Bond Street, Green Park, map 5
Modern French | £105
16 Carlos Place, Mayfair, W1K 2AL
Tel no: (020) 3147 7200
the-connaught.co.uk

An evening at The Connaught is every bit as classy as a night at the opera. The sultrily lit interiors of the outrageously comfortable dining room, patrolled by staff in choreographic throngs, are an invitation to an old-school treat. Choosing from the menu involves tediously rearranging marbles, marked with the day's ingredients, on a solitaire board, but the reward is Hélène Darroze's thoughtfully composed modern French cuisine. There are surprising juxtapositions all over the show, but nothing too jolting, and much in the way of east Asian reference. The Cornish lobster is got up in Vietnamese garb with spring onions and enoki, while the tandoori-spiced scallop with carrot purée and orange is a long-running hit. Meats are top-drawer, whether in a dish of Basque pork with morels, wild garlic and anchovy, or in the indispensable Challans duck given sweetness and citric power with beetroot and blood orange. A spin on boozy baba with tropical fruits is drenched in the Darroze family's Armagnac, while the rhubarb comes from a Yorkshire grower and is partnered with lemongrass, almonds and ginger. There is a large and splendid wine list, and the option of taking a pre-selected flight to go with your menu choices.

Chef/s: Hélène Darroze. **Meals:** set L £55 (3 courses). Set D £105 (5 courses). Tasting menu £185. **Details:** 65 seats. V menu. Bar. Wheelchairs. Music.

★ NEW ENTRY ★

Hide Above

Cooking score: 6
⊖ Green Park, map 5
Modern British | £95
85 Piccadilly, Mayfair, W1J 7NB
Tel no: (020) 3146 8666
hide.co.uk

£5 OFF

A prime Piccadilly spot represents Ollie Dabbous' latest move on the Monopoly board, and no one in the huge and humming three-tiered space – well hardly anyone – is demurring at the rental he has to pay for landing on Mayfair. Visitors conclude that the new production has restored the élan lately missing in the chef's former homes. The double-height timber front door is the stuff of fairy tales, as is the sweeping oak staircase that leads to Hide Above, a comfortable mezzanine that's all neutrals and blond wood with plenty of natural light from floor-to-ceiling windows. That natural theme pulls through to the food, where an opener of whole baby vegetables, with sunshine-yellow chamomile mayonnaise, is simplicity itself, a light pickling showing great restraint (a theme throughout our inspection meal). It's a prelude to showstoppers such as avocado with gooseberries and basil in a chilled osmanthus infusion, a slice of ice-white, steamed turbot with a masterly combination of pea-green nasturtium broth and pickled yellow courgette, and a cut of tender barbecued Herdwick lamb, which plays beautifully

against the sweetness of a rich, glossy lamb jus and savoury pine nut praline. After that, cherry ripple ice cream is an Instagrammable joy. The slick Hide Ground makes for an egalitarian sort of space, where you can pop in for breakfast, graze on home-cured charcuterie or splash the cash on lunch or dinner – the Mayfair location dictates top-end prices. The wine list has magnificent vintages and rare bottles, but for those of us who live in the real world, staff will recommend affordable wines by the glass or bottle.
Chef/s: Ollie Dabbous, Luke Selby and Josh Angus. **Closed:** 25 Dec. **Meals:** tasting menu £95. **Details:** 62 seats. V menu. Bar. Wheelchairs. Music.

★ NEW ENTRY ★

The Holborn Dining Room

Cooking score: 3
⊖ Holborn, map 5
Modern British | £40
Rosewood Hotel, 252 High Holborn, Holborn, WC1V 7EN
Tel no: (020) 3747 8633
holborndiningroom.com

'The food here is simple and straightforward but it is very, very well done,' notes a fan of this grand British brasserie housed in the equally grand Rosewood Hotel. Huge and high-ceilinged, the dining room is studded with pillars, red leather upholstery and a brass seafood counter, which delivered a 'simple and very good' Cornish crab toast with avocado and Bloody Mary jelly at inspection. But it's not all about fish – this place is known for pies. Consider a golden, deep-filled, hand-raised, buttery puff-crust pie filled with chunks of chicken, girolle mushrooms and a not too-creamy sauce with exactly the right amount of tarragon: 'really one of the best chicken pies I can remember eating'. If pies aren't your thing, there is much besides: 'faultless' grilled octopus with native-breed chorizo and aïoli, for example, or a beef burger with Cheddar, smoked pancetta and truffle fries. Finish with a sticky toffee pudding. There's a secluded dining terrace, too. A European-focused wine list does the job, and the gin bar stocks over 50 bottles.
Chef/s: Calum Franklin. **Meals:** main courses £16 to £44. **Details:** 184 seats. 40 seats outside. Bar. Wheelchairs.

Honey & Co.

Cooking score: 3
⊖ Warren Street, map 2
Middle Eastern | £35
25a Warren Street, Fitzrovia, W1T 5LZ
Tel no: (020) 7388 6175
honeyandco.co.uk

Sarit Packer and Itamar Srulovich's Middle Eastern eatery remains one of the best of its kind in London, proving to be a beacon of hospitality in an area not generally noted for good places to eat. It's so cramped it's a wonder so many people can work and eat in such a tiny space, but the diminutive size certainly doesn't deter regulars who are drawn back by favourite dishes. For some it's the chicken pastilla, for others the prawn tagine with preserved lemon, fennel, artichoke and Pink Fir potatoes. Most, however, seem united in their addiction to the mixed meze selection (singling out spiced cinnamon falafel with tahini for special praise), and the shawarma – slow-cooked lamb shoulder served with burnt pitta, mint yoghurt and pomegranates. There's a selection of tempting cakes, and booking is essential, even if you're planning to drop in for breakfast – we recommend the shakshuka. Cocktails are fun, and wines, from a short, serviceable list, are mainly European.
Chef/s: Sarit Packer and Itamar Srulovich. **Closed:** Sun, 24 to 27 Dec, 31 Dec to 3 Jan. **Meals:** main courses £17. Set L and D £31 (2 courses) to £35. **Details:** 28 seats. 6 seats outside. Music.

Honey & Smoke

Cooking score: 4
⊖ Great Portland Street, Warren Street, map 5
Middle Eastern | £40
216 Great Portland Street, Fitzrovia, W1W 5QW
Tel no: (020) 7388 6175
honeyandco.co.uk

Few capture the intoxicating flavours of the Middle East better than Sarit Packer and Itamar Srulovich of Honey & Co. fame (see entry) and, with Honey & Smoke, they've done it again, creating a simple space, brightened by colourful artwork, where fabulously fresh ingredients get treated with love, respect and spice. Start with a meze plate for the table – herby falafel with creamy tahini, roasted aubergine and tomato salad served with Moroccan sourdough – then move on to something from the grill: charred octopus, say, with crispy potatoes covered in a paprika and garlic dressing, or smokey aubergine filled with tahini and topped with a burnt egg yolk, and hamama (roasted pigeon with onion and golden raisin rice). When it comes to something sweet, look no further than the already iconic feta and honey cheesecake. Breakfast brings spinach and feta börek and Moroccan pancakes. The short wine list is bolstered by stimulating cocktails and a few beers.

Chef/s: Sarit Packer and Itamar Srulovich. **Closed:** Sun, Mon, 24 to 27 Dec, 31 Dec to 3 Jan. **Meals:** main courses £17 to £18. Set L and D £32. **Details:** 80 seats. Bar. Wheelchairs. Music.

Hoppers Soho

Cooking score: 3
⊖ Tottenham Court Road, map 5
Sri Lankan | £29
49 Frith Street, Soho, W1D 4SG
hopperslondon.com

A 'hopper' (or appam) is a Sri Lankan pancake made from fermented rice and coconut milk, and is 'a lot nicer than it sounds'. The Sethi family's walk-in eatery (you can't book) looks like an urban shack and is busy much of the time – a 'virtual queue' system means you could always choose to wait for a table in the comfort of a local hostelry. Those hoppers and dosas arrive with vibrant chutneys and sambals, while full-flavoured curries include tender black pork and crab versions. Small plates of mutton rolls, goat roti, and tamarind and ginger chicken wings are good for sharing, and if you're looking to push the boat out, check out the Ceylonese spit chicken roast with gutukola (Sri Lankan greens) sambal and pol (coconut) roti, or go for the full-on feast menu. Drink cool cocktails such as saffron and almond sour, Sri Lankan beers, or wines from £14. There's a second, bookable, Marylebone branch (see entry).

Chef/s: Renjith Sarath Chandran. **Closed:** Sun, Christmas, bank hols. **Meals:** main courses £9 to £21. Feasting menu £29. **Details:** 40 seats. V menu. Bar. Music.

★ NEW ENTRY ★

Hoppers St Christopher's Place

Cooking score: 3
⊖ Bond Street, map 6
Sri Lankan | £29
St Christopher's Place, 77 Wigmore Street, Marylebone, W1U 1QE
Tel no: (020) 3319 8110
hopperslondon.com

The second branch of Hoppers, which has brought family-style Sri Lankan cooking to Marylebone, is distinguished from the first, in Soho (see entry), by its willingness to take bookings. Divided across two floors, with bench seating and sharing tables, there's a vibrant ambience with cooking to match. Armed with the glossary on the menu, you might feel emboldened to eschew the set banqueting options and pick your way through lamb kothu roti, a soft flatbread stuffed with flavourful meat, egg and greens in a chilli-warm sauce, classic (and huge)

masala dosas filled with mildly spiced potato, sambal of Maldive fish with ground coconut, onion, lime and red chilli, or karis of chicken, prawns, crab or lamb shank. Then there are the hoppers themselves: fermented rice batter cooked in a bowl shape, with an optional soft-cooked egg. And for dessert? An ice cream sandwich. Regional punches, some based on Ceylonese arrack, supplement a small wine selection from £28.

Chef/s: Renjith Sarath Chandran. **Closed:** Sun, Christmas, bank hols. **Meals:** main courses £7 to £20. Feasting menu £29. **Details:** 100 seats. 6 seats outside. V menu. Bar. Wheelchairs. Music.

★ NEW ENTRY ★

Ikoyi

Cooking score: 4
⊖ Piccadilly Circus, map 5
West African | 50

1 St James's Market, St James's, SW1Y 4AH
Tel no: (020) 3583 4660
ikoyilondon.com

A small but stylishly outfitted unit in the somewhat soulless new St James's Market development is the unlikely home of this West African-inspired restaurant, one of London's most original new openings by far. Named after a well-to-do Lagos suburb, Ikoyi may be cramped but it looks the part with its terrazzo floor, earthenware lights and handmade ceramics. Waiters combine plate-carrying duties with translation services. Mbongo, ndolé, ehuru, sinasir... they know their way around the menu, the ingredients used and the techniques involved. A curious-looking dish, buttermilk plantain dusted in raspberry salt with smoked Scotch bonnet mayo is a primer on the house style: surprising, accomplished and humming with heat. Octopus, ndolé and blackened calçot onions is the standout starter, faultlessly tender flesh against a lurid green watercress and spinach purée. Monkfish, banga (palm fruit) and citrus asaro is beautifully cooked. Mango parfait with ogbono (seed paste) suggest puddings are not a forté. Prices are punchy and wines, from £32, spice-friendly.

Chef/s: Jeremy Chan. **Closed:** Sun, 25 and 26 Dec. **Meals:** main courses £26 to £35. Tasting menu £50 (4 courses) to £70. **Details:** 42 seats. Bar. Wheelchairs. Music.

★ NEW ENTRY ★

Indian Accent

Cooking score: 4
⊖ Green Park, map 5
Indian | £55

16 Albemarle Street, Mayfair, W1S 4HW
Tel no: (020) 7629 9802
indianaccent.com

The much-travelled Manish Mehrotra returned to London in 2017 to open this third branch of Indian Accent, which has siblings in Delhi and New York. An aubergine-fronted Mayfair address with marble tables and sultry lighting feels right for the aspirational reinventions of traditional Subcontinental food that the group has honed. From the off, your culinary moorings are loosed, as things look and taste unusual: an espresso cup of pumpkin and coconut soup comes with a naan filled with blue cheese, its pungency working unexpectedly well with the spices. Intermediate dishes comprise the likes of phulka, a pair of flatbreads topped with pulled pork, chilli and scratchings. Ghee-rich lamb curry comes in a copper pan, its deeply spiced meat flaking into the sauce, while seared scallops and rava prawns on dried shrimp rice is a crisp and sweet treat. Dessert might be a thrilling treacle tart with vanilla ice cream, or a comfortingly bland pink-tinged cylinder of sweet rice, dotted with dried barberries and sauced with almond milk. Swinging cocktails and aromatic wines by the glass feature on an enterprising list that's up to the mark.

Chef/s: Manish Mehrotra. **Closed:** Sun, 25 and 26 Dec, 1 Jan, 28 and 29 May, bank hols. **Meals:** main courses £16. Set L £25 (2 courses) to £30. Set D £55 (3 courses) to £65. Tasting menu £45 to £80. **Details:** 70 seats. 4 seats outside. Music. Children over 10 years.

The Ivy

Cooking score: 2
⊖ Leicester Square, map 5
Modern European | £50
1-5 West Street, Covent Garden, WC2H 9NQ
Tel no: (020) 7836 4751
the-ivy.co.uk

It seems fitting that this West End legend should be located opposite the theatre showing 'the world's longest-running play' – although *The Mousetrap* is a mere stripling compared to The Ivy's 100-year run. The A-listers may have moved on to playgrounds new, but some of our national treasures still feel right at home amid the harlequin stained glass, retro table lamps, green leather banquettes and glittering vintage-style bar in the centre of the dining room. Of course, it's all about the experience, but the international menu also plays a vital supporting role: the signature hamburgers are properly charred and meaty, the fishcakes appear like old friends and there are surprises from faraway lands, too – perhaps salmon ceviche with blackened corn, butter chicken masala or crispy duck and watermelon salad. To finish, encores ring out for the knickerbocker glory and baked Alaska. Wines suit any occasion, although pushing the boat out is almost *de rigueur*.

Chef/s: Gary Lee. **Closed:** 25 and 26 Dec. **Meals:** main courses £16 to £35. **Details:** 120 seats. Bar. Wheelchairs. Music.

J. Sheekey

Cooking score: 4
⊖ Leicester Square, map 5
Seafood | £55
28-35 St Martin's Court, Covent Garden, WC2N 4AL
Tel no: (020) 7240 2565
j-sheekey.co.uk

This crimson-fronted seafood restaurant in the heart of theatreland looks every inch the part with a few terrace tables outside, and a cocooning ambience of old panelling within. The action is centred on a sweeping horseshoe-shaped bar, where the bounty of the sea is served on tiered stands as though Edward VII still occupied the throne. One or two more speculative modernities have inveigled their way in, such as stone bass and salmon ceviche dressed in jalapeños and black quinoa, but mostly you won't err if you plough the time-honoured furrow of fish stew with braised fennel and aïoli, fried skate wing in caper butter or fully loaded fish pie. With dressed crab, potted shrimps and caviar to ease you in, it's all good, and the heart-warming pudding might be gooseberry pie with elderflower ice cream. French-led wines are good, though the financial centre of gravity is high, from a starting price of £27.

Chef/s: Andy McLay. **Closed:** 25 and 26 Dec, 1 Jan. **Meals:** main courses £18 to £44. Set L £24 (2 courses) to £29. **Details:** 75 seats. 40 seats outside. Bar. Wheelchairs. Music.

Jamavar

Cooking score: 5
⊖ Bond Street, Green Park, map 5
Indian | £60
8 Mount Street, Mayfair, W1K 3NF
Tel no: (020) 7499 1800
jamavarrestaurants.com

Since the last edition of the Guide there have been changes in the kitchen here, with Mehernosh Mody now at the helm. The colonial-style interior remains inviting, filled with marble, gold mirrors, dark wood panelling and tables inset with mother-of-pearl. Despite such luxury, there's an informal feel and staff are attentive and good at putting diners at ease. The simple descriptions on the menu mask craft and subtlety and while prices are high, set menus help to cushion the blow. One visitor was particularly impressed by a chicken tikka – 'very good indeed, perfectly balanced' – that came with sweet basil purée, pickled radish and raita. Beautifully cooked king prawns in a vivid yellow, impeccably spiced creamy coconut curry also impressed, while accompaniments of basmati rice, naan, spinach with cream cheese and yellow dhal have garnered praise. To finish, consider rhubarb and saffron rabri kulfi. Indian-inspired cocktails and wines (from £35) have been thoughtfully chosen to support the food, but prices reflect the Mayfair address. A second restaurant, Bombay Bustle, has opened in Maddox Street (see entry).

Chef/s: Surende Mohan and Mehernosh Mody. **Closed:** Sun, 25 and 26 Dec, 1 Jan. **Meals:** small plates £8 to £15. Main courses £18 to £30. Set L and early D £24 (2 courses) to £29. Tasting menu £70. **Details:** 108 seats. 8 seats outside. V menu. Music.

★ NEW ENTRY ★

Jean-Georges at the Connaught

Cooking score: 5
⊖ Bond Street, Green Park, map 5
Modern British | £55
16 Carlos Place, Mayfair, W1K 2AL
Tel no: (020) 7107 8861
the-connaught.co.uk

New York's superstar chef Jean-Georges Vongerichten is back and he's taken up residence in a glamorously sleek, high-gloss room at The Connaught, with wraparound windows overlooking Mount Street. An all-day casual dining menu brings a touch of luxury, which plays to the well-heeled clientele. Expect modern British classics with broad appeal, such as posh fish and chips (with sweet pea gribiche), Dover sole, lamb chops and the like sharing the limelight with 'an addictive' black truffle and fontina cheese pizza and the chef's French-Asian creations. Tuna tartare is predictably paired with avocado but given zip by a chilli oil and ginger vinaigrette. A venison main arrives with beetroot, a chestnut purée lightly infused with ginger and a side of pomme purée, all finished off by a truffle-infused jus. Desserts are handled with supreme dexterity, especially a flamboyant sugar-work orange, filled with bergamot foam and served with shortbread, orange curd and mandarin sorbet. Cocktails head the drinks list, but wines are expensive, with only a handful below £50.

Chef/s: Jean-Georges Vongerichten. **Meals:** main courses £15 to £49. Tasting menu £88 (7 courses).

★ NEW ENTRY ★

Jidori Yakitori

Cooking score: 3
⊖ Covent Garden, map 5
Japanese | £25
Covent Garden
jidori.co.uk

Styled after Tokyo's yakitori joints, this minimalist, pastel-toned space is set over three narrow levels with a basement karaoke room. Japanese-style skewered chicken is the main attraction and almost no part of the bird goes unused. Only free-range specimens qualify for skewering and grilling: thigh is paired with spring onions, tender heart with bacon, and tsukune (minced chicken) skewers – a Japanese street-food staple – come with raw egg yolk and tare (dipping sauces) for dunking. Feeling indecisive? Then opt for the omakase menu (chef's choice) – three yakitori with rice, sides and soft-cooked egg. Veering away from poultry doesn't disappoint as red prawn sashimi, katsu Scotch egg and miso-glazed aubergine skewers showcase the kitchen's talents. Don't stop here – ginger ice cream with miso caramel, sweet potato crisps and black sesame has won legions of fans. Craft beers, cocktails, saké and whisky head up the fun drinks list.

Chef/s: Shunta Matsubara. **Closed:** Sun. **Meals:** small plates £3 to £12. Set D £10 to £18.

★ NEW ENTRY ★

Jugemu

Cooking score: 3
⊖ Piccadilly Circus, map 5
Japanese | £35
3 Winnett Street, Soho, W1D 6JY
Tel no: (020) 7734 0518

It may be located on a Soho back street but tiny Jugemu, with its strong Japanese following, feels more Tokyo than London.

Look beyond the cramped tables and tight-packed counter seating and concentrate instead on Yuya Kikuchi's sparkling fresh sushi and glistening sashimi. With several menus and a number of specials, choosing can be difficult, so it pays to order the omakase (chef's choice) sashimi or nigiri sushi: yellowtail, sea bass, mackerel, turbot, eel, razor clams and more have passed the quality test. Then build a meal from a list of small dishes, say soba and mixed seafood tempura, prawn dumplings or beef tataki, add on a more experimental 'special', perhaps fried squid with sweet chilli and mozzarella. If you are sitting at the counter, the made-to-order hand rolls are a must. Service is welcoming, booking advisable and prices reasonable – provided you don't get carried away. To drink, there's tea, beer or saké, plus a few wines (by glass and bottle) selected to complement the food.
Chef/s: Yuya Kikuchi. **Closed:** Sun. **Meals:** small plates £4 to £10. Assorted sushi/sashimi £13 to £33.

★ NEW ENTRY ★

Kettners

Cooking score: 2
⊖ Leicester Square, Tottenham Court Road, map 5
French | £40
29 Romilly Street, Soho, W1D 5HP
Tel no: (020) 7375 061
kettnerstownhouse.com

Kettners is a Soho legend. Opened in 1867, it was the first restaurant to bring French cooking to the capital. Now owned by Soho House, it has been remodelled as a hotel and restaurant – the sympathetic re-creation of the interior (Art Nouveau plasterwork, mirror-lined walls) feels 'like a warm hug of nostalgia' – and there is a 'terrific lively ambience' to the place. The menu, too, has been revamped; the culinary compass now points to Britain, the style simple, seasonal and unfussy. Small bites ('warm and cheesy' Gruyère gougères), salads, sandwiches, raw seafood and oysters lead on to more substantial dishes of, say, wild sea bass with monk's beard or roast breast of Banham chicken with black truffles, the leg meat stuffed with duxelles, and served with pommes Anna. Panna cotta lightly infused with ginger and lifted by crushed salted caramel biscuit and excellent Yorkshire rhubarb makes a soothing finish. Drink cocktails or look to the enterprising wine list with some good choices at fair prices.
Chef/s: Jackson Berg. **Meals:** set L, and early and late D £20 (2 courses) to £24. Sun L £30 (3 courses). **Details:** 65 seats. 12 seats outside. Bar. Wheelchairs. Music.

Kiku

Cooking score: 3
⊖ Green Park, map 5
Japanese | £40
17 Half Moon Street, Mayfair, W1J 7BE
Tel no: (020) 7499 4208
kikurestaurant.co.uk

Slate-grey stone, blond wood and fretwork screens create a simple, clean look at this popular, long-standing family restaurant (established 1978) just round the corner from the Japanese Embassy on Piccadilly. The à la carte cruises its way through hot and cold appetisers, soup, salads, grills, hotpots and the like, or you can opt for the full kaiseki works (set menus). Sushi and sashimi is of the highest quality, and there has been praise for the tempura, both prawn and assorted, and grilled chicken with teriyaki sauce. Otherwise, the repertoire covers everything from an assorted fresh seaweed salad and dobin mushi (clear soup) to hotpots of sukiyaki and shabu-shabu (for two or more). This is an enjoyable place where a single luncher can come for a good-value Kiku set, or the slightly more elaborate fixed-price menus built around sushi, sashimi, beef teriyaki or oroshi tonkatsu (fried pork cutlet). Drink saké, beer or wine from £17.50.
Chef/s: F Shiraishi and Y Hattori. **Closed:** 24 to 28 Dec, 1 Jan. **Meals:** main courses £15 to £78. Set L £24 (4 courses) to £34. Set D £59 (7 courses) to £82. **Details:** 100 seats. Wheelchairs.

Kiln

Cooking score: 4
⊖ Piccadilly Circus, map 5
Thai | £26
58 Brewer Street, Soho, W1F 9TL
kilnsoho.com

The queues can be a 'nightmare' and the 'waiting game' prior to securing a table a real kerfuffle, but that's a small price to pay for some of the most mould-breaking Thai food currently available in London. Make no mistake, Kiln is red-hot – a dark, cramped and noisy place with a long stainless-steel counter and seats right next to a BBQ grill that not only blasts out waves of blistering heat, but also does the business on assorted specialities from northern Thailand, Burma and China's Yunnan province. Indigenous ingredients are supplemented by supplies of British seasonal produce (notably day-boat fish and rare-breed meat) and the results receive an emphatic thumbs-up: skewers of cumin-spiked aged lamb line up alongside turmeric-infused smoked sausages, while seafood might include Laos-style skate wing or a jungle curry of pollock. Kiln also specialises in richly flavoured claypots, along with sides including must-order stir-fried Cornish greens. Beers, ferments and cocktails flow, but don't ignore Kiln's wine list – a short, snappy and 'unusually intelligent' slate that's properly tailored to the explosive demands of the food.

Chef/s: Nick Molyviatis. **Closed:** 25 and 26 Dec, 1 Jan. **Meals:** plates £7 to £34. **Details:** 50 seats. Music.

Kitchen Table

Cooking score: 6
⊖ Goodge Street, map 5
Modern British | £125
70 Charlotte Street, Fitzrovia, W1T 4QG
Tel no: (020) 7637 7770
kitchentablelondon.co.uk

After waiting in the fervour of fast-casual favourite, Bubbledogs, a tap on the shoulder indicates that you're ready to be led through the brown leather curtains and into a wildly different space. A highly functional kitchen awaits, with 20 counter seats giving a window into the intricate mind of James Knappett. Meticulous care and attention manifests in a mesmeric culinary performance, and a respectful hush fills the room. Sandia Chang, co-owner, sommelier and wife to James, greets you with genuine warmth and sets the tone for a hugely personal evening. Provenance is absolutely key here. A stunning array of produce from across the British Isles is engaged to memorable effect across 14 courses, intertwined with subtle nods to Knappett's kitchen experiences across the world – so Cornish lobster is decadently paired with Australian black truffle and a charcoal cream, and roasted black bream appears with green asparqagus, sweet woodruff, black garlic and lovage. Heavenly oven-fresh Parker House rolls are served with a trio of butters: brown, garlic and wild garlic. 'Chicken', a snack of crispy skin topped with rosemary mascarpone and bacon jam is a bite-size reboot of this classic flavour combination reinvented for the modern palate. Expert wine advice allows for the list to be explored and enjoyed as it should, and while the experience will take an entire evening, it is time well spent.

Chef/s: James Knappett. **Closed:** Sun, Mon, Tue. **Meals:** tasting menu £125. **Details:** 20 seats. Wheelchairs. Music. Children over 12 yrs.

Kitty Fisher's

Cooking score: 5
⊖ Green Park, map 5
Modern British | £50
10 Shepherd Market, Mayfair, W1J 7QF
Tel no: (020) 3302 1661
kittyfishers.com

Diminutive Kitty Fisher's stands in sharp contrast with the swank and swagger of its Mayfair peers. Essentially a neighbourhood restaurant, this atmospheric split-level bistro is perfect for a cosy meal (the few outside tables are in high demand on sunny days). Chef George Barson, dividing his time between here and new Covent Garden sibling Cora

Pearl (opening as we went to press), is going great guns in the kitchen with contemporary, considered dishes on which every ingredient earns its place. 'Delicious is an understatement,' observed an inspector of the toasted brown sourdough and whipped butter with charred leek ash. Barson introduces the flavour of the wood grill judiciously, in charred rounds of juicy octopus with chilli, tomatoes and mellow lovage purée, or an extraordinarily good piece of cod with brown shrimp and cauliflower. Shiny silken chocolate ganache, malt ice cream and stout mousse to finish is a treacly delight. House wine at £4.50 a glass is almost unheard of in Mayfair.

Chef/s: George Barson. **Closed:** Sun, 24 to 27 Dec, 31 Dec to 2 Jan, bank hols. **Meals:** main courses £28 to £31. Set L £30 (2 courses) to £35. Sun L £50. **Details:** 36 seats. 8 seats outside.

Little Social

Cooking score: 5
⊖ Oxford Circus, map 5
Anglo-French | £60
5 Pollen Street, Mayfair, W1S 1NE
Tel no: (020) 7870 3730
littlesocial.co.uk

Jason Atherton's London portfolio covers a range of eclectic dining options, this atmospheric bistro being considered the dress-down alternative to the flagship Pollen Street Social (see entry) opposite. It's a rather inviting, if noisy, room of ox-blood booth seating, dark wood and French posters, where the mood is casual and Cary Docherty's menu a confident fusion of Anglo-French styles. Dishes are always comforting and big flavoured. Cumbrian bavette tartare with quail's egg yolk and gaufrette potatoes (waffle crisps), followed by whole roasted Dover sole à la meunière or 40-day aged Buccleuch Estate côte de boeuf represent the old guard, while warm smoked eel with beetroot, horseradish cream and watercress, and spaghetti with chilli, garlic, crab, mint and Parmesan strike a more contemporary note. Finish with clementine pavlova and passion fruit sorbet or excellent French cheeses from La Fromagerie. There's also a bargain set (and pre-theatre) menu, and interesting cocktails, and the equitably spread wine list does the job with good choice by the glass and carafe.

Chef/s: Danny Hewett and Cary Docherty. **Closed:** Sun, 25 Dec, 2 Jan. **Meals:** main courses £23 to £37. Set L and early D £20 (2 courses) to £25. **Details:** 50 seats. Wheelchairs. Music.

Locanda Locatelli

Cooking score: 4
⊖ Marble Arch, map 6
Italian | £95
8 Seymour Street, Marylebone, W1H 7JZ
Tel no: (020) 7935 8390
locandalocatelli.com

Step through the doors of this glossy, discreet Italian on the ground floor of the Hyatt Regency Churchill Hotel and be prepared to be impressed. Giorgio Locatelli's food offers a distinct blend of creativity and fashion, backed up by solid technique. The sheer quality of ingredients stands out on a menu that's traditionally divided into five sections, from antipasti to dolci. Locatelli knows his audience, tempting diners with the likes of an oh-so-simple broad bean, rocket and ewe's cheese salad, or a splendid rendition of a classic – minestrone di verdure. Perfect pasta, say a silky linguine with lobster, tomato, garlic and sweet chilli, a robust dish of roasted monkfish with walnut and caper sauce and monk's beard, or squab pigeon with lentils and garlic give an idea of the kitchen's mightily impressive capabilities. Desserts are clever and innovative, perhaps liquorice semifreddo with lime jelly, Branca Menta sauce and finger lime caviar. Expect a tremendous bill, something the wine list, which explores Italy with insightful selections, will do little to alleviate.

Chef/s: Giorgio Locatelli and Rino Bono. **Meals:** main courses £27 to £37. **Details:** 85 seats. Bar. Wheelchairs.

Lorne

Cooking score: 4
⊖ Victoria, map 3
Modern British | £40
76 Wilton Road, Victoria, SW1V 1DE
Tel no: (020) 3327 0210
lornerestaurant.co.uk

Something of a domestic feel has been conjured in this narrow Pimlico venue, with its bare-boarded floor, indoor planters and kitchenette stools, as well as a row of seats at a marble counter. A flooding calamity closed Lorne for a while in early summer 2018, but the reopening sees Peter Hall's carefully worked, eclectic menus maintaining their resourceful raids on Mediterranean technique for main dishes such as harissa-lashed cod and octopus with colour-coded accompaniments of black ink gnocchi, rainbow chard and white beetroot, or veal with puntarelle, apple, bacon, garlic and sage. Prior to that, there could be salmon aromatically cured in gin, bergamot and linseed, with populist pile-ups for afters, in the manner of chocolate, banana, peanut and caramel, or pineapple, coconut and ginger, the latter spiked with tepache, a Mexican drink of fermented pineapple rind. An enjoyably diverse wine list unrolls across both hemispheres, even finding room for a clutch of German Rieslings. Bottles start at £22.

Chef/s: Peter Hall. **Closed:** Sun, 23 Dec to 2 Jan, bank hols. **Meals:** main courses £19 to £24. Set L and early D £22 (2 courses) to £27. **Details:** 40 seats. Music. No children.

Lurra

Cooking score: 2
⊖ Marble Arch, map 6
Spanish | £45
9 Seymour Place, Marylebone, W1H 5BA
Tel no: (020) 7724 4545
lurra.co.uk

Thanks to Melody Adams and Nemanja Borjanovic falling in love with Basque cuisine on a wine-tasting trip, London has not just one, but two restaurants devoted to celebrating the region's distinct flavours and cooking techniques. First, there was Donostia (see entry), then – just a few yards away – Lurra. The pared-down Nordic-style dining room, all pale wood and marble, with mint-green stools surrounding the open kitchen, echoes the simplicity of the food, much of which comes off the traditional Basque-style wood and charcoal grill. Bites and tapas include sourdough with grilled bone marrow, jamón croquetas and Padrón peppers, or a wooden board of delicate crab pintxo. If you're after something more substantial, follow with a signature sharing plate: either grilled dry-aged steak from the celebrated 14-year-old Rubia Gallega cow, a whole wild turbot or slow-cooked lamb. Finish with burnt cheesecake, the classic San Sebastián pintxos bar dessert. A glass of lightly sparkling txakoli from the almost exclusively Spanish list makes for an accommodating pairing.

Chef/s: Charlie Bourn. **Meals:** main courses £12 to £22. Set L £25 (3 courses) to £32. **Details:** 70 seats. 25 seats outside. Music.

★ NEW ENTRY ★

Magpie

Cooking score: 6
⊖ Piccadilly Circus, map 5
Modern British | £40
10 Heddon Street, Mayfair, W1B 4BX
Tel no: (020) 3903 9096
magpie-london.com

The Regent Street area is beginning to fill up with exceptionally good eating, and Sam Herlihy and James Ramsden's Magpie is a case in point. Decor-wise it's not much – a bit scuffed, a bit dark, almost bare walls, plain wood tables, dangly lights – but staff are genuinely committed and the food is a delight, a masterclass in the new British cuisine. Mainly small plates (sharing, of course) focus on the best seasonal produce with some welcome inflections from further afield – sea trout crudo, say, with a tahini and tangerine sauce ('so good we almost ordered another plate'). It is possible to eat

conventionally, sharing a couple of appetisers (crudités with a fabulous miso 'bagna cauda', and delicious nuggets of deep-fried cod brandade), picking a small plate as a starter ('next time I go I'm having that fried chicken coq au vin all to myself') and going on to a bigger plate each, say pork collar with endive, lentils and apricot, or cod with sushi rice cake and pickled pak choi. Desserts are pitch-perfect, too, especially a creamy black bean mousse, a layer of passion fruit cutting its richness, with chilli sorbet giving heft. As for drinks, imaginative cocktails and modern, well-chosen wines suit the food admirably.
Chef/s: Adolfo de Cecco. **Closed:** 24 Dec to 2 Jan. **Meals:** small plates £4 to £11, main courses £13 to £16. **Details:** 50 seats. 12 seats outside. Bar. Wheelchairs. Music.

LOCAL GEM

Mele e Pere

⊖ Piccadilly Circus, map 5
Italian | £35
46 Brewer Street, Soho, W1F 9TF
Tel no: (020) 7096 2096
meleepere.co.uk

Soho's very own trattoria and vermouth bar now has a few tables on the ground floor, but most of the action is going on in the basement, down the mele e pere (apples and pears, for those who know their Cockney rhyming slang). They 'infuse, blend and keg' their own vermouth on site, to be served in the lively bar. The kitchen turns out focaccia that's 'divine... straight out of the oven' – dip it in smoked garlic aïoli, a punchy companion to a 'sharing plate' of deep-fried squid. Prefer to keep your food to yourself? Order one of the bigger plates, such as tagliatelle with a rich beef ragù, or a hearty fish stew.

Mere

Cooking score: 4
⊖ Goodge Street, map 5
Modern European | £60
74 Charlotte Street, Fitzrovia, W1T 4QH
Tel no: (020) 7268 6565
mere-restaurant.com

With the 'M' logo on everything from the water jugs, coasters and loo-door handles to the alphabetically appropriate dusting of chocolate powder atop cups of cappuccino, *MasterChef* judge Monica Galetti's cleverly designed, light-filled basement dining room isn't short on self-promotion – although nothing distracts from the elegant food. Galetti's approach reflects her time as senior sous-chef at Le Gavroche (see entry), so expect harmonious, high-end partnerships ranging from steamed halibut with leeks, celeriac purée and hazelnut crumb to loin of rose veal accompanied by glazed sweetbread, brown-butter mash and Madeira sauce. To finish, reinvented classics such as pear vacherin with candied chestnuts and spiced bread ice cream strike a more reassuring seasonal note. Some have found the service 'efficient but disinterested', although those with deep pockets can always console themselves with a choice bottle from the thoughtfully composed upper-crust wine list.
Chef/s: Monica Galetti. **Closed:** Sun, bank hols. **Meals:** main courses £23 to £39. Set L £29 (2 courses) to £35. Set D £45 (2 courses) to £60. Tasting menu £70 (6 courses). **Details:** 55 seats. V menu. Bar. Wheelchairs. Music.

Murano

Cooking score: 6
⊖ Green Park, map 5
Modern European | £70
20 Queen Street, Mayfair, W1J 5PP
Tel no: (020) 7495 1127
muranolondon.com

As a major-league dining establishment in the heart of Mayfair, it's not surprising that comfort levels are high. The long, narrow, shades-of-white dining room may be looking a little dated after eight years, and readers would like to see Angela Hartnett in the kitchen more often, but Oscar Holgado has taken up the reins and his food is 'certainly an enjoyable experience'. A board of charcuterie (San Daniele ham), lovely salty grissini, two kinds of focaccia, olive oil and pickled vegetables open all meals, preceding, perhaps, spring vegetable tortellini with peas, broad beans and dabs of Rove des Garrigues goat's curd, then a thick piece of very fresh halibut in a grassy green parsley velouté. To finish, there may be a lovely creamy take on tiramisu as a pre-dessert, followed by a well-made apricot soufflé. Italy and France lead the charge on a wine list that has an interesting global spread, too. Markups are high, but the informed sommelier gives good advice.

Chef/s: Angela Hartnett and Oscar Holgado. **Closed:** Sun, 5 days Christmas. **Meals:** set L £28 (2 courses) to £33. Set D £55 (2 courses) to £80. Tasting menu £90 (5 courses) to £100. **Details:** 55 seats. Wheelchairs.

Neo Bistro

Cooking score: 3
⊖ Bond Street, map 5
Modern British | £35
11 Woodstock Street, Mayfair, W1C 2AE
Tel no: (020) 7499 9427
neobistro.co.uk

That familiar look of exposed brick, schoolroom chairs and bare bulbs is used to good effect at this bistro just off Oxford Street, part of Mark Jarvis's small group of restaurants (see entries for Anglo and Stem). The open kitchen adds the usual sizzle and interest with a menu that offers tried-and-trusted bistro classics of the dressed pork terrine and hanger steak variety. Alongside these are modern European dishes – the warm shallot tart beautifully matched with a silky goat's cheese ice cream that so impressed one reader, or chicken breast with curried carrot and an onion bhaji, tempura Cornish cod, and crisp-fried gnocchi served with fresh peas, wild garlic and Parmesan. A side dish of deep-fried cheesy pressed potatoes is a winner, too. Coffee meringue cake or cheeses from La Fromagerie bring up the rear. The wine list opens with a Trebbiano D'Abruzzo for £20.

Chef/s: Mark Jarvis, Nazmal Hassan and Stefano Sabotino. **Closed:** Sun. **Meals:** main courses £15 to £18. Set D £40.

The Ninth

Cooking score: 5
⊖ Goodge Street, Tottenham Court Road, map 5
French-Mediterranean | £60
22 Charlotte Street, Fitzrovia, W1T 2NB
Tel no: (020) 3019 0880
theninthlondon.com

It's not on the ninth floor, it's not even at number 9 Charlotte Street, but the number nine clearly means something to Jun Tanaka, and he's worth following even if the ninth was to refer to another dimension – though it's probably referring to the fact that this is the ninth restaurant with which the chef has been involved. The two-storied designscape has a sort of faded luxury that looks rather like a film set depicting some dystopian future, but if that sounds like style over substance, it's not; the real focus is on small plates designed for sharing, and they show real craft and clear-headed thinking. It's a bit French, a bit Med, and a bit more. If burrata with beetroot, blood orange and walnuts is aimed at the genteel new wave, veal tongue tonnato and roe deer in a salt crust reveal a penchant for big, hearty flavours and ingredients. And if you want to avoid disappointment, make sure you order enough oxtail croquettes and Carlingford oysters for everyone. Langoustine ravioli and pappardelle with black winter truffles show pasta is taken seriously, and, among sweet courses, pain perdu with vanilla ice cream is as comforting as you would hope. The mostly European-minded wine list opens at £24.

Chef/s: Jun Tanaka. **Closed:** Sun, 23 Dec to 4 Jan, bank hols. **Meals:** main courses £21 to £30. Set L £21 (2 courses) to £27. **Details:** 90 seats. 8 seats outside. Wheelchairs. Music.

Noble Rot

Cooking score: 5
⊖ Holborn, Russell Square, map 5
Anglo-French | £47
51 Lamb's Conduit Street, Bloomsbury, WC1N 3NB
Tel no: (020) 7242 8963
noblerot.co.uk

A bricks-and-mortar mission statement from the owners of the cult oenophile journal *Noble Rot*, this enterprising wine-bar-cum-restaurant is a runaway success. It's no surprise that the wine list is a glorious one-off – an idiosyncratic collection of undervalued tipples by the glass alongside esoteric gems from world-leading producers – but not all eyes are on the wine. Paul Weaver has settled into his stride, his cooking a brilliant amalgam of flavours, textures and combinations, but then he did learn his craft at London's St John Bread & Wine, and Kent's The Sportsman (see entries). Wonderfully seasonal dishes are straightforward, mostly simple assemblies and inspired finishing touches – a delicate, creamy burratina, perhaps, served with romesco and calçot onions, or a perfectly cooked slip sole dressed with a punchy smoked butter. At a February meal there was also a simple tart of wild garlic, leek and goat's curd, grilled Tamworth pork chop with white beans and apple sauce, and monkfish braised in oxidised Meursault. Focaccia is the star of the trio of homemade breads, and desserts are equally reassuring, perhaps a rhubarb and custard tart. The mood is relaxed and the decor atmospherically dark thanks to wood panelling, bare floorboards and candles, and the service is spot-on.

Chef/s: Paul Weaver. **Closed:** Sun, 25 and 26 Dec, 1 Jan. **Meals:** main courses £18 to £29. Set L £16 (2 courses) to £20. **Details:** 55 seats. Bar.

Nopi

Cooking score: 3
⊖ Piccadilly Circus, map 5
Middle Eastern/Mediterranean | £50
21-22 Warwick Street, Soho, W1B 5NE
Tel no: (020) 7494 9584
nopi-restaurant.com

Yotam Ottolenghi's Soho restaurant shares its DNA with the better-known Ottolenghi brand. Where Ottolenghi is casual, however, Nopi is a more formal affair, especially the street-level dining room with its white marble surfaces, tactile white walls and brushed brass accents; the basement's more casual with communal tables around an open kitchen. Open from breakfast until late, one can start the day with the ever-reliable shakshuka (baked eggs) and smoked labneh, or scrambled tofu with rose harissa and avocado salsa. Flavours are vibrant and audaciously paired. Vegetables hog the spotlight; among Nopi's signature small plates (designed for sharing) are courgette and Manouri cheese fritters with cardamom yoghurt and Valdeón cheesecake, pickled beetroot and thyme honey. There are a few mains, too, say Gigha halibut, nori, ginger and fried capers. Melon sorbet with cucumber, arak and basil is a light finish. The wine list looks beyond the obvious to Palestine, Georgia and some volcanic and orange wines.

Chef/s: Yotam Ottolenghi and Spyros Koufalakis. **Meals:** main courses £20 to £26. Set early D (Mon to Fri) £26. **Details:** 108 seats. Bar. Music.

Ormer Mayfair

Cooking score: 6
⊖ Green Park, map 5
Modern British | £60
Flemings, 7-12 Half Moon Street, Mayfair, W1J 7BH
Tel no: (020) 7499 0000
ormermayfair.com

Ormer now has its own entrance within Flemings Hotel in the heart of Mayfair, but the descent to the lower ground floor – into a world of subdued beige luxe – still feels appealingly like leaving the West End hurly-burly behind. A labyrinth-patterned carpet, panelled walls and capably professional staff help distinguish the Shaun Rankin experience, which brings more than a touch of the wind-blown coasts to central London. Start as bracingly, with tuna sashimi and scallop ceviche in wasabi with Bloody Mary jelly, or as richly, as in lobster ravioli in crab and tomato bisque, as you fancy: presentations are carefully considered and flavours resonantly sea-deep. If you're sticking with the marine route, go on to pistachio- and pinenut-crusted turbot with pickled cockles, but there is authoritative meat cookery too – perhaps loin and glazed sweetbreads of lamb with goat's curd agnolotti and minted peas. The signature treacle tart with raspberries and Jersey clotted cream is a must. Wines are rather brutally categorised by price bracket, but there is plenty of exciting drinking for the plentifully resourced, starting at £23.

Chef/s: Shaun Rankin. **Closed:** Sun, Mon, 25 to 27 Dec, 30 Dec to 2 Jan. **Meals:** main courses £29 to £40. Set L £30 (2 courses) to £32. Tasting menu £84. **Details:** 85 seats. V menu. Vg menu. Bar. Wheelchairs.

Orrery

Cooking score: 4
⊖ Baker Street, Regent's Park, map 6
French | £55
55 Marylebone High Street, Marylebone, W1U 5RB
Tel no: (020) 7616 8000
orrery-restaurant.co.uk

While the Marylebone dining scene has developed all around it, Orrery has maintained a steadfast presence at the narrow top end of the high street, its half-moon windows letting light into a long, predominantly white first-floor room that looks glossy and sleek enough for an occasion. Igor Tymchyshyn continues to cook the kind of lightly modernised French food in which the place has always specialised, on a menu that may take in a velvety chicken liver parfait matched with apple chutney, a well-timed fillet of plaice with cucumber, a dollop of horseradish cream and rich velouté, and a variant on tournedos Rossini with discreetly truffled sauce Périgourdine. It's all designed to comfort and reassure. Similar contentment is to be found among desserts of lightly poached cherries topped with yoghurt and dots of crisp meringue or apricot tart with vanilla ice cream. The wine list feels top-heavy, with not enough at the gentler end, but a reasonable glass selection starts at £7.50.

Chef/s: Igor Tymchyshyn. **Meals:** main courses £20 to £39. Set L £25 (2 courses) to £29. Set D £54 (2 courses) to £59. Tasting menu £69. **Details:** 100 seats. 20 seats outside. V menu.

The Other Naughty Piglet

Cooking score: 4
⊖ Victoria, map 5
Modern European | £30
The Other Palace, 12 Palace Street, Victoria, SW1E 5JA
Tel no: (020) 7592 0322
theothernaughtypiglet.co.uk

Hats off to Lord Lloyd-Webber for encouraging Margaux and Joe Sharratt to open a second venue in his theatre near Buckingham Palace (see Naughty Piglets, south London). Reached via a curving marble staircase that feels very 'Any Dream Will Do', the mezzanine dining room is filled with plank-topped tables and café chairs, has an open-to-view kitchen and a relaxed, laid-back feel. The food format is small plates, from 'utterly splendid' ham croquettes, 'properly oozy and creamy' burrata with romesco and almonds, and 'hysterically good' XO linguine with cured egg yolk – an impressive Chinese take on carbonara – to brilliant Herdwick lamb with aubergine and wild garlic. Not everything is as good as everything else but the hits are legion, not forgetting a dessert of honeycomb, chocolate mousse and salted caramel. The wine list puts its best foot forward, a headline attraction in itself, bursting with biodynamics, oxidation and artisan gems.

Chef/s: Joseph Knowlden. **Closed:** Sun, 24 Dec to 3 Jan. **Meals:** small plates £2 to £18. Set L £22 (2 courses) to £25. **Details:** 60 seats. Bar. Wheelchairs. Music.

Otto's

Cooking score: 3
⊖ Chancery Lane, map 5
French | £46
182 Gray's Inn Road, Bloomsbury, WC1X 8EW
Tel no: (020) 7713 0107
ottos-restaurant.com

Otto's offers an old-school French dining experience that is, for many, an antidote to today's modernisation of the industry – totally devoid of industrial styling and nary a tattoo in sight, it's like stepping back in time. Marilyn Monroe's form in photos and cushions acknowledges one 20th-century icon, but otherwise the mood is formal and conservative. *Gueridon* (trolley) service sees the waiting staff in hands-on tableside action, with the specialities of the house undoubtedly being the Challans duck, Bresse chickens and Scottish lobsters that find their way into the old silver pressing machines – it's pure culinary theatre, and ensures every ounce of flavour is extracted. The traditional repertoire extends from starters like snails in parsley and garlic butter, and smoked haddock soufflé, via roast milk-fed Pyrenean lamb with dauphinois potatoes, to quince tart or Grand Marnier soufflé. The wine list pretty much stays loyal to France, with just a few interlopers to add depth to a comprehensive collection.

Chef/s: Otto Tepassé and Michael Bocquiren. **Closed:** Sun, Mon, Christmas, bank hols. **Meals:** main courses £23 to £37. Set L £24 (2 courses) to £28. **Details:** 40 seats. No children.

★ NEW ENTRY ★

The Oystermen

Cooking score: 2
⊖ Leicester Square, Covent Garden, map 5
Seafood | £40
32 Henrietta Street, Covent Garden, WC2E 8NA
Tel no: (020) 7240 4417
oystermen.co.uk
£5 OFF

'This has to be one of the smallest restaurants I've ever squeezed myself into – even the one loo is touted as the smallest in London,' observed one visitor. The kitchen occupies a back corner of the narrow room, with dining space at a real premium – 'I felt I was going to knock food off the neighbouring table'. It's not terribly comfortable, but one has to warm to fresh seafood at such kind prices. Come here for oysters, lovely snacks such as crab arancini with brown crab mayo, or delicious smoked cod brandade with sesame lavosh (thin, crisp slivers of bread), or tuck into whole crab. Starters could run to 'really tasty' squid served in a tangle with diced fried aubergine, green olive, pine nuts and pickled raisins, while monkfish tail with yellow Malaysian curry, pak choi and jasmine rice makes a satisfying main. The short, interesting wine list is good value, too.

Chef/s: Alex Povall. **Closed:** 25 Dec to 1 Jan. **Meals:** main courses £17 to £22. **Details:** 26 seats. Music.

The Palomar

Cooking score: 5
⊖ Piccadilly Circus, map 5
Middle Eastern | £35
34 Rupert Street, Soho, W1D 6DN
Tel no: (020) 7439 8777
thepalomar.co.uk

Punchy flavours and a lively vibe burst from this joyful Soho restaurant that unites the warm-hearted best of Mediterranean, North African and Middle Eastern food in a menu that is as broad in its appeal as the space is intimate. Book ahead for a seat in the back dining room, or grab a spot at the zinc bar to see chefs prepare a Tel Aviv mix (squid and octopus that dance with Maghreb spices), or a plate of cured trout with za'atar, plum and almonds. It's a place to share food, so pull apart pitta or yeasted Yemeni kubaneh to sweep through baba ganoush or sumac-fragrant burnt courgette tzatziki before, say, a dish of citrussy roasted poussin with sage and black rice, or grilled sea bream with fennel and herb oil. Finish with a rich malabi (creamy Arabic pudding) with sweet-tart hibiscus syrup and pistachios. The cocktail list is spirited, and there's wine from £30.

Chef/s: Jeremy Borrow. **Meals:** main courses £10 to £26. **Details:** 50 seats. Music. Children in dining room only.

★ NEW ENTRY ★

Parsons

Cooking score: 4
⊖ Covent Garden, map 5
Seafood | £30
39 Endell Street, Covent Garden, WC2H 9BA
Tel no: (020) 3422 0221
parsonslondon.co.uk

This diminutive restaurant is an impressive newcomer to London's growing seafood scene. With its modern white decor and mix of counter seating and close-packed tables, it may lack comfort but it makes up for it with warm, welcoming service and a short menu of dishes you really want to eat. There are nibbles to have with a drink, say excellent salt cod fritters or half a dozen oysters, followed by sea trout tartare with a punchy Bloody Mary jelly. Next, look to the wall mirrors displaying the day's catch: perhaps whole sea bream, perfectly timed and enough for two to share, served with the lobster mash so loved by readers. There's also fish pie and a token meaty offering – maybe steak tartare or a steak sandwich. Desserts are limited; we had a perfectly serviceable apple tarte fine, but wish we'd ordered the Welsh rarebit. The food is impressively supported by an enterprising wine list, long on fish-friendly whites from northern and southern hemispheres, plus a handful of reds and a good selection by the glass, all reflecting Parsons' relationship to the excellent 10 Cases wine bar across the road.

Chef/s: Goemon Ishikawa. **Closed:** Sun. **Meals:** main courses £15 to £27. **Details:** 30 seats.

★ NEW ENTRY ★

Pastaio

Cooking score: 3
⊖ Oxford Circus, map 5
Italian | £25
19 Ganton Street, Soho, W1F 9BN
pastaio.london

Fresh pasta joints are proliferating at a rate of knots, and Pastaio is one of the latest to follow the trend for making it by hand every morning with doors opening at midday to inevitable queues – no bookings are taken. Diners are seated at communal tables in the canteen-like space with its bold, geometric mural at one end and open kitchen at the other. The single-sheet menu features some eight pastas, as well as antipasti and pudding options. To start, a toasted sandwich of fried mozzarella, 'nduja and honey that was so good we immediately ordered another. Next up, cacio e pepe, a Roman favourite of pungent pecorino, freshly ground Tellicherry pepper and fat bucatini pasta bound together to form 'a heavenly dish'. Stuffed pastas – perhaps agnoli parcels of wild boar, rabbit and pork – are equally stellar. Finish with a 'generous wedge' of tiramisu. Affordable wines from a short all-Italian list are available by the glass and carafe.

Chef/s: Stevie Parle. **Meals:** main courses £7 to £12. **Details:** 72 seats. Music.

★ NEW ENTRY ★

Picture

Cooking score: 3
⊖ Oxford Circus, Goodge Street, map 5
British | £30
110 Great Portland Street, Fitzrovia, W1W 6PQ
Tel no: (020) 7637 7892
picturerestaurant.co.uk

Halfway up Great Portland Street, opposite the BBC, the original branch of Picture (there's an offshoot in Marylebone) is a bare-bones kind of place, with stripped-back decor under the double skylight. Smallish plates are the drill, divided into starters, fish, meats and desserts, with the option of a six-course taster, on a menu that evolves in part from day to day. At inspection, there were good things in the form of a beetroot tartare with goat's curd, radishes and crumbled hazelnuts, silky ravioli of caramelised onion with butternut and pecorino, and a textbook reading of smoked haddock brandade with a breadcrumbed poached egg and purple broccoli. Heavy salting is something of an issue, and occasionally a dish misfires where it ought to be winning – the sweetbread croquette that came with excellent slow-cooked Welsh lamb was an apologetic afterthought – but there is enough excitement generally to fill the place. Finish with vanilla panna cotta, rhubarb, crushed gingerbread and meringue. Wines by the glass need a little more variety across the board, but start at £5.80.

Chef/s: Alan Chiste. **Closed:** Sun. **Meals:** main courses £12 to £16. Set L £19 (2 courses) to £23. Tasting menu £45 (6 courses). **Details:** V menu.

Pied à Terre

Cooking score: 4
⊖ Goodge Street, map 5
Modern French | £95
34 Charlotte Street, Fitzrovia, W1T 2NH
Tel no: (020) 7636 1178
pied-a-terre.co.uk

Following the departure of Andy McFadden in 2017, Asimakis Chaniotis has been promoted from sous-chef to run the kitchen at this long-standing dining destination. Cooking here is complex with ambitious plate presentations. Amuse-bouche curiosities included red-tinted chocolate lips, filled with salmon cream cheese – as one reader remarked, they 'encouraged us to imagine delights to come'. Pretty as a picture, a first course of Pembrokeshire flaked crab, encased in a white radish wrap was complemented by pickled green strawberries, peppery British-grown wasabi and a cloudburst of lime-ginger foam. A tender roast squab was cooked to juicy perfection and matched with blackberries and creamy potato sabayon. It wasn't all plain sailing – duck wellington came with a rather bitter-tasting black curry sauce. But spirits lifted with a faultless millefeuille stacked with cubed apples and served with a tart green apple and celery sorbet. Two doorstopper manuals provide an indication of the legendary wine list, which is overseen by a warmly enthusiastic sommelier.

Chef/s: Asimakis Chaniotis. **Closed:** Sun, 2 weeks Christmas and New Year, bank hols. **Meals:** set L £30 (2 courses) to £38. Set D £65 (2 courses) to £80. Tasting menu £75 to £145. **Details:** 44 seats. V menu. Vg menu. Bar. Wheelchairs. Music.

Symbols

Accommodation is available

Three courses for less than £30
£5 off voucher scheme
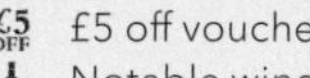
Notable wine list

★ TOP 10 ★

Pollen Street Social

Cooking score: 9
⊖ Oxford Circus, map 5
Modern British | £98
8-10 Pollen Street, Mayfair, W1S 1NQ
Tel no: (020) 7290 7606
pollenstreetsocial.com

The pulling power of Jason Atherton's restaurants shows no sign of weakening, if the relentless busyness of his flagship Mayfair restaurant is anything to go by. A Monday lunchtime thrums with the sort of numbers that, for many a chef, are but the stuff of dreams, some diners savouring the nine-course tasting menu, others taking a more conventional à la carte or set lunch approach. To deliver daily the stellar quality expected of Atherton is no mean feat, and early summer visits shine with the flashes of brilliance you'd expect. Afternoon tea canapés continue to delight, especially the cep and Parmesan velouté whose texture is as light on the tongue as its savouriness is lingeringly deep, and a starter of smoked eel memorable for its yielding flesh, delicious against sprightly cucumber, apple, buttermilk, and a beetroot reduction. Sweet, poached quail comes with tender young courgettes, peas, just blanched carrots, a scattering of petals and basil leaves, with depth of flavour from a duck broth. Butter-soft nuggets of fillet and best end of Lake District lamb are the highlight of a main course that includes a fabulous collection of broad beans and peas and the sweet-sharp taste of mint. A soufflé is as much an architectural masterclass as a triumph of flavour, harmonising as it does dark chocolate with Sicilian pistachios and Madagascan vanilla ice cream, while the basil sorbet that accompanies a gorgeous lemon, lime and olive oil sponge topped with a fine disc of honey crackling is probably 'the standout mouthful of the whole meal'. There are some spectacular wines by the glass, and though the list opens at £25 a bottle, be warned that it doesn't tarry there for long.

Chef/s: Jason Atherton and Dale Bainbridge. **Closed:** Sun, 25 Dec, 2 Jan. **Meals:** main courses £35 to £90. Set L £37. Tasting menu £98 (8 courses). **Details:** 58 seats. V menu. Vg menu. Bar. Wheelchairs. Music.

Portland

Cooking score: 5
⊖ Great Portland St, Oxford Circus, map 5
Modern British | £50
113 Great Portland Street, Fitzrovia, W1W 6QQ
Tel no: (020) 7436 3261
portlandrestaurant.co.uk

If some find the pared-back look of this modern bistro a little austere, it's partly mitigated by young, amiable staff whose attentive, clued-up approach is a great asset. Merlin Labron-Johnson extracts maximum flavour from his rough-edged urban food, as is demonstrated by an opening nibble of chicken liver parfait on a shard of paper-thin chicken skin – 'I could have eaten ten'. Treacly sourdough with beef-tallow butter brings a full-on fat assault before you get into the menu proper, which might compensate with a clean-edged starter of slivered raw scallop on cod's roe with green apple and massaged kale, or fabulous new-season asparagus with ricotta gnudi and an egg yolk, showered with grated pecorino. Mains could be Old Spot in thick pink slices with braised endive and quince purée in a rich puddle of demi-glace, or sea bass with Dorset blewits and sea leeks. A dessert of granola-crusted lavender parfait failed to fire at inspection, but for its vibrant rhubarb coulis. An assiduous approach to wine results in a clutch of excellent, often youthful, growers on a list supplemented by a slate of specials available by the glass, as well as single bottles of aristocratic treasures.

Chef/s: Merlin Labron-Johnson and Zachary Elliott-Crenn. **Closed:** Sun, 22 Dec to 2 Jan. **Meals:** main courses £22 to £32. Set L £30 (2 courses) to £35. Tasting menu £55 to £65. **Details:** 35 seats. Wheelchairs. Music.

LOCAL GEM

Princi

⊖ Tottenham Court Road, Piccadilly Circus, map 5

Italian | £22

135 Wardour Street, Soho, W1F 0UT
Tel no: (020) 7478 8888
princi.com

Striking good looks, an animated atmosphere, all-day opening and reasonable prices make this Italian self-service café a useful Soho destination. The food displayed on the counter (pizza slices, salads, hot pasta dishes, pastries) is fresh and good quality, and the coffee is excellent. Head to the adjoining restaurant, though, for waiter service and decent renditions of Italian staples, from popular wood-fired pizzas, and pasta – tagliatelle bolognese or spaghetti carbonara, say – to thinly sliced bresaola with rocket and shaved Parmesan, or bruschetta topped with roasted peppers, garlic, anchovies and olive oil. You can't book so expect to queue at busy times. A brief Italian wine list starts at £23.50.

Quilon

Cooking score: 4

⊖ St James's Park, Victoria, map 5

Indian | £55

41 Buckingham Gate, Westminster, SW1E 6AF
Tel no: (020) 7821 1899
quilon.co.uk

Once upon a time they put up visitors to Buckingham Palace in this handsome old block. It's easy to see why. It's a Taj hotel these days, and has been home to one of the capital's most compelling modern Indian restaurants since 1999. With its own entrance, and identity, Quilon's dining room positively shimmers with a gloss that suits the postcode. Sriram Aylur has led the line from the start – inspiration coming from the south-west of India, specifically the coastal areas. Thus lobster broth is a good place to start, flavoured with coriander, or how about chargrilled scallops with papaya, poppy seeds and chilli relish? Meat and vegetarian options are no less well considered: a mini masala dosa starter, say, or venison chilli fry main course. Powerful flavours are well handled, as when lemon sole is matched with Goan spices, and crispy fried squid arrives with samphire and chilli. Chai latte crème brûlée is a creative finale. Tasting menus include a version with accompanying beers, and the wine list opens at £33.

Chef/s: Sriram Aylur and Ramesh Ganiga. **Closed:** 25 Dec. **Meals:** main courses £12 to £45. Set L £27 (2 courses) to £31. Tasting menu L £36, D £60. **Details:** 83 seats. Bar. Wheelchairs. Music.

Quirinale

Cooking score: 3

⊖ Westminster, map 3

Italian | £42

North Court, 1 Great Peter Street, Westminster, SW1P 3LL
Tel no: (020) 7222 7080
quirinale.co.uk

This upmarket Italian in the heart of Westminster has the airy lightness and clean lines of an art gallery, its white-clad tables set far enough apart to give its regulars (many of them politicians) a feeling of privacy. The menu is packed with a deli-full of Italian ingredients – Parma ham with Andria burrata; Sardinian smoked ricotta with baby spinach, honey-glazed walnuts and cherry tomatoes; octopus with Borettane onions and peppers – and that's just the antipasti. Elsewhere there could be orecchiette with Italian sausage, sprouting broccoli and Sardinian pecorino, or fillet of red mullet with tomato and Taggiasca olives. Of course, desserts include tiramisu but here it is a liquorice version with caramelised nuts. Alternatively, you could try warm semolina budino with rhubarb and mint or a ricotta and blueberry tart. Italian to the end, the wine list offers good regional coverage.

Chef/s: Stefano Savio. **Closed:** Sun. **Meals:** main courses £15 to £29. **Details:** 50 seats. Music.

Quo Vadis

Cooking score: 4
⊖ Tottenham Court Road, map 5
Modern European | £50
26-29 Dean Street, Soho, W1D 3LL
Tel no: (020) 7437 9585
quovadissoho.co.uk

'The scaled down room really suits Quo Vadis – very intimate and charming – a big thumbs-up from me,' noted a regular, returning for the first time since the restaurant gave up space to accommodate Barrafina Dean Street (see entry). It's the kind of place that inspires loyalty – the draw being Jeremy Lee's seasonally influenced menus packed with classic French and modern European-inspired dishes of consistently high standard. You could take the well-tried route with the signature sandwich of smoked eel or whole artichoke vinaigrette, go on to that day's pie and mash, perhaps chicken and bacon, and finish with St Emilion au chocolat. Otherwise, head off into the world of grilled chicken skewers with coriander chutney before sampling baked coquelet with braised fennel, celeriac and green sauce or a hake, crab and tarragon broth, and finish with a damson, walnut and blackcurrant mess. The wine list offers satisfying scope, with a good selection by the glass or carafe; bottles start at £28.
Chef/s: Jeremy Lee. **Closed:** Sun, bank hols. **Meals:** main courses £17 to £28. Set L and D £18 (2 courses) to £23. **Details:** 26 seats. 12 seats outside.

Rex Whistler Restaurant

Cooking score: 3
⊖ Pimlico, map 3
British | £36
Tate Britain, Millbank, Pimlico, SW1P 4RG
Tel no: (020) 7887 8825
tate.org.uk
£5 OFF

Deep in the basement of Tate Britain, the Rex Whistler dining room made a stand for decent museum catering in the days when there was only one Tate. Its white-linened tables and wraparound mural by the titular artist create a clubbable atmosphere, while the lunch menus have made a creditable attempt to reflect the changing times. Coffee-cured duck breast with mustard-dressed winter leaves, perhaps followed by roast halibut in veal stock sauce with Jerusalem artichoke, or the cheek, belly and ears of pork with black pudding and pistachios, sauced with cider, are what to expect these days. The cheese trolley is an invitation to indulgence, or look to Nahua chocolate tart with goat's milk ice cream, honeycomb and hazelnuts. Wine is taken seriously here: there's a sommelier's recommendation for each main dish (small glasses from £4.90), dozens of lunchtime half bottles, and mature French classics to beat the band. Bottles open at £28.
Chef/s: Alfio Laudani. **Closed:** 24 to 26 Dec. **Meals:** set L £30 (2 courses) to £36. Sun L £36. **Details:** 80 seats. 50 seats outside. Bar. Wheelchairs.

★ TOP 50 ★

The Ritz

Cooking score: 7
⊖ Green Park, map 5
British | £80
150 Piccadilly, Mayfair, W1J 9BR
Tel no: (020) 7493 8181
theritzlondon.com

Opened in 1906, The Ritz was conceived as the last word in *bon ton* splendour, an ambition it has never relinquished. Its dining room, surely the most beautiful in London, guarded by a gilded Poseidon at one end, with French windows overlooking the park, is an experience destination if ever there was, and is currently at the top of its culinary game. The cooking under John Williams, awarded the MBE in 2008, claims to be British, even while speaking the language of culinary appropriation: truffled artichoke royale, langoustine à la nage, sole meunière, gâteau St Honoré. That said, there is a recognisable streak of gently applied modernism running through the menus to great effect these days, producing finely judged dishes that maintain interest where machine repetitions of classics fall short. Lobster with heirloom beetroot and marigold might pave the way for main courses that reflect the changing times. Sika venison fillet with red cabbage, chestnuts and elderberries, or pigeon with walnuts, prunes and swede, speak eloquently of contemporary thinking. Sharply defined flavours at dessert throw the copious appearance of chocolate into welcome relief: blood orange with sour cream and honeycomb, perhaps, or crêpes Suzette flamed at the table by a delighted maître d'. There is now a vegan menu. The wine list takes no prisoners, with bottles starting at £59.

Chef/s: John Williams. **Meals:** main courses £40 to £56. Sun L £67. Tasting menu £105. **Details:** 85 seats. 26 seats outside. V menu. Vg menu. Bar. Wheelchairs. Music.

★ NEW ENTRY ★

Rochelle ICA

Cooking score: 2
⊖ Charing Cross, map 5
Modern British | £35
ICA, The Mall, St James's, SW1Y 5AH
Tel no: (020) 7766 1424
arnoldandhenderson.com

Margot Henderson and Melanie Arnold's reworking of their Shoreditch original (Rochelle Canteen, see entry) occupies what designers might call a difficult space – a mezzanine restaurant tucked away in the Institute for Contemporary Arts overlooking the Mall. Some find the look 'too cafeteria' and the service comes in for some stick, but the food and the reasonable prices are generally of more interest to diners. The menu – brief, simple, seasonal – delivers some real treats: quail, 'deliciously charry from the grill' or a couple of tasty salt hake croquettes with sorrel mayonnaise. Main courses are straightforward and satisfying, whether a generous rabbit, bacon and wild garlic pie or beautifully cooked cod on monk's beard tangled with tomatoes. Desserts are classics along the lines of a pillowy meringue with a huge dollop of very good cream and perfectly poached rhubarb. Drink cocktails or choose from a brief but poorly laid-out list of French wines.

Chef/s: Ben Coombs. **Closed:** Mon. **Meals:** main courses £13 to £19. **Details:** 50 seats. Bar. Wheelchairs.

★ TOP 50 ★

★ NEW ENTRY ★

Roganic

Cooking score: 8
⊖ Baker Street, Bond Street, map 6
Modern European | £80
5-7 Blandford Street, Marylebone, W1U 3DB
Tel no: (020) 337 06260
roganic.uk

Whisper it: Simon's back in town, and he's here to stay. But keep it hush so that you don't find yourself struggling to get into this delicious, understated, Marylebone restaurant, the permanent home of Rogan's wildly successful two-year pop-up. As you'd expect from this grounded chef and his protégé in charge here, Oli Marlowe, the largely plant-based menu sways with an easy seasonal rhythm. The components of individual dishes, and the pace of the whole meal, are so pitch-perfect that you finish eight courses (or the full 13-movement symphony) wanting more. Ingredients from Rogan's Our Farm in Cumbria are woven melodiously with the best from elsewhere, in dishes that applaud the humble as enthusiastically as the glamorous. The silkiest carrot purée and tender roasted carrot is anything but a vegetal afterthought – without it (or indeed the fleeting note of char on slender brassicas) the tender 21-day aged Cumbrian pork with its wisp of crackling would not be the dish it is. Similarly, it's the peppery notes of a sorrel sauce and radish that linger long after accompanying cured mackerel has had its moment, and it's the sea kale and seaweed butter that lodge a monkfish dish in the mind. Clarity of flavour sings out to the end: rhubarb hides under snowy, cleansing buttermilk, and the finale of chamomile ice cream with bittersweet honey and shards of

burnt milk is thrilling. The wine flight (£50/£75) is a superbly paired sequence of sips, but do enjoy the list, which charts a route round some predictable – and less predictable – vineyards after opening at £35.
Chef/s: Oli Marlowe. **Closed:** Sun, Mon, , 23 Dec to 7 Jan, 27 Aug to 3 Sept. **Meals:** set L £35 (3 courses). Tasting menu £75 (8 courses) to £95. **Details:** 40 seats. V menu. Vg menu. Music.

Roka

Cooking score: 3
⊖ Goodge Street, map 5
Japanese | £60
37 Charlotte Street, Fitzrovia, W1T 1RR
Tel no: (020) 7580 6464
rokarestaurant.com

Regulars sit at the counter for a ringside seat by the robata at this, the original Roka, launched in 2004. Drink cool Japanese cocktails in the stylish subterranean Shochu Lounge. For main entry, see Canary Wharf branch, east London.
Chef/s: Hamish Brown and Luca Spiga. **Closed:** 25 Dec. **Meals:** main courses £15 to £72. Tasting menu £70 to £90. **Details:** 88 seats. 24 seats outside. Bar.

Roka Aldwych

Cooking score: 2
⊖ Temple, map 5
Japanese | £60
71 Aldwych, Aldwych, WC2B 4HN
Tel no: (020) 7294 7636
rokarestaurant.com

The fourth London site for Rainer Becker's glam Japanese robata concept. Expect good-value lunch and pre-theatre menus and a very popular Sunday brunch service. For main entry, see Canary Wharf branch, east London.
Chef/s: Hamish Brown and Cristian Bravaccini. **Meals:** main courses £15 to £72. Tasting menu £70 to £90. **Details:** 150 seats. V menu.

Roux at Parliament Square

Cooking score: 4
⊖ Westminster, St James's Park, map 5
Modern European | £59
11 Great George Street, Parliament Square, Westminster, SW1P 3AD
Tel no: (020) 7334 3737
rouxatparliamentsquare.co.uk

Given its location within the hushed environs of the Royal Institution of Chartered Surveyors and its proximity to Westminster's political amphitheatre, it's no surprise that this branch of Michel Roux Jr's evolving empire is all about well-considered dining in well-upholstered surroundings. Chef Steve Groves understands the house style and provides politicos of all shades with food that has elegance, style and just enough innovation to keep minds and palates alert. There's comfort and familiarity in a dish of asparagus with morels, Spenwood cheese and wild garlic, while a combination of pig's cheek, carrot, ale and Mangalitsa black pudding strikes a more bullish note. Elsewhere, a plate of dry-aged duck partnered by beetroot, chicory and Yukon Gold potato strikes a more progressive note than a pairing of halibut, cauliflower, grapes and tarragon. Roux's shadow also hovers over fancy desserts such as an apple soufflé with muscovado, Calvados and oats, while impressive French labels lead the way on the respectable wine list.
Chef/s: Steve Groves. **Closed:** Sat, Sun, 1 week Christmas and New Year, 2 weeks Aug. **Meals:** set L £42. Set D £59. Tasting menu L £65 (6 courses), D £79 (8 courses). **Details:** 60 seats. Bar. Wheelchairs.

Send us your review

Your feedback informs the content of the *GFG* and will be used to compile next year's reviews. To register your opinion about any restaurant listed, or a restaurant that you wish to bring to our attention, visit our website.

Roux at the Landau

Cooking score: 5
⊖ Oxford Circus, map 5
French | £52
The Langham, 1c Portland Place, Marylebone, W1B 1JA
Tel no: (020) 7965 0165
rouxatthelandau.com

£5 OFF

The Roux dining room at The Langham has undergone a creative refurb that introduces a centre island, with bar-style seating, to the opulently panelled elliptical space. It's all change in the kitchen too, where Nicolas Pasquier has been installed, maintaining the contemporary French style set by Michel Roux Jr. Opening 'snacks' are mere morsels of loveliness – thin prosciutto on ricotta-stuffed 'grissini' with Kalamata olive purée, or salmon tartare on calamansi with horseradish crème fraîche. Starters proper might aim for the stars with an XL Orkney scallop dappled with oscietra caviar in beurre blanc, before equally ambitious mains of roasted turbot with a lobster and fennel raviolo in foaming tarragon-scented bisque, or a thick hunk of beef fillet with white asparagus and morels, served with buttery pomme purée, its central hollow filled with a bone-marrow-laced demi-glace. It's as though Escoffier never left us. Finish with chocolate moelleux and cardamom ice cream, hiding under a billowing cloud of caramel. A whopping French-led wine list gathers the pick of each region, with Coravin glasses permitting modest entry to the magic kingdom and a commendable range by the bottle starting at £32.

Chef/s: Nicolas Pasquier. **Closed:** Sun, Mon. **Meals:** main courses £16 to £38. Set L £25 (2 courses) to £30. Tasting menu £65 (5 courses). **Details:** 100 seats. V menu. Bar. Wheelchairs. Music.

Rules

Cooking score: 3
⊖ Covent Garden, Leicester Square, map 5
British | £49
35 Maiden Lane, Covent Garden, WC2E 7LB
Tel no: (020) 7836 5314
rules.co.uk

To call Rules 'retro' would be to suggest that it had ever gone anywhere from which it might retrogress. London's oldest public eatery could well have been mentioned in the 1798 edition of the *Good Food Guide*, had we existed. Suffice to say it's been in the game a while, and game is its principal draw. Once the season is on, braised hare haunch with port-glazed chicory, lentils and pear, or a crown of pheasant for two, served with sausage, smoked bacon and pickled cabbage, are what lure the crowds, though there are homelier dishes too, for when nothing but steak and kidney suet pud will do (for another quid, they'll chuck in an oyster). One or two more modern touches may be noted in starters like smoked eel with beetroot jam and dandelion, or the Frenched-up version of bread-and-butter pudding made from brioche, with Armagnac-slicked prunes inveigled into the custard. The ambience of antique mirrors, oil paintings and framed cartoons, not to mention old-school service, add immeasurably to the appeal. A mostly French wine list starts at £29.

Chef/s: David Stafford. **Closed:** 24 to 27 Dec. **Meals:** main courses £20 to £43. **Details:** 90 seats. Bar.

★ NEW ENTRY ★

Sabor

Cooking score: 4
⊖ Piccadilly Circus, map 5
Spanish | £35
35-37 Heddon Street, Mayfair, W1B 4BR
Tel no: (020) 3319 8132
saborrestaurants.co.uk

This confident tapas bar is the first solo venture for Nieves Barragán, who made her name as executive chef at Barrafina. It works to a familiar formula: no bookings, fast-paced chefs cooking in full view behind the counter. Get your timing right and you'll avoid the queues, though you can always perch at the adjacent bar if there's a wait. Low counter seating has been designed for comfort: 'it was lovely to sit on normal seats (with backs), feet firmly on the floor'. A frequently changing line-up of sharply executed small plates demonstrates the kitchen's flavour-first approach – start perhaps with frit mariner, a seafood concoction of squid, prawns, aubergine and pepper, or superb quail served with a good, slightly tart romesco sauce. Tapas classics have a place, too: 'the best pan con tomate' topped with wafer-thin slices of cecina (jamón); crisp, flavourful prawn croquetas; and a creamy made-to-order salt cod ajoarriero tortilla. A short list of Spanish wines has a good selection by the glass and bottles from £25. Upstairs is El Asador, the place to come if your fancy turns to wood-roasted suckling pig or kid goat, and where tables are bookable, though communal.

Chef/s: Nieves Barragán. **Closed:** Sun, Mon. **Meals:** tapas £9 to £15. **Details:** 56 seats. Bar. Wheelchairs. Music.

Salt Yard

Cooking score: 2
⊖ Goodge Street, map 5
Spanish/Italian | £30
54 Goodge Street, Fitzrovia, W1T 4NA
Tel no: (020) 7637 0657
saltyard.co.uk

More versatile than some of its compatriots in the capital, the Salt Yard Group's flagship delivers exactly what its freewheeling Goodge Street location demands. Sit outside with a glass of sherry and some boquerones, nibble on charcuterie and cheese in the boisterous bar (try the three Manchegos with membrillo) or head down to the spacious basement room if you fancy a full run through the kitchen's repertoire of Spanish and Italian small plates. Stuffed courgette flowers drizzled with blossom honey remain the headline act, but ring the changes by ordering torched mackerel and mackerel tartare with pistachio pesto and sour cream, truffled mac 'n' cheese or Ibérico pork loin partnered by celeriac purée, morcilla crumb and charred apple. If you're after something sweet, consider the baked chocolate ganache with caramelised clementine and lavender cream. Back-up comes from a zippy list of Iberian and Italian wines (no-corkage BYO on Monday nights).

Chef/s: Dan Sherlock and Joe Howley. **Closed:** 24 to 26 Dec, 30 Dec to 1 Jan. **Meals:** tapas £5 to £12. **Details:** 74 seats. 8 seats outside. Bar.

Savoy Grill

Cooking score: 2
⊖ Charing Cross, map 5
Anglo-French | £58
The Savoy, Strand, Covent Garden, WC2R 0EU
Tel no: (020) 7592 1600
gordonramsay.com

Immune to the breathless persuasions of 'next food trend' lists, the velvety, low-lit Savoy Grill is an anachronism, and all the more precious for it. Where others pare back, champion plants and ferment like fury, this place continues to flambé crêpes Suzette, fillet Dover sole or lift the lid of a gleaming trolley to carve whatever precise creation lies beneath, all under the rapt gaze of diners. Tuesday lunchtime means succulent slices of spinach-stuffed Dingley Dell pork, served with the butteriest of mash; on Wednesday it's beef wellington. Escoffier-esque cuisine and unashamedly luxurious ingredients – lobster (thermidor or bisque), beluga caviar, chateaubriand – crowd the menu. Service is glidingly smooth, as you'd expect, and though the hefty wine list (everything is north of £30) might startle, do enjoy the sommelier's advice. Finish, if not with an Instagrammable crêpe moment, then with a millefeuille, cut *à table* – no mean feat given how paper-fine the pastry, how giving the sweet cream, how pert the raspberries.

Chef/s: Ben Waugh. **Meals:** main courses £12 to £48. Set L £26 (2 courses) to £30. Set early D £31 (2 courses) to £35. Tasting menu £98. **Details:** 100 seats. V menu. Vg menu.

Scott's

Cooking score: 4
⊖ Green Park, map 6
Seafood | £51
20 Mount Street, Mayfair, W1K 2HE
Tel no: (020) 7495 7309
scotts-restaurant.com

Scott's makes a heroic attempt at bringing the foaming briny to the shores of landlocked Mayfair with seafood and fish specialities served in an atmosphere of old-school luxe. A construction that looks like a speedboat is piled with ice and crustaceans behind the bar, and the Art Deco styling gives the place the feel of a cruise liner. Oysters from all over open the menu, with three grades of caviar not far behind, and the classic preparations to follow include crab that is not so much dressed as bespoke tailored, yellowtail and salmon sashimi, ceviche variations, and seared sea bass in lemon and herb butter. Let there be no bashfulness in ordering deep-fried haddock and mushy peas, or indeed a meat main, perhaps veal cutlet in sage butter with salsify and ceps. It all comes at a fair old whack, as one would expect from the equation of fresh seafood plus Mayfair, but it all feels worth it, through to the chocolate and salt caramel fondant with stracciatella ice cream. Wines start at £31.

Chef/s: David McCarthy. **Closed:** 25 and 26 Dec. **Meals:** main courses £20 to £43. **Details:** 150 seats. V menu. Wheelchairs.

Seven Park Place by William Drabble

Cooking score: 6
⊖ Green Park, map 5
French | £75
St James's Hotel and Club, 7-8 Park Place, Mayfair, SW1A 1LS
Tel no: (020) 7316 1600
stjameshotelandclub.com
£5 OFF

Reassuringly unfashionable, yet curiously outré in its outlook, chef William Drabble's bijou dining room within the palatial surrounds of the St James's Hotel is nothing if not optically challenging, involving exotic decorative tendrils and equally brash carpets with mirrors, geometrically patterned banquettes and off-kilter artworks. Thankfully, the kitchen is totally grounded in its pursuit of modern French cuisine as Drabble and his team fashion polished dishes from a storehouse of fine British ingredients: poached native lobster tail with cauliflower purée, roasted cauliflower and lobster butter sauce has become something of a signature over the years, while saddle of Lune Valley lamb might appear with onion, rosemary and wild garlic leaves. Although luxuries are given the full treatment, there is also room for humbler ideas, as in baked fillet of red mullet with blood orange and calamari pasta, slow-cooked veal cheek in Madeira or vanilla rice pudding with caramel poached pear. The 'wine book' is just that – a masterly tome running to more than 40 illuminating pages, with elite producers and desirable vintages at every turn (albeit at eye-watering prices), plus a host of top-ranking Coravin selections by the glass.

Chef/s: William Drabble. **Closed:** Sun, Mon, 20 to 27 Dec. **Meals:** set L £28 (2 courses) to £33. Set D £65 (2 courses) to £75. Tasting menu £95 (6 courses). **Details:** 26 seats. Bar. Wheelchairs. Children over 12 yrs.

★ TOP 50 ★

Sketch, Lecture Room & Library

Cooking score: 7
⊖ Oxford Circus, map 5
Modern European | £120
9 Conduit Street, Mayfair, W1S 2XG
Tel no: (020) 7659 4500
sketch.london

The Lecture Room & Library at Sketch is something to behold, the eye-popping interior setting the tone for some of the West End's most dazzling assaults on the palate. Under Johannes Nuding, the house style of Pierre Gagnaire retains its competitive edge, and the conceptual formats, which centre on dishes presented in carefully classified components on separate plates, to be eaten in a recommended order, remain inviolate. There is so much going on in each dish that the title can do no more than indicate a thematic approach, in which 'Sea Garden', for example, finds room for transparent clam ravioli in potato cream, scallop and coral glazed in mandarin, razor clams and squid in anchovy water and cava, and pumpkin ice cream with seaweed jelly. Assorted takes on a single meat are *de rigueur* these days, but here the kitchen really puts its primary ingredients through their paces, so that pork is presented as grilled rack in hay cocotte, stuffed trotter, pig's ear salad in mango vinegar, and luscious black pudding velouté boosted with spiced rum and chestnuts. Somehow, despite the heterogeneity of the presentations, it all hangs together, even unto the grand dessert show, which encompasses poppy flower chantilly with redcurrant gel and aloe vera, mango mousse with burrata and Campari ice cream, a mini baba in coconut and cachaça syrup, and much, much else. The star-studded wine list, from £29.50, makes a creditable effort to keep up.

Chef/s: Pierre Gagnaire and Johannes Nuding. **Closed:** Sun, 2 weeks Dec, 2 weeks Aug. **Meals:** main courses £50 to £68. Tasting menu £120. **Details:** 48 seats. V menu. Children over 6 yrs.

Social Eating House

Cooking score: 6
⊖ Oxford Circus, map 5
Modern British | £50
58 Poland Street, Soho, W1F 7NR
Tel no: (020) 7993 3251
socialeatinghouse.com

As one would expect from a restaurant in Jason Atherton's Social group, the overall feel is smart and modern: a dark wood and leather sort of place with a bit of funky industrialism thrown in and a bar upstairs (The Blind Pig) that has a semi-secret feel. Paul Hood heads the kitchen, sailing confidently through the tricky waters of intricate modern cuisine, fashioning clever contemporary dishes from superlative raw materials, perhaps pairing finely sliced raw scallops and wafer-thin discs of Jerusalem artichoke with a lime and avocado purée to create 'a lovely refreshing dish'. Equally impressive is roasted cod with a light crust of herbed crumbs atop apple-braised turnip, silky turnip purée and a barely caramelised apple-based sauce – a surprisingly delicious combination. A lavish venison dish was also praised: two thick medallions of pink haunch with fondant swede, a dab of glazed red cabbage, walnut shavings and glossy, butter-loaded mash. Service is 'formal but engaging' and the set lunch is seen as a bargain. With its collection of French classics and cannily chosen, thought-provoking bottles from elsewhere, the wine list really scores, and a good by-the-glass selection offers fruitful drinking throughout.

Chef/s: Paul Hood and Daniel Birk. **Closed:** Sun, bank hols. **Meals:** main courses £28 to £43. Set L £22 (2 courses) to £27. Tasting menu £65 (6 courses) to £85. **Details:** 76 seats. V menu. Bar. Wheelchairs. Music.

Social Wine & Tapas

Cooking score: 4
⊖ Bond Street, map 6
Modern European | £29
39 James Street, Marylebone, W1U 1DL
Tel no: (020) 7993 3257
socialwineandtapas.com

With an atmosphere of warm informality, menus that encourage grazing and a heroic wine list that demands exploration, Jason Atherton's tapas and wine bar is a reliable favourite on a street lined with restaurants. It's arranged over several levels, each done out tastefully and expensively with dark woods, copper tones and soft lighting, with an open kitchen on the ground floor that affords views of Marcus Rohlen and his team hard at work. Charcuterie and cheeses are a given, but the menu also wends its way from crunchy Szechuan-fried chipirones and squid ink aïoli, or grilled octopus with chickpea purée, chorizo and feta, to an outstanding Cornish cod with bacon marmalade and Roscoff onion, or tender Ibérico pig's cheeks with sherry vinegar and baby gem. Vegetables are given the star treatment in a dish of chargrilled carrots given heft by burnt aubergine, miso and walnut pesto. Laure Patry's formidable, wide-ranging wine list suits the food admirably.

Chef/s: Jason Atherton and Marcus Rohlen. **Closed:** Sun, bank hols. **Meals:** tapas £6 to £18. Set L and early D £26 (2 courses) to £20. **Details:** 45 seats. Wheelchairs. Music.

Spring

Cooking score: 5
⊖ Temple, Waterloo, map 5
Modern European | £60
Somerset House, Lancaster Place, Aldwych, WC2R 1LA
Tel no: (020) 3011 0115
springrestaurant.co.uk

The Spring experience at Skye Gyngell's Somerset House restaurant comes 'at a price' but is, say repeat visitors, 'worth it'. The handsomely proportioned room 'lifts the spirits' with sprays of seasonal blooms, tactile linens and flattering lighting. Service is attentive and warm. It's an English country garden of a menu featuring first-class biodynamic produce from Herefordshire's Fern Verrow farm in the form of nettle and sheep's milk ricotta dumplings and an asparagus and wild garlic garnish with lamb cutlets and lovage salsa verde. Lemon sole with sprout tops and Café de Paris butter is 'a perfect exemplar of the classic simplicity that is this elegant venue's hallmark'. Ice creams and tarts are excellent: try apple and prune tart with crème fraîche and Armagnac. Budget-watchers will appreciate the £20 pre-theatre menu of 'waste' ingredients but should note that though the Europhile wine list starts at £26, it hits its stride above £50.

Chef/s: Skye Gyngell and Rose Ashby. **Closed:** Sun, 23 to 26 Dec, 17 Jun, bank hols. **Meals:** main courses £27 to £35. Set L £28 (2 courses) to £32. **Details:** 100 seats. Wheelchairs.

★ NEW ENTRY ★

Stem

Cooking score: 4
⊖ Oxford Circus, map 5
Modern British | £45
5 Princes Street, Mayfair, W1B 2LF
Tel no: (020) 7629 9283
stem-byneo.co.uk

Having scored resounding hits with Anglo and Neo Bistro (see entries), Mark Jarvis has picked a super-central site just off Regent Street for his third venture. Occupying a Grade II-listed townhouse, Stem's interior combines purple leather banquettes, wishbone-style chairs and copper light fittings, while the kitchen means business with a menu that's short, modern and resolutely ambitious. The seasonal repertoire might offer anything from Cornish sea trout with green strawberries and rainbow carrots to aged beef sirloin alongside wobbly bone marrow, pickled cucumber and shiso – although the 'clear winner' on our visit is a dish of lightly charred green asparagus spears with white asparagus shavings, blobs of confit duck egg and tarragon cream. Sides of creamed sweetcorn and smoked kernels are exactly what's required, and there's the novelty of hay ice cream with moist hazelnut cake to finish. Service is utterly charming and chatty (without ever seeming 'overzealous'), and the wine list includes some unusually interesting bottles.

Chef/s: Mark Jarvis and Sam Ashton-Booth. **Meals:** main courses £15 to £25. Set L £23 to £27. Tasting menu £60 (7 courses). **Details:** 36 seats. V menu. Vg menu. Bar. Music.

Average price

The figure given in bold denotes the average price of a three-course dinner without wine.

★ NEW ENTRY ★

Sushi Atelier

Cooking score: 4
⊖ Oxford Circus, map 5
Japanese | £37
114 Great Portland Street, Fitzrovia, W1W 6PH
Tel no: (020) 7636 4455
sushiatelier.co.uk

Eating Japanese in Mayfair traditionally means rigorous ritual, reverential service, formalised cuisine and very big bills, but Sushi Atelier is one of a more approachable new breed – so expect Western tweaks, pally staff and a polyglot gang of blowtorch-wielding chefs, plus garish graffiti art and a pumping soundtrack. Lunches at the long counter (solo or otherwise) promise affordable sashimi-style sustenance, but it's worth making inroads into the carte if you're seeking something more refined. Sample butterfish carpaccio with a ponzu-like sauce and lotus-root crisps, for example, or tiny slices of cured razor clam with Japanese spring ginger, lime zest and a 'chewy' agar jelly laced with peaty whisky – all concealed under a smoke-filled cloche. Elsewhere, 'sensitively seasoned' sushi sets ramp up the creativity several notches, from artistically twisted horse mackerel with diced ginger to raw deep-red tuna with a dot of sweet-sour garlic and coriander syrup. Saké samplers will get you in the mood, and there's a short but interesting wine list, too.
Chef/s: Robert Kemeny. **Closed:** Sun. **Meals:** main courses £16 to £33. **Details:** 40 seats. Music.

Tamarind Kitchen

Cooking score: 3
⊖ Tottenham Court Road, map 5
Indian | £40
167-169 Wardour Street, Soho, W1F 8WR
Tel no: (020) 7287 4243
tamarindkitchen.co.uk

Mayfair's sophisticated Tamarind is closed for refurbishment, due to reopen in late 2018 with a new menu. For those who don't mind the 'cool hipster vibe' or the 'ambient club music' blaring through the speakers, this upmarket Soho seedling might fill the gap. Spread over two lavishly designed floors (velvet seating, elevated booths, dark wood, dim lighting), it provides a sultry backdrop for Indian food with familiar overtones – although execution is several notches above the norm. Minty pudina lamb chops from the tandoor are one of the standouts, while the choice of mains spans everything from luxurious chicken korma and tamarind-spiked South Indian fish curry to a traditional 'dum' biryani and guchi kofta (morel and paneer dumplings in a spiced creamy sauce). Sides, rice and breads are all up to the mark, while desserts feature some distinctly Westernised concoctions – a trifle, say – given an exotic twist from mango jelly, pistachio sponge, coconut bavarois and tropical fruits. Other plus points include pain-free prices, frisky cocktails and a commendable list of spice-friendly wines.
Chef/s: Peter Joseph. **Closed:** 25 and 26 Dec, 1 Jan. **Meals:** main courses £11 to £16. **Details:** 85 seats. Music.

Tandoor Chop House

Cooking score: 2
⊖ Charing Cross, map 5
Indian | £29
8 Adelaide Street, Covent Garden, WC2N 4HZ
Tel no: (020) 3096 0359
tandoorchophouse.com

Adelaide Street is a typical thoroughfare linking Charing Cross with Theatreland. Rather than rushing past on your way to a show, make time to linger at No. 8, the love child of a British chop house and a North Indian communal canteen. With its wood panels and exposed ducting, it's an urban interpretation of the genre in which three huge brass tandoor ovens take pride of place. Expect vivid spicing and evocative aromas in masala boti-rubbed ribeye steak, crisp lamb chops, whole roasted cauliflower or the house tandoor chicken, and it's all the better if you're happy to share. Kick off with crispy bhajis, or chickpea chaat with tamarind chutney, and be sure to order one of the tandoor-cooked

breads, such as the bone-marrow butter naan. There's even a sweet version with Nutella, salted nuts and coconut ice cream. Drink British craft beer and cider, or something off the concise wine list (opening at £25).
Chef/s: Mitz Vora and Ross Clarke, Kundon Singh and Kapil Joyand. **Meals:** main courses £9 to £17. **Details:** 48 seats. Wheelchairs. Music.

Temper

Cooking score: 3
⊖ Piccadilly Circus, map 5
International | £40
25 Broadwick Street, Soho, W1F 0DF
Tel no: (020) 3879 3834
temperrestaurant.com

The firepit glowing at the heart of Neil Rankin's vast BBQ bunker is the engine room of his Soho restaurant. This is where the action happens, where hunks of lamb, goat and beef (all butchered in-house) are cooked low and slow, while chefs press tortillas to order for the eclectic South American-influenced menu. There's seating all around at a marble and brass counter or at generous booths for those who wish to assemble a spread of flatbreads, tostadas and sides. The cooking's full-on, the flavours ramped up with every last bit of the animal: see burnt-end Thai larb, lamb-fat béarnaise with grilled corn and black beans, and pork skin with crab tostadas. Cheeseburger tacos and 'tofu al pastor' are clever crossovers. Drinks are taken seriously too, from G&Ts and soft drinks to uncompromising wines served with flair. Temper's younger siblings, Temper City and Temper Covent Garden, specialise in tandoor cooking and pizza respectively.
Chef/s: Neil Rankin and George Wood.
Meals: main courses £9 to £25. **Details:** 183 seats. Bar. Wheelchairs. Music.

10 Greek Street

Cooking score: 3
⊖ Tottenham Court Road, map 5
Modern European | £42
10 Greek Street, Soho, W1D 4DH
Tel no: (020) 7734 4677
10greekstreet.com

Six years on and this small, easy-going all-day Soho eatery remains plain, bare and cramped. Staff squeeze you in where they can – the popular bar stools give a ringside view of the chefs at work – they don't take bookings and queuing is inevitable, yet a young crowd floods in to devour the simple, pared-back modern sharing plates. Blame the excellent down-to-earth cooking and ferociously seasonal British produce. Asparagus, wild garlic and Jersey Royals all appear the very day you first crave them, but at the heart of things the kitchen excels at dishes such as razor clams with blood orange, 'nduja, fennel and monk's beard, and larger plates of clay-baked pigeon with bread pudding, cavolo nero and plum, or monkfish with chickpeas, sea lettuce and saffron. Hot chocolate mousse with espresso ice cream and hazelnuts adds the finishing touch and a short, modern wine list, with good choice by the glass, rounds things off.
Chef/s: Cameron Emirali. **Closed:** Christmas. **Meals:** main courses £18 to £27. **Details:** 35 seats. 2 seats outside. Music.

Terroirs

Cooking score: 1
⊖ Charing Cross, map 5
Modern European | £32
5 William IV Street, Covent Garden, WC2N 4DW
Tel no: (020) 7036 0660
terroirswinebar.com

A spirited, close-packed wine bar spread over two floors (the cellar restaurant is more chilled out), Terroirs celebrated its tenth birthday in 2018. It runs to a simple formula: a terrific list of exciting modern wines (from £23) is combined with a menu of punchy, rustic Med-

inspired food. Plates of charcuterie or French cheeses suit snacking with a glass of something, or go the whole hog and order burrata and confit fennel or smoked cod's roe with radish and salmon caviar, then roasted calf's tongue with pomme purée and Madeira jus, or stone bass with celeriac purée and salsa verde. An uncommonly good frangipane cake with blood orange and yoghurt is more than just an afterthought. Wines are predominantly French with plenty of large format and natural bottles. There's a second branch at 36-38 Lordship Lane, East Dulwich SE22 8HJ.
Chef/s: Simon Barnett. **Closed:** Sun, 25 and 26 Dec, 1 Jan, bank hols. **Meals:** main courses £17 to £24. **Details:** 100 seats. 6 seats outside. Bar. Music.

Texture

Cooking score: 5
⊖ Marble Arch, map 6
Modern French/Nordic | £75
34 Portman Street, Marylebone, W1H 7BY
Tel no: (020) 7224 0028
texture-restaurant.co.uk

The elemental flavours and clean presentation of dishes at this über-classy Marylebone restaurant are a crystal-clear indication of how the mind of Reykjavik-born chef, Aggi Sverrisson, works. The kitchen stylishly celebrates the natural world, taking its lead from enduringly popular Scandinavian cuisine. Dive deep into the notion with lightly salted cod or langoustines fished from chill North Atlantic waters, Norwegian king crab, or a plate of Icelandic cheeses – a two-year aged Gouda maybe. There are nods to more southerly foods too, the likes of milk-fed lamb (saddle, shoulder, belly) from the Pyrenees served with suitably delicate baby carrots and grelot onions, or asparagus, cut from Wye Valley beds and pepped up with Asian flavours. Finish a meal back in Iceland with skyr, rye bread crumbs and sweet Gariguette strawberries, or Icelandic liquorice with chocolate, cardamom, hazelnuts and lemongrass. The vast wine list sweeps the globe but can find nothing for less than £35.
Chef/s: Agnar Sverrisson. **Closed:** Sun, Mon, 2 weeks Dec, 19 to 22 Apr, 2 weeks Aug. **Meals:** main courses £35 to £48. Set L £29 (2 courses) to £34. Tasting menu £95. **Details:** 50 seats. Vg menu. Bar. Wheelchairs. Music.

Theo Randall at the InterContinental

Cooking score: 6
⊖ Hyde Park Corner, map 6
Italian | £70
InterContinental London Hotel, 1 Hamilton Place, Mayfair, W1J 7QY
Tel no: (020) 7318 8747
theorandall.com

Park Lane is a famous address best known for grand hotels and luxurious dining rooms. Theo Randall's Italian restaurant at the InterContinental, although established a dozen years ago, belongs to a different tradition. Randall, a chef still strongly associated with the River Café, where he spent 17 years, leaves flashy flourishes to his neighbours; his goal is to serve simple, seasonal flavours in comfortably smart surrounds. Where luxury does appear on the plate, it's in the form of perfectly seared calf's liver with sage and pancetta, say, or lobster linguine or a quivering panna cotta laced with grappa. Fish around on the website for special offers before you dine: the set dinner menu (£35 with a glass of Prosecco) is worth a look, though the full and very fairly priced menu of antipasti, primi, secondi and dolci is where the thrills lie. The wine list, fittingly Italophile, is organised unusually by season.
Chef/s: Theo Randall and Luis Eduardo Rendon Rodriguez. **Meals:** main courses £20 to £38. Set L and D £29 (2 courses) to £35. Tasting menu £70. **Details:** 160 seats. Vg menu. Bar. Wheelchairs. Music. Parking.

Tredwells

Cooking score: 2
⊖ Leicester Square, map 5
Modern British | £30
4a Upper St Martin's Lane, Covent Garden, WC2H 9NY
Tel no: (020) 3764 0840
tredwells.com

Of the multifarious eating and drinking opportunities around Seven Dials, this 'bright, lively' big-city eatery from Marcus Wareing is one of the more compelling. Split over three levels, with a leather and brass-studded bar dominating the ground floor, it's a contemporary space that suits the casual vibe. It's never going to win any prizes for inventiveness, although the timely introduction of a five-course plant-based tasting menu drew applause from one visitor 'pleased to be able to eat out with my vegan husband'. Good calls from the brasserie-style à la carte include 'thin and delicately made' duck ravioli matched with bright pickled radish and mooli, crunchy peanuts and micro herbs, and a simple dish of beautifully charred Ibérico Secreto pork, with a combo of gordal olives, blood orange, radicchio and salted ricotta. Bread is good, too, with diners praising a 'lovely little oval-shaped potato and rosemary loaf'. To drink, the global wine list has reasonable choice in the £30 to £45 range.

Chef/s: Chantelle Nicholson. **Closed:** 24 to 26 Dec, 1 Jan. **Meals:** main courses £18 to £33. Set L £22 (2 courses) to £26. Set D £25 (2 courses) to £30. Sun L £30. Vegan tasting menu £35. **Details:** 134 seats. 12 seats outside. Vg menu. Bar. Wheelchairs. Music.

Trishna

Cooking score: 4
⊖ Baker Street, Bond Street, map 6
Indian | £65
15-17 Blandford Street, Marylebone, W1U 3DG
Tel no: (020) 7935 5624
trishnalondon.com

Colourful Air India posters on the whitewashed walls may well showcase the international destinations touched by the global carrier, but the Sethi family's restaurant transports you to the coastal regions of south-western India. A pin-sharp contemporary output recalls the flavours and aromas of Kerala, Cochin and Mangalore, in a setting that owes more to mid-century Denmark than it does to the Indian Subcontinent. Start with pumpkin samosa with coconut chutney and murabba (a sweet fruit preserve) or shrimps spiced up with Tellicherry pepper and matched with coconut and mango chutney. The tandoor turns out hariyali bream (with smoked tomato kachumber) and subz seekh kebab (with organic sprout chaat and mint chutney), while Dorset brown crab is equally hard to resist. A curry might be hake with raw mango and tamarind, and wild mushroom and morel pilau will appeal to all. Finish with pistachio and fig kheer (rice pudding). The wine list flies you first class around the world, with a cracking choice by the glass.

Chef/s: Sajeev Nair. **Closed:** Christmas, bank hols. **Meals:** main courses £15 to £25. Set L £15 (2 courses). Tasting menu £60 (5 courses) to £70. **Details:** 80 seats. 6 seats outside.

Visit us online

For the most up-to-date information about *The Good Food Guide*, go to thegoodfoodguide.co.uk

28°-50°

Cooking score: 4
⊖ Bond Street, map 6
Modern European | £38
15-17 Marylebone Lane, Marylebone, W1U 2NE
Tel no: (020) 7486 7922
2850.co.uk

While the City branch of this 'wine workshop & kitchen' closed in 2018, the Marylebone address – the first to open – continues to breathe life into the wine bar genre. Spread over two stylish floors, wine and food get equal attention, with the former aided by the Coravin system to allow for tantalising options by the glass in three different sizes. France is the mainstay of a wine list that covers the globe, with classic cocktails adding to the mix. Owner Agnar Sverrisson of Texture (see entry) hails from Iceland, so look out for the house-cured gravadlax and Icelandic fish pie that sit alongside a top-notch burger, mushroom and truffle lasagne, and suckling pork belly with spring greens and bacon. A charcuterie plate and oysters make good sharers, and your waiter will likely have good ideas as to what to drink with cheeses from La Fromagerie.

Chef/s: Julien Baris. **Closed:** Sun, 25 and 26 Dec, 1 Jan, Easter Mon. **Meals:** main courses £15 to £22. Set L and early D £19 (2 courses) to £22. **Details:** 50 seats. 14 seats outside. Bar. Wheelchairs. Music.

Umu

Cooking score: 6
⊖ Green Park, Bond Street, map 5
Japanese | £150
14-16 Bruton Place, Mayfair, W1J 6LX
Tel no: (020) 7499 8881
umurestaurant.com
£5 OFF

The entrance is expertly camouflaged amid the narrow passageways of Bruton Place, its sliding door activated by passing a hand over the sensor in *Star Trek* fashion. Inside, a cocooned world of unruffled gentility is conjured, and virtually everything you see, from the ikebana flower displays to the exquisitely presented Kyoto kaiseki dishes are the work of Yoshinori Ishii himself. Umu is what's known as a labour of love, a plutocrat's journey into the subtleties and piquancies of Japanese cuisine, probably best appreciated via the seasonal set menus. Spring undertakes a journey from kombu-cured Arctic char with rhubarb, white asparagus, wasabi and vinegar jelly to a concept dessert called 'Cherry Blossom' on the Shore made with Ki no bi Kyoto gin. Along the way there may be a clear soup of eel and elvers, the day's outstanding fish specials, and the all-important wagyu beef with morels, potato mochi (dumplings) and mountain vegetables. A glazed rice ball with butterbur (coltsfoot relish) and pickles is worth the journey. For another £95, you can have wine and saké pairings with the dishes.

Chef/s: Yoshinori Ishii. **Closed:** Sun, 24 Dec to 4 Jan. **Meals:** main courses £32 to £85. Kaiseki menu £155 (8 courses). **Details:** 50 seats. Wheelchairs. Music.

Veeraswamy

Cooking score: 3
⊖ Piccadilly Circus, Oxford Circus, map 5
Indian | £70
Victory House, 99 Regent Street, Mayfair, W1B 4RS
Tel no: (020) 7734 1401
veeraswamy.com

With a prime West End location and more than 90 years of history, London's oldest Indian restaurant is a sure-fire target for tourists seeking a taste of right royal cooking. Extravagantly revamped and now part of a group that also includes Amaya and Chutney Mary (see entries), Veeraswamy's thickly carpeted dining room looks rather splendid with its silver ceiling, tinted glass lanterns and sepia photos of the old Raj. The menu features a version of Hyderabadi lamb biryani that was on the menu when the restaurant opened in 1926, and the kitchen shows considerable panache and precision when it comes to the regional stalwarts (smokey chicken tikka,

Kashmiri rogan josh et al). That said, it's also worth investing in less familiar dishes such as crumbed beetroot 'chops', roast duck vindaloo and venison mutta kebab (a tamarind-glazed Scotch egg). Classic and fine vintages dominate the sophisticated wine list.

Chef/s: Uday Salunkhe. **Meals:** main courses £17 to £41. Set L 26 (2 courses). Sun L £33 (2 courses) to £37. **Details:** 110 seats. V menu.

Viet Food

Cooking score: 2
⊖ Piccadilly Circus, map 5
Vietnamese | £25
34-36 Wardour Street, Soho, W1D 6QT
Tel no: (020) 7494 4555
vietnamfood.co.uk

'It's great to see places like Viet Food opening in Chinatown', and there's no doubt that Jeff Tan's vibrant Vietnamese cooking is clearly a cut above the food currently available elsewhere in the area. The two-tiered all-day eatery is solidly designed – 'shoestring startup this is not' – with cramped tables and service that ranges from 'efficient but informal' to not always believing the customer is right. However, everyone agrees that the dishes (mainly designed for sharing) are a delight: 'really fresh and extremely tasty'. One reader was impressed by tender pork belly and by the balance of spice and sweetness in a free-range chicken curry; others have praised the bun (vermicelli noodle), the stir-fry duck breast with green papaya, freshwater prawn salad with sweet chilli sauce, and the spring rolls. It's a popular place and booking is recommended. The wine list has been carefully chosen to complement the food.

Chef/s: Jeff Tan. **Closed:** 25 Dec. **Meals:** tapas £5 to £10. Main courses £11 to £16. **Details:** 70 seats. Bar.

Vinoteca Marylebone

Cooking score: 2
⊖ Marble Arch, map 6
Modern European | £33
15 Seymour Place, Marylebone, W1H 5BD
Tel no: (020) 7724 7288
vinoteca.co.uk

As with all the Vinotecas, this Marylebone restaurant, wine bar and shop offers a huge range of bottles with ungreedy mark-ups, alongside simple European dishes, each with a suggested wine pairing. There's private dining in the basement. For main entry, see King's Cross branch, north London.

Chef/s: Lloyd Morse. **Closed:** bank hols. **Meals:** main courses £9 to £19. Set L £15 (2 courses) to £18. **Details:** 55 seats. Bar. Music.

Vinoteca Soho

Cooking score: 2
⊖ Oxford Circus, Piccadilly Circus, map 5
Modern European | £33
53-55 Beak Street, Soho, W1F 9SH
Tel no: (020) 3544 7411
vinoteca.co.uk

Spread over two floors in the heart of Soho, the location of this wine bar and bistro – part of a six-strong chain – is handy if you're catching a show. There's a good-value pre-theatre menu alongside the Vinoteca formula of Med-inspired dishes and, of course, a stonking wine list. For main entry, see King's Cross branch, north London.

Chef/s: Klaudiusz Wiatrak. **Meals:** main courses £14 to £19. Set L and early D £15 (2 courses) to £18. **Details:** 80 seats. Bar. Wheelchairs. Music.

Stay in the know

For the latest restaurant news, look out for the weekly *GFG Briefing*. Visit thegoodfoodguide.co.uk

★ NEW ENTRY ★

The Wigmore

Cooking score: 3
⊖ Oxford Circus, Bond Street, map 5
Modern British | £28
15 Langham Place, Marylebone, W1B 3DE
Tel no: (020) 7965 0198
the-wigmore.co.uk

Tucked into the south-east corner of the swanky Langham and spread over two large, high-ceilinged rooms, The Wigmore brings shoppers, tourists and local suits up to date on the great British pub experience. It starts with a classy look – racing green walls, dark wood, leather, marble and brass – moves on to beer (taken very seriously) and then goes the whole hog with a crowd-pleasing menu of pub classics designed by Michel Roux Jr. Bar snacks of masala-spiced Scotch egg, stove-top cheese and mustard toastie, buttered crumpet with crab, and Bloody Mary salted chips have garnered a loyal following. A 'belting' roast chicken served with paprika-coated fingerling potatoes and topped with roasted calçot onions and pea shoots is 'more than enough for two'. Other standouts include a cheeseburger with ox tongue and crispy shallots, and butter-poached cod with mussels, monk's beard and sherry. There's no going hungry here, so you may want to share a treacle and orange tart. A modest wine list opens at £21.

Chef/s: Michel Roux Jr and James Howley. **Meals:** main courses £14 to £15. **Details:** 160 seats. Bar. Wheelchairs. Music.

Wild Honey

Cooking score: 4
⊖ Oxford Circus, Bond Street, map 5
Modern European | £50
12 St George Street, Mayfair, W1S 2FB
Tel no: (020) 7758 9160
wildhoneyrestaurant.co.uk

More than a decade after opening, Anthony Demetre's confident, modern cooking continues to draw a savvy cosmopolitan crowd. Everything feels right, from the 'clubby, discreet and comfortable' dining room with its beautiful dark wood panelling, white tablecloths and striking contemporary art, to attentive service and seasonal menus so full of good things that you're planning a return visit before you've ordered. A meal in March could bring a salad of crab combined with avocado cream, black radish and fennel, ahead of roast saddle of venison with sweet potato, beetroot and onion, while May might deliver spring garlic leaf and young spinach velouté with ricotta dumpling and asparagus, followed by 'superb' rabbit à la moutarde with spring greens and carrots. The set menus at lunch and dinner are justifiably popular, praise continues for the wild honey ice cream with crushed honeycomb, but look out, too, for the excellent lemon curd tart and the very good cheeseboard. There's acclaim, too, for the sommelier whose knowledge of his aristocratic cellar is impressive, and whose advice should be followed.

Chef/s: Anthony Demetre and Greg Csaba. **Closed:** Sun, bank hols. **Meals:** main courses £18 to £29. Set L and D £35 (3 courses). **Details:** 55 seats. Music.

Wiltons

Cooking score: 4
⊖ Green Park, map 5
British | £67
55 Jermyn Street, Mayfair, SW1Y 6LX
Tel no: (020) 7629 9955
wiltons.co.uk

'There is something reassuring about an establishment that is impervious to fashion,' thought one visitor to this thoroughly British institution, which started life as a shellfish stall in the Haymarket in 1742 and became a restaurant in the 1840s. Thick carpets, starched white tablecloths, cerise velvet seats and dark wood-panelled booths keep noise levels low. The cooking, equally old-school, focuses on a classical British repertoire, one where shellfish takes pride of place, and the lunchtime carvery is 'a welcome dose of nostalgia'. Everything is impeccably sourced, from a 'very fresh' Devonshire crab or smoked wild Scottish salmon to Rhug Estate venison. Monkfish tail, served on the bone, with seaweed butter and sides of Jersey Royals and leaf spinach has been applauded, as has passion fruit soufflé with mango compôte and white chocolate ice cream. Prices can be punishing, but 'this restaurant knows what its customers like and want, and it gives it to them in spades' and faultless service helps to soften the blow. The wine list, notably strong on France, rises sharply from £30.

Chef/s: Daniel Kent. **Closed:** Sun, 23 Dec to 2 Jan, bank hols. **Meals:** main courses £18 to £68. Set L and D £35 (2 courses) to £43. **Details:** 100 seats. Wheelchairs.

Anonymous

At *The Good Food Guide*, our inspectors dine anonymously and pay their bill in full every time.These impartial review meals, along with feedback from thousands of our readers, are what informs the content of the *GFG*. Only the best restaurants make the cut.

The Wolseley

Cooking score: 2
⊖ Green Park, map 5
Modern European | £38
160 Piccadilly, Mayfair, W1J 9EB
Tel no: (020) 7499 6996
thewolseley.com

If Messrs Corbin and King had not already dreamed up The Wolseley, then film director Richard Curtis surely would have done by now. This high-status Piccadilly address – note the avuncular doorman and ornate façade – seduces movie stars, tourists, tweedy out-of-towners and pin-striped powerbrokers. White linen tablecloths and bread and butter account for the unpopular £2 cover charge, though it might equally be a people-watching surcharge. One comes for the scene, not the food, not that the latter isn't enjoyable: omelette Arnold Bennett, chopped liver and steak frites are among the all-day classics. Breakfast is a London tradition: silver coffee pots and crisply uniformed waiting staff lend even porridge a sense of occasion. Afternoon tea, less expensive than the grand hotel variety, luxuriates in the spectacular, chandeliered setting too. Fine wines, cocktails and Champagne are delivered with panache though service in general can be patchy.

Chef/s: David Stevens. **Meals:** main courses £13 to £49. **Details:** 170 seats. V menu. Bar. Wheelchairs.

Wright Brothers Soho

Cooking score: 2
⊖ Oxford Circus, map 5
Seafood | £45
13 Kingly Street, Soho, W1B 5PW
Tel no: (020) 7434 3611
thewrightbrothers.co.uk

Poké bowls and po' boys are bright additions to the menu at the Soho Wright Brothers, off Carnaby Street, with alfresco dining in Kingly Court. For main entry, see Spitalfields branch, east London.

Chef/s: Gareth Clelland. **Closed:** 25 and 26 Dec, 1 Jan. **Meals:** main courses £13 to £23. **Details:** 90 seats. 30 seats outside. Bar. Wheelchairs. Music.

Xu

Cooking score: 4
⊖ Piccadilly Circus, map 5
Taiwanese | £35
30 Rupert Street, Soho, W1D 6DL
Tel no: (020) 3319 8147
xulondon.com

Located where Chinatown morphs into Soho, this grander sibling of Bao (see entry) takes its inspiration from the 1930s tea rooms of Taiwan, right down to the Art Deco lights, ceiling fans and vintage leather booths. The deal here is fashionable small plates – perhaps grilled quail, Szechuan oil and hazelnut sauce, or pan-fried aged pork pancake with vinegar and chilli oil, fennel and glass noodles – and Taiwanese classics. When it comes to main courses, the signature shou pao chicken (marinated chicken with fresh ginger, spring onion, white pepper and fried chicken skin) continues to impress readers, but try the chilli egg-drop crab (white and brown crabmeat with salmon roe, egg-drop sauce, red chilli, fermented shrimp and garlic) and silken tofu with mapo sauce made from green peppercorns. Ma lai cake (steamed brown sugar sponge cake with condensed milk and orange butterscotch) provides a sweet, fragrant finale. A short wine list does the job, though cocktails are worthy of exploration.

Chef/s: Erchen Chang. **Meals:** main courses £14 to £19. Set L and D £40. **Details:** 68 seats.

Yauatcha

Cooking score: 4
⊖ Tottenham Court Road, map 5
Chinese | £40
15-17 Broadwick Street, Soho, W1F 0DL
Tel no: (020) 7494 8888
yauatcha.com

The original branch of what is now a global brand, Yauatcha's Soho venue is a seductive place rather than a practical one. Ground-floor tables are closely packed and small for all the dim sum baskets that can stack up – and the later it gets, the more like a club the moodily lit basement dining area becomes. Stick to the ground floor and come for the suitably varied dim sum. Help in choosing them may not be forthcoming, but the har gau prawn dumplings, scallops shui mai and char siu buns all come recommended, as do wagyu beef fried dumplings, mushroom spring roll and the famous venison puffs. Among the larger plates, look out for Thai-style chicken, jasmine tea-smoked ribs, or stir-fry pepper chilli seafood with asparagus. Western desserts include a fine raspberry délice with Madirofolo chocolate and lychee. To drink, there's a wide range of teas and cocktails, and a wine list that's tailored to the food.

Chef/s: Tong Chee Hwee. **Meals:** main courses £8 to £31. Set L £28. **Details:** 190 seats. Bar. Music.

Zoilo

Cooking score: 3
⊖ Bond Street, map 6
Argentinian | £40
9 Duke Street, Marylebone, W1U 3EG
Tel no: (020) 7486 9699
zoilo.co.uk

Expect a modern take on the multifarious flavours of Argentina here, served up to an appreciative crowd ('the atmosphere is buzzing'). The beef the country is so famous for is present and correct – flank steak with grilled hispi cabbage, a whopping 400g ribeye or outstanding empanadas. Small plate dining is the way to go, so share black pudding croquettes with squid and apples, a salad of winter tomatoes with creamy burrata, ox tongue carpaccio, or sea bass ceviche with avocado and pickled radishes. It's all done with style. Finish with dulce de leche crème brûlée and 'banana split' ice cream. The wine list includes regional options from the home country, including fizz, and some fun cocktails such as the Patagonian Poncho (Rum Sixty Six, Cointreau, cinnamon and cacao), which go down a treat in the basement bar.

Chef/s: Diego Jacquet. **Closed:** Sun, 1 week Christmas, bank hols. **Meals:** sharing plates and main courses £7 to £32. Set L £15 (2 courses) to £19. **Details:** 51 seats. Bar. Wheelchairs. Music.

LOCAL GEM

L'Absinthe

⊖ Chalk Farm, map 2
French | £27
40 Chalcot Road, Primrose Hill, NW1 8LS
Tel no: (020) 7483 4848
labsinthe.co.uk

Now in its eleventh year, locals are vociferous in support of Jean-Christophe Slowik's relaxed French bistro, a 10-minute walk from the Roundhouse. Indeed, one visitor reckoned she was 'the only person there who didn't live in the area'. It's a convincing slice of France, noted for such classics as leeks vinaigrette with poached eggs, chicken liver parfait, Toulouse sausage with Puy lentils and mustard sauce, boeuf bourguignon with pomme purée, and of course, steak frites. The cooking may not be the most adventurous, but it is satisfying and good value. The short wine list opens at £21.95.

Bellanger

Cooking score: 2
⊖ Angel, map 2
Modern European | £35
9 Islington Green, Islington, N1 2XH
Tel no: (020) 7226 2555
bellanger.co.uk

Named after a certain Monsieur Bellanger (purveyor of Delaunay-Belleville automobiles), this gregarious neighbourhood asset brings the Corbin & King house style to Islington – and locals love it. From the breads and pastries in the window to the polished woodwork and aged mirrors in the *belle époque* dining room, Bellanger breathes warmth and authenticity, while dapper staff are on hand to deliver full-flavoured brasserie fare with unmistakable Alsatian influences. The menu trundles from salades râpées and quiche lorraine to Black Forest gâteau and classic millefeuilles, taking in mains of ready-to-burst Toulouse sausages, calf's liver with black bacon and lemon sole with morel butter as well as bestsellers such as veal Holstein. Corbin & King's restaurants are known for giving good breakfast, and Bellanger is no exception with its viennoiserie, bircher muesli, eggs, crêpes and suchlike. As for drinks, traditional Alsace beers and cocktails vie with smart wines from the region and beyond.

Chef/s: Dalmaine Blignaut. **Meals:** main courses £14 to £28. Set L and early D £16 to £19.
Details: 200 seats. 32 seats outside. V menu. Bar. Wheelchairs. Music.

Bradleys

Cooking score: 2
⊖ Swiss Cottage, map 2
French | £40
25 Winchester Road, Swiss Cottage, NW3 3NR
Tel no: (020) 7722 3457
bradleysnw3.co.uk

'I've been cooking here for 25 years and still love the change of seasons,' notes Simon Bradley, chef proprietor of this neighbourhood restaurant close to Hampstead Theatre (it's a popular pre- and post-theatre spot). At other times locals pack the smart contemporary dining room for food that strikes a modern note with its amalgam of calendar-tuned British ingredients and solid French technique. A starter of Dorset crab and mullet ceviche with fennel, grapefruit and brown crab tartare signals the kitchen's intentions, while mains might feature venison smoked over pine (with onion farci, charred king cabbage and pickled pear) as well as fish from Brixham – perhaps whole lemon sole pointed up with salsify, purple broccoli and blood orange or grilled fillet of turbot with kale, ceps, celery and basil. When it comes to dessert, try something simple such as raspberry crème brûlée. Special menus abound, and the appealing French-led wine list is a credit to the place.

Chef/s: Simon Bradley. **Closed:** bank hols.
Meals: main courses £18 to £24. Set L and D £20 (2 courses) to £24. Sun L £28 (2 courses) to £32.
Details: 60 seats. V menu. Vg menu.

The Bull & Last

Cooking score: 3
⊖ Tufnell Park, Kentish Town, map 2
Modern British | £39
168 Highgate Road, Hampstead, NW5 1QS
Tel no: (020) 7267 3641
thebullandlast.co.uk

This laid-back and characterful Victorian hostelry has all the rustic charm of a country bolthole rather than an old pub within striking distance of Parliament Hill and Hampstead Heath. A pint of London-brewed Five Points So Solid Brew in the bar might be just the ticket after a walk on the heath, but the daily changing menu of seasonal dishes packs in the diners upstairs, too. Dishes are broad-shouldered and unfussy, a typical meal beginning with handmade pappardelle with slow-cooked lamb ragù, crème fraîche, marjoram and lemon. It might precede sea trout with cauliflower, daikon and kohlrabi salad, tempura prawn and sesame, or chargrilled onglet with triple-cooked chips, a mixed leaf salad and garlic butter. Finish off with blueberry cheesecake ice cream sundae or a board of well-kept British cheeses. A carefully chosen wine list starts at £22 and there's a great range of real ales.

Chef/s: Oliver Pudney. **Closed:** 25 Dec. **Meals:** main courses £15 to £24. **Details:** 45 seats. Music.

★ NEW ENTRY ★

Ceremony

Cooking score: 3
⊖ Tufnell Park, map 2
Vegetarian | £30
131 Fortess Road, Tufnell Park, NW5 2HR
Tel no: (020) 3302 4242
ceremonyrestaurant.london/

Ceremony bills itself as a restaurant that 'just so happens to be vegetarian', wearing its meat-free credentials lightly and pitching itself at both the herbivores and carnivores of NW5. It also just so happens to occupy a rather dapper space, with a smattering of tables arranged around a turquoise-tiled bar that dispenses cocktails to North London media types. The menu, meanwhile, is something of a magpie, representing eastern Europe, east Asia and various coordinates in between. An inspection began with addictive butternut squash pierogi, although other options might be as uncomplicated as whole globe artichoke, lemon garlic butter and hollandaise. Bright colours and clean flavours defined the mains: vivid green linguine with a thick pesto of wild garlic, rocket and cashew with goat's curd, or crunchy sweet potato curry with coconut and biryani. Round off with a flourless chocolate cake, or better still, ice cream from Ruby Violet (over the road). Ceremony also wins bonus points for prompt, pomp-free service, and its small but diligently curated wine and beer selection.

Chef/s: Kinga Jablonka. **Closed:** Mon. **Meals:** main courses £15 to £16. **Details:** 30 seats. V menu.

Dishoom

Cooking score: 2
⊖ King's Cross, map 2
Indian | £30
5 Stable Street, King's Cross, N1C 4AB
Tel no: (020) 7420 9321
dishoom.com

Just a short walk from King's Cross station, this branch of the Indian café/restaurant chain is arranged over three stories of a grand Victorian warehouse with outside seating. As with all Dishooms, it's open from breakfast to dinner. Soup up the lamb-on-the-bone special with supplementary lamb brains. For main entry, see Shoreditch branch, east London.

Chef/s: Naved Nasir. **Closed:** 25 and 26 Dec, 24 Jul. **Meals:** main courses from £6 to £22. **Details:** 250 seats. 28 seats outside. V menu. Bar. Wheelchairs. Music.

LOCAL GEM

500 Restaurant

⊖ Archway, map 2
Italian | £27
782 Holloway Road, Archway, N19 3JH
Tel no: (020) 7272 3406
500restaurant.co.uk

£5 OFF £30

Mario Magli and Giorgio Pili's Archway Italian eatery may be looking a little tired around the edges these days, but it remains an intimate, much-loved asset to the local community. A meal might start with silky burrata from Puglia served with chestnut purée, followed by a deeply comforting dish of ravioli filled with slow-cooked venison in a tomato and red wine sauce. Then consider chargrilled sea bream fillets with braised fennel, saffron, raisins and pine nuts, and tiramisu for dessert. Italian wines start at £18.50.

★ NEW ENTRY ★

Ham

Cooking score: 3
⊖ West Hampstead, map 1
Modern British | £33
238 West End Lane, West Hampstead, NW6 1LG
Tel no: (020) 7813 0168
hamwesthampstead.com

David Houten and Rose Tuckey reputedly named their restaurant after the Old English word for 'home' but whatever the etymology, Ham has caused a stir in the neighbourhood. Brunch is already a shoo-in for locals, although the real action takes place in the evening when Australian Matt Osborne, ex-The Ledbury and Terroirs (see entries) masterminds proceedings from his visible perch in a mezzanine kitchen overlooking the contemporary-style dining room. The menu promises enticing new-British seasonal fare with oriental and Antipodean influences, ranging from crisp-skinned Norfolk quail with artichokes and kombu seaweed to a vibrant dish of super-fresh pollock accompanied by spring asparagus, crab dumplings and shiitake mushrooms or a meat-free amalgam of seedless Trombetta courgettes, tomato, barley, olives and shiso. To conclude, desserts such as banana mousse with white chocolate, coconut, mango and basil show a commendably light touch, while the food is supported by an eclectic wine list.

Chef/s: Matt Osborne. **Closed:** Mon, Tue. **Meals:** main courses £14 to £21. **Details:** 45 seats. 6 seats outside. Bar. Music.

★ NEW ENTRY ★

The Hero of Maida

Cooking score: 2
⊖ Warwick Avenue, map 6
Anglo-French | £35
55 Shirland Road, Maida Vale, W9 2JD
Tel no: (020) 3960 9109
theheromaidavale.co.uk

£5 OFF

A proper pub for modern-day London, The Hero is as welcoming to drinkers as to diners, with bottles of cider and pints from Timothy Taylor's given the same billing on the menu as wine. There are bar snacks – homemade sausage rolls and the like – but those who come for a proper meal receive classic Anglo-French dishes from a kitchen that knows what it's doing, accompanied by simple seasonal produce that's allowed to speak for itself. Smoked trout, for example, is lifted with a perfectly cooked duck egg and enriched with a watercress mayonnaise, while brown crabmeat makes a piquant sauce for simply poached asparagus, the white crab used as a garnish. Elsewhere, a pile of pink-as-you-like calf's liver sits on a bed of buttery mash and black bacon. Follow with all time champions – tarte tatin, crème caramel or petit pot au chocolat. Cutting edge it isn't, but for familiar classics cooked with care and flare, it's hard to beat.

Chef/s: Henry Harris and Stephen Collins. **Closed:** 25 to 26 Dec, 1 Jan. **Meals:** main courses £13 to £20. **Details:** 60 seats. 42 seats outside. Bar. Music.

Jin Kichi

Cooking score: 2
⊖ Hampstead, map 2
Japanese | £30
73 Heath Street, Hampstead, NW3 6UG
Tel no: (020) 7794 6158
jinkichi.com

Simple, unaffected charm and good-value food brings the crowds to this animated Japanese eating house in the heart of Hampstead, where options on a long, user-friendly menu abound. Top-drawer, ultra-fresh sushi is the restaurant's trump card and the range is extensive, taking in turbot and sea urchin as well as the more familiar tuna, eel and sea bass – mixed sushi (and sashimi) sets are a good way in. Beyond raw fish, the kitchen delivers popular dishes such as mixed vegetable tempura, pork katsu with tonkatsu sauce, and chicken yakitori. Familiar appetisers from edamame beans to gyoza dumplings (filled with minced pork) start the ball rolling, and meals end simply with ice cream – which can include red bean and green tea flavours. Lunch brings one-plate meals (teriyaki, sushi, sashimi, for example, all served with rice and miso soup), and wines are limited, so drink saké, shochu, beer or green tea.

Chef/s: Rei Shimazu. **Closed:** Mon. **Meals:** main courses £6 to £20. Set L £10 (2 courses) to £19. **Details:** 42 seats. V menu. Music.

Odette's

Cooking score: 4
⊖ Chalk Farm, map 2
Modern British | £50
130 Regent's Park Road, Primrose Hill, NW1 8XL
Tel no: (020) 7586 8569
odettesprimrosehill.com

The striped awning and outdoor tables mark what has been a place of neighbourhood pilgrimage for many a long year. It's been a decade since Bryn Williams acquired Odette's, and at the start of 2018, established sous-chef Tom Dixon stepped up to head the kitchen. The comfortable rooms with their books and prints indicate something of the cultural orientation of the regular customer base, people who enjoy modern interpretations of traditional European cooking. Proceedings might open with a serving of smoked eel, pickled turnips and apple to set the taste buds alight, a waft of smoked rosemary adding aromatic depth, before halibut grenobloise with potted shrimps, or the glorious Welsh beef fillet and braised cheek with pommes Anna and broccoli, make their appearances. Dishes are carefully weighted and cleanly presented, perhaps with a side of BBQ potatoes dressed in cheese, onion and truffle. Finish with the house take on Jaffa cake with almonds and caramelised cream, or maple syrup parfait with spiced pumpkin and chocolate. A good glass selection, including some Coravin goodies, leads off a cosmpolitan wine list, with bottles from £25.

Chef/s: Bryn Williams and Tom Dixon. **Closed:** Mon, 2 week Christmas. **Meals:** main courses £18 to £29. Set L £17 (2 courses) to £22. Set early D £22 (2 courses) to £27. Sun L £33 (3 courses). Tasting menu £55. **Details:** 55 seats. 25 seats outside. V menu. Music.

Oldroyd

Cooking score: 3
⊖ Angel, map 2
Modern European | £35
344 Upper Street, Islington, N1 0PD
Tel no: (020) 8617 9010
oldroydlondon.com

Three years on, Tom Oldroyd's tiny restaurant continues to enjoy faithful support. A rare independent in an area dominated by chains, it is defined by tightness of space, sharing plates of Mediterranean-accented, no-nonsense food, and reasonable prices. Scrupulously seasonal, the kitchen moves from winter dishes of squid ink risotto, and duck breast with celeriac mash and spiced red cabbage, to springtime hits such as gnocchi fritti with wild garlic and Parmesan, and grilled calçots with salsa romesco and toasted almonds.

Ingredients are top-drawer, as evidenced by roast lamb rump served with braised baby gem and fennel with ramson and anchovy sauce, and monkfish tail with celeriac purée, agretti, shrimps and brown butter. After that, pudding (should you have the wherewithal) could be chocolate mousse with poached pears and walnut. As befits the food, imaginative cocktails are offered together with a concise European wine list with everything offered by the glass, carafe or bottle.

Chef/s: Matt Hiltemann. **Closed:** 25 and 26 Dec, 31 Dec to 1 Jan. **Meals:** main courses £7 to £22. Set L £16 (2 courses) to £19. Set D £20 (2 courses) to £30. **Details:** 32 seats. 6 seats outside. Music.

Osteria Tufo

Cooking score: 2
⊖ Finsbury Park, map 2
Italian | £25
67 Fonthill Road, Finsbury Park, N4 3HZ
Tel no: (020) 7272 2911
osteriatufo.co.uk

A beam of Neapolitan sunshine landing on a quiet back street in Finsbury Park, Osteria Tufo wears its heritage lightly: with an elegant dining room sporting charcoal-grey walls, chessboard flooring, lofty windows and linen-clad tables. The menu, however, is a stridently Italian affair, with dishes representing the whole country but showing a bias to all points south. Simple, elemental flavours prevail among the antipasti: homemade meatballs in ragù, or baby octopus alongside cherry tomato, olives and capers. Primi dishes represent Italian comfort food at its most big-hearted, with homemade pasta starring – from folds of pappardelle in luganica pork sausage ragù, to stubby Neapolitan paccheri paired with fresh Devon crab and mussels. Carne and pesce options cater to those of more substantial appetites – while desserts include crowd-pleasers like tiramisu. The all-Italian wine list sees bottles starting from £20.

Chef/s: Diego Monticelli-Cuggio. **Closed:** Mon, 23 Dec to 4 Jan. **Meals:** main courses £13 to £16. Sun L £22 (2 courses). **Details:** 30 seats. 20 seats outside. Vg menu. Wheelchairs. Music.

LOCAL GEM

Ottolenghi

⊖ Highbury & Islington, Angel, map 2
Middle Eastern | £35
287 Upper Street, Islington, N1 2TZ
Tel no: (020) 7288 1454
ottolenghi.co.uk

Yotam Ottolenghi's impact on Britain's culinary landscape has been remarkable: his pioneering approach put vegetables at the centre of the plate and enlivened the nation's spice cupboards. At this all-day operation, one of four deli-cafés, the pristine white-on-white space directs the eye to the vibrant food. Order a selection of signature salads, a riot of bold flavours that head to the Middle East one moment, to Asia the next; perhaps roasted aubergine with feta yoghurt, almonds, pomegranate and mint, or crushed peas and edamame with wasabi, cucumber and pumpkin seeds, or opt for a hot main of baked Cornish hake with za'atar onions or a Cabrito goat kofta. The abundance of sweet things shouldn't be missed.

Parlour

Cooking score: 2
⊖ Kensal Green, map 1
Modern British | £35
5 Regent Street, Kensal Green, NW10 5LG
Tel no: (020) 8969 2184
parlourkensal.com

The old Grey Horse has been dusted down and reconfigured as a proper foodie pub for our times, making the most of original features and creating an agreeable local at the same time. Jesse Dunford Wood knows what's what when it comes to feeding the crowds who pack the place, putting butch British ideas (the famed cow pie and three-cheese macaroni) alongside dishes where European flavours and the seasons are at play (chicory, blood orange and blue cheese salad, and sea bass with mussels, monk's beard and Pink Fir potatoes). Burger night is every Tuesday, there are snacks to share, say chestnut houmous with rosemary pitta bread or popcorn chicken nuggets, or you can settle in for a seasonal supper that could include baked mackerel with rhubarb, radishes and mint, and finish with sticky toffee pudding, butterscotch and crème fraîche. Drinks run from craft beers to a short global list of wines.

Chef/s: Jesse Dunford Wood. **Closed:** Mon, Christmas to New Year, Aug bank hol. **Meals:** main courses £16 to £18. Set L £15 (2 courses) to £18. Set D £21 (2 courses) to £29. Tasting menu £45. Chef's table L £75, D £85. **Details:** 125 seats. 65 seats outside. Bar. Wheelchairs. Music.

Perilla

Cooking score: 4
⊖ Canonbury, Dalston Kingsland, map 2
Modern European | £44
1-3 Green Lanes, Newington Green, N16 9BS
Tel no: (020) 7359 0779
perilladining.co.uk
£5 OFF

'This is my kind of food – seasonal, light, all about fresh ingredients and flavour, not too much mucking about and utterly delicious,' was the verdict of one first-time visitor to Ben Marks and Matthew Emmerson's unfussy, rough-round-the-edges eatery on the edge of Newington Green. What Perilla lacks in comfort it makes up for with really engaged service and a short menu that obsessively plays off the seasons and looks to Europe for inspiration. The understated, purposeful cooking is all about small plates (order two or three per person), first-class ingredients and the big, bold flavours seen in seaweed sourdough and lamb-fat butter (a real crowd-pleaser) and dishes such as velvety smooth, nutty onion soup (served in a whole burnt onion) or octopus bolognaise. Pot-roast broccoli with cabbages and a thick, curd-like yoghurt, or grilled calf's liver with a baked Maris Piper potato and dulse also draw praise, while juniper and myrtle crème caramel makes an excellent finish. The modern European wine list opens at £24.

Chef/s: Ben Marks. **Closed:** 24 to 26 Dec, 1 and 2 Jan. **Meals:** main courses £12 to £34. Tasting menu £38. **Details:** 44 seats. Wheelchairs. Music.

Restaurant Michael Nadra

Cooking score: 3
⊖ Chalk Farm, map 2
Modern European | £39
42 Gloucester Avenue, Primrose Hill, NW1 8JD
Tel no: (020) 7722 2800
restaurant-michaelnadra.co.uk

More expansive and ambitious than his Chiswick original (see entry), Michael Nadra's Primrose Hill offshoot is quaintly housed in a Grade II-listed 'horse tunnel' by the Regent's Canal. It comes with a dedicated martini bar, a bright conservatory and an elegant alfresco terrace, although the focus is on the atmospheric brick-walled dining room with its stone floors and caramel-toned leather banquettes. Value for money is the key to Nadra's endeavours, and he achieves his goal via a choice of eclectic fixed-price menus. Flavours are true, and readers have found much to enjoy – from greener-than-green broccoli, kale and spinach soup with garlic crostini to steamed sea bass with prawn and chive dumplings, oriental greens and crab bisque sauce. Meat eaters might veer towards loin of Welsh lamb accompanied by stuffed savoy cabbage, potato terrine, rainbow chard and smoked aubergine, while sticky toffee pudding and chocolate fondant both pass muster in the dessert department. The wine list ventures far and wide in search of quality, with an enlightened choice of growers and ample selections by the glass or carafe.

Chef/s: Michael Nadra. **Closed:** Mon, 24 to 28 Dec. **Meals:** set L £23 (2 courses) to £28. Set D £ 33 (2 courses) to £39. Tasting menu L £50, D £60 (6 courses). **Details:** 80 seats. 33 seats outside. Bar. Wheelchairs. Music.

LOCAL GEM

Roti King

⊖ Euston, map 2
Malaysian | £10
40 Doric Way, Euston, NW1 1LH
Tel no: (020) 7387 2518
rotiking.info

Frequently dubbed the ambassador of Malay food in London, Roti King is sequestered in a basement on an unprepossessing Euston back street, but don't let that put you off. The local student population and anyone yearning for home-style south-east Asian flavours queue round the block for the roti canai – flaky, buttery flatbread, cooked to order at the open kitchen, stuffed or as it comes, for dipping into bowls of curry, humming with spice, pan-Asian favourites such as nasi goreng, bowls of steaming laksa and a gamut of noodle dishes – at prices that are a steal. It's BYO, cash-only, and no reservations.

Season Kitchen

Cooking score: 2
⊖ Finsbury Park, map 2
Modern British | £25
53 Stroud Green Road, Finsbury Park, N4 3EF
Tel no: (020) 7263 5500
seasonkitchen.co.uk

There's a sense of understated chic about this Finsbury Park neighbourhood venue (handy for the Park Theatre), done in sober grey with a bare-boarded floor, a miscellany of pictures and a plethora of linened tables. Ben Wooles' menu breaks with the straitjacket of the three-course format, offering everything in small or large sizes for your own coordinating. That said, devilled whitebait with real mayonnaise, gnocchi with wild garlic, hazelnuts and Parmesan, or wood-pigeon breast with polenta in blackberry gravy all sound like bankable appetisers, while the dishes that feel like aspirants to main status take in stone bass with pickled anchovies, tomatoes and olives, and breast, heart and sweetbreads of lamb with apricot. The aged steaks are an obvious draw, while vegetarian dishes might encompass courgette koftas with rice curd. End things on an aromatic high with a chocolate pot laced with rosemary, or a plate of British cheeses with carta di musica crispbread and blood orange marmalade. A tempting list of modern wines applies a fair markup policy throughout.

Chef/s: Ben Wooles. **Closed:** Sun, Mon, 24 to 30 Dec. **Meals:** main courses £12 to £20. **Details:** 35 seats. Music.

Trullo

Cooking score: 3
⊖ Highbury & Islington, map 2
Italian | £40
300-302 St Paul's Road, Islington, N1 2LH
Tel no: (020) 7226 2733
trullorestaurant.com

Feeding Islington with full-flavoured Italian food since 2010, Trullo is the sort of restaurant most neighbourhoods just aren't lucky enough to have. Spread over two floors, the design aesthetic hits the nail on its contemporary urban-rustic head – enamel lamps, filament bulbs – and the service helps it all go along smoothly, despite the inevitable throng. Antipasti lead the way on a menu that changes twice a day: wild sea bass carpaccio with fennel seeds and chilli; or bruschetta topped with cuttlefish, Datterini tomatoes and basil. Pasta is good, too, perhaps tagliolini with 'nduja and mascarpone, or ravioli of ricotta with sage butter. The charcoal grill might offer up Cornish monkfish with Trombetta courgettes, or rabbit leg with Violetta artichokes and chips. It's the sort of food you could eat every day if time and budget allowed, right through to desserts of cherry and almond tart. The helpfully annotated, all-Italian wine list opens at £24.

Chef/s: Tim Siadatan and Conor J Gadd. **Closed:** 23 Dec to 3 Jan. **Meals:** main courses £16 to £22. **Details:** 78 seats. Music.

Scoring explained

Local Gems, scores 1 and 2
Scoring a 1 or a 2 in *The Good Food Guide*, or being awarded Local Gem status, is a huge achievement. We list the very best restaurants in the UK; for the reader, this means that these restaurants are well worth visiting if you're in the area - and you're extremely lucky if they are on your doorstep.

Scores 3 to 6
Further up the scale, scores 3 to 6 range from up-and-coming restaurants to places to watch; there will be real talent in the kitchen. These are the places that are well worth seeking out.

Scores 7 to 9
A score of 7 and above means entering the big league, with high expectations of the chef. In other words, these are destination restaurants, the places you'll long to talk about - if you're lucky enough to get a booking.

Score 10
This score is extremely rare, with chefs expected to achieve faultless technique at every service. In total, only eight restaurants have achieved 10 out of 10 for cooking since the scoring system was introduced in 1998.

See page 13 for an in-depth breakdown of *The Good Food Guide*'s scoring system.

Vinoteca

Cooking score: 1
⊖ King's Cross, map 2
Modern European | £33
One Pancras Square, King's Cross, N1C 4BU
Tel no: (020) 3793 7210
vinoteca.co.uk

Those who remember the bad old days of restaurant wine service – the cork-sniffing sommeliers, the exorbitant clarets – can only be glad of Vinoteca. The friendly six-strong group's mission statement is best exemplified by its regularly updated, amusingly annotated list of over 200 world wines (England to Australia via Luxembourg) and 25 ever-changing by-the-glass pours. Prices are transparent: both shop and restaurant prices are listed (each restaurant has its own bottle shop) and there's a world of choice in the sub-£30 bracket (London restaurants, take note!). Adventurous drinking is positively encouraged: 'Who would have thought of retsina and mozzarella?' enthuses a reader. It's a clever concept, but an inspection meal at the industrial-chic King's Cross branch was patchy. Bavette and chips, a group signature, was good, but crab and Jersey Royals with vichyssoise and a vegetarian main of grilled Mediterranean vegetables with scamorzone were rather old-fashioned. Breakfasts and good-value weekday set lunches are a bonus.
Chef/s: Kieren Steinborn. **Meals:** main courses £8 to £23. Set L £15 (2 courses) to £18. **Details:** 80 seats. 40 seats outside. Wheelchairs. Music.

LOCAL GEM

Walnut

⊖ Finsbury Park, map 2
Modern European | £29
The Arts Building, Morris Place, Finsbury Park, N4 3JG
Tel no: (020) 7263 5289
walnutdining.co.uk

Emma Duggan has turned an unprepossessing spot hard by Finsbury Park station into a nifty little neighbourhood meeting place. Shape-shifting smartly, weekday Walnut segues from modern breakfasts (shakshuka, perhaps, or avocado on toasted sourdough) to casual lunches of multi-coloured salads and aubergine parmigiana. At the weekend, brunch rules. Duggan's Angela Hartnett schooling comes through best at dinner: her rich and creamy Portland crab risotto is just as it should be. Vegetables get a lot of love (asparagus and a crispy egg, or courgette ribbons, hazelnuts and gremolata) but Dedham Vale steaks are a mainstay. Drink wine, coffee, whatever you fancy.

★ NEW ENTRY ★

Westerns Laundry

Cooking score: 5
⊖ Holloway Road, map 2
Modern British | £28
34 Drayton Park, Islington, N5 1PB
Tel no: (020) 7700 3700
westernslaundry.com

The hinterland between Highbury, Islington and Holloway seems an unlikely setting for such a hot spot. That Westerns Laundry is considered a destination is partly down to the pitch-perfect atmosphere and the friendly, informed staff, but mainly to the 'deceptively simple, satisfying and stunning' food. The interior, which opens on to a summer terrace, brought to mind an old-fashioned school hall for one reader: think high white walls, school-style coat pegs, communal tables ('not as hateful as it sounds'), and blackboard (listing the small sharing plates of the daily changing menu). The cooking allows the very best ingredients to shine, so a simple plate of pickled anchovies is on song, just spiky enough to whet the palate. Similarly, 'rosy and salty, deeply flavoured' paleta Ibérica needs nothing more, while crisp croquettes of creamy smoked haddock with mustard mayo are a masterclass in frying. These were the indispensable preludes to an inspection meal that went on to 'beautifully, delicately cooked' cod given spring-like notes from lettuce, celery and peas, with salty bacon adding depth and richness; and featherblade with Jerusalem artichoke that was 'such a satisfying, beautifully considered plate of food'. A light rum baba (for two), utterly drenched in a boozy syrup, made a perfect finish. The wine choices fully live up to the ethos of the cooking, an up-to-the-minute list of low intervention wines from European vineyards.
Chef/s: David Gingel. **Closed:** Mon. **Meals:** small plates £2 to £24. **Details:** 55 seats. Wheelchairs. Music.

READERS RECOMMEND

Xi'an Impression

Chinese
117 Benwell Road, Highbury, N7 7BW
Tel no: (020) 3441 0191
xianimpression.co.uk
'A tiny place opposite Arsenal's Emirates Stadium. It's famed for hand-pulled noodles – try the biangbiang noodles in chilli sauce with chunky beef – but we also go for the steamed pulled pork burger or the chicken and mushroom pot sticker. We've heard rumours of a larger Spitalfields offshoot.'

Readers recommend

These entries are genuine quotes from a report sent in by one of our readers. We intend to follow up these suggestions in the year to come.

Angler

Cooking score: 6
⊖ Moorgate, map 4
Modern British | £65
South Place Hotel, 3 South Place, Moorgate, EC2M 2AF
Tel no: (020) 3215 1260
anglerrestaurant.com

The location on the top floor of the gleaming South Place Hotel, surrounded by office blocks, may not be the obvious setting for a seafood restaurant, but Angler's long, mirror-lined dining room suits Gary Foulkes' focused cooking. Expect dishes that are inventive but restrained, classical yet able to embrace broader influences: take a simple tuna tartare, where tiny cubes of yellowfin are topped with dots of avocado, wasabi purée and a few leaves of purple shiso. Or slow-cooked octopus tentacles roasted to develop a nice crust, anointed with taramasalata, and served with tempura chipirones, slices of new potato and a sweetly acidic red wine bagna cauda to counter the richness. Meat isn't ignored, but seafood is the star, as in steamed turbot on 'noodles' made from finely sliced squid and served with shimeji mushrooms in a clear dashi stock, or Cornish cod with roasted parsley root and purée and a rich, meaty, glossy sauce. A milky, almost mousse-like chocolate pavé is an indulgent finish. You can drink well here without breaking the bank: bottles start at £28 and there's plenty of fish-friendly choice below £40.

Chef/s: Gary Foulkes. **Closed:** Sun, bank hols. **Meals:** main courses £30 to £40. Set L £28 (2 courses) to £32. Tasting menu £65 (6 courses) to £98. **Details:** 60 seats. 25 seats outside. Bar. Wheelchairs. Music.

Anglo

Cooking score: 6
⊖ Farringdon, map 5
Modern British | £42
30 St Cross Street, Farringdon, EC1N 8UH
Tel no: (020) 7430 1503
anglorestaurant.com

'Love it. Absolutely my sort of place in terms of food, space, service and ethos . . . it did not put a foot wrong from the moment we arrived.' So ran the notes of a first-time visitor to Mark Jarvis's shining beacon to new British cuisine. Like its restrained interior – neutral colours, concrete floor, bare tables and black pendant lights – the food is confidently no-frills, with the kitchen's focus on the best of seasonal British produce. Choose two or three courses from a short, fixed-price list at lunch, or the full tasting menu of six, seven or eight courses. Dishes show a lightness of touch combined with bold flavours, and every detail makes sense, so the subtle depth of egg yolk might be partnered by puréed potato, watercress and truffle, while the intense hit of green tomato and aromatic lemongrass might lift a plate of sweet prawns. The breathtaking richness of beef cheeks is perfected paired with earthy celeriac and clean-tasting parsley. Equally deft is the cheese and onion malt loaf. Desserts are innovative, scaling the heights with a daring assemblage of chocolate, cranberry and rhubarb. Wines, mainly from European vineyards, suit the food admirably.

Chef/s: Mark Jarvis. **Closed:** Sun, Mon, 24 Dec to 4 Jan. **Meals:** set L £23 to £28. Tasting menu £48 (7 courses) to £60. **Details:** 32 seats. Music.

Symbols

 Accommodation is available
 Three courses for less than £30
£5 OFF £5 off voucher scheme
Notable wine list

LOCAL GEM

Berber & Q Grill House

⊖ Haggerston, map 2
Middle Eastern | £29
338 Acton Mews, Haggerston, E8 4EA
Tel no: (020) 7923 0829
berberandq.com

Railway arches are ideal if you're after that edgy, urban feel, and Berber & Q looks the business – dangling lamps here, communal rough-hewn wooden tables there, and plenty of atmosphere (or noise, if you're over 40). Inspired by the Middle East and North Africa and cooked over charcoal, expect burnt beetroot with hazelnut dukkah, lamb chops, or baharat-spiced short rib, with meze plates ideal as sharers (fight over the smokey chicken wings). Drink a bespoke local beer (or something from Morocco or Israel), and inspired cocktails. If you're in Exmouth Market, check out the sister establishment: Shawarma Bar, EC1R 4QE.

Bistrotheque

Cooking score: 2
⊖ Bethnal Green, map 1
Modern British | £40
23-27 Wadeson Street, Bethnal Green, E2 9DR
Tel no: (020) 8983 7900
bistrotheque.com

Bistrotheque was the original off-the-radar spot when it opened in a former sweatshop in Bethnal Green in 2004. Fifteen years later, age has not diminished its edgy appeal. The young and fashionable flock here at the weekend for the fast-paced brunch scene, when Bloody Marys and pancakes, bacon and maple syrup keep hangovers at bay. The new soft-shell crab Benedict with spiced hollandaise is popular, too. The 'New York-y' loft vibe is awfully cool but awfully noisy so shout up to order your fish and chips or spicy, hand-chopped steak tartare (both comforting, constant presences here). Dinner is in the bistro spirit with a vogueish dash of seasonality: consider tempura cabbage and parsley mayonnaise or roast cod, pickles and chilli pepper emulsion. Pudding could be panna cotta, poached rhubarb and shortbread or a liquid finish of espresso martini at the bar. French wines, some surprisingly conservative, dominate the list.

Chef/s: Blaine Duffy. **Closed:** 24 to 26 Dec. **Meals:** main courses £17 to £39. Early and late D £25 (3 courses). **Details:** 80 seats. Bar.

Blacklock

Cooking score: 2
⊖ Monument, map 4
British | £25
13 Philpot Lane, City, EC3M 8AA
Tel no: (020) 7998 7676
theblacklock.com

Blacklock, purveyor of chops and drops, may have started in Soho (see entry) but it's found its spiritual home in the City. Monday to Friday, the Square Mile's hungry pile into the brick-lined basement for steaks, guffaws and bottles of Châteauneuf-du-Pape – 'Del Boy's favourite claret' as the tasting notes remind us. The menu is easy to navigate, with clearly priced sections for pre-chop bites, starters, big chops, £5 cocktails etc. The 'all-in' option at £20 a head gets you a plate of the day's chops (from Philip Warren in Cornwall) and a side apiece. It's easy to get silly with the sides and sauces (garlic marrow spread, say) so keep it simple with a chilli-smothered starter of pig's head on toast, a few chops (fattier cuts such as smoked bacon fare well on the grill), a salad and a portion of crisp beef-dripping chips. House wines are on tap, starting at £4.50 a glass.

Chef/s: Mirek Dawid. **Closed:** Sat, Sun, 25 and 26 Dec. **Meals:** main courses £12 to £18. Set L and D £20 (2 courses). **Details:** 92 seats. Bar. Music.

★ NEW ENTRY ★

Brat

Cooking score: 5
⊖ Shoreditch High Street, map 4
British | £35
First Floor, 4 Redchurch Street, Shoreditch, E1 6JL
bratrestaurant.com

Tomos Parry's decision to up sticks from Kitty Fisher's in Mayfair (see entry) and move to the first floor of a former boozer in Shoreditch's Tea Building led to one of the most awaited openings of 2018. It has given the chef more room to expand on his wood-fired obsession – the first thing you see on entering the wood-panelled dining room is the open grill and blazing oven. And if you have heard anything at all about Brat, then you know about the turbot ('brat' in Old English) offered in three sizes (the smallest a whopping 1kg), which comes wood-roasted on the bone, some of its skin deeply charred without drying out the rich white meat beneath. Parry takes the same approach with Herdwick lamb, Dexter fillet and the like. Wonderfully meaty oysters, lightly roasted with seaweed; two flavourful wild rabbit patties with creamy white beans topped with blood sausage; or delicately soused red mullet, served on a zesty tangle of pickled vegetables, are terrific openers that hammer home the kitchen's MO of sourcing prime ingredients and treating them with the utmost simplicity. Squeeze in at tightly packed tables or the narrow counter – there's no pretense of formality here, yet the service is remarkable, talkative and enthusiastic. The short, European wine list is modern and keenly priced, with everything available by the glass or bottle.

Chef/s: Tomos Parry. **Closed:** Mon. **Meals:** main courses £17 to £65. **Details:** 64 seats. Music.

Brawn

Cooking score: 4
⊖ Hoxton, map 2
Modern European | £35
49 Columbia Road, Hoxton, E2 7RG
Tel no: (020) 7729 5692
brawn.co

Perched on a corner of one of east London's prettiest streets, Brawn is very much what modern London eating is all about. With stools for sitting at the counter, and what look like old-fashioned kitchenette tables in the main room, it's definitely the no-frills, pared-back look. A first sight of Ed Wilson's straightforwardly written menus might suggest the same thing, but the food is full of dynamism, with energetic seasonings and satisfying textures throughout. Nibble some pungent Gers andouille, or crunchy fiery radishes, to get going, before considering the likes of a raw scallop dressed in celery, capers and colatura di alici (a fish sauce of fermented anchovies). Afterwards come robust meat mains such as pork collar with white mogette beans, sprout tops and wholegrain mustard sauce, bracing fish like cod brandade with radicchio and olives, or perhaps a crossover dish of black pudding and squid with bitter greens. A fix of dark chocolate comes in savoury guise with olive oil and sea salt to finish, or look to blood orange and almond tart for sweet relief. A stunning compendium of modern wines accompanies, its tentacles reaching far and wide, with oxidative natural whites and bottles from the lesser-known French regions, including a whole portfolio from Anne and Jean-François Ganevat in the Jura. There are small glasses from £4.50, bottles from £19.

Chef/s: Ed Wilson and Doug Rolle. **Closed:** 24 Dec to 3 Jan, bank hols. **Meals:** main courses £14 to £25. Sun L £28. **Details:** 70 seats. Bar. Wheelchairs. Music.

Breddos

Cooking score: 1
⊖ Barbican, map 5
Mexican | £25
82 Goswell Road, Clerkenwell, EC1V 7DB
Tel no: (020) 3890 8545
breddostacos.com

Swift success led this former taco shack to put down roots and open a second bricks-and-mortar site in Soho (see entry), yet the formula here remains the same: take prime British produce and apply a no-borders approach to flavour. Take the carne asada, a steak-topped taco, finished with grelot onion cream and punchy nam jim (a Thai dipping sauce), or a snack of corn esquites (salad) spiced with 'nduja. The hallmark tortillas, made from scratch by grinding the corn in a volcanic stone mill, are more than just mere vessels for other ingredients. Tacos are served in pairs with fiery salsas, but tortillas appear in other guises, too: try pickled chili quesadilla with tangy Oaxaca cheese or sashimi-grade tuna tostada. The street-food aesthetic remains, with communal or stool seating reinforcing the fact that no one's getting too serious. Tequila lovers are spoilt for choice, though there's wine, beer and thirst-quenching agua fresca if you want to leave steadier on your feet.

Chef/s: Artur Lasota. **Closed:** 24 to 30 Dec. **Meals:** tacos £4 to £5. Tostadas £9 to £10. **Details:** 42 seats. Bar. Wheelchairs. Music.

★ NEW ENTRY ★

Brigadiers

Cooking score: 3
⊖ Bank, Mansion House, map 4
Indian | £40
1-5 Bloomberg Arcade, City, EC4N 8AR
Tel no: (020) 3319 8140
brigadierslondon.com

The Sethi siblings (Gymkhana, Hoppers x 2, see entries) have clearly had fun creating their newest concept Brigadiers, a barbecue restaurant and drinking den inspired by India's army mess bars. There's a warren of rooms, including one with a pool table, whisky vending machine, self-serve beer taps and screens for live sports. The theming's OTT – shield your eyes from the leopard-print carpet and monkey lamps – but it's a fabulously original place in which to celebrate payday over schooners of draught beer from a monthly changing list. It would take several visits to work your way through all the bar snacks, kebabs, biryanis, grills and paos. Even poppadoms come in multiple forms: crimped potato, lentil, puffed tapioca and fenugreek. Ingredients are fine quality, notably in gamey ox cheek vindaloo 'cocktail samosas' and juicy goat chops slathered in bhuna ghee masala, though there's one component too many in beef chuck keema with boiled egg, straw potatoes, chilli cheese naan and bone marrow. If beer or whisky aren't your thing, choose from an extensive global wine list starting at £28.

Chef/s: Satya Jena. **Closed:** 25 to 27 Dec, 1 to 3 Jan. **Meals:** set L £20 (2 courses) to £25. Set D £30 (2 courses) to £40. Sun L £40 (2 courses). Tasting menu £50 (8 courses). **Details:** 140 seats. 40 seats outside. V menu. Bar. Wheelchairs. Music.

Cabotte

Cooking score: 3
⊖ Bank, map 4
French | £40
48 Gresham Street, City, EC2V 7AY
Tel no: (020) 7600 1616
cabotte.co.uk

£5 OFF

'Busy with City types and costly bottles; clearly the two-bottle lunch is not dead,' said one visitor to this smart mirror-lined bistro that takes its inspiration – both vinous and gastronomic – from Burgundy. For the meatiest and most regionally unimpeachable route through the menu, look to roast lamb sweetbreads and peas in minted lamb jus, followed by the indispensable beef cheek bourguignon with savoy cabbage and smoked bacon. There are seafood offerings, too – rock oysters in Chardonnay vinegar, and Loch

Duart salmon with roasted cauliflower, wild leeks and gremolata. Sides include leek gratin, gratifyingly doused in Comté, and if you're closing a deal – either business or romantic – what better way than with a tatin for two, adorned with clods of clotted cream? A *cabotte* is a little hut, of the kind seen throughout the vineyards of the Côte d'Or, and the 500-strong wine list is fittingly loaded with their output, at prices that slowly but surely relax their grip on common sense. Bottles of other stuff start at £25.

Chef/s: Edward Boarland. **Closed:** Sat, Sun, 21 Dec to 4 Jan. **Meals:** main courses £18 to £24. **Details:** 75 seats. Wheelchairs. Music.

Café Spice Namasté

Cooking score: 2
⊖ Tower Hill, map 4
Indian | £42
16 Prescot Street, Tower Hill, E1 8AZ
Tel no: (020) 7488 9242
cafespice.co.uk

As time has passed, a publishing and TV career has blossomed for Cyrus Todiwala, but fame first beckoned in the mid 1990s with the opening of Café Spice Namasté in this red-brick former courthouse. It's a riot of colour inside, while on the plate ethically sourced British ingredients loom large in dishes full of the spirit of India, north and south. Bhel puri is as good a place to start as any, displaying the distinct spicing that is the norm here, or go for the rich meatiness of the 'addictive' lamb dosa. There are some classic curries, but with a twist (ostrich bhuna, for example), and inventive ideas such as grilled halibut served on a risotto fired up with red chilli and garlic. Vegetarians fare very well indeed – split-pea and spinach fritter, say, with a spicy Goan-style coconut sauce – and there's a tasting menu that kicks off with a pomegranate Bellini. A concise, food-friendly wine list starts at £24.75.

Chef/s: Cyrus Todiwala. **Closed:** Sun, 25 Dec to 1 Jan, bank hols. **Meals:** main courses £17 to £23. Set L and D £30 (2 courses) to £40. Tasting menu £70. **Details:** 120 seats. Music.

LOCAL GEM

Ceviche

⊖ Old Street, map 4
Peruvian | £25
2 Baldwin Street, Old Street, EC1V 9NU
Tel no: (020) 3327 9463
cevicheuk.com

A sister to Ceviche in Soho (see entry), the Old Street venue occupies a prime piece of real estate and presents a rather more formal face to the world than its colourful older sibling. Cocktails remain a crowd-puller (pisco sour, paloma spritz...), while the trademark ceviches take you the 6,000km to Lima in a heartbeat. The rotisserie turns out pollo a la brasa (with thick-cut chips and amarillo salsa), Japanese flavours infuse wang wei octopus, and artichoke and asparagus pie is a satisfying meat-free dish. Beers and wines have South American soul to match.

Cinnamon Kitchen

Cooking score: 3
⊖ Liverpool Street, map 4
Indian | £50
9 Devonshire Square, City, EC2M 4YL
Tel no: (020) 7626 5000
cinnamon-kitchen.com

Cinnamon Kitchen sees Vivek Singh reimagine his grand Cinnamon Club concept for City hotshots. The spin-off's a little lighter on the wallet: £19 at lunch gets you two courses that might feature chicken leg or a vegetarian trio (Padrón peppers, paneer and achari cauliflower) given the tandoor treatment. The £39 kebab platter for two is an easy decision. Things get even more interesting later in the day (after cocktails at the adjacent Anise Bar maybe) when you'll find such Singh signatures as tandoori-spiced red deer with pickled root vegetables, Lucknow and Hyderabadi biryanis and long-standing sides of masala mash or tomato curry-leaf quinoa. Lighter dishes including cured salmon with green pea wasabi jhalmuri (puffed rice) appear on both carte and tasting menu (with wine pairings). For a fusion finish, try Neal's Yard Dairy cheese with quince chutney and Peshwari naan. Classic international wines start at £24.50.

Chef/s: Vivek Singh and Rakesh Nair. **Closed:** Sun, 25 Dec. **Meals:** main courses £17 to £37. Set L £19 (2 courses) to £24. Set D £24 (2 courses) to £29. Tasting menu £70 (7 courses). **Details:** 110 seats. 40 seats outside. V menu. Music.

City Social

Cooking score: 6
⊖ Liverpool Street, map 4
Modern British | £58
Tower 42, 25 Old Broad Street, City, EC2N 1HQ
Tel no: (020) 7877 7703
citysociallondon.com

Wrapped around the 24th floor of the old NatWest tower, this outpost of Jason Atherton's empire offers window seats on every side. While many sky-scraping venues fail to deliver food to match the views, City Social succeeds handsomely, and a change of chef – Daniel Welna now heads the stoves under the continued stewardship of executive chef Paul Walsh – has gone smoothly. The suave interior – parquet floors, modernist wood and leather chairs, horseshoe banquettes and a glossy, mirrored ceiling – exudes luxury and confidence, and so does the food. Brixham crab with pickled kohlrabi, nashi pear and pink grapefruit typifies the lightness of the cooking, the seemingly simple ingredients given depth by the addition of a delicate layer of jelly carrying the richer flavour of brown crabmeat. Mains are equally classy and the ingredients are second to none: Herdwick lamb, for example, with white asparagus, almond, olive tapenade and pomme soufflé; or Cornish sea trout with grilled courgette, broad beans, sorrel and cucumber vinaigrette. For pudding, rum baba wins special praise – 'possibly the lightest I have ever tasted' – complemented with sweet mango and a just-right sharp pineapple carpaccio. The wine list is quite a tome, with a great selection of intriguing wines by the glass.

Chef/s: Paul Walsh. **Closed:** Sun, bank hols. **Meals:** main courses £24 to £41. **Details:** 100 seats. Vg menu. Bar. Wheelchairs. Music.

The Clove Club

Cooking score: 6
⊖ Old Street, Shoreditch High Street, map 4
Modern British | £75
Shoreditch Town Hall, 380 Old Street, Shoreditch, EC1V 9LT
Tel no: (020) 7729 6496
thecloveclub.com

'Fabulous', 'bliss', 'ace'... Isaac McHale's forward-thinking British cooking at The Clove Club moves readers to superlatives. In the half decade since it launched at Shoreditch Town Hall out of a pop-up in a pub, The Clove Club has become an integral part of the UK's fine dining landscape. It's grown up now but never stuffy; the understated room with palms, wooden tables and blue-tiled open kitchen feels tranquil. There's a choice of menus: a seven-course taster or shorter five-course version. Among McHale's best-known dishes are buttermilk chicken with pine salt, and a dessert of warm blood orange sheep's milk yoghurt and wild fennel granita but some newer ideas are establishing supremacy. Among them, Japanese-inflected sardine sashimi, smoked sardine and whisky broth and thornback ray, chrysanthemum, brown butter and spruce. You can add wine, tea or soft-drink pairings, or take your pick from the wide-reaching, intelligent wine list. Note: reservations take the form of 'tickets' purchased in advance.

Chef/s: Isaac McHale. **Closed:** Sun, 2 weeks Dec. **Meals:** tasting menus £75 to £110. **Details:** 60 seats. V menu. Bar. Music. Children at L only.

Club Gascon

Cooking score: 5
⊖ Barbican, Farringdon, map 5
Modern French | £50
57 West Smithfield, City, EC1A 9DS
Tel no: (020) 7600 6144
clubgascon.com

Club Gascon has celebrated 20 years with a face-lift, creating more space and allowing the magnificent marble panelling to stand out. The food may not have the direct and earthy appeal of its earlier days but such skilful cooking, applied to fine ingredients, ensures a high success rate. Pascal Aussignac is famous for championing the produce of his native Gascony, though the once ubiquitous foie gras is now, happily, all but absent. Seasonality is characteristic of the output, and highlights of our winter dinner included a cep pie and wild mushroom fricassée with deeply flavoured parsley oil, and a perfectly cooked nugget of barbecued black cod with bisque-like foamy oceanic jus, sea urchin pearl and a tiny ball of sweet-sour nashi pear that brought a welcome hint of acidity. A pre-dessert prune soaked in Armagnac with orange and Armagnac cream was 'utterly delicious'. Among the many incidentals, bread with lobster-infused butter comes in for praise. The white-gloved Gallic service knows what it's about, while the extensive wine list is a treasure trove of wines from France's south-west region.

Chef/s: Pascal Aussignac and Arturo Granato. **Closed:** Sun. **Meals:** main courses £21 to £29. Set L £25 (2 courses) to £45. Set D £45. Tasting menu £80. **Details:** 42 seats.

Anonymous

At *The Good Food Guide*, our inspectors dine anonymously and pay their bill in full. These impartial review meals, along with feedback from thousands of our readers, are what informs the content of the *GFG*.

★ NEW ENTRY ★

The Coach

Cooking score: 2
⊖ Farringdon, map 5
Modern French | £35
26-28 Ray Street, Clerkenwell, EC4V 2BA
Tel no: (020) 3954 1595
thecoachclerkenwell.co.uk

£5 OFF

Careful refurbishment of this historic inn has reinvigorated the bar area, where proper pints are pulled amid a hubbub of chatter. But there's a constant stream of hungry folk, too, finding their way to the back room or up the creaky stairs, drawn by Henry Harris's honest, generous and well-prepared grand-mère-style French cooking (and who leave some hours later with a satisfied air about them). Most of the offering here is bang on the nail. There's relish for the enormous porterhouse steaks, and lamb rump served with fresh white beans and rosemary is as good a dish as anything in London. But it's not all perfect: horseradish sauce and celeriac rémoulade that accompany smoked salmon and Bayonne ham lack a certain subtlety, and our onglet was cooked hot enough to char on the outside but remain cold in the middle. Crème caramel, on the other hand, is the real deal, as is the decent, sensible wine list.

Chef/s: Aurelien Durand and Henry Harris. **Closed:** 25 and 26 Dec, 1 Jan. **Meals:** main courses £7 to £36. **Details:** 82 seats. 20 seats outside. Bar. Music.

Comptoir Gascon

Cooking score: 3
⊖ Farringdon, Barbican, map 5
French | £28
61-63 Charterhouse Street, Clerkenwell, EC1M 6HJ
Tel no: (020) 7608 0851
comptoirgascon.com

£5 OFF £30

A homely feel pervades the smaller offshoot of Club Gascon (see entry), where shelves of French products form a backdrop to the mix of farmhouse-style bench seating, counter stools and dinky little tables for two. As at the mother ship, the cooking of south-west France is wholeheartedly celebrated on an informally structured menu that encompasses plenty of duck, from slow-cooked egg with crushed Jerusalem artichokes and watercress, to properly rendered confit with potato cake and salad leaves, as well as traditional cassoulet. Even chips are done in duck fat and 'crazy salt'. Not a duck fan? There are fish dishes such as the rather grand whole sea bass with pipérade, or perhaps a veal onglet steak with white asparagus, chicory and orange zest. It's all presented with appreciable flair by knowledgeable staff, although textbook crème brûlée requires no explanation. The south-western wines include many of the much-improved aromatic dry whites of the region, with glass prices from £5.50.

Chef/s: Pascal Aussignac. **Closed:** Sun, Mon, 22 Dec to 7 Jan. **Meals:** main courses £10 to £33. **Details:** 40 seats. 8 seats outside. Wheelchairs. Music.

★ BEST NEW ENTRY, LONDON ★

Cornerstone

Cooking score: 6
⊖ Hackney Wick, map 1
Seafood | £40
3 Prince Edward Road, Hackney Wick, E9 5LX
cornerstonehackney.com

Cornerstone could be the template for the latter-day urban restaurant: a big square, white room with concrete floor, lots of light, a dominant open kitchen and simple modern furniture. It's a look many London venues aspire to, but few achieve with even half the brio of Tom Brown's casual new opening near Hackney Wick station. There's the same studied craft that earned him accolades at Outlaw's at the Capital (see entry), and a winning way with seafood that enlivens a compact menu of ferociously seasonal small plates. Everything is on point: from 'sublime' raw hand-dived scallop with Isle of Wight tomato dressing; a well-judged dish of cured monkfish flecked with toasted almonds, dots of yoghurt, grapes and the tang of sherry vinegar; to a delicate plaice fillet served with nuggets of sweet, tender lobster in a slick of buttery paprika sauce with diced courgette. And the token meat offering is not to be missed if the 'outstanding' crisp lamb shoulder kiev with anchovy, pea and mint butter is anything to go by. Potted shrimp crumpet has the makings of a signature dish, and a rich saffron-infused Cornish burnt cream with sweet strawberries, shards of sweet brittle and a hint of ginger, is an indulgent finish. Staff are engaging, cocktails just complicated enough to get your attention, and every bottle on the brief wine list is natural, organic, biodynamic and refreshingly priced.

Chef/s: Tom Brown. **Closed:** Sun, Mon. **Meals:** main courses £12 to £16. Tasting menu £35 (6 courses) to £45. **Details:** 46 seats. Wheelchairs. Music.

The Culpeper

Cooking score: 2
⊖ Aldgate East, map 4
Modern European | £33
40 Commercial Street, Whitechapel, E1 6LP
Tel no: (020) 7247 5371
theculpeper.com

Culpeper's inspirational rooftop garden and growing patch has been redesigned and re-branded as 'Piculpeper' to reflect the venue's seasonal obsession with pickling and preservation – although it continues to pay homage to the namesake 17th-century botanist, physician and astrologer. A year-round harvest of medicinal and edible herbs, vegetables and flowers finds its way downstairs to the first-floor kitchen, where it's put to use in a succinct menu of full-flavoured seasonal dishes. Wild garlic pesto adds pungency to a starter of burrata and 'nduja, while Tarbais beans, glazed carrots and salsa verde complement a serving of confit pork belly. Otherwise, share a whole lemon sole with new potatoes, brown butter, capers and almonds, before rounding off with chocolate lava cake, griottine cherries and praline parfait. Spread over four floors, this multipurpose pub and restaurant with rooms also includes a street-level bar where drinkers can sup local beers, cocktails (herb-infused, naturally) and fashionable wines at fair prices.

Chef/s: Antonio Santos da Mota. **Closed:** 24 Dec to 2 Jan. **Meals:** main courses £13 to £17. **Details:** 110 seats. 42 seats outside. Bar. Wheelchairs. Music.

La Dame de Pic

Cooking score: 6
⊖ Tower Hill, map 4
French | £85
Four Seasons Hotel London at Ten Trinity Square, Tower Hill, EC3N 4AJ
Tel no: (020) 3297 3799
ladamedepiclondon.co.uk

The Four Seasons at Tower Hill is a hunk of Thames-side corporate luxe in one of the more overtly historic parts of London. Its principal dining room has been got up in hard-edged chic, with caramel-seated booths and mirrored pillars creating a faintly disorienting space, but the true touch of dazzlement is provided by Anne-Sophie Pic, who brings a modernist French sensibility to this corner of Britain. Her dishes, ably executed by head chef Luca Piscazzi, combine delicacy of construction with intensity of flavour, hardly more evident than in berlingots, her signature starter of pyramidal pasta filled with smoked Brillat-Savarin, green asparagus, bergamot and mint. An enjoyment of nature furnishes pine-tree buds in a geranium bouillon to accompany seared langoustines and heirloom carrots, while main course might deliver Dover sole with gnocchi and mussels in an emulsion of saffron and shiso leaf, or Brittany pigeon marinated in batak (Indonesian peppercorns) and Nikka Japanese whisky, served with Jerusalem artichoke and blackberries. The house dessert is a millefeuille layered with bourbon coffee cream and pepper foam, and sharpened with preserved kumquat. Rhône wines are a speciality on a quality-drenched list, where prices start at £35 for a white Ventoux.

Chef/s: Anne-Sophie Pic and Luca Piscazzi. **Closed:** Sun. **Meals:** main courses £37 to £43. Set L £29 (2 courses) to £39. Early D £45. Tasting menu £115 (6 courses). **Details:** 50 seats. Bar. Wheelchairs. Music. Children over 5 yrs at D.

Dishoom

Cooking score: 2
⊖ Old Street, Liverpool Street, map 4
Indian | £30
7 Boundary Street, Shoreditch, E2 7JE
Tel no: (020) 7420 9324
dishoom.com

'No wonder it is so popular' is one inspector's verdict on the successful Dishoom chain (est. 2011), now with five grand sites in London and one in Edinburgh. This loving homage to the Irani cafés of mid-century Mumbai (themselves a throwback to the European 'grand café'), with their rotating ceiling fans, marble tables, bentwood chairs and faux faded beauty, are elaborately realised productions, up and running by 8am for bacon naans. The all-day menu bristles with such temptations as spicy lamb chops, jackfruit biryani, chicken tikka rolls on 'handkerchief bread' and chargrilled corn on the cob 'Chowpatty-beach style'. Each branch has its own signature dish, which at Shoreditch, one of the liveliest Dishooms, is overnight-braised lamb raan, whole or in a soft bun. Friendly prices and the fast-paced informality of the experience have a wide appeal. Drinks are fun too: cool cocktails, craft beers and inventive alcohol-free sherbets, lassis and chais, plus wines from £22. Evening reservations for parties of six or more only.

Chef/s: Naved Nasir. **Closed:** 25 and 26 Dec, 1 and 2 Jan. **Meals:** main courses £8 to £13. **Details:** 235 seats. Vg menu. Bar. Wheelchairs. Music.

The Don

Cooking score: 3
⊖ Bank, Cannon Street, map 4
Modern European | £42
The Courtyard, 20 St Swithin's Lane, City, EC4N 8AD
Tel no: (020) 7626 2606
thedonrestaurant.co.uk

A shoo-in for business lunches of the lingering kind, The Don is famed for its tranquil courtyard location far from the City's madding crowd – although John Hoyland's abstract artworks lend the dining room a surprising contemporary edge. Chefs come and go, but Lorenzo Merolle isn't about to change The Don's ways – expect mainstream cooking with a broad European slant and a smattering of name-checked British ingredients among the terrines, tartares and risottos. Starters of grilled octopus salad with tomato fondue, lemon oil and saffron aïoli could give way to roast Cornish cod with ratatouille or suprême of corn-fed chicken with petits pois à la française, while dessert might be tarte tatin with clotted cream. Alternatively, summon the Anglo-French cheese trolley – a well-endowed, pungent tribute. The Don's majestic all-encompassing wine list is replete with ports, sherries and other fortified tipples alongside and a host of superior vintages for all palates and pockets – including some bottles from the owners' Trinity Hill Vineyard in New Zealand.

Chef/s: Lorenzo Merolle. **Closed:** Sat, Sun. **Meals:** main courses £16 to £29. Set L and D £21 (2 courses) to £25. **Details:** 90 seats. Bar.

The Eagle

Cooking score: 2
⊖ Farringdon, map 5
Modern European | £20
159 Farringdon Road, Clerkenwell, EC1R 3AL
Tel no: (020) 7837 1353
theeaglefarringdon.co.uk

'We keep it simple at The Eagle, and we think it works,' writes Michael Belben, describing a formula that has proved successful since the pub opened in 1991, when it virtually defined a new genre. No bookings, daily blackboard menus and a deconstructed look are pretty ubiquitous now, but were considered bold and edgy then. Now, with more competition in the area, there's less of a scrum for tables (for both drinkers and diners), but the tiny kitchen still punches above its weight, its robust British-Mediterranean dishes ranging from skrei cod with green lentils and salsa cruda, and Napoli sausages with soft white polenta and roast red onions in red wine. A pint or a glass of wine (from £3.90) and a plate of good food is what The Eagle has always been about – there may be a short tapas menu now, and a couple of desserts, but never a choice of two or three courses.

Chef/s: Ed Mottershaw. **Closed:** 1 week Christmas, bank hols. **Meals:** main courses £9 to £17. **Details:** 65 seats. 24 seats outside. Music.

Galvin Hop

Cooking score: 2
⊖ Liverpool Street, map 4
Modern British | £28
35 Spital Square, Spitalfields, E1 6DY
Tel no: (020) 7299 0404
galvinrestaurants.com

While the Galvin brothers' grand La Chapelle is all about the grape, their 'pub deluxe', Galvin Hop, celebrates the grain. The 'house beer' – unpasteurised Pilsner Urquell, delivered weekly from the Czech Republic and stored in polished copper tanks above a pewter bar – takes the after-work pint to the next level. This is a city boozer reimagined as an all-day hangout with a broad remit covering everything from takeaway breakfasts to weekend brunching, superior snacking (duck-egg Scotch eggs, Saddleback scratchings), set lunches and smart wines 'on tap'. There's even sport on the box when occasion demands. British pub classics dominate the menu: pork pie and piccalilli, Cumbrian sirloin steak and onion rings and Jubilee chicken curry are well made but unfussy. The Galvins, usually such Francophiles, are not immune to trends: Korean chicken, gourmet 'dogs', doughnuts and spicy michelada cocktails have proved a successful departure.

Chef/s: Chris Barrett and Jeff Galvin. **Meals:** main courses £13 to £20. Set L and D £17 (2 courses) to £20. Sun L £15. **Details:** 70 seats. 50 seats outside. Bar. Wheelchairs. Music.

Galvin La Chapelle

Cooking score: 5
⊖ Liverpool Street, map 4
French | £65
35 Spital Square, Spitalfields, E1 6DY
Tel no: (020) 7299 0400
galvinrestaurants.com

As the setting for the Galvin brothers' magnum opus in the City, La Chapelle creates quite a dash with its vaulted ceilings, soaring granite columns, arched windows and glassed-in mezzanine. Such an awe-inspiring interior cries out for fine food, and the kitchen obliges with luxurious cooking underpinned by pin-sharp technique. French accents shine through in dishes such as halibut fillet with Jerusalem artichoke purée, artichoke barigoule and Bayonne ham, although Jeff Galvin is equally at home matching a velouté of wild garlic with crispy Hereford snails or dressing a carpaccio of Cumbrian beef with pickled shimeji mushrooms. Visitors also speak of 'stunning flavours and beautiful presentation', from a textbook wild mushroom risotto enlivened with winter truffle and fine herbs to an aromatic tagine of spice-crusted Bresse pigeon with couscous, confit lemon and harissa sauce. After that, there might be silky truffle brie de Meaux with walnuts or a crowning dessert such as hot Valrhona chocolate fondant with blood orange sorbet. Extravagantly priced verticals from Paul Jaboulet's Hermitage La Chapelle naturally take pride of place on the sophisticated French-led wine list, but there's plenty of serious drinking from other quarters too.

Chef/s: Jeff Galvin and Saffet Bayram. **Closed:** 24 to 26 Dec, 1 Jan. **Meals:** main courses £29 to £42. Set L and early D £34 (2courses) to £38. Tasting menu £85 (7 courses). **Details:** 110 seats. 30 seats outside. V menu. Vg menu. Bar. Wheelchairs. Music.

Gunpowder

Cooking score: 2
⊖ Liverpool Street, Aldgate East, map 4
Indian | £30
11 White's Row, Spitalfields, E1 7NF
Tel no: (020) 7426 0542
gunpowderlondon.com

The tables may be tightly packed and the brick-walled, modest dining room rather cramped, but three years after opening, Gunpowder continues to be a big hit, with reports of queues even on wintry evenings (you can't book). Diners are drawn by the fact that the creative kitchen goes where more mainstream Indian restaurants fear to tread, moving beyond the high-street clichés to authentic modern Indian cooking. It's a small menu and sharing plates are very much the thing here, arriving in a seemingly haphazard way and ranging from excellent vegetable dishes (aloo chaat, moreish porzhi okra fries, sigree-grilled mustard broccoli) to mustard fish steamed in a banana leaf, tender kashmiri lamb chops with a spicy dip, a venison and vermicelli doughnut, crispy pork ribs with tamarind kachumber, and organic baby chicken chargrilled in tandoori spices. Drink London-brewed beer or choose from a handful of spice-friendly wines (from £20).

Chef/s: Nirmal Save. **Closed:** Sun, 25 and 26 Dec, 31 Dec, 1 Jan. **Meals:** main courses £8 to £16. **Details:** 28 seats. Music.

Hawksmoor Guildhall

Cooking score: 4
⊖ Bank, map 4
British | £60
10-12 Basinghall Street, City, EC2V 5BQ
Tel no: (020) 7397 8120
thehawksmoor.com

A cavernous wood-panelled City steakhouse, best known for its superb breakfasts (try the bacon chop or sausage and egg HkMuffin). For main entry, see Knightsbridge branch, west London.

Chef/s: Phillip Branch. **Closed:** Sat, Sun, 24 Dec to 1 Jan, bank hols. **Meals:** main courses £15 to £55. Set L and early D £25 (2 courses) to £28. Tasting menu £70 (6 courses). **Details:** 160 seats. Bar. Wheelchairs. Music.

Hawksmoor Spitalfields

Cooking score: 3
⊖ Liverpool Street, Aldgate East, map 4
British | £60
157a Commercial Street, City, E1 6BJ
Tel no: (020) 7426 4850
thehawksmoor.com

The original Hawksmoor has a basement bar for cocktails, burgers and superior bar snacks. For main entry, see Knightsbridge branch, west London.

Chef/s: Pavlos Costa. **Closed:** 25 and 26 Dec. **Meals:** main courses £12 to £55. Set L and early D £25 (2 courses) to £28. Sun L £21. **Details:** 118 seats. Bar. Wheelchairs. Music.

James Cochran EC3

Cooking score: 5
⊖ Aldgate, map 4
Modern British | £40
19 Bevis Marks, City, EC3A 7JA
Tel no: (020) 3302 0310
jcochran.restaurant
£5 OFF

If you're unfamiliar with the City, Bevis Marks is not a street you're going to stumble across, but persevere – the food here is latter-day dining undiluted. The space is utilitarian, contemporary, fronted by a bar with a counter and window-ledge seating, but the cooking aims high, belted out of a basement kitchen and sent up by dumb waiter – though one visitor thought that 'this cooking, this chef, demands an open kitchen with chefs swaggering out to serve the food'. What is on offer is a simple small-plates menu of ferociously seasonal food. Sourdough bread and whipped smoked bone-marrow butter is a crowd-pleaser, while Jamaican jerk buttermilk chicken with Scotch bonnet jam, maize and coriander, a ravishing dish of cauliflower with shallot and hazelnut, and roast haunch of venison with braised red cabbage, beetroot, pine milk and smoked bone marrow have been winter hits. Start with a house-infused Douglas fir G&T or look to the short list of affordable wines (from £28); the extravagant should look to the flagship list.

Chef/s: James Cochran. **Closed:** Sun, 24 to 27 Dec, 31 Dec to 6 Jan. **Meals:** small plates £6 to £15. Main courses £20 to £26. Tasting menu £60 (7 courses). **Details:** 45 seats. V menu. Bar.

Jidori

Cooking score: 2
⊖ Dalston Kingsland, map 2
Japanese | £20
89 Kingsland Road, Hackney, E8 2PB
Tel no: (020) 7686 5634
jidori.co.uk

Named after the robustly flavoured free-range chickens that Japanese yakitori joints frequently skewer and grill, Jidori prides itself on sourcing fine British fowl for the same purpose. Styled after these yakitori-yas, the sparse yet inviting room has stools at the pale wood bar, an open grill area and utilitarian table seating. The skewer-centric menu majors on said bird, broken down into different parts for true beak-to-claw eating and each portion of two sticks is slow cooked to order on the smouldering charcoal grill imported from Tokyo: try thigh meat with spring onion, wings, impaled hearts or minced chicken with egg yolk, slathered with the umami house-made tare dipping sauce. Small plates designed for sharing turn a snack into a meal: try sushi-grade salmon, silken tofu, mizuna, radish and pickled ginger salad or katsu curry Scotch egg, alongside palate-invigorating pickled vegetables. End on a high with ginger ice cream, miso caramel, sweet potato crisps and black sesame praline. Drinks include Japanese beer and several sakés.

Chef/s: Shunta Matsubara. **Closed:** Sun. **Meals:** small plates £3 to £10. **Details:** 44 seats. Wheelchairs. Music.

José Pizarro

Cooking score: 2
⊖ Liverpool Street, map 4
Spanish | £28
36 Broadgate Circle, City, EC2M 1QS
Tel no: (020) 7256 5333
josepizarro.com

You can't call Broadgate Circle, that shiny complex of brand-name restaurants near Liverpool Street, soulless – not when José Pizarro is in the mix. Even at this, his third restaurant after José tapas bar (see entry) and Pizarro, both in SE1, Pizarro cooks with real heart, serving produce he is proud of. The jamón Ibérico is the real acorn-fed thing, expensive, but one can build a meal around it from the extensive tapas menu. Old favourites crop up (croquetas, tortilla de patata et al) and are hard to resist, but look to new ideas, too, such as spicy prawn fritters with allioli, octopus with black olives and celery or grilled asparagus with fried egg, Manchego, romesco and optional jamón. Ibérico pork is big here; consider pluma tartare with piparra peppers and presa with salvitxada sauce. Follow gin tonicas on the terrace with a bottle from the all-Spanish list.

Chef/s: José Pizarro. **Closed:** Sun. **Meals:** main courses £7 to £20. **Details:** 40 seats. 24 seats outside. Wheelchairs. Music.

Lardo

Cooking score: 2
⊖ London Fields, map 1
Italian | £27
205 Richmond Road, Hackney, E8 3NJ
Tel no: (020) 8985 2683
lardo.co.uk

Lardo makes good use of the generous industrial space provided by this one-time commercial laundry to create an undeniably urban interior – polished concrete, chunky wood, mismatched chairs, dangling filament light bulbs – and an open kitchen with wood-fired oven. Natural light floods in through the huge windows, with a few bench tables outside by the road. That oven turns out stonking Neapolitan-style pizzas, perhaps topped with smoked tomato and clams, or with cauliflower, Tuscan sausage and chilli flakes. The kitchen deals in fresh, seasonal produce, so check out the daily changing pasta and secondi (duck spiedino, say, with roast grapes and orange). There's something for everybody among the eye-catching antipasti (salumi, salt cod with chickpea purée, or warm beetroot with goat's curd and pickled walnuts). Get a sweet hit from almond granita with brioche, and to drink, organic wines and cocktails with an Italy-meets-London twist go down a treat.

Chef/s: Matthew Cranston. **Closed:** 7 days over Christmas. **Meals:** main courses £9 to £15. **Details:** 60 seats. 60 seats outside. Wheelchairs. Music.

The Laughing Heart

Cooking score: 3
⊖ Bethnal Green, Hoxton, map 1
International | £35
277 Hackney Road, Hackney, E2 8NA
Tel no: (020) 7686 9535
thelaughingheartlondon.com

Behind a dark, narrow frontage, the Laughing Heart opens up into a long, ram-jammed room with rough brickwork and fluted glass lampshades above bare tables. Neatly constructed small plates draw on the produce of artisan British producers, as well as the culinary traditions of, well, the whole world. Expect to snack on sea kale tempura, or a Morecambe Bay oyster in horseradish, before following with tortellini of Speckled Face mutton and broad beans, Dorset crab with peas and avocado, or pak choi in richly boozy Shaoxing broth. Continuing that Chinese theme, they've Szechuaned the crème brûlée, and fashioned something apt for the summer swelter with peach and elderflower tart. The Heart is also a wine bar and retail outlet, with a monster list of well-crafted, forward-thinking wines, from £25, including Werlitsch's austere south Styrian masterpieces and that vanishingly rare resource, a spread of mature cru Beaujolais. Night-Tubers note that the licence extends until 2am.

Chef/s: Tom Anglesea. **Closed:** Sun. **Meals:** small plates £9 to £18. **Details:** 40 seats. Bar. Music.

★ NEW ENTRY ★

Leroy

Cooking score: 4
⊖ Shoreditch High Street, map 4
Modern European | £35
18 Phipp Street, Shoreditch, EC2A 4NU
Tel no: (020) 7739 4443
leroyshoreditch.com

Leroy is one letter short of an anagram for Ellory, the Hackney restaurant it was born out of. Owners Jack Lewens and Ed Thaw shut Ellory last year for 'cheaper rents' in EC2 and found this wedge-shaped wine bar (formerly Edwin's) now with marble counter, bistro chairs and print-lined walls. It's a calm spot by day, revved up at night by the owners' vinyl collection. In the manner of a cool Paris cave à vins, Leroy lists natural wines (some refined, some eccentric) with charcuterie, cheese and small plates. Some of it is just good shopping but the more elaborate endeavours, such as grilled asparagus with smooth almond sauce and grated egg, spider crab and super-ripe tomatoes on toast and gorgeous golden Sauternes crème caramel demonstrate real flair. Roast chicken with a few leaves of green chicory and a spoon of harissa is a mark of its newfound confidence.

Chef/s: Sam Kamienko. **Closed:** Sun, 24 Dec to 3 Jan, Easter Sun and Mon. **Meals:** small plates £8 to £17. Set L £16 (2 courses) to £20. **Details:** 50 seats. Bar. Music.

Luca

Cooking score: 3
⊖ Farringdon, Barbican, map 5
Italian | £50
88 St John Street, Clerkenwell, EC1M 4EH
Tel no: (020) 3859 3000
luca.restaurant

Opened in 2016 and now firmly part of Clerkenwell's gastronomic scene, Luca's connection with The Clove Club (see entry) is not immediately apparent until you study the short, produce-led menu. From the same team as the Shoreditch trailblazer, this 'Britalian' turns out Italian-inflected dishes with no superfluous frippery to an appreciative crowd. In the smartly turned out dining room, with more than a nod to Art Deco, you can expect to eat roast Orkney scallops with Jerusalem artichoke and 'nduja, or tagliatelle of braised rabbit with green olives and marjoram. Follow with braised pig's cheeks with lemon polenta, yellow raisins and toasted hazelnuts, and finish with Sicilian lemon tart with roast fennel and black pepper ice cream. Everyone loves the Parmesan fries, praises the service and considers the set lunch and theatre menus (available in the bar) a bit of a bargain. The extensive all-Italian wine list is a spot-on match for the food.

Chef/s: Robert Chambers. **Closed:** Sun, 2 weeks Christmas. **Meals:** main courses £13 to 35. **Details:** 60 seats. Bar. Music.

★ NEW ENTRY ★

Lutyens Grill

Cooking score: 2
⊖ Bank, map 4
British | £55
The Ned, 27 Poultry, City, EC2R 8AJ
Tel no: (020) 3828 2000
thened.com

Soho House's foray into the City – a 250-room luxury hotel and restaurant complex in the former Midland Bank HQ – can seat 850 people at any one time. They were all in on the evening of our visit (lunchtimes are calmer). Of the Ned's 10 restaurants, Lutyens Grill, its small wood-panelled steakhouse, is the most exclusive (read: expensive). Less formal options include Millie's Lounge (open 24 hours) and Californian Malibu Grill. Once past the Cerberus on the door and out of earshot of the live-music stage, we settled into this haven of white-jacketed waiters, polished crystal and trolley service with relief. There's not much room to innovate even gently on a classic grill menu but the kitchen succeeds with hay-smoked venison carpaccio and beetroot, and Orkney scallops (perfectly cooked) with salsify and Morecambe Bay shrimps. The main deal is steaks, a choice of 16. Ours, Hereford bone-in sirloin (£42, but the cheapest by weight) was poor: tough and underseasoned. Grilled halibut won hands down. Bills are, inevitably, stratospheric (the list offers few wines under £50) but there's no denying, especially if head office is paying, the Ned has got it.

Chef/s: Jason Loy. **Closed:** Sun. **Meals:** main courses £24 to £110. **Details:** 50 seats. Bar. Wheelchairs.

Lyle's

Cooking score: 5
⊖ Shoreditch High Street, map 4
Modern British | £59
Tea Building, 56 Shoreditch High Street, Shoreditch, E1 6JJ
Tel no: (020) 3011 5911
lyleslondon.com

Restaurants in Shoreditch may come and go but some – like Lyle's – seem here to stay. Thank goodness, for the cooking is confident and thoughtful, guided by the supreme quality of the (few) ingredients on each plate, and the determination of the chefs to deliver taste over technique. Roasted beetroot with sorrel and nuggets of givingly gelatinous bone marrow is a delight of sweet-sour balance. Fleshy monkfish with slivers of artichoke and early Jersey Royals is as tender as the suckling kid goat that follows, paired with mild Tropea onions and wild garlic that strokes, rather than hammers, the dish with spring flavour. A dessert that marries flavours of coffee, caramel and pillowy, scorched Italian meringue is bravely bittersweet. With a sequence of smallish plates making up the evening set menu, the meal feels coherent (it's à la carte at lunchtime) and it was good to see the bar stools full with diners enjoying the evening bar menu: 10 to 12 small dishes from the lunch menu, plus the snacks from the evening set. A considered wine list offers interesting bottles from £24 and advice is knowledgeable.

Chef/s: James Lowe. **Closed:** Sun, Christmas, 4 and 5 Jan, bank hols. **Meals:** main courses £14 to £24 (L only). Set D £59 (4 courses). **Details:** 48 seats. V menu. Vg menu. Bar. Wheelchairs. Music.

Average price

The figure given in bold denotes the average price of a three-course dinner without wine.

The Marksman

Cooking score: 3
⊖ Cambridge Heath, Hoxton, map 1
Modern British | £36
254 Hackney Road, Hackney, E2 7SJ
Tel no: (020) 7739 7393
marksmanpublichouse.com

A private cellar room for celebratory feasting is the latest addition to this stylishly revamped hostelry, although there's still an enduring pubby resilience about the refurbished ground-floor bar (order craft beer and nibbles here). Upstairs, strikingly patterned lino floors, leather banquettes and an eye-catching 'woven' ceiling provide the backdrop for attention-grabbing food that chimes with London's culinary zeitgeist: The Marksman's beef and barley buns are not to be missed, but the terse, plain-speaking menu also promises everything from Tamworth pork chops with green onions and mustard to gurnard with devilled mussels and white beans. There are splendid pies to share and tarts of every description (from pumpkin and goat's curd to brown butter and honey), or you could round off by refreshing your palate with a zingy vermouth-spiked blood orange sorbet. Eight wines by the glass or carafe open the bidding on the succinct all-European wine list.

Chef/s: Tom Harris and Jon Rotheram. **Meals:** main courses £16 to £21. Set L Fri and Sat £22 (2 courses) to £26. Sun L £29 (2 courses) to £33. Feasting menu £39 to £59. **Details:** 80 seats. 12 seats outside. Bar. Wheelchairs. Music.

Merchants Tavern

Cooking score: 4
⊖ Old Street, map 4
Modern European | £45
36 Charlotte Road, Shoreditch, EC2A 3PG
Tel no: (020) 7060 5335
merchantstavern.co.uk

Where the City meets Shoreditch, suits meets trainers and VCs meet start-ups, Angela Hartnett and Neil Borthwick's Merchants Tavern is a local haunt for a singular neighbourhood. It's a vast space carved up into bar, dining room and open kitchen. One could quite easily lose an afternoon over sausage rolls, spicy deep-fried oysters and a pint or two in the bar. The brick-lined dining room is a more civilised affair, with amply upholstered chairs around generously spaced tables at which to explore Borthwick's expressive style and hidden gems, bin ends and choice pours from the wine list. At its best, the cooking's vivid and precise: try gin-cured salmon with fennel and orange, or simple maltagliati pasta with pesto ahead of cod, mussels and artichokes barigoule, or pork belly, grilled baby leeks and carrots. Weekend brunches add bacon sandwiches and shakshuka to the mix, and an accessible wine list offers plenty by the glass and carafe.

Chef/s: Neil Borthwick. **Meals:** main courses £9 to £23. **Details:** 108 seats. Bar. Wheelchairs.

The Modern Pantry

Cooking score: 3
⊖ Farringdon, map 5
Fusion | £37
47-48 St John's Square, Clerkenwell, EC1V 4JJ
Tel no: (020) 7553 9210
themodernpantry.co.uk

On an attractive cobbled square on the fringes of Farringdon and Clerkenwell, The Modern Pantry takes a two-tiered approach. There are tables outside and on the ground floor for café eating and afternoon teas, with interlinked restaurant rooms upstairs. The bare-boarded style recalls rooms above a Soho pub, but the menu reaches out to culinary traditions across the globe. Salmon sashimi marinated in beetroot and soy is dressed in pomegranate seeds and yuzu crème fraîche, and the sugar-cured prawns thickly stuffed into an omelette with spring onion, coriander and chilli are appealing too. Main-course meats were a little tepid at inspection, but of unarguable quality – rough-cut onglet with Kalamata olive salsa and cassava chips, and mature lamb rump with delicate Persian spicing, onions both braised and puréed and some braised romaine lettuce. A rich milk chocolate mousse comes in a thin cocoa-dusted shell with gorgeous blackcurrant and liquorice sorbet. Wines from a short but serviceable international list start at £4.50 a glass.

Chef/s: Robert McLeary. **Closed:** 25 and 26 Dec, Aug bank hol. **Meals:** main courses £16 to £24. **Details:** 100 seats. 36 seats outside. Wheelchairs. Music.

Monty's Deli

Cooking score: 2
⊖ Hoxton, map 2
Jewish | £20
227-229 Hoxton Street, Hoxton, N1 5LH
Tel no: (020) 7729 5737
montys-deli.com

'This is Ashkenazi Jewish grub, of the sort I was brought up on and love,' noted one first-time visitor to Mark Ogus and Owen Barratt's Hoxton deli (they have a Spitalfields Market stall too). The brunch, all-day and dinner menus are inspired by, but by no means encumbered by, Jewish culinary tradition. The space has been sensitively restored to echo its former life as a butcher and bakery yet it's a US-style diner through and through: slide into a booth or watch the trademark Reuben – a tower of impossibly succulent salt beef, sauerkraut, Russian dressing, mustard and cheese, bookended with rye – being made to order at the bar while you drink a root beer float. Make a beeline for the slow-proved bagels, too, and exemplary latkes or chopped liver on glossy challah buns. There's baked cheesecake for afters, natch, plus classic cocktails and a short wine list.

Chef/s: Mark Ogus and Owen Barratt. **Closed:** Mon, Tue. **Meals:** small plates £5 to £9. Main courses £9 to £15. **Details:** 65 seats.

LOCAL GEM

Mora

⊖ Leytonstone High Road, map 1
Italian | £29
487 High Road, Leytonstone, E11 4PG
Tel no: (020) 8539 1731
moraitalianrestaurant.co.uk

This 'wedge-shaped slice of southern Italy' is modest and modern, its interior spare but comfortable. Daily specials are simple in execution: Apulian burrata, for example, is unfussily served with two fat al dente asparagus spears and a drizzle of olive oil. This is heartfelt, unrefined fare that's reliably fresh and satisfying. Homemade pasta is the main draw, so look out for the likes of malloreddus (little Sardinian gnocchi) in a tomato and sausage ragù, or saffron tagliatelle with broad beans. A thoughtful selection of reasonably priced wines and beers from small Italian producers helps to seal the deal.

Morito Exmouth Market

Cooking score: 3
⊖ Farringdon, map 2
Spanish/North African | £30
32 Exmouth Market, Clerkenwell, EC1R 4QE
Tel no: (020) 7278 7007
morito.co.uk

The backbone of this tiny-but-mighty tapas and meze bar, like its venerable older sibling next door, is spirited Mediterranean Basin cooking. Pull up a stool at the orange counter or settle at one of the titchy tables to enjoy the rustic, life-enhancing flavours of North Africa, Spain and the eastern Med. Emerald-green Padrón peppers, jamón, patatas bravas and salt cod croquetas are mainstays on the list of small plates. Grilled tetilla cheese with membrillo and walnuts, and crispy aubergine, whipped feta and date molasses characterise creative offerings for vegetarians. Expect some plancha-grill char on impeccably sourced fish and meat, plenty of allioli and good bread, and try not to get carried away. At weekends, start the day with a full Catalan or

huevos any which way. You can book for lunch and dinner Monday to Wednesday and Sunday, but convivial queuing is otherwise to be expected. Spanish wines kick off at £20.
Chef/s: Samantha Clark. **Meals:** tapas £2 to £10. **Details:** 36 seats. 6 seats outside. Wheelchairs. Music.

Morito Hackney

Cooking score: 4
⊖ Hoxton, map 2
Spanish/North African | £30
195 Hackney Road, Hackney, E2 8JL
Tel no: (020) 7613 0754
moritohackneyroad.co.uk

With Cretan head chef Marianna Leivaditaki at the stove, Sam and Samantha Clark's Hackney branch of Morito has developed a character distinct from the Exmouth Market original. The room itself is large and clattery (that's down to the concrete floors, metal chairs and marble bar) but it's attractive too – all the more so when filled with the boho locals sipping on chilled cava spiked with pomegranate. One could almost forget the gritty Hackney Road setting. The menu is a mash-up of Moorish, Spanish and Cretan influences and yet it somehow makes perfect sense. Fried aubergines with date molasses and feta are a wonderful sticky tangle of salt and sweet. Also worth a look are chargrilled lamb chops with anchovy and paprika butter and a refreshing Cretan salad with crunchy dakos (rusks) and mizithra cheese. Finish with crisp filo, creamy custard and apricot. The short Spanish wine list opens at £30.
Chef/s: Marianna Leivaditaki. **Meals:** tapas £3 to £15. **Details:** 72 seats.

Visit us online

For the most up-to-date information about *The Good Food Guide*, go to thegoodfoodguide.co.uk

Moro

Cooking score: 5
⊖ Farringdon, map 2
Spanish/North African | £40
34-36 Exmouth Market, Clerkenwell, EC1R 4QE
Tel no: (020) 7833 8336
moro.co.uk

Back in 1997 we all got caught up in Sam and Sam Clark's love affair with the cooking of the southern Mediterranean – that evocative blend of clean, fresh flavours and the pungent spicing of North Africa and Moorish Spain. Today, the region's cooking is truly entrenched in the UK's culinary landscape... and we still love Moro, one of its original champions (booking remains essential). The zinc-topped counter, bare tables and white walls of this airy Exmouth Market hot spot remain contemporary, while the wood-fired oven still works its magic on everything from black bream to pork belly. Start with a crab brik fired up with harissa, or charcoal-grilled asparagus with a pinenut tarator, before tender slow-roasted kid with broad bean purée and spring vegetable and tarragon sauce, or that aforementioned bream, with braised chard, green almonds and chickpeas. Among sweet courses, you can always depend on yoghurt cake with pistachios and pomegranate. Spain and Portugal dominate the wine list, opening at £25.50.
Chef/s: Sam and Samantha Clark. **Closed:** 24 Dec to 1 Jan. **Meals:** main courses £18 to £24. **Details:** 100 seats. Wheelchairs.

Oklava

Cooking score: 3
⊖ Shoreditch High Street, map 4
Turkish | £35
74 Luke Street, Shoreditch, EC2A 4PY
Tel no: (020) 7729 3032
oklava.co.uk

For a burst of sunshine on your plate, and an easy-going, sociable vibe that could find you lingering at the table for longer than you expected, head to this Turkish-Cypriot restaurant just off Great Eastern Street. Selin Kiazim brings her native cuisine bang up to date with a small-plate menu that is packed with fragrant, fresh flavours. Medjool date butter lifts baharat-spiced bread, and grilled halloumi hits just the right sweet-salty notes, needing nothing more than its accompanying lemon, honey and oregano. Elsewhere, smokey urfa chillis give oomph to lamb chops, just as za'atar crumb and lime mayonnaise do to crunch-coated chilli-garlic chicken. Flaky künefe made with layers of mozzarella and crisp kataifi pastry, drizzled with verjus and topped with pistachios, remains the pick of the desserts but there is love, too, for spiced rice pudding brûlée. A line-up of Turkish wines opens at £24. There's a sister restaurant, Kyseri, in Fitzrovia: 64 Grafton Way, W1T 5DP; tel: (020) 7383 3717.

Chef/s: Selin Kiazim. **Closed:** Sun, Mon, bank hols. **Meals:** small and sharing plates £6 to £18. **Details:** 46 seats. 12 seats outside. Wheelchairs. Music.

★ NEW ENTRY ★

Ombra

Cooking score: 4
⊖ Bethnal Green, map 1
Italian | £30

1 Vyner Street, Hackney, E2 9DG
Tel no: (020) 8981 5150
ombrabar.restaurant

£5 OFF

What a clever idea to open a Venetian bacaro along a London canal. This informal bar and restaurant offers the traditional cooking of Venice with a quirkiness all its own. Small plates (cicchetti) and larger dishes are prepared with great care, quality ingredients and Instagrammable appeal: razor clams balanced on a plate of mussel shells are topped with shards of blood orange and chopped hazelnuts; authentic sweet and sour sardines with onions, raisins, vinegar and pine nuts; a magnificent curl of octopus in a bowl of fragrant broth with chopped tomatoes and bright green strands of monk's beard; or ravioli of burrata and spinach bathed in butter that just begs to be mopped up with a slice of sourdough. Puddings are simple but delicious, ranging from custard tart to tiramisu or panna cotta. Wines are sourced from across Italy with many from the Veneto and a handful of on-trend orange wines.

Chef/s: Mitshel Ibrahim. **Closed:** Mon. **Meals:** main courses £13 to £17. Sun L £20 (3 courses). **Details:** 33 seats. 30 seats outside. Music.

Palatino

Cooking score: 3
⊖ Old Street, map 2
Italian | £35

71 Central Street, Clerkenwell, EC1V 8AB
Tel no: (020) 3481 5300
palatino.london

Stevie Parle's Palatino, the canteen component of a cool Clerkenwell shared working space, takes Rome as its starting point. The menu changes with the seasons that stream in through the windows, though there are some constants – most significantly, the square-cut tonnarelli pasta with Tellicherry pepper and pecorino cheese, creamy with a slosh of cooking water as is the traditional way (a Palatino favourite that appears on the 'presto' menu served lunchtimes and pre-theatre). Wandering away from the Eternal City, one might also find chickpea farinata from Liguria with asparagus and ricotta salata or Venetian risi e bisi. We're back in Rome for main courses of vignarola (spring vegetable stew with artichokes) or classic saltimbocca. Alternatively, there might be simply roasted whole fish such as sea bass with marjoram and olive oil. Finish with tiramisu or ricotta panna cotta and sour cherries. Interesting Italian wines start at a very reasonable £22.

Chef/s: Stevie Parle and Richard Blackwell. **Closed:** Sun. **Meals:** main courses £14 to £21. **Details:** 70 seats. Bar. Music.

Petit Pois

Cooking score: 2
⊖ Old Street, Hoxton, map 4
French | £30
9 Hoxton Square, Hackney, N1 6NU
Tel no: (020) 7613 3689
petitpoisbistro.com

This pint-sized modern bistro, all brick walls and bare floorboards with an attractively light air, continues to delight a London purlieu that may think it's gone all quinoa, but is as much a pushover for classic Parisian bistronomy as the rest of us. Asparagus served with hollandaise and a crisp of Bayonne ham is the right way to greet the early onset of summer, while mussels take their place among wads of cabbage and seaweed in tart Breton cider. When it comes to mains, there's tender Barbary duck breast with salt-baked beetroot, or perhaps cod with sea veg in beurre blanc, but many will be those who fail to resist the atavistic lure of a whomping great hunk of steak with crunchy frites and béarnaise. Dessert is chocolate mousse, served *à table* to emphasise its richly aerated texture, or Paris-Brest. There are fine French cheeses, too. Wines from £24 are mostly, though not quite all, French.

Chef/s: Gino Tighe. **Meals:** small plates £4 to £12. Main courses £18 to £20. **Details:** 25 seats. 10 seats outside.

Pidgin

Cooking score: 5
⊖ Hackney Central, map 1
Modern British | £49
52 Wilton Way, Hackney, E8 1BG
Tel no: (020) 7254 8311
pidginlondon.com

From a kitchen the size of other restaurant's walk-in refrigerators, this Hackney micro-bistro turns out a new four-course menu every single week. Since it opened in 2015, the unlikely hotbed of culinary creativity has yet to repeat a dish. It helps that no ingredient is off-limits, no combination of flavours too audacious. Hence pork with corn kernel, apricot, hibiscus, nettle and romanesco and, from the same week's offering, malted cajeta mousse (similar to dulce de leche), pine ice cream, preserved cherries and peanut. New head chef Adolfo de Cecco (previously at Magpie, Pidgin's West End sister establishment) brings with him a level of technical wizardry that can corral such disparate influences to create one harmonious whole. Seasonality shines forth on an early summer menu that introduces crab, buttermilk, borage and cucumber and Parisian gnocchi with broad beans and chicken liver. Wine pairings change weekly as does the short, oddball wine list.

Chef/s: Adolfo de Cecco. **Closed:** Mon, Tue, 23 Dec to 2 Jan. **Meals:** set L and D £49 (4 courses). **Details:** 27 seats. 4 seats outside. V menu. Wheelchairs. Music.

Popolo Shoreditch

Cooking score: 4
⊖ Old Street, map 4
Italian | £35
26 Rivington Street, Shoreditch, EC2A 3DU
Tel no: (020) 7729 4299
popoloshoreditch.com
£5 OFF

The industrial neutrality embraced by most East End restaurants – exposed brick, concrete and suchlike – is on full display at this densely packed little slice of urban cool. It's young and fun and no-nonsense, with the kitchen on view from the counter seats on the cramped ground floor (there's a further dining room upstairs), and some very good things to eat. The brief menu of small sharing plates focuses on Italy with a sprinkling of Mediterranean-basin flavours – panzanella salad, and bavette with inzimino (chickpea stew), alongside grilled octopus with baba ganoush and za'atar, and spiced lamb with carrot tahini and Sardinian flatbread. But what distinguishes Jon Lawson's kitchen is the spectacular pasta – the ex-Theo Randall chef makes some of the best in town – and recent highlights have included agnolotti filled with melt-in-the-mouth pig's cheek with porcini butter, prawn and artichoke taglierini, and hare pappardelle. A short list of predominantly Italian wines opens at £28.

Chef/s: Jon Lawson. **Closed:** Sun, 23 Dec to 8 Jan. **Meals:** main courses £9 to £15. **Details:** 33 seats. Bar. Music.

Quality Chop House

Cooking score: 4
⊖ Farringdon, map 5
Modern British | £38
94 Farringdon Road, Clerkenwell, EC1R 3EA
Tel no: (020) 7278 1452
thequalitychophouse.com

Once a humble 19th-century working men's canteen serving simple sustenance, this glorious relic of the Victorian era is, perhaps surprisingly, under the same ownership as ultra-modern Fitzrovia restaurants Clipstone and Portland (see entries). Eat in the original listed dining room with its chequerboard floor, wooden booths and unforgiving pew-style seats, now slightly extended for larger 21st-century bottoms – or the more conventional bistro-style room next door. You could say the kitchen has gone back to basics, offering prime, intensely seasonal ingredients, simply served. Creamy buffalo mozzarella offset by a splash of delicious, intense Fontodi olive oil and the sharpness of elder capers; perhaps a roasted turbot head, 'no marks for presentation, but loads of tasty meaty fish' or a superb Middle White pork chop. Similar contentment is to be found among desserts, especially 'a light and surprisingly delicate lemon curd with sloe berry and oats'. Service could hardly be more knowledgeable, and there's intelligence written all over the wine list and real choice by the glass.

Chef/s: Shaun Searley. **Closed:** 1 week Christmas, bank hols. **Meals:** main courses £17 to £47. Set L £20 (2 courses) to £25. **Details:** 86 seats. Music.

Rochelle Canteen

Cooking score: 2
⊖ Shoreditch High Street, Old Street, map 4
Modern British | £30
Arnold Circus, Shoreditch, E2 7ES
Tel no: (020) 7729 5677
rochelleschool.org/rochellecanteen

Margot Henderson and Melanie Arnold set up Rochelle Canteen in 2006 to feed and water Shoreditch's creative community, following it up with a second site at the Institute of Contemporary Arts (ICA) in late 2017 (see entry). While the latter basks in the limelight, the original – an idiosyncratic set-up in a converted school bikeshed – continues to charm its many regulars. Summer shows the hidden schoolyard garden at its best, when Mediterranean flavours and regional French wines (from a fiver a glass) beg to be enjoyed alfresco. One feels the seasons keenly all year round, thanks to a daily menu that, at inspection, fizzed with vernal promise: wild garlic and bean soup; grilled Tropea onions with nutty, forceful romesco; and saffron-laced crab tart, its egg filling still slightly aquiver. There's some inconsistency, however; tough grilled lamb's leg with fennel and potato bake simply did not compare. Pudding is a toss-up between seasonal ice cream or a classic tart.

Chef/s: Elian Farner. **Closed:** 23 Dec to 2 Jan, bank hols. **Meals:** main courses £12 to £18. **Details:** 36 seats. 20 seats outside.

Roka Canary Wharf

Cooking score: 3
⊖ Canary Wharf, map 1
Japanese | £50
4 Park Pavilion, Canary Wharf, E14 5FW
Tel no: (020) 7636 5228
rokarestaurant.com

Rainer Becker's Japanese grill concept has been cooking over the coals since 2004. It has evolved from the first Charlotte Street site to become a collection of four in affluent areas, including Canary Wharf where the first-floor restaurant, bar and terrace is the well-travelled

trader's go-to for VIP wining and dining. Evenings are low-key, lunches hopping. At inspection, the room at full volume, we struggled to make out the waiter's spiel – there's an unfathomable array of tasting menus, set lunches, sushi, salads, seafood and more – so chose the 'premium lunch menu' for ease. It gave a good overview of the Roka style, all 'wow' presentation and dialled-up flavours. From iceberg salad with seaweed, sesame and onion dressing (a crunchy, refreshing umami bomb) to juicy Korean spiced lamb cutlets from the robata grill via sashimi and jalapeño tempura maki, it made its impact. Saké, shochu, cocktails and big-ticket wines easily match the food.
Chef/s: Cristian Bravaccini. **Meals:** dishes from £9 to £72. Set L £35 (2 courses) to £42. Tasting menu £70. **Details:** 89 seats. 40 seats outside. Vg menu. Bar. Wheelchairs. Music.

Rotorino

Cooking score: 2
⊖ Haggerston, Dalston Junction, map 2
Italian | £30
434 Kingsland Road, Hackney, E8 4AA
Tel no: (020) 7249 9081
rotorino.com

There's little about Stevie Parle's crepuscular Dalston Italian, all vintage tiles and vinyl booths, that immediately suggests sun-kissed days in southern Italy. Other than the menu, that is, a clever collection of flavour-forward antipasti, roasts, grills and pasta from Calabria, Sicily, Puglia and beyond. Accessibility is the watchword. Sure, one can get stuck into some splashy wines over a multi-course feast, but alternative points of entry include risotto (nettle and Taleggio) and a glass of wine for a tenner on Mondays and 'Britalian' Sunday roasts at £15. Wines start at £22, with plenty of choice under £30, plus reserve wines and monthly specials. Bring friends, order plenty – dishes are designed to be divvied up – and be sure to include some hand-rolled pasta (perhaps spaghetti puttanesca), served in large and small sizes, the zingy watermelon and ricotta salata salad, roast Sasso chicken and gelato to finish.
Chef/s: Stevie Parle and Luigi del Giupice.
Meals: main courses £9 to £19. **Details:** 90 seats. Bar. Wheelchairs. Music.

Rök

Cooking score: 2
⊖ Shoreditch High Street, map 4
Scandinavian | £36
26 Curtain Road, Shoreditch, EC2A 3NZ
Tel no: (020) 7377 2152
roklondon.com

Super-cool Scandi-style Rök borrows freely from the new (and old) Nordic kitchen. Both here and at its Islington sister site, it makes full use of the wood grill and larder of pickled, fermented and smoked ingredients to offer a menu bursting with colour throughout the year. Rök sources well, as seen in lunchtime offerings of Swaledale mutton open sandwich with wild garlic pesto or Skagen shrimp toast, as well as in more elaborate specials such as smoked langoustine with sea urchin roe sauce or octopus with cucumber, barley and smoked and fermented celeriac purée. Vegetables aren't forgotten: consider smoked kohlrabi salad with peanuts and dandelion. While the white-painted brickwork and plain wooden tables may look casual, the kitchen's approach is anything but. Its creativity extends to the wild drinks list where cardamom and toasted oat mead and apple and rhubarb cider are up against more conventional vinous offerings.
Chef/s: Matt Young. **Closed:** Sun. **Meals:** main courses £16 to £17. **Details:** 40 seats. Bar.

Sager + Wilde

Cooking score: 3
⊖ Bethnal Green, map 1
Modern British | £32
250 Paradise Row, Bethnal Green, E2 9LE
Tel no: (020) 7613 0478
sagerandwilde.com

The old railway arches by Bethnal Green station have become a hive of gastronomic activity in recent times, and Sager + Wilde has played a prominent part in their renaissance. With a private space at mezzanine level, as well as a terrace and dimly lit restaurant, the place is given over to a mix of dead simple informal eating and stylish drinking. In the former category, expect the appetising likes of smoked cod's roe with Pink Firs and radishes, or cotechino with pickled veg, before a filling plate of pasta such as fusilli with nettles, dandelions and Spenwood cheese in a creatively retooled pesto, or grey mullet with chicory and monk's beard in anchovy sauce. Finish with cannoli or tiramisu, or Neal's Yard Dairy cheeses. The wines are a joy to behold, with Veneto Garganega and red Bierzo among the glasses, before a cavalcade of modern classics passes in review. Bottles start at £23.
Chef/s: Matt Ziemski. **Closed:** 24 to 27 Dec. **Meals:** main courses £11 to £20. **Details:** 60 seats. 70 seats outside. Bar. Wheelchairs. Music.

St John

Cooking score: 5
⊖ Farringdon, map 5
Modern British | £40
26 St John Street, Clerkenwell, EC1M 4AY
Tel no: (020) 7251 0848
stjohngroup.uk.com

The unmistakable St John style – modern British by way of provincial France – was set at this former smokehouse in 1994. Since then it's spawned several siblings and many an imitator. But few take their commitment to seasonality and nose-to-tail cooking as seriously as St John. It takes guts to pare dishes back to just 'terrine' or 'kohlrabi', while the signature bone marrow and parsley salad, ox heart with chips and pickled walnuts, and a wonderfully wan white cabbage and brown shrimp salad are similarly unapologetic. Desserts might include cherry trifle or apricot jelly. Group feasting menus of whole suckling pig are pure sleeves-rolled-up hedonism. Away from the plate, the white-walled restaurant and bar make few concessions to creature comforts though warm-hearted waiters jolly things up nicely. The wine list's a romp through regional France (from £28).
Chef/s: Jonathan Woolway. **Meals:** main courses £13 to £25. **Details:** 80 seats. Bar. Wheelchairs.

St John Bread and Wine

Cooking score: 3
⊖ Liverpool Street, map 4
British | £35
94-96 Commercial Street, Spitalfields, E1 6LZ
Tel no: (020) 7251 0848
stjohngroup.uk.com

One can pinpoint the time of year down to the month or even week from the daily changing menu at this offshoot of Fergus Henderson's legendary St John (see entry). The kitchen gives a masterclass on cooking with the seasons and from the old-fashioned English larder. A snapshot from June: globe artichoke vinaigrette, crayfish and hot butter and strawberry ice cream. Another, from December: braised cuttlefish, red wine and aïoli, beef mince on duck-fat toast and spiced apple crumble. Happy-making stuff that's designed to be shared. Of the year-round classics, the sugared custard doughnuts, madeleines and famous bacon sandwich (from the breakfast menu) have a cult following. This Spitalfields venue squeezes in a bakery counter, wine shop of sorts and dining space, leaving little room for frills. White walls, blackboards and wooden chairs mirror the rustic-minimalist cooking and regional French wines (from £6.50 for a 175ml glass) to perfection.
Chef/s: Farokh Talati. **Closed:** 25 and 26 Dec. **Meals:** small plates £4 to £10. Large plates £13 to £20. **Details:** 64 seats. Bar.

★ NEW ENTRY ★

St Leonards

Cooking score: 3
⊖ Old Street, Shoreditch High Street, map 4
Seafood | £30
70 Leonard Street, Shoreditch, EC2A 4QX
Tel no: (020) 7739 1291
stleonards.london

Named after the ancient parish of Shoreditch in which it stands, St Leonard's is now resident in the former premises of Eyre Brothers, freshly spruced up with traditional E1 concrete surfaces and mid-century furniture. As often in saintly affairs, St Leonards makes a keen division between the fiery flames (dishes cooked on a log-burning hearth in one corner) and the celestial cool of the ice bar in another corner. With the latter, bivalves take centre stage – start with cherrystone clams submerged in a tangy pool of Szechuan oil and coriander. A small plate of wild bass crudo with burnt kohlrabi and lardo made for a divine pairing on our inspection, though simpler things are also done well: Dexter bavette with cured bone marrow came tinged with notes of woodsmoke from the hearth. Desserts kept up the momentum – especially salt caramel and East India sherry tart with a dollop of cardamom ice cream. An Old World-leaning wine list has bottles starting at £23.
Chef/s: Andrew Clarke and Jackson Boxer. **Closed:** Sun. **Meals:** main courses £14 to £55. **Details:** 70 seats.

Sardine

Cooking score: 2
⊖ Old Street, map 2
French | £35
15 Micawber Street, Hoxton, N1 7TB
Tel no: (020) 7490 0144
sardine.london

It's as if the ghost of Elizabeth David is watching over the goings-on at Stevie Parle's pocket-handkerchief-sized space attached to the Parasol Unit Foundation for Contemporary Art off busy City Road. Since last year, chef Alex Jackson has made some ace additions to the bistro's offering, including weekend brunch (how about 'breakfast cassoulet'?), 'Les Plats Familiaux' feasting menus (whole leg of lamb à la ficelle), monthly 'Grande Bouffe' dinners (le Grand Aïoli), and even a £5.50 daily sandwich. The southern French wood-fire cooking and Provençal styling will have Francophiles dreaming of *les vacances* all year round. The menu's rustic, pleasingly so, with unfashionable (or rather, never-not-fashionable) classics such as duck liver parfait, prunes and toast and soupe au pistou keeping company with onglet with ceps sauce and an apricot and brown-butter tart. There's a prix fixe from £16 and wines from the Mediterranean list, from £22.
Chef/s: Stevie Parle and Alex Jackson. **Meals:** main courses £15 to £20. **Details:** 45 seats.

Smokestak

Cooking score: 4
⊖ Shoreditch High Street, map 4
Modern British | £25
35 Sclater Street, Shoreditch, E1 6LB
Tel no: (020) 3873 1733
smokestak.co.uk

The rust-coloured frontage gives notice of the dressed-down ambience of Smokestak, where counter seats and spindly stools at bare tables are the style. A smoker and grill take centre stage for the expertly barbecued and roasted meats that are the principal stock-in-trade. Hefty servings deliver the goods, with brisket enjoying Most Favoured Cut status, whether for a fully loaded bun and pickled red chilli on brown parcel paper, a single mustard-barbecued serving, or the whole caboodle for the table on 24-hour pre-order. Elsewhere, expect aged pork belly with gochujang chilli paste, or thick-cut pork rib with pickled cucumber, along with sides of jacket potato and smoked rarebit, or January King cabbage with chickpeas and chorizo. It all gets topped and tailed, if you've the stamina, with tempura-battered calçots and aïoli, and poached rhubarb and hazelnut crumble with sheep's ricotta ice cream, so come hungry. Sour and bitter cocktails and a clutch of big-structured wines from £20 enhance the entertainment.

Chef/s: David Carter and Phillip Eagle. **Closed:** 24 to 26 Dec. **Meals:** main courses £9 to £17. **Details:** 79 seats. 40 seats outside. Bar. Music.

★ NEW ENTRY ★

Smoking Goat

Cooking score: 3
⊖ Shoreditch High Street, Old Street, map 4
Thai | £20
64 Shoreditch High Street, Shoreditch, E1 6JJ
smokinggoatbar.com

The original Smoking Goat quit Soho in early 2018 but the Thai barbecue name lives on in the ground floor of a former pub and strip club in Shoreditch. Rowdy and raucous at peak times, buzzy at others, it's populated by that east London mix of stranded tourists, solo foodies, suits and cool kids. There's a strong German showing on the dozen-strong wine list, but on a hot day, watermelon juice and cold beer win. There's no better way to take on the street-style sharing menu's attack of flavours, textures and supercharged chilli. From a section winningly entitled 'drinking foods', we enjoyed sticky, salty chilli wings, a Goat signature, and delicate steamed oysters with roasted chilli, two very different dishes. A good start. 'Large plates' – everything's served on canteen-style melamine – range from simply salted fried lemon sole, with nam prik pao, a lesson in restraint, to extraordinarily savoury smoked brisket noodles. Breakfast served Thursday to Sunday.

Chef/s: Ali Borer. **Closed:** 25 and 26 Dec, 1 Jan. **Meals:** main courses £9 to £24. **Details:** 96 seats. Music.

Som Saa

Cooking score: 2
⊖ Aldgate East, map 4
Thai | £30
43a Commercial Street, Spitalfields, E1 6BD
Tel no: (020) 7324 7790
somsaa.com

Making no concessions to Western palates, Som Saa revels in introducing diners to the lesser-known flavours of northern and north-eastern Thailand. The former warehouse in Spitalfields retains its industrial aesthetic, albeit warmed up with plenty of wood, pendant lighting and vintage decor. Start in the bar, where gloriously heady snacks (try the fermented sausage) and cocktails revivify and hint at what's to come. Intensely fragrant, technicolour iterations of regional Thai food are made to be shared, so order four or five dishes between two (plus sticky or jasmine rice) and let yourself be guided by staff if you're averse to chilli sweats. An aromatic salad of papaya with snake beans, dried shrimp, peanuts and cherry tomatoes pre-empts rich, complex curries, perhaps a Kanchanaburi Province curry with chalk stream trout, mussels and wild ginger, or signature whole deep-fried sea bass. Top-drawer British meat and fish, Asian produce, a surfeit of fresh herbs, and Thai spices make for intoxicating combinations. The wine list is designed to hold its own with the food.

Chef/s: Andy Oliver and Mark Dobbie. **Closed:** Sun. **Meals:** small plates £9 to £18. **Details:** Bar. Music.

Sosharu

Cooking score: 4
⊖ Farringdon, map 5
Japanese | £45
64 Turnmill Street, Clerkenwell, EC1M 5RR
Tel no: (020) 3805 2304
sosharulondon.com

The chef is Romanian, the produce British, the cuisine Japanese, but Alex Craciun has managed to pull all these strands together with great success. He delivers 'an exciting and harmonious dining experience' in a seductively lit room with swathes of wood and stone that reminded one reader 'of a few modern restaurants in Shinjuku'. There have been a few tweaks to the menu since the last edition of the Guide: the roster of izakaya-inspired dishes is now more accessible, and includes simple ramens and tonkatsus. Otherwise, raw and cooked salmon served in a crispy seaweed taco makes a tantalising start, broccoli tempura with kimchi and aged Parmesan is superb (prawn tempura is excellent, too) and sukiyaki with wagyu beef, glass noodles and shiitake, cooked at the table, is 'rustic and fun'. End on an exotic note with apple with shaved ice, salty caramel and Calvados foam. Service is 'spot-on'. There are some exciting choices on the wine list (from £29) and a splendid selection of saké. If cocktails are more your thing, head downstairs to the bar.

Chef/s: Alexandru Craciun. **Closed:** Sun, bank hols. **Meals:** main courses £14 to £45. Set L and D £25 (2 courses) to £29. Tasting menu £45. **Details:** 78 seats. Bar. Wheelchairs. Music.

Tayyabs

Cooking score: 1
⊖ Whitechapel, Aldgate East, map 1
Pakistani | £25
83-89 Fieldgate Street, Whitechapel, E1 1JU
Tel no: (020) 7247 6400/9543
tayyabs.co.uk

As much an East End institution as jellied eels and pearly kings, Tayyabs has grown an evangelical following since it opened in 1972. The premises may have expanded (with room for 350 diners) but the formula is unchanged: meaty, moreish Punjabi cuisine. Start with the legendary lamb chops, or perhaps chunks of masala fish or mutton tikka arriving on sizzling hot plates. Mains focus on karahi curries – keema and king prawn among them – though vegetarians also rave about the baby pumpkin tinda masala. Tayyabs is unlicensed, so an expedition to a Whitechapel off-licence is generally part of the experience.

Chef/s: Wasim Tayyab. **Meals:** main courses £6 to £14. **Details:** 350 seats. Wheelchairs. Music.

Tratra

Cooking score: 3
⊖ Shoreditch, Old Street, map 4
Modern French | £39
Boundary Hotel, 2-4 Boundary Street (entrance in Redchurch Street), Shoreditch, E2 7DD
Tel no: (020) 7729 1051
theboundary.co.uk

Tratra at Prescott & (Sir Terence) Conran's Boundary Project has erased all memories of the haute French restaurant that preceded it. French chef and writer Stéphane Reynaud has tweaked the concept, introducing a sharing menu better suited to his rustic style. He's made his presence felt – indeed, he was actually in the house when we inspected – and brought life to the double-height basement. Brown-paper tablecloths, candlelight and an expanded bar area issue a warm bienvenue. Reynaud's renowned for charcuterie so start with slices of ventrèche or chorizo de Bigorre and look out for early-evening 'bottomless' deals. Split a few small plates such as wafer-thin pork belly carpaccio anointed with horseradish and scattered with Roscoff onion, peppercorns and perfumed basil – ingenious in its simplicity – or seared mackerel, caramelised shallots and not-quite-punchy-enough Dijon cream. Lightly salted caramel fondant is the mellow signature dessert. An all-French wine list now starts at an approachable £21.

Chef/s: Stéphane Reynaud and James Warburton. **Closed:** Mon, 26 Dec, 1 Jan. **Meals:** small plates £5 to £19. **Details:** 100 seats. Bar. Wheelchairs. Music.

★ NEW ENTRY ★

Vinoteca City

Cooking score: 2
⊖ Cannon Street, map 4
Modern European | £33
21 Bloomberg Arcade, City, EC4N 8AR
Tel no: (020) 3150 1292
vinoteca.co.uk

This smart, new all-day Vinoteca offers counter dining, weekend brunch and weekday breakfasts (from 7.30am). As well as the usual 200-strong list, the 'wine ledger' is updated daily and includes very limited supplies of rare vintages and aged bottles. For main entry, see King's Cross branch, north London.
Chef/s: Fabrizio Pusceddu. **Meals:** main courses £8 to £23. Set L £15 (2 courses) to £18. **Details:** 100 seats. 50 seats outside. Bar. Music.

Vinoteca Farringdon

Cooking score: 2
⊖ Farringdon, Barbican, map 5
Modern European | £33
7 St John Street, Farringdon, EC1M 4AA
Tel no: (020) 7253 8786
vinoteca.co.uk

Compact and cosy, this Farringdon wine shop and bistro was the original Vinoteca. Expect the winning formula of Med-influenced dishes, a cracking wine list and friendly staff, plus private dining in the basement. For main entry, see King's Cross branch, north London.
Chef/s: Pawel Jankowiak. **Closed:** Sun, bank hols. **Meals:** main courses £9 to £19. Set L £15 (2 courses) to £18. **Details:** 35 seats. 8 seats outside. Music.

Send us your review

Your feedback informs the content of the *GFG* and will be used to compile next year's reviews. To register your opinion about any restaurant listed, or a restaurant that you wish to bring to our attention, visit our website.

Wright Brothers Spitalfields

Cooking score: 2
⊖ Liverpool Street, map 4
Seafood | £40
8a Lamb Street, Spitalfields, E1 6EA
Tel no: (020) 7324 7730
thewrightbrothers.co.uk

The Wright Brothers (in fact, brothers-in-law) were oyster wholesalers before they were restaurateurs so don't pass up the chance to indulge at their five London seafood restaurants (est. 2005 in Borough). Sourced from the British Isles and beyond, their oyster are impeccable au naturel and can even survive the barrage of purist-baiting techniques we tried at their Spitalfields site: fried with Louis sauce, with grapefruit, mint and chilli granita, or smoked with pickled cucumber (particularly delicious). Classic dressed crab was also good. The shellfish bar is where it's at: we were less convinced by the kitchen's contributions – scallops with smokey aubergine purée, and heavily battered soft-shell crab with sriracha mayo were crying out for seasoning. Menus are large, with room for both classics and innovations. The group downplays the luxury status attached to swanky shellfish, hence the sound selection of sub-£40 wines and the restaurants' low-key brand of glamour.
Chef/s: Michal Heins. **Closed:** 25 and 26 Dec, 1 Jan. **Meals:** main courses £13 to £23. **Details:** 120 seats. 30 seats outside. Music.

The Anchor & Hope

Cooking score: 3
⊖ Waterloo, Southwark, map 5
Modern European | £31
36 The Cut, South Bank, SE1 8LP
Tel no: (020) 7928 9898
anchorandhopepub.co.uk

Sixteen years on, this take-us-as-you-find-us pub is as popular as ever. The drill remains the same: no-frills décor and cramped tables, a robust British-inspired menu and no bookings – but you can wait in the bar until a table becomes vacant. The menu changes daily from lunch to dinner, the cooking a tribute to great British produce. Dishes vary, some are simple assemblies (leek and crab vinaigrette with crushed hazelnuts, or a warm snail and bacon salad), while others are more complex, as in a pumpkin, chestnut and Parmesan tart served with a cep sauce or Swaledale meats in broth with lentils, mustard fruits and salsa verde, and a well-reported dish of pheasant – the breast wrapped in ham and sage, a confit leg – with winter coleslaw and hazelnuts. The bread is considered delicious, and blood orange and raspberry queen of puddings a fitting finish. To drink there's beer and a European wine list with good choice in the £20 to £40 range.

Chef/s: Alex Crofts. **Closed:** 23 Dec to 2 Jan, bank hols. **Meals:** main courses £11 to £25. Set L £15 (2 courses) to £17. **Details:** 50 seats. 32 seats outside. Bar.

Artusi

Cooking score: 3
⊖ Peckham Rye, map 1
Italian | £28
161 Bellenden Road, Peckham, SE15 4DH
Tel no: (020) 3302 8200
artusi.co.uk

'I would go as far as saying this is one of my favourite Italian restaurants in London', is the view of one visitor, in no doubt that this much-loved venue on Bellenden Road is the kind of neighbourhood eatery you'd be thankful to have on your doorstep. A sleek, minimalist finish and an all-round energetic buzz add to the easy-going appeal, the upbeat attitude maintained by keen staff. The menu is brief and regularly changing, passion for quality runs through every aspect, from puntarelle with anchovy, chilli and soft-boiled egg to hispi cabbage served with bagna cauda and olives, from pappardelle of ox cheek ragù to leg of lamb with borlotti beans, minestra nera (broccoli-flavoured leaves) and mint gremolata. Desserts flit between the likes of pear and almond cake with crème fraîche and ice cream and it's all washed down with classic Italian cocktails and a short modern wine list.

Chef/s: Emily Sansom. **Closed:** 1 week Christmas. **Meals:** main courses £12 to £18. Sun L £20. **Details:** 42 seats. 6 seats outside. Wheelchairs. Music.

Babur

Cooking score: 2
map 1
Indian | £35
119 Brockley Rise, Forest Hill, SE23 1JP
Tel no: (020) 8291 2400
babur.info

What would happen if the life-sized model of a tiger ever left the roof of Babur? Sounds like a ravens in the Tower of London scenario but, after nearly 35 years, neither tiger nor restaurant are going anywhere. The dining room, an unpretentious space with exposed brick walls and vibrant Indian artworks, is watched over by a charming team, while the menu delivers diverse dishes that avoid the average curry-house clichés. No wonder that for many loyal fans it's 'a local institution'. Openers such as griddled scallops with spiced pea purée, Gurkhali ostrich tikka, and beetroot 'cutlet' with a crispy tapioca coating, and mains such as kasundi king prawns, rabbit soweta, and Lucknowi chicken biryani, continue to impress with vivid spicing and sound thinking. To finish, cumin chocolate fondant with salted caramel gelato is fusion heaven. The wine list, opening at £24.95, is a carefully considered edit of spice-friendly bottles, though the house cocktails are well worth a try, too.

Chef/s: Jiwan Lal. **Closed:** 26 Dec. **Meals:** main courses £15 to £19. Sun L £16 (buffet). **Details:** 72 seats. V menu. Music.

The Begging Bowl

Cooking score: 2
⊖ Peckham Rye, map 1
Thai | £30
168 Bellenden Road, Peckham, SE15 4BW
Tel no: (020) 7635 2627
thebeggingbowl.co.uk

Competition might be fierce in restaurant-heavy Peckham, but diners heartily endorse this well-established, no-reservations Thai eatery. A light-filled and spacious dining room, fronted by a narrow conservatory, it's plain, neat and well cared for. The kitchen offers a tight, regularly changing list of sharing plates delicately balanced between hot, sour, salty and sweet, and while its food may not be groundbreaking, it simply cooks the way more Thai restaurants should. There are plenty of hits: crispy squid with red turmeric, kaffir lime leaf and sour chilli dip; a turmeric- and sesame-infused chickpea tofu; pomelo salad with blood orange, cashew nuts and lemongrass; piquant charcoal-grilled sausages. One sure bet is to order the deep-fried whole sea bass as a centrepiece, with the coconut-sesame banana fritter with tamarind, peanut brittle and turmeric custard making a fine finale. Cocktails are worth exploring, and there's a short beer list and spice-friendly wines (from £21).

Chef/s: Jane Alty. **Closed:** 25 and 26 Dec, 1 Jan. **Meals:** sharing plates £4 to £17. Set L £16. **Details:** 50 seats. 24 seats outside. Wheelchairs. Music.

Bistro Union

Cooking score: 3
⊖ Clapham South, map 3
British | £30
40 Abbeville Road, Clapham, SW4 9NG
Tel no: (020) 7042 6400
bistrounion.co.uk

A neighbourhood bistro as imagined by Adam Byatt was always going to be one to watch, and so it has proved here in Clapham's 'Abbeville Village'. Given the culinary fireworks going off at Trinity (see entry), Bistro Union is the sort of place you could eat every day if time and budget allowed. A contemporary interior of natural wood and dangling light bulbs provide an urban backdrop to rustic dishes such as Gloucester Old Spot chop with cannellini beans, fennel and preserved lemons. The produce is top stuff: note the burrata that brings a creamy hit to a salad of blood orange, chilli and mint, or the Wye Valley asparagus that comes with smoked cod's roe and crispy CackleBean egg, a speciality import from the Cotswolds. Cornish pollack baked in seaweed butter, toad-in-the-hole with onion gravy – it's comfort and joy all the way to a dessert of chocolate cremosa with toffee popcorn. Weekend brunch is a local institution. Drink wines from £20, draught beers or cocktails.

Chef/s: Adam Byatt and Joshua Hooper. **Closed:** 23 to 28 Dec. **Meals:** main courses £14 to £30. Sun supper £26. **Details:** 45 seats. 12 seats outside. Bar. Wheelchairs. Music.

Camberwell Arms

Cooking score: 2
map 1
Modern British | £30
65 Camberwell Church Street, Camberwell, SE5 8TR
Tel no: (020) 7358 4364
thecamberwellarms.co.uk

At first glance you might be forgiven for thinking this was a run-of-the-mill city boozer, with its Victorian façade and busy roadside location. In reality, visitors have branded the Camberwell Arms a great neighbourhood asset, its crowd-pleasing menus offering plenty of interest. There's a good buzz about the place – from the scuffed front bar with its high tables and stools, to the crowded back restaurant with its mismatched tables and dangly lights. It pushes all the dining buttons, too, with a heavy reliance on seasonal produce, good pricing and eager young staff. What's not to like? Caponata (diced, fried aubergine) and burrata toast has been justly celebrated, as has the house-cured salmon with dill and crème fraîche, and fortifying cold-weather dishes such as slow-cooked ox cheek with red wine, porcini and mash. Sunday lunch is book-well-ahead popular, when big flavours and hearty portions come into play – a magnificent Hereford beef, ale, onion and bone-marrow pie to share, for example. House French opens the wine list at £18.

Chef/s: Michael Davies. **Closed:** 24 to 29 Dec, 1 and 2 Feb. **Meals:** main courses £12 to £25. **Details:** 100 seats. Bar. Wheelchairs. Music.

The Canton Arms

Cooking score: 1
⊖ Stockwell, map 3
Modern British | £29
177 South Lambeth Road, Stockwell, SW8 1XP
Tel no: (020) 7582 8710
cantonarms.com

Dark and moody, the deep red walls set off by glowing lights and shelves stocked with jars of homemade pickles and ferments, this genuine local is a consistently good choice for food, although the busy bar can sometimes detract. Head for the rear, book-lined dining area – they don't take reservations – and expect a gutsy, muscular riff on British themes; this is a sibling of The Anchor & Hope and Great Queen Street (see entries) after all. At inspection an earthy starter of whipped bass roe with radishes and seeds made 'no concessions to elegance' but was no less satisfying for it, while a piri-piri spatchcock poussin with gem lettuce and buttermilk dressing had a well-judged peppery punch. Gooseberry fool also hit the spot, combining 'lip-smackingly tart fruit, pillowy cream and the shortest little shortbread biscuit'. The keenly priced wine list gives good global coverage and plenty by the glass.

Chef/s: Trish Hilferty and Andrew Lambert. **Closed:** 24 Dec to 2 Jan, bank hols. **Meals:** main courses £15 to £18. **Details:** 68 seats. 48 seats outside. Bar. Music.

Casse-Croûte

Cooking score: 4
⊖ London Bridge, Borough, map 1
French | £35
109 Bermondsey Street, Bermondsey, SE1 3XB
Tel no: (020) 7407 2140
cassecroute.co.uk

The postcode may be London SE1, but everything about Casse-Croûte speaks of *la belle France*. It's effortlessly rustic, endearingly charming and totally devoted to food, with a huge helping of familial bonhomie on the side. There are gingham cloths on the tables, posters on the walls and – at the centre of things – a daily blackboard menu written entirely in French, with just three choices at each stage. Drop by in June and you might find a ragoût of cuttlefish and tomatoes, or veal kidneys in mustard sauce, followed by hake with artichokes barigoule, or mignons of pork with petits pois and broad beans. Plates of artisan cheese and charcuterie are ideal with a glass or two of well-selected French regional wine, while dessert might bring apricot tart or pain perdu with red fruits. Prices are *très bon* and the whole crammed-in set-up is joyfully gregarious, right down to the last double kiss.

Chef/s: Sylvain Soulard. **Closed:** 24 to 30 Dec. **Meals:** main courses £17 to £21. **Details:** 25 seats. 2 seats outside. Wheelchairs. Music.

Chez Bruce

Cooking score: 6
⊖ Balham, map 3
British | £58
2 Bellevue Road, Wandsworth, SW17 7EG
Tel no: (020) 8672 0114
chezbruce.co.uk

Chez Bruce has been a steady presence on Wandsworth Common since 1995. It has the distinction of being both a destination restaurant and a neighbourhood darling, largely thanks to a very fine classical wine list (which doesn't overlook half bottles, dessert wines and older vintages) and two safe pairs of hands: those of Bruce Poole and long-serving head chef Matt Christmas. Call their style old-fashioned, they take it as a compliment: such richly pleasing dishes as tagliatelle with braised rabbit, truffle cream sauce and mousserons, and sautéed calf's liver with pancetta, mashed potato and retro stuffed mushroom are surely ripe for revival. As for the cheese trolley, it's a rare treat to encounter so many well-kept British and French cheeses. Modernity hasn't gone unnoticed, however: sugared chocolate doughnuts with salted caramel are a vogueish finish. Service is smooth and professional; the setting simple but soigné.

Chef/s: Matt Christmas. **Closed:** 24 to 26 Dec, 1 Jan. **Meals:** set L £33 (2 courses) to £38. Set D £49 (2 courses) to £58. Sun L £42. Tasting menu £65 (4 courses) to £75. **Details:** 80 seats. Wheelchairs. Children at L only.

Symbols

Accommodation is available
Three courses for less than £30
£5 off voucher scheme
Notable wine list

★ NEW ENTRY ★

Cinnamon Kitchen Battersea

Cooking score: 1
⊖ Battersea Park, map 3
Indian | £35
4 Arches Lane, Battersea, SW11 8AB
Tel no: (020) 3955 5480
cinnamon-kitchen.com

Vivek Singh's latest opening, in a railway arch by Battersea Power Station, is a play of contrasts, its brick walls softened by velvet and woven cane. Lunches are casual: lamb bhuna heaped on soft naan is a generous, inexpensive option. Service is stiff – better suited to dinnertime formalities when cocktails and punchy (but predictable) global wines come into play. Bright ideas abound, perhaps Ibérico presa with vindaloo sauce (nicer than it sounds) and bitter melon with spicy soya ragoût. We found the signature Malabari mussels and dates on brioche too sweet but finished on a high with saffron-laced double ka meetha bread pudding.

Chef/s: Rakesh Nair and Vivek Singh. **Closed:** Sun, 25 Dec. **Meals:** main courses £14 to £12. Set L £12 (1 course) to £21. Tasting menu £38 (9 courses). **Details:** 250 seats. V menu. Bar. Wheelchairs. Music.

★ NEW ENTRY ★

Coal Rooms

Cooking score: 4
⊖ Peckham Rye, map 1
Modern British | £29
11a Station Way, Peckham, SE15 4RX
Tel no: (020) 7635 6699
coalroomspeckham.com

There's no doubt that this casual eatery in the former ticket office of Peckham Rye station has heaps of character: grill flames flare as you squeeze past the open kitchen, the small dining room is surprisingly, delightfully light and bright, and the loos are not-to-be-missed listed. Service keeps well on track even during busy periods and the food is bold, simple and modern, with inspiration from just about everywhere, pulling in Mediterranean, Asian and South American flavours, updating English classics and generally getting it all right. Sharing plates run to punchy corn tacos with pumpkin mole, chimichurri and London Fettle cheese, or smoked pig's head blood pudding with apple ketchup, and 'just awesome' Bermondsey Frier croque-monsieur with coppa ham and red-eye mayonnaise. Chops, possibly Gloucester Old Spot or Cabrito goat, feature among mains, and there could be mackerel and potted shrimp pasty or a whole spit-roast chicken to share for Sunday lunch. Cocktails and bottled craft beers supplement a short, global wine list.

Chef/s: Sam Bryant. **Closed:** 22 to 28 Dec. **Meals:** main courses £14 to £17. **Details:** 65 seats. Bar. Wheelchairs. Music.

Craft

Cooking score: 3
⊖ North Greenwich, map 1
Modern British | £38
Peninsula Square, Greenwich, SE10 0SQ
Tel no: (020) 8465 5910
craft-london.co.uk

This sleek, glass-fronted, three-floor operation by the O2 Arena on Greenwich Peninsula takes in a ground-floor café and shop, a rooftop bar and a glamorous first-floor dining room festooned with striking contemporary lighting. In contrast to its internationalist, futuristic surroundings, Stevie Parle's venture champions small-scale domestic farmers and growers and (true to its name) cures, ferments, pickles, smokes and bakes in-house, too. The kitchen identifies its food as 'new British' and majors in various tasting menus, with à la carte for the traditionalist. Innovative snacks kick things off, perhaps vegetable ferments and foragings with salted yoghurt or crispy oxtail; pollock comes with leek and wild cabbage, smoked cod's roe and dulse; and Denver steak with white artichokes, Pink Fir, ale and bittercress. Try wild chamomile set cream with gingerbread ice cream and brown-butter sponge to finish. The open-minded list of wines from progressive small producers takes in Welsh rosé and London-made wine alongside enterprising bottles from independent operators and co-operatives further afield.

Chef/s: Stevie Parle and Thomas Greig. **Closed:** Sun, Mon. **Meals:** main courses £15 to £22. Set menu £38 (4 courses). Tasting menu £55 (7 courses). **Details:** 84 seats. Bar. Wheelchairs. Music. Parking.

LOCAL GEM

The Crooked Well

⊖ Oval, map 1
Modern British | £30
16 Grove Lane, Camberwell, SE5 8SY
Tel no: (020) 7252 7798
thecrookedwell.com

Delivering the usual mix of bare brick, dark wood, bold wallpaper and dangling lights that we've come to expect in a modern urban pub, it's no surprise that the Well is as pleasantly laid-back as most of its customers. Outside tables on the quiet residential street and a fair booking system that keeps tables back for walk-ins ensure regulars return for cooking that plays off the seasons. Artichokes with broad beans; goat's curd and chargrilled focaccia; and corn-fed chicken breast with petits pois à la française are typical choices. Wines from £19.50.

The Dairy

Cooking score: 5
⊖ Clapham Common, map 3
Modern European | £48
15 The Pavement, Clapham, SW4 0HY
Tel no: (020) 7622 4165
the-dairy.co.uk

'You'd never know this was a temple to up-to-the-minute seasonality,' noted one visitor, eyeing up the distressed walls, wallpapered ceiling and wonky tables. But then Robin Gill's flagship restaurant (see also Sorella) has

never taken itself too seriously – and prides itself on reasonable prices. The kitchen takes market-fresh ingredients and puts them together in winning combinations that fully exploit contrasting flavours and textures – in the piquancy of elderberries teamed with a 'snack' of boozy chicken liver mousse, and in the sweet, sour and herbaceous notes found in a simple assembly of asparagus, lovage, pink grapefruit and St Tola cheese, for example. Two good-sized discs of monkfish could be pepped up with youthful broad beans, peas and baby spinach, while aged bavette – three thick, charred slices, medium-rare and beautifully seasoned – might be teamed with new-season shallot, hazelnuts for crunch and beef-fat hollandaise that's 'thick, rich and made for dipping'. It's all washed down with cocktails that keep to the seasonal theme, and a short, modern wine list.
Chef/s: Ben Rand. **Closed:** Mon, Christmas. **Meals:** small plates £9 to £13. Set L £28 (4 courses). Sun L £32. Tasting menu £48. **Details:** 65 seats. 30 seats outside. V menu. Vg menu. Bar. Wheelchairs. Music.

★ NEW ENTRY ★

Duddell's

Cooking score: 2
⊖ London Bridge, map 4
Chinese | £60
9 St Thomas Street, London Bridge, SE1 9RY
Tel no: (020) 3957 9932
duddells.co

It's easy to walk past the former St Thomas' church and not realise it's a restaurant, let alone a Chinese one, so discreet is the signage. Once inside, you can't help but admire the sensitive remodelling that maintains the original features (wall panelling, altarpiece), while a half mezzanine makes full use of the ecclesiastical dimensions. Now home to a high-end import from Hong Kong, you can expect pricey Cantonese cooking, including crisply battered yin yang prawns with a yuzu-lime leaf dressing, and monkfish with earthy morel mushrooms, fresh, al dente garlic shoots and crispy dough. For a much cheaper experience, come for lunchtime dim sum where prawn har gau and scallop dumpling are textbook versions of classic dishes, and black pepper duck pumpkin dumpling and Ibérico char siu bun are successful twists on the dim sum repertoire. From the unusual cocktail list try the St Thomas Antidote – an Asian take on a pisco sour – otherwise keep costs down by drinking tea.
Chef/s: Daren Liew. **Closed:** 25 Dec. **Meals:** set L £25 (2 courses) to £30. Tasting menu £82 (for 2, sharing). **Details:** 102 seats. Bar. Wheelchairs.

Edwins

Cooking score: 1
⊖ Borough, map 5
Modern European | £30
202-206 Borough High Street (Upstairs), Borough, SE1 1JX
Tel no: (020) 7403 9913
edwinsborough.co.uk

A pared-down interior of wood and reclaimed furniture sets the tone for a refreshingly unpretentious slice of high-street dining in a room hidden above the Trinity pub. Hugely likeable in a simple, low-key way, the no-airs-and-graces food is a zesty Euro-inspired assortment of small and large plates. Of the former, cod cheeks with chickpea tempura and sauce gribiche, and scallops in filo with harissa mayo define the style, with extra possibilities in the shape of, say, whole lemon sole meunière, or duck breast with cabbage parcel and redcurrant jelly jus. Finish with British cheeses or rhubarb trifle. Wines from £27.
Chef/s: Salim Massouf. **Meals:** main courses £13 to £30. Early D £20 (2courses). **Details:** 35 seats.

Stay in the know

For the latest restaurant news, look out for the weekly *GFG Briefing*. Visit thegoodfoodguide.co.uk

El Pastor

Cooking score: 2
⊖ London Bridge, map 4
Mexican | £25
7a Stoney Street, Borough, SE1 9AA
tacoselpastor.co.uk

Authenticity is somewhat thin on the ground when it comes to eating Mexican on this side of the Atlantic, but for brothers Sam and James Hart, and mate Crispin Somerville, inspiration comes from having lived in Mexico (Sam and Crispin), so nothing less than the real thing will do. That means heritage corn for the tacos (made fresh daily), and a long list of mezcal by the shot, glass or carafe. They don't take bookings, so head to the railway arch in Borough Market and be lucky. Choose your salsa – the el diablo is for 'massive show-offs' – and set your temperature gauge for those blue and white corn tacos: chicken with a chipotle and cumin rub, say, an umami-rich number with mushrooms and caramelised onions, or the stonking 24-hour-marinated pork shoulder. Flavours hit home, as does the drinks list: Mexican beers, tequilas and wines, and tequila and mezcal-based cocktails.

Chef/s: Tomasz Baranski. **Closed:** bank hols. **Meals:** main courses £3 to £9. **Details:** 60 seats. 16 seats outside. Wheelchairs. Music.

40 Maltby Street

Cooking score: 3
⊖ Bermondsey, map 1
Modern British | £30
40 Maltby Street, Bermondsey, SE1 3PA
Tel no: (020) 7237 9247
40maltbystreet.com

Maltby Street may no longer be the diminutive market it once was, but 40 Maltby Street, one of its original railway-arch traders and an extension of natural wine merchant Gergovie Wines, seems oblivious to the bustling foodie scene that now hems it in. Bar-stool seating, scruffy wood floors and bare-brick walls befit the unstructured format of the lively restaurant whose blackboard menu is based on ever-changing seasonal produce. The techniques employed may be classic Anglo-French but what you eat is never predictable. Commence with small plates, perhaps pork terrine or duck rillettes, or battered cuttlefish with wild garlic mayo and shaved fennel. Larger plates take in the likes of lamb ragoût with fried green peppers and fresh curd. The riveting all-natural wine list ('absolutely baffling to the uninitiated') turns classification-led rules on their head, championing small producers, unfamiliar regions and little-known grapes. Fortunately, staff double-up as natural wine movement ambassadors and deliver perfect pairings. Note no bookings are taken.

Chef/s: Steve Williams. **Closed:** Mon, Tue. **Meals:** main courses £7 to £16. **Details:** 40 seats. 4 seats outside. Wheelchairs. Music.

Franklins

Cooking score: 2
map 1
Modern British | £30
157 Lordship Lane, East Dulwich, SE22 8HX
Tel no: (020) 8299 9598
franklinsrestaurant.com

Franklins has two hats (or three if you include its Farm Shop across the road), and it wears them very well indeed, being both a proper little boozer and big-hearted restaurant. Tablecloths and an open kitchen mark out the dining area, where 'lovely staff' serve up a seasonal daily menu that sits just the right side of rustic. Get off the mark with wet garlic and potato soup, or quail with coleslaw and green sauce, and move on to ox tongue, pease pudding and carrots, or guinea fowl with garlic courgettes. There's an honesty and integrity to the kitchen's output that has earned it a loyal following. Fish figures too – hake with samphire and salsify, say – and vegetarians might get a butternut squash and chickpea combo with saffron mayonnaise. Bakewell tart is a classic finish, or keep it savoury with English cheeses or Welsh rarebit.

Cocktails, draught beer and well-chosen wines go down nicely, as does the excellent value set lunch.
Chef/s: Ralf Wittig. **Closed:** 25 and 26 Dec. **Meals:** main courses £15 to £24. Set L £14 (2 courses) to £17. **Details:** 70 seats. 12 seats outside.

Ganapati

Cooking score: 2
⊖ Peckham Rye, map 1
Indian | £30
38 Holly Grove, Peckham, SE15 5DF
Tel no: (020) 7277 2928
ganapatirestaurant.com

A stalwart of the Peckham dining scene, this reliable Indian proclaims itself with a turmeric-coloured frontage. It is noted for unpretentious but enthusiastic staff and offers something a little different to an appreciative and loyal clientele, namely regional home cooking and street food inspired by the southern Indian states of Kerala, Tamil Nadu, Karnataka and Andhra Pradesh. Richly spiced duck leg, for example, is cooked north Kerala style with roasted spices, coconut and garam masala; sea bass fillet comes with lemon, green chilli, ginger and coconut milk. Chutneys and all the incidentals are a cut above and there's plenty of choice for non-meat eaters: from vegetarian street snacks and thalis to baby aubergine and chickpea in a light masala sauce flavoured with coconut, tomato, tamarind and mint leaves. A brief wine list starts at £22, though most people prefer beer or lassi.
Chef/s: Aboobacker Pallithodi Koya. **Closed:** Mon. **Meals:** main courses £11 to £15. **Details:** 38 seats. 14 seats outside. Music.

Average price

The figure given in bold denotes the average price of a three-course dinner without wine.

★ NEW ENTRY ★

Garden Café

Cooking score: 2
⊖ Lambeth North, map 3
Modern British | £32
Garden Museum, 5 Lambeth Palace Road, Lambeth, SE1 7LB
Tel no: (020) 7401 8865
gardenmuseum.org.uk

'It's a fair schlep from the tube... but your efforts will be rewarded,' notes a visitor who ventured out to Lambeth's Garden Museum – a 'quirky cultural space' with a glass and bronze-tiled extension housing a revamped café-cum-restaurant, plus a delightful courtyard garden... and burial ground. The daily menu is an 'exercise in simplicity' with pithy descriptions and robust seasonal ideas ranging from jellied pig's ear, pickled radish and dandelion to pollock with peppers and black olives. The gutsy deep-flavoured fish soup 'makes few concessions to aesthetics', while a plate of fat, garlicky Toulouse sausages with white beans and green sauce is hearty peasant fare. There are also some gentler compositions, as in a 'wonderfully restrained' starter involving lightly steamed white sprouting broccoli, tangy crème fraîche and crunchy pangrattato. Although it's primarily a lunchtime spot, the café also serves dinner on Tuesday and Friday evenings. Wines avoid box-ticking clichés in favour of more enterprising stuff.
Chef/s: Harry Kaufman. **Closed:** first Mon of each month. **Meals:** main courses £13 to £19. **Details:** Wheelchairs.

Hawksmoor Borough

Cooking score: 4
⊖ London Bridge, map 4
British | £60
16 Winchester Walk, Borough, SE1 9AQ
Tel no: (020) 7234 9940
thehawksmoor.com

Housed in a converted hops warehouse near Borough Market, this branch of the popular steak chain hires out its basement Cooks'

Room (with its own kitchen) for private dining and events, or check it out on the last Friday of the month at the Cooks' Room Supper Club. For main entry, see Knightsbridge branch, west London.
Chef/s: Simon Cotterill. **Closed:** 24 to 26 Dec, 1 Jan. **Meals:** main courses £12 to £55. Set L and early D £25 (2 courses) to £28. Sun L £21. **Details:** 140 seats. Wheelchairs. Music.

LOCAL GEM

★ LOCAL RESTAURANT AWARD ★ REGIONAL WINNER

Home SW15

⊖ East Putney, Putney, map 3
Modern British | £30
146 Upper Richmond Road, Putney, SW15 2SW
Tel no: (020) 8780 0592
homesw15.com

There's a strong local following at this appealing all-day bar and restaurant, a reworking of restaurateur Rebecca Mascarenhas' Bibo. Sip 'a remarkably affordable daiquiri' in the spacious front bar, or head to the dining room where the service is enthusiastic and engaging and the kitchen is noted for generosity and boldness. A homemade shrimp burger sings with Vietnamese herbs, spices and harissa mayo; cod-cheek popcorn comes with properly made tartare sauce; and a huge chicken Caesar lacks for nothing in taste, dressing or crispy bacon. And don't ignore the chocolate and hazelnut mousse – it's a winner. Daily brunch and Sunday roasts add to the appeal. As for drink, once you get past the cocktails, a global selection of wine suits the food admirably.

José

Cooking score: 3
⊖ London Bridge, Borough, map 1
Spanish | £23
104 Bermondsey Street, Bermondsey, SE1 3UB
Tel no: (020) 7403 4902
josepizarro.com

Elbows in as you enter José Pizarro's weeny tapas corner-bar on the developing gastronomic stretch of Bermondsey Street. A seat at the counter for the true *comida rápida* experience may well have you letting the afternoon engagements go hang, so convivial is the ambience and so welcoming the staff. Everything is chalked up on the board, and nothing seems to disappoint, from tender razor clams with jamón, and prawns sizzled up with garlic and chilli, to wine-soaked chorizo with the optimal balance of paprika and fat, and satisfyingly robust cheesy croquetas. If fried goat's cheese in honey doesn't quite satiate the sweet-savoury tooth, olive-oiled and salted chocolate pot, or strawberries in vermouth vinegar can fill any gaps. A list of wines served in small measures from £4 showcases the diversity of modern Spanish viticulture, and there are deeply traditional dry amontillados and olorosos among the sherries. Just up the road, Pizarro offers similar fare with more conventional table seating.
Chef/s: José Pizarro. **Meals:** tapas £4 to £14. **Details:** 17 seats. Wheelchairs. Music.

LOCAL GEM

Kashmir

⊖ Putney, map 3
Indian | £30
18-20 Lacy Road, Putney, SW15 1NL
Tel no: (07477) 533888
kashmirrestaurants.co.uk

In-the-know locals make a beeline for this Indian restaurant, unsurprisingly, for it's a cut above the rest. The menu has plenty of reassuringly familiar dishes for the non-adventurous: a papad basket (fried and roasted poppadoms) with chutneys, onion bhajia, samosas, masalas and biryanis all feature, the better for being prepared fully on the premises and cooked to order. More inquisitive diners are rewarded when trying the kitchen's real specialities: lamb ribs fried after first being boiled in milk, leaving a crisp outer shell with an unctuously soft meatiness within; or choq wangan, slow-cooked aubergine soured with tamarind. There's an adequate wine list, and the lassis are lovely.

★ NEW ENTRY ★

Kudu

Cooking score: 4
⊖ Queens Road Peckham, map 1
Modern European | £40
119 Queens Road, Peckham, SE15 2EZ
Tel no: (020) 3950 0226
kudu-restaurant.com

Blink and you might miss this low-key little eatery in a parade of shops close to Queens Road station. A stripped-back look of parquet floor, bare tables, artfully distressed walls and open kitchen sets a relaxed mood. South African Patrick Williams adds a taste of his home nation's cuisine to some modern European ideas. There's much to like about a kitchen that bakes such good bread (and serves it with melted seafood butter), and it might be hard to choose between small plates of onion and beer tarte tatin with goat's curd, or pig's head tortellini with mushroom and hay broth and crispy onions. 'Medium plates' are satisfying portions of, say, braai lamb neck, teamed with smoked yoghurt, lettuce and sprouting broccoli, or roasted skate wing with charred calçots and samphire. Burnt milk tart with rhubarb marmalade stands out from a list of comforting desserts. South London locals have warmly embraced the weekend brunches, and service, led by Amy Corbin, is wonderfully welcoming. Most bottles on the brief, kindly priced list come by the glass; good cocktails too.

Chef/s: Patrick Williams. **Closed:** Mon, Tue, 23 Dec to 6 Jan, 26 Mar to 1 Apr, 27 Aug to 1 Sept. **Meals:** main courses £10 to £16. **Details:** 47 seats. Wheelchairs. Music.

Lamberts

Cooking score: 2
⊖ Balham, map 3
Modern British | £30
2 Station Parade, Balham High Road, Balham, SW12 9AZ
Tel no: (020) 8675 2233
lambertsrestaurant.com
£5 OFF

Joe Lambert's neighbourhood spot, a stone's throw from Balham tube and train station, has built up a strong following since opening 16 years ago, its success down to sound cooking and sensible prices (the midweek market menu is considered a bargain). The food brims with freshness and flavour, the winter menu revealing an abundance of well-sourced seasonal British produce along the lines of ox tongue and pickled red cabbage, pot-roast guinea fowl with lentils, parsnip and bacon, and baked apple and pumpkin with sultanas and salted caramel. More eye-catching dishes might include roasted, pickled and smoked cauliflower with toasted almonds, sea trout gravadlax with pickled cockles and dill and, from the traditional Sunday lunch menu, whole roast partridge with roast potatoes, carrots, parsnips, greens and red onion. Cocktails are imaginative riffs on classics, there are London-brewed beers and a modestly priced wine list arranged by style.
Chef/s: Miro Dohnal. **Closed:** Mon, 25 and 26 Dec, 1 and 2 Jan. **Meals:** main courses £14 to £20. Set D £17 (2 courses) to £20. **Details:** 53 seats. 8 seats outside. Music.

★ NEW ENTRY ★

Llewelyn's

Cooking score: 3
⊖ Herne Hill, map 1
British | £32
293-295 Railton Road, Herne Hill, SE24 0JP
Tel no: (020) 7733 6676
llewelyns-restaurant.co.uk

The inhabitants of Herne Hill look kindly on this modern café-style restaurant next door to the train station. Decor is simple – wood floors, white-topped tables, white-painted walls and not much else in between – as everything revolves around the food. The kitchen is scrupulously seasonal and deserves credit for its lack of ostentation. Flavours are direct and enjoyable, with no pretensions or unnecessary garnish, whether in a classic house terrine studded with pistachios, or in creamy burrata given a lift by fennel and blood orange. Mains bring the likes of a hearty plate of braised duck leg with bacon, prunes and mashed potato, or whole grilled lemon sole with good, crisp thick-cut chips and a homemade tartare sauce. Desserts will tempt, even if you don't think you need one – a zingy, well-made Sicilian lemon tart, perhaps, or a rich, sweet Muscat caramel custard. The drinks list is fun, too, ranging from house cocktails and sherries to reliable European wines.
Chef/s: Warren Fleet. **Closed:** Mon. **Meals:** main courses £16 to £33.

★ NEW ENTRY ★

Lupins

Cooking score: 4
⊖ Borough, London Bridge, map 5
Modern European | £25
66 Union Street, Borough, SE1 1TD
Tel no: (020) 3908 5888
lupinslondon.com

What we love about this place is that it ticks so many of the boxes of other on-trend restaurants – snacks and small plates of super-fresh, brilliantly seasoned, well-sourced, seasonal ingredients – but with none of the po-facedness. Instead, what you get is happy, sunshiny food in a dinky first-floor dining room done out in pastel sweetie colours – a breath of fresh air on the rather industrial road between Borough High Street and Waterloo. Dishes are finely balanced and beautifully thought out. A snack of tomato croquettes with olive tapenade and feta is a generous portion of expertly crisped arancini-style balls, with a yielding, silken filling. A puck of ruby red beef tartare combines brilliantly with pickled pear, while cornmeal spring onions with chipotle mayonnaise are 'insanely moreish' – the greens shredded, deep-fried and served in a hot, tangled heap. Desserts – perhaps shiny quenelles of indecently dense dark chocolate ganache served with a swirl of salt caramel and sesame brittle – are please-all, and please they do. Wines include many organic and biodynamic labels.
Chef/s: Natasha Cooke. **Closed:** Mon, 24 Dec to 1 Jan, bank hols. **Meals:** small plates £2 to £12. **Details:** 28 seats. Music.

Marcella

Cooking score: 2
map 1
Italian | £28
165a Deptford High Street, Deptford, SE8 3NU
Tel no: (020) 3903 6561
marcella.london

Jack Beer of Peckham's much-loved Artusi (see entry) is the driving force behind this regularly bursting-at-the-seams Italian eatery. It's struck just the right chord with locals, offering a basic but contemporary interior, albeit rather close-packed and frequently noisy, with easy-going service, gentle pricing and a sure hand in the kitchen. A daily changing blackboard lists a handful of small and large plates, pasta dishes, plus two larger sharing plates – perhaps a veal chop, whole bream or lemon sole. Very good beef shin ragù with tagliatelle kept one visitor happy, and other recent hits have been crab arancini, pasta al pomodoro, fried artichoke with aïoli, and porchetta with cime di rapa and polenta. Sweet things include an olive oil cake or baked custard with quince. Creative cocktails are another attraction, as is the brief, all-Italian wine list that's reasonably priced by the glass, carafe and bottle.

Chef/s: Jack Beer. **Meals:** main courses from £14. Sun L £20. **Details:** 57 seats. Music.

LOCAL GEM

Milk

⊖ Balham, map 3
Modern European | £10
18-20 Bedford Hill, Balham, SW12 9RG
milk.london

You'll find reliably good coffee and cake at this popular café which keeps locals sweet with its all-day brunch regulars of sweetcorn fritters (served with halloumi, smashed avo and kasundi), and weekly changing buttermilk pancakes. Seasonally led specials such as an Israeli-inspired aubergine soup with butter drenched sourdough, or a fat homemade bagel stuffed with salmon tail tartare, fenugreek rémoulade and pickled wild garlic show real flair in the kitchen. Queues are inevitable at busy times, though there are bookable dinners (Thursday to Saturday). Exposed brick walls and quirky neon signs suit the relaxed mood.

LOCAL GEM

Mr Bao

map 1
Taiwanese | £20
293 Rye Lane, Peckham, SE15 4UA
Tel no: (020) 7635 0325
mrbao.co.uk

'Feels like a real neighbourhood place with couples, with or without babies, and groups of friends,' recalled one visitor to this basic, intimate eatery known for its cheerful staff and kind prices. A tick-box order sheet offers a handful of bao (steamed buns) perhaps with a classic filling of pork with pickles and peanut powder, or a mushroom version with shiitake, teriyaki, miso mayo and crispy shallots. Don't neglect openers, such as pork dumplings or Tenderstem broccoli with ponzu, and there's one very sweet bao for dessert (best shared). Cocktails are recommended, and there's a sibling in Tooting – Daddy Bao, 113 Mitcham Road, SW17 9PE.

LOCAL GEM

Naughty Piglets

⊖ Brixton, map 1
Modern European | £29
28 Brixton Water Lane, Brixton, SW2 1PE
Tel no: (020) 7274 7796
naughtypiglets.co.uk

It's double trouble for those Naughty Piglets, with number two taking over the first floor of Andrew Lloyd Webber's theatre near Buckingham Palace (The Other Naughty Piglet, see entry). Here in Brixton, there's a new basement bar for walk-ins, and the same prospect of compelling small plates with the focus on global flavours: BBQ pork belly with Korean spices; roast cod with St George mushrooms and wild garlic; and asparagus with cured egg yolk and Berkswell ewe's milk cheese. The 'fabulous' wine list focuses on small producers.

Padella

Cooking score: 2
⊖ London Bridge, map 4
Italian | £20
6 Southwark Street, Borough, SE1 1TQ
padella.co

Tim Siadatan and Jordan Frieda are clearly doing something right, if the perpetual queue of pasta lovers that snakes around Borough Market is anything to go by. In turning a plate of pasta into something decadent yet affordable, the duo have hit on a winning formula. Stroll past Padella's plate-glass frontage in the morning and see the pasta being rolled by hand, then come back and score a counter stool or a table in the basement dining room. The single-sheet menu kicks off with antipasti, perhaps house-baked bread with oil, salame or salad, then segues to that pasta. Inspired by, but no slave to, Italian tradition, sauces are composed of seasonal British ingredients at their best. Gnocchi bathed in a silky cloak of nutmeg butter comes in at an astounding £4, fat Tuscan noodles (pici) might be dressed in marjoram, golden garlic and lemon, or there's the signature pappardelle with eight-hour Dexter beef shin ragù. Finish with lemon tart or chocolate sorbet and opt for a refreshing aperitivo or wine straight from the barrel.

Chef/s: Ray O'Connor. **Meals:** main courses £4 to £12. **Details:** 75 seats.

The Palmerston

Cooking score: 1
map 1
Modern British | £40
91 Lordship Lane, East Dulwich, SE22 8EP
Tel no: (020) 8693 1629
thepalmerston.co.uk

£5 OFF

Real ales, scuffed floors and mismatched tables reinforce this spacious Victorian pub's credentials as a neighbourhood boozer, but dark wood panelling and soft lighting in the dining room complement a strong profile on the food front. The kitchen has a generally cosmopolitan outlook and while some dishes may sometimes struggle to make their expected impact, among successes have been game terrine with chilli jam, cod and mussels with saffron broth, ratte potatoes and aïoli, and 40-day aged Galloway ribeye steak with marchand du vin butter. The food is supported by a clear, passionately accumulated wine list of global reach. An extensive by-the-glass selection provides an unmissable introduction and markups are friendly.

Chef/s: Jamie Younger and Celia Dickerson. **Closed:** 25 and 26 Dec, 1 Jan. **Meals:** main courses £17 to £28. Set L £16 (2 courses) to £19. **Details:** 60 seats. 20 seats outside. Wheelchairs. Music.

Peckham Bazaar

Cooking score: 2
⊖ Peckham Rye, map 1
Eastern Mediterranean | £35
119 Consort Road, Peckham, SE15 3RU
Tel no: (020) 7732 2525
peckhambazaar.com

Inspiration here comes from former Ottoman territory, from the Balkans in the north to Greece and Turkey further south. Around a dozen dishes include some lighter vegetable meze to begin, such as courgette fritters, cucumber, radishes and tarator, after which the grill takes over, tackling seafood and meat with equal aplomb. Octopus appears often, the blackened tentacles served over Cyprus potatoes, white tarama, capers and herbs. Meat dishes might include pork and lamb adana kebabs, baba ganoush and adjika (red pepper paste) or a more dressed-up lamb saddle stuffed with pine nuts and graviera cheese. Geographically, wines are a match for the food, with interesting picks from Greece, Hungary and Croatia. Service is friendly but can be slow.

Chef/s: John Gionleka. **Closed:** Mon. **Meals:** main courses £8 to £17. **Details:** 33 seats. 22 seats outside. Wheelchairs. Music.

LOCAL GEM

Pedler

⊖ Peckham Rye, map 1
Modern European | £25
58 Peckham Rye, Peckham, SE15 4JR
Tel no: (020) 3030 5015
pedlerpeckhamrye.com

Honest cooking, a low-key local vibe and bags of good cheer all contribute to Pedler's neighbourhood appeal. Diners are crammed in but no one minds when this is the 'best place for brunch in the area' and dinner brings beetroot and goat's cheese arancini, smoked haddock mac and cheese, or chicken and bacon puff pastry pie with cream, leeks and peas. Portions are generous, so you may want to share the brioche French toast with

Negroni ice cream and grilled pineapple. Drinking is fun, too, from cocktails to the reasonably priced, global wines with everything offered by the glass or bottle.

Pique-Nique

Cooking score: 3
⊖ London Bridge, Bermondsey, map 1
French | £50
Tanner Street Park, Bermondsey, SE1 3LD
Tel no: (020) 7403 9549
pique-nique.co.uk

Tanner Street Park is the epitome of an urban park, squeezed in between new-builds and industrial units behind Bermondsey Street with a café carved out of an old shelter in the corner. It may have a municipal look, but Pique-Nique is a volubly *sympathique* French bistro offering a brief menu of dishes honed by tradition, a generous marble-topped bar for casual counter eating (croque-monsieur, perhaps) and rows of chickens turning on the spit. It's a valuable neighbourhood asset, related to nearby Casse-Croûte (see entry) and is the place to come for pâte en croûte de volaille, the famed anchois de Collioure with shallots, suckling pig with Jerusalem artichokes, kale and raisins, and chateaubriand with potato purée and sauce aux cèpes (for two or three to share). After that there's a daily tart, soufflé or chocolate dessert. Most of the wines on the short, reasonably priced French list come by the glass.
Chef/s: Sylvian Soulard. **Closed:** 23 to 30 Dec. **Meals:** main courses £22 to £25. Tasting menu £41 (5 courses). **Details:** 45 seats. 12 seats outside. Wheelchairs. Music.

Le Pont de la Tour

Cooking score: 3
⊖ London Bridge, Tower Hill, map 1
French | £46
36a Shad Thames, Bermondsey, SE1 2YE
Tel no: (020) 7403 8403
lepontdelatour.co.uk

By the southern end of Tower Bridge, the coveted terrace tables enjoying the best of the riverside views, the Pont still enjoys considerable cachet. In the evenings, it's the distillation of glam: mirrored pillars and extravagant floral displays, with all the splendour of a luxurious railway dining car. Service is 'stiffly proper, although the Spanish sommelier is more approachable'. The menu formats will baffle the unfamiliar: you can eat three of the courses from the carte at a cheaper prix fixe tariff, but it isn't the sort of place to count the pennies. Dishes are more adventurous than the classic French norm, particularly for fish: start with cured salmon, miso and lime with charcoal tuiles and pickled cucumber, or Gruyère-crusted halibut in curry velouté and mussels, a better-balanced dish than it sounds. Where there are letdowns, they are surprising: a layer of raggily carved braised lamb shoulder topped with ratatouille, topped again with lamb fillet, all a bit of a *petit déjeuner du chien*. Desserts run the range from classic tarte tatin to chocolate délice with caramel crémeux and passion fruit ice cream. The wine list is mostly stunning, at markups that will also stun. There are some very well-chosen selections by the glass, but they too quickly leave their £9 base behind.
Chef/s: Julien Imbert. **Meals:** main courses £19 to £32. Set D £25 (2 courses) to £30.

★ TOP 50 ★

Restaurant Story

Cooking score: 8
⊖ London Bridge, map 4
Modern British | £120
199 Tooley Street, Bermondsey, SE1 2JX
Tel no: (020) 7183 2117
restaurantstory.co.uk

Since it opened in 2013, Tom Sellers' pace-setting restaurant has never lacked for enthusiastic, solid support. A reboot in early 2018 has produced an understated, more grown-up dining room, one with white tablecloths but a relaxed feel, reinforced by exceptionally personable service from staff who are knowledgeable, attentive and totally at ease. You won't be shown a menu (allergies are checked on booking) but the variously priced, beautifully balanced multi-course tasting menus are full of small delights and unexpected flavours. Crucially, some old favourites remain: the opening nibbles of crisp, savoury confit rabbit sandwich, the squid ink 'Storeos' looking just like the cookie, the beef-dripping candle; but these are now boosted by some stunning new dishes. Platinum caviar and golden beetroot with oh-so-delicate buttermilk blinis is a multi-layered sensation. So is a little dish of tomato and vanilla, a delightful interplay of sweetness and acidity. Other revelations have been the straightforward pleasure of turbot perfectly matched with a foamy Champagne sauce and salty, tangy sea herbs; the luxury juxtaposed with simplicity in veal sweetbread with grated hazelnut, turnip, white chocolate beurre blanc and a teaspoon of oscietra caviar, and the exquisite flavours in a morsel of chicken with morels, lettuce and a rich jus – just enough to satisfy. Almonds and dill (almond ice cream, toasted almonds, dill snow and oil) is as sensational as when we first tried it in 2015 and the cavalcade of sweeties still rounds off the meal. To drink, there is a matching option that includes cocktails and wines, or ask the sommelier's advice on a substantial list that's strong in France with shorter, but still interesting, shrift elsewhere.

Chef/s: Tom Sellers. **Closed:** Sun, 22 Dec to 3 Jan, Aug bank hol weekend. **Meals:** set L £45. Tasting menu £80 (8 courses) to £120. **Details:** 36 seats. V menu. Wheelchairs. Music. Children over 8 yrs.

★ NEW ENTRY ★

Salon

Cooking score: 4
⊖ Brixton, map 3
Modern European | £36
18 Market Row, Coldharbour Lane, Brixton, SW9 8LD
Tel no: (020) 7501 9152
salonbrixton.co.uk

Spread over two floors in Brixton Village market, the ground level of this modern bistro is home to a bustling bar peddling quirky cocktails, such as the Dirty Dill – a gin-based concoction with house-made pickle juice and dill – and a casual menu for drop-in diners. Upstairs offers a vegetable-focused, seasonal set menu in a more intimate setting. A springtime visit opened with a delicate starter of squid in brown butter with fresh peas and a sublime elderflower vinaigrette. Jersey Royals poached in a seaweed broth with sea vegetables and toasted buckwheat had a mineral saltiness made even more brilliant by a tamari-cured egg yolk, which, once broken, turned the broth soft and silky. Expect thoughtfully balanced, elegant mains such as Blackdown Hills hogget with nettles and chargrilled leaves, and puddings such as pear with spelt, rosemary and honey. Bar diners can enjoy simpler dishes such as merguez sausages with pickled red cabbage and yoghurt, or nettle gnocchi with lemon ricotta. The wine list opens at £23.50.

Chef/s: Nicholas Balfe. **Closed:** Mon. **Meals:** set L and D £36 (3 courses) to £49.

LOCAL GEM

Santo Remedio

⊖ London Bridge, map 4
Mexican | £30
152 Tooley Street, London Bridge, SE1 2TU
Tel no: (020) 7403 3021
santoremedio.co.uk

£5 OFF

In 2017, Natalie and Edson Diaz-Fuentes moved Santo Remedio from Shoreditch and brought a taste of Mexican taquerias to London Bridge. It's split over two floors, but visitors advise booking a ground-floor table, where there is a 'really nice buzz'. The kitchen motors industriously, delivering 'big-ish small plates' of guacamole ('chunky, fresh, very garlicky with a slight kick of chilli'), delicious quesadillas, perhaps hibiscus flower fried with onions and served with a goodly amount of Chihuahua cheese and 'delightfully smokey' tomato and chilli salsa, tender short-rib tacos, and beautifully crisp churros with a dipping sauce of cajeta – a Mexican caramel sauce. Drink 'excellent' Margaritas, Mexican beer or explore the several native wines offered on a brief list.

LOCAL GEM

Silk Road

map 1
Chinese | £15
49 Camberwell Church Street, Camberwell, SE5 8TR
Tel no: (020) 7703 4832

The cooking in this basic dining room is based mainly on the north-west frontier province of Xinjiang – known for strong flavours and the use of wheat noodles (made in-house). Do book, as low prices and dishes with a rare home-cooked quality (no sweet-and-sour here) mean inevitable queues. Lamb skewers are popular, and the cumin-flavoured red snapper version is well reported, as are pork dumplings, and the soupy bowl of chicken on the bone with flat noodles (the medium plate enough for three). Expect brisk, efficient service; to be placed where there is space; and no desserts. Cash only.

Soif

Cooking score: 1
⊖ Clapham South, map 3
Modern European | £32
27 Battersea Rise, Battersea, SW11 1HG
Tel no: (020) 7223 1112
soif.co

Soif is a paradise for oenophiles. The huge wine list starts in France but meanders its way around the world, calling in on interesting, independent wine growers, with staff happy to advise if needed. It would be a mistake however to overlook the food. There's an exemplary selection of charcuterie, but the competent kitchen has no trouble in sending out a daily changing menu of vibrant Mediterranean dishes, perhaps a simple salad of tomatoes, broad beans and anchovies softened with goat's curd, or a great chunk of on-the-bone smoked mackerel with celeriac rémoulade. So-called small plates are generous; large plates are strictly for larger appetites.

Chef/s: Anthony Hodge. **Meals:** small plates £8 to £10. Large plates £14 to £22. **Details:** 56 seats. Bar. Music.

Sorella

Cooking score: 4
⊖ Clapham Common, Clapham North, map 3
Italian | £35
148 Clapham Manor Street, Clapham, SW4 6BX
Tel no: (020) 7720 4662
sorellarestaurant.co.uk

Robin Gill is a dab hand at opening down-to-earth restaurants that only draw attention where it matters: on the plate. He has a finger on the city's culinary pulse, too, and his repurposing and renaming of The Manor, shifting the focus from modern British to Italian, has proved to be a shrewd and popular move. The double-shop-fronted restaurant is unchanged, an unassuming place done out in sparse, contemporary style, and continues the sharing plates concept (with both small and large dishes) with the emphasis on prime seasonal ingredients. Cicchetti are a good starting point, especially the crisp, creamy truffle arancini that were such a hit at inspection. Punchy small plates could bring Jersey milk ricotta, which works well with a vibrant, earthy courgette and basil purée, then a rich, umami-laden tagliatelle with porcini and shavings of summer truffle. Alternatively, opt for larger plates of Saddleback pork with borlotti beans or turbot on the bone. There's good service, too, plus impressive cocktails and an interesting list of Italian wines.

Chef/s: Dean Parker. **Closed:** Mon, 25 Dec. **Meals:** main courses £12 to £26. Tasting menu £45. **Details:** 55 seats. Bar. Wheelchairs. Music.

Sparrow

Cooking score: 2
⊖ Lewisham, map 1
International | £30
2 Rennell Street, Lewisham, SE13 7HD
Tel no: (020) 8318 6941
sparrowlondon.co.uk

This likeable eatery, a few steps from Lewisham train station, is a great addition to an area with limited eating options. A hard-edged aesthetic with large plate-glass windows, wood floors and bare tables means it can be noisy, but with seasonality underpinning the cooking, there's little chance of locals tiring of the ever-changing repertoire. Excellent focaccia arrives still warm and the menu is a refreshingly eclectic assortment of small plates, allowing you to choose a number of dishes to share (or keep to yourself). Tuck into kale and smoked cod's roe; fried chicken with a lovely tart plum sauce; roast Jerusalem artichoke with hazelnut pesto and bitter leaves; squid ink linguine; or braised pork shoulder with buttery mash. Desserts are no slouch either, perhaps blood orange panna cotta or double-baked chocolate cake. Sharpen up with a cocktail of the day or a glass of something from the brief European wine list.

Chef/s: Terry Blake and Yohini Nandakumar. **Closed:** Mon. **Meals:** main courses £8 to £17. **Details:** 30 seats.

★ NEW ENTRY ★

Swan

Cooking score: 3
map 5
Modern British | £40
21 New Globe Walk, Bankside, SE1 9DT
Tel no: (020) 7928 9444
swanlondon.co.uk
£5 OFF

Picture-postcard views of St Paul's from the spacious, light-filled dining room, sited above a bustling bar and next to the Globe Theatre, makes the Swan a popular destination for tourists. The menu centres on regional British produce and is overseen by Allan Pickett, former chef at the now-closed Piquet. At inspection, a simple first-course salad of salt-baked heritage beetroot, Kentish goat's cheese and caramelised hazelnuts scored highly for contrasting textures and flavour. Top marks also to a perfectly cooked sea trout fillet, matched with wilted garlic leaves and astringent samphire. The good news continued with a resolutely French-style roast chicken breast, partnered with buttery celeriac cream and a meaty jus. Desserts hit the sweet spot and fly the Union Jack for the likes of steamed pudding, fruit crumble and an apple-topped Bakewell tart. Afternoon teas are available from the unorthodox time of noon (it's never too early for scones) and the sizeable wine list includes established classics and newer wineries.

Chef/s: Allan Pickett. **Closed:** 26 Dec, 1 Jan. **Meals:** main courses £18 to £30. Set L £25 (2 courses) to £28. Sun L £27 (2 courses) to £30. **Details:** 90 seats. Bar. Wheelchairs. Music.

Trinity

Cooking score: 6
⊖ Clapham Common, map 3
Modern European | £75
4 The Polygon, Clapham, SW4 0JG
Tel no: (020) 7622 1199
trinityrestaurant.co.uk

A stalwart of the Clapham dining scene, this light, contemporary venue has long been a beacon of quality. At heart it's a neighbourhood restaurant, one where the bold, assured cooking draws locals back again and again. Adam Byatt's menu is a glorious roll call of top-notch ingredients, his dishes a wonderful amalgam of flavours, textures and combinations, as seen in a splendid spring opener of soused Cornish mackerel with white gazpacho, grapes and tarragon, or a stunning smoked eel pissaladière with red wine, garlic and black olives. There is much to applaud, from meat dishes that tap into the Gallic mainstream, say pigeon (from Bresse) served with rainbow chard, blood orange and spiced barbajuan fritters, or maize-fed chicken with new season's morels, wild garlic and sauce albufera, to a dish of roast cod with squid ink linguine and sardine bolognese. Desserts have included the much-praised choux à la crème with warm chocolate and cocoa sorbet, while the wine list boasts quality producers from across the globe, with the French leading the pack. For a more casual experience there is Upstairs at Trinity, where you can watch the chefs in action while you tuck in to small plates of salt cod fritters with seaweed aïoli, say, or crab risotto, steamed mussels in bouillabaisse, broccoli with anchovy sauce, or BBQ T-bone lamb with smoked aubergine and spiced yoghurt.

Chef/s: Adam Byatt. **Closed:** 24 to 27 Dec. **Meals:** set L £30 (2 courses) to £40. Set D £55. Tasting menu £68 (4 courses). **Details:** 46 seats. 18 seats outside. V menu. Wheelchairs. Children at L only.

The White Onion

Cooking score: 3
⊖ Wimbledon, map 3
Modern French | £42
67 High Street, Wimbledon Village, Wimbledon, SW19 5EE
Tel no: (020) 8947 8278
thewhiteonion.co.uk

Classical cooking with quirky, modern twists, lovely presentation and clued-up service all mean this neighbourhood restaurant 'suits the Wimbledon crowd to a T'. Seasonal produce plays its part – expect fresh peas, local asparagus and wild garlic leaves in spring. On our visit we enjoyed a rich pillow of cauliflower purée, baked under scallops moistened with lardo, which absorbed the cooking juices, making the bivalves sweeter and more tender than ever. Lamb rump, served with a croquette of slow-cooked lamb shoulder and paired with coco beans, was given heft with the addition of chorizo and aïoli. Generous first courses make main courses seem slightly small, but leave room for the indulgent desserts – poached rhubarb, say, with a 'crumble' of caramelised popcorn and hazelnuts and white chocolate ice cream. The wine list has plenty by the glass and carafe, but those in the know look to the 'Off the Beaten Track' section for proper bargains.

Chef/s: Frédéric Duval. **Closed:** Mon, 24 Dec to 9 Jan, 6 to 15 Aug. **Meals:** main courses £15 to £29. Set L £20 (2 courses) to £24. Sun L £22 (2 courses) to £26. **Details:** 70 seats. Wheelchairs. Music.

★ NEW ENTRY ★

Wright Brothers Battersea

Cooking score: 2
⊖ Battersea Park, map 3
Seafood | £34
26 Circus West Village, Battersea Power Station, Battersea, SW8 4NN
Tel no: (020) 7324 7734
thewrightbrothers.co.uk

The riverside site of this popular seafood chain is in a new restaurant enclave by Battersea Power Station. Exclusive to this branch are dishes cooked over charcoal in the Josper. For main entry, see Spitalfields branch, east London.

Chef/s: Richard Kirkwood. **Closed:** 25 and 26 Dec, 1 Jan. **Meals:** main courses £9 to £33. **Details:** 120 seats. 40 seats outside. Bar. Wheelchairs. Music.

Wright Brothers Borough Market

Cooking score: 2
⊖ London Bridge, map 4
Seafood | £40
11 Stoney Street, Borough, SE1 9AD
Tel no: (020) 7403 9554
thewrightbrothers.co.uk

The original and, some say, the best of this upmarket seafood chain. Enjoy the atmosphere of Borough Market over oysters and Muscadet at the barrel tables out front. For main entry, see Spitalfields branch, east London.

Chef/s: Rob Malyon. **Closed:** 25 and 26 Dec, 1 Jan. **Meals:** main courses £18 to £24. **Details:** 70 seats. 5 seats outside. Wheelchairs. Music.

Albertine

Cooking score: 1
⊖ Shepherd's Bush Market, Shepherd's Bush, map 1
Modern British | £30
1 Wood Lane, Shepherd's Bush, W12 7DP
Tel no: (020) 8743 9593
albertine.london

After co-founding the Leon chain and briefly running her own restaurant, Allegra McEvedy has returned to her family roots by rescuing and taking over Albertine, which her mother first opened in 1978. At ground level there's a welcoming wine bar with stripped floors and church pew seating. Stairs lead up to the homely dining room, where no-frills seasonal menus might bring smoked eel with Pink Fir potatoes, samphire and preserved lemon butter, or Barnsley lamb chop with tzatziki, pea shoots and harissa. Finish with cheesecake, strawberries and Italian meringue. An exciting, modern wine list with persuasive tasting notes opens at £20. Exactly what you need after escaping the gargantuan Westfield shopping centre, just opposite.

Chef/s: Roberto Freddi. **Closed:** Sun. **Meals:** main courses £14 to £17. **Details:** 24 seats. Bar.

Amaya

Cooking score: 4
⊖ Knightsbridge, map 6
Indian | £70
15 Halkin Arcade, Motcomb Street, Knightsbridge, SW1X 8JT
Tel no: (020) 7823 1166
amaya.biz

'We're lucky in London to have some of the best high-end Indian restaurants outside the Subcontinent,' noted one returning visitor to this long-running, upmarket Indian restaurant (and sibling of Chutney Mary – see entry). Spacious and dimly lit, its seductive feel is enhanced by black leather, red furnishings, dark wood and terracotta statues, while the mood is relaxed, with an appreciative buzz from diners. It's all helped by friendly, well-executed service. Prices match the Belgravia location, although the menu offers much flexibility with sharing plates and smaller portions (which can be tiny), and enticing vegetarian options. The food from the open-view kitchen continues to thrill: two yellow Bolivian peppers, filled with soft cheese, are perked up by a smash of heat; griddled crab cakes are beautifully presented; a wild venison seekh kebab is warm and smokey; and don't miss the perfect, buttery naan. Finish with sweet blackberry and toffee kulfi. To drink, there are cocktails and spice-friendly wines (from £30) plus 35 wines by the glass (from £8).

Chef/s: Sanchit Kapoor. **Meals:** main courses £25 to £43. Set L £26 (3 courses). Tasting menu £45. **Details:** 98 seats. V menu. Bar. No children after 8pm.

LOCAL GEM

L'Amorosa

⊖ Ravenscourt Park, Stamford Brook, map 1
Italian | £35
278 King Street, Hammersmith, W6 0SP
Tel no: (020) 8563 0300
lamorosa.co.uk

'I can happily confirm that it's changed not a jot, unassumingly going about its business as a pitch-perfect neighbourhood restaurant,' noted a satisfied reader, returning to the 'elegant simplicity' of L'Amorosa after a three-year absence. Andy Needham's cooking here is satisfyingly simple, the menu a run-through of Italian classics: Venetian-style sardines; burrata and oregano ravioli with prawns; agnolotti with lamb ragù; or roast chicken with polenta and herb salsa verde. For dessert there's tiramisu, of course. The all-Italian wine list is as accessibly priced as the food.

Apero

Cooking score: 2
⊖ South Kensington, map 3
Mediterranean | £27
The Ampersand Hotel, 2-10 Harrington Road, South Kensington, SW7 3ER
Tel no: (020) 7591 4410
aperorestaurantandbar.com

The decor in the vaulted cellars of this smart hotel not far from South Kensington tube may favour cool whites, but the menu is all zip and zing and sunshine brights. Settle at a marble-topped bar or in a smart leather chair and take a ramble through the Mediterranean sharing dishes. All the usual suspects are here – patatas bravas, roasted almonds, crispy fried squid – but much more besides: fat queen scallops with Espelette butter and bottarga; fried Crottin de Chavignol with truffle honey; chicken thighs cooked with sherry, cream and mushrooms. Fish and seafood make a good showing (try grilled octopus with artichoke and burnt tomato salsa) and substantial meat offerings could include bavette steak with savoy cabbage and smoked potato purée. There's a reasonable selection of meat-free options – not least courgette and basil arancini with smoked mozzarella. Drinks include cocktails, continental beers and European wines.

Chef/s: Mark Woolgar. **Meals:** small plates £4 to £14. Set L £13 (2 courses) to £16. **Details:** 48 seats. Bar. Wheelchairs. Music.

Bombay Brasserie

Cooking score: 3
⊖ Gloucester Road, map 3
Indian | £51
Courtfield Road, South Kensington, SW7 4QH
Tel no: (020) 7370 4040
bombayb.co.uk

Opening its doors the year 'Come On Eileen' ruled the charts (1982, if you're not of that vintage), Bombay Brasserie was a class act from the get-go and has held its own against the rise of the Indian new wave. That's partly because it was never really old school, never a curry house cliché, and if its menu contains tandoori chicken and chicken biryani, there's also guinea fowl dakshini and masala sea bass, and the conservatory dining room is still dressed up to the nines. There's a tasting menu if you want to surrender the decision making, while the Sunday buffet remains a draw. Grilled scallops with a coarsely pounded spice mix is one way to start, moving on to adraki lamb chops cooked in the tandoor, with pricey vegetable accompaniments and decent breads. Orange jamun cheesecake is a fusion finish. The wine list is arranged by style and has nowt below 30 quid by the bottle.

Chef/s: Prahlad Hegde. **Closed:** 25 Dec. **Meals:** main courses £17 to £28. Set L £27. Set D £51. Sat and Sun L £37 (buffet). Tasting menus £58 to £64. **Details:** 100 seats. 120 seats outside. Bar. Wheelchairs. Music.

Cambio de Tercio

Cooking score: 5
⊖ Gloucester Road, map 3
Spanish | £45
163 Old Brompton Road, Earl's Court, SW5 0LJ
Tel no: (020) 7244 8970
cambiodetercio.co.uk

'Any restaurateur would give his eye teeth for the prosperous, loyal and sophisticated clientele who pack this place seven days a week,' notes one Chelsea local who heartily applauds this Spanish high-flyer. Yes, the interconnecting rooms are slightly scruffy and the tables are too close together, but the vibe is carefree, service energetic and the food is a 'far cry from the paella and sangria clichés of folk memory'. How about stone bass tiradito with apricot tartare and pickled red onion, sweet heritage carrots with smoked aubergine purée and macadamia pesto, or caramelised oxtail with Colombian tamarillo, cabbage and potato purée? Such bold flights of fancy are delivered with consummate skill, but the kitchen also gives old faithfuls such as patatas bravas and boquerones the kind of makeover that makes them seem brand-new. The thrills continue right to the end, when the arrival of caramelised papaya with frozen yuzu-coconut ice cream and raspberry 'snow'. Cambio's 350-bin, all-Spanish wine list matches the food blow for blow.

Chef/s: Alberto Criado. **Meals:** main courses £26 to £30. Tapas £4 to £26. Tasting menu £55. **Details:** 80 seats. 6 seats outside. V menu. Bar. Music.

Charlotte's Bistro

Cooking score: 3
⊖ Turnham Green, map 1
Modern European | £35
6 Turnham Green Terrace, Chiswick, W4 1QP
Tel no: (020) 8742 3590
charlottes.co.uk

Pitched between a brasserie and a fine-dining destination, Charlotte's Bistro has much in common with its sister, Charlotte's W5 in Ealing. The setting is clean and uncluttered – think brown leather banquettes, simple wood tables and plenty of natural light – so there's nothing to distract you from the task at hand, which is an unfussy, modern European menu of bright flavours and a rollcall of familiar dishes such as beef carpaccio, charred asparagus, risotto and roasted meats. As to the rest of the food, duck rillettes with apple and pear chutney is typical of the style, preceding, say, pan-fried sea bass with crushed new potatoes, samphire and mussels. A side of dauphinois potatoes has been a good call, and for dessert, consider classics such as panna cotta with summer berries and an almond biscuit. The bar favours small-batch spirits, craft beers and natural European wines.

Chef/s: Pierre-Alain Simonin. **Meals:** set L Mon to Fri £20 (2 courses) to £25, Sat and Sun £25 (2 courses) to £30. Set D £29 (2 courses) to £35. **Details:** 80 seats. Bar. Music.

Clarke's

Cooking score: 4
⊖ Notting Hill Gate, map 6
Modern British | £50
124 Kensington Church Street, Notting Hill, W8 4BH
Tel no: (020) 7221 9225
sallyclarke.com

Since opening her Notting Hill restaurant in 1984, Sally Clarke has earned herself an MBE, had her portrait painted by Lucian Freud and staked her claim as a doyenne of artisan bread in London. You can sample her bakery's wares by calling in for breakfast, although the staff of life is also an ever-present prelude to lunch or dinner in this urbane dining room. Once famous as a champion of healthily charged California-style chargrilling, Sally's heart is now in the Mediterranean – although she's still fervently committed to all things seasonal, British and (preferably) organic. Warm purple artichoke with bottarga, lemon and puntarelle is a typically vivid starter, while mains might bring Scottish halibut dressed with a sauce of dill and Prosecco alongside monk's beard, kale sprouts and romanesco. Strong true flavours are also the key to desserts such as baked quince with quince ice cream. Meanwhile, California dreamers and Burgundy fanciers alike will find inducements on the elite, handpicked wine list.

Chef/s: Sally Clarke and Michele Lombardi. **Closed:** Sun (occasional opening; check website), 1 week Christmas, 1 week Aug, bank hols. **Meals:** main courses £28 to £33. Set L £27 (2 courses) to £33. Set D £39. **Details:** 90 seats. Bar. Wheelchairs.

Send us your review

Your feedback informs the content of the *GFG* and will be used to compile next year's reviews. To register your opinion about any restaurant listed, or a restaurant that you wish to bring to our attention, visit our website.

★ TOP 10 ★

Claude Bosi at Bibendum

Cooking score: 9
⊖ South Kensington, map 3
French | £90
Michelin House, 81 Fulham Road, South Kensington, SW3 6RD
Tel no: (020) 7581 5817
bibendum.co.uk

A year on and Claude Bosi has adjusted well to his new surroundings. The Art Deco splendour of the Bibendum building seems to have provided the chef with further motivation to demonstrate his enormous talent and the result is a real treat – modern French cuisine that is a serious contender on the international food scene. From the elegant first-floor dining room with its trademark stained-glass windows and high comfort level, to the meticulous staff led by Enrico Molino, the whole operation appears to run on castors. And as for the food, the sheer quality of it can be gauged immediately from the terrific opening salvo of canapés and amuse-bouches (highlights being the light, warm, moreish cheese gougères, and an egg shell 'en cocotte', filled with coconut cream and pea mousse). The same theme of dazzling flavours continues right across the board: a single grilled langoustine, served chilled and bathed in iced consommé, delicately complemented by smoked pike roe and silky tofu, for example, or the sweetness of crab offset by tart rhubarb jelly flecked with herbs and cardamom. Equally deft is the umami hit of a mushroom custard that accompanies a crisp-skinned fillet of sea bream, the fish given vigour thanks to tarragon, morels and an exquisitely rich sauce, and the foamy, caper-studded brown-butter sauce of a signature turbot à la grenobloise. There are hits in other departments, too: the boldness, texture and flavour in 'my mum's tripe and cuttlefish gratin' that arrives in a cast-iron dish with a cake of pig's ear and ham, and a 'sensational' rabbit with langoustine and artichoke barigoule. Taste, texture and visuals are also uppermost in clever, innovative desserts, whether a grown-up rhubarb millefeuille filled with yuzu and coconut cream, or a cep vacherin that's a surprising riff on the classic, combining crisp meringue, cream, white chocolate, banana and cep powder. There's a comprehensive job being done in the wine department: clued-up staff are on hand to guide diners through the impressive list, or to suggest matches from the by-the-glass selection.

Chef/s: Claude Bosi. **Closed:** Mon, Tue, 25 to 27 Dec, 1 to 10 Jan, bank hols. **Meals:** main courses L only £28 to £48. Set L £35 (2 courses) to £40. Set price alc D £80 (2 courses) to £100. Tasting menu £120 (6 courses). Sun L £50 (3 courses). **Details:** 45 seats. Bar. Wheelchairs. Music.

Claude's Kitchen

Cooking score: 4
⊖ Parsons Green, map 3
Modern British | £36
51 Parsons Green Lane, Parsons Green, SW6 4JA
Tel no: (020) 3813 3223
amusebouchelondon.com

When your business in the Amuse Bouche Champagne bar is concluded, climb the stairs to Claude's Kitchen, a neighbourhood resource for intimate dining with a sense of style and real heart, just over the road from Parsons Green tube station. At unclothed tables under bare bulbs, the food has an appealingly rustic quality, but looks reliably dramatic on the plate, and delivers strong, assured flavour. Stuffed squid in its ink with wild garlic, fennel and crunchy rye might kick things off, before a tranche of crumbed monkfish arrives in the company of green tomatoes, anchovies and green beans. Alternatively there might be a vigorously Indian-spiced duck dish, accompanied by smoked aubergine, leeks and a Calvados-poached pear. Lively sides include gratinated Portobello mushroom, or harissa potatoes, and it all concludes with something like passion fruit curd and vanilla cream, scented with mint. 'Questions are expected and encouraged,' the menu advises, so don't hang back. The short wine list does its job within a narrow varietal compass, with sparklers categorised under the faintly alarming heading 'Spray'. For £165, you can spray a bottle of Krug.

Chef/s: Claude Compton. **Closed:** Sun.
Meals: main courses £17 to £19. Tasting menu £55.
Details: 40 seats. No children.

★ TOP 10 ★

★ NEW ENTRY ★

Core by Clare Smyth

Cooking score: 10
⊖ Notting Hill Gate, map 6
Modern British | £75
92 Kensington Park Road, Notting Hill, W11 2PN
Tel no: (020) 3937 5086
corebyclaresmyth.com

That Clare Smyth has made a virtually seamless transition from Restaurant Gordon Ramsay (see entry) to her own establishment and maintained such an impeccably high standard is a remarkable achievement. She is, without doubt, one of the country's best chefs. Her skill has always been in packing intriguing ingredients into one composition and coaxing all into harmony. And the flavours invoked are strikingly vivid, as seen in the subtle hits of sweet and sour in a braised whole carrot topped with slow-cooked lamb and sheep's milk yoghurt or the perfectly cooked nugget of skate that arrives with Morecambe Bay shrimps in nutmeg-infused brown butter, mimicking the flavour of potted shrimps. Singling out winning dishes is difficult, but sauces are definitely a highlight. Rich and light in turn, they complement and play off ingredients of outstanding quality, be it the humble potato opener that is fast achieving cult status, where salty herring and trout roe and a velvety, caramel-sweet dulse beurre blanc add deep notes, or the tantalising combination of Sharpham spelt, morels, asparagus, and shaved Parmesan in an umami-rich morel and wild garlic juice – a spoon ensuring that every drop

This year's highlights

Elizabeth Carter, consultant editor, picks her standout dishes

A humble potato opener at **Clare Smyth's Core** teamed with salty herring and trout roe and a caramel-sweet dulse beurre blanc proved good enough to be served at Harry and Meghan's wedding.

At **Ynyshir**, Gareth Ward's mini wagyu burger is an amazing nugget of meat, crisp on the outside, tender within, and topped with pickled lettuce and a blob of sourdough mayo in place of the bread.

Birmingham's **Harborne Kitchen** gave me one of the best chicken liver parfaits I've ever had. Dotted with white chocolate and served with strawberries, macadamia nuts and shards of crisp chicken skin, the mix of umami and sweet flavours is incredible.

At Tom Brown's **Cornerstone**, a delicate fillet of plaice paired with sweet, tender lobster in a puddle of buttery paprika sauce was sublime. Elsewhere in London, **Magpie**'s 'coq au vin' is two chunks of deep-fried chicken in a thick red wine sauce offset by a red wine-pickled onion.

The strawberry ice cream sandwich at **Restaurant Nathan Outlaw** was one of my desserts of the year. At **The Small Holding** in Kent, sweet strawberries, basil ice cream, crumbly shortbread and dots of lemon cream was a winning combo.

is savoured. Desserts are handled with supreme dexterity and even minor details can be star attractions, whether a canapé of warm, fluffy Périgord truffle gougère or crispy smoked duck wing with burnt orange and spices, or a delicate chocolate tart petit four. This is serious dining, one with a high comfort level afforded by well-spaced tables and padded chairs, with slightly formal but ever so attentive service under the watchful eye of Rob Rose. It isn't easy matching wine to the myriad of flavours, so advice from the sommelier provides verbal notes to a wine list that ticks the boxes for serious intent and quality.

Chef/s: Clare Smyth. **Closed:** Sun, Mon, 24 to 26 Dec, 27 Aug. **Meals:** set L £65. Set D £75. Tasting menu £85 (5 courses) to £105. **Details:** 54 seats. V menu. Vg menu. Bar. Wheelchairs. Music. No children.

★ TOP 50 ★

Dinner by Heston Blumenthal

Cooking score: 8
⊖ Knightsbridge, map 6
British | £80
Mandarin Oriental Hyde Park, 66 Knightsbridge, Knightsbridge, SW1X 7LA
Tel no: (020) 7201 3833
dinnerbyheston.com

The culinary jewel in the Mandarin Oriental's recently polished crown exemplifies luxury dining in the capital. A restrained sense of glamour and comfort is woven into the spacious dining room overlooking Hyde Park. With its kitchen on full view through glass screens and smooth, focused service, it is far from stuffy. Dinner is Heston Blumenthal's interpretation of British food history, deftly executed by Ashley Palmer-Watts and his team, with every dish date stamped for authenticity. Meat fruit (c.1500), a staple on the menu since opening, provides an interesting textural meld of mandarin gel and chicken liver parfait but is, perhaps, more a triumph of aesthetics than flavour. Lobster and cucumber soup (c.1730) provides a more fitting grand opening, refreshing and cleansing with smoked onion and rock samphire adding body and bite in equal measure. Pease pudding works well with a hefty roast Ibérico chop, cooked on the bone, and teamed with black pudding, pickled onion and mint oil. Sweet treats include another fixture from day one – a Georgian-era tipsy cake served with spit-roasted pineapple. The wine list is big and diverse, but helpful advice is on hand whether you want just a glass or something colossally expensive.

Chef/s: Ashley Palmer-Watts and Jonny Glass. **Meals:** main courses £33 to £52. Set L £45 (3 courses). **Details:** 149 seats. Wheelchairs. Children over 4 yrs.

★ NEW ENTRY ★

Dishoom

Cooking score: 2
⊖ High Street Kensington, map 6
Indian | £30
4 Derry Street, Kensington, W8 5SE
Tel no: (020) 7420 9325
dishoom.com

The newest London venue of the Mumbai-inspired Irani-style café group, this Art Deco-styled branch is based in the former Barkers department store. The house special, mutton pepper fry, comes recommended. For main entry, see Shoreditch branch, east London.

Chef/s: Naved Nasir. **Closed:** 25 and 26 Dec, 24 Jul. **Meals:** main courses £9 to £13. **Details:** 150 seats. V menu. Vg menu. Wheelchairs. Music.

Elystan Street

Cooking score: 6
⊖ South Kensington, Sloane Square, map 3
Modern British | £70
43 Elystan Street, Chelsea, SW3 3NT
Tel no: (020) 7628 5005
elystanstreet.com

Opening in 2016 under distinguished new management, Elystan Street is the latest episode in the illustrious careers of restaurateur Rebecca Mascarenhas and super-chef Philip Howard. First-timers may need a little while to find it, tucked away in Chelsea's hinterland as it is, but the reward is a fresh, elegant, wood-toned space with café-style tables and an agreeable air of informality. The kitchen brings novelty and assured technique to modern menus that might open with a complicated tartare of langoustines, scallops, sea bream and salmon, with turnips, apple and lovage, before moving on to peppered ribeye and glazed short rib with bacon and stout jam, potato galettes and chanterelles, or magnificent veal sweetbreads with girolles. Desserts try variations on classic themes, fashioning cheesecake from Brillat-Savarin, a tatin from pears, or smashing up a brownie, layering it in chocolate foam and pairing with hazelnut ice cream. An enterprising drinks list might offer a rhubarb and vanilla sour to start, before a parade of distinctive wines by the glass and carafe.

Chef/s: Philip Howard and Toby Burrowes. **Closed:** 25 and 26 Dec, 1 Jan. **Meals:** main courses £19 to £46. Set L £35 (2 courses) to £43. Set D £65. Sun L £50. **Details:** 64 seats. Wheelchairs.

Enoteca Turi

Cooking score: 4
⊖ Sloane Square, map 3
Italian | £48
87 Pimlico Road, Chelsea, SW1W 8PH
Tel no: (020) 7730 3663
enotecaturi.com

Having earned his stripes as sommelier and maître d' at The Connaught, Giuseppe Turi later become the toast of Putney before moving his Enoteca to its current home in Belgravia. The postcode may have changed, but the concept remains the same – a marriage of forthright, ingredients-led Italian cooking with superlative wines from all corners of the geographical 'boot'. Cut-outs of the regions decorate the gold-painted brick-walled dining room – a clean-lined contemporary backdrop for cooking that lifts the traditions of 'cucina rustica' to sophisticated new heights. Pasta is one of the benchmarks (perhaps buckwheat pizzoccheri with Swiss chard, potato, cabbage and a fonduta of Bitto cheese). Elsewhere, you might find garlicky slow-cooked rabbit with chickpea and pickle salad alongside cipollata (Umbrian 'onion soup') and radichetta (aka asparagus chicory). Moving on to dolci, there are equally pleasurable confections such as pistachio tiramisu or Amalfi lemon sponge with strawberry salad. Enoteca's crowning glory is, of course, its magisterial wine list – a generously priced tribute to the diversity of Italian viticulture, with famous labels, oddball discoveries and ample pickings by the glass.

Chef/s: Massimo Tagliaferri. **Closed:** Sun, 25 and 26 Dec, 1 Jan. **Meals:** main courses £19 to £32. Set L £25 (2 courses) to £29. **Details:** 70 seats. 8 seats outside.

The Five Fields

Cooking score: 6
⊖ Sloane Square, map 3
Modern British | £75
8-9 Blacklands Terrace, Chelsea, SW3 2SP
Tel no: (020) 7838 1082
fivefieldsrestaurant.com
£5 OFF

Rarely is a restaurant so perfectly in tune with its neighbourhood, in this case a discreet and prosperous part of Chelsea. There are no gimmicks here, just top-class cooking with every accompanying detail – from linen and cutlery to playful design and flattering lighting – just right. No wonder the well-heeled customers love it; there's a real sense of occasion. On the plate you'll find dots, smears, flowers, herbs and even gold leaf, but Taylor Bonnyman's workmanship is undeniably first class, whether in an appetiser of chicken teriyaki with cucumber, finger lime and bonito hollandaise, or a starter of cabbage, oxtail, oyster and dill. Though breaking new ground is not Bonnyman's game, his cooking shows off superlative produce and everything is produced with great assurance, from a visually dramatic venison with morels, celeriac, oak moss and cooked sorrel to pigeon flavoured with za'atar and dressed with hop shoots and lemony miner's lettuce. Eye-catching desserts include rhubarb with lime and pepper, and cheesecake freshened with mango and pineapple. To drink, there's a first-class wine list, but modest selection by the glass.

Chef/s: Taylor Bonnyman and Marguerite Keogh. **Closed:** Sat, Sun, Christmas to first 2 weeks Jan, 2 weeks Aug, bank hols. **Meals:** set D £65 (2 courses) to £75. Tasting menu £90 (8 courses). **Details:** 35 seats. V menu. Bar. Music. Children over 12 yrs.

The Goring

Cooking score: 5
⊖ Victoria, map 3
Modern British | £60
15 Beeston Place, Belgravia, SW1W 0JW
Tel no: (020) 7396 9000
thegoring.com

Pitching up here in the thrashing rain of a British August, a couple found themselves securely and courteously looked after through a perfectly British lunch of pea and ham soup, steak and kidney pie, and black fig trifle. The Goring, in contrast to most other five-star hotels in London, is not corporately owned, and so manages to deliver a personal experience from top to bottom. Shay Cooper sources from end to end and side to side of the British Isles for materials that are treated with respect and a certain haute cuisine classicism, but there are imaginative touches aplenty. The Orkney scallop comes with kedgeree, shiso and lime, before Kentish salt marsh lamb arrives in the company of a braised lamb and haggis bun, shallot purée and a tapenade of seaweed. Cornish cod is more traditionally attired in Jersey Royals, asparagus and peas with a smooth velouté of cockles and bacon. Trolley presentations of roasts, desserts and cheeses add to the theatre in a spacious, elegant dining room. Bottle prices on the magnificent wine list open at £33.

Chef/s: Shay Cooper. **Meals:** set L £52 (3 courses). Set D £64 (3 courses). Sun L £58 (3 courses). **Details:** 70 seats. 30 seats outside. V menu. Bar. Wheelchairs. Parking.

Harwood Arms

Cooking score: 5
⊖ Fulham Broadway, map 3
British | £49
Walham Grove, Fulham, SW6 1QP
Tel no: (020) 7386 1847
harwoodarms.com

Sally Abé's menu at the Harwood Arms, a rejuvenated boozer in a smart residential street, reads as if an eccentric English aristo has taken her on as private cook and told her to help herself to anything she needs from the estate. A springtime menu proffers wood pigeon and prune faggots with onion cream and thyme; roast fallow deer with baked crapaudine beetroot, smoked bone marrow and walnut; and Eccles cake with goat's milk ice cream. The posh pub's culinary concerns can be traced to its founders, Mike Robinson and The Ledbury's Brett Graham, champions of game and wild food. The rustic feel of the restaurant – wooden tables, blackboard menus, mix-and-match chairs – suits it to a T. Set-price menus are supplemented by Sunday roasts and the all-important venison Scotch egg. Serious wines suit serious food: Burgundy, Bordeaux and Rioja are well represented.

Chef/s: Sally Abé. **Closed:** 24 to 26 Dec. **Meals:** set L £25 (2 courses) to £30. Set D £40 (2 courses) to £49. Sun L £49. **Details:** 50 seats. Bar. Wheelchairs. Music.

Hawksmoor Knightsbridge

Cooking score: 3
⊖ Knightsbridge, South Kensington, map 3
British | £60
3 Yeoman's Row, Knightsbridge, SW3 2AL
Tel no: (020) 7590 9290
thehawksmoor.com

The Hawksmoor group, six-strong in London (and with outposts in Manchester and Edinburgh) has sought out sites of architectural and historical interest for its new generation British steakhouses. Wow factor matters when one's forking out for beef:

Hawksmoor's grass-fed, dry-aged variety does not come cheap. The menu is a choose-your-own-adventure offering of whopping steaks, sides and sauces including such signatures as textbook triple-cooked chips, Doddington Caesar salad, bone-marrow gravy and anchovy hollandaise. At inspection, Knightsbridge showed Hawksmoor on its best behaviour, all fancy wines and flash ingredients in wood-panelled surrounds – there's even gold leaf on the otherwise rather inelegant 'Ambassador's Reception' chocolate hazelnut dessert. Rock oysters had an expressive flavour beneath their Vietnamese dressing, and crab on toast was a generous hillock with a nifty little watercress salad. Sadly a sriracha lobster roll lacked punch. Sunday roasts and express menus represent good value in general, but above all in SW3. Waiting staff, clad in civvies, ooze personality. Clearly, Hawksmoor values its independent spirit even as it grows.

Chef/s: Flamur Zeka. **Closed:** 25 and 26 Dec. **Meals:** main courses £12 to £55. Set L and D £25 (2 courses) to £28. Sun L £21. **Details:** 130 seats. Bar. Music.

★ TOP 50 ★

Hedone

Cooking score: 7
⊖ Chiswick Park, map 1
Modern European | £95
301-303 Chiswick High Road, Chiswick, W4 4HH
Tel no: (020) 8747 0377
hedonerestaurant.com

With very little signage outside and a heavy door and full curtain to negotiate to gain access, there are unlikely to be diners who eat here on a whim – a visit here is booked and eagerly anticipated. It's a small space: some choose to sit at a stool in front of the open-plan kitchen; those who want to talk are better placed in the comfortable Nordic-style dining area. The menu, either a seven- or ten-course taster, with added canapés and pre-desserts, becomes an astonishingly long and complex journey of taste and texture. It pays to give careful attention to the announcement of each dish, even to take notes – diners are given no written copy of what they eat even as they leave, making moments of culinary genius too ephemeral. The lack of menu allows the kitchen to cook for each table individually, and to use the best produce available at any time, but some of the best dishes crop up with regularity: superb sourdough bread (happily diners are given a loaf to take home with them); 'fish and chip', comprising a square potato crisp wrapped around monkfish, accompanied by a gorgeous mayonnaise garnished with chopped cornichon and caper as a mix-your-own tartare sauce; gently poached crab, served with a hazelnut mayonnaise, with a sprinkling of finger lime caviar giving it an unexpected lift. Given the lack of information, the wine matching offered seems a sensible way to order – go off-piste and the bill can shoot up.

Chef/s: Mikael Jonsson. **Closed:** Sun, Mon. **Meals:** tasting menu £95 to £135. **Details:** 20 seats.

Hereford Road

Cooking score: 3
⊖ Bayswater, map 6
British | £28
3 Hereford Road, Notting Hill, W2 4AB
Tel no: (020) 7727 1144
herefordroad.org

The abstract work on one wall of Tom Pemberton's split-level Notting Hill eatery looks a lot like a series of exclamation points, which could well be intended to echo the emphatic flavours and good-humoured, straightforward approach of his kitchen. Meat is very much the order of the day, with mains that run a gamut from Blythburgh pork chops and grilled onglets to a seasonal offering of red-legged partridge with lentils and butternut squash. Everything is timed to a nicety, with succulence and sharply etched seasoning the watchwords, and you might prepare with a bowl of steamed cockles in cider and thyme, or with a winter warmer of beef broth and bone marrow. Fortifying puddings such as sticky date or rhubarb crumble fill any remaining gaps, or else opt for the single cheese, perhaps Colston Bassett Stilton with fennel biscuits. The short wine list is evenly split between reds and whites, with house selections from £24.50.

Chef/s: Tom Pemberton. **Closed:** 23 Dec to 4 Jan. **Meals:** main courses £14 to £17. Set L £14 (2 courses) to £16. **Details:** 53 seats. 10 seats outside. Wheelchairs.

Hunan

Cooking score: 3
⊖ Sloane Square, map 3
Chinese | £68
51 Pimlico Road, Chelsea, SW1W 8NE
Tel no: (020) 7730 5712
hunanlondon.com

Michael Peng's Hunan is not like most Chinese restaurants, which may explain why this modest (but highly esteemed) destination has been sailing quietly under the radar since 1982. What sets it apart is the fact that there's no menu: simply spell out your preferences, highlight any no-go ingredients and indicate your chilli tolerance before allowing the kitchen to work its magic. In return, you can expect a bespoke banquet of up to 18 little dishes, normally presented in clusters of three: stir-fried pig's kidney with preserved vegetables; spicy cod tongue; cuttlefish and aubergine salad, for example. Specialities from Hunan do feature on the menu, but the kitchen's geographical remit is much broader than that, which is why you might also be served Shanghai dumplings, double-cooked crispy lamb and steamed sea bass with sesame, ginger and onion dressing (a Cantonese classic). To finish, diners celebrating the Chinese New Year can expect sticky rice cakes with candied melon. The wine list is a true oenophile marvel, studiously compiled, trustworthy and fascinating in every department.

Chef/s: Mr Peng. **Closed:** Sun, 2 weeks Christmas, bank hols. **Meals:** set L £46 (12 courses). Set D £68 (18 courses). **Details:** 44 seats. V menu. Vg menu.

Indian Zing

Cooking score: 2
⊖ Ravenscourt Park, map 1
Indian | £35
236 King Street, Hammersmith, W6 0RF
Tel no: (020) 8748 5959
indian-zing.co.uk

£5 OFF

Manoj Vasaikar opened on King Street in 2005 and has been doing a roaring trade ever since, delivering Indian food that is a cut above and has genuine – what's the word? – zing. The neutral decor is run through with vivid colours from Indian artworks and there's a small covered terrace out back. The menu delivers distinctive courses that match the promise of their descriptions. Start with a vegetable-filled samosa with tamarind relish, spicy chicken kebab with artichokes and tomato relish, or lamb salli rasilla (lamb mince, fresh fenugreek and Indian cottage cheese). Among main courses, Keralan fish stew is full of the flavours of the south of the Subcontinent, and chicken makhani has a rich, fresh and piquant sauce. For dessert, dried apricots get the tandoor treatment, flavoured with Cointreau, cinnamon and cardamom. The annotated wine list opens at £20.

Chef/s: Manoj Vasaikar. **Meals:** main courses £11 to £29. Set L £16 (2 courses) to £19. Sun L £16 (2 courses) to £19. **Details:** 50 seats. 10 seats outside. Wheelchairs. Music.

Kitchen W8

Cooking score: 5
⊖ High Street Kensington, map 6
Modern European | £48
11-13 Abingdon Road, Kensington, W8 6AH
Tel no: (020) 7937 0120
kitchenw8.com

Located on a quiet road just off Kensington's high street, Philip Howard and Rebecca Mascarenhas' elegant restaurant is well-patronised by local residents and businesses. The decor, with its olive green upholstery, retro mirrors and crisp table linen is understated, and Mark Kempson's modern European menu is characterised by clean flavours and seasonal ingredients. At a spring meal, a starter of lamb raviolo was especially impressive for its supporting cast of buttery girolles, sweet garden peas and zesty mint dressing. Main courses proved to be equally considered, with a precision-roasted chicken breast harmonised with wild garlic cream and earthy mousseron mushrooms. Desserts, although simple, are finely tuned. A soft pistachio sponge and creamy almond ice provided a marvellous foil to the floral flavour of Gariguette strawberries. Dining here isn't cheap, but the set lunchtime menu is splendid value at under £30 for three courses, and there's a generous listing of New and Old World wines served by the glass and carafe. Service is attentive yet unobtrusive.

Chef/s: Mark Kempson. **Closed:** 24 to 26 Dec, bank hols. **Meals:** main courses £25 to £30. Set L £25 (2 courses) to £28. Set D £27 (2 courses) to £30. Sun L £39. Tasting menu £75. **Details:** 70 seats. Wheelchairs.

Launceston Place

Cooking score: 5
⊖ Gloucester Road, map 3
Modern European | £60
1a Launceston Place, South Kensington, W8 5RL
Tel no: (020) 7937 6912
launcestonplace-restaurant.co.uk

Having wowed edgy east London at the short-lived Woodford (where he was the Guide's *Chef to Watch*), impressively tattooed Ben Murphy now finds himself cooking for the well-to-do residents of South Ken. Famously lauded as one of Princess Diana's local favourites, Launceston Place has a smooth, subdued look with muted grey colour schemes setting the tone in its various dining rooms – although the cooking is as bold as brass, clever, fashion-conscious and playful. Whether you plump for the carte or the tasting menu, expect terse descriptions and emoji-style pictorial clues alongside each dish: a pink-faced porker signals presa Ibérica with carrot and pork neck; a smiley bunny heralds rabbit with basil and squid. Such epigrams conceal a huge amount of detailing and witty transformation – just consider a rebooted carbonara involving celeriac and silky lardo or a surprising alliance of scallop, artichoke and vanilla. At the other end of the scale, desserts might bring an equally unexpected concoction involving violet, coffee and mango. By contrast, the cosmopolitan wine list is deeply serious – and seriously pricey.

Chef/s: Ben Murphy. **Closed:** Mon, 25 to 28 Dec. **Meals:** set L £23 (2 courses) to £28. Set D £55 (2 courses) to £60. Pre-theatre menu £30. Sun L £35. Tasting menu £79 (8 courses). **Details:** 50 seats. V menu. Bar. Wheelchairs. Music.

★ TOP 50 ★

The Ledbury

Cooking score: 8
⊖ Notting Hill Gate, Westbourne Park, map 6
Modern British | £125
127 Ledbury Road, Notting Hill, W11 2AQ
Tel no: (020) 7792 9090
theledbury.com

If the location in deepest Notting Hill might lead first-timers to expect laid-back waiting staff sashaying about to the throb of a permanent mix tape, they should probably think again. The scene is one of smoothly geared professionalism, of a stripe that wouldn't let down a five-star West End hotel, a marvel to see when the place is in full flow, and yet managed with a personal touch throughout. The diner who discreetly asked for his menu to be signed, and was promptly whisked backstage to be given a tutorial by Brett Graham in the fabled hen of the woods dish was left in awe. You let the mushroom sit in kombu dashi, then parboil it, then barbecue it, wrap it in wafer-thin aged pork lardo and dress it with potato emulsion and rosemary oil. Yes, Graham's cooking is as technically intricate and thought-provoking as that sounds but the results, confirmed that visitor, are 'simply stunning'. Other dishes have become fixtures on the tasting menus, the white beetroot baked in clay, seasoned with caviar salt and served with smoked eel among them. Layers of resonance imbue every offering, though, as when concentrated bonito butter adds sharp focus to Cornish monkfish, or when the game season turns up roast snipe with rhubarb. That mushroom preparation is the preferred accompaniment to New Forest sika deer, its pinkly succulent flesh an object lesson in acutely sensitive meat cookery, while the outrider for the pair of desserts might be passion fruit curd with Sauternes and olive oil. Vegetarian dishes lack nothing in innovative heft, and to cap it all, there is a wine list to write home about. Glass selections embrace Canberra Riesling, Burgenland rosé and Georgian Saperavi, while the bottles head off into Elysian viticultural pastures such as the Strathbogie Ranges (for a Shiraz called Ladies Who Shoot Their Lunch). Bottles start at £35.

Chef/s: Brett Graham and Greg Austin. **Closed:** 24 to 27 Dec, Aug bank hol. **Meals:** set L £80. Set price alc L and D £125 (4 courses). Tasting menu £150 (8 courses). **Details:** 56 seats. V menu. Vg menu. Wheelchairs. Children over 12 yrs.

★ TOP 50 ★

Marcus

Cooking score: 8

⊖ Hyde Park Corner, Knightsbridge, map 6

Modern European | £85

The Berkeley, Wilton Place, Belgravia, SW1X 7RL

Tel no: (020) 7235 1200

marcusrestaurant.com

The subtle gleam from polished wood and rich leather induces a feeling of wellbeing in this elegant, cosseted dining room, especially when you factor in the comfortable chairs, fine linen and generous elbow room. Mark and Shauna Froydenlund have settled into their roles as joint chef patrons, reinterpreting Marcus Wareing's intricately worked modern European style with a span of contemporary references from 'very good' sourdough crumpets with cockle butter and 'really lovely' Jersey Royals with trompette mushrooms and Tunworth custard, to a standout halibut with pickled egg, clams and monk's beard. Excellent raw materials are cooked with precision timing, and the seasonal menus offer an intriguing array of dishes: note the pheasant egg with short-rib ragù, wild garlic and asparagus, and the Cornish turbot with artichoke, courgette and mint that were the highlights of a spring meal for one reader. Or the scallop tartare with shellfish bisque and coriander, which preceded Cumbrian rose veal neck with pea, morel and miso that left another diner equally impressed. Salted milk chocolate aero with sorrel and clementine is an indulgent finale. Prices reflect the postcode and the five-star deluxe hotel setting, but with 'staff doing a fantastic job of making us feel special' and a more gently priced five-course lunch menu, this 'smart and glamorous setting' is definitely the place for an old-fashioned special occasion. The massive wine list deals in classic names from France and around the globe, and is best experienced by one of the selected wine flights – although the sommelier's advice is worth taking.

Chef/s: Mark and Shauna Froydenlund. **Closed:** Sun. **Meals:** set L £55. Set D £65 to £85. Tasting menu £105 (5 courses) to £120. **Details:** 80 seats. Bar. Wheelchairs. Parking. Children over 8 yrs.

Medlar

Cooking score: 5

⊖ Sloane Square, Fulham Broadway, map 3

Modern European | £60

438 King's Road, Chelsea, SW10 0LJ

Tel no: (020) 7349 1900

medlarrestaurant.co.uk

The location at the leafier end of the King's Road makes Joe Mercer Nairne's neighbourhood west Londoner a firm favourite with locals, who know their way sufficiently around the menu to be disapproving of the untoward vanishing of favoured dishes. A recent refurbishment has added artificial trees, and those pavement tables in the sunshine remain a lure. Modern

European dishes with strong appeal are the principal business, territory that covers the long-running crab raviolo in bisque with samphire, brown shrimps and leek fondue, and mains such as roast lamb and tongue with a tartlet of Portobellos and Reblochon, as well as artichokes and onion purée, or grilled turbot in Japanese livery, with shimejis, dashi broth and baby squid, greened up with monk's beard and sea kale. A side of triple-cooked chips and béarnaise rounds out the spread, but allow space for a serving of rhubarb with pistachio cake, Greek yoghurt and orange zest. An unexpectedly resourceful wine list opens at £28, and covers a lot of global vineyard land, including mature Médoc claret and Vega Sicilia by the Coravin glass.

Chef/s: Joe Mercer Nairne. **Closed:** Mon. **Meals:** set L £30 (2 courses) to £35. Set D £45 (2 courses) to £53. Sun L £35. Tasting menu £60 (5 courses) to £70. **Details:** 90 seats. 6 seats outside. Music.

Ognisko

Cooking score: 3
⊖ South Kensington, map 6
Polish | £30
55 Exhibition Road, South Kensington, SW7 2PG
Tel no: (020) 7589 0101
ogniskorestaurant.co.uk

Founded in 1939, Ognisko Polski (Polish Hearth Club) is one of the oldest Polish clubs in London. It now occupies a rather grand, colonnaded Victorian townhouse and its elegant ground-floor restaurant and cocktail bar pay homage to the winter-warming world of Polish cuisine and the head-spinning pleasures of vodka. Old school and charming, this is the place to come for marinated herring blinis, excellent pierogi – dumplings filled with cheese, potato and onion – or a hot smoked salmon salad with beetroot, watercress and horseradish dressing. Pork schnitzel (with sautéed potatoes, capers, anchovies and fried egg) is 'just as it should be', as is roast hake with mushrooms, leeks and kasza (roast buckwheat groats). The set lunch is a bargain, and a gazebo-covered outdoor terrace is particular appealing on sunny days. Just about every Polish vodka imaginable waits to be sampled; alternatively look to the imaginative cocktails, or wines from £19.50.

Chef/s: Jarek Mlynarczyk. **Meals:** main courses £13 to £20. Set L and early D £19 (2 courses) to £23. **Details:** 80 seats. 70 seats outside. Bar.

108 Garage

Cooking score: 6
⊖ Westbourne Park, map 1
Modern British | £40
108 Golborne Road, Notting Hill, W10 5PS
Tel no: (020) 8969 3769
108garage.com

Packing a major punch on the Golborne Road, Luca Longobardi and Chris Denney's high-achieving restaurant offers some exciting contemporary cooking. The dining room (and it really was once a garage) follows current fashion: open kitchen, hard surfaces (wall, floor, tables, chairs) with natural light from the shop-front windows. Loyal regulars are voluble in their support for the seasonally driven plates. For one, it was the surprising delicacy and sweetness of scallop ceviche topped with thinly sliced apple and dill that impressed. For another, the highlight was salt-baked celeriac with Einstok pale ale rarebit. Elsewhere, visitors have praised the vivid flavours in a dish of lamb, onion and capers, or sea bass with monk's beard and mussel korma, and everybody loves the warm sourdough served with chicken liver parfait, cod's roe taramasalata and seaweed butter. Desserts are a standout, especially a beautifully presented pear poached in whey and served with chervil sorbet and buttermilk ice cream, or the popular chocolate crémeux and miso goat's yoghurt. Cocktails are good and the short, modern wine list has been chosen to match the food.

Chef/s: Chris Denney. **Closed:** Sun, Mon. **Meals:** main courses £13 to £27. Set L £55 (7 courses). Tasting menu £65 (7 courses). **Details:** 38 seats. 4 seats outside. Wheelchairs. Music.

Outlaw's at the Capital

Cooking score: 6
⊖ Knightsbridge, map 6
Seafood | £69
Capital Hotel, 22-24 Basil Street,
Knightsbridge, SW3 1AT
Tel no: (020) 7591 1202
capitalhotel.co.uk

A small discreet dining room, which makes up in elegance what it lacks in glitz, is the home of an outpost of Nathan Outlaw's slowly expanding empire, aptly housed in The Capital Hotel. Canny Londoners flock here, gratefully aware of the 12-hour round trip to the Cornwall mothership, Restaurant Nathan Outlaw (see entry) they are saving themselves. The keen-eyed can watch the kitchen at work through a small window but most are more concerned with what's in front of them. Our inspection meal took in the good-value set lunch and dishes from the à la carte; Andrew Sawyer and his team delivered an exceptionally tender, slow-cooked octopus, crisped outside and set in a pool of deep-green clear chervil sauce, a dollop of almond bread sauce bringing contrasting texture, while grape slices added bursts of sweetness. Equally impressive was megrim sole, one fillet fried in breadcrumbs green with herbs, the other simply poached and served on a warm version of a tartare sauce, with an accompanying bowl of Jersey Royals. Fish dominates, but meat is handled equally well – we enjoyed duck scrumpet with pickled chicory and a parsley and anchovy mayonnaise, as well as ewe's curd dumpling with peas, beans and pistachio. For dessert, a beautifully presented honey ice cream sandwich with Champagne strawberry sorbet. The wine list is truly international.

Chef/s: Andrew Sawyer. **Closed:** Sun. **Meals:** set L £33 (2 courses) to £39. Set D £55 (2 courses) to £69. Tasting menu £95. **Details:** 32 seats. Bar. Music. Parking.

Pétrus

Cooking score: 6
⊖ Knightsbridge, map 6
Modern French | £85
1 Kinnerton Street, Knightsbridge, SW1X 8EA
Tel no: (020) 7592 1609
gordonramsay.com

There's no mistaking the principal focus of Pétrus. A glass-fronted wine room occupies central pride of place, to the extent that tables look a little as though they are courteously making space for it. Neutral tones and blinded windows contribute to the air of calm refinement, while the kitchen turns out modern French cooking in the Ramsay manner, in which elements of a dish build up in subtle potency to create one unforgettable impression after another. Even a mixture of messages such as seared curried scallop with braised kombu and bacon in egg sabayon is a masterpiece of controlled intensity, while roast loin of fallow deer with its bone marrow acquires productive sour and earthy notes from pickled blackberries and salt-baked beetroot. A pairing of Gigha halibut and cuttlefish in bouillabaisse is the last word in bracing sea-freshness, with fennel and rouille adding depth. Piercing sorbets light up the dessert repertoire: cherry with kirsch mousse, coconut and lime with passion fruit soufflé. The deeply traditional French-led wine list opens with small glasses from £8.

Chef/s: James 'Jocky' Petrie. **Closed:** 26 to 28 Dec. **Meals:** set L £35 (2 courses) to £45. Set D £65 (2 courses) to £85. Tasting menu £110 (8 courses). **Details:** 55 seats. Wheelchairs. Music.

Get social

Follow us on social media for the latest news, chef interviews and more.
Twitter: @GoodFoodGuideUK
Facebook: TheGoodFoodGuide

Popeseye Steak House

Cooking score: 1
⊖ Olympia, map 3
British | £35
108 Blythe Road, Olympia, W14 0HD
Tel no: (020) 7610 4578
popeseye.com
£5 OFF

Steak, the whole steak and nothing but the steak... that's the message at Popeseye, a highly individual eatery named after a Scottish term for rump steak. Since 1995, Ian Hutchinson has been going his own way, offering a seductively simple menu of five different cuts, all served with sauces, chips and an optional salad. The meat is from grass-fed Aberdeen Angus herds, aged for a minimum 28 days and chargrilled without recourse to oil or the salt cellar. The result is unadulterated red-blooded joy. That's it – apart from homemade puddings, some farmhouse cheese and a cluster of beefy red wines. Cash only. Branches in Putney and Highgate Hill.
Chef/s: Ian Hutchinson. **Closed:** Sun. **Meals:** steaks £12 to £65. **Details:** 34 seats. Wheelchairs.

Portobello Ristorante Pizzeria

Cooking score: 2
⊖ Notting Hill Gate, map 6
Italian | £33
7 Ladbroke Road, Notting Hill, W11 3PA
Tel no: (020) 7221 1373
portobellolondon.co.uk
£5 OFF

For nigh on 10 years, Portobello Ristorante has been a destination address for appreciative locals. Those in the know recommend bagging tables in the canopied and heated all-weather front terrace, preferring it to the close-packed dining room inside. There's skill in the kitchen, though it delivers straightforward and comforting cooking rather than culinary fireworks, perhaps huge wood-fired Neapolitan pizzas and mighty trattoria staples such as parmigiana di melanzane and saltimbocca alla romana, backed up by the likes of Parma ham with creamy burrata, and grilled corn-fed baby chicken with roast potatoes. Fish continues to be a strength, with praise this year for stone-baked fillets of sea bass with cherry tomatoes, carrots, celery, garlic, chilli and olive oil. When it comes to dessert, torta caprese (chocolate and almond cake) with vanilla ice cream is hard to trump. The likeable wine list canters through the Italian regions offering plenty of interesting stuff from £23.
Chef/s: Gazmir Tefa. **Closed:** 25 Dec, 1 Jan, Easter, Aug bank hol. **Meals:** main courses £18 to £26. Set L £15 (2 courses). **Details:** 60 seats. 30 seats outside. Music.

Rabbit

Cooking score: 1
⊖ Sloane Square, map 3
Modern British | £28
172 King's Road, Chelsea, SW3 4UP
Tel no: (020) 3750 0172
rabbit-restaurant.com

Four years on, Oliver and Richard Gladwin's charmingly *rus in urbe* Chelsea eatery continues to enjoy loyal support. The cooking, a tribute to great British produce (with much from the Gladwins' own farm in West Sussex), plays off the seasons via a series of small sharing plates, moving from winter hits of partridge breast with salsify, pear, winter purslane and pearl barley to spring vegetable pappardelle with wild garlic and sunflower seed pesto. There's been praise, too, for malt-braised pig's cheeks with elderflower gel, spinach, nutmeg and crackling, and crunchy honeycomb with mascarpone and tarragon sugar deserves a mention. Reasonable prices extend to the mainly European wine list.
Chef/s: Richard Lovemore. **Closed:** 24 Dec to 2 Jan, bank hols, Easter Sun. **Meals:** small plates £5 to £15. Set L and D £15 (2 courses) to £20. Tasting menu £42 (7 courses). **Details:** 64 seats. Vg menu. Wheelchairs. Music.

★ TOP 10 ★

Restaurant Gordon Ramsay

Cooking score: 9
⊖ Sloane Square, map 3
French | £120
68 Royal Hospital Road, Chelsea, SW3 4HP
Tel no: (020) 7352 4441
gordonramsayrestaurants.com

Long before it turned 20 in 2018, Gordon Ramsay's flagship restaurant had achieved classic status. Though it boasts the attributes of many larger places, its small scale and relative intimacy have always been part of its appeal. Without fireworks of design or ornament, the dining room lays out its stall clearly: a light space devoted to the service of food in supreme comfort. In particular, Jean-Claude Breton, who heads front of house, has set the bar for how things should be done at this level. And Matt Abé, now firmly ensconced in a brand-new kitchen, is following suit. Though you can still find a few Gordon Ramsay classics on the menu (lobster ravioli, for example), Abé's approach is to be lavish with punctiliously cared-for ingredients, and to outfit each dish sparingly. A beautiful illustration is the Herdwick lamb – supernaturally tender cuts of loin and rack, with slow-cooked shank, belly and shoulder – served with a simple but vibrant spring vegetable navarin. Or take a starter of Jérôme Galis green asparagus teamed with wild garlic and juicy morels, the whole given a bit of punch from dots of smokey confit egg yolk. And in a strikingly presented dish of Cornish brown crab, bitter sweet with almond and almond foam, slight acidity from elderflower and served with mini English muffins, the chef reveals a knack for combining flavours that seem to get more interesting as you go along. Then there is Dover sole, very sweet and pure, enlivened with shiso, razor clams, celtuce and shiitake, which promises – and delivers – a lightness entirely befitting of a springtime lunch. As for desserts, soufflés are a certified hit, but there's admiration, too, for a take on pavlova with Gariguette and wild strawberries, Sarawak pepper and lemon verbena. The rest of the meal – bread, sensational cheese gougères, a springtime-sweet amuse-bouche of fresh peas in a pool of intense, green pea velouté, or some rather good, nutty milk-salted chocolate to take away – all march in unison. A wine list of surpassing finesse accords France its due, but is diligent elsewhere, too. All handled with great insight by head sommelier James Lloyd, whether by the wine flight, glass or bottle.

Chef/s: Matt Abé. **Closed:** Sun, Mon. **Meals:** set L £70. Set D £120. Tasting menu £155 to £185. **Details:** 42 seats. V menu. Wheelchairs.

Restaurant Marianne

new chef/no score
⊖ Royal Oak, map 6
Modern European | £100
104a Chepstow Road, Notting Hill, W2 5QS
Tel no: (020) 3675 7750
mariannerestaurant.com
£5 OFF

Diminutive, delightful and delicious, this tucked-away Notting Hill spot with just five tables gathered in a pale-toned dining room is a place that firmly ticks the 'intimate' and 'neighbourhood' boxes. The appropriately compact kitchen – you can peep in through a narrow window, past a defensive-looking row of kitchen knives – is a place where the few chefs move around each other with practised grace and calm. We learned of the departure of Marianne Lumb as the Guide was going to press; she is to be replaced by her right-hand man, Myles Strotton. We are told he'll continue with the style regulars have come to love, so expect contemporary, fresh dishes with luxury ingredients at their core. Ceps, summer truffles, native lobster, turbot, scallops and wagyu beef pop up on a daily changing set menu – five courses at lunch, six at dinner, plus a few extras, of course. Previously there has been praise for an amuse-bouche that combines sticky candied pecans with parsnip foam and tart apple, a dish of Cerney Ash cheese, tomato gelée, turnip, lemon sorrel and smoked eel, and a piece of

Gloucestershire muntjac on 'perfect' cavolo nero with a pear purée and Szechuan pepper. Sommelier Roberto della Pietra remains front of house, and his superbly curated, compact wine list offers bottles from £40.

Chef/s: Myles Strotton. **Closed:** Mon, 22 Dec to 7 Jan, 20 Aug to 3 Sept. **Meals:** tasting menu L £95, D £110. **Details:** 14 seats. Music. Children over 12 yrs.

Restaurant Michael Nadra

Cooking score: 3
⊖ Turnham Green, map 1
Modern European | £39
6-8 Elliott Road, Chiswick, W4 1PE
Tel no: (020) 8742 0766
restaurant-michaelnadra.co.uk

A smart new refurb at the beginning of 2018 has refreshed the Chiswick sister of Michael Nadra's Primrose Hill venue (see entry). Stefano Aiani takes charge here of interpreting the house style of modern Eurasian cooking with innovative flourishes, bold presentations and assured impact. A six-course tasting menu is on hand to test the kitchen's mettle, alongside some daring liquid pairings (luxuriously silky U'Luvka vodka from Poland is served with the bouquet of sorbets), but there are interesting propositions all over the standard carte, too. The on-trend Japanese approach to seafood produces tuna sashimi dressed in yuzu and soy with tempura soft-shell crab on purple shiso, as prelude to roasted mallard breast with a salad of confit leg, accompanied by liver pâté crostini, freekeh, pomegranate and fondant sweet potato in Madeira jus. Desserts take a more traditional tack for vanilla cheesecake with berry compôte, or treacle tart with clotted cream. A wine list full of good things at manageable prices runs from half-bottle carafes of Languedoc blends from £13, all the way to the aristocracy of France and Tuscany.

Chef/s: Michael Nadra and Stefano Aiani. **Closed:** Mon, 24 to 28 Dec. **Meals:** set L £23 (2 courses) to £28. Set D £33 (2 courses) to £39. Tasting menu L £50, D £60 (6 courses). **Details:** 50 seats. Music.

The River Café

Cooking score: 5
⊖ Hammersmith, map 1
Italian | £90
Thames Wharf, Rainville Road, Hammersmith, W6 9HA
Tel no: (020) 7386 4200
rivercafe.co.uk

As it embarks on its fourth decade of operations, the River Café still draws the hordes to Hammersmith, many of them from much further afield than London. With its terrace on the Thames, and the light-filled interior space, it's pre-eminently a venue for lunches and summer evenings, but the implicit understanding of the virtues of straightforward Italian food are what have kept it popular in all seasons. Fixed-price lunch menus are a good way in for the newcomer, running the range in winter from chargrilled squid with rocket and red chilli, via Gorgonzola polenta, to the majesty of wild sea bass roasted with fennel, lemon zest and Pinot Bianco, then dressed with spinach. The principal carte ups the ante for whole wood-roasted Anjou pigeon with bruschetta and green beans, sauced in Allegrini's Valpolicella. At dessert, the much-imitated but never replicated chocolate nemesis awaits, as do stracciatella ice cream or panna cotta with grappa and raspberries. The wine list is resplendent with thoroughbred Italian gear, beginning at £35 before getting airborne.

Chef/s: Ruth Rogers, Joseph Trivelli and Sian Owen. **Closed:** 25 Dec to 3 Jan, Mon bank hols in Aug. **Meals:** main courses £18 to £40. Set L £28 (2 courses) to £42. **Details:** 120 seats. 100 seats outside. Bar. Wheelchairs. Parking.

LOCAL GEM

Rosso

⊖ Earl's Court, map 6
Italian | £25
276-280 Kensington High Street, Kensington, W8 6ND
Tel no: (07384) 595191
enotecarosso.com

An informal and sociable space, more wine bar than restaurant, the 'delightful' Rosso occupies a spacious, high-ceilinged room with modish touches throughout; it makes a good spot for a quick bite washed down with Italian wines. The menu is flexible with many dishes in three sizes: 'rustic' wild boar pappardelle appears among pasta dishes, while sharing plates of charcuterie and cheese are a perfect match for the wines. Elsewhere, tender lamb fillet comes with celeraic mash and broad beans, and desserts such as panna cotta and wild berry coulis round things off. The copious, good-value, all-Italian wine list seeks out regional producers and there are an admirable 35 options by the glass.

★ NEW ENTRY ★

San Pietro

Cooking score: 2
⊖ High Street Kensington, Earl's Court, map 3
Italian | £45
7 Stratford Road, South Kensington, W8 6RF
Tel no: (020) 7938 1805
san-pietro.co.uk

The white-painted, two-tiered restaurant on the corner of a Kensington side street is a charming prospect, projecting itself as low-key and relaxed with its pale, rough-stone walls, white-clad tables, gold leather banquettes and chatty, friendly staff. The lengthy menu features a similar collection of classic pasta, pizza and fresh fish (delivered daily) to that of big brother Portobello Ristorante Pizzeria in Notting Hill (see entry). Highlights at inspection were 'fabulous' salty focaccia, zucchini fritti ('delightful long laces of crispy courgettes'), 'simple, delicious' linguine with clams and mussels, perfectly cooked sea bass with a black olive tapenade and baby artichoke, and a 'light and perfect' pizza with mozzarella, Parma ham and rocket. In addition, there's a very good-value set lunch. To finish, both vanilla panna cotta or tartufo bianco are classics. A good selection of Italian regional wines comes by the glass, carafe or bottle.

Chef/s: Andrea Ippolito. **Closed:** 25 Dec, 1 Jan. **Meals:** main courses from £10 to £30. Set L £15 (2 courses). **Details:** 60 seats. Bar. Music.

The Shed

Cooking score: 3
⊖ Notting Hill Gate, map 6
Modern British | £30
122 Palace Gardens Terrace, Notting Hill, W8 4RT
Tel no: (020) 7229 4024
theshed-restaurant.com

In an ace position just off Notting Hill Gate's main drag, the Gladwin brothers' artfully chaotic venue outperforms its ancestral duty as an urban eatery, incorporating a tiny sun-spot of a terrace, a dinky bar inside and a main, sunny dining room with a retro, ramshackle 50s vibe. The come-as-you-are ambience seems perfect for working your way through a small plates menu divided into things on toast, slow cooking and fast cooking. A delicate grilled scallop, teamed with cucumber, cherry tomato and rapeseed salsa contrasted well with the heartier flavours found in toasted sourdough with a big dollop of soft, 'nduja-style chorizo on kale topped with a perfectly fried egg, and terrifically deep-flavoured lamb with a glossy lamb jus, purple potatoes, spring greens and peas, all zinged up with slices of subtly pickled red onion. Don't leave without trying the indecent pleasure that is honeycomb crunchie with mascarpone and tarragon sugar. There's a short but decent selection of wines; cocktails, too.

Chef/s: Ross Dunk. **Closed:** Sun, 24 Dec to 2 Jan, bank hols. **Meals:** small plates £7 to £16. **Details:** 70 seats. 20 seats outside. Vg menu. Bar. Wheelchairs. Music.

Shikumen

Cooking score: 3
⊖ Shepherd's Bush Market, map 1
Chinese | £35
Dorsett Hotel, 58 Shepherd's Bush Green, Shepherd's Bush, W12 8QE
Tel no: (020) 8749 9978
shikumen.co.uk
£5 OFF

Although the name references an East-West architectural style popular in Shanghai during the 1860s, Shikumen's designers have gone for a modernist look that blends high ceilings and leather banquettes with slate-grey floors, oriental screens and a hand-carved bar. It's a sleek and rather glamorous backdrop for cooking that absorbs a few occidental ideas while hopping and skipping between the Chinese regions. A list of superior hand-crafted dim sum includes different-coloured versions of xiao long bao (Shanghai's signature 'soup dumplings') as well as more familiar shumai, char-siu cheung fun and deep-fried turnip puffs. You can also trade up to Peking duck (presented authentically in two servings), baked sea bass in Champagne sauce, braised pork belly with Chinese buns or a king prawn curry with almond slices and fresh lily bulbs. The results are stylish and convincing, right down to desserts of black sesame balls in ginger tea. Chinese 'liquor', saké and cocktails are alternatives to the international wine list.
Chef/s: Kan Choon Lai. **Closed:** 25 Dec. **Meals:** main courses £7 to £39. Set L and D £30 to £50. **Details:** 148 seats. Wheelchairs. Music.

Six Portland Road

Cooking score: 2
⊖ Holland Park, map 1
Modern European | £45
6 Portland Road, Holland Park, W11 4LA
Tel no: (020) 7229 3130
sixportlandroad.com

Tucked away down a little street off Holland Park Avenue, not far from the tube station, this light, simply decorated neighbourhood restaurant and wine bar continues to prosper. Expect a laid-back vibe and obliging service, and the kitchen pumps out a short, regularly changing menu of European-influenced dishes underpinned by first-class produce. From platters of Italian charcuterie and starters of, say, jambon persillé with sauce gribiche or lamb souvlaki with tzatziki, tomato and red onion, it's all simple, good-value cooking. Main courses include rabbit leg with chickpeas, chorizo and aïoli, or hake with peas, girolles, pancetta and gem lettuce, and if the outstanding lemon tart is not on the menu, there's usually chocolate mousse. The choice of wines complements the food, the large selection featuring plenty of small growers while leaving ample room for European classics and offering a generous clutch by the glass.
Chef/s: Pascal Wiedemann. **Meals:** main courses £17 to £34. Set L £18 (2 courses) to £20. **Details:** 36 seats.

★ NEW ENTRY ★

Southam Street

Cooking score: 4
⊖ Westbourne Park, map 1
International | £38
36 Golborne Road, Notting Hill, W10 5PR
Tel no: (020) 3903 3591
southamstreet.com

This vibrant newcomer from the owners of 108 Garage (see entry) occupies an imposing building on several levels. The decor throughout is witty and extravagant – no safe, corporate style here – and the prosperous local crowd loves it all: from the ground-floor

dining room and open kitchen, via the several bars, snug corners and large west-facing terrace with heaters for chilly nights, to the lowest level, where a secret open-air space is for informal barbecues and general hanging out. The menu is effortlessly modern, a wildly eclectic ramble through the Far East and Japan, Europe, the USA and Central America, with prime American beef and Australian wagyu from the robata grill alongside tartares and ceviches, sushi and sashimi, soft-shell crab, bao buns and Korean fried chicken. Plenty of European dishes appear, too, among them creamy burrata with wild garlic and beetroot, cherry vine tomatoes with horseradish mascarpone, and Spanish Ibérico pluma partnered with pickled pears. Prices are reasonable, but portions are small and the bill can mount up, especially if you explore the short European wine list in any depth.
Chef/s: Chris Denney and Charles Lee. **Closed:** Mon. **Meals:** main courses £14 to £30.

La Trompette

Cooking score: 5
⊖ Turnham Green, map 1
Modern European | £55
3-7 Devonshire Road, Chiswick, W4 2EU
Tel no: (020) 8747 1836
latrompette.co.uk

There's a lot of competition in Chiswick these days, but La Trompette is still a cut above – a genuinely cherished neighbourhood haunt that keeps its prices in check without ever stinting on quality or style. Everything is in the best possible taste, from the polished floors, contemporary artworks, neutral colours, flattering lighting and big picture windows to the daily line-up of well-considered modern European dishes. Clever ideas, elaborate detailing and a proper respect for natural flavours typify chef Rob Weston's output, from calf's sweetbreads with hen of the woods mushrooms, salt-baked turnip, lemon and miso to aged Anjou pigeon, Jerusalem artichoke, winter greens and quince. This is food with real impact, and there's nothing timid about Weston's approach to fish either – note loin of cod partnered by mussels, cauliflower, crosnes, cider and spinach. After that, the stupendous cheeseboard is unmissable, although it would be sinful to bypass the muscovado custard tart with Earl Grey ice cream and medjool dates. The gloriously comprehensive 600-bin wine list has superb pickings across the range, while a dozen top-drawer selections by the glass offer outstanding value.
Chef/s: Rob Weston and Olly Pierrepont. **Closed:** 25 to 27 Dec, 1 Jan. **Meals:** set L £30 (2 courses) to £35. Set D £45 (2 courses) to £55. Sun L £40. Tasting menu L £65, D £75 (7 courses). **Details:** 88 seats. 14 seats outside. Wheelchairs. No young children.

Vinoteca

Cooking score: 2
⊖ Turnham Green, map 1
Modern European | £33
18 Devonshire Road, Chiswick, W4 2HD
Tel no: (020) 3701 8822
vinoteca.co.uk

The Vinoteca formula of well-priced wines and simple, European dishes translates well to this relaxed neighbourhood site. For main entry, see King's Cross branch, north London.
Chef/s: James Robson. **Closed:** 25, 26 and 31 Dec, 1 Jan. **Meals:** main courses £14 to £19. Set L £15 (2 courses) to £18. **Details:** 48 seats. Music.

Wright Brothers

Cooking score: 2
⊖ South Kensington, map 3
Seafood | £35
56 Old Brompton Road, South Kensington, SW7 3DY
Tel no: (020) 7581 0131
thewrightbrothers.co.uk

Handy for the museums, the South Ken outpost of the popular seafood chain has a separate cocktail and oyster bar, The Mermaid, in the basement. For main entry, see Spitalfields branch, east London.

Chef/s: Jonathan Stray. **Closed:** 25 and 26 Dec, 1 Jan. **Meals:** main courses £17 to £23. Set L £18 (2 courses) to £20. **Details:** 56 seats. Bar. Music.

Zuma

Cooking score: 5
⊖ Knightsbridge, map 6
Japanese | £80
5 Raphael Street, Knightsbridge, SW7 1DL
Tel no: (020) 7584 1010
zumarestaurant.com

Zuma is as global a brand as a couture designer label, with iterations across the known world from Vegas to Phuket via the Emirates and Knightsbridge. Its inspiration is the informal, take-it-as-it-comes eating style of Japan's izakaya taverns, only transported into the world of multi-textured interior design, sepulchrally lit grottos and perforated screens. A sushi counter and robata grill, not to mention a semi-secluded tosho table, provide atmospheric hitching posts for the immaculately rendered classic morsels. Sliced seared tuna of velveteen texture is dressed in chilli daikon and ponzu for a cold starter bite, while hot options include grilled unagi eel with avocado and sweet omelette, and the robata turns out sizzling triumphs such as spiced beef tenderloin doused in sesame, red chilli and sweet shoyu. A house special is the poussin marinated in barley miso and then roasted over cedarwood. To finish, the cheesecake is disguised as an oshibori hot towel, and served with raspberry and lychee sorbet. A well-stocked saké bar helps acclimatise the venturesome diner, while others can fall back on a list of top-drawer, price-pumped wines.
Chef/s: Rainer Becker and Michael Calenzo.
Meals: sharing plates £5 to £79. Tasting menu £76.
Details: 150 seats. Bar. Wheelchairs. Music.

Inspector highlights

Our undercover London inspectors reveal their most memorable dishes from a year of extraordinary eating.

'The jasmine and wild pea-flower religieuse at **Hide Above**, Mayfair was sensational; such a joy to encounter a pastry kitchen with both classical skills and the desire to do something decidedly different.'

'A plate of pickled aubergines at **Albertine**'s wine bar in Shepherd's Bush, London. Sitting on creamy tahini and sprinkled with crispy fried capers and served with flatbread for scooping, it had me almost licking the plate clean.'

'In Soho, London, **Pastaio**'s 'nduja, mozzarella and honey toasted sandwich was a messy, joyful mouthful. I had to order another.'

'Nieves Barragàn Mohacho is a brilliant but modest chef who sweats the small stuff, such as in the balance of acidity in the dressing on a simple winter tomato salad at **Sabor** in Mayfair.'

'My most memorable dish? Raspberry powder buttermilk plantain with smoked scotch-bonnet mayonnaise at **Ikoyi**, a West African restaurant in St James's.'

A Cena

Cooking score: 2
⊖ Richmond, map 1
Italian | £35
418 Richmond Road, Twickenham, TW1 2EB
Tel no: (020) 8288 0108
acena.co.uk

On the main drag close to the eastern end of Richmond Bridge, A Cena 'does the job whether you feel like dressing up or dressing down', whether there's a birthday to celebrate or there's simply nothing in the fridge. The black-and-white neutrality is softened by candles in the evening, the bar can knock up a decent Bellini, and the wine list is a regional tour of the Italy. The menu takes on the classic dishes and does them well – Caesar salad, say, or gamberetti fritti with a spicy mayonnaise – or you might start with sweet-and-sour fried slip sole. The fresh pasta is a good bet (rigatoni with tomato, chilli, oregano and a hit of vodka), with secondi of beef braised in Tuscan red wine or fillet of sea bass with inzimino di ceci (chickpeas and kale). For dessert, tiramisu is hard to resist.

Chef/s: Nicola Parsons. **Closed:** 5 days Christmas, 1 Jan, 2 weeks Aug, bank hols. **Meals:** main courses £18 to £24. Set L £10 (2 courses). Sun L £21 (2 courses) to £25. **Details:** 50 seats. Bar. Wheelchairs. Music.

The Bingham

Cooking score: 4
⊖ Richmond, map 1
Modern British | £45
61-63 Petersham Road, Richmond, TW10 6UT
Tel no: (020) 8940 0902
thebingham.co.uk

The classical Georgian architecture and idyllic riverside setting would be reason enough to visit The Bingham. But that's not all this glamorous Richmond address has to offer. Inside, chandeliers glister and mirrors sparkle as guests sip cucumber martinis on the balcony overlooking manicured lawns. It's pure escapism, enhanced by staff who anticipate one's every need. There's some crossover between the six-course tasting, carte and good-value Market Menu, which makes the latter quite a steal. At inspection, the kitchen demonstrated a leaning towards delicacy both on the plate and the palate. After a powerful amuse of Parmesan custard, the confit sea trout starter with marinated heirloom tomatoes and the baked cod with kohlrabi, puffed wild rice, lemon purée and mushroom tea were ethereally pretty, but a little underpowered. Dessert was a strong finish, however, with dense, dark chocolate mousse, supported by hazelnut sponge and refreshingly acidic yoghurt sorbet. Wine flights available.

Chef/s: Andrew Cole. **Meals:** set L £19 (2 courses) to £21. Set D £37 (2 courses) to £45. Sun L £34 (2 courses) to £38. Tasting menu £50 (6 courses). **Details:** 40 seats. 15 seats outside. V menu. Bar. Wheelchairs. Music.

LOCAL GEM

Bombetta

⊖ Snaresbrook, map 1
Italian | £35
Units 1-5 Station Approach, Wanstead, E11 1QE
Tel no: (020) 3871 0890
bombettalondon.com

This popular Italian eatery, found on the approach to Snaresbrook tube station, may not be much to look at, but it's ideal for a bit of midweek comfort food and a nice glass of wine. Look beyond the basic interior to the open kitchen dominated by a charcoal grill, and to the popular cured meat and cheeseboards. Readers have mixed feelings about the bombette (parcels of wood-grilled offcuts of meat and cheese) and recommend sticking with the sharing plates of pig's head bruschetta, deep-fried arancini and beef meatballs. Italian wines from £19.50.

Brilliant

Cooking score: 2
⊖ Hounslow West, map 1
Indian | £29
72-76 Western Road, Southall, UB2 5DZ
Tel no: (020) 8574 1928
brilliantrestaurant.com

This is one of those places with a bit of a cult following that 'those in the know' speak about in hushed tones, bragging about how they used to frequent it when it first opened in 1975. The menu, seriously long and wide-ranging, is a mix of familiar Indian restaurant fare, regional Punjabi dishes and occasional Kenyan accents. It's vivid, eye-catching food that the interior tries a little too hard to compete with, offering a blingy blend of orange leather chairs, sparkly table tops and black string curtains. Good pickles – including a particularly lip-smacking salted lime – along with exemplary poppadoms, lead into lamb chops nicely charred from the tandoor, and tender chunks of karahi chicken in a rich, spicy gravy with red and green peppers, served with fluffy pilau rice dotted with peas and fragrant with ginger, cumin and garlic. Drinks include the usual Indian lagers and a handful of popular, good-value wine offerings.

Chef/s: Dipna Anand. **Closed:** Mon. **Meals:** main courses £6 to £14. Set L and D £25. **Details:** 265 seats. V menu. Bar. Music. Parking.

La Buvette

Cooking score: 3
⊖ Richmond, map 1
French | £30
6 Church Walk, Richmond, TW9 1SN
Tel no: (020) 8940 6264
labuvette.co.uk

Chequered tablecloths, bentwood chairs and big blackboards all scream neighbourhood bistro, so it's no surprise that La Buvette's heart-warming take on French provincial cooking is unashamedly old-school. Reassuring signature dishes such as rustic fish soup with rouille, chargrilled onglet with frites and crème brûlée might suggest the stoic world of classic French cooking although the kitchen isn't afraid to try out a few new ideas: red onion tarte fine comes with a dollop of labneh, salmon replaces beef as the core ingredient of a bourguignon, and desserts could include a pairing of Yorkshire rhubarb with fromage blanc, ginger-biscuit crumb and cardamom syrup. Excellent-value prix fixe deals, numerous chalked-up specials and 'marvellous' Sunday lunches get the thumbs-up, and the owners even stage special fondue evenings in the restaurant's lovely, secluded courtyard – further good news for locals. The all-French wine list includes some agreeable tipples by the glass or carafe, and imaginative wine flights, too.

Chef/s: Buck Carter. **Closed:** 25 to 28 Dec, Good Fri, Easter Sun. **Meals:** main courses £15 to £19. Set L and D £20. **Details:** 34 seats. 34 seats outside.

The Dysart Petersham

Cooking score: 5
⊖ Richmond, map 1
Modern British | £45
135 Petersham Road, Richmond, TW10 7AA
Tel no: (020) 8940 8005
thedysartpetersham.co.uk

This former Arts and Crafts pub has a fine position – overlooking the gates of Richmond Park – and an interior with its own wow factor: towering ceilings, an expanse of stone-tiled floor, ornately leaded windows, metal chandeliers and seriously chunky wooden tables – there's even a grand piano. Now run as a restaurant, Kenneth Culhane's cooking is a beacon in south-west London, his modern approach underpinned by a classical theme and driven by an awareness of the seasons and a grasp of flavour combinations that work. Tastes are rounded with no sharp edges and among highlights this year have been 'a cracking halibut and sashimi starter', oxtail risotto with pickled chilli, shiitake dashi and bone-marrow sauce, and wild stone bass with spinach and sauce

Jacqueline. This is cooking that achieves what it sets out to, be it exemplary warm treacle and almond bread or a roasted peanut financier with umeboshi plum, clementine curd and yuzu sorbet as a finale. The wine list offers a package tour of the vinous world, with prices from £22.50.

Chef/s: Kenneth Culhane. **Closed:** Mon, Tue. **Meals:** main courses £22 to £34. Set L and D £24 (2 courses) to £28. Sun L £35. Tasting menu £70. **Details:** 46 seats. 25 seats outside. V menu. Vg menu. Wheelchairs. Music. Parking. No children after 8pm.

Eat17

Cooking score: 2
⊖ Walthamstow Central, map 1
British | £26
28-30 Orford Road, Walthamstow, E17 9NJ
Tel no: (020) 8521 5279
eat17.co.uk

There's no doubt owners Chris O'Connor and James Brundle know how to win friends; they did invent bacon jam after all. And readers consider Walthamstow lucky to play host to their casual British bistro – it feels like a neighbourhood asset. And what a smart bolthole it makes, too, with its copper bar, leather banquettes and mid-century-style furniture. A winning combination of well-priced food, and a menu that strikes the right note between traditional and contemporary, helps to add to the buzz. Everyone praises the US-style hot wings, the cheeseburger (with bacon jam, natch) and the shepherd's pie made with slow-cooked shoulder of lamb, but there's also duck pappardelle with sage, truffle, onion jus and pecorino, or a tagine of chickpea, sweet potato and pepper. Round it all off with apple and rhubarb crumble and custard. Service is slick and friendly, the wine list brief and markups not too greedy.

Chef/s: Rowen Babe. **Closed:** 25 to 31 Dec. **Meals:** main courses £13 to £21. **Details:** 60 seats. 12 seats outside. Bar. Wheelchairs. Music.

The French Table

Cooking score: 3
map 1
French | £45
85 Maple Road, Surbiton, KT6 4AW
Tel no: (020) 8399 2365
thefrenchtable.co.uk

More than 17 years down the line, Eric and Sarah Guignard are still running their hugely popular Surbiton restaurant with vim and vigour, offering locals the sort of sophisticated French-inspired cuisine that beckons in the heart of the capital. First choice for a special occasion, the clean-lined grey-toned dining room also attracts well-heeled diners eager to try the Gallic classics that are here in abundance, from honey-roast quail with a crispy quail's egg, pistachio purée and brioche to pear tarte tatin with pecans and cinnamon ice cream. But it's also worth investigating more unusual ideas – perhaps a starter of carrot crème brûlée with heritage carrots, blue cheese and walnut dressing or a main course that pairs pan-fried stone bass with creamy salsify and miso, samphire and matelote sauce. The fixed-price format works well, especially when complemented by one of the 'monthly specials' from Sarah Guignard's thoughtfully composed wine list.

Chef/s: Eric Guignard. **Closed:** Sun, Mon, 25 Dec to 3 Jan, 19 Aug to 3 Sept. **Meals:** set L £22 (2 courses) to £27. Set D £39 (2 courses) to £45. Tasting menu L £30 (5 courses), D £52. **Details:** 70 seats.

The Glasshouse

Cooking score: 5
⊖ Kew Gardens, map 1
Modern European | £55
14 Station Parade, Kew, TW9 3PZ
Tel no: (020) 8940 6777
glasshouserestaurant.co.uk

'I'm very hard to please, but I can't wait to go back,' admitted a reader who has been frequenting this likeable Kew evergreen for more than 20 years. Over that time The Glasshouse has been 'consistently excellent' in all departments, and little seems to have changed with the arrival of chef Greg Wellman. Textured walls, beige tones and flattering lighting set the scene for generously flavoured, Euro-inspired dishes 'served in just the right quantities' – from a harmonious starter of white asparagus with watercress emulsion, blood orange and toasted almond pesto, to a 'simply perfect' Yorkshire rhubarb and Sauternes trifle. Pasta such as pappardelle with morels, black truffle and Parmesan is 'silky smooth', and seasonality is also writ large in dishes of roast cod with seaweed butter, monk's beard and brown shrimps; or venison haunch and pie accompanied by smoked creamed potato, rainbow chard and pickled walnuts. The welcome is always warm, service 'hits exactly the right note', and the thoughtfully constructed global wine list offers serious pickings at very accommodating prices with numerous half bottles and by-the-glass selections.

Chef/s: Greg Wellman. **Closed:** Mon, 24 to 26 Dec, 1 Jan. **Meals:** set L £30 (2 courses) to £35. Set D £45 (2 courses) to £55. Sun L £40. Tasting menu L £45 (4 courses), D £70 (5 courses). **Details:** 60 seats. Wheelchairs. Children at L only.

Grand Trunk Road

Cooking score: 3
⊖ South Woodford, map 1
Indian | £38

219 High Road, South Woodford, E18 2PB
Tel no: (020) 8505 1965
gtrrestaurant.co.uk

High-achieving Indian restaurateur Rajesh Suri shunned his favourite big-money postcodes in favour of London's outer regions when setting up this confident addition to his portfolio. Wedged into a parade of suburban shops and named after the 16th-century trade route that stretched from Kabul to Kolkata, Grand Trunk Road conjures the spirit of the old Subcontinent with its warm copper tones, spicy colour schemes and invigorating cooking. Billed as a 'food journey', the menu spans everything from the barbecue delights of Peshawar to the sweetmeats of Bengal via street-food snacks, Moghul feasts and seafood from India's coastal provinces. Appetisers might include Punjabi potato and paneer tikki with tamarind chutney, while mains could range from tandoori rabbit with long peppers to a Delhi-style masala gosht with dried kalpasi flowers. To finish, take comfort from the evocatively named 'Last Milestone 2500' (mango brûlée with ajwain biscuits). Fancy East-West cocktails are an alternative to the upmarket wine list.

Chef/s: Daya Shankar Sharma. **Closed:** Mon, 25 and 26 Dec, 1 Jan, bank hols. **Meals:** main courses £15 to £34. Set L £17 (2 courses) to £20. Set D £39. Sun L £29. Tasting menu £43. **Details:** 52 seats. V menu. Wheelchairs. Music. Children at L only.

READERS RECOMMEND

Homies on Donkeys

Unit 38, 98 Wood Street, Walthamstow, E17 3HX
homiesondonkeys.com

'There are only five seats at the counter of this basic taqueria in the indoor market. Squeeze in to try the best tacos around: our favourite is the pork cooked "low and slow" in smokey chipotle sauce, piled high with "gauc" and cheese. It's a great lunchtime refuelling stop.'

Madhu's

Cooking score: 2
map 1
Indian | £28

39 South Road, Southall, UB1 1SW
Tel no: (020) 8574 1897
madhus.co.uk

One of the slickest and sleekest players in Southall, long-running Madhu's gets its high-gloss look from mirrors, metal and shiny black surfaces – a glamorous backdrop for food that neatly sidesteps the Indian new wave in favour of something more traditional. The cooking is generous and full-blooded to a fault, with due respect for the old ways, some East African undertones and a deft touch when it comes to dipping into the spice box. Specialities flagged with a red 'M' are always worth trying – perhaps mogo jeera (fried cassava with roasted cumin seeds), gloriously rich butter chicken made to a family recipe, or keema mutter (minced lamb and peas) cooked 'in the old style'. Tandooris and tikkas show a meaty allegiance to India's northern provinces, but vegetarians also do particularly well here (try the Punjabi-style vegetable dumplings in a sour yoghurt curry tempered with mustard seeds). Wines from £16.

Chef/s: Rakesh Verma. **Closed:** Tue, 25 Dec. **Meals:** main courses £6 to £13. Set L £20 (2 courses) to £25. Set D £20 (2 courses) to £25. **Details:** 100 seats. V menu. Wheelchairs. Music. Parking.

★ NEW ENTRY ★

Madhu's Heathrow

Cooking score: 2
⊖ Heathrow Terminal 1, 2, 3
Indian | £35
Sheraton Skyline Hotel, Bath Road, Harlington, UB3 5BP
Tel no: (020) 8564 3380
madhusheathrow.com

Within the confines of Heathrow's Sheraton Skyline Hotel, this offshoot of Madhu's in Southall (see entry) feels rather corporate despite the dramatic red and black decor. But the welcome is warm, service is polite and efficient, and the menu broad enough to please all-comers. A robata grill in the kitchen allows for more flexibility than a tandoor – marinated sea bass can be cooked alongside salmon-stuffed baby calamari or chicken malai kebabs, marinated in mascarpone with a hint of cardamom. Machuzi kuku (slow-simmered chicken) and nalli gosht (a rich spiced lamb dish) are long-term specialities of Madhu's, alongside flavoursome naan breads, but it's worth looking at the chef's recommendations for lighter dishes: peppered soft-shell crab with a sweet mango mayo dip; lovely wild mushroom and truffle pilau rice. Spicing tends to be light, but the kitchen is happy to dial up the heat if asked. The wine list includes fragrant spice-friendly whites and punchy reds, and of course there's Cobra on draught.

Chef/s: Sanjay Anand. **Meals:** main courses £6 to £13. Set D £33 (3 courses). Tasting menu £45 (4 courses). **Details:** 130 seats. Wheelchairs. Music. Parking.

LOCAL GEM

Olympic Studios Café & Dining Room

⊖ Hammersmith, map 1
Modern British | £30
Olympic Studios, 117-123 Church Road, Barnes, SW13 9HL
Tel no: (020) 8912 5170
olympicstudios.co.uk

The Olympic Studios is quite the hive of activity: swing by for breakfast, lunch, coffee and cake, dinner, catch a film, record an album (the latter by invitation only, sadly). The Café & Dining Room is open all day turning out feel-good food like deep-fried squid, cauliflower mac and cheese and the Olympic hot dog, alongside butter-bean stew with braised freekeh and herb-crusted rack of lamb, and it's all done with attention to detail. Cocktails and well-chosen wines, and the presence of six different Champagnes, show its mettle.

Petersham Nurseries Café

Cooking score: 3
⊖ Richmond, map 1
Modern European | £60
Church Lane, off Petersham Road, Richmond, TW10 7AG
Tel no: (020) 8940 5230
petershamnurseries.com

Awkward to get to (there's limited parking and it's a bus ride from the nearest station) and occupying the back of a giant greenhouse, on paper, this restaurant has little to recommend it. But the boho-chic setting, with pounded earth floor and mismatched tables, and enthusiastically foodie waiters wearing wellies in the winter and shorts in the summer, is utterly beguiling. 'It's like a really good version of a mountain restaurant in Ibiza – cool, beautiful, relaxed and really expensive,' thought one visitor. The kitchen's ethos is all about fine ingredients simply prepared: monkfish served 'crudo', dressed in a peppery olive oil and Amalfi lemon juice, and garlanded with fennel leaves and edible flowers; chicken breast atop a bed of fresh peas, asparagus and braised cos lettuce; a classic apricot and almond tart enlivened with a little lemon thyme. Beautiful presentation is a given but, in keeping with the image, cutlery has seen better days, though there's nothing shabby about the all-Italian wine list or glasses.

Chef/s: Damian Clisby and Ambra Papa. **Closed:** Mon. **Meals:** main courses £21 to £30. **Details:** 120 seats. 120 seats outside. Wheelchairs.

The Petersham

Cooking score: 2
⊖ Richmond, map 1
Modern British | £56
Nightingale Lane, Richmond, TW10 6UZ
Tel no: (020) 8003 3945
petershamhotel.co.uk

The somewhat old-fashioned feel to this hotel dining room – 'thick carpet and acres of tablecloth give the place a comfortable hushed feeling' – is entirely mitigated by an idyllic country view from the panoramic floor-to-ceiling windows (best to visit at lunchtime or in the summer). For those not facing outwards, the interior walls are covered in mirrored panels, so few are without the entrancing vista. The kitchen seems to have taken this as a starting point: utterly beautiful presentation relies on flowers and herbs lifting each dish. The main menu features grand versions of classics – steak tartare adorned with caviar and quail's egg, or tomato and mozzarella dressed with balsamic pearls and olive oil powder. Most diners opt for the well-priced set option where Jerusalem artichoke soup might be poured on to artichoke crisps and nasturtiums, and pan-fried salmon jazzed up with a curry foam and garnished with pea sprout sprigs. Coupled with the good-value, interesting wine list, it's a hit with locals of a certain age.

Chef/s: Jean-Didier Gouges. **Closed:** 25 Dec. **Meals:** main courses £26 to £40. Set L and D £25 (2 courses) to £29. Sun L £40. **Details:** 90 seats. Bar. Music. Parking.

Sonny's Kitchen

Cooking score: 2
map 1
Modern European | £30
94 Church Road, Barnes, SW13 0DQ
Tel no: (020) 8748 0393
sonnyskitchen.co.uk

Sonny's may have changed its colours and its complexion during its 30-year residency in Barnes, but it remains a neighbourhood favourite for young and old alike. Long-standing restaurateur Rebecca Mascarenhas knows her customers, and (with help from co-owner Phil Howard) has created a venue that satisfies all requirements, offering good-value, sound cooking and a gregarious vibe in stylish, airy surroundings (note the modern artworks dotted around the white-tiled dining room). The kitchen works to a daily menu, adding specials such as Galician beef fillet with beetroot purée and oxtail croquette to its line-up of accessible, unchallenging brasserie-style dishes. Burgers, confit duck and daube of beef sit easily alongside mustard-glazed chicken wings with apple and celeriac slaw, or steamed sea bream with radish, agretti and prawn consommé, while desserts could offer yoghurt panna cotta or profiteroles with muscovado cream. Well-chosen wines, a daytime café menu and a food shop next door complete an all-round package.

Chef/s: Andrew Chelley. **Closed:** Christmas and New Year. **Meals:** main courses £15 to £30. Set L and D £20 (2 courses) to £23. Sun L £27. **Details:** 85 seats. Bar. Music.

Tangawizi

Cooking score: 2
⊖ Richmond, map 1
Indian | £30
406 Richmond Road, Twickenham, TW1 2EB
Tel no: (020) 8891 3737
tangawizi.co.uk

At first glance Tangawizi seems like any other spruced up neighbourhood Indian. But look closer. Though the prices are a shade higher, the deep purple room, the elegantly dressed staff and the careful lighting all combine to lift eating here to another level. The kitchen follows suit: the menu has all the familiar classics – tandoori chicken and biryanis abound – but thanks to excellent produce and astute spicing and marinating, they bear little relation to normal high-street versions. Chutneys are clean and vibrant, tandoori king prawns are juicy and huge, rice is delicate and moreish, lamb saagwala tender and flavoursome. Most of the well-dressed crowd of regulars know their way around the menu, but staff are happy to guide those wanting to go a little off-piste. The multiple-dish set menus are best kept for the really hungry. Booking during the week is advised and essential at the weekend. The short wine list offers options by the glass, as well as Indian-inspired cocktails.
Chef/s: Surat Singh Rana. **Closed:** 25 and 26 Dec, 1 and 2 Jan. **Meals:** main courses £7 to £16. **Details:** 60 seats. Music.

The Victoria

Cooking score: 3
⊖ Richmond, map 1
Modern British | £35
10 West Temple Sheen, East Sheen, SW14 7RT
Tel no: (020) 8876 4238
victoriasheen.co.uk

Richmond Park's dog walkers drop by for breakfast, rugby teams pop in for a restorative pint and families with kids take full advantage of The Victoria's BBQs and summertime playground – the pub is in a residential area close to a primary school, so it has a captive audience. It is helmed by chef Paul Merrett and the whole place trades on the quality of its cooking. Careful sourcing and top-drawer ingredients define the menu, which offers burgers, bangers and beer-battered fish alongside more upbeat contemporary ideas: perhaps homemade labneh with pomegranate, sumac and toasted focaccia; asparagus and pecorino ravioli; or slow-cooked lamb breast with wild garlic polenta, hispi cabbage and crispy capers. There are some fashionable vegan options too, while desserts span everything from strawberry parfait with basil meringue to sticky toffee pudding with salted caramel ice cream. The grown-up wine list includes a dozen by-the-glass selections.
Chef/s: Paul Merrett and Damien Ciolek. **Meals:** main courses £13 to £18. **Details:** 80 seats. 50 seats outside. Bar. Music. Parking.

ENGLAND

Bedfordshire, Berkshire, Bristol,
Buckinghamshire, Cambridgeshire,
Cheshire, Cornwall, Cumbria, Derbyshire,
Devon, Dorset, Durham, Essex,
Gloucestershire, Greater Manchester,
Hampshire & the Isle of Wight,
Herefordshire, Hertfordshire, Kent,
Lancashire, Leicestershire and Rutland,
Lincolnshire, Merseyside, Norfolk,
Northamptonshire, Northumberland,
Nottinghamshire, Oxfordshire, Shropshire,
Somerset, Staffordshire, Suffolk, Surrey,
Sussex, Tyne & Wear, Warwickshire,
West Midlands, Wiltshire, Worcestershire,
Yorkshire

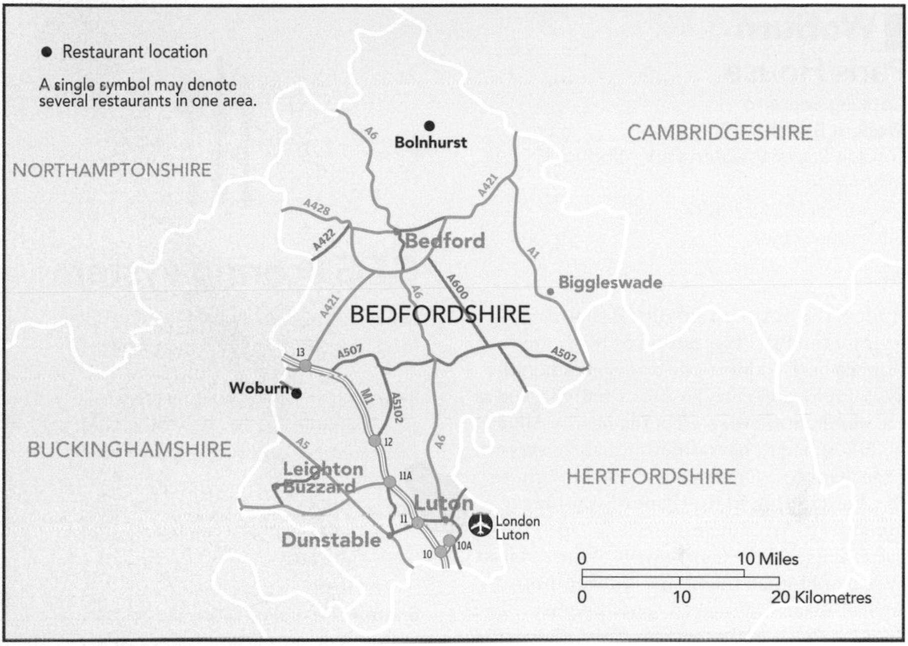

Bolnhurst

The Plough

Cooking score: 4
Modern British | £40
Kimbolton Road, Bolnhurst, MK44 2EX
Tel no: (01234) 376274
bolnhurst.com

Is it a pub? Is it a restaurant? In truth, this singular venue is a bit of both, although massive black beams, thick stone walls, tiny windows, chirpy staff and a fully functioning bar testify to its roots as a local watering hole. Martin and Jayne Lee have been here since 2005, honing their innkeeping skills while serving up food with clear, clean flavours and a modern edge. Steaks and day-boat fish are shown the Josper grill, but the day's menu has a great deal more to offer – from roast Orkney scallops with smoked celeriac, walnut and garlic crisps to venison loin accompanied by butternut squash purée, a venison cottage pie, pancetta and pickled red cabbage. To finish, the Neal's Yard Dairy cheese list is well worth a patriotic sniff, while desserts include a classic Amalfi lemon tart with crème fraîche (also from Neal's Yard). Despite the odd suggestion that the place is 'coasting', there's much to admire and enjoy here – not least an authoritative wine list offering classy, eclectic bottles at generous drinker-friendly prices, including 15 rousing selections by the glass or carafe.

Chef/s: Martin Lee. **Closed:** Mon, 2 weeks Jan. **Meals:** main courses £17 to £32. Set L and D £20 (2 courses) to £25. Sun L £25. **Details:** 80 seats. 30 seats outside. Bar. Wheelchairs. Parking.

Send us your review

Your feedback informs the content of the *GFG* and will be used to compile next year's reviews. To register your opinion about any restaurant listed in the Guide, or a restaurant that you wish to bring to our attention, visit: thegoodfoodguide.co.uk/feedback

Woburn

Paris House

Cooking score: 6
Modern British | £96
London Road, Woburn Park, Woburn,
MK17 9QP
Tel no: (01525) 290692
parishouse.co.uk
£5 OFF

Built in the northern English Renaissance style for the Paris Exposition of 1878, and then shipped back in bits to be reassembled on the Woburn Estate, Paris House initially served as accommodation for staff at the nearby Abbey. In 2017, it had its latest interior makeover, with a much more contemporary look brought to the dining room in the shape of sky-blue upholstery, Art Nouveau-style foliage patterning and the banishment of linen. Head chef Ben Hyman maintains Phil Fanning's style of Asian-influenced contemporary cooking, with multi-course tasters all over the show. Dishes to conjure with have included dim sum-style mantou bun with kimchi, spring onion and hoisin, butter-poached hamachi fish with caramelised white miso, caviar and sea kale, and venison with aduki beans, black pudding and cranberries. The vegetarian version is quite as replete with invention, perhaps including chou farci with turnips and violet grape mustard, and desserts often mobilise sweet vegetables to great advantage, as in the carrot production that's enriched with kuromitsu (Japanese sugar syrup) and carrot and buttermilk sorbet. Well-chosen wines by the glass from £7.

Chef/s: Phil Fanning and Ben Hyman. **Closed:** Mon, Tue, Wed, 24 Dec to 3 Jan. **Meals:** tasting menu L £49 (6 courses), D £96 (8 courses) to £115 (10 courses). Sun L £67 (5 courses). **Details:** 32 seats. V menu. Music. Parking.

GFG scoring system

Score 1: Capable cooking with simple food combinations and clear flavours.

Score 2: Decent cooking, displaying good technical skills and interesting combinations and flavours.

Score 3: Good cooking, showing sound technical skills and using quality ingredients.

Score 4: Dedicated, focused approach to cooking; good classical skills and high-quality ingredients.

Score 5: Exact cooking techniques and a degree of ambition; showing balance and depth of flavour in dishes.

Score 6: Exemplary cooking skills, innovative ideas, impeccable ingredients and an element of excitement.

Score 7: High level of ambition and individuality, attention to the smallest detail, accurate and vibrant dishes.

Score 8: A kitchen cooking close to or at the top of its game. Highly individual with impressive artistry.

Score 9: Cooking that has reached a pinnacle of achievement, making it a hugely memorable experience.

Score 10: Just perfect dishes, showing faultless technique at every service; extremely rare and the highest accolade.

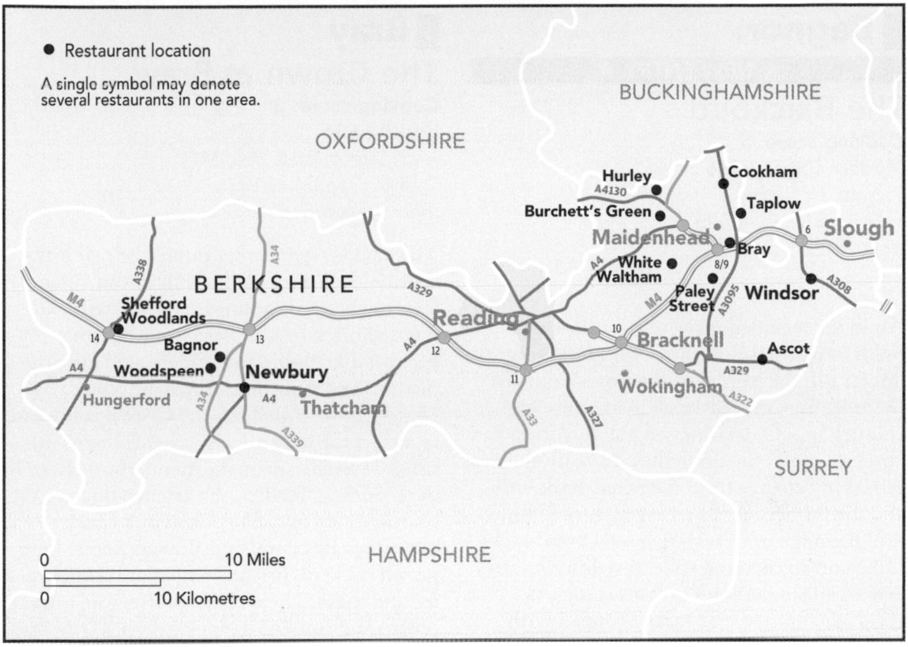

Ascot

Restaurant Coworth Park

Cooking score: 6
British | £75
Blacknest Road, Ascot, SL5 7SE
Tel no: (01344) 876600
dorchestercollection.com

Built for an East India merchant in 1776, Coworth is a broad white slice of Georgiana sitting amid ancient woodland and meadows in the vicinity of Windsor. Its cottages and stables now transformed into rooms and suites, and its lofty-ceilinged interiors preserving all their original splendour, it's the very model of a Home Counties country retreat. Since taking over the stoves in 2016, Adam Smith has spread his wings here, and produces an exciting repertoire of innovative food that's seen to its best advantage on the seven-course tasting menu. A caviar tart with Cornish crab and yuzu suggests there is no inhibition about pulling out the stops, and attractive ideas come thick and fast. A pairing of sautéed duck liver with gingered rhubarb shows exemplary balance, while fish could be steamed turbot with truffled cauliflower, sauced in Champagne. Fine Fettle, a Yorkshire sheep's milk cheese, helps enrich superlative herb-crusted lamb with courgettes and mint, while dessert could be Tahitian vanilla mousse in the tropical guise of pineapple, lime and coconut. If you can get past the battalions of vintage Champagnes, a star-studded lineup of producers awaits on the main list, opening at £32.

Chef/s: Adam Smith. **Closed:** Mon, Tue. **Meals:** set L £30 (2 courses) to £35. Set D £50 (3 courses) to £75. Sun L £50 (3 courses). Tasting menu £95 (7 courses). **Details:** 55 seats. Bar. Wheelchairs. Music. Parking. Children over 8 yrs after 7pm.

Bagnor

★ NEW ENTRY ★

The Blackbird

Cooking score: 5
Modern British | £36
Bagnor, RG20 8AQ
Tel no: (01635) 40005
theblackbird.co.uk

Amid the secluded mansions, streams and fields of pastoral Berkshire, with Donnington not far off, the hamlet of Bagnor is home to Dom Robinson's red-brick, half whitewashed country inn. Old-fashioned pub furniture and crockery, not to mention the odd doily, make a refreshing change from the pared-back look, and the service takes a relatively formal tone, too. A wodge of treacle-rich soda bread kicks things off in cheering style. A willingness to leave well alone shows in starters such as classically dressed crab tartare topped with blanched asparagus, as do layers of appealing depth in a foaming cup of onion soubise popping with haricots and garnished with Alsace bacon. Prime ingredients get the respect they deserve in a main course of crisp-fatted lamb loin with its sweetbread, coarse polenta and a sauce of chopped Kalamatas, courgettes and pine nuts. Fish could be wild sea bass in bouillabaisse with saffron potatoes and grilled onions, and the finale will be an unreformed slice of French classicism such as rum-drenched baba with rum and raisin ice cream, or a more venturesome glassy-topped rooibos tea crème brûlée with mandarin sorbet and rosemary shortbreads. The fairly brief wine list has a broad glass selection from £5.30.

Chef/s: Dom Robinson. **Closed:** Mon, Tue, 25 and 26 Dec, 1 Jan. **Meals:** main courses £18 to £26. Set L and D £19 (2 courses) to £24. **Details:** 32 seats. 16 seats outside. Bar. Parking.

Bray

The Crown at Bray

Cooking score: 3
British | £36
High Street, Bray, SL6 2AH
Tel no: (01628) 621936
thecrownatbray.com

The duck-as-you-enter pub is the real 16th-century deal, a proper local in a posh village. It feels unchanged, unmessed-about with, all gnarled black beams, bare stone hearths, parquet-like floors and understated historic pictures and paintings. It may be owned by Heston Blumenthal but the Crown is not out to attract the telly-tourist crowd: there's not a single Heston-ism on the menu, the walls or in the branding. Rather, the kitchen does a roaring trade in well-cooked pub classics – mainstays are crispy cauliflower cheese, king prawn cocktail, fish and chips, and confit duck leg and mash. There's been praise, too, for a potato and smoked haddock soup, a trug of (seasonal) vegetables that came with a generous pot of well-made bagna cauda for dipping, and a 'stonking' white chocolate bread-and-butter pudding with a scoop of vanilla ice cream popped on top. The sprawling beer garden is a local secret, since 'nowhere else in Bray can you enjoy a pint at a pub bench on a well-kept secluded lawn'. Wines from £22.

Chef/s: Matt Larcombe. **Closed:** 25 Dec. **Meals:** main courses £16 to £29. **Details:** 50 seats. 70 seats outside. Bar. Parking.

★ TOP 10 ★

The Fat Duck

Cooking score: 8
Modern British | £325
1 High Street, Bray, SL6 2AQ
Tel no: (01628) 580333
thefatduck.co.uk

'Curiouser and curiouser!' says Alice when, after tripping down the rabbit hole, she finds herself sucked into madcap adventures, spinning through preposterous experiences in which predictability and convention are abandoned to the four winds. 'Question Everything' says Heston Blumenthal on his coat of arms, presumably because if you don't, you end up accepting the status quo. And that is something Blumenthal would never do. Even at 20-odd years old, the Fat Duck remains untouchable, the *ne plus ultra* of mind- and palate-bending cooking; it occupies, in this unassuming whitewashed building, a universe parallel to uber-proper Bray high street where, for a prepaid £325 ticket, you, too, can channel your inner Alice. Suspend disbelief, allow Storytellers with their practised lines to take you on the nostalgia-laden trip to the seaside that is the framework for this multi-course, multi-sensory experience. Forgive that, as the hours pass, their spontaneity sometimes slips, and accept that there will be elements on a meal of this length that you may dislike. There's a harshness to the hot-cold stock 'tea'; and the 'Sounds of the Sea' foam is surely a tired trope by now. Indeed, for those of us who have had enough of foam on our plates (or framed sheets of glass in this case) it is the *concept* of this dish, the listening to splashing waves on earphones, that lingers long after the flavour of cured mackerel, abalone, clams and sea vegetables has ebbed – and even that feels dated. But, oh my, the shining gems! An aerated beetroot macaron, horseradish cream pricking its sweet earthiness, disappears in a puff of delicious memory; spirited nitro-poached 'cocktails' sparkle, dance and evaporate on the tongue; a gold fob watch dissolves into an intensely flavoured consommé before your eyes, part of the captivating 'mock turtle picnic' dish; the crab and passion fruit '99' is exquisite. 'Damping through the boroughgroves' may take you from Wonderland to Jabberwocky-land, but the diversion through a mist-swirled forest floor of mushroomy textures and flavours – morels, mealworms, a truffle 'log' – is the stuff of spellbinding genius, and delicious with it. All this theatricality is perhaps a tease for the exceptional 'main meal', however. Pigeon breasts are ineffably tender, conventionally and supremely enjoyable in a glossy red wine reduction, rich and sweet with onions. Mythical, appley, taffety tart is so impossibly perfect and fragile that it was surely made by fairies, the very same, perhaps, that keep a levitating pillow spinning as dimmed lights suggest the end of play. The soporific whiteness of this course with its taste and textures of marshmallow, meringue, white chocolate, orange blossom and malt is soothing to some; others find its softness, and the spoon with its fluffy, baby-powdery handle, unsettling. This isn't 'going out for lunch' in any conventional sense; it's going out for an experience, and it's worth knowing that when you buy your ticket. It's worth also being prepared for the galactic scope of the wine list and its correspondingly stratospheric pricing – you'd be wise to choose a recommended flight. It may come as a relief, however, to know that heavenly salt glazed brioche and double cream butter are just that – bread and butter – and that back home, when you dip into your Fat Duck memory by opening the goody-bag of sweets, the Queen of Hearts playing card is – phew – just a piece of decorated white chocolate. Back to reality.

Chef/s: Heston Blumenthal and Edward Cooke.
Closed: Sun, Mon, 2 weeks Christmas.
Meals: tasting menu £325. **Details:** 42 seats. V menu. Wheelchairs. Parking.

The Hind's Head

Cooking score: 4
British | £48
High Street, Bray, SL6 2AB
Tel no: (01628) 626151
hindsheadbray.com

£5 OFF

Bray truly is straight out of *Midsomer Murders*. It's all so perfect, and walking into this twee Heston Blumenthal pub does nothing to alleviate the idea that you're on a film set. This is what a British boozer looks like in a Hollywood movie: waistcoated staff, wood panelling, pewter tankards on the mantel. But the lack of draught ales and the high prices mean the pub comparison ends there, for The Hind's Head is more of a destination restaurant these days. There's no doubting the quality of the ingredients, though, and recommendations have come for silky-smooth smoked chicken liver parfait under a layer of dark brown limpid jelly; for chicken breast, the skin nicely crisped, the meat juicy, sitting on a smooth purée of broad beans and mint oil with a few nuggets of smoked lardons and grilled gem lettuce; and for an exemplary raspberry tart with a good, biscuity pastry, juicy sharp raspberries, crushed pistachios, Earl Grey ice cream and powdered raspberry. Wines start at £28 for a Picpoul, rising fairly steeply to three figures for big-hitting Burgundies, Bordeaux and the like.

Chef/s: Peter Grey. **Closed:** 25 Dec. **Meals:** main courses £20 to £40. Set L Mon to Fri £25 (3 courses). Sun L £44 (3 courses). Tasting menu £62 (5 courses). **Details:** 90 seats. Bar. Music. Parking.

★ TOP 50 ★

The Waterside Inn

Cooking score: 7
French | £165
Ferry Road, Bray, SL6 2AT
Tel no: (01628) 620691
waterside-inn.co.uk

'The one thing you can confidently say about The Waterside Inn is that the food is always delicious,' one reader was moved to note, adding that he found the setting 'magical' and the service 'so willing and friendly'. This is grand dining in old-fashioned style – ladies' menus still come unpriced. Most visitors want to sit in the front part of the large dining room with views over the willow-fringed Thames; to the rear you'll glimpse the river over the heads of those who bagged the best tables. Alain Roux's food is built around the enduring values of French cookery: his brand of rare refinement is applied to impeccable ingredients and the place generally lives up to diners' expectations, especially those for whom money is no object. An inspection meal included a superb fillet of turbot alongside fish mousse wrapped in carrot strips and topped with a mushroom duxelle and a single morel, the plate finished with an exemplary vin jaune sauce. Equally impressive was a lobster starter – half a fat tender tail and a massive claw – served in its shell and bathed in a syrupy ginger and white port sauce with tiny strips of blanched carrot. Seasonal dishes encompass a springtime milk-fed lamb from the Pyrenees, its shoulder, leg, chops and kidney all roasted to different degrees of excellence and served with asparagus, slices of potato, an almost consommé-clear reduced lamb sauce and a first-class sauce paloise. Desserts, like a rhubarb soufflé with rhubarb compôte, will put the finish on any celebration. Wines remain resolutely French and very expensive.

Chef/s: Alain Roux. **Closed:** Mon, Tue, 26 Dec to 31 Jan. **Meals:** main courses £54 to £67. Set L Wed to Fri £52 (2 courses) to £64. Set L Sat and Sun £80. Tasting menu £168 (6 courses). **Details:** 70 seats. Bar. Parking. Children over 9 yrs.

Burchett's Green

The Crown

Cooking score: 6
Anglo/French | £35
Burchett's Green, SL6 6QZ
Tel no: (01628) 824079
thecrownburchettsgreen.com

'A really excellent recommendation in the Guide, so here is another thumbs-up for it,' reported a very satisfied visitor much taken by Simon Bonwick's brick-built village hostelry. It still works as a pub – you enter straight into a tiny fire-warmed bar – but the focus is on food, with the cooking deeply rooted in French technique and served in a small dining room whose decorative style could be described as smart country chic. Bonwick buys wisely and cooks ably within limitations: he works alone in the kitchen, with members of his family doing duty as kitchen porters and waiting staff. Such a set-up dictates a short menu, perhaps marinade of anchovies with flavours of Provence or rillette of rabbit with French pickles to start, then rump of salt marsh lamb with a 'gorgeous sauce' or the glorious delight that is the braised haunch of venison pie. There could be raspberry bavarois or the house speciality, coffee and walnut cigar, to finish. Home-baked sourdough rolls, impressive cheeses from La Fromagerie and the 'sincere and genuine' welcome from eldest son Dean and his various siblings have also been praised. Keen prices extend to the short wine list, which opens at £21.

Chef/s: Simon Bonwick. **Closed:** Mon, Tue, 2 weeks New Year, 2 weeks Aug. **Meals:** main courses £18 to £24. **Details:** 18 seats. Bar. Music. Parking. No children under 12 yrs.

Cookham

The White Oak

Cooking score: 3
Modern British | £31

The Pound, Cookham, SL6 9QE
Tel no: (01628) 523043
thewhiteoak.co.uk

£5 OFF

Smartly refurbished for the good folk of Cookham, the White Oak satisfies the needs of thirsty drinkers and their hungry counterparts – with a hidden garden pleasing both camps. Prime Highland steaks hold a special place on the menu, although the kitchen embarks on a user-friendly tour through the contemporary brasserie repertoire, taking in everything from pickled mackerel with rhubarb and chilli jam, horseradish and radish to steamed chicken and ham hock pudding or lemon sole with Bombay potatoes, brown shrimps and spiced yoghurt. After that, brioche 'donuts' or lardy cake with salted caramel and vanilla ice cream deliver a satisfying calorific punch. Readers also like the 'modestly priced' set menu, which has yielded crispy ox cheek croquettes, soft and moist calf's liver on chard and mustard mash, commendable cheeses and tangy raspberry fool. Around 40 trusty wines include a respectable showing by the glass. Related to the Three Oaks, Gerrards Cross (see entry).

Chef/s: Graham Kirk. **Meals:** main courses £15 to £28. Set L and D £16 (2 courses) to £19. **Details:** 76 seats. 30 seats outside. Bar. Wheelchairs. Music. Parking.

Hurley

Hurley House

Cooking score: 4
Modern British | £45

Henley Road, Hurley, SL6 5LH
Tel no: (01628) 568500
hurleyhouse.co.uk

£5 OFF

Built on the site of a long-neglected roadside pub, Hurley House combines the attributes of a boutique hotel with the allure of an elegant rustic-chic restaurant in the modern style (black slate floors, clubby green leather banquettes, bare brickwork). Local ales and posh snacks are served at the high-ceilinged bar; progress to the dining room for skilfully rendered, ingredients-led cooking. Although lots of components jostle for attention on the plate, the results are never overworked – just consider a starter involving Jerusalem artichoke, celeriac, hazelnuts and Périgord truffle or an equally busy main course pairing of North Sea cod and Scottish haddock with smoked bacon, potato, samphire, leeks and mussels. Elsewhere, wood pigeon wellington with mushroom ketchup keeps things seasonal, as do desserts such as rhubarb tarte fine with white chocolate crumble. Back-up comes from an overtly ambitious wine list.

Chef/s: Emanuele Privitera. **Meals:** main courses £17 to £36. Set L £18 (2 courses) to £24. **Details:** 38 seats. 68 seats outside. Bar. Wheelchairs. Music. Parking.

Newbury

The Vineyard

Cooking score: 4
Modern French | £69

Stockcross, Newbury, RG20 8JU
Tel no: (01635) 528770
the-vineyard.co.uk

£5 OFF

There's a little corner of Berkshire that is forever California, and it's here at Sir Peter Michael's Dionysian ranch where, behind a flaming water feature, the tiled expanses of a slick boutique hotel open before you. The dramatic split-level dining room with its wrought-iron foliage is backed by a space-age wine store where glass walls keep an air-conditioned watch on 3,000 listings. Before you start on that, there's Robby Jenks' modern European cooking to consider, which makes a virtue of strong seasonings and bold combinations. A starter of soy and treacle tuna, beetroot, avocado and ginger might herald a serving of Indian-spiced cod with cauliflower and coconut, or duck breast with blackberries and beetroot, accompanied by celeriac purée. Finish with cassis-laced blackcurrant soufflé and liquorice ice cream. And so to the wine: new plantings in the Napa will soon buttress the owner's established estates in Knights Valley, Sonoma County and the environs, with Chardonnay, Pinot Noir and red Bordeaux blends awaiting (re)discovery by fans of American viticulture, but there are wondrous treasures from the whole world over. Complex English sparklers, zesty Alsace Rieslings, Sauvignon's finest hours in Pouilly-Fumé, Super Tuscans, starry Douros, arriviste Greeks, and a rolling lava flow of botrytised and late-harvested stickies will help to while away a month-long stay. Start the meter running at £25 a bottle.

Chef/s: Robby Jenks. **Meals:** set L £24 (2 courses) to £29. Set D £48 (2 courses) to £69. Sun L £39. Tasting menus £89 (7 courses) to £99. **Details:** 80 seats. 100 seats outside. V menu. Vg menu. Bar. Wheelchairs. Music. Parking. No children after 7pm

Old Windsor

The Oxford Blue

Cooking score: 5

Modern British | £65

10 Crimp Hill, Old Windsor, SL4 2QY
Tel no: (01753) 861954
oxfordbluepub.co.uk

Some places manage to marry classic French cooking and precise presentation with a relaxed pub setting so happily that nobody thinks to question the partnership. The Oxford Blue is one such place. There's beer on tap from a long bar, bare floors and tables, lots of tweed and tartan, and a powerful menu from Steven Ellis, who demonstrates his top-flight pedigree in every dish. Begin with his signature braised pig's trotter, an exquisitely crafted ballotine, with its perfect companions of black pudding, apple (prettily arranged slivers of red- and green-skinned varieties) and a sharp sauce gribiche; continue with pheasant (from Windsor Great Park) with celeriac, confit leg and more apple, or a magnificent raised chicken pie. This is a nostalgia-laden masterclass, the confit meat inside the crisp golden pastry tender, the accompanying mash smooth and rich. Finish with a silky Cambridge burnt cream with pine and juniper biscuits that you won't need, but won't leave, either. There is a separate vegan menu with choices, and a wine list that opens at £18.50.

Chef/s: Steven Ellis. **Closed:** Mon, Tue, 1 week Christmas, 23 to 31 Jul. **Meals:** main courses £29 to £36. Set L £20 (2 courses) to £25. Tasting menu £75. **Details:** 45 seats. 16 seats outside. Vg menu. Bar. Music. Parking.

Paley Street

The Royal Oak

Cooking score: 4

Modern British | £40

Littlefield Green, Paley Street, SL6 3JN
Tel no: (01628) 620541
theroyaloakpaleystreet.com

Nick Parkinson's 'smart but unshowy dining pub' continues to fly high on the food front. Behind a traditional white-painted façade lies an elegant wood-floored interior with old beams and standing timbers in the bar, and striking modern artwork in the L-shaped dining room, with terrace doors giving on to a sheltered stone garden. As for food, Leon Smith's clear-sighted, thoughtful approach pays dividends all year round; his appealing menus are built on good, seasonal produce and sensible combinations. Wood pigeon with caramelised chicory, walnuts and port, and dressed crab with blood orange, radicchio and sorrel are typical of the restrained starters.

Mains include truffled polenta with roasted spring onions and heritage carrots, Cornish brill with crab bisque, borlotti beans, clams and samphire, or the roasted saddle of Crown Estate venison that came with a venison sausage roll, lightly braised radishes, chard, celeriac and a glossy meat sauce and so impressed at inspection. The wine list 'is still cracking', ranging from obscure little treats (from £25) to pricey Bordeaux, with good choice by the glass.

Chef/s: Leon Smith. **Meals:** main courses £18 to £36. Tasting menu £65 (7 courses). **Details:** 80 seats. Bar. Music. Parking.

Shefford Woodlands

LOCAL GEM

The Pheasant Inn

Modern British | £30

Ermin Street, Shefford Woodlands, RG17 7AA
Tel no: (01488) 648284
thepheasant-inn.co.uk

With a rural aspect, though just a few minutes from junction 14 of the M4, the partly weatherboarded Pheasant is well groomed and eager to please. The kitchen looks to Europe and beyond for its modern repertoire: Moroccan lamb parcels, tempura courgette flower with feta and toasted quinoa, and tarte tatin to share. There's fish and chips and a posh burger, too, and classic Sunday lunches including whole roast chicken and chateaubriand sharers. Drink real ales from the pumps, or wines from £17.

Local Gem

These entries highlight a range of neighbourhood venues, delivering good, freshly cooked food at great value for money.

Taplow

★ TOP 50 ★

André Garrett at Cliveden

Cooking score: 8

Modern French | £75

Cliveden House, Bourne End Road, Taplow, SL6 0JF
Tel no: (01628) 607100
clivedenhouse.co.uk

'Immaculate service that the redoubtable Lady Astor would have approved of, and superb food,' a report concludes. 'Turning into the driveway, the house looked really quite special . . . the whole experience lived up to that first impression', commented another. There's nothing quite like Cliveden, the grandest of country house hotels. The darkly panelled, tapestry-hung entrance hall has a time-warp charm, the extremely elegant restaurant bags the view (of the splendid parterre and glorious English countryside beyond), and it is all run with a sense of unarguable civility and grace. André Garrett's contemporary French cooking certainly matches the setting, offering a mix of classic techniques with bold, modern touches. What gives his food vitality, indeed its identity, is the use of sharp flavours to point up the main item: for example, a twice-baked Lincolnshire Poacher soufflé with apple and truffle salad, or a fresh-tasting garden beetroot salad with ewe's yoghurt, hazelnut, fennel pollen and ice wine dressing. Or take a disarmingly simple and meaty chunk of Cornish turbot, perfectly timed, with gem lettuce, clams, leeks, lemon and olive oil, or locally stalked fallow deer with braised shoulder, watercress, chestnut and pickled blackberry. These are dishes full of vibrancy. Concluding our meal, a Bramley apple soufflé (with a basil ice cream) matched the brilliance of the opening cheese version, but the gold star went to an intense, zingy lemon sablé. The comprehensive wine list contains an embarrassment of riches

(especially in France), for which you'll need to be embarrassingly rich as just a handful of bottles are in the £35 to £45 category.
Chef/s: André Garrett. **Meals:** main courses £21 to £58. Set L £36. Sun L £60. Tasting menu £98 (7 courses). **Details:** 70 seats. Bar. Music. Parking. No children after 7pm.

The Astor Grill

Cooking score: 3
British/American | £40
Cliveden House, Taplow, SL6 0JF
Tel no: (01628) 668561
clivedenhouse.co.uk

Hotels really don't come any more impressive than Cliveden, a dazzling country pile with acreage and annexes – one of which houses the Astor Grill. The gastronomic flagship may be André Garrett at Cliveden (see entry), but this more flexible and casual restaurant is also overseen by Garrett – and his team put on a convincing show. Fronted by a large sheltered terrace (the perfect spot for a summer lunch), the former stable block has been smoothed over with rich wood tones, deep blue leather banquettes and soft lighting. It is open all day for brunch, lunch and dinner, and the menu, though brief, has broad appeal, romping through classics such as omelette Arnold Bennett, Cornish mussels with grilled sourdough, chargrilled Ibérico pork or lamb chops and chateaubriand for two to share, as well as offering superfood salads, buttermilk chicken sandwiches and a beef burger with smoked raclette cheese. Desserts such as English trifle with port jelly meet with readers' approval, too. A short, global wine list starts at £30.
Chef/s: André Garrett and Paul O'Neill. **Meals:** main courses £16 to £32. **Details:** 40 seats. 30 seats outside. Bar. Wheelchairs. Music. Parking.

White Waltham

The Beehive

Cooking score: 6
British | £38
Waltham Road, White Waltham, SL6 3SH
Tel no: (01628) 822877
thebeehivewhitewaltham.com

£5 OFF

Dominic Chapman is the driving force and guiding light behind this upmarket country pub overlooking White Waltham's cricket pitch. Indeed, he has built up a loyal following since opening in 2014, thanks in part to a careful balance of pubby approachability – a spacious bar offering genuine civility and warmth – and an equally spacious and well-arranged dining room offering simple yet alluring cooking of first-class ingredients. When a meal can open with 'very good' rosemary and sea salt bread rolls 'piping hot from the oven' and go on to wild rabbit lasagne with wood blewits and chervil, it is clear that cooking is taken seriously. Everybody seems to find everything 'beautifully cooked', and readers have applauded a sharing platter (for two) of roast rib of medium-rare Black Angus beef with spinach, greens, shallots and persillade, chips and béarnaise sauce on one occasion, on another whole Brixham lemon sole, complemented by splendid brown shrimps, dill and lemon butter sauce and some 'super mash'. Desserts have been a particular highlight for many, lemon curd and passion fruit tart garnering as much praise as a luxurious chocolate fondant with almond biscuit, a real toffee sauce and indulgent coffee ice cream. A wide-ranging wine list provides a good, varied selection, with several choices also by glass and carafe.
Chef/s: Dominic Chapman. **Closed:** 25 and 26 Dec. **Meals:** main courses £16 to £28. Set L and D £20 (2 courses) to £25. **Details:** 70 seats. 50 seats outside. Bar. Wheelchairs. Music. Parking.

Woodspeen
The Woodspeen

Cooking score: 6
Modern British | £46
Lambourn Road, Woodspeen, RG20 8BN
Tel no: (01635) 265070
thewoodspeen.com
£5 OFF

John Campbell brings his considerable experience to bear on the confident, classy food at this well-established restaurant. Formerly a roadside pub, the building retains some of its old looks, but the feel is bright, clean and fresh, the kitchen open to view, with a sleek contemporary finish to the dining room. There's a pleasing seasonal rhythm to menus featuring celeriac soup with beetroot, shiitake, pine nut and parsley, and pheasant breast with parsley root, chard and caper sauce, or smoked Cheddar ravioli with onion broth and beef cheek, and cod with salsify, braised onion and potted shrimps. And with upbeat classics offered, say a sharing plate of Middle White pork chop and belly, with crackling and homemade black pudding, the kitchen has judged nicely what local people want. The Woodspeen's bread is irresistible, and you can indulge in desserts such as buttermilk parfait with rhubarb, ginger cake and blood orange. The amiable service has the warmth required to get people coming back, while the wine list, a majestic tome, ventures along lesser-known byways, as well as giving full rein to big hitters.

Chef/s: John Campbell. **Meals:** main courses £18 to £36. Set L and early D £24 (2 courses) to £29. **Details:** 66 seats. 36 seats outside. Vg menu. Bar. Wheelchairs. Music. Parking.

Inspector highlights

Our undercover inspectors reveal their most memorable dishes from a year of extraordinary eating.

'At **New Yard** near Mawgan, Cornwall, a thick slice of barbecued beetroot topped with whipped goat's curd, paper thin slices of pickled beetroot and beer vinaigrette. It had earthiness, umami and acidity. It looked terrific, too.'

'Two from **A. Wong**, Victoria: first a dainty, Zhou dynasty-style crab claw, cut open at table and filled with diced, cured scallop and wasabi, then Xi'an City 'lamb burger' with sesame, coriander and chilli.'

'Pig's head terrine at **Audela**, Berwick-upon-Tweed was a paradise of porcine perfection, while simple, sautéed spring-lamb offal at **The Feathers Inn**, Hedley on the Hill was a tasty plateful that many places don't have the confidence to offer.'

'Two tartes tatin were memorable for different reasons: the delicacy of Rogan's apple tartlet at **Roganic** and the unreconstructed, sticky charm of the version at **Evelyn's Table**.'

'**Jidori**'s ginger ice cream with miso caramel, sweet potato crisps and black sesame is a triumphant pud. A riot of sweet and salty flavours, the miso caramel takes it to another level.'

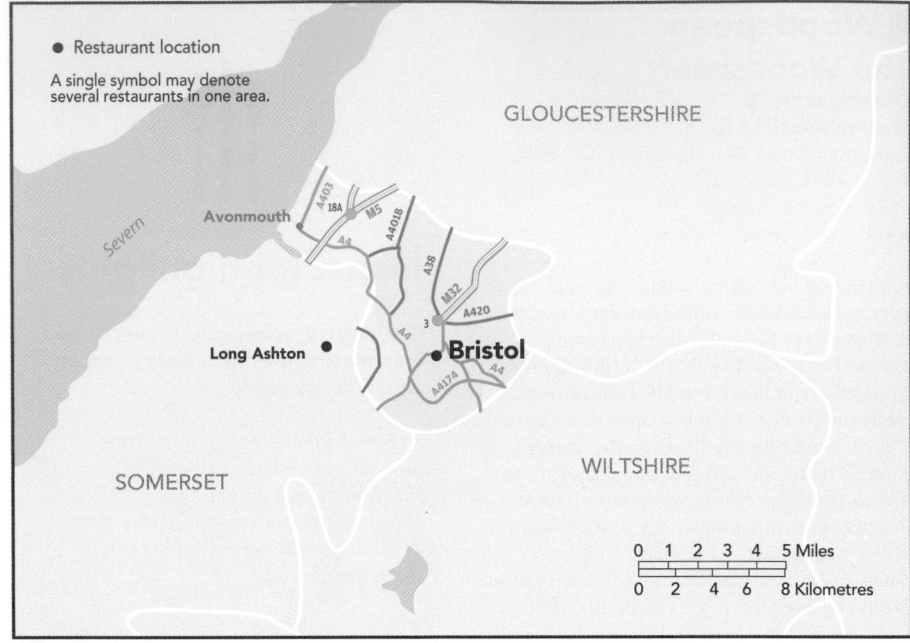

Bristol

Adelina Yard

Cooking score: 4
Modern European | £41
3 Queen Quay, Welsh Back, Bristol, BS1 4SL
Tel no: (0117) 911 2112
adelinayard.com

Jamie Randall and Olivia Barry's venture continues to thrive with its Nordic-influenced British cooking, and is well established at the heart of Bristol's dining scene. The introduction of a chef's table in front of the open-view kitchen has added much-needed covers to what is a compact, narrow space, but the menus remain as terse as before, with three choices per course if you aren't swayed by the bargain tasting menu. Crab, kohlrabi and lovage is a delicate way to start a meal, or perhaps pork jowl, pear, fermented Jerusalem artichoke and hazelnut will catch your eye. For mains, how about roast skrei cod, crisp chicken wings, leeks and baby spinach or salt-baked celeriac, shiitake gel, mushroom, kale and truffle? Combinations are well considered, not least at the dessert stage when semolina cake is teamed with blood orange, mascarpone and panko breadcrumbs. The European-focused wine list opens at £21, with taster-size glasses from £2.50.

Chef/s: Jamie Randall and Olivia Barry. **Closed:** Sun, Mon, 23 Dec to 8 Jan, 3 Mar, 22 Jul. **Meals:** main courses £19 to £24. Tasting menu £57 to £65. **Details:** 34 seats. 10 seats outside. Wheelchairs. Music.

Bell's Diner

Cooking score: 3
Mediterranean | £25
1-3 York Road, Montpelier, Bristol, BS6 5QB
Tel no: (0117) 924 0357
bellsdiner.com
£30

Down a Montpelier backstreet, Bell's Diner has built a reputation as the go-to place for beautifully cooked Mediterranean and North African-inspired small plates. The setting and

location may be bohemian, but don't let the rickety chairs and wine menus in old record sleeves fool you – the cooking here is serious. Seasonal ingredients are impeccably sourced, resulting in 'wonderfully fresh, lemony' winter tabouleh accompanying charcoal-roasted kohlrabi and squash, or three fat juicy prawns barbecued and drenched in lime and chilli butter, and grilled sardines with rich, spicy, slightly sweet muhammara with pangrattato and smoked oil. The fish dishes might have stolen the show, but a pinxto of tender pieces of chicken breast marinated in buttermilk with nora peppers and spiced yoghurt was equally enjoyable, while a slice of dense cheesecake with caramelised white chocolate sauce 'provided a joyous end'. The eclectic drinks list takes in wines from Turkey and Greece, offers 'tastes' as well as glasses and bottles, and features local beers, ciders and intriguing aperitifs.
Chef/s: Dan Brookes. **Closed:** 24 to 28 Dec, 1 Jan. **Meals:** small plates £4 to £13. **Details:** 55 seats. Bar. Music. No children after 8pm.

Bellita

Cooking score: 2
Mediterranean | £25
34 Cotham Hill, Bristol, BS6 6LA
Tel no: (0117) 923 8755
bellita.co.uk

'You want to order everything on the menu,' noted one visitor to this warmly welcoming, informal restaurant serving Spanish and North African small plates and moreish snacks. The lighting is pretty dim, dining a mix of counters with high stools and banquette seating, which gives a jumbled, bar-like feel – if you're not content to perch, phone ahead to bag one of the tables. Dinner is a succession of big-hitting flavours: jamón croquetas alone are worth the trip, but there's also Ibérico pork cheeks with prunes, star-anise-flavoured white bean purée and purple sprouting broccoli, locally grown asparagus with an intensely rich pine nut mayonnaise, or a Valencian squid rice with tangy mojo verde. Puddings are bite-size bursts of sweetness, say two pieces of homemade rosemary, fig, grapefruit and pistachio nougat or a dark chocolate pot accompanied by a few Málaga raisins steeped in sherry. With a variety of quirkily named cocktails, homemade cordials and digestifs, not to mention a wine list sourced exclusively from female winemakers, the drinks list is almost as exciting as the food.
Chef/s: Sam Sohn-Rethel and Pash Peters. **Closed:** Sun, 25 and 26 Dec. **Meals:** small plates £5 to £15. **Details:** 42 seats. Bar. Wheelchairs. Music.

Box-E

Cooking score: 4
Modern British | £29
Unit 10, Cargo 1, Wapping Wharf, Bristol, BS1 6WP
boxebristol.com

Want to really be a part of the action? The four 'chef's table' seats here are possibly as close to working in a professional kitchen as you can get. But then all tables in this harbourside restaurant, fashioned out of two shipping containers, enjoy a view of chef Elliott Lidstone cooking single-handedly in the open kitchen as wife Tessa runs front of house. Big on flavour, Lidstone's menu delivers beautifully presented, skilful cooking from the outset. Look to chopped fillet of raw beef, Jerusalem artichoke crisps and horseradish, or baked duck egg with smoked trout to start, perhaps leading on to hake, crushed potatoes and seaweed butter, or tender crispy pork belly, black lentils and rainbow chard. Desserts offer equal satisfaction, with vanilla panna cotta, poached rhubarb, blood orange and pistachio providing a show-stopping finale. A wine list that rarely strays outside Europe opens at £23, with a dozen by the glass.
Chef/s: Elliott Lidstone. **Closed:** Sun, Mon. **Meals:** main courses £14 to £17. Tasting menu £45. **Details:** 18 seats. Wheelchairs. Music.

Bravas

Cooking score: 2
Spanish | £15
7 Cotham Hill, Bristol, BS6 6LD
Tel no: (0117) 329 6887
bravas.co.uk

It's small, cramped and, local spies tell us, bookings are essential whether it's Monday lunchtime or Saturday night, but it is worth making an effort to eat at this Bristol hot spot. Kieran and Imogen Waite really have built their own corner of Barcelona with this lively tapas bar where drinkers and diners squeeze on to high stools at the elmwood bar or grab tables under the stairs at the back. Dishes from a concise and frequently changing menu are sent out by chefs working in a diminutive open kitchen behind the bar, perhaps chorizo and mushroom croquetas, charred cauliflower salad with chimichurri and almonds, Newlyn sardines with garlic and chilli dressing, or braised Hereford ox cheek with celeriac purée. Finish with Seville orange, hazelnut and almond meringues or salted chocolate truffles. Apart from a few carefully chosen Bristol beers and around 25 premium gins, the drinks list rarely looks beyond Spain, with 10 sherries and wines from £18.40.

Chef/s: Mark Chapman and Alice Hart. **Closed:** Sun, 24 to 26 Dec, 1 Jan. **Meals:** tapas £3 to £8. **Details:** 40 seats. Bar. Music.

Bristol Lido

Cooking score: 1
Spanish | £35
Oakfield Place, Bristol, BS8 2BJ
Tel no: (0117) 332 3970
lidobristol.com

'A genuine find, an oasis of calm hidden behind houses, you really wouldn't know it's there,' noted one regular to Clifton's restored Victorian lido and spa. The window seats overlooking the heated infinity pool are highly prized, as are tables looking into the partially open kitchen with its wood-fired oven. Chef Freddy Bird divides his time between here and the new Reading Lido, but his mark is all over menus of colourful, seasonal food with influences from Spain, North Africa and the Middle East seen in the likes of smokey, charcoal-grilled aubergine, mint, chilli, garlic and labneh, or lamb leg with arrocina beans, grelos, crispy sweetbreads and salsa verde. Largely drawn from Spain and Italy, the wines start at £19.50.

Chef/s: Freddy Bird. **Closed:** 25 and 26 Dec, 1 Jan. **Meals:** main courses £17 to £30. Set L and D £16 (2 courses) to £20. **Details:** 130 seats. 24 seats outside. Bar. Wheelchairs. Music.

Bulrush

Cooking score: 5
Modern British | £60
21 Cotham Road South, Bristol, BS6 5TZ
Tel no: (0117) 329 0990
bulrushrestaurant.co.uk

£5 OFF

Look for the deep violet frontage of a modest neighbourhood restaurant on a rather unpromising stretch of road in Cotham, and prepare to be astonished. Old chairs at bare tables amid whitewashed brick walls are the unplugged setting in which George Livesey's kitchen turns up the modern British burners for jet-propelled cooking that's all about novelty and ingenuity. Barbecued ox heart with apple, turnips and seaweed was a counterintuitive hit at a reader's retirement do, and the fondness for oddball ingredients adds coal purée to the beetroot tartare and crab apple. At main, it might be roast brill with tulip, crab and green tea or a distinctly more mainstream, but no less effective, Aylesbury duck breast with leeks and black garlic. To finish, there's bee pollen with the honey parfait and yoghurt sorbet, or ceps and burnt apple with a mousse of roasted white chocolate. 'Above all else,' reports our reader, 'the welcome and service were warm, unobtrusive and efficient in equal measure' – the gold standard. On-trend aperitif cocktails usher in a tiny wine list that starts at £27 for a fruit-driven Gascon white.

Chef/s: George Livesey. **Closed:** Sun, Mon, 23 Dec for 3 weeks, 1 week May, 2 weeks Sept. **Meals:** main courses £18 to £22. Tasting menu £60. **Details:** 18 seats. V menu. Music.

★ TOP 10 ★

Casamia

Cooking score: 9
Modern British | £98
The General, Lower Guinea Street, Bristol, BS1 6SY
Tel no: (0117) 959 2884
casamiarestaurant.co.uk

The listed Victorian building overlooking Bathurst Basin used to be a hospital, its ground floor now taken up by Peter Sánchez-Iglesias's intimate and innovative restaurant. This is an everybody-should-do-it-once sort of place, though it helps to be prepared for the underlying concept – first-timers may well find themselves quite at sea. The 10-course, seasonally inspired tasting menu lists dishes by their main component only, so sit back and leave the rest to the open-to-view kitchen – the soaring sophistication of the food is sensational. Plates are small, even the main acts, with delivery coming from chefs willing and able to fill in the gaps on the sparingly written menu. 'Salad' is a super mix of vegetables and leaves in miniature – fresh, pickled, jam, barbecued, dried – given depth by punchy Aztec mint and dots of sheep's curd, while 'Beetroot' is a masterly combination of warm (sweet beetroot risotto) and cold (yoghurt sorbet), with pickled fennel and pistachio for extra texture. A nugget of confit trout loin, enlivened by crab bisque, on the side a delicate trout belly mousse topped with roe and served with skin crisps, is totally irresistible. And then there are the little flavour bombs: the umami hit of a delicate tartlet filled with aged Parmesan, and the rich, fleeting contrasts of carabinero (red) prawn tartare in a sweet shell of seaweed meringue. Equally notable is butter- and lemon-poached turbot with a glorious Champagne sabayon, sweet slices of grape and earthy shaved summer truffle, and duck breast, salt-brined and as tender and tasty as could be, cleverly supported by dabs of chia seed, lentils and fondant potato. Tarragon mousse, pulled into focus by layers of passion fruit seeds, crisp tarragon meringue and passion fruit granita and jam, is the perfect curtain-raiser for a riff on rhubarb textures, with a cube of delicate lemon and juniper Turkish delight and an intense porcini mushroom fudge the final trump card. And the wine? It's a fascinating list with many desirable bottles and small, interesting producers galore (from £30), so it's worth thinking about a matching flight or giving sommelier Tom Lakin a budget to get the best out of it.

Chef/s: Peter Sánchez-Iglesias and Jim Day. **Closed:** Sun, Mon, Tue, 24 Dec to 9 Jan. **Meals:** tasting menu £98 to £118. Set L Fri £48 (4 courses). **Details:** 28 seats. V menu. Wheelchairs. Music.

Flour & Ash

Cooking score: 1
Italian | £20
203b Cheltenham Road, Bristol, BS6 5QX
Tel no: (0117) 9083228
flourandash.co.uk

In a parade of shops close to railway arches spanning Cheltenham Road, this compact pizzeria is a simple enough proposition: wood-fired pizzas and homemade ice cream in a modest, hard-edged setting of wood floor and metal-topped bench sets. Pizzas range from a classic margherita to onglet steak with mozzarella, wood-roast jalapeños and cowboy butter. Regulars add a dip, say Parmesan aïoli, for the 'well cooked' crusts. A handful of starters – maybe wood-roast quail with za'atar and aïoli – and sides of salads or truffle polenta chips add to the appeal. Bottled beers are mainly Bristol brewed, while everything on the brief list of global wines comes by the glass. Booking is recommended.

Chef/s: Brendan Baker. **Closed:** 24 to 26 Dec, 31 Dec, 1 Jan. **Meals:** main courses £9 to £14. **Details:** 41 seats. Music.

Vegetarian and vegan

While many restaurants offer individual dishes suitable for non-meat eaters, those marked 'V menu' (vegetarian) and 'Vg menu' (vegan) offer separate menus.

Greens

Cooking score: 3
Modern European | £28
25 Zetland Road, Bristol, BS6 7AH
Tel no: (0117) 924 6437
greensbristol.co.uk

When it comes to opening a neighbourhood restaurant, you've got to know your neighbourhood, and Greens is spot-on for Redland. In business since 2012, it's relaxed and easy-going enough for eating out on a whim, but celebrating a special occasion here wouldn't feel amiss, either. The menu deals in judicious flavour combinations. A first-course ham hash cake with poached egg and hollandaise is full of bistro attitude, with grilled sea bream escabèche a lighter, sharper alternative. Follow on with hake with king prawns and butter bean and chorizo casserole, or pork belly with dauphinois and apple sauce. Steaks get their own menu, featuring 28-day dry-aged sirloin, ribeye or fillet from a local butcher. Pear frangipane tart with rhubarb compôte and clotted cream sends you home happy. A decent slate of vegan and vegetarian options, plus set lunch and midweek set dinner menus, broaden the appeal still further. The concise wine list opens at £19.50, and includes options by the glass and carafe.

Chef/s: Martin Laurentowicz. **Closed:** 24 to 28 Dec. **Meals:** main courses £15 to £28. Set L £13 (2 courses) to £17. Set D £18 (2 courses) to £24. Sun L £19. **Details:** 40 seats. 8 seats outside. V menu. Music.

★ NEW ENTRY ★

The Kensington Arms

Cooking score: 1
Modern British | £25
35-37 Stanley Road, Bristol, BS6 6NP
Tel no: (0117) 944 6444
thekensingtonarms.co.uk

Josh Eggleton of the Pony & Trap and Root (see entries) co-owns this Victorian corner pub tucked away in the backstreets of Redland. Known as the Kenny, it's a vibrant local with a well-supported bar, where a short menu includes a brilliant burger ('one of the best in Bristol'), and a smart dining room with an open-view kitchen where you can watch chef Luke Hawkins at work. Here the menu has a seasonal feel, mixing well-honed pub staples (fish and chips; ham, egg and chips) with crab cakes with curry mayo and pickled turnip, or fillet of sea bass with mussels, sea vegetables, new potatoes and salsa verde. Finish with orange crème brûlée and cardamom ice cream. Wines from £19.

Chef/s: Luke Hawkins. **Closed:** 25 Dec. **Meals:** main courses £12 to 17. Set L £12 (2 courses) to £18. Sun L £21 (2 courses) to £25. Tasting menu £35. **Details:** 100 seats. 40 seats outside. Bar. Wheelchairs. Music.

Mesa

Cooking score: 2
Tapas | £25
2B North View, Bristol, BS6 7QB
Tel no: (0117) 970 6276
mesabar.co.uk

A galaxy of filament light bulbs shine down on the happy throng at Mesa as they tuck into small plates inspired by Spain, North Africa and the Middle East. It's Spain that leads the line, with boquerones and classic tortilla with allioli in support of pan-fried chorizo simmered in Asturian cider, and smoked sardines and sweet peppers on toast. These Iberian flavours are joined by more contemporary numbers such as a salad of raw fennel and Braeburn apples dressed with Moscatel vinaigrette, while Syrian lentils with cumin yoghurt remains a firm favourite with vegetarians and non-vegetarians alike. Everything looks enticing on the plate – neighbour envy is a real possibility. To finish, smashed cherry and feta cheesecake with almonds and Campari ties it all up nicely. Iberian wines are at the forefront of a drinks list that runs to creative cocktails, sherries and Spanish beers and ciders.

Chef/s: Olly Gallery. **Closed:** Sun, Mon. **Meals:** tapas £4 to £11. **Details:** 50 seats. Music.

No Man's Grace

Cooking score: 2
Modern European | £32
6 Chandos Road, Bristol, BS6 6PE
Tel no: (0117) 974 4077
nomansgrace.com
£5 OFF

Simply furnished premises in the Redland district of the city house John Watson's aspirational neighbourhood venue. Watson (ex-Casamia) opened here in 2014, and aims to offer an affordable version of cutting-edge contemporary cooking via a traditional carte and seven-course tasting menu. Dishes are constructed from solid building blocks of flavour, as in a duck liver faggot with bashed swede and peppered granola followed, perhaps, by hake with roasted cauliflower and monk's beard, dressed in hazelnut oil. There is an assertive boldness to these compositions, which may not always be the most elegant, but deliver where it matters. The tasting menu might hinge on smoked haddock in cockle chowder, and then 40-day aged sirloin with celeriac and shallots, before one of the signature desserts appears: warm hazelnut mousse with chocolate brownie and salt caramel ice cream, for example. Attractive cocktails include rhubarb gimlet and the house take on a classic negroni, while the concise, varietally arranged wine list, from £20, does an efficient job.

Chef/s: John Watson. **Closed:** Mon, Tue. **Meals:** set L £18 (2 courses) to £20. Set D £22 (2 courses) to £27. Sun L £25. Tasting menu £45. **Details:** 30 seats. 25 seats outside. Bar.

The Ox

Cooking score: 3
British | £35
The Basement, 43 Corn Street, Bristol, BS1 1HT
Tel no: (0117) 922 1001
theoxbristol.com

Hopes rarely rise when descending stairs to a basement dining room, but this former bank vault is such a unique setting, it doesn't disappoint. The spiral marble staircase takes you into a darkly lit room of oak panels, vintage mirrors and rich colours. Here, beef is the star: sourced from a local butcher, dry-aged for at least 35 days, and flame-grilled over charcoal. And with D-rump, sirloin, ribeye, fillet, USDA prime, or bone-in rib to share, plus a range of sauces, Ox offers umpteen ways to have your pound of flesh. In addition, there's hickory-smoked sticky ribs or chargrilled squid to start, and pan-fried skate wing with brown shrimp butter or glazed pig's cheeks with potato gratin as alternative main courses. Sunday roast is a big thing, taking in rump of beef or leg of Somerset lamb with all the trimmings. A short wine list features big-hitting reds and food-friendly whites. There's a second branch on Whiteladies Road, BS8 2QX.

Chef/s: Luke Angus. **Closed:** 24 to 27 Dec. **Meals:** main courses £13 to £31. Set L £12 (2 courses) to £15. Sun L £18 (2 courses). **Details:** 80 seats.

Stay in the know

For the latest restaurant news, look out for the weekly *GFG Briefing*. Visit thegoodfoodguide.co.uk

Paco Tapas

Cooking score: 5
Spanish | £35
3a The General, Lower Guinea Street, Bristol, BS1 6SY
Tel no: (0117) 925 7021
pacotapas.co.uk

What started life as a low-key bolt-on to neighbouring Casamia (see entry) has quickly become a must-visit destination in itself. With an equally popular terrace overlooking the harbour basin, this busy Andalusian-style bar takes tapas to a different level thanks largely to the use of a charcoal-fuelled grill in the open kitchen. Cooking over fire with such precision and consistency takes a great degree of skill and Peter Sanchez-Iglesias and his team combinine traditional techniques with the cutting-edge skills learnt at Casamia. Raw materials from Spain (lomo Ibérico de bellota, carabineros prawns) and closer to home (fish arrives daily from Cornwall) are treated with great respect and care at every stage. Galician beef cecina is impeccably presented as razor-thin slices, a pair of scallops come grilled in their shells and basted with rosemary-scented pork fat, smokey gambas al ajillo are just seasoned with lemon and salt, while pink Pyrenean lamb rack has its tenderness emphasised by an initial marinade in milk. Finish with a silky crema catalana topped with fennel pollen. The all-Spanish wine list opens at £27, but there are also 14 sherries served by the glass, bottle or mixed into cocktails.

Chef/s: Peter Sanchez-Iglesias and Dave Hazell. **Closed:** Sun, Mon, 24 to 26 Dec, 1 Jan. **Meals:** tapas £2 to £22. **Details:** 25 seats. 20 seats outside. Wheelchairs. Music.

Pasta Loco

Cooking score: 3
Italian | £28
37a Cotham Hill, Bristol, BS6 6JY
Tel no: (0117) 973 3000
pastaloco.co.uk

The city-centre opening of sibling Pasta Ripiena (see entry) has not made it any easier to get a seat at Dominic Borel and Ben Harvey's original site, particularly at weekends, when tables still need to be booked two months in advance. Pasta Loco quickly made its mark, with Dominic's ebullient front of house style matched by Ben's broad-minded take on modern Italian cooking. Seasonal ingredients turn up with various types of pasta (handmade daily), say orzo 'risotto' and sun-dried tomato pesto with seared scallops and Tenderstem broccoli, or bucatini with cream, black pepper and Gorgonzola. Before that, there are mussels steamed in sherry with spicy 'nduja, parsley and cream, but make sure you leave room for orange and almond cake with cardamom ice cream and Earl Grey caramel satsuma. A carefully considered wine list with a number of Italian big hitters starts at £17.

Chef/s: Ben Harvey. **Closed:** Sun, 23 Dec to 3 Jan. **Meals:** main courses £9 to £19. **Details:** 33 seats.

★ NEW ENTRY ★

Pasta Ripiena

Cooking score: 3
Italian | £28
33a St Stephen's Street, Bristol, BS1 1JX
Tel no: (0117) 329 3131
pastaripiena.co.uk

The second venture from the Pasta Loco team (see entry), this city-centre eatery was one of Bristol's most avidly anticipated openings of 2018. Tiny and simply decorated in the same bare wood, DIY style as its big brother, the restaurant has an open kitchen from which issues a series of exquisite stuffed pastas and other Italian delicacies. At inspection, a starter of imported Sicilian tomatoes with goat's curd, pangrattato, mint and basil, dressed with white balsamic and grass-green olive oil, proved to be a masterclass in letting top-notch ingredients speak for themselves. A main course of salt-cod-stuffed squid ink ravioli in a creamy soup of crayfish, samphire-like agretti and roast tomatoes spiked with mint, dill and chilli was perfectly balanced. For pudding there's homemade gelato, or try the poached pear with meringue and mascarpone. A short but carefully chosen wine list includes several organic and biodynamic bottles.

Chef/s: Joe Harvey. **Closed:** Sun. **Meals:** main courses £12 to £17.

Prego

Cooking score: 3
Italian | £30
7 North View, Bristol, BS6 7PT
Tel no: (0117) 973 0496
pregobar.co.uk

British and Italian ingredients come together at this neighbourhood restaurant, which has a summer terrace out front and a happy hum all year round. An antipasto of fritto misto sums it up nicely. Brixham fish, lightly dusted in flour and fried until crisp, with rocket and dill aïoli to dip. Pasta and pizza are well executed: try wild mushroom agnoletti with wood-roasted artichoke and agrodolce tomatoes, or a slow-proven sourdough crust topped with homemade sausage, red onion and house chillies. Among well-drawn secondi, English rose veal is flavoured with Marsala and lemon, while John Dory arrives with spiced chickpeas and saffron aïoli. The set lunch menu comes at a canny price, while Monday is all about bargain pizzas. Finish with a classic tiramisu or an Italian cheese plate. The all-Italian wine list opens at £16.50, with bellinis and vermouths to up the ante.

Chef/s: Julian Faiello, Olly Gallery and Ricky Stephenson. **Meals:** main courses £15 to £24. Set L £13 (2 courses) to £18. **Details:** 52 seats. 16 seats outside.

The Pump House

Cooking score: 3
Modern British | £31
Merchants Road, Bristol, BS8 4PZ
Tel no: (0117) 927 2229
the-pumphouse.com

A Victorian pumping station perched by the water's edge where Bristol's docklands open out to the Avon, Toby Gritten's venue has a lot going for it in the location stakes. Tables on the terrace facing the river are a summertime must, and the kitchen offers a seasonally changing brasserie menu of unpretentious food, beginning with great nibbles – pulled pork and Cheddar rarebit made with Worcestershire sauce – perhaps accompanied by the gin of the day. Pub classics will divert the attention of those who can't resist the likes of smoked haddock and salmon fishcakes with hollandaise and a poached egg, while the more adventurous look to seared scallops with parsnip purée, apple and chicken, and mains such as pork belly with Puy lentils, parsley root and smoked garlic mash, or a vegetarian option of semolina gnocchi with beetroot, walnuts and kefir. Desserts out of the ordinary include almond milk panna cotta with apple and fennel. Wines categorised by style start at £20 for the Languedoc house selections.

Chef/s: Toby Gritten and Nick Fenlon. **Closed:** 25 Dec. **Meals:** main courses £13 to £27. Sun L £17. Tasting menu £40 (6 courses). **Details:** 114 seats. 60 seats outside. Bar. Wheelchairs. Music. Parking.

Symbols

Accommodation is available
Three courses for less than £30
£5 off voucher scheme
Notable wine list

★ NEW ENTRY ★

Root

Cooking score: 4
Modern British | £32
Cargo, Gaol Ferry Steps, Wapping Wharf, Bristol, BS1 6WP
Tel no: (0117) 930 0260
eatdrinkbristolfashion.co.uk
£5 OFF

A lively new entrant on the Bristol dining scene, this forward-thinking shipping container restaurant, in the city's waterfront Cargo development, has a Scandi look with functional furniture and trailing pot plants. It's owned by Josh Eggleton of the Pony & Trap (see entry) and run by ex-Pony & Trap chef Rob Howell, who puts the focus firmly on vegetables. From the open kitchen, Howell sends out small plates of predominantly meat-free creations. A spring meal produced 'standout' asparagus topped with Cheddar rarebit and dusted with a spicy seeded dukkah, with a well-made spring risotto of broad beans and peas, puffed rice and garlic oil proving another highlight. Those looking beyond veg-based dishes might find chicken schnitzel with garlic butter and anchovies, or bavette with roasted carrot. Cheddar strawberries with shortbread crumbs and coconut sorbet was a 'perfect summer dessert on a sunny May day'. Wines from £24.

Chef/s: Rob Howell. **Closed:** Sun, 25 and 26 Dec. **Meals:** small plates £4 to £9. **Details:** V menu. Wheelchairs. Parking.

Tare

Cooking score: 3
Modern European | £30
Unit 14, Museum Street, Wapping Wharf, Bristol, BS1 6ZA
Tel no: (0117) 929 4328
tarerestaurant.co.uk
£5 OFF

With its open-view kitchen and 20 covers, this compact restaurant fashioned out of two shipping containers displays plenty of ambition, not to mention a clever use of space. Part of the Cargo development in Bristol's old docks, this is chef Matt Hampshire's first solo outing, and Tare has quickly established itself as one of the city's go-to places. There has been a change of tack since we last visited, with an à la carte now running alongside the original no-choice tasting menu format. We opened an inspection meal with a well-made Stream Farm chicken and leek terrine lifted by pickled and puréed beetroot, before moving on to a dark and sticky glazed pork neck with broccoli, creamy celeriac mash, sweetish rhubarb and crushed hazelnuts for texture. To finish, a light and zingy lemon tart boasting crisp, buttery pastry was teamed with crème fraîche and spicy ginger crumb. A small but interesting clutch of wines is fairly priced, starting at £22.

Chef/s: Matt Hampshire. **Closed:** Sun, Mon. **Meals:** main courses £16 to £19. Tasting menu £45 (7 courses). **Details:** 20 seats. V menu. Wheelchairs. Music. Parking.

Wallfish Bistro

Cooking score: 4
Seafood | £40
112 Princess Victoria Street, Clifton, Bristol, BS8 4DB
Tel no: (0117) 973 5435
wallfishbistro.co.uk

This proper little bistro is simplicity itself, run by a keen couple with a passion for seasonal, regional ingredients. A little off the beaten Clifton track, it's a real local asset; the unpretentious setting and cheerful service fit the bill, while the perfectly formed menu, with its focus on fish and seafood, offers up some good contemporary cooking. Orkney scallops, roasted in the shell, star in a first course with chorizo, sherry and breadcrumbs; lemon sole is matched with brown shrimps, burnt apple and capers. For those looking beyond piscine delights, rack of lamb comes with Marmite-glazed sweetbreads. As a finale, ginger parkin with toffee sauce, or blood orange and almond tart are testament to a kitchen with excellent pastry skills. There's a terrific value weekday lunch and early dinner deal, and the mainly European wine list starts at £15.

Chef/s: Seldon Curry. **Closed:** Mon, Tue. **Meals:** main courses £15 to £22. Set L and early D £14 (2 courses) to £17 (Wed to Fri). **Details:** 38 seats. Music.

Wilks

Cooking score: 6
Modern French | £58
1-3 Chandos Road, Bristol, BS6 6PG
Tel no: (0117) 973 7999
wilksrestaurant.co.uk

A refurbishment in summer 2017 successfully rebooted Wilks six years after it opened in one of Bristol's more desirable suburbs. James Wilkins was clearly paying attention when he trained under the Galvin brothers in London and Michel Bras in France – he displays a solid understanding of classic techniques. His dishes are big on flavour and conjured from the best available produce, whether it's local or sourced directly from Paris. A typical meal might begin with hand-dived Orkney scallops tartare teamed with fresh English wasabi, sesame, apple and ginger. It might go on to roe deer saddle and haunch served with chervil and alexander root purée, ceps, organic collard greens, deer jus poivrade and white Penja peppercorn. Desserts are a high point, as per a green-tea meringue sphere with white chocolate, Seville orange coulis, saffron and quince sorbet. The carefully curated, French-leaning wine list opens at £26.

Chef/s: James Wilkins. **Closed:** Mon, Tue, 3 weeks Christmas, 3 weeks Aug. **Meals:** set L £25 (2 courses) to £29. Set D £48 (2 courses) to £58. Tasting menu £58 to £88. **Details:** 34 seats. V menu. Bar. Wheelchairs. Children over 6 yrs at D.

Bristol's best bites

Rob Howell of Root shares his favourite local places to eat and drink

Little Victories in Wapping Wharf is the one for **coffee**. A lovely little spot with high ceilings and lots of greenery. Sit up on the high bench and enjoy their outstanding coffee or if you're there for **lunch**, grab a **toastie** - they're great!

We are lucky enough to live just off the harbourside by Baltic Wharf, so we usually head to **The Cottage** for a pint of **Butcombe**; it's a great little spot on the docks with possibly the best and most classic Bristol views. Also being **dog friendly** it's pretty handy for us. If you want something stronger, then head across the water to the **Pump House** for a **gin**, they have quite a few!

Wallfish Bistro on a Saturday and Sunday is the only place in the city people need to know about for **brunch**. Whether it's for the best **full English**, **Bloody Mary** or a load of oysters, it's the perfect place for weekend brunch.

For **food shopping**, the three **Better Food** shops around Bristol are great, serving only local and organic ingredients. Head up to Clifton Village to **Reg the Veg** for some fresh produce and then to **Source Food Hall** in St Nicholas Market for the best meat, fish and shellfish in the city.

Wilsons

Cooking score: 5
Modern British | £35
22a Chandos Road, Bristol, BS6 6PF
Tel no: (0117) 973 4157
wilsonsrestaurant.co.uk

Super-fresh vegetables straight from owners Jan Ostle and Mary Wilson's smallholdingare one of the reasons why locals are returning again and again to this modest former shop. Just down the road from fellow Bristol stars Wilks and No Man's Grace (see entries), the dining room is stripped back with dark floorboards and white walls, the only splashes of colour coming from flowers (grown by the owners, naturally) and jars of homemade pickles on the counter of the tiny bar. There's nothing pared-down when it comes to the vibrant flavours of Ostle's formidable seasonal cooking, however. At inspection the blackboard-only menu kicked off with a perfectly balanced but robust red mullet and blood orange soup, followed by pan-roasted cod fillet teamed with a light and verdant combination of peas, parsley, snails and pancetta. After that, expect a perfectly wobbly crème caramel paired with smoked ice cream. A dependable wine list opens at £21.

Chef/s: Jan Ostle. **Closed:** Sun, Mon, 2 weeks Aug, 1 week May, Christmas week. **Meals:** main courses £16 to £18. **Details:** 28 seats. Wheelchairs. Music.

LOCAL GEM

The Cauldron

International | £28
98 Mina Road, Bristol, BS2 9XW
Tel no: (0117) 914 1321
thecauldron.restaurant

The wood-fired oven works its spell on pork belly with miso and caramelised onions, while cast-iron cauldrons sizzle over fire pits – perhaps filled with braised pig's cheek to be served with creamy polenta. Smokeless lumpwood charcoal and beech logs fuel the grill to offer up Dexter beef burger or flat-iron steak. Meat-free options might be subject to the cauldron treatment, too, as in linguine cooked with a rich tomato sauce, capers and charred aubergine. Drink vegan wines or bottled beers.

LOCAL GEM

Hart's Bakery

British | £8
Arch 35, Lower Approach Road, Bristol, BS1 6QS
Tel no: (0117) 992 4488
hartsbakery.co.uk

Turning arches beneath Bristol Temple Meads into a thriving bakery and café is no mean feat, especially when the place is so hidden – first-timers should ask for directions at the station. There's an industrial-meets-utilitarian vibe, a few trestle tables and an inevitable queue from breakfast through to mid-afternoon (when most things will have run out). Laura Hart is famous for her bread, sausage rolls, almond croissants and creamy custard tarts, but there are also lunch specials such as Greek pork with tzatziki, Kalamata olives, shredded cabbage and pickled carrots in an oregano bun, and Bristol-roasted coffee.

LOCAL GEM

Pi Shop

Italian | £19
The General, Lower Guinea Street, Bristol, BS1 6FU
Tel no: (0117) 925 6872
thepishop.co.uk

It seems Peter Sanchez-Iglesias's pizzeria adjoining Casamia (see entry) has settled into a nice groove since opening in 2016. The waterfront terrace adds a little something special and, inside, a giant, gleaming wood-burning pizza oven dominates the cool white room. Starters are simple, perhaps raw artichoke with shavings of Parmesan or buffalo mozzarella with beetroot and pine nuts, then classic pizzas (margherita or marinera, say) alongside specialities such as aubergine with ewe's curd, Parmesan and basil. The fresh herb dip is perfect for the crusty crusts, there's ice cream for dessert, great cocktails and a brief list of Italian wines.

LOCAL GEM

Sky Kong Kong

Korean | £15

Unit 2, Haymarket Walk, Bristol, BS1 3LN
Tel no: (0117) 239 9528
skykongkong.co.uk

The menu changes every day at Wizzy Chung's dinky organic Korean café, and a good deal of her vegetables and herbs are from an allotment; she makes her own soy sauce, miso and chilli paste, too. Lunchtime bento boxes are a popular choice, but it's also great value in the evening when you might dive into seared scallops with local strawberries and avocado, pan-fried salmon or sea bass with summer salad, and classic bulgogi stir-fry (all with sides, pickles and vegetables). It's unlicensed, so BYOB.

LOCAL GEM

Spoke & Stringer

Spanish | £30

The Boathouse, Unit 1, Lime Kiln Road, Bristol, BS1 5AD
Tel no: (0117) 925 9371
spokeandstringer.com

Biking and surfing, eating and drinking . . . This combo of shop and adjacent café occupies a prime corner of the harbour with views across to the SS Great Britain. Daytime brunch includes the house breakfast (plus a vegetarian version) and steak sandwich, while the evening looks to Spain with pintxos at the bar, and creative tapas. Opt for grilled pollock enriched with chorizo, broad beans and lentils, calamares fired up with chilli and lime, or lamb koftas with harissa and mint yoghurt. Drink cool cocktails or wines from indie producers.

Long Ashton

The Bird in Hand

Cooking score: 2
Modern British | £34

17 Weston Road, Long Ashton, BS41 9LA
Tel no: (01275) 395222
bird-in-hand.co.uk

A short drive from Bristol city centre (where you will find Toby Gritten's sister pub The Pump House – see entry) brings you to this quintessential dining pub in a rural village. Popular with both locals and visitors, the menu offers simple, honest food focused on foraged and seasonal British produce. There's a traditional bar, but you may choose to hunker down in front of the fire in winter, or lounge in the patio garden when the weather cooperates. Wherever you choose, it's worth kicking things off with a black pudding Scotch egg with brown sauce, which makes the perfect accompaniment to a pint of one of the excellent local ales. The menu combines classic flavours – crab salad with green apple, cucumber and Amalfi lemon, say, followed by cod with mash, wild mushrooms and shellfish butter sauce – while dessert might be chocolate fondant with banana and peanut brittle. A short international wine list has bottles from £16.50.

Chef/s: Felix Rayment and Toby Gritten. **Closed:** 25 Dec. **Meals:** main courses £16 to £25. **Details:** 47 seats. 40 seats outside. Music.

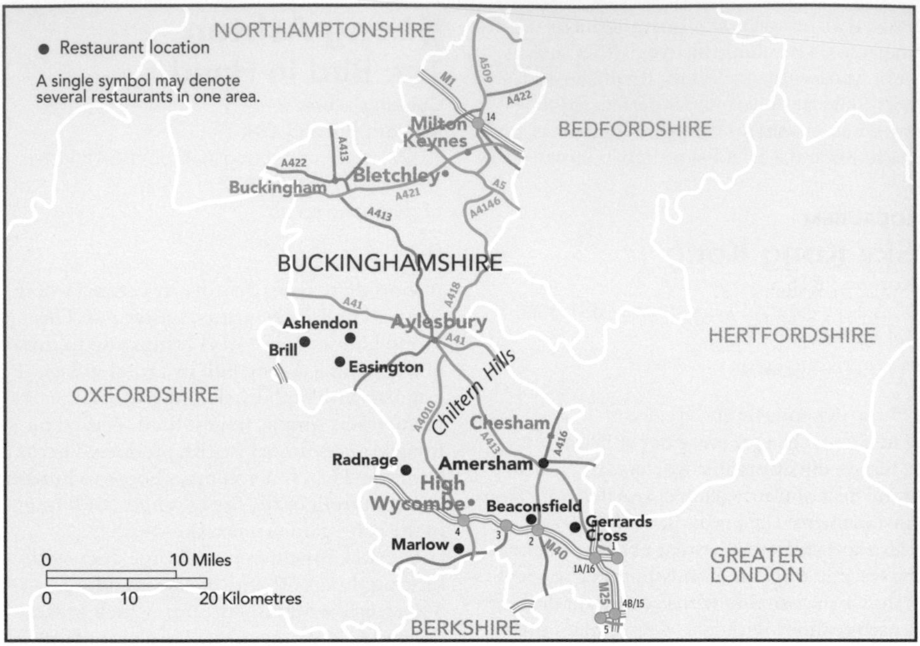

● Restaurant location

A single symbol may denote several restaurants in one area.

NORTHAMPTONSHIRE
BEDFORDSHIRE
BUCKINGHAMSHIRE
HERTFORDSHIRE
OXFORDSHIRE
GREATER LONDON
BERKSHIRE
Milton Keynes
Bletchley
Buckingham
Aylesbury
Ashendon
Brill
Easington
Chiltern Hills
Chesham
Amersham
Radnage
High Wycombe
Beaconsfield
Gerrards Cross
Marlow

0 10 Miles
0 10 20 Kilometres

Amersham

★ TOP 50 ★

Artichoke

Cooking score: 7
Modern European | £48
9 Market Square, Amersham, HP7 0DF
Tel no: (01494) 726611
artichokerestaurant.co.uk

Looking freshly minted after its recent refurb, with new seating boosting the comfort factor in the original part of the restaurant, the Artichoke is not only held in high esteem but cherished like a dear friend. All is cool, calm and collected in the open kitchen, while the cooking shows an unswerving commitment to the clear, clean, exhilarating flavours of ingredient-led seasonal cooking. Sea trout is smoked over Fuggle hops from the Chiltern Brewery, and plates of Buckinghamshire-stamped venison 'always eat well' – perhaps accompanied by smoked celeriac purée, a tangily stimulating blue-cheese crumble, pickled red onions, poached quince and shredded cavolo nero. Chef patron Laurie Gear's magpie instincts also yield thrilling results – as in a Japanese-themed dish of glazed roast cod (*à point*) partnered by a squid ink and prawn 'dumpling', artichokes and rich, deep shellfish and miso sauce. Regulars say that 'presentation has reached new heights', particularly when it comes to desserts such as a lemon bavarois 'of lovely flavour and texture' with olive oil gel, citrus fruit salad and thyme sherbet ice – puds don't come more satisfyingly fresh or invigorating than this. Alternatively, relish the sweet and savoury brilliance of goat's curd, poached gooseberries, gooseberry sorbet and puffed spelt grains. Really confident staff clearly love their work, and it shows in service that's 'abundant but never overwhelming'. Meanwhile, the wine list continues to improve, with many new bottles, impressive global coverage and a telling balance between classic and on-trend viticulture.

Chef/s: Laurie Gear and Ben Jenkins. **Closed:** Sun, Mon, 2 weeks Dec to Jan, 1 week Easter, 2 weeks Aug. **Meals:** main courses £24 to £26 (L only). Set L £28. Set D £43 (2 courses) to £48. Tasting menu L £38 (5 courses) to £44, D £68 (7 courses). **Details:** 48 seats. V menu. Children over 6 yrs at D.

LOCAL GEM

Gilbey's

Modern British | £37
1 Market Square, Amersham, HP7 0DF
Tel no: (01494) 727242
gilbeygroup.com

Ultra-dependable and much-loved locally, Gilbey's is the epitome of a neighbourhood bistro – equally suited to a quick solo lunch or a garrulous significant birthday bash. Housed in a converted grammar school with a desirable courtyard terrace attached, it majors in eclectic modern food with lots of bright flavours – from Cornish cod with clementine, charred radicchio, fennel dressing and seaweed dumplings to pork belly with candied apple, oyster mushrooms and Calvados jus. The Gilbeys are wine importers, so expect plenty of decent drinking to boot.

Ashendon

The Hundred

Cooking score: 4
British | £29
Lower End, Ashendon, HP18 0HE
Tel no: (01296) 651296
thehundred.co.uk
£5 OFF

Matthew Gill's quirkily rustic 16th-century pub with rooms, a few miles from Waddesdon Manor, is full of warmth, honest intent and gastronomic pleasures. The aim is to combine first-rate, well-sourced ingredients with uncomplicated modern cooking to produce a menu with broad appeal, which Gill achieves with his clear flavours and a feel for what is right. There's a please-all quality to classics – for example, the well-reported beef and kidney pie, and the skirt steak with fries and aïoli – but the kitchen is better known for starters of lamb's tongue with lentils and green sauce, and mains of braised rabbit with chorizo and potato or guinea fowl with white beans and bacon, and the chocolate slice with crème fraîche ice cream and ginger snap that makes such a fine finish. The homemade bread comes in for praise, and the short, reasonably priced wine list has been compiled with care.
Chef/s: Matthew Gill. **Closed:** Mon, 1 week Jan. **Meals:** main courses £14 to £18. **Details:** 40 seats. 30 seats outside. Bar. Music. Parking.

Beaconsfield

LOCAL GEM

No. 5

Modern British | £32
London End, Beaconsfield, HP9 2HN
Tel no: (01494) 355500
no5londonend.co.uk

A beacon in Beaconsfield, this lively split-level restaurant is a godsend for the town's residents and 'has been packed since the day it opened'. The menu offers plenty of good things from 'amazing' ox cheek fritters or torched mackerel with avocado purée and kimchi mayo to grilled sea bream with mussels, dill emulsion and nori crumb. It's also great for top-end burgers (no skimping on the meat here), while puddings might include hot brioche doughnuts with salted caramel. Wines start at £19. Related to the White Oak, Cookham and the Three Oaks, Gerrards Cross (see entries).

Brill

The Pointer

Cooking score: 3
Modern British | £40
27 Church Street, Brill, HP18 9RT
Tel no: (01844) 238339
thepointerbrill.co.uk
£5 OFF

Cynics might say that this is a 'hospitality plaything for super-rich owners', but since taking over the Pointer in 2012, David

Howden and co have turned what was an average boozer into the hub of the village. The big bar looks as deliberately manicured as a set for a glossy photo-shoot, while the heavily branded restaurant feels snazzily rustic, with 'ultra-scripted' staff attending to every detail. There's also a deliberately voguish feel to the food, with its home-grown and home-reared ethos: on the plus side, a chunkily plated salad involving beetroot of many colours, raw pear, tangy goat's curd and croûtons has been well received; on the minus side, a dish called 'Peter Rabbit' is one of the chef's 'less successful molecular experiments'. In between, the star attraction is Middle White suckling pig from the owner's farm, perhaps served with kale, haricot beans and scrumpy sauce. The trend-conscious wine list highlights organic, biodynamic and vegan-friendly bottles.
Chef/s: James Graham. **Closed:** Mon. **Meals:** main courses £20 to £30. Set L £18 (2 courses) to £23. **Details:** 60 seats. 40 seats outside. Music.

Easington
The Mole & Chicken

Cooking score: 2
Modern British | £32
Easington Terrace, Easington, HP18 9EY
Tel no: (01844) 208387
themoleandchicken.co.uk

This creeper-covered restaurant with rooms has blazing fires in the cold months, a rustic interior and warm atmosphere all year round, but you can't beat a table on the terrace when the sun is shining and the view across Buckinghamshire and Oxfordshire countryside is laid out before you. The menu takes a modern route through the pub catalogue, so the Scotch egg is a haggis version with wild garlic aïoli, and squid gets the salt and pepper treatment. Among main courses, pan-fried liver, bacon and kidneys is a joy to behold, beer-battered fish and chips plays to the gallery, and slow-cooked pork belly with cauliflower purée and burnt onion shows a contemporary touch. For dessert, banana tarte tatin comes with chestnut ice cream. Breakfast is available to non-residents, and Sunday lunch includes a choice of four roasts. The concise wine list opens with house Chilean at £19.50.
Chef/s: Steve Bush. **Closed:** 25 Dec. **Meals:** main courses £15 to £28. Set L and D £18 (2 courses). **Details:** 62 seats. 60 seats outside.

Gerrards Cross
The Three Oaks

Cooking score: 4
Modern British | £31
Austenwood Common, Gerrards Cross, SL9 8NL
Tel no: (01753) 899016
thethreeoaksgx.co.uk
£5 OFF

Readers' enthusiasm for this solid, brick and timber sibling of the White Oak, Cookham (see entry) continues, with both locals and visitors drawn by the smart interior of polished wood tables, soft colours, big windows and a very civilised atmosphere. It is also a place for some accomplished cooking. True food values and a passion for sourcing the finest seasonal produce are at the heart of Mikey Seferynski's cooking, and the chef has a raft of appealing ideas up his sleeve. He offers a compact, bang-up-to-date menu with the food driven by well-sourced local and regional produce. Readers have praised a starter of charred broccoli salad with burrata, smoked almonds and harissa dressing, and a main course of red wine marinated chicken served with roast Jerusalem artichoke purée, white bean cassoulet, truffle and house frites. And for pudding? It's a hard choice between sticky toffee pudding with linseed caramel and brown-butter cream, and milk chocolate délice with dark chocolate 'aero' and passion fruit parfait. A French-leaning wine list opens at a modest £19.
Chef/s: Mikey Seferynski. **Closed:** 25 Dec. **Meals:** main courses £15 to £26. Set L £15 (2 courses) to £19. **Details:** 74 seats. 40 seats outside. Bar. Music. Parking.

Marlow

The Coach

Cooking score: 5
Modern British | £30
3 West Street, Marlow, SL7 2LS
thecoachmarlow.co.uk

Tom Kerridge's casual but slick Coach is a real paradox: it's ostensibly a pub, but you can't simply drop by for a pint at the long gleaming bar; it's also a restaurant, but you can't book and the food consists of a jumble of plates served in come-as-you-please style by staff and chefs alike. There's sport on the (silent) TV screens, it's open all day and the whole place rocks along nicely. The menu is split into 'meat' and 'no meat', with tapas-style sharing and grazing as the preferred modus operandi and a dramatic rotisserie at the heart of things (check out the whole stuffed quail with black pudding and a coconut-inflected moilee sauce). Elsewhere, you could could pick crispy pig's head with celeriac rémoulade and spiced date sauce, or venison chilli with red wine, chocolate and toasted rice cream; others might prefer mushroom risotto 'Claude Bosi', fish fritters or smoked haddock thermidor. It's a sure-fire hit list, executed with enviable pizazz and proficiency. To conclude, opt for spiced gypsy tart or rhubarb and custard fool. Ales, cocktails and wines keep the mood upbeat.

Chef/s: Nick Beardshaw and Tom De Keyser.
Meals: main courses £7 to £17. **Details:** 45 seats.

The Hand & Flowers

Cooking score: 5
Modern British | £65
126 West Street, Marlow, SL7 2BP
Tel no: (01628) 482277
thehandandflowers.co.uk

To a passer-by on the A4155, the Hand & Flowers could be a common or garden English pub: a humble setting on the edge of a market town, blooming flower boxes on the outside, russet red brickwork and dusky beams within. This being the pub of TV royalty Tom Kerridge, however, getting a table can be the Wonka's golden ticket of dining, with fans keen to see familiar pub fare elevated to a minor art form (and prices to match). Staff are informal and informed, shuttling whitebait with Marie Rose for pre-dinner snacking at tightly packed tables. Old-school British flavours are recast in elaborate starters: moreish haggis and 'lamb chorizo' tart with carrot, fennel and chartreuse whipped cheese, or gala pie with onion and cider purée, pickled gherkin and pork bordelaise sauce. Choosing mains, you might be torn between the gamey glory of Cotswold venison with sprouting broccoli and game and bacon pommes duchesse (a standout on our inspection), or slow-cooked duck breast, piquant blood-orange and oat crumble. Everyone, however seems to agree on very pinchable Hand & Flowers chips, which disappear as soon as they land on the table. Desserts seem a tad less inspired – vanilla crème brûlée, or chocolate and ale cake with salted caramel and muscovado ice cream. No such grumbles with the wine list – a weighty tome where prices head skyward, from £28 a bottle, with offerings from the local Rebellion brewery on the taps. Not the cheapest pub meal, but based on our visit the Hand & Flowers is still in bloom.

Chef/s: Tom Kerridge and Aaron Mulliss.
Meals: main courses £34 to £42. Set L £25 (2 courses) to £30. **Details:** 52 seats.

Sindhu

Cooking score: 5
Indian | £40
Compleat Angler, Bisham Road, Marlow, SL7 1RG
Tel no: (01628) 405405
sindhurestaurant.co.uk

With its view over Marlow weir, the dining room at the Compleat Angler has always been considered a lovely spot, though the clubby old-British decor was not something that screamed spice. Sindhu has addressed this with lots of mirrors, plain mahogany tables, chairs

well upholstered in canary yellow or duck-egg blue and by painting walls off-white. Add a sense of warmth and generosity, especially when it comes to the food – 'I felt like I was truly indulging and being spoilt' – and you have 'Indian cooking in a high-end style and setting'. Highlights this year include properly made uthappam with white crabmeat, sweetcorn, samphire and an apple-based sauce spooned over at table; a tandoori breast of New Forest guinea fowl with a little adana kebab of leg meat and a thick, lightly creamy curry sauce with a dash of watercress oil; and a lamb chop cooked to a tender pink in the tandoor with a slice of rump served in a 'rogan jus'. To drink, there are 22 by-the-glass options (or by the 500ml carafe), and the main list is a nice balance of affordable and quality.
Chef/s: Prabhu Ganapati. **Meals:** main courses £22 to £28. **Details:** 56 seats. V menu. Wheelchairs. Music. Parking.

The Vanilla Pod

Cooking score: 4
Modern European | £45
31 West Street, Marlow, SL7 2LS
Tel no: (01628) 898101
thevanillapod.co.uk
£5 OFF

It may never have been at the cutting edge of cooking, but that isn't chef proprietor Michael Macdonald's style. Since 2002, he has been quietly going about his business, producing food of a high standard in this tall, narrow townhouse that once belonged to the poet TS Eliot. The mood is low-key, quietly civilised, a tad old-fashioned here and there – qualities that often extend to the chef's capably executed food. The cooking mines a rich vein of satisfying Anglo-French cuisine, adding a few influences from the Mediterranean along the way. In the mood for fish? Go for seared scallops with Jerusalem artichoke purée and chestnut ahead of pan-fried plaice with white beans and mushrooms, while meatier offerings could bring duck breast and confit leg with prunes, followed by venison with creamed cabbage and bacon. Desserts such as apple streusel with hot buttered rum are a perfect fit, and the wide-ranging wine list promises quality as well as value.
Chef/s: Michael Macdonald. **Closed:** Sun, Mon, 23 Dec to 10 Jan, Easter weekend, 28 May to 6 Jun, 27 Aug to 5 Sept. **Meals:** set L £16 (2 courses) to £20. Set D £20 (2 courses) to £25. Tasting menu £60 (7 courses). **Details:** 42 seats. V menu.

Radnage

The Mash Inn

Cooking score: 5
Modern British | £60
Horseshoe Road, Radnage, HP14 4EB
Tel no: (01494) 482440
themashinn.com

Since 2016, Nick Mash's new generation inn has had travellers beating a path to its door for Jon Parry's open-fire cooking. Parry cooks in the contemporary vernacular, foraging and fermenting like the best of his better-known peers, only with the weight of the picture-perfect inn's history and geography on his side. His food enjoys a real affinity with its surroundings, however unexpected some combinations, viz smoked eel and bone marrow with ramson 'capers', and poached rhubarb with beeswax and gorse from the full tasting menu. The shorter menu offers choices at main course – consider buttermilk lamb leg with sprouting broccoli from the garden and lamb 'bacon' or halibut with turmeric cauliflower, golden raisins and samphire-like 'salty fingers' – and for dessert where there might be beef-dripping canelé with grilled pineapple, or chocolate cremoso with lovage granita. Real ales and fine wines (some biodynamic choices) sit comfortably together.
Chef/s: Jon Parry. **Closed:** Sun, Mon, Tue, 24 Dec to 2 Jan. **Meals:** set L (Wed to Fri) £23 (2 courses) to £25. Set L and D £60 (6 courses). Tasting menu £80 (10 courses). **Details:** 32 seats. Bar. Wheelchairs. Music. Parking. Children over 14 yrs.

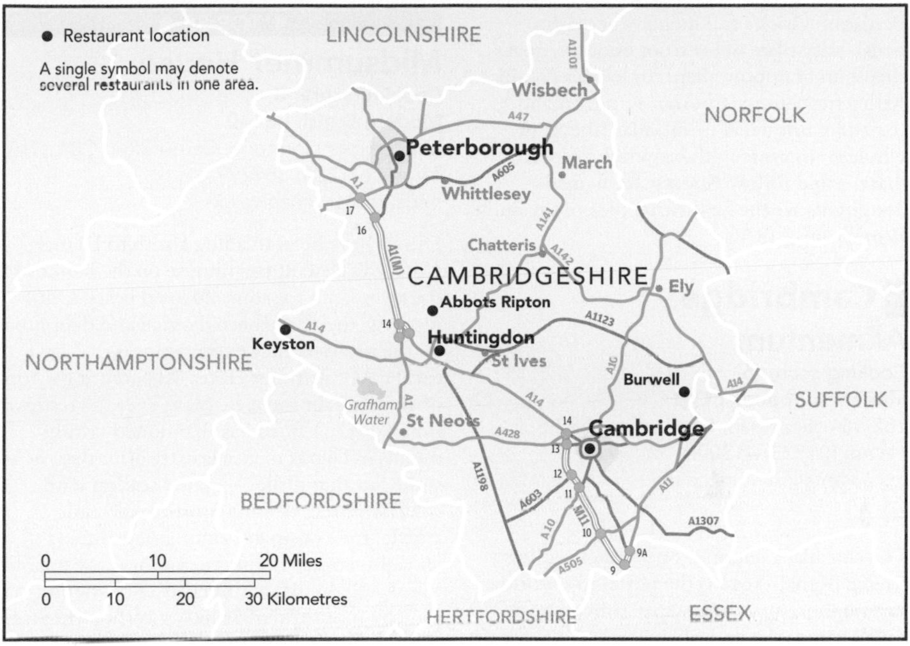

● Restaurant location
A single symbol may denote several restaurants in one area.

LINCOLNSHIRE
NORFOLK
CAMBRIDGESHIRE
NORTHAMPTONSHIRE
SUFFOLK
BEDFORDSHIRE
HERTFORDSHIRE
ESSEX
Wisbech
Peterborough
March
Whittlesey
Chatteris
Ely
Abbots Ripton
Keyston
Huntingdon
St Ives
Burwell
Grafham Water
St Neots
Cambridge
0 10 20 Miles
0 10 20 30 Kilometres

Abbots Ripton

The Abbot's Elm

Cooking score: 2
Modern European | £32
Abbots Ripton, PE28 2PA
Tel no: (01487) 773773
theabbotselm.co.uk

After a spell of early 'retirement' in 2017, Julia Abbey is now back at the helm here, overseeing the kitchen and easing the new brigade into their duties. With its thatched roof, cosy interiors, real ales and sizeable outside dining space, Abbot's Elm is a tempting proposition – especially as it offers a mix of classy pub-style food and confidently rendered restaurant dishes. Take a traditional route with a fricassée of lamb's kidneys, black pudding and wild mushrooms followed by fish pie with broccoli almondine, or be more up to date and plump for hand-picked Portland crab with citrus salad and wasabi cream ahead of sea bream with braised potatoes, cavolo nero, parsley and lemon butter sauce. As a finale, opt for orange and Grand Marnier pancakes or passion fruit panna cotta with coconut sorbet. There's a varied selection of well-priced wines by the glass or carafe

Chef/s: Julia Abbey. **Meals:** main courses £11 to £29. Set L £14 (2 courses) to £18. Sun L £27. **Details:** 70 seats. 40 seats outside. Parking.

Burwell

LOCAL GEM

The Anchor

Modern British | £31
63 North Street, Burwell, CB25 0BA
Tel no: (01638) 743970
theanchorburwell.net

Bluebell, the pub border collie, and her equally welcoming humans, are reason enough to visit this unassuming Fenland village spot. Come for a drink and bar snacks (try the brie fritters), or linger longer over

Benjamin Crick's full menu – perhaps a sweet-salty plate of beetroot gnocchi, goat's cheese and rainbow chard, or lobster ravioli with a freshening lemongrass, ginger and coriander bisque. A spectacular ribeye, or whole lemon sole with brown shrimps to share, could follow. Sugary, fresh-made doughnuts are the lip-licking pick of the puds. Wine from £18.50.

Cambridge

Alimentum

Cooking score: 6
Modern European | £70
152-154 Hills Road, Cambridge, CB2 8PB
Tel no: (01223) 413000
restaurantalimentum.co.uk
£5 OFF

The chic black entrance on a rather soulless stretch of main road is the portal to a world of thoroughgoing culinary experimentation. Small bare tables and a bare floor in a room inbued with a sense of space and light make a neutral backdrop for ingenious menus of contemporary European food. Aromatic uplift distinguishes dishes such as celeriac with rosemary and truffle, or salmon with its caviar in buttermilk with dill and horseradish. The beef main course is a show-stopping presentation of 80-day aged meat, perhaps the rump cap and cheek with morels and gnocchi in red wine. As a pre-dessert, the gin and tonic sorbet makes a sensational attempt to steal the show, but there could be coffee curd to follow, illuminated with passion fruit and saffron, and trend-conscious reworkings of Battenberg and Black Forest. Then again, it would be a shame to let the cheese trolley pass by unheeded. A thrilling wine list represents the best in modern thinking, with Deltetto's citrus-fresh Favorita and a great Oregon Pinot Noir among the glass selections alone. Bottles open at £22, and encompass many dynamic producers.

Chef/s: Samira Effa. **Closed:** 24 to 30 Dec, bank hols. **Meals:** set L £28 (2 courses) to £35. Set D £55 (2 courses) to £70. Tasting menu L £60, D £80. **Details:** 40 seats. Bar. Wheelchairs. Music.

★ TOP 50 ★

Midsummer House

Cooking score: 8
Modern British | £140
Midsummer Common, Cambridge, CB4 1HA
Tel no: (01223) 369299
midsummerhouse.co.uk

Diners have been treading a path to Daniel Clifford's elegant townhouse on the banks of the river Cam for some 20 loyal years. Until recently, they have been dazzled and delighted by the multi-course extravaganzas that have earned Midsummer House its perch at the top of Britain's dining tree. Now, ever the restless innovator, Clifford has abandoned tasting menus in favour of an à la carte offer that tucks some familiar dishes – seared scallop with celeriac purée, Granny Smith apple and truffle, for example – among new ones (and an eight-course tasting menu for those unable to forget). A curl of gingerbread containing a punchy mouthful of Stinking Bishop cheese is a palate-awakening amuse-bouche, and sets the tone for a generous meal of precise yet robust flavours. Delicate crab and fleshy, just-sautéed tiger prawns summon up the sea in one detailed starter, while elsewhere chicken wings, smoked eel and sautéed duck liver come together harmoniously in a marriage of sweet, savoury, tender and crisp. The tyrannical richness of veal kidneys and snails with a glossy onion soubise left one diner overwhelmed by a 'clumpiness' that seemed out of kilter with the airy elegance elsewhere, but butter-poached cod with roasted langoustines, cauliflower, salty caviar and peppery oyster leaf is a triumph. Kumquats hide deep in a fairy-light Grand Marnier soufflé; sweet Gariguette strawberries are celebrated with the late-spring joy they deserve, alongside edgy lovage and set ewe's milk. The superlative front of house team delivers effortlessy smooth service. Note that though the wine list is one of extraordinary length, breadth and depth, there's little choice around the £30 mark.

Chef/s: Daniel Clifford and Mark Abbott. **Closed:** Sun, Mon, 22 Dec to 10 Jan. **Meals:** alc £97 (2 courses) to £118. Set L £69. Tasting menu £145. **Details:** 50 seats. Bar. Children over 14 yrs.

★ NEW ENTRY ★

Restaurant Twenty-Two

Cooking score: 3
British | £35
22 Chesterton Road, Cambridge, CB4 3AX
Tel no: (01223) 351880
restaurant22.co.uk

Word has spread fast about the young new owners (chef Sam Carter and his partner Alex Olivier) of this discreet townhouse restaurant. The service is as unaffected and light as the intimate interior is elegant – but come for the food! A mini Guinness loaf, paired with Guinness butter, is a bouncy, malty nibble alongside an amuse-bouche of chilled cucumber velouté, sprightly with lime and dill. Asparagus with mild ricotta and feathery hen of the woods mushrooms, animated by peppery leaves and crunchy puffed wild rice, is a joyfully balanced plate of food. Hereford beef, 60-day aged, is extraordinarily tender, the fat rendered into luscious submission, with peas, beans and turnip giving texture and freshness next to a crisp croquette, beef-fat Jersey Royals and horseradish cream. Leave space for baked yoghurt and raspberries with minty, citrussy shiso granita, or pistachio cake with lemon sorbet, its sharpness offset by white chocolate. The menu is refreshingly compact, and if you fancy everything, there's a tasting menu. The wine list skips around the world but settles on a £20 opener.

Chef/s: Sam Carter. **Closed:** Sun, Mon, 25 to 26 Dec. **Meals:** main courses £16 to £20. Tasting menu £45 (7 courses). **Details:** 22 seats. Music.

LOCAL GEM

The Dumpling Tree

Chinese | £17
8 Homerton Street, Cambridge, CB2 8NX
Tel no: (01223) 247715
thedumplingtree.com

You cannot capture the essence of Yunnan food in a few dishes or flavours, so varied is the region's cuisine – which is perhaps why the scope of the menu at this friendly, family-run spot ranges so wide. Come, obviously, for plump homemade dumplings (steamed, fried or in a spicy soup) filled generously with pork and Chinese chives, fresh prawns or chicken and mushroom. A Thai-style tom yum soup, fragrant with lemongrass, chilli and lime, earns praise, as does super spicy 'dare-devil's fish'. To finish? Crisp, hot, sweet pineapple fritters, of course. Wine from £19.

LOCAL GEM

Fitzbillies

Modern British | £20
51-52 Trumpington Street, Cambridge, CB2 1RG
Tel no: (01223) 352500
fitzbillies.com

Fitzbillies has been a dedicated refuelling point for dons, students and tourists since 1920, and has hit exactly the right spot with readers since it was saved from recessional ruin eight years ago by Tim Hayward and Alison Wright. It's as busy and buzzy at breakfast as it is for lunch and, with no reservations taken, folk are happy to queue – though a second branch has opened across town in Bridge Street. Inventive salads, buck rarebit (topped with a poached egg) and a savoury tart of the day are typical lunch offerings, and there's also a classic afternoon tea and great cakes, including the famed Chelsea bun. Wine from £21.

Huntingdon

LOCAL GEM

The Old Bridge Hotel

Modern British | £34

1 High Street, Huntingdon, PE29 3TQ
Tel no: (01480) 424300
huntsbridge.com

The Great Ouse flows past John and Julia Hoskins' ivy-fronted hotel, where their passion for food and wine has been on show for 25 years (2019 is the big anniversary). From their dapper contemporary restaurant with a fabulous wine shop attached, expect brasserie-style cooking such as grilled whole king prawns with samphire and garlic butter, before confit duck pudding, chargrilled steak, or sea trout with lobster butter. Almond and orange give a Mediterranean spin to bread and butter pudding. The splendid wine list runs to an equally splendid selection by the glass.

Keyston

The Pheasant

Cooking score: 2
Modern British | £30

Loop Road, Keyston, PE28 0RE
Tel no: (01832) 710241
thepheasant-keyston.co.uk

A Raleigh bicycle displayed high on a wall indicates that this large, lovely thatched pub has a quirky streak to counterbalance its old-world rural charm. Likewise, the time-honoured fittings – heavy wooden furniture, ancient beams, hunting-print wallpaper – are leavened by ales from local microbreweries, a global wine list full of exciting labels, and a seasonal menu that embraces both 'traditional classics' (including marvellously meaty Toulouse sausages with spring greens and crushed Jersey Royals) and tender lamb slices with potato fondant, caponata and beetroot in mint and red wine sauce. Slips aren't unheard of – at inspection, slightly off-hand service failed to inform us that peas and (rather oddly) pickled ginger replaced the broccoli fritters in a smoked monkfish biryani starter – but pudding of nutty muscovado and hazelnut torte with raspberry compôte left us smiling. A 'wine of the month' bolsters the ample by-the-glass options.

Chef/s: Simon Cadge. **Closed:** Mon, 2 to 15 Jan. **Meals:** main courses £10 to £24. Set L and D £15 (2 courses) to £20. Sun L £26. **Details:** 80 seats. 30 seats outside. Bar. Wheelchairs. Parking.

Peterborough

Prévost

Cooking score: 3
Modern British | £33

20 Priestgate, Peterborough, PE1 1JA
Tel no: (01733) 313623
prevostpeterborough.co.uk

£5 OFF

Lee Clarke's highly accomplished venue is a snapshot of where we are in 21st-century restaurateuring. An expansive space with laminate floor, smartly clothed tables and a view into the black-tiled kitchen creates a wholly relaxed atmosphere, and the menu formats allow for a succession of three, five or nine courses, supplemented by a bargain lunchtime set menu. It's all in the art of combination, an approach that mostly works with the grain of principal ingredients rather than trying to trip them up. Salmon is matched with horseradish and beetroot, a clam with monk's beard and cauliflower, while the main-course alternatives (the only stage requiring a choice) might be baked brill with parsnip and anchovy butter, or full-flavoured hogget with artichoke and rosemary gravy. For the cheese course, a crumpet makes an elegant vehicle for brie and celery, and the closing note could be opulently rich chocolate marquise with whisky ice cream. Wines include some vivid southern hemisphere varietals in among the high-toned European classics. The starting price is £20.

Chef/s: Lee Clarke. **Closed:** Sun, Mon, first 2 weeks Jan. **Meals:** set L £19 (3 courses). Set D £33 (3 courses) to £75. **Details:** 34 seats. V menu. Bar. Wheelchairs. Music. No children at D.

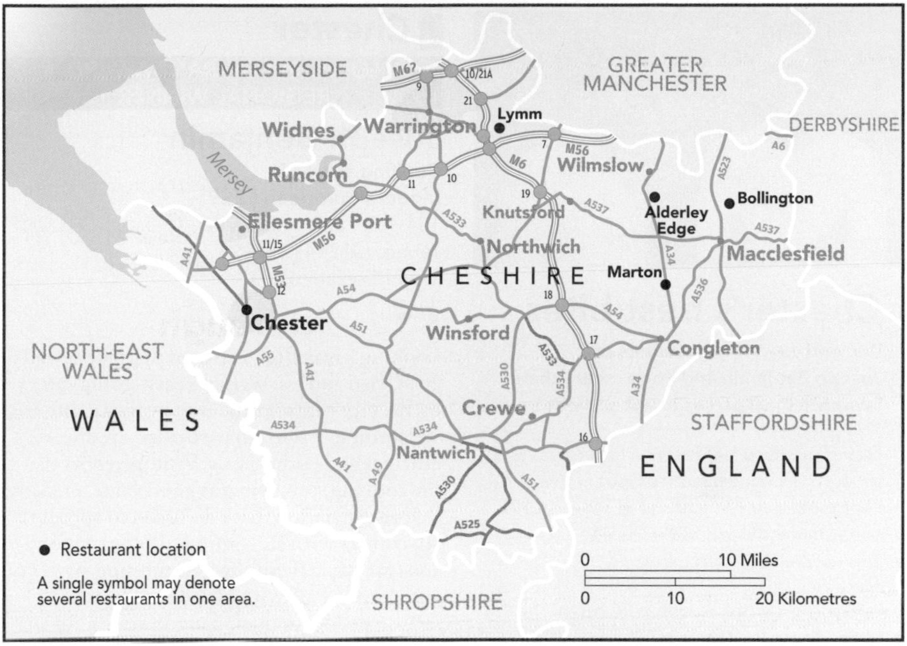

Alderley Edge

LOCAL GEM

Yara

Lebanese/Syrian | £25

29 London Road, Alderley Edge, SK9 7JT
Tel no: (01625) 584040
yara2eat.co.uk

A mini group of family-run restaurants dotted across the North West, Yara serves up a blend of Lebanese and Syrian cuisine that's equally suited to festive sharing or a quick fill-up. Around 30 cold and hot starters span everything from silky baba ganoush and mutabal to falafel, kibbeh and spicy sujuk sausages, while mains are the usual grills, kebabs, couscous and the odd vegetable stew. 'Bring a ferocious appetite', advises one reader. House wine is £14.50, or you can BYO (corkage £2). There are branches at 23 Oxford Road, Altrincham; and 7 Wilmslow Road, Cheadle.

Bollington

LOCAL GEM

The Lime Tree

British | £30

18-20 High Street, Bollington, SK10 5PH
Tel no: (01625) 578182
limetreebollington.co.uk

For six years, Patrick Hannity has been the driving force behind this amenable wine bar and restaurant housed in a pair of converted Victorian shops. He knows his customers well – this is the younger sibling of the Lime Tree in Manchester's West Didsbury (see entry) – and the kitchen turns out commendable food based on fresh ingredients, the style comforting rather than assertive. Typical choices include caramelised onion tarte tatin with goat's cheese, roast loin and slow-cooked shoulder of Cheshire lamb with potato rösti, and Grand Marnier crème brûlée. Wines from £18.

Chester's best bites

Ben and Joe Wright, owners of Joseph Benjamin and Porta, share their favourite local places to eat and drink

Going out for **breakfast** is a rare treat for us, but we love **Jaunty Goat** in the centre of town. On a Monday, when our restaurant is closed, we're sure to bump into most of our staff there.

Located on Brook Street, new kid on the block, **Moss Coffee**, is perfectly located for grabbing a takeaway for the train, and the **coffee** is fantastic.

A serene canalside location that's great for **brunch** meetings or a hangover recovery fry-up is **Artichoke Bistro**. It also happens to have one of the best-stocked bars in the North.

Local stalwart **Telford's Warehouse** is a great place for a quiet **beer** during the day and is also a local institution for live music. There's a brilliant atmosphere and an ace **beer selection**. Get a highly prized bench in the sun if you can.

For **dinner**, it'd be a toss-up between **Chef's Table** and **Sticky Walnut**. Both class acts serving absolutely great food and wine. Alongside these places, we're proud to be part of **Chester's thriving food scene**.

Chester

★ LOCAL RESTAURANT AWARD ★
REGIONAL WINNER

Joseph Benjamin

Cooking score: 3
Modern European | £29
134-138 Northgate Street, Chester, CH1 2HT
Tel no: (01244) 344295
josephbenjamin.co.uk

Looking great after a tasteful upgrade in early 2018, Ben and Joe Wright's easy-going eatery by the city gate continues to be lively and welcoming – staff, in particular, are cheery, efficient and enthusiastic. Visitors report that the cooking, too, remains good value, praising a clever operation that's designed to appeal to all-comers with its confidently cooked food and café-style flexibility. A stunning starter of cured stone bass with blood orange and saffron pickled fennel, bang in season for late winter, reveals the trouble taken over sourcing quality raw materials, while Goosnargh corn-fed chicken breast is teamed with mushroom fideuà (pasta) and a piquillo pepper rouille. Finish with homemade fruitcake with Colston Bassett Stilton and a glass of chilled oloroso or cinnamon rice pudding and fig jam. To drink, there are appealing, international wines at kind prices, a good gin list and craft beers. Related to Porta tapas bar next door (see entry).

Chef/s: Jose Garzón. **Closed:** Mon, 25 Dec to 1 Jan. **Meals:** main courses £11 to £19. **Details:** 36 seats. Bar. Wheelchairs. Music.

Porta

Cooking score: 2
Spanish | £22
140 Northgate Street, Chester, CH1 2HT
Tel no: 01244 344295
portatapas.co.uk

'Slick operation in a small space' sums up Ben and Joe Wright's take on a Spanish tapas bar, an offshoot of their restaurant, Joseph Benjamin, next door. An effusive welcome, open-to-view kitchen and pared-back interior set the mood, with a few picnic tables outside if the weather cooperates. Anchor yourself on a bar stool at a high table and discover some very good things to eat, perhaps air-dried beef cecina (similar to ham) with pickled chillies, or tender Ibérico presa pork with mojo verde, slow-roast ox cheek with pickled walnuts, and seared broccoli with almonds and romesco sauce. Tapas classics have their place, too – croquetas (perhaps squid ink and prawn), tomato bread, patatas bravas, prawns a la plancha, and tortilla – while chocolate mousse with honeycomb makes a good finish. To drink, there's a brief list of Spanish wines, some sherries and a few British and Spanish beers. No bookings, just turn up.

Chef/s: Joe Wright and José Catala. **Meals:** tapas £4 to £10. **Details:** 38 seats. 24 seats outside. Wheelchairs. Music.

★ TOP 50 ★

Simon Radley at the Chester Grosvenor

Cooking score: 7
Modern French | £75
Eastgate, Chester, CH1 1LT
Tel no: (01244) 324024
chestergrosvenor.com

The portico entrance to the Grosvenor, hard by the Eastgate Clock, leads into a beautiful marble lobby, and from there it's a short step to the intimately lit, gleaming opulence of Simon Radley's lounge bar and dining room. Glass cases of Pol Roger under a blinded skylight, with a magnificent icicle chandelier, give notice of the level at which the game is played, confirmed when a mobile bread counter is wheeled up to the table and a long recitation of its wares begins. Everything about this operation is city-slick and flawlessly professional, with Simon Radley and his head chef Raymond Booker's culinary output at its heart. There is a palpable determination to mix grand hotel dining with forward-thinking culinary ideas, so that first courses might see pairings of lightly seared halibut and long-stewed oxtail with red wine risotto and bone-marrow butter, or a creamily truffle-glazed cannelloni roll of veal sweetbreads with a corpulent langoustine. Main-course meats are dazzling in quality: the Pyrenean mountain lamb full of aromatic intensity with its offaly faggot, morels and parsley root purée; or there may be sea bass with Menai oysters and caviar in cauliflower cream. Any overload of richness is carefully avoided through judicious balancing, despite the numerous extras, and desserts try out some novel propositions in the form of a broken milk chocolate cylinder of black figs, caramel ganache and honey cake, or a Turkish Delight study that combines saffron cake with lemon sorbet, sweet curd and crystallised crimson rose petals. An authoritative and accessible wine list is confident in all regions, with featured sections on individual vineyards including Lethbridge in Victoria, Australia, and Gusbourne in Kent. Glass selections start at £9.

Chef/s: Simon Radley and Raymond Booker. **Closed:** Mon, 25 Dec. **Meals:** set D £75. Tasting menu £99 (8 courses). **Details:** 45 seats. Bar. Wheelchairs. Children over 12 yrs.

Sticky Walnut

Cooking score: 4
Modern European | £30
11 Charles Street, Chester, CH2 3AZ
Tel no: (01244) 400400
stickywalnut.com

Arranged over two floors and with an unadorned, modern feel, Sticky Walnut is the original of Gary Usher's ever-growing chain of North West bistros. Hidden in a parade of shops down a back street in Chester, and open all day from noon, it is considered quite a find by readers, and it does exactly what it sets out to do: serve imaginative, seasonal British food at reasonable prices. Menus change monthly, with the kitchen delivering gutsy, broad-shouldered dishes, perhaps roast beetroot salad featuring those eponymous sticky walnuts, spiced pumpkin seeds and ricotta, or crispy

pig's head terrine with salt-baked turnip, miso, watercress and pear. Come here, too, for steamed cod with warm potato salad, pancetta and dill butter or braised featherblade of beef with caramelised onion purée and a side of chunky truffle and Parmesan chips. To finish, spiced coconut rice pudding arrives with poached pineapple and sugared hazelnuts. There's a short list of cocktails, gin, beer and cider, and a kindly priced wine list.
Chef/s: Jack Huxley. **Closed:** 25 and 26 Dec. **Meals:** main courses £15 to £22. Set L £16 (2 courses). Set D £18 (3 courses, Mon to Thur). Sun L £18 (2 courses) to £22. **Details:** 55 seats.

Lymm

The Church Green

Cooking score: 2
Modern British | £30
Higher Lane, Lymm, WA13 0AP
Tel no: (01925) 752068
aidenbyrne.co.uk
£5 OFF

Chef Aiden Byrne has celebrity status in the environs of Manchester and beyond, but still finds time to take care of business at this expansive pubby venture in a Cheshire village. All possibilities are covered here, whether you're after breakfast, a kids' meal or a Sunday roast. The 'lounge' menu brings a host of small plates (aka 'snacks'), prime marrow-bone burgers, pies and other self-styled 'homely classics', but the real action is in the restaurant. Here, the repertoire takes in thoroughly modern ideas such as pan-fried scallop with smoked apple and hazelnut gnocchi or pork belly with squid, chorizo and rosemary mash – all on a bedrock of great Northern produce. Slabs of home-reared beef (served with beef-dripping chips and classic sauces) justify the tagline 'British Grill', while desserts could be as homespun as sticky toffee pudding or lemon cheesecake. Cocktails provide an alternative to the substantial wine list.
Chef/s: Aiden Byrne. **Closed:** 25 Dec. **Meals:** set L and D £24 (2 courses) to £30. **Details:** 120 seats. 130 seats outside. Bar. Wheelchairs. Music. Parking. No children after 8pm on Sat.

Marton

La Popote

Cooking score: 1
French | £45
Church Farm, Manchester Road (A34), Marton, SK11 9HF
Tel no: (01260) 224785
la-popote.co.uk
£5 OFF

Everyone mentions the engaging, friendly service and happy vibes pervading this converted coach house, which looks on to a 13th-century church. Beams, old brick, a flower-filled garden and orangery may speak of 'ye olde' England, yet you can expect a strong French accent to the food. Daily specials can take in moules marinière, pheasant coq au vin or Dover sole meunière, but visitors are equally delighted with old favourites such as chicken liver pâté, Goosnargh duck breast à l'orange, and Herefordshire beef fillet au poivre. Finish with a trio of crème brûlée or tarte tatin. A well-annotated wine list opens at £19.75.
Chef/s: Victor Janssen. **Closed:** Mon, Tue, 26 Dec to 5 Jan, 1 week Aug. **Meals:** main courses £20 to £30. Set L £18 (2 courses) to £23. Sun L £25. **Details:** 60 seats. 25 seats outside. Bar. Wheelchairs. Music. Parking. No small children at D.

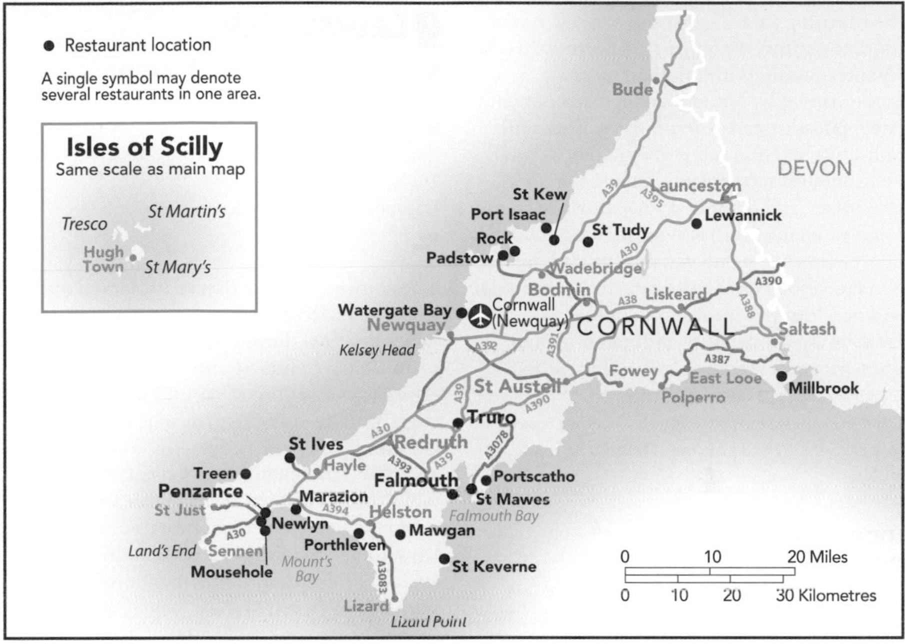

Falmouth

Oliver's

Cooking score: 3
Modern British | £33
33 High Street, Falmouth, TR11 2AD
Tel no: (01326) 218138
oliversfalmouth.com

Doing simple things well is the hallmark of this cheerful little bistro on Falmouth's 'quirky High Street', run with great warmth and energy by Ken and Wendy Symons. Cornish sardines, grilled to a perfect crisp, need nothing more than their garnish of caramelised lime and a splash of vinaigrette. Charred goat's cheese gives a pleasing smokiness to a beetroot and blood orange salad. Plaice, landed that morning, shines with buttered 'Cornish news' – potatoes, that is. Nor is it all fish. Try lamb's liver and bacon or meatballs with pea and courgette risotto. Dessert could bring raspberry millefeuille with raspberry sorbet. White walls, wooden tables and fish-themed artwork is the extent of the decor. With a serviceable wine list, French Sauvignon Blanc at a fiver a glass, and a big bottle of Doom Bar ale at £4.50, 'it's no surprise that business is booming'.

Chef/s: Ken Symons. **Closed:** Sun, Mon, 5 weeks Dec to Jan, bank hols. **Meals:** main courses £16 to £24. Set L £17 (2 courses) to £23. Tasting menu £40 (7 courses). **Details:** 28 seats. Vg menu. Music. Children over 12 yrs at D.

Star & Garter

Cooking score: 2
British | £28
52 High Street, Falmouth, TR11 2AF
Tel no: (01326) 316663
starandgarterfalmouth.co.uk
£5 OFF £30

'We live eight hours away and have driven for a night's stay so we could eat at this restaurant' is praise indeed for a full-of-life Georgian inn that's 'a real asset, badly needed in this area'. There's a good rustic feel in the bar with its real ales, but head to the restaurant at the back for the stunning views across the estuary. As for food, the culinary compass points towards the Mediterranean, with Puglian burrata accompanied by blood orange, marjoram and new season Tuscan olive oil or sardines with radicchio, sultanas and pomegranate, as well as venison with sage polenta, cavolo nero and gremolata, and octopus with cannellini beans, rainbow chard, chilli and mint. South Devon's Sharpham cheeses are worth a try if chocolate and raw honey tart with buttermilk ice cream and hazelnut praline doesn't appeal. Everything on the well-annotated, global wine list comes by the glass, and there are expertly crafted cocktails, too.

Chef/s: Andi Richardson. **Meals:** main courses £15 to £19. Set L £18 (3 courses). **Details:** 60 seats. Bar. Music.

LOCAL GEM

Rick Stein's Fish

Seafood | £30

Discovery Quay, Falmouth, TR11 3XA
Tel no: (01326) 330050
rickstein.com

A casual outpost of Rick Stein's ever-expanding empire, this Falmouth eatery is a cheery, upbeat spot with a menu to match. As ever, it promises an intriguing snapshot of the chef's global escapades, featuring anything from salt and pepper prawns to grilled whole plaice with lemongrass butter or hake with savoy cabbage, beer and bacon. The takeaway counter does a brisk trade in fish and chips fried in beef dripping. To drink, try a G&T made with Tarquin's Cornish gin, or stay with the commendable wine list.

Local Gem

These entries highlight a range of neighbourhood venues, delivering good, freshly cooked food at great value for money.

Lewannick

Coombeshead Farm

Cooking score: 6
British | £65

Lewannick, PL15 7QQ
Tel no: (01566) 782009
coombesheadfarm.co.uk

The communal table that so unnerved one solo diner last year has given way to separate tables in a new dining room and everyone seems to have entered into a much more relaxed, welcoming rhythm. The restored, rustic 18th-century farmstead is a congenial labour of love from proprietor Tom Adams and chef Tim Spedding, who match bare tables and an unfussy mood with a home-grown gastronomy that embraces produce from their 66-acre farm, whether fresh, foraged, pickled, fermented or cured, along with ethically reared meat. The result is intensely seasonal cooking that sings with flavour, from the opening spread of pork terrine, crisp pickled vegetables, their own young cheese and home-cultured butter served with 'the best sourdough in the country,' to the 'lovely, subtle flavours' of a single oyster grilled in beef fat and served in a delicate broth with a little grated horseradish. Add in a lovage soup with potato, peas, beans and some superb cured pork, and a main course of aged duck (breast with milk-soft fat under a crisp glazed skin, duck sausage and heart) and you have the components of a meal that is worth a special trip. Dessert could be rosemary and milk sorbet with salted caramel and a beef-fat biscuit crumb, then a vast rhubarb and custard millefeuille. Nibbles with pre-dinner drinks might include delicate Stithians cheese gougères, and an incredible éclair-like gnocchi draped in a slice of ethereal home-cured lardo. As for drinks, imaginative cocktails and modern, well-chosen European wines suit the food admirably.

Chef/s: Tim Spedding. **Closed:** Mon, Tue, Wed, 25 and 26 Dec. **Meals:** set D £65 (5 courses). Sun L £28. **Details:** 30 seats. Wheelchairs. Music. Parking. Children at Sun L only.

Marazion

Ben's Cornish Kitchen

Cooking score: 5
Modern British | £35
West End, Marazion, TR17 0EL
Tel no: (01736) 719200
benscornishkitchen.com
£5 OFF

Outstanding value for money is the immediate selling point at this agreeable bistro-style restaurant on Marazion's main street. Inside, all is suitably understated, with polished wood floors, white-painted stone walls and modest furnishings playing second fiddle to chef proprietor Ben Prior's confident and intelligent cooking. Locally sourced seasonal ingredients (especially fish) are treated with considerable skill and invention, from a starter of pan-fried scallops with roast cauliflower purée, apple and pistachio dukkah to smoked loin of venison with a sausage roll, choucroute, salt-baked celeriac and beetroot. You can also expect the unexpected: perhaps kid goat cutlets with spiced couscous and tomato relish. Catch of the day comes with truffle mash, roasted broccoli and coppa ham, before a finale of cleverly constructed desserts such as lemongrass and kaffir lime cream or muscovado and star anise parfait with hazelnut and poached pear. Prior and his team buy their wines in small batches, so the list is a constantly evolving compendium of cannily selected bottles – at extremely friendly prices.

Chef/s: Ben Prior. **Closed:** Sun, Mon, 25 Dec to 10 Jan. **Meals:** set L £19 (2 courses) to £24. Set D £29 (2 courses) to £35. **Details:** 28 seats. Wheelchairs. Music.

Mawgan

New Yard

Cooking score: 4
Modern British | £35
Trelowarren Estate, Mawgan, TR12 6AF
Tel no: (01326) 221595
newyardrestaurant.co.uk
£5 OFF

'This place is so tucked away that you really need to know it's there – you'd never stumble upon it otherwise – and it has serious wow factor.' So ran the notes of one visitor to this beautifully designed converted coach house on Sir Ferrers Vyvyan's delightfully remote Trelowarren Estate. New Yard capitalises on its bucolic location by sourcing 90 per cent of raw materials from within a 15-mile radius. With log-burning stoves at either end of a long room, and summer courtyard tables, a meal here is a year-round celebration of the best Cornish produce: estate game, fish from day boats and locally grown fruit and vegetables. Simplicity is the mantra of the open kitchen, from which comes a menu of 'the sort that makes you want to eat everything on it'. Our winter meal opened with 'innovative, fresh and delicate' cured monkfish with sea buckthorn caramel, spring onion, yoghurt and coriander, and went on to whole lemon sole with wild garlic and lemon dressing and mashed potato. A baked rice pudding with Caramac custard, raisin and burnt sugar was 'comfort food of the highest order'. A carefully considered drinks list opens at £15 for house wine and includes English sparklers and around 10 Cornish beers and ciders.

Chef/s: Jeffrey Robinson. **Closed:** Mon, 3 weeks Jan. **Meals:** main courses £13 to £29. Set L and D £19 (2 courses) to £25. **Details:** 50 seats. 12 seats outside. Bar. Wheelchairs. Music. Parking.

Nick Hook Photography

Cornwall's best bites

Bruce Rennie of The Shore in Penzance shares his favourite local places to eat and drink

The best **breakfast** is at **Sunset Surf Café, Gwithian**. There is nothing quite like having breakfast overlooking the sea, especially after a good surf!

The **Jubilee Pool Café, Penzance** has good **coffee** and nice service in the sunshine. It's by the recently refurbished Art Deco seawater **lido** which makes for a great way to chill and relax.

For **brunch**, **Duke Street Café** is a buzzing **family-run** place with very friendly service in the gorgeous fishing village of **Newlyn**.

The Mexico Inn, Longrock is great for **lunch**, and particularly known for having some satisfying, freshly cooked **pub food** in the winter when the fire is toasty warm.

Thornes Fruit & Veg, Causewayhead, Penzance is the most central place to get produce from local farms as well as great cheese, dairy, sausages and fudge, all from **Cornwall**.

Head to **The Gurnard's Head** at Zennor for a **pint**. This is as close as we get to having a local. We love to take the dog out for a walk along the coastal paths followed by a drink and snack in the bar.

Millbrook

The View

Cooking score: 3
Modern British | £38
Treninnow Cliff, Millbrook, PL10 1JY
Tel no: (01752) 822345
theview-restaurant.co.uk

They don't call it The View for nothing. Perched a little above the clifftop road, Matt Corner's place enjoys an imperious wide-screen vista over Whitsand Bay. The place itself is light and welcoming, with bold abstract artworks on clean white walls and banquettes in sky blue. It's justifiably popular with an enthusiastic local crowd, who flock in for modern British cooking of precision and elegance. A starter serving of crab risotto with lemon, oregano and Parmesan was beautifully wrought at inspection, while a vegetarian main dish of caramelised onions on layered puff pastry with a gratinated topping of Yarg cheese was a delight. Lamb rump of good flavour comes with pomegranate and sunflower seeds and nuts, as well as sweetly braised red cabbage, though the fatty foam that sauces it isn't quite right. Finish with creamily dense vanilla panna cotta with a brace of roasted plums, or warm chocolate mousse cake in fennel and orange syrup. Wines are an eclectic bunch from sound growers at demonstrably fair prices.

Chef/s: Matt Corner. **Closed:** Mon, Tue, seasonal opening winter. **Meals:** main courses £17 to £24. Set L £15 (2 courses) to £18. **Details:** 45 seats. 30 seats outside. Music. Parking.

Mousehole

The Old Coastguard

Cooking score: 3
Modern European | £28
The Parade, Mousehole, TR19 6PR
Tel no: (01736) 731222
oldcoastguardhotel.co.uk
£5 OFF £30

Run along similar 'eat, drink, sleep' lines as its siblings (the Gurnard's Head in nearby Treen and the Felin Fach Griffin in Brecon, see entries), this revamped hotel boasts majestic views across Mount's Bay – best enjoyed from its enclosed subtropical garden. Otherwise, eat in the vividly decorated dining room from a menu that shows ardent support for local and regional produce, albeit with plenty of global bedfellows: cider-braised squid, for example, might sit with white beans, gremolata and tempura sea vegetables, while vegetarians should be intrigued by a dish of crispy salsify with a duck egg, turnips and lentil dressing. The kitchen also makes a good fist of the classics (braised beef cheek with horseradish mash, say), and there's praise for desserts such as rhubarb and lemon verbena trifle. The drinks side of things covers everything from Cornish ales and zesty aperitifs to a list of colourfully described wines.

Chef/s: Matt Smith. **Closed:** 25 Dec, 5 days Jan. **Meals:** main courses £14 to £22. Set L £18 (2 courses) to £21. Set D £20 (2 courses) to £25. Sun L £25. **Details:** 70 seats. 30 seats outside. Bar. Wheelchairs. Music.

2 Fore Street

Cooking score: 3
Modern British | £33
2 Fore Street, Mousehole, TR19 6PF
Tel no: (01736) 731164
2forestreet.co.uk

More than 10 years down the line, Joe Wardell's disarmingly unassuming restaurant by Mousehole harbourside is still a family-run local asset to treasure. The setting is all neutral colours and distressed wooden tables, while the food owes much to the location: fish from the Cornish day boats is always a good call, from twice-baked crab and Parmesan soufflé to mixed seafood stew or wild sea bass accompanied by smokey Puy lentils, candied bacon, pea shoots and fennel mayo. Meat dishes such as wild boar terrine with shallot purée or organic local ribeye with green peppercorn sauce and skinny fries show a keen eye for sourcing, while dessert ushers in comforting treats ranging from rhubarb and ginger crumble tart with clotted cream to caramelised rice pudding with cinnamon and honeycomb. Hot drinks and cream teas are a fillip for seasonal visitors, and the wine list offers decent drinking at easy-going prices.

Chef/s: Joe Wardell. **Closed:** 3 Jan to 10 Feb. **Meals:** main courses £15 to £22. Sun L £15 (2 courses) to £18. **Details:** 36 seats. 30 seats outside. Music.

Newlyn

The Tolcarne Inn

Cooking score: 3
Seafood | £32
Newlyn, TR18 5PR
Tel no: (01736) 363074
tolcarneinn.co.uk
£5 OFF

'It is on a backstreet of Newlyn and you would never imagine it served such good food,' noted one surprised visitor to this unassuming tucked-away pub. More confidence comes from knowing that Ben Tunnicliffe is the man behind the stoves, having 'made his name at far swankier establishments in Cornwall'. And with Newlyn's fish market virtually next door 'you can be confident it's going to be good'. At one midweek spring lunch, a variety of seafood was chalked up: John Dory, hake, gurnard, mussels, salt cod and ling, as well as fishcakes and fish soup, and Tunnicliffe allows this best of Cornwall's catch to be the star. It's all simply prepared: that John Dory fillet is braced with cauliflower purée, spinach and raisin and onion chutney, salt cod fritters are pepped up with a ginger, chilli and apple salsa, while hake is matched with smoked bacon and hazelnuts, and gurnard with creamed fennel and mussels. To drink, Tribute draught ale and Chilean Sauvignon Blanc at £18.50.

Chef/s: Ben Tunnicliffe. **Closed:** 25 and 26 Dec. **Meals:** main courses £16 to £21. **Details:** 40 seats. 24 seats outside. V menu. Parking.

Padstow

Paul Ainsworth at No. 6

Cooking score: 7
Modern British | £62
6 Middle Street, Padstow, PL28 8AP
Tel no: (01841) 532093
paul-ainsworth.co.uk

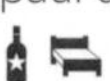

Paul Ainsworth maintains his exacting style at this Georgian townhouse on Middle Street. Tables in the former courtyard, restfully decorated in white and soft greys, take the pressure off the more compact front room. The food remains impeccably Ainsworth, concentrating on meat and fish, though two-course vegetarian and vegan menus are available on request. Dinner may start with an amuse-bouche of deep-fried Porthilly oyster, good sourdough and Cornish and caramelised butter. Highlights of our visit were a fresh, light dish of sea bream with lime and Japanese katsuobushi, with crunch coming from a shrimp slaw, and an intensely flavoured slow-cooked hogget wrapped in a thin suet crust and served with red garlic ketchup and a sweetbread fricassée – 'a robust and full-bodied dish'. Desserts, another high point, credited Gary Rhodes circa 1998 with a cleverly reworked bread-and-butter pudding topped with vanilla ice cream and a shot of Pedro Ximénez, which 'tasted like an old-fashioned bread-and-butter pudding but lighter and more elegant'. A smart front of house team pulls off the tricky feat of delivering flawless service without being remotely stiff or stuffy, while the prestigious wine list has many outstanding wines by the glass (from £9) and bottle (£35 for a South African Shiraz-Grenache).

Chef/s: Paul Ainsworth and John Walton. **Closed:** Sun, Mon, 25 and 26 Dec. **Meals:** main courses £31 to £45. Set L £25 (2 courses) to £29. **Details:** 46 seats. V menu. Vg menu. Bar. Music. Children over 4 yrs.

The Seafood Restaurant

Cooking score: 4
Seafood | £69
Riverside, Padstow, PL28 8BY
Tel no: (01841) 532700
rickstein.com

The Seafood Restaurant has been the HQ of Rick Stein's extensive and still expanding empire since 1975. It's close to the harbour, where Padstow's fishing boats are moored, and the large, white-painted dining room is filled with vast, striking contemporary canvases, with the seafood counter (which now, finally, takes bookings) a focal point as chefs prepare platters of fruits de mer. Prices are high, and some diners might ask why, when so many of the star dishes are created from seafood landed across the road: £45 for roast tronçon of wild turbot; £57 for a small Padstow lobster. Dishes are inspired by Rick Stein's travels throughout Europe and Asia: a starter of Cornish crab, for example, could be teamed with wakame, cucumber and dashi salad and wasabi mayonnaise, while a more classic Normandy dish of seafood dieppoise with sea bass, gurnard, hake, scallop, mussels and langoustines might follow. The wine list opens at £25 and is packed with fish-friendly big hitters.

Chef/s: Stephane Delourme. **Closed:** 25 and 26 Dec. **Meals:** main courses £20 to £60. Set L £41. **Details:** 120 seats. V menu. Wheelchairs. Children over 3 yrs.

LOCAL GEM

Rick Stein's Café

Seafood | £24

10 Middle Street, Padstow, PL28 8AP
Tel no: (01841) 532700
rickstein.com

The café arm of the Stein empire occupies a period building just back from the harbour, where breakfast, coffee and cakes, light lunches, and dinner are served in a simple, smart space that fuses the Cornish seaside with Scandi neutrality. So come for lunchtime slow-cooked pork tacos, or kick off an evening meal with deep-fried squid with aïoli or hake laksa, followed by moules-frites or chargrilled rump steak. The children's menu is far more interesting than the norm. Drink cool cocktails or wines from £19.50.

Penzance

The Shore

Cooking score: 3
Seafood | £46

13-14 Alverton Street, Penzance, TR18 2QP
Tel no: (01736) 362444
theshorerestaurant.uk

'Bruce Rennie is an energetic chef who doubles as waiter at quiet times, and serves the freshest fish from the Newlyn day boats,' begins a report on this stylish little restaurant about 10 minutes' walk from Penzance seafront. Bits of driftwood and candles in conch shells give the dining room a vaguely maritime feel that chimes perfectly with Rennie's imaginative cooking, presented as a five- or seven-course tasting menu. Lemon sole with asparagus, tarragon and lemon represents the classical side of things, but most dishes have a more contemporary edge, as in cured line-caught pollack with citrus dressing, passion fruit, fermented cabbage and dill, or diver-caught Salcombe scallops in a ceviche with rose, yuzu, white peach and rosemary. Desserts might include white chocolate délice or strawberries with basil sorbet. Wines have been thoughtfully chosen with fish in mind.

Chef/s: Bruce Rennie. **Closed:** Sun, Mon. **Meals:** Tasting menu £46 (5 courses) to £66 (7 courses). **Details:** 26 seats.

Port Isaac

Outlaw's Fish Kitchen

Cooking score: 5
Seafood | £50

1 Middle Street, Port Isaac, PL29 3RH
Tel no: (01208) 881183
outlaws.co.uk

£5 OFF

'Small in stature, big in reputation' is how one visitor summed up the snug proportions of this harbourside seafooder. It's shoehorned into the picturesque fishing village's oldest building, and may demand a certain amount of squeezing in, but the necessary bookings suggest, rightly, that the food is the real draw. It's all very lively, simple and unfussy, letting the fresh fish and its treatment shine through. Tim Barnes takes a global view and has a sublime knack for uniting harmonious flavours and textures, his captivating tapas-sized sharing plates shot through with vivid contrasts. Thin slivers of gurnard ceviche with orange, fennel and radish, and cured brill with apple, fennel and celeriac dressing are just two of the dishes that have made an impression on readers. There's been praise, too, for the lightest, crispiest ling with chilli jam; for monkfish with a red onion salad, coriander and yoghurt; delicate sole with crispy oyster and oyster mayonnaise; and marinated whole mackerel with garlic mayonnaise. The kitchen rarely puts a foot wrong, and that also goes for desserts along the lines of rhubarb sponge with lemon crème fraîche, and the plate of local cheeses. Expect kindly, attentive service and a brief, fish-friendly wine list.

Chef/s: Tim Barnes. **Closed:** Sun, Mon, 1 week Christmas, Jan. **Meals:** small plates £7 to £20. **Details:** 24 seats. V menu. Vg menu. Music.

★ NUMBER ONE RESTAURANT ★

Restaurant Nathan Outlaw

Cooking score: 10
Seafood | £130
6 New Road, Port Isaac, PL29 3SB
Tel no: (01208) 880896
nathan-outlaw.com

£5 OFF

Even by Cornish standards, the view across Port Isaac Bay from this tiny, unprepossessing restaurant is arresting, yet the real draw here is Nathan Outlaw's confident cooking, which combines considerable skill with a knack for deploying first-rate seafood to its ultimate advantage. There's a refreshing lack of pomp, especially when you consider that RNO is a must-do for anyone on the serious gastronomic circuit. The no-choice tasting menu is ingenious in its simplicity, yet continues to surprise. A meal may open with the serving of two dishes in tandem. At our late spring lunch, fingers of house-cured brill in a light, mint-infused dressing, a scattering of sweet peas and dots of yoghurt sharply pointing up the flavour, played perfectly against raw gilthead bream, neatly fanned out like sashimi in a dill dressing, topped with tiny orange and grapefruit segments and young broad beans. What appeals about the cooking is that there is no needless experimentation, just a collection of fine ingredients, all sensitively prepared and working in harmony. That is why a beautiful piece of crisp-skinned gurnard, matched by an aromatic saffron aïoli, with a disc of pickled kohlrabi adding a welcome note of acidity, continues to impress. As does a dazzling hazelnut-encrusted John Dory ('a triumphant standout'), in a precisely balanced, sweet yet punchy red wine dressing. There's nothing wacky or cheffy about a piece of turbot, either, simply served with St Enodoc asparagus and smoked hollandaise; everything in this virtuoso dish rests on the sheer quality and freshness of the ingredients. Desserts are no mere afterthought, with an exceptionally luscious strawberry ice cream sandwich scaling the heights. The service, under the brilliant supervision of Stephi Little, is pitch-perfect. There has been praise, too, for sommelier Damon Little, whose cellar knowledge is impressive, and whose advice is valuable whether you're taking the wine flight or just seeking the right glass or bottle.

Chef/s: Nathan Outlaw. **Closed:** Sun, Mon, Tue, 22 Dec to 1 Feb. **Meals:** tasting menu £130 (8 courses). **Details:** 30 seats. V menu. Music. Children over 10 yrs.

LOCAL GEM

Fresh from the Sea

Seafood | £18
18 New Road, Port Isaac, PL29 3RE
Tel no: (01208) 880849
freshfromthesea.co.uk

It's not hard to work out that Calum and Tracey Greenhalgh's no-fuss daytime café is all about fish and shellfish. The crabs and lobsters are landed in the *Mary D*, Calum's boat, and responsible fishing is the name of the game. Tracey serves up the daily catch (from early March to the end of November), and crab sandwiches remain a favourite. Specials might include spider crab or homemade fishcakes, and the feast platter is just that (whole lobster, crab, Porthilly oysters). Drink house wine, Prosecco or local beers.

Porthleven

Kota

Cooking score: 4
Fusion/Modern European | £40
Harbour Head, Porthleven, TR13 9JA
Tel no: (01326) 562407
kotarestaurant.co.uk

£5 OFF

'Eating at Kota is a huge pleasure, even on a cold December evening' is an enthusiastic endorsement of Jude and Jane Kereama's converted corn mill in a fabulous location on Porthleven's harbour head. With Maori heritage and Chinese and Malaysian roots, Jude creates food with a global outlook that stays faithful to Cornish produce, especially seafood, and the result is unfussy dishes with well-defined flavours. On our visit the food was very much on point. A silky raviolo of perky crab, teamed with a few mussels and briny sea greens, was lifted by a combo of lemongrass, lime leaf and turmeric root. Next up were slices of roast five-spiced duck breast with a sweet, sticky orange-inflected teriyaki glaze accompanied by crispy duck croquettes, carrots, turnips and winter greens. A delicate rhubarb and custard millefeuille with a refreshing, almost tingling ginger beer sorbet made a splendid finale. Spice- and seafood-friendly wines start at £18, with emphasis on Antipodean big players. For something a little more informal and family-friendly, the owners also run the Kota Kai Bar and Kitchen a few doors down.

Chef/s: Jude Kereama. **Closed:** Sun, Mon, 24 to 26 Dec, Jan. **Meals:** main courses £15 to £25. Set L and D £22 (2 courses) to £27. Tasting menu £50. **Details:** 40 seats. Bar. Wheelchairs. Music. No children under 10 yrs after 7pm.

Portscatho

Driftwood

Cooking score: 5
Modern European | £70
Rosevine, Portscatho, TR2 5EW
Tel no: (01872) 580644
driftwoodhotel.co.uk

The hotel's elegant, sun-filled dining room decorated in fresh seaside shades and hung with sailcloth drapes overlooks a beautiful stretch of Gerrans Bay on Cornwall's south coast. In this well-dressed setting, Chris Eden's food weaves ingredients, tastes and textures into a menu of complex, multi-layered dishes. Helford crab and thinly sliced raw asparagus, asparagus sauce, watercress, sea purslane, caviar and shards of savoury fish tuile typifies his exacting but delicious work. Lamb loin given a crust of herbs and hen of the woods with a seaweed-wrapped lamb dolma, is another. Desserts are 'very intricate'. There are minor irritations, with vegetables – perhaps mixed greens of kale, spinach and sprouting broccoli dressed with olive oil and toasted almonds – costing extra on a £70 dinner. Service from the white-jacketed team can be laboriously formal. The compensations are Eden's food adventures culled from the county's larder and local catch. The extensive wine list starts with a Verdejo at £23 and rises sharply.

Chef/s: Chris Eden and Adam Muddock. **Closed:** 11 Dec to 2 Feb. **Meals:** set D £60 (2 courses) to £70. Tasting menu £85 (6 courses) to £100 (8 courses). **Details:** 34 seats. Bar. Wheelchairs. Music. Parking. Children over 6 yrs at D.

Rock

The Mariners

Cooking score: 2
British | £35
Rock, PL27 6LD
Tel no: (01208) 863679
themarinersrock.com
£5 OFF

The food at this whitewashed pub is courtesy of Nathan Outlaw, draught ales are supplied by Sharp's Brewery, and the Camel Estuary view out front is unsullied by development. The best of those views come from the first-floor dining room, especially the terrace, while the ground-floor bar has been opened up (with a fair amount of noise generated off natural hard surfaces). The Cornish waters do provide their bounty for the menu, but it's not all about seafood here, judging by the 10oz pork chop with apple and cider sauce, and top-notch local steaks. From the concise carte, fishcakes get a welcome hit of acidity from accompanying pickled vegetables, breaded hake with tartare sauce and gem salad stands in for trad fish and chips and, to finish, rhubarb and almond pavlova hits the spot. Those draught ales get support from bottled beers and a short, well-judged wine list.

Chef/s: Zack Hawke. **Closed:** 3 weeks Jan. **Meals:** main courses £16 to £25. Sun L £27 (3 courses). **Details:** 100 seats. 50 seats outside. Bar. Music.

St Ives

Alba

Cooking score: 2
Modern British | £37
Old Lifeboat House, Wharf Road, St Ives, TR26 1LF
Tel no: (01736) 797222
alba-stives.co.uk

An enviable collection of contemporary artworks from the St Ives school certainly catches the eye at this two-tier restaurant and cocktail bar in a converted lifeboat house, although the bracing harbour view from the first-floor dining room is stiff competition. Locally landed fish is a standout on the menu, and the catch is handled with a degree of dexterity – think crab linguine or confit sea trout with choucroute, smoked mackerel, potato salad and wholegrain mustard beurre blanc. Meat eaters and vegetarians are also generously accommodated, with options ranging from pork tenderloin with braised Puy lentils, cavolo nero and salsa verde to a jungle curry of butternut squash and spinach with jasmine rice and Asian slaw. For afters, consider something left-field, such as miso and verjus panna cotta with honey ice cream and rice tuiles. The mood is relaxed and convivial, helped along by a substantial list of carefully chosen wines.

Chef/s: Grant Nethercott. **Closed:** Sun to Wed (Nov to Feb only), 25 and 26 Dec. **Meals:** main courses £20 to £30. Set D £25 (2 courses) to £29. **Details:** 34 seats. Bar. Music.

Porthgwidden Beach Café

Cooking score: 1
Seafood | £30
Porthgwidden Beach, The Island, St Ives, TR26 1PL
Tel no: (01736) 796791
porthgwiddencafe.co.uk

This secluded beachside café is a local institution, its terrace delivering sea and sunset views, and the please-all menu that, given the location, is a predictably – though not exclusively – fishy affair, a triumph of fresh, lively flavours. You won't go far wrong with smoked haddock chowder, seafood paella or roasted hake with smoked bacon mash, steamed mussels and fresh peas. Fish and chips and lunchtime panini are bestsellers, too, and it's worth noting the place is open for breakfast (bacon roll, hot crumpets, scrambled egg and smoked salmon). Wines from £15.95.

Chef/s: Robert Michaels. **Meals:** main courses £13 to £20. **Details:** 32 seats. 40 seats outside.

Porthmeor Beach Café

Cooking score: 1
International | £25
Porthmeor, St Ives, TR26 1JZ
Tel no: (01736) 793366
porthmeor-beach.co.uk

Whether you are in the conservatory-style dining room or on the terrace, this beachside café just below the Tate is a prime spot to catch the glorious St Ives sunsets. The lime green chairs and pink plastic buckets of cutlery are as vibrant as the global dishes emerging from the open kitchen. The contemporary tapas (available lunchtime and evening) might include grilled halloumi with roasted courgette, or crispy fried sea bass with Asian salad. More substantial mains (evenings only) might include grilled gurnard fillet with local crab and crushed new potatoes, or cider-braised pork belly, cassoulet, spring greens and gribiche. Sip a sundowner from a short list of classic cocktails, or explore seafood-friendly wines from £18.30.

Chef/s: Louis Wardman. **Closed:** 3 weeks from 4 Jan. **Meals:** main courses £13 to £19. Tapas £3 to £9. **Details:** 31 seats. 60 seats outside. Bar. Wheelchairs. Music.

Porthminster Beach Café

Cooking score: 3
Seafood | £40
Porthminster Beach, St Ives, TR26 2EB
Tel no: (01736) 795352
porthminstercafe.co.uk

This striking white Art Deco building occupies a rather special position, right on the golden sands of a Blue Flag beach. With unbeatable panoramic views over the sea, it's a magnificent setting in summer, but is equally alluring when the waves are crashing below on a blustery winter's evening. Whether you dine in the whitewashed dining room or on the heated terrace there is a decidedly Antipodean feel to the offering, even though Australian executive chef Michael Smith's tantalisingly original dishes make the most of Cornish seafood. Innovative starters include ginger-cured turbot with sweet-and-sour plum, yoghurt and hyssop, while mains take in pan-fried Cornish hake fillet with bubble and squeak, bacon, hollandaise sauce, winter truffle and spinach. Finish with manuka panna cotta and fresh figs with rum syrup, pistachio biscotti and thyme. A white-heavy wine list grouped by style kicks off at £17.50.

Chef/s: Michael Smith. **Closed:** 25 Dec. **Meals:** main courses £16 to £32. **Details:** 48 seats. 60 seats outside. V menu. Wheelchairs. Music.

LOCAL GEM

Blas Burgerworks

Burgers | £17
The Warren, St Ives, TR26 2EA
Tel no: (01736) 797272
blasburgerworks.co.uk

This great little burger joint, found down a narrow street behind the harbour, is a laudable independent operation, owned and run by Lisa Taylor for 13 years. It's an honest kitchen, offering ten beef varieties and reasonable price tags, and is a fine proponent of thoughtful regional sourcing – 100% Cornish beef, Primrose Herd bacon – with various chicken burgers (just as carefully sourced), and a selection of vegetarian and vegan burgers extending the range. To drink, there's Cornish beer and a brief list of wines.

St Keverne

★ NEW ENTRY ★

The Greenhouse

Cooking score: 4
Modern British | £29
6 High Street, St Keverne, TR12 6NN
Tel no: (01326) 280800
tgor.co.uk

'A wonderful restaurant run by wonderful people' is one diner's verdict of Leonie and Neil Woodward's modest bay-windowed cottage bistro just off the village square. It's a sentiment shared by many readers, impressed by the own-made bread, and dishes that are 'local, traditional, innovative and beautiful', perhaps with a touch of the Levant and Maghreb. Start with gin-cured gravadlax served on a corn tostada with squid ink aïoli, softened onions and dukkah, or a generous Cornish mackerel ceviche with pink grapefruit, finished with papaya and chilli. Mains might be roast duck breast with a cumin-infused duck pastilla or a plate of eight scallops, in their shells, with orange hollandaise and a pine nut and parsley crumb. To finish, there could be Turkish coffee crème brûlée with almond shortbread, or a plate of Cornish cheeses. There's a good beer and wine list with organic Italians at £18 and five Lizard Ales 'brewed in the old nuclear bunker' at Coverack. You can also BYO.

Chef/s: Neil and Leonie Woodward. **Closed:** Sun, Mon, Tue, Jan. **Meals:** main courses £13 to £16. Set L £19 (2 courses) to £25. **Details:** 28 seats. Music.

Vegetarian and vegan

While many restaurants offer individual dishes suitable for non-meat eaters, those marked 'V menu' (vegetarian) and 'Vg menu' (vegan) offer separate menus.

St Kew

St Kew Inn

Cooking score: 2
Modern British | £29
Churchtown, St Kew, PL30 3HB
Tel no: (01208) 841259
stkewinn.co.uk

An inn for over 500 years, the St Kew's solid granite walls have doubtless borne witness to a few escapades over the centuries. With its unreconstructed interior of flagstones, oak beams, chunky wooden tables and a huge iron range in the bar, it's not hard to picture the old days, especially in winter, when blazing fires warm drinkers and diners. The garden is a draw in fine weather, with views over the church, and ample space to spread out. A good amount of regional produce finds its way on to the menu, and the kitchen keeps in mind its role as a classic old pub, while also revelling in culinary ambition: proper fish and chips appear alongside a well-reported halibut with 'very tasty' saffron mash, asparagus and shrimp with seaweed. Kidneys make a welcome showing among first courses, sautéed with shiitake mushrooms, and main courses take in chicken and mushroom pie and Porthilly mussels in cider. Drink St Austell ales, or wines from £17.50.

Chef/s: Martin Perkins and Ryan Fisher. **Closed:** 25 and 26 Dec. **Meals:** main courses £14 to £20. Sun L £14. **Details:** 70 seats. 80 seats outside. Bar. Parking.

St Mawes

Hotel Tresanton

Cooking score: 3
Modern European | £42
27 Lower Castle Road, St Mawes, TR2 5DR
Tel no: (01326) 270055
tresanton.com

With its own 'beach club', gorgeous private terraces, equally gorgeous views and even an eight-metre yacht for hire, Olga Polizzi's dashing seaside bolthole is a darling of Cornwall's urbane weekend crowd. The cool, calm dining room summons up visions of a sunny Mediterranean, an impression reinforced by Paul Wadham's vibrant seasonal cooking and his deft handling of local seafood – perhaps Newlyn sardines with pangrattato and lemon or John Dory partnered by roast celeriac, heritage carrots and red onion marmalade. Cornish meats are also given their full due (best end of Launceston lamb with a jumble of roast peppers, aubergine, courgette and tapenade, for example), while desserts span everything from burnt English custard with rhubarb to a lush ice cream sundae with maple syrup and pecan nuts. The setting cries out for cocktails, but there are plenty of sophisticated boutique wines, too, especially from Italy.

Chef/s: Paul Wadham. **Meals:** main courses £18 to £28. Set L £25 (2 courses) to £29. **Details:** 70 seats. 90 seats outside. Bar. Wheelchairs. Parking. Children over 6 yrs at D.

St Tudy

St Tudy Inn

Cooking score: 2
Modern British | £30
Churchtown, St Tudy, PL30 3NN
Tel no: (01208) 850656
sttudyinn.com

With its stone walls, slate roof and wood-burning stove, this village pub with rooms is the very model of a go-getting Cornish local. Visitors have been 'very impressed' with the food, so it's worth booking a berth in one of three nautically themed dining rooms for dishes with a strong seasonal bias and a liking for West Country produce. Strong, clear flavours and no-frills presentation are hallmarks of chef owner Emily Scott's cooking, from summertime treats such as lemon sole with asparagus and herb dressing to winter warmers including baked figs with Helford White cheese, thyme and honey or duck leg with red cabbage and kale. Elsewhere a 'delicate and very successful' risotto dressed with courgette flowers signals the chef's undoubted capabilities, while puds might feature vanilla panna cotta with rhubarb. Fancy G&Ts and pints of Padstow-brewed St Tudy Ale are alternatives to a succinct list of 'well-priced' wines by the glass or carafe.

Chef/s: Emily Scott. **Closed:** 25 and 26 Dec. **Meals:** main courses £13 to £21. Set L (Mon only) £15 (2 courses) to £18. **Details:** 80 seats. 20 seats outside. Bar. Wheelchairs. Music.

Treen

The Gurnard's Head

Cooking score: 2
Modern British | £34
Treen, TR26 3DE
Tel no: (01736) 796928
gurnardshead.co.uk

£5 OFF

With its ochre-coloured exterior and piscine name writ large on the roof, there's little danger of missing or mistaking this windswept Cornish inn – or, indeed, the rocky outgrowth from which it takes its name. Inside, open fires, sofas and Cornish ales warm the cockles, while the kitchen makes much of its regional supplies, especially seafood. As you might expect, the namesake fish often puts in an appearance, while John Dory comes dressed up with celeriac, pancetta and chicken butter. Elsewhere, humble cuts of beef rump, pork collar and lamb breast are much favoured for more robust meat dishes, ahead of desserts such as iced banana parfait with peanuts and caramel. The drinks list covers everything from punchy cocktails, aperitifs and sherries to an enterprising assortment of colourfully described, idiosyncratic wines. Related to the Old Coastguard in Mousehole and the Felin Fach Griffin in Brecon (see entries).

Chef/s: Max Wilson. **Closed:** 3 to 6 Dec. **Meals:** main courses £18 to £21. Set L £19 (2 courses) to £22. Set D £21 (2 courses) to £27. Sun L £24. **Details:** 70 seats. 30 seats outside. V menu. Music. Parking.

Truro

Tabb's

Cooking score: 5
Modern British | £33
85 Kenwyn Street, Truro, TR1 3BZ
Tel no: (01872) 262110
tabbs.co.uk

It may not look much from the outside, but this lovingly polished little restaurant has accrued a solid reputation since opening nigh on 15 years ago. Much depends on Nigel Tabb's kitchen and his fruitful connections with the local food network. His cooking is at the gentler end of the modern British spectrum, with combinations that make sense: pigeon breast, for example, is accompanied by fennel, apple and Cornish Gouda, while hog's pudding, celeriac and cauliflower stir-fry offset perfectly cooked scallops. An occasional foray into Asian flavours may bring grilled fillet of ray wing with soy, pak choi and a seafood sesame broth given heft with chilli oil, while fillet of beef stroganoff with red wine reduction, celeriac and horseradish cream keeps things traditional. Unwavering consistency and skilled execution are the hallmarks of desserts, say a hot chocolate fondant with black treacle ice cream. Wines from France and elsewhere are available at very fair markups.

Chef/s: Nigel Tabb. **Closed:** Sun, Mon, 25 and 26 Dec, 1 Jan. **Meals:** main courses £16 to £21. Set L and D £20 (2 courses) to £25. Sun L (monthly) £33. **Details:** 28 seats. Bar. Music.

Send us your review

Your feedback informs the content of the *GFG* and will be used to compile next year's reviews. To register your opinion about any restaurant listed, or a restaurant that you wish to bring to our attention, visit our website.

Wadebridge

READERS RECOMMEND

The Ship Inn

Gonvena Hill, Wadebridge, PL27 6DF
Tel no: (01208) 813845
shipinnwadebridge.co.uk

'We like the cosy, low-beamed dining room, friendly, well-informed staff and excellent wine list (not too big, but lots of variety). The steamed mussels, cooked in a classic marinière style, are very nice indeed – no grit and just the right amount of sauce. Also try the monkfish with sautéed chorizo and chickpeas.'

Watergate Bay

Fifteen Cornwall

Cooking score: 3
Italian | £65

On the beach, Watergate Bay, TR8 4AA
Tel no: (01637) 861000
fifteencornwall.co.uk

Watching the sun setting over Watergate Bay is one of the treats (if you're lucky) of dinner at Jamie Oliver's Fifteen, but by day or dusk the spacious dining room of exposed beams, teardrop lamps and bentwood chairs has an 180-degree view of the bay's thundering Atlantic rollers. Former sous-chef Adam Banks has returned from Australia to take up the top job in the kitchen where he and his team (black hats) train young apprentices (white hats) as part of Oliver's Cornwall Food Foundation. Spinach, sage and pistachio ravioli was an uncomplicated starter with a £13 price tag that suggests you're paying for that view. From mains, local brill with fried capers and sprouting broccoli was elevated by the salty nip of pig's cheek, while monkfish with caponata was sour-sweet with smokiness from the charcoal grill. Carrots with lentils and yoghurt impressed, as did a pine nut and honey tart agreeably paired with foraged gorse flower gelato. A bottle of house Veneto opens the wine list at £22.50.

Chef/s: Adam Banks. **Closed:** 2 weeks Jan.
Meals: main courses £9 to £30. Tasting menu £65.
Details: 100 seats. V menu. Bar. Wheelchairs. Music. Parking. Children over 4 yrs at D.

LOCAL GEM

The Beach Hut

British | £28

Watergate Bay Hotel, Watergate Bay, TR8 4AA
Tel no: (01637) 860877
the-beach-hut.co.uk

With the waves of sandy Watergate Bay all but lapping at the door at high tide, this busy, boisterous 'hut' with faux ships' lamps and canvas chairs is no homespun shack but part of the Watergate Bay Hotel, and caters for all tastes and ages. For those fresh from the surf and hungry, the menu will fill any gap. The generous mackerel salad special would stretch a wetsuit to bursting point. Or there could be a bowl of crab spaghetti, equally generous and doused with olive oil and garlic, fried squid, Cornish mussels, beef chilli, pad thai and ever popular burger and fries. Bottled beers, cocktails and Prosecco at £6 a glass enhance the holiday mood.

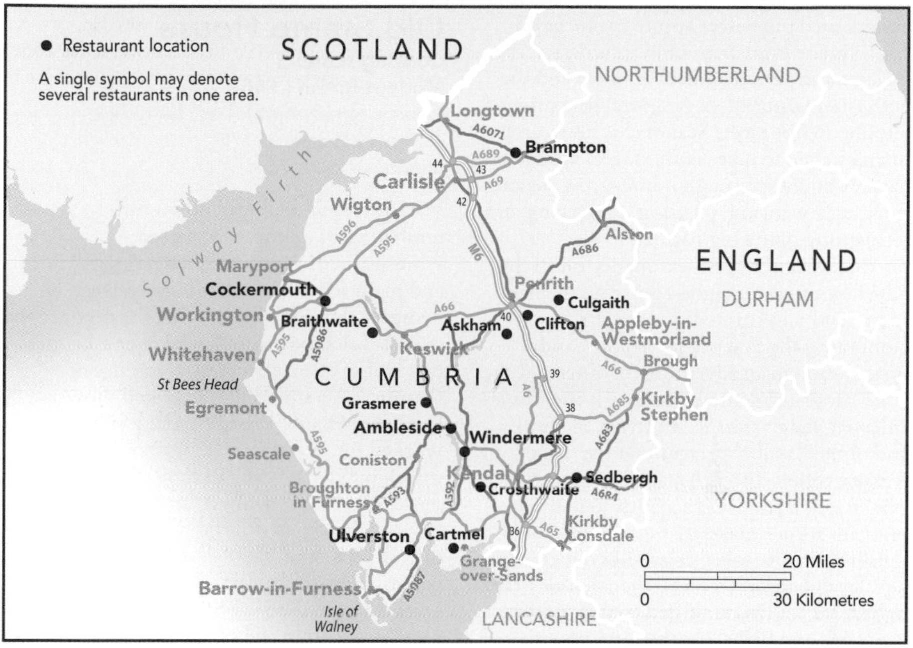

Ambleside

The Drunken Duck Inn

Cooking score: 3
Modern British | £38
Barngates, Ambleside, LA22 0NG
Tel no: (015394) 36347
drunkenduckinn.co.uk

'I've never had a duff pint here,' notes a regular visitor to this justly renowned Lakeland inn – not surprising, since the pub boasts its own on-site brewery producing a range of Barngates ales. Boozy attributes aside, the Drunken Duck seems to have it all: glorious views, warming fires, a dog-friendly bar, fishing rights, splendid accommodation and food with seasonal sensibilities. Lunches are all about feeding the holidaymakers (sandwiches, chips, mussel chowder, sticky ribs, waffles), but dinner is a more ambitious and thought-provoking prospect. Bao buns with fermented oyster mushrooms, kimchi and plum ketchup throw down the gauntlet for Lakeland tourists, and kimchi also turns up in a Japanese-inspired dish of halibut with gyoza and wasabi. Elsewhere, kipper Scotch eggs seek to reassure, likewise pork fillet and shoulder with savoy cabbage, cider and bacon. For pudding, try the lemon tart or a chocolate dessert with passion fruit and coconut. Well-chosen wines from £19.50.

Chef/s: Jonny Watson. **Closed:** 25 Dec. **Meals:** main courses £10 to £22. **Details:** 60 seats. 46 seats outside. Bar. Wheelchairs. Parking.

★ TOP 50 ★

Lake Road Kitchen

Cooking score: 7
Modern European | £65
3 Sussex House, Lake Road, Ambleside, LA22 0AD
Tel no: (015394) 22012
lakeroadkitchen.co.uk

'True North' describes one's ethos in having a clear and authentic path through life, and James Cross's take on true northern cuisine exudes such purpose. Despite the focus on cool climate ingredients and techniques, the welcome and environment is warm and the enthusiasm unbridled. A neutral backdrop of 'mountain hut meets Scandi chic' allows the open kitchen to take centre stage. Harnessing nature's bounty through home-growing and foraging see curing, pickling, preserving and fermenting play a big part. Bespoke purchasing and hyper-seasonality mean the no-choice five- or eight-course set menus (described, not printed) change daily – combining the best of opportunity and imagination in an adventure for diner and chef alike. Slow-fermented sourdough and home-cultured, hand-churned butter at the funky end of the flavour spectrum set the scene for a sensory rollercoaster. A starter of French-brined quail, fried and accompanied by pungent spruce mayonnaise and fermented mushroom juice takes finger-licking good to a new level. Greater finesse is then demonstrated in delicate yet flavour-filled courses of root vegetable and barley broth enriched with herbed rapeseed, and firm, flaky skrei cod partnered solely with truffled miso for maximum impact. A main course might feature aged Saddleback pork, cooked rare over an open flame until its fat renders to unadulterated naughtiness, served with a punchy salad of more than 20 different leaves from the polytunnel. Desserts have similar local integrity – think wild elderflower custard with rhubarb and granola. Whether enjoying educated recommendations from the cleverly designed drinks menu or the direct attentions of a chef who serves his own food, Lake Road Kitchen offers an engaging blend of expertise, obsession and passion wrapped in informed informality.

Chef/s: James Cross. **Closed:** Mon, Tue. **Meals:** tasting menu £65 (5 courses) to £90. **Details:** 21 seats. Music. Children over 12 yrs.

Old Stamp House

Cooking score: 5
Modern British | £45
Church Street, Ambleside, LA22 0BU
Tel no: (015394) 32775
oldstamphouse.com

Narrow stone steps lead down into a semblance of a simple farmstead – whitewashed stone walls, slate-flagged floor and plain wooden furnishings overseen by pedigree sheep portraits. From the decor to the cup of welcome broth that presages the menu, this is chef Ryan Blackburn's 'essence of Cumbria' – a simmered, seasoned showcase of local ingredients. Freddy Garside's beef is worked into a tartare with oyster emulsion, sorrel, pickled elf caps and rye crumb giving a sense of balance, richness, acidity and crunch. Herdwick hogget offers flavoursome morsels of pale pink loin, slow-cooked shoulder and panko-crumbed breast, cleverly accompanied by chicken of the woods mushrooms and a punchy anchovy and mint emulsion; a mini stockpot of braised barley with spring vegetables brings some welcome solidity to the dainty portions. Desserts have a more international flavour and might include a chocolate and chicory mousse with passion fruit. Cumbrian ales, gins and vodkas sit happily alongside a compact wine list.

Chef/s: Ryan Blackburn. **Closed:** Sun, Mon, 24 to 26 Dec, first 2 weeks Jan. **Meals:** main courses £24 to £27. Set L £20 (2 courses) to £25. Tasting Menu L £35, D £50 (5 courses) to £65. **Details:** 20 seats.

Askham

Allium at Askham Hall

Cooking score: 5
Modern British | £50
Askham, CA10 2PF
Tel no: (01931) 712350
askhamhall.co.uk

As a descendant of the Earls of Lonsdale, Charles Lowther is a busy man, overseeing the George & Dragon at Clifton (see entry) as well as maintaining Askham Hall – the family's ancient country seat a few miles from Ullswater, now an enchanting hotel. Fixed-price multi-course dinners are served in Allium – a conservatory-style restaurant overlooking the kitchen garden, which contributes its own valuable harvest throughout the year. Star billing, however, goes to the owner's home-reared Shorthorn beef, rare-breed pigs and chickens – the latter served with cauliflower cheese and truffle, perhaps. Curing, pickling and other sidelines are reminders that this is an industrious enterprise, although the surrounding region also contributes much seasonal bounty – as in loin and neck of Rough Fell lamb with carrots, onions, beer and barley. If it sounds deceptively simple, the results are elegant and sophisticated, especially when it comes to fish – think roast hake with oyster mushrooms, King cabbage, crosnes and sweet soy. Desserts such as geranium set cream with Yorkshire rhubarb, blood orange and Campari granita are in similar vein, while France is the main player on the international wine list.

Chef/s: Richard Swale. **Closed:** Sun, Mon, 24 to 26 Dec, 2 Jan to mid Feb. **Meals:** set D £50. Tasting menu £65 (5 courses). **Details:** 54 seats. Wheelchairs. Music. Parking. Children over 10 yrs.

Braithwaite

The Cottage in the Wood

Cooking score: 5
Modern British | £45

Magic Hill, Whinlatter Forest, Braithwaite, CA12 5TW
Tel no: (01768) 778409
thecottageinthewood.co.uk

£5 OFF

'The address is a giveaway as it really is a magic location,' enthused a visitor to Kath and Liam Berney's restaurant with rooms, as much taken with the 'jaw-dropping views of Bassenthwaite on the way up' as with the majesty of Skiddaw seen from the dining room windows. Ben Wilkinson now heads the kitchen, celebrating food that is local and seasonal, whether on the 'Taste Cumbria' menu or the short carte. Excellent cooking techniques, great balance and depth of flavour and 'super ingredients' were all on display at an evening inspection that opened with English asparagus on fried rye bread with confit egg yolk, almond, pea salad and Fine Fettle sheep's cheese, and a crab and tomato salad with 'layer upon layer of lovely flavours' from brown crab royale, chilled watercress and garden herbs. A fabulous piece of line-caught pollack followed, served with a young leek, chive and Champagne sauce and deeply flavoured oyster mushroom; and perfectly cooked dry-aged beef with violet artichokes, green olives, grilled gem lettuce, Jersey Royals, lardo and tomato. A chocolate marquise with yoghurt crumble and yoghurt sorbet offered a superb contrast of sweet and sour. Homemade sourdough and little treacle loaves, excellent local cheeses and helpful wine suggestions add to the experience.

Chef/s: Ben Wilkinson. **Closed:** Sun, Mon, 25 and 26 Dec, first 3 weeks Jan. **Meals:** set L £30. Set D £45. Tasting menu £65. **Details:** 36 seats. V menu. Wheelchairs. Parking. Children over 10 yrs at D.

Brampton

Farlam Hall

Cooking score: 2
Modern British | £49

Hallbankgate, Brampton, CA8 2NG
Tel no: (01697) 746234
farlamhall.co.uk

For more than four decades the Quinion family has offered warm hospitality in this 'very beautiful, old-fashioned retreat'. In keeping with English country-house tradition, the evening meal is one sitting, with drinks and canapés served in the drawing room at 7.30pm before dinner at 8 in the 'impressive' ornate dining room. The daily changing four-course menu offers the best of local produce – perhaps a smoked chicken and wild mushroom ramekin ('delicately smokey with that hit of umami'), a medallion of tender local Cumbrian beef with braised red onions, pink peppercorn and brandy sauce; or Lancashire guinea fowl breast with sweet

potato purée, plum and apple sauce and a plum tartlet. A 'wonderfully ripe' Stilton is served from the whole round and offered with a choice of Blue Shropshire, Cumbrian Blue or Wensleydale, and a 'delicate, silky' vanilla panna cotta provides the sweet finale. A wide-ranging wine list starts at £24.
Chef/s: Barry Quinion. **Closed:** 25 to 30 Dec, 6 to 25 Jan. **Meals:** set D £49 (4 courses). **Details:** 40 seats. Bar. Wheelchairs. Parking. Children over 5 yrs.

Cartmel

★ TOP 10 ★

L'Enclume

Cooking score: 10
Modern British | £145
Cavendish Street, Cartmel, LA11 6PZ
Tel no: (015395) 36362
lenclume.co.uk

£5 OFF

Since opening in this small South Lakes village sixteen years ago, Simon Rogan has achieved something of a miracle. His farm-to-table operation has influenced chefs right across the country; it's beyond dispute that British food owes him a lot. The obsessive search for flavour begins on the farm and continues in the kitchen where Rogan's approach is to extract maximum flavour from produce that is already pretty intense. You find yourself thinking that each new ingredient may well be the finest example of its kind you've ever tasted. 'One of the best meals in the last year – full of the surprises that happen when chefs, at full creative tilt, evolve ideas, and try different combinations,' opined one visitor. Choose a number – eight (lunch only) or 18 – and settle back as a rolling carnival of small bites, delivered hot-foot by the chefs, tell their own story. The freshness of Morecambe Bay in an oyster 'pebble'; the spectacular full-on crunch of a pork and eel cracker dotted with sweetcorn purée and summer savoury leaves; luscious cod mousse scattered with chopped parsley and scooped up with crisp chicken skin; rich, buttery salt-baked celeraiac topped with caviar and sweetened kelp; slices of Cornish scallop in an inky mushroom broth, strewn with shaved black truffle; the peppery note of nasturtium leaves in raw, diced aged beef run through with anchovy mayonnaise. This is scintillating cooking that excites without intimidating as in a wonderfully fatty nugget of roasted lamb loin with 'a focused, refined taste that set it apart from any lamb I've had before'. Rogan isn't one to stand still and is forever launching new ideas, such as turbot steamed in horseradish leaf with a pike-perch roe sauce, on the side a tartare of the fish topped with peas. Desserts represent a final creative flourish: with standouts running to an almost tart spiced rhubarb mousse with apple marigold, and an amazingly satisfying nougatine sandwich of woodruff ice cream, birch syrup and hazelnut. Of course, prices are high but L'Enclume delivers a complete package, with unobtrusive but attentive service that underscores the impressive food and drink. The exemplary wine list combines both quality and breadth with plenty of choice by the glass and a capable sommelier is ready to give clear and insightful advice.
Chef/s: Simon Rogan and Paul Burgalieres. **Closed:** Mon, 1st week Jan. **Meals:** set L £59 (8 courses). Tasting menu £155 (18 courses). **Details:** 44 seats. V menu. Wheelchairs. Children at L only.

Rogan & Co

Cooking score: 6
Modern British | £34
Devonshire Square, Cartmel, LA11 6QD
Tel no: (015395) 35917
roganandco.co.uk

£5 OFF

Ex-L'Enclume head chef Tom Barnes is now manning the stoves at Simon Rogan's informal brasserie-style restaurant just around the corner from the mothership, putting the spotlight on simplicity and flavour to make the very best of local produce, much of it from Rogan's farm. A bright seam of invention runs through Barnes' sensibly compact menus: the classic smoked eel and potato combination is given fresh life in a pairing with a sensational herby buttermilk sauce, while a summery bowl of chilled tomato juice, dotted prettily with flowers, is set off by a purée of black garlic and lovage. Confit shoulder of spring lamb, a slick of puréed potato, and tangy baby nasturtium leaves, all in a rich lamb jus, delivers well-balanced, emphatic flavours without over-elaboration. To follow there are delights aplenty: sweet woodruff from the farm scents vanilla ice cream, served with caramelised brioche; and delicate apple marigold flavours a foamy custard accompanying a chocolate fondant. The short but well-chosen wine list sets out on its global journey with a Slovenian white and French red at £22.

Chef/s: Tom Barnes. **Closed:** Tue, Wed (Nov to Apr). **Meals:** main courses £17 to £26. Set L £20 (2 courses) to £26. **Details:** 42 seats. Wheelchairs. Music.

Clifton

George & Dragon

Cooking score: 2
Modern British | £30
Clifton, CA10 2ER
Tel no: (01768) 865381
georgeanddragonclifton.co.uk
£5 OFF

With its rug-strewn stone floors and heritage colours, this tastefully renovated 18th-century coaching inn is a popular spot – for its rustic bar where local ales and wood-burner keep the pub side of the bargain, and for the quality of its home-grown or locally sourced ingredients. Most meat has been reared or dry-aged at its sister establishment, Allium at Askham Hall (see entry), so expect homemade black pudding and Askham Saddleback pork rissole (with bacon jam and fresh apple), and spiced Boer goat burger, topped with chilli jam, cucumber yoghurt and crisp gem lettuce (with fantastic dripping chips), as well as a hearty pheasant and partridge hotpot with chestnut dumplings, red cabbage and creamy mash 'that definitely passed muster on a winter evening'. If there is room still, then dark chocolate and orange tart or a homely nutmeg-infused egg custard with poached rhubarb might just hit the spot. Some 80 wines are arranged by style, starting at £18.

Chef/s: Gareth Webster. **Closed:** 26 Dec. **Meals:** main courses £17 to £25. **Details:** 104 seats. 60 seats outside. Vg menu. Bar. Wheelchairs. Music. Parking.

Cockermouth

Quince & Medlar

Cooking score: 1
Vegetarian | £28
11-13 Castlegate, Cockermouth, CA13 9EU
Tel no: (01900) 823579
quinceandmedlar.co.uk

Named after the two fruit trees out back, Colin and Louisa Le Voi's singular vegetarian restaurant continues to blossom as it approaches its 30th birthday. The location (a handsome Georgian townhouse) is certainly not your average 21st-century meat-free eatery – the cooking is immune to vegetarian fashion, although it championed vegan cooking long before plant-based menus became the latest thing. Dishes such as a celeriac, almond and buckwheat 'bomb' with charred salsify and tarragon sauce show the style, and there might be quince cheesecake to finish. A modest list of organic wines completes the package.

Chef/s: Colin Le Voi. **Closed:** Sun, Mon, 24 to 26 Dec, 2 weeks Jan. **Meals:** main courses £16. **Details:** 26 seats. V menu. Music.

Anonymous

At *The Good Food Guide*, our inspectors dine anonymously and pay their bill in full every time.These impartial review meals, along with feedback from thousands of our readers, are what informs the content of the *GFG*. Only the best restaurants make the cut.

Crosthwaite

The Punch Bowl Inn

Cooking score: 2
Modern British | £35
Lyth Valley, Crosthwaite, LA8 8HR
Tel no: (015395) 68237
the-punchbowl.co.uk

With the church opposite and the Lyth Valley providing such a lovely backdrop, it's easy to see the attraction of this smart country inn. The decor is pitched agreeably between rural hostelry and upper-crust inn-with-rooms, while the menu celebrates regional produce, say Morecambe Bay shrimps or Mrs Kirkham's Lancashire cheese (in a twice-baked soufflé). However, inspiration for dishes tends to come from wider-spread European roots, so expect Cumbrian beef carpaccio teamed with salt-baked celeriac, roasted hazelnuts, Colston Bassett cheese and bitter leaves, then a duo of Cumbrian lamb (with mint sauce, roasted carrot and oyster mushroom) or baked chalk stream trout (with baby leeks, anchovy emulsion, Scottish mussels and mushrooms à la grecque). Dessert could bring a classic custard tart or 'a deliciously beautiful cranberry soufflé served with ice cream and a lovely sauce'. Sandwiches and pub classics form part of the lunchtime offering. Wines from £24.

Chef/s: Arthur Bridgeman Quinn. **Meals:** main courses £15 to £26. Tasting menu £55 (5 courses). **Details:** 90 seats. 40 seats outside. V menu. Vg menu. Bar. Wheelchairs. Music. Parking.

Symbols

- Accommodation is available
- Three courses for less than £30
- £5 off voucher scheme
- Notable wine list

Culgaith

LOCAL GEM

Mrs Miller's

Modern British | £28
Hazel Dene Garden Centre, Culgaith, CA10 1QF
Tel no: (01768) 882520
mrsmillersculgaith.co.uk

Wend your way through the higgledy-piggledy Hazel Dene Garden Centre, past boxes of seed potatoes and other horticultural paraphernalia, then negotiate the gift shop before alighting on Mrs Miller's relaxed tearoom-cum-café. Breakfast and lunch menus sustain the visitors with filling treats (homemade venison burgers, Caesar salad, smörgåsbord toasts, scampi and chips), but the kitchen ups its game for dinner on Friday and Saturday evenings. Expect plenty of regional produce in dishes such as slow-cooked Cumbrian beef with truffle mash and bourguignon sauce. Wines from £12.50.

Grasmere

★ TOP 50 ★

Forest Side

Cooking score: 7
Modern British | £60
Keswick Road, Grasmere, LA22 9RN
Tel no: (015394) 35250
theforestside.com

A Victorian country house just up the road from Grasmere has been transformed into a boutique hotel for the times, complete with staff attired in country-interiors mode, and an expansive dining room, where reclaimed materials and views of the gardens encourage you to feel well bedded into the environs. As, indeed, does the output of Kevin Tickle's limitlessly imaginative kitchen, where ingredients both bought and found come together in various multi-course parades of exploratory dishes. A spring dinner produced numerous highlights for one diner: crisp toasted quinoa with charred cauliflower on Dale End Cheddar purée; simultaneously 'chewy and gloopy' pig's ear terrine with kimchi; venison pastrami dressed in juniper yoghurt. These were the outriders for principal dishes that tend towards boldly simple: translucent cod with crosnes and dill; and a slice of ultra-rare hogget shoulder alongside tender sweetbread with a set custard of smoked potato. There's nothing obvious about the sweet items, not when nitro-frozen balls of sweet cicely in sheep's curd, rhubarb in duck egg custard, and dandelion root with Carvetii coffee and walnuts are on the agenda. It's food that inevitably tends to divide opinion, often between two dining together, but when 'the most intense, tingling, sharp flavours' crop up in dish after dish, it's hard to argue with the thought-provoking nature of it all. Commendable efforts have been made with the wine list, too, which opens with enterprising small-glass selections from £7.

Chef/s: Kevin Tickle. **Meals:** set L £35 (3 courses). Set D £60 (3 courses). Tasting menu £80 (6 courses) to £95. **Details:** 50 seats. V menu. Bar. Wheelchairs. Parking. Children over 8 yrs.

The Jumble Room

Cooking score: 1
International | £40
Langdale Road, Grasmere, LA22 9SU
Tel no: (015394) 35188
thejumbleroom.co.uk
£5 OFF

The Jumble Room has been going its own way since it opened its doors in 1996. Chrissy Hill has always cooked the kind of food she likes to eat (luckily it turns out lots of other people do, too), while the decor is bold and 'definitely full of personality'. The food ignores international borders, with regional ingredients starring in a global panoply that might take you from Spanish salad with Manchego and baby figs, to Persian lamb rump, Malaysian seafood curry, or fish and chips. The wine list is a good read and fairly priced.

Chef/s: Chrissy Hill and James O'Campo. **Closed:** Tue, 8 to 27 Dec. **Meals:** main courses £15 to £23. **Details:** 48 seats. Music.

Sedbergh

Three Hares

Cooking score: 2
Modern European | £30
57 Main Street, Sedbergh, LA10 5AB
Tel no: (015396) 21058
threeharescafe.co.uk
£5 OFF

This bistro and bakery is the vision of James Ratcliffe and Nina Matsunaga, a fabulous fusion of Nina's heritage (Japan via Germany) and the bounty of this part of the world. It is a top-drawer café during the day, open for breakfast, lunches, and amazing pastries, breads and cakes, then for dinner on three evenings. The ethos is field to fork; passion for regional produce, including rare-breed meats, is heartfelt, and just about everything is made on the premises. Pheasant gyoza with soy makes a tantalising nibble before small plates such as the full-flavoured duck gizzards with haggis, blood orange and curd, or mackerel and confit squid with hits of rhubarb. Among big plates, British White beef hotpot competes with wild turbot and curried mussels – 'share and spare yourself the envy'. To finish, bitter chocolate tart comes with Jerusalem artichoke ice cream. The wine list focuses on small independent producers, and do ask about the saké options.

Chef/s: Nina Matsunaga. **Closed:** Mon, 25 and 26 Dec. **Meals:** main courses £13 to £23. Tasting menu £40 (5 courses) to £50. **Details:** 25 seats. 2 seats outside. Music.

Nina Matsunaga's best bites

Nina Matsunaga of Three Hares in Cumbria shares her favourite places to eat and drink around the North West and beyond

For **breakfast**, **The Pentonbridge Inn** at Penton, near Carlisle, for their amazing cinnamon eggy bread.

The Music Room by Atkinsons Coffee Roasters in Lancaster is consistently good, which is what you need when you're a caffeine addict.

Northcote at Langho, Blackburn, is a classic spot for **lunch**. Good service, great wine and food.

For **food shopping**, we get all our meat and a lot of veg straight from farmers and friends, otherwise the Chinese grocers in Lancaster, Preston and Manchester are always a treat for me.

The Scran & Scallie pub in Edinburgh is a great place to go with the **family**.

The best place for dinner is **Lake Road Kitchen** at Ambleside. James and Sally are a couple of grafters and it comes across in all they do.

If I could eat only one thing, it would have to be... local meat, whether it's hogget, beef, pork or game from the shoots nearby.

Ulverston

★ NEW ENTRY ★

Virginia House

Cooking score: 5
Modern British | £45
24 Queen Street, Ulverston, LA12 7AF
Tel no: (01229) 584844
virginiahouseulverston.co.uk

£5 OFF

Ulverston is a pretty market town best known for catering to hungry fell walkers: 'you certainly don't expect exceptional cooking in a guesthouse'. But Craig Sherrington trained with David Everitt-Matthias at Le Champignon Sauvage (see entry) as well as Eric Chavot, although his tasting menus are entirely his own, inspired by the natural larder of Cumbria. He piles on diverse flavours with brio: in a goat's cheese bonbon with pear purée, say, or a shot glass of tomato water that's 'the fresh essence of summer', and by serving celeriac velouté with rhubarb and kale doughnut or a duck breast with asparagus and caramelised onions. Elsewhere, sea bass is invigorated with roast and puréed cauliflower, buttermilk and parsley oil and leaf, while a pork dish uses fillet, belly, black pudding and pancetta, with a wild garlic barley risotto and broccoli spears for balance. Puddings include a mini soufflé with jam and custard and with coffee, vanilla fudge, chocolate and fig jelly. Service, led by Louise Sherrington, is 'clearly bursting with pride with so much talent in the kitchen'. There's a well-stocked gin bar, too, and a short but well-targeted wine list.
Chef/s: Craig Sherrington. **Closed:** Sun, Mon, Tue, first 2 weeks Jan. **Meals:** tasting menu £45 (5 courses) to £75. **Details:** 34 seats. V menu. Bar. Music. Children over 12 yrs at D.

Windermere

Holbeck Ghyll

new chef/no score
Modern British | £68
Holbeck Lane, Windermere, LA23 1LU
Tel no: (015394) 32375
holbeckghyll.com
£5 OFF

Among the most seductively sited hotels in the Lake District, Holbeck Ghyll confronts Windermere as though a team of cinematic set designers had just finished it moments before you arrive, and a sense of unruffled calm pervades the inner spaces. As we went to press, the energetically creative Jake Jones had recently departed the kitchen and a new chef was yet to be announced. Highlights from the seven-course tasting menu taken during Jones's tenure included Shetland mussel broth of 'tremendous taste', Gigha halibut with stupendous sand-grown carrots, and a stunning dessert that featured poached pear and meringue on pistachio sponge with chocolate honeycomb flakes. On the carte were dishes of aged roe deer venison scented with truffle, while the vegan menu centred on truffled mushroom risotto with mushroom ketchup, fried kale and chestnuts. We believe Jones's successor plans to continue the ethos of successfully combining regional produce with Scottish seafood. A wine list that promises 'classics and mavericks' represents a progressive evolution from the old grand-hotel format, and makes space for leafy Chilean Sauvignon Gris, Romania's full-blooded red Feteasca, and Louis Roederer's benchmark California sparklers. Bottles start at £30.

Closed: first week Jan. **Meals:** set L £35 (2 courses) to £45. Set D £68 (3 courses). Tasting menu £88. **Details:** 50 seats. 25 seats outside. Vg menu. Bar. Wheelchairs. Parking. Children over 8 yrs at D.

Hrishi at Gilpin Hotel & Lake House

Cooking score: 6
Modern British | £70
Crook Road, Windermere, LA23 3NE
Tel no: (01539) 488 818
thegilpin.co.uk

High in the Fells, Gilpin Hotel provides a luxurious retreat where the rugged surroundings and classic country-house atmosphere sit easily alongside meditative spa facilities and Asian-inspired water landscapes. As head chef, Hrishikesh Desai fuses his diverse inspirations equally successfully, delivering a seamless blend of classical technique and precision with Pan-Asian riffs on texture and flavour. The gracious calm of Hrishi's formal dining rooms accented with notes of gold against white linen is an appropriate canvas for the vibrancy and colour of the food. From à la carte to tasting menus, diners note the 'excellent creativity with subtle Asian notes along the way'. Dishes might include slow-poached loin of Cumbrian veal with celeriac textures, pickled mushrooms and milk foam followed by slow-roast salt-aged pork belly with cabbage fermented with coconut and turmeric and served with a five-spice reduction. Desserts deliver artistry for eye and palate – an inspired lime leaf panna cotta in a white chocolate shell with rhubarb textures and honeycomb granola crunch is a treasure trove of sensations. An extensive cellar covers all the classic bases of Old World production, as well as a few interesting takes on the New World.

Chef/s: Hrishikesh Desai. **Meals:** set D £70 (3 courses). Sun L £38 (3 courses). Tasting menu £90 (7 courses). **Details:** 58 seats. 26 seats outside. V menu. Bar. Wheelchairs. Music. Parking. Children over 7 yrs.

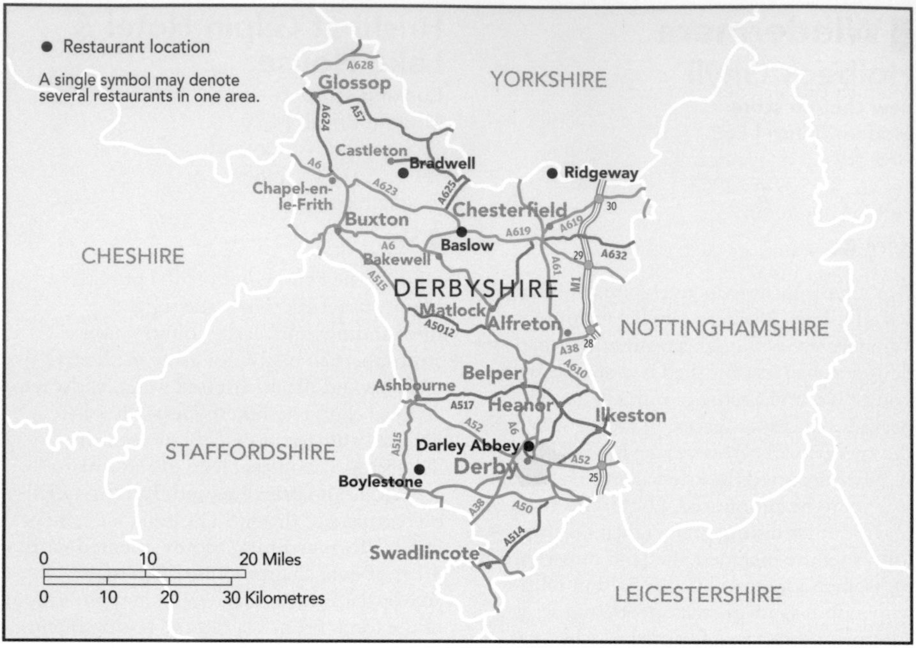

● Restaurant location

A single symbol may denote several restaurants in one area.

YORKSHIRE
CHESHIRE
DERBYSHIRE
NOTTINGHAMSHIRE
STAFFORDSHIRE
LEICESTERSHIRE

Glossop
Castleton
Bradwell
Ridgeway
Chapel-en-le-Frith
Buxton
Chesterfield
Baslow
Bakewell
Matlock
Alfreton
Belper
Ashbourne
Heanor
Ilkeston
Darley Abbey
Derby
Boylestone
Swadlincote

0 10 20 Miles
0 10 20 30 Kilometres

Baslow

Fischer's Baslow Hall

Cooking score: 6
Modern European | £78
Calver Road, Baslow, DE45 1RR
Tel no: (01246) 583259
fischers-baslowhall.co.uk

Constructed in the early 20th century, towards the close of the great era of architectural pastiche, Baslow is a stone-built mansion in the 17th-century style, with leaded windows and gabled wings, acquired in its early days by the Ferranti electrical dynasty. Under its present ownership, it has moved with the times, from the country-house era of the 1980s to the present world of kitchen gardens and chef's tables. Rupert Rowley is in charge, overseeing those vegetable and herb plots, arranging attractive presentations on hand-thrown stoneware made by the in-house potter, and cooking to a seasonal template with Asian influences woven in. Crab tempura with yuzu and cucumber precedes sautéed brill with an onion bhajia on the winter menu, before a triumphant serving of Shorthorn beef with snails and parsley makes its entrance. Three-dimensional flavours are in evidence throughout, as in a starter of tandoori quail with mango and lime, a main dish of sea bass with Parmesan, lemon, fennel and artichoke, and a finale of prune, Armagnac and jasmine parfait with honeycomb and brioche. Wines take a classical approach, with some Coravin treats to back up the main glass selection from £5.50.

Chef/s: Rupert Rowley. **Closed:** 25 and 26 Dec. **Meals:** set L £25 (2 courses) to £34. Set D £65 (2 courses) to £79. Sun L £38 (2 courses) to £45. Tasting menu £68 to £97. **Details:** 74 seats. V menu. Bar. Parking. Children over 8 yrs.

Rowley's

Cooking score: 1
Modern British | £27
Church Lane, Baslow, DE45 1RY
Tel no: (01246) 583880
rowleysrestaurant.co.uk

No more than a proverbial stone's throw from big brother Fischer's at Baslow Hall (see entry), Rowley's is a world away in style and attitude. Part stone-walled village pub, part brasserie, it mixes traditional features with swaggering purple-hued interiors, and the food covers all bases. Lunch means sandwiches, steaks, fish and chips, etc, and dinner brings a more sophisticated line-up involving anything from steak tartare with a fried quail's egg to Derbyshire venison with salsify, hay-baked celeriac, game chips and cocoa sauce. To finish off, perhaps sample the iced banana parfait. Thornbridge beers and international wines suit any occasion.
Chef/s: Adam Harper. **Closed:** 25 Dec. **Meals:** main courses £16 to £24. Mon to Fri set L £17 (2 courses) to £21. Set D £23 (2 courses) to £31. Sun L £25. **Details:** 78 seats. 16 seats outside. Wheelchairs. Music. Parking.

Boylestone

The Lighthouse Restaurant

Cooking score: 4
Modern British | £55
New Road, Boylestone, DE6 5AA
Tel no: (01335) 330658
the-lighthouse-restaurant.co.uk

It's easy enough to find the pub in this quiet village deep in pretty countryside, but the Lighthouse is another matter. The restaurant is behind the Rose and Crown, in a beamed barn extension not visible from the road. The big draw here is Jon Hardy's cooking. His intricate, light, modern eight-course evening-only tasting menu is delivered with bags of flair and surprise, the opening statement of intent a nibble of tandoori pork kebab pointed up with sriracha (hot chilli sauce) and garlic mayo, and underpinned by a subtle smokiness. Pot-roasted celeriac comes with assertive flavours every which way – Lincolnshire Poacher cheese sauce, black truffle, chive and apple – before sensational sticky ox cheek with mustard mash and Wild Beer Co gravy or aged dairy-cow tartare with an oscietra caviar cornet. The picture is completed by superb sourdough bread with sweet cultured butter, effective, informed service and by the cleverly put together, well-annotated wine list.
Chef/s: Jon Hardy. **Closed:** Sun, Mon, Tue, first 2 weeks Jan. **Meals:** tasting menu £55 (8 courses). **Details:** 40 seats. V menu. Bar. Wheelchairs. Music. Parking. Children over 12 yrs.

Bradwell

The Samuel Fox Country Inn

Cooking score: 4
Modern British | £36
Stretfield Road, Bradwell, S33 9JT
Tel no: (01433) 621562
samuelfox.co.uk

In the middle of the Dales, close to Matlock, Bakewell and Buxton, and with food taking precedence over pints, this comfortable, well-run village inn makes a great pit stop. Chef proprietor James Duckett's aim is to combine first-rate, seasonal ingredients with unfussy modern cooking to produce a menu with broad appeal. Ham hock and black pudding terrine with pickled cauliflower, beef cheek braised in red wine with walnut mash, or fillet of sea bream with a pearl barley and mussel risotto, charred lettuce and aïoli typify the largely European influences, though elsewhere there might be cured sea trout with pickled fennel, beetroot and sumac. There's bittersweet chocolate tart with mandarins, pistachios and chocolate sorbet to finish, while a couple of local ales and a short list of reasonably priced wines satisfy drinkers.
Chef/s: James Duckett. **Closed:** Mon, Tue, 2 to 23 Jan, 1 week Aug. **Meals:** set L and D £29 (2 courses) to £36. Sun L £28. Tasting menu £55 (7 courses). **Details:** 40 seats. V menu. Wheelchairs. Parking.

Darley Abbey
Darleys

Cooking score: 3
Modern British | £50
Darley Abbey Mill, Haslams Lane, Darley Abbey, DE22 1DZ
Tel no: (01332) 364987
darleys.com
£5 OFF

The newly refurbished terrace offers pole-position outdoor seating overlooking the Derwent, the logical extension of the Hobsons' weirside restaurant, housed in a converted mill. It's a soothing setting indeed for some adventurous modern cookery that gathers influences from around the world. Skrei cod has its Icelandic cockles – or rather its accompanying mussels – warmed with curried green lentils for one cosmopolitan starter, while pork belly takes another Asian route, being glazed in hoisin and teamed with spring onions and gingered black kale. They could be followed by something relatively traditional, perhaps breast and confit leg of chicken with apple and hazelnuts in sherry vinegar sauce, while black seaweed and steamed pak choi adorn a serving of stone bass that comes with wild rice risotto. At the finishing stage, pistachio ice cream adds lustre to red berry soufflé, and an eye-catching triple-layered chocolate dessert is partnered with vanilla parfait. The concise international wine list starts at £18.95, or £4.95 a glass.

Chef/s: Jonathan Hobson. **Closed:** Mon, 25 Dec for 2 weeks. **Meals:** main courses £23 to £26. Set L £20 (2 courses) to £25. Sun L £30. Tasting menu £50 (7 courses). **Details:** 60 seats. 30 seats outside. V menu. Bar. Music. Parking.

Ridgeway
The Old Vicarage

Cooking score: 6
Modern British | £60
Ridgeway Moor, Ridgeway, S12 3XW
Tel no: (0114) 247 5814
theoldvicarage.co.uk

It's barely a 10-minute drive from the home of crucible steel and *The Full Monty*, but this enchanting Victorian vicarage could be from a different time and place with its hidden copses, wildflower meadows and croquet lawns. Inside, it's all about personal comfort and civilised contentment, whether you're relaxing by the fire or sitting in the restaurant surrounded by botanical prints. Tessa Bramley has been in residence for three decades, adding authority and wisdom to the kitchen's seasonal endeavours while ensuring that native produce is never far from the chef's hands. The results show an instinctive feel for what is right on the plate, whether it's a perfectly seared fillet of Whitby cod with sea herbs, courgette ribbons, chervil purée and a lemon butter sauce or a serving of local pork fillet with carrot purée, buttered kale, crab apple and sage jelly and a 'fantastic' spiced pork crackling. Elsewhere, a delightful alliance of a 'memorable' butter-roasted fillet of brill with wild mushrooms, thyme gnocchi and a Riesling chive sauce brings freshness to the table without resorting to flashy in-vogue gestures. The kitchen breaks a few rules, though, when it comes to spicily aromatic desserts such as caramelised shallot ice cream with rhubarb and pepper puffed rice. With personal links to some of the world's leading producers, the illustrious all-inclusive wine list blurs the boundaries between terroir and technology – look to the splendid house recommendations for starters.

Chef/s: Tessa Bramley and Nathan Smith. **Closed:** Sun, Mon, 26 Dec to 4 Jan, 2 weeks Jul to Aug, bank hols. **Meals:** set L £40. Set D £60 (4 courses). Tasting menu £70 (7 courses). **Details:** 44 seats. V menu. Wheelchairs. Parking. Children over 8 yrs at D.

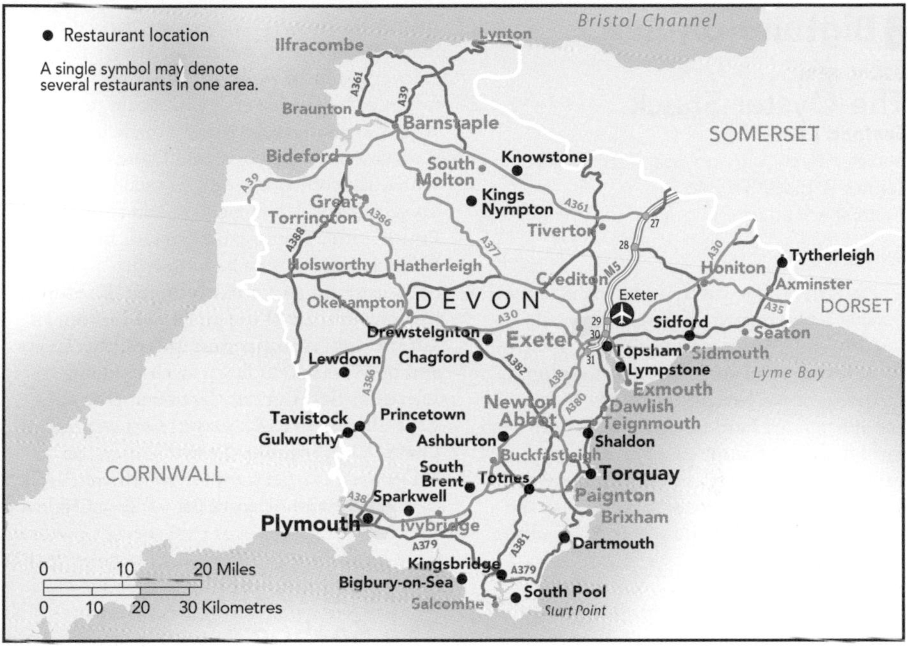

● Restaurant location

A single symbol may denote several restaurants in one area.

Bristol Channel
Lynton
Ilfracombe
Braunton
Barnstaple
SOMERSET
Bideford
South Molton
Knowstone
Great Torrington
Kings Nympton
Tiverton
Tytherleigh
Holsworthy
Hatherleigh
Crediton
Honiton
Axminster
DORSET
Okehampton
DEVON
Exeter
Sidford
Seaton
Drewsteignton
Exeter
Topsham
Sidmouth
Lewdown
Chagford
Lympstone
Lyme Bay
Exmouth
Newton Abbot
Dawlish
Teignmouth
Tavistock
Princetown
Gulworthy
Ashburton
Shaldon
Buckfastleigh
CORNWALL
South Brent
Totnes
Torquay
Paignton
Sparkwell
Brixham
Plymouth
Ivybridge
Dartmouth
Kingsbridge
Bigbury-on-Sea
South Pool
Salcombe
Start Point
A361 A39 A386 A388 A377 A30 A35 M5 A382 A38 A380 A381 A379 27 28 29 30 31
0 10 20 Miles
0 10 20 30 Kilometres

Ashburton

The Old Library

Cooking score: 3
Modern European | £38
North Street, Ashburton, TQ13 7QH
Tel no: (01364) 652896
theoldlibraryrestaurant.co.uk

'Just what this area needed,' a local confirmed, gladdened at the success of Amy Mitchell and Joe Suttie's café-style operation (accessed from the car park behind the library building). A whitewashed room hung with framed food photos, the kitchen an integral part of it, is very much in the modern manner. The short menus that change every few weeks are supplemented by blackboard specials. A trio of scallops come in 'crispy pig' guise, each sitting on a chunk of belly with matchsticks of bacon on top, as well as sweetcorn purée and forthrightly pickled shallots, or start with beetroot carpaccio in Gorgonzola dressing and toasted seeds. To follow, local beef fillet is a mainstay, or there may be duck breast with chicory, roast squash and salted lemon relish, as well as the day's fish in crab velouté with sautéed fennel. Carb-heavy desserts include banana and marmalade cake, or dark chocolate and stout pudding, but there might also be a splodge of cardamom white chocolate and honey with poached rhubarb. The short wine list has been carefully considered, with standard glasses from £5.

Chef/s: Amy Mitchell and Joe Suttie. **Closed:** Tue, 23 Dec to 15 Jan. **Meals:** main courses £17 to £23. Sun L £20. **Details:** 28 seats. 10 seats outside. Wheelchairs. Music. Parking.

Send us your review

Your feedback informs the content of the *GFG* and will be used to compile next year's reviews. To register your opinion about any restaurant listed, or a restaurant that you wish to bring to our attention, visit our website.

Bigbury-on-Sea

LOCAL GEM

The Oyster Shack

Seafood | £30
Stakes Hill, Bigbury-on-Sea, TQ7 4BE
Tel no: (01548) 810876
oystershack.co.uk

£5 OFF

The bright orange sail that acts as shade for the outside tables is hard to miss, and it's all suitably chilled and seasidey. Those oysters come *au naturel* or with a host of toppings, including seaweed salsa, while the local crab and lobsters are hard to resist. Start with Thai mussels or Vulscombe goat's cheese on bruschetta, and keep an eye out for the daily catch. The approach road changes with the tide, so do check tide times before travelling. Wines start at £18.

Chagford

Gidleigh Park

Cooking score: 4
Modern European | £125
Chagford, TQ13 8HH
Tel no: (01647) 432367
gidleigh.co.uk

Change has been afoot at dear old Gidleigh since Michael Wignall departed the kitchens in the autumn of 2017. The front of house approach hasn't registered so much as a blip, maintaining formidable levels of professional courtesy and genuine warmth. The view from the panelled dining rooms over the descending ground of the Teign Valley still bestows a restorative feeling of benign isolation, and the house itself is a treasure. Chris Simpson took on his first big gig here in early 2018, having come from Nathan Outlaw's Cornwall team, and there is a definite sense of gear change to the kitchen's output. Dishes are undeniably simpler; there is much less reliance on the dazzlements of technical ingenuity, and a distinct air of retrenchment. A first course of lemon sole fillet with brown shrimps, caramelised celery, lemony wild garlic purée and a deep-fried fish cracker is appealing enough, as might be the tartlet of Salcombe crab and asparagus topped with Exmoor caviar. Main-course meats showcase salt-aged beef and Dartmoor lamb, while fish could be monk dressed in chicken jus with Jerusalem artichoke and seaweed. Finish with a flying saucer of chocolate and banana parfaits, which comes with a side dish of lime granita for self-dolloping. The wine list remains one of the glories of Devon, an astonishing, commanding roll call of classics and new-wave oenology, with Coravin selections fleshing out the offering by the glass. Prices are high; glasses start at £12.

Chef/s: Chris Simpson. **Closed:** 10 days Jan. **Meals:** set L £65. Set D £125. Tasting menu £145 (10 courses). **Details:** 48 seats. Bar. Parking. Children over 8 yrs.

Dartmouth

The Seahorse

Cooking score: 4
Seafood | £45
5 South Embankment, Dartmouth, TQ6 9BH
Tel no: (01803) 835147
seahorserestaurant.co.uk

£5 OFF

The pink and white fondant frontage on the Dartmouth quayside shimmers invitingly on a dazzling day, advertising the flagship of Tonks and Prowse's seafood empire. A big brasserie-style room has a towering wall of wine shelves on one side, and windows on to the kitchen. From the moment the nibbles are set before you – caper-laden anchoïade and garlicky bacalhau with dippers – the intentions are clear. The menu deals in daily changing fish and shellfish specials, with main dishes divided into plancha and charcoal oven preparations. A fillet of John Dory on blanched Datterini tomatoes and oregano is a straightforward pleasure, or go for Dover sole or plaice served whole, or spiny lobster with rice. There are a few meat options, too, mostly cuts of beef. Start with razor clams and sobrasada, or a small portion of meaty pappardelle, and close the deal with amber-hued Sicilian lemon tart, or milhojas (the Spanish take on millefeuille) with Moscato-poached pear. The wine list is a dream date, its sections classified by price in multiples of ten, teeming with excellent growers. Constantly changing specials served by the small glass (from £5) or half-bottle carafe are always worth a look.

Chef/s: Jake Bridgwood. **Closed:** Sun, Mon, 24 to 26 Dec, 1 and 2 Jan. **Meals:** main courses £21 to £32. Set L and early D £20 (2 courses). **Details:** 40 seats. 4 seats outside. Bar. Wheelchairs. Music.

LOCAL GEM

Rockfish

Seafood | £25

8 South Embankment, Dartmouth, TQ6 9BH

Tel no: (01803) 832800

therockfish.co.uk

This welcoming little haven overlooking the river Dart, the first in what is now a mini chain of Devon seafood restaurants, is considered a local asset, and deservedly popular. Service is efficient and cheerful, coping with children, groups and the like, and serving traditional fish and chips and fresh seafood with pride, all day from noon. Leigh-on-Sea cockles, crisp Torbay calamari or sprats, Devon crab and locally caught and smoked mackerel, all reflect a commitment to local and sustainable sourcing. Fish-friendly wines from £19.95.

Drewsteignton

The Old Inn

Cooking score: 4

Modern European | £55

Drewsteignton, EX6 6QR

Tel no: (01647) 281276

old-inn.co.uk

It's certainly 'old' (more than three centuries old, to be precise) and it used to be a staging post, but that's about it as regards rose-tinted heritage appeal. Duncan Walker runs this one-time village inn as a personable restaurant-with-rooms with a professional outlook, while his cooking is all about confident technique, sound sourcing and cosmopolitan ideas. He keeps fashions and trends at arm's length, preferring to make his point with more thoughtful gestures – as in a saffron-tinged lasagne of crab, red peppers and roast shellfish velouté or sautéed calf's sweetbreads simply dressed with frisée, almonds and balsamic. West Country ingredients play a starring role in dishes such as roast loin of Dartmoor lamb with boulangère potato and creamed spinach, while desserts tend to be assured takes on the classics – a perfectly executed tarte tatin or apricot soufflé, for example. Around 40 wines show impeccable taste and a nose for good value.

Chef/s: Duncan Walker. **Closed:** Sun, Mon, Tue, 3 weeks Jan. **Meals:** set D £48 (2 courses) to £55. **Details:** 15 seats. Bar. Children over 12 yrs.

Gulworthy

The Horn of Plenty

Cooking score: 3

Modern British | £50

Gulworthy, PL19 8JD

Tel no: (01822) 832528

thehornofplenty.co.uk

With entrancing views of the Tamar Valley and a prevailing mood of soul-soothing relaxation, this small country house hotel is a lovely prospect. In business for 50 years, the Horn of Plenty was once the domain of acclaimed chef, Sonia Stevenson, although a lot has changed since those pioneering days. Luckily, current chef Ashley Wright understands the seasons and applies vivid strokes to a bountiful selection of West Country produce – a terrine of Creedy Carver duck accompanied by slow-cooked duck egg and truffle, say, or Cornish venison paired with orange, heritage beetroot and chocolate jus. Fish from the region's ports also features strongly (perhaps Brixham skate with winkles, salsify, black garlic and chicken jus), while desserts wander further afield for the

likes of 'banoffee' banana parfait with dulce de leche and white chocolate textures. Sixty dependable wines include a dozen by the glass.
Chef/s: Ashley Wright. **Meals:** set L £20 (2 courses) to £25. Set D £50. Tasting menu £65 (5 courses). **Details:** 60 seats. 20 seats outside. Bar. Wheelchairs. Music. Parking.

Kings Nympton

LOCAL GEM

The Grove Inn

British | £22

Kings Nympton, EX37 9ST
Tel no: (01769) 580406
thegroveinn.co.uk

Kings Nympton is naught but a hamlet, a straggle of cottages along a tiny road, and at its centre, the Grove Inn. There's no car park, so squeeze the car in on the side of the road. It's a great old-fashioned place: ancient, low-ceilinged, noted for its warm fire and welcoming service and for dealing in real ales and honest cooking. So tuck into Exeter lamb faggots with gravy and buttered mash or a burger of rose veal topped with mature Cheddar. There are also various steaks, 'proper' ham with two fried free-range eggs and chips, and hot chocolate pudding for afters. Everything on the wine list comes by the glass and bottles start at £15.

Kingsbridge

LOCAL GEM

Beachhouse

Seafood | £30

South Milton Sands, Kingsbridge, TQ7 3JY
Tel no: (01548) 561144
beachhousedevon.com

Set in a jaw-dropping location above a pretty sandy shoreline, this whitewashed wooden shack is well worth the drive down a vertigo-inducing, high-hedged lane. There's a tiny open kitchen and a blackboard menu that's carried table to table offering buckets of local mussels, bowls of 'blissful' crab linguine, deep-fried whitebait, and crusty bread with dukkah and feta. The lunchtime sandwich selection might include a mackerel club made with local Salcombe Smokie. Outdoor tables draw the crowds in fine weather, and there's a serviceable list of seafood-friendly wines.

Knowstone

The Masons Arms

Cooking score: 4

Modern British | £48

Knowstone, EX36 4RY
Tel no: (01398) 341231
masonsarmsdevon.co.uk

This 13th-century thatched inn on the edge of Exmoor has oodles of character with a beamed front bar, huge inglenook and a dining room that, though relatively modern, offers charming views across the fields and has a fabulously eccentric Renaissance-style painted ceiling. Chef patron Mark Dodson's cooking displays a discipline, refinement and technical mastery that comes from a background in classic French cuisine, and his exquisite amuse-bouches raise expectations high. At inspection, a starter of confit duck and duck liver terrine with celeriac, walnut and celery had a wonderfully rich texture and deep, pleasing flavours, while a generous portion of pink, tender lamb loin came with a rectangle of textbook-perfect boulangère potatoes, smokey aubergine purée and baby carrots. Puddings are elegantly presented, whether a burnt rhubarb custard with tiny meringues, poached rhubarb and stem ginger ice cream or a chocolate délice with apricot sorbet. The kindly priced wine list is predominantly French.
Chef/s: Mark Dodson. **Closed:** Sun, Mon, first week Jan, Feb half-term, last week Aug. **Meals:** main courses £26 to £28. Set L £21 (2 courses) to £25. **Details:** 28 seats. 16 seats outside. Bar. Wheelchairs. Music. Parking. Children over 5 yrs at D.

Lewdown

Lewtrenchard Manor

Cooking score: 5
Modern British | £50
Lewdown, EX20 4PN
Tel no: (01566) 783222
lewtrenchard.co.uk

The creaky floors and venerable panelling at Lewtrenchard bear witness to its Jacobean origins, via an uplift given it by the Victorian divine, Sabine Baring-Gould. It's an atmospheric treasure trove, with extensive gardens in which Gertrude Jekyll had a hand, and a pair of dining rooms in which oil portraits of bygone worthies keep a vigilant eye. The cooking is partly supplied by the Manor's own walled kitchen plot, and Matthew Peryer favours a finely detailed country-house style – local goat's cheese pavé with lightly pickled red and white beetroot from the garden, candied walnuts, apple and a beetroot sauce set the tone for one visitor. The outstanding dishes at that meal were poached Loch Duart salmon, which was matched with superb West Country smoked eel, Jerusalem artichoke, toasted hazelnuts and a garnish of sea vegetables; and garlic and thyme roasted lamb rump with shredded breast, haricots, morels and wild garlic. Britain's growing vegan clientele is furnished with its own menu, centring perhaps on roasted cauliflower with crispy kale and girolles in caper and raisin dressing. Desserts include a rich trio of chocolate with crunchy praline, and a delightful salted caramel ice cream. The French-led wine list opens at £27.50.

Chef/s: Matthew Peryer. **Meals:** set L £21 (2 courses) to £26. Set D £55. Sun L £28. Tasting menu £69 (7 courses). Private chef's table £79 (8 courses). **Details:** 40 seats. 20 seats outside. V menu. Vg menu. Bar. Wheelchairs. Parking. Children over 8 yrs at D.

Lympstone

Lympstone Manor

Cooking score: 6
Modern British | £125
Courtlands Lane, Lympstone, EX8 3NZ
Tel no: (01395) 202040
lympstonemanor.co.uk

In due course, it will be possible to sit on the south-facing terrace at Lympstone, Devon's acres unrolling from the banks of the Exe before you, and drink a glass of the Manor's own sparkling wine. The planting of a vineyard in spring 2018 gives notice both of the vigour of English viticulture and of Michael Caines' ambitions for the place. Inside, in a trio of contemporary dining rooms hung with decent original artworks, he offers a full hand of menu formats: a three-per-course carte, an eight-course taster, an Estuary fish menu, and vegetarian and vegan alternatives. The highlights are legion, in a style that combines a certain delicacy of construction with finely honed flavours and seasonings throughout: quail tartlet with onion confit and black truffle in a light quail jus; sea bass roasted in star anise with bouillabaisse; the majestic local venison loin with braised red cabbage, glazed figs and chestnut purée. To finish, soufflés with matching ice creams – perhaps prune and Armagnac – are the last word in airy fragility, and chocoholics are looked after with mahogany-coloured ganache, ivory-white ice cream and a parfait of milk with hazelnut. The wine list has been compiled with verve, with a fine selection by the glass from £10, or £14.50 for the house blanc de blancs while you wait for the Cuvée Lympstone to come on stream.

Chef/s: Dan Gambles and Michael Caines MBE. **Meals:** set L £38 (2 courses) to £60. Set D £125 (3 courses). Sun L £60. Tasting menu £140 (9 courses). Estuary menu £130 (8 courses). **Details:** 50 seats. 40 seats outside. V menu. Vg menu. Bar. Wheelchairs. Music. Parking. Children over 5 yrs.

Devon's best bites

Jake Bridgwood of The Seahorse in Dartmouth shares his favourite local places to eat and drink

Yarn in **Dartmouth** is owned by an ex-fisherman and his partner. Will and Jade run the cool little bar with a relaxed vibe and offer something a bit different for **breakfast** - such as **mince on toast**, which pays homage to Jade's original home in New Zealand.

The Steam Packet at **Kingswear** is a new favourite of mine. A warm and cosy little **bar**, it's extremely popular with the locals with the added bonus of views over the River Dart. They have a few great **West Country ales** and if you get peckish the **pizzas** are awesome.

Woodroast in **Dartmouth** serves really great **artisan coffee**, blended by hand right in front of you and it comes with **biscotti** from Ancona in Italy.

Totnes is heaving with great **little shops**, I can spend hours wandering around picking things up for home and often for the restaurant.

Ancherstone Café is a short, scenic ferry trip from us at **Dittisham**. Stepping on to the same pontoon where they land the **crab and lobster** for the café all adds to the experience. On a hot day eat a bowl of **Elberry Cove mussels** outside.

Plymouth

The Greedy Goose

Cooking score: 4
Modern British | £35

Prysten House, Finewell Street, Plymouth, PL1 2AE
Tel no: (01752) 252001
thegreedygoose.co.uk

£5 OFF

Built in 1498 and widely regarded as Plymouth's oldest building, the imposing stone-walled Prysten House currently provide the backdrop for Ben Palmer's gastronomic endeavours. Eat in the historic dining room, or in the courtyard on fine days, from an incisive monthly menu full of seasonal and West Country produce – perhaps a combo of hand-picked Devon crab, crispy oyster, cucumber and lemongrass mayonnaise or 'cellar' goat's curd with beetroots, pickled red onion and hazelnut dukkah. Dry-aged native beef from Philip Warren of Launceston pleases, too, likewise hay-smoked guinea fowl with salt-baked celeriac or Wild Hart venison accompanied by pearl barley, piccolo parsnip and celery. The GG chocolate mousse with milk ice cream is an ever-present winner when it comes to dessert. Tasting menus and cut-price 'five-ten-five' deals (for lunch and early supper) ensure that the restaurant caters to a broad constituency. To drink, inspired local G&T pairings sit alongside a well-constructed wine list.

Chef/s: Ben Palmer and Thomas Dodd. **Closed:** Sun, Mon, 24 Dec to early Jan. **Meals:** main courses £16 to £28. Set L and early D £15 (2 courses) to £20. Tasting menu £60 (7 courses) to £90 (11 courses). **Details:** 65 seats. 30 seats outside. Bar. Music. Parking. Children over 4 yrs.

Rock Salt

Cooking score: 2
Modern British | £30
31 Stonehouse Street, Plymouth, PL1 3PE
Tel no: (01752) 225522
rocksaltcafe.co.uk
£5 OFF

If Plymouth city centre could be said to have a wrong side of the tracks, nobody would snap your head off for identifying it as Stonehouse. And yet, the area boasts the Jenkins family's Rock Salt, a corner site that was once a Victorian pub, and now fair looks the part as a chunky-tabled bistro and all-day breakfast stop. Dave Jenkins is determined not to scare people off with over-ambitious prices, resulting in a three-course lunch menu at an affable £16, perhaps taking in a black pudding Scotch egg with pickles and bacon jam, a hunk of pan-roasted stone bass on chorizo and chickpeas, and a tumbler of honey panna cotta topped with mandarin sorbet, peach syrup and honeycomb. Evenings bring on the likes of seared venison loin with its cottage pie and maple-glazed parsnip, or butter-roasted guinea-fowl breast and confit leg with creamed cabbage and walnuts. Wines start at £4.75 a standard glass.

Chef/s: David Jenkins. **Closed:** 25 and 26 Dec. **Meals:** main courses £11 to £23. Set L and D £12 (2 courses) to £16. Sun L £15. Tasting menu £50 (7 courses). **Details:** 60 seats. V menu. Vg menu. Bar. Music.

Princetown

Prince Hall Hotel

Cooking score: 3
British | £35
Princetown, PL20 6SA
Tel no: (01822) 890403
princehall.co.uk
£5 OFF

Prince Hall is far enough from local clusters of civilisation as to feel positively misanthropic, but makes a cracking base for tramping about Dartmoor and, anyway, the warm welcome within is a contrast to the brooding isolation. The Dalys describe their culinary approach as 'relaxed fine dining', meaning there are no outré combinations or inscrutable technicalities, just an extensive menu of locally based cooking that tells you exactly what you're going to get. That could be seared scallops dressed in lemon oil to start, with a coppa ham crisp and celeriac purée, prior to fennel-salted guinea fowl breast in white wine jus, or pan-roast skrei cod with saffron mash in caper, lemon and herb butter. At dessert, the temptations keep on coming, in the varied shapes of white chocolate and honey cheesecake with black cherry sorbet, or crème brûlée with crushed pistachios; or there are fine West Country cheeses, including Yarg, Sharpham and Vulscombe goat. The little wine list just about does.

Chef/s: Luke Daley. **Meals:** main courses £15 to £25. Set L £30. Set D £30 to £35. Tasting menu £65 (6 courses). **Details:** 30 seats. 30 seats outside. V menu. Vg menu. Bar. Parking.

Shaldon

Ode & Co.

Cooking score: 1
Italian | £20
Coast View Holiday Park, Torquay Road, Shaldon, TQ14 0BG
Tel no: (01626) 818450
odetruefood.com
£5 OFF £30

Ode Dining's high-end mothership (closed for refurbishment at the time of going to press) has spawned a cluster of more casual but equally eco-minded venues, including this glass-fronted eatery in a smart holiday park overlooking Lyme Bay. The short menu centres on smokey wood-fired pizzas with organic sourdough bases, but don't ignore the soups, salads and 'pickers' (small plates of English cold cuts, day-boat fish goujons, ham and piccalilli croquettes, etc) – or, indeed, puds such as dough fingers sprinkled with cinnamon sugar. On Sundays, 'firewall roasts' are cooked in the wood-fired pizza oven using

the traditional 'brick' technique. To drink, wines, beers and juices generally come with an organic or biodynamic seal of approval.
Chef/s: Tim Bouget and David Bundros. **Closed:** Mon, Tue, 25 Dec, winter months. **Meals:** small plates £3 to £8. Pizzas £9 to £11. Sun L £17 (2 courses). **Details:** 60 seats. 60 seats outside. Bar. Music. Parking.

Sidford
The Salty Monk
Cooking score: 2
Modern British | £35
Church Street, Sidford, EX10 9QP
Tel no: (01395) 513174
saltymonk.co.uk

There isn't much to Sidford beyond a hairdresser, a Spar and a chippy, but there is also the Salty Monk, the Witheridges' long-running restaurant with rooms in a historic monastic salt-storage facility. It's run with bundles of personable charm out front, and motors along on Andy Witheridge's solid bistro cooking, which doesn't try to overreach itself with technical whizz-bangs, but does build comforting dishes from well-sourced materials. The homemade breads with mustard and truffle butters deserve a mention in despatches in themselves, as a winning intro to homely starters such as black pudding on pea purée with ham jelly and Serrano crisps, and sturdily constructed mains. Creedy Carver duck breast is offered as pink as gammon, but full of flavour, along with buttery champ and a swipe of celeriac purée, or there may be hake fillet on lentils and coconut with Thai-spiced sauce. The orange tart would work better cold than red-hot from the oven, but comes with inviting mascarpone enriched with honey and tonka, and cubes of blood-orange jelly. Appreciable efforts have been made with the wine list, which opens at £18.50.
Chef/s: Andy Witheridge. **Closed:** Mon, Jan, 1 week Nov. **Meals:** main courses £17 to £30. Tasting menu £65. **Details:** 28 seats. 18 seats outside. V menu. Bar. Wheelchairs. Music. Parking.

South Brent
Glazebrook House
Cooking score: 4
Modern British | £43
Wrangaton Road, South Brent, TQ10 9JE
Tel no: (01364) 73322
glazebrookhouse.com

Sitting proud above a B-road on the southern fringes of Dartmoor, Glazebrook House feels a bit like the home of a true British eccentric with an eye for exotic curios. By comparison, the kitchen plays it straight, offering routine sustenance at lunchtime (salads, steak sandwiches, risottos and the like), then more ambitious offerings in the evening. Name-checked West Country ingredients are given satisfyingly accomplished treatments, from pan-fried smoked mackerel with Earl Grey gel and pickled shallots to rump of lamb with braised salsify, Jerusalem artichoke and Dawlish mushrooms. Elsewhere, dry-aged Cornish steaks receive the classic treatment, while the day's 'market fish' might be presented with shellfish orzo and crispy soft-shell crab. After that, dip into pleasurable desserts such as pear and ginger cake with miso caramel. A well-curated wine list provides sound back-up.
Chef/s: Ben Palmer and Joshua Ackland.
Meals: main courses £16 to £36. Set L £15 (2 courses) to £20. Sun L £25. Tasting menu £45 (5 courses) to £64 (8 courses). **Details:** 40 seats. 24 seats outside. Bar. Wheelchairs. Music. Parking. Children over 5 yrs at D.

South Pool

The Millbrook Inn

Cooking score: 2
French | £35
South Pool, TQ7 2RW
Tel no: (01548) 531581
millbrookinnsouthpool.co.uk
£5 OFF

South Pool sits by the Kingsbury estuary, where little boats either bob on the water, or sit beached in mud at low tide. It's a narrow-roaded village with a whitewashed inn tucked neatly in sideways between the cottages. An air of low-ceilinged rustic conviviality prevails, a wood-burner (and a boutique guest apartment up top) the only concessions to modernisation. Jean-Philippe Bidart adopts a twin-track approach. He cooks a seasonally changing, simple lunch menu of, perhaps, honey- and mustard-glazed ham hock with pickled cabbage, and plum frangipane tart with apple and blackberry ice cream. In the evenings, a more obviously French ambience takes over: you might try escargots and wild mushrooms in garlic butter on homemade brioche, breasts of pigeon and pheasant in a gamey jus with lyonnaise potatoes, and luxuriously laden pavlova to finish. The drinks list features a handful of local ales, as well as carefully chosen wines at sensible prices.

Chef/s: Jean-Philippe Bidart. **Meals:** main courses £14 to £24. Set L £13 (2 courses) to £16. Set D £25 (3 courses). Sun L £18. **Details:** 60 seats. 100 seats outside.

Sparkwell

The Treby Arms

Cooking score: 4
Modern British | £30
6 Newtons Lane, Sparkwell, PL7 5DD
Tel no: (01752) 837363
thetrebyarms.co.uk

Brunel built the Treby in the 1850s for the amenity of workers on his railway bridge over the Tamar, and just a few clicks up the road is the Dartmoor Zoo, star of the Hollywood comedy, *We Bought A Zoo* (2011). So don't imagine that a low-slung whitewashed inn in a mere slip of a village near Plymouth is all sheltered rusticity. The head chef's position has been a bit of a revolving door of late and, at the moment, there is an attempt to consolidate with a more popularly based menu that doesn't cock any snooks at luscious fillet steaks with doorstop chips, or bowls of sticky toffee pudding. That doesn't, however, preclude the retention of a more inventive streak that brings on nibbles of buttermilk fried chicken and battered anchovies, a starter such as Salcombe crab under a coat of radish slices with elderflower gel and strawberries, main-course fish like herb-fringed pollock with brandade croquette, white asparagus and pour-it-yourself beurre blanc, and superlative light desserts. Those last might embrace lemon parfait with Calvados-soused apple and piercing lime gel, or a summery white wine and rosemary jelly with strawberries, honeycomb and white chocolate. A concise wine list has a few gems, with prices from £19 for Romanian varietals.

Chef/s: Paul Crump. **Closed:** Mon, Tue, 25 and 26 Dec, 1 Jan. **Meals:** main courses £12 to £35. Set L Tue to Fri £15 (2 courses) to £20. **Details:** 60 seats. 20 seats outside. Bar. Music. Parking.

Tavistock

The Cornish Arms

Cooking score: 3
Modern British | £26
15-16 West Street, Tavistock, PL19 8AN
Tel no: (01822) 612145
thecornisharmstavistock.co.uk
£5 OFF £30

Don't be blown off course by the name: this Cornish Arms is firmly rooted in Devon, in a market town on the western fringes of Dartmoor, to be precise. Originally built as a refuelling point for travellers en route to the namesake county, the pub has been seriously extended and now puts the emphasis on plates of food, rather than pints of ale. Although the daytime menu has its stalwarts (lasagne, ploughman's, liver and bacon), the kitchen also tackles more serious modern stuff, especially in the evenings. Three courses might take you from wood mushroom and truffle arancini via Loch Duart salmon fillet with steamed cockles and seaweed béarnaise to warm banana loaf with peanut parfait and banoffee ice cream. Meaty grills also feature, and it's worth keeping an eye out for seasonal game – perhaps seared venison loin with parsnip, pork belly, spiced prunes and juniper jus. Three dozen wines from £19.95.

Chef/s: John Hooker and William Norrie. **Meals:** main courses £14 to £24. Set L £20. **Details:** 75 seats. 75 seats outside. Vg menu. Bar. Wheelchairs. Music. Parking.

Topsham
Salutation Inn

Cooking score: 4
British | £43
68 Fore Street, Topsham, EX3 0HL
Tel no: (01392) 873060
salutationtopsham.co.uk
£5 OFF

The stylish conversion of this imposing Georgian coaching inn into a restaurant with rooms includes the light-filled Glasshouse, an informal all-day café that's custom-built for the local crowd. From here, turn your attention to dinner in the formal dining room, where the contemporary cooking of Tom Williams-Hawkes is offered via various multi-course menus (including a vegetarian option). Here, really good food strikes a balance between classical and contemporary, nothing is outlandish or challenging, and the kitchen shows a steadfast commitment to British seasonal produce, whether Lyme Bay scallop (teamed with fennel and ketchup), local beef sirloin that arrives with mushroom raviolo, celeriac and Madeira sauce, or West Country cheeses. Desserts draw plenty of enthusiasm, especially a dark chocolate tart with salted caramel and caramelised banana. Some feel the dining room, an interior room, lacks character, though well spaced white-clad tables are appreciated, as is the warm, welcoming service. Wines from £21.50.

Chef/s: Tom Williams-Hawkes. **Closed:** first 2 weeks Feb. **Meals:** set L £20 (2 courses) to £25. Set D £43 (4 courses). Tasting menu £69 (6 courses) to £90 (8 courses). **Details:** 42 seats. V menu. Wheelchairs. Music. Parking.

Torquay
The Elephant

Cooking score: 5
Modern British | £45
3-4 Beacon Terrace, Torquay, TQ1 2BH
Tel no: (01803) 200044
elephantrestaurant.co.uk
£5 OFF

Enveloped within an 1830s rising terrace just off the harbour, the Elephant is now into its second decade of provisioning Torquay with contemporary British food. Simon Hulstone's own allotment provides excellent fresh produce for the menus, to support the Brixham fish and locally reared meats, as well as some enterprising vegetarian cooking, perhaps roast pumpkin fondant in spiced carrot jus with cauliflower and pine nut pesto. Delicately constructed openers such as scallop in sherry vinegar with pancetta and date chutney are full of strong flavour contrasts, while main courses take a more mainstream approach for Crediton duck breast with Roscoff onion, savoy cabbage and black garlic in thyme jus, or the long-running cod fillet in a butter sauce of verjus and spring onions. A rhubarb dessert built around baked custard with blood orange sorbet and pepper meringue is a spring treat, and there are artisan cheeses from the South West, served with green tomato chutney and medlar jelly. Wine markups show commendable restraint, bottles opening at £20.

Chef/s: Simon Hulstone. **Closed:** Sun, Mon, 2 weeks Jan. **Meals:** main courses £17 to £27. Set L £20 (2 courses) to £22. Tasting menu £73. **Details:** 60 seats. Bar. Music.

The Orange Tree

Cooking score: 2
Modern European | £35
14-16 Parkhill Road, Torquay, TQ1 2AL
Tel no: (01803) 213936
orangetreerestaurant.co.uk

Tucked away discreetly between the bustle of restaurant-loaded Torwood Street and the harbour, the Orange Tree is very much the preserve of those in the Torbay know. They return with tenacious loyalty, both for the old-fashioned sense of occasion with which Sharon Wolf runs front of house, and for Bernd Wolf's confident modern European cooking. A seared piece of fish is a popular starter, perhaps John Dory with cashew crumble, gingery butternut squash and sautéed pak choi. Main-course meats are of reliable local provenance, the herb-crusted lamb loin with roast fennel and tapenade jus a palpable hit, and truffle-scented beef fillet with mushroom duxelles in Madeira the perennial showstopper. Desserts range from a brittle-topped crème brûlée laced with Grand Marnier to Belgian chocolate fondant with morellos and honeycomb ice cream. A five-course tasting menu with extras gives a reliable tour of the territory. The wine list keeps prices sensible, starting at £19.50 for Languedoc varietals, standard glasses from £4.90.

Chef/s: Bernd Wolf. **Closed:** Sun, Mon, 26 and 27 Dec, first week Jan, 2 weeks Oct to Nov. **Meals:** main courses £16 to £27. Tasting menu £52. **Details:** 42 seats. Music.

Totnes

Rumour

Cooking score: 1
International | £30
30 High Street, Totnes, TQ9 5RY
Tel no: (01803) 864682
rumourtotnes.com

Despite a change of ownership in 2017, this all-day wine bar and restaurant remains at the boho heart of the Totnes scene. Come here for world beers, cocktails and a modest assortment of wines or stake your claim for some free-ranging eclectic food. Chef Lee Hegarty still fronts the kitchen, and he's keeping up with all the trends when it comes to small (and big) plates of global food: bao bun tacos with Mongolian lamb, bowls of coconut laksa, and roasted cauliflower with crispy tofu give way to burgers, steaks, pizzas and wood-fired chicken with burnt leeks and morcilla. To finish, how about popcorn panna cotta?

Chef/s: Lee Hegarty. **Closed:** 25 and 26 Dec, 1 Jan. **Meals:** main courses £12 to £17. **Details:** 60 seats. Wheelchairs. Music.

Tytherleigh

LOCAL GEM

The Tytherleigh Arms

Modern British | £35
Tytherleigh, EX13 7BE
Tel no: (01460) 220214
tytherleigharms.com

The former coaching inn on the Dorset/ Devon border still looks like a proper pub inside, with beams, bare boards and an open fire, but the focus is firmly on food these days. The kitchen goes in for big, belting flavours and keeps one foot firmly on British soil, deftly deploying the likes of Devon crab (with kohlrabi, Jersey Royals, sea rosemary and brown-meat mayonnaise), locally reared steaks or slow-cooked belly and pork tenderloin teamed with heritage carrots, roasted celeriac and pickled rhubarb. Pub classics, salads and sandwiches appear on the good-value lunch menu.

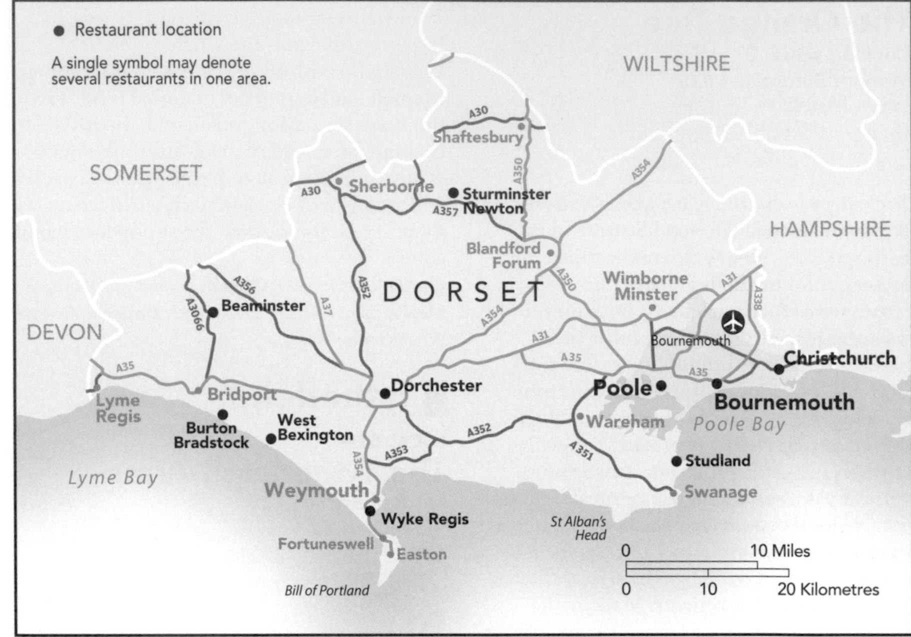

Beaminster

Brassica

Cooking score: 4
Modern British | £30
4 The Square, Beaminster, DT8 3AS
Tel no: (01308) 538100
brassicarestaurant.co.uk

'A charming place where the food is inventive enough to be interesting and delicious, without being pretentious any way,' enthused one visitor to Cass Titcombe and Louise Chidgey's well-run modern brasserie, which occupies a listed former toll house in the town square. A warm, calm space with rough stone walls, colourful cushions and a wood-burner for the colder months, Brassica has become a local asset since it opened five years ago, with visitors impressed by Titcombe's assured and seasonal cooking. At inspection, four plump, crisp haggis croquettes, teamed with watercress, pickled celery and a mustard dressing, proved to be full-flavoured and remarkably light. Precisely timed grilled hake fillet followed, served with nutty haricot beans, cavolo nero and a swirl of 'properly piquant' anchovy sauce, while Yorkshire rhubarb cheesecake pavlova made a great finish. Set menus are particularly good value, as is the concise, well-considered Eurocentric wine list, which opens at £21.

Chef/s: Cass Titcombe. **Closed:** Mon, 25 and 26 Dec. **Meals:** main courses £15 to £23. Set L £15 (2 courses) to £20. Sun L £20 (2 courses) to £25. **Details:** 40 seats. 6 seats outside. Music.

Bournemouth

The Larder House

Cooking score: 2
Modern European | £35
4 Southbourne Grove, Bournemouth, BH6 3QZ
Tel no: (01202) 424687
thelarderhouse.co.uk

'Unrivalled...we are lucky to live so close,' declares one local who appreciates this 'quirky' restaurant's many attributes – from the welcoming staff and spot-on service to the eclectic food with its noticeable Spanish overtones. To start, you can share the spoils from the 'Social Suzannes' (boards of cured artisan meats, fish and larder provisions) or nibble on some international tapas – perhaps crispy lamb's sweetbreads with devilled aïoli, fish fingers or honey and mustard chicken wings. After that, the 'main event' might bring fillet of hake paired with pork belly, heritage carrots, mini fondants and dukkah nuts or roast guinea fowl with soft polenta, wild mushrooms, salsify and Parmesan, before desserts such as sticky toffee stout cake bring proceedings to a patriotic conclusion – although regulars also recommend the tiptop cheese selection with homemade chutneys. Curious drinkers should check out the 'amazing' Library of Liquor speakeasy upstairs for unusual wines, sherries and cocktails.

Chef/s: Nick Hewitt. **Closed:** 24 to 26 Dec. **Meals:** main courses £15 to £26. **Details:** 48 seats. 48 seats outside. Bar. Wheelchairs. Music.

Roots

Cooking score: 3
Modern European | £40
141 Belle Vue Road, Bournemouth, BH6 3EN
Tel no: (01202) 430005
restaurantroots.co.uk

The blink-and-you'll-miss-it location in a quiet row of shops – main window frosted so passers-by can't see in – and simple, white-washed interior don't quite prepare first-time visitors for the ambitious and dazzling dishes prepared by chef proprietors Jan and Stacey Bretschneider. There's no carte at dinner, just a choice of three tasting menus. After 'snacks' including baba ganoush with yoghurt, and cucumber with sweet chilli and peanut, highlights of the eight-course Classic menu included poached halibut teamed with courgette, saffron, baby gem and artichoke; truffle butter poached chicken, baby leek, morels, sauce Viognier and the 'Roots Signature', comprising an intense celeriac ice cream, shaved raw celeriac, celeriac broth, hazelnuts and grapes. To finish, New Forest strawberry mousse, elderflower and an innovative white asparagus ice cream. Service may be over-enthusiastic – bordering on stifling – but you can't accuse the front of house of lacking passion for food, drink and hospitality. An intelligently curated wine list featuring some German big hitters opens at £19, with plenty offered by the glass.

Chef/s: Jan Bretschneider. **Closed:** Sun, Mon, 23 Dec to 5 Jan. **Meals:** set L £26. Tasting menu £40 (6 courses) to £60. **Details:** 18 seats. V menu. Music.

LOCAL GEM

West Beach

Seafood | £33
Pier Approach, Bournemouth, BH2 5AA
Tel no: (01202) 587785
west-beach.co.uk

'Still one of the best dining options in Bournemouth,' noted a regular of this glass-fronted seaside veteran that is separated from the beach only by a slim promenade. Tables on the decked terrace, with its stunning views across Poole Bay, are much sought after in fine weather. Come here for local fish and seafood, from shellfish platters and mussels cooked various ways to blackboard specials of cod fillet, samphire, cockles, crushed potatoes and wild garlic sauce vierge. There's fillet of beef with Jerusalem artichoke purée, or ribeye steak with peppercorn sauce, for those who must. Seafood-friendly wines from £19.

Burton Bradstock

★ NEW ENTRY ★

Seaside Boarding House

Cooking score: 3
Seafood | £30
Cliff Road, Burton Bradstock, DT6 4RB
Tel no: (01308) 897205
theseasideboardinghouse.com

This stylish hotel, at the cliff-front spot where stairs up from Chesil Beach meet the coastal path, has all the bright light and sea views you could ask for – in fine weather the terrace comes into its own. The dining room has the feel of a smart French bistro, very traditional without being formal, while the kitchen looks to the locality for ingredients and mixes up influences in a true modern British way. Fish tops the bill: 'squid, chilli, peas' proves to be barely more than that, served with the buttery juices from the pan with a little lemon added; a gutsy and indulgent crab and avocado salad comes with a tom yum dressing that adds a slight sweet note and some vibrant heat; while a vast tranche of turbot with buttery hispi cabbage and a white wine and smoked mussel cream is 'classic stuff, well executed'. There's also grilled bavette, and chocolate semifreddo with pistachio brittle and passion fruit to finish. Wines from £21.

Chef/s: Craig Whitty. **Meals:** main courses £12 to £22. **Details:** 60 seats. Wheelchairs. Parking.

LOCAL GEM

Hive Beach Café

Seafood | £30

Beach Road, Burton Bradstock, DT6 4RF
Tel no: (01308) 897070
hivebeachcafe.co.uk

There's a splendid view of the Jurassic Coast from the marquee-style heated awnings of this laid-back seaside café, while a mix of picnic sets and metal tables and chairs reflect the uncomplicated approach of the kitchen, which champions local seafood. Whole crab is fired up with Cajun potato salad and garlic mayonnaise, plaice arrives simply grilled with rock salt, samphire and crayfish, or you can tuck into a massive shellfish platter or good old fish and chips. Open all year for breakfast and lunch (and early suppers in summer); no bookings are taken.

Anonymous

At *The Good Food Guide*, our inspectors dine anonymously and pay their bill in full. These impartial review meals, along with feedback from thousands of our readers, are what informs the content of the *GFG*.

Christchurch

The Jetty

Cooking score: 1

Modern British | £40

Christchurch Harbour Hotel & Spa, 95 Mudeford, Christchurch, BH23 3NT
Tel no: (01202) 400950
thejetty.co.uk

A glass box in the garden of the Harbour Hotel, part of a growing chain, makes a light and airy restaurant. It sits on the edge of the water overlooking Christchurch Harbour, with the beach huts of Mudeford twinkling in the distance. It's a wonderful setting to tuck into the extensive choice of local seafood offered on a variety of menus overseen by Alex Aitken. After nibbling on crisp cockle popcorn, start with pan-seared scallops, crab tortellini and truffle foam before a whole sea bream roasted with chilli and garlic served with greens and beurre blanc. Apple tarte tatin with prune and Armagnac ice cream makes for a brasserie classic finale. Wines from £18.95.

Chef/s: Alex Aitken. **Meals:** main courses £20 to £30. Set L and early D £23 (2 courses) to £26. Sun L £35. Tasting menu £28 (5 courses) to £65. **Details:** 70 seats. 30 seats outside. V menu. Vg menu. Bar. Wheelchairs. Music. Parking.

Dorchester

★ NEW ENTRY ★

Sienna

Cooking score: 4

Modern British | £55

36 High West Street, Dorchester, DT1 1UP
Tel no: (01305) 250022
siennadorchester.co.uk

Following the departure of Russell and Eléna Brown in 2015, this one-time Guide stalwart has made an impressive comeback, thanks to the arrival of chef proprietor Marcus Wilcox. The restaurant's frontage reminded one visitor of a garishly orange kebab shop, but the 'absolutely tiny' dining room has a magic all its own. Meals now revolve around a series of tasting menus, plus a set lunch featuring similar dishes in different combinations. From the latter, you might find a 'wonderfully refreshing' starter of blowtorched mackerel with compressed watermelon and pickled cucumber, or big-flavoured, buttery steak tartare dotted with confit egg yolk and peppery nasturtium leaves. To follow, squid-ink-crumbed halibut fillet arrives atop juicy charred leeks, pickled cauliflower and roasted artichoke purée, while desserts such as a set custard with braised rhubarb, hibiscus jelly and rhubarb purée maintain the 'simple but delicious' standard. The well-priced wine list packs lots of interest into a small space – a bit like Sienna itself.

Chef/s: Marcus Wilcox. **Closed:** Mon. **Meals:** set L £20 (2 courses) to £25. Tasting menu L £35 (4 courses), D £55 (6 courses) to £70. Sun L £35. **Details:** 14 seats. V menu.

Poole

LOCAL GEM

Guildhall Tavern

French | £40

15 Market Street, Poole, BH15 1NB
Tel no: (01202) 671717
guildhalltavern.co.uk

'I didn't know restaurants like this still existed outside France,' cooed one nostalgic diner. After 19 years there is still a strong appetite for this unashamedly old-school French veteran in Poole's Old Town. Booking is advisable both for dinner or for the great-value set lunch. Expect generous portions of traditional bistro classics, with an emphasis on fish and seafood. Start with light, creamy crab and scallop tarte fine, followed by chargrilled whole sea bass flambéed with Pernod at the table, and finish with pear, ginger and chocolate sphere. The wine list is French-accented – *bien sûr* – and opens at £18.95.

Studland

LOCAL GEM

Pig on the Beach

Modern British | £40

Manor House, Manor Road, Studland, BH19 3AU
Tel no: (01929) 450288
thepighotel.com

With extensive gardens, views of Studland beach beyond, a laid-back interior of bare boards and auction-room finds and a greenhouse-style restaurant, this boutique country hotel (part of a growing chain) appears to have it all. The kitchen has forged dependable links with the local food network and leavens its menus with produce from the hotel's own garden – as in black pudding ('from our pigs') with garden leaves and pickled quail's egg or South Coast hake with purple sprouting broccoli and Poole Bay clams. West Country cheeses are worth exploring, and desserts could include lemon curd meringue pie. Wine from £25.

Sturminster Newton

Plumber Manor

Cooking score: 2

Anglo-French | £38

Sturminster Newton, DT10 2AF
Tel no: (01258) 472507
plumbermanor.com

£5 OFF

The Prideaux-Brunes have definitely stamped their mark on this ancient manor house – it's been in the family since the 17th century. Converted to a hotel in 1972 (and listed in this Guide ever since), it still feels like walking into someone's home. Dinner begins with drinks and canapés in the bar, then into the dining room with its well-spaced, white-clothed tables and slightly old-fashioned air – a perfect setting for a menu that celebrates traditional favourites such as smoked salmon paupiettes with smoked trout mousse. Mains such as supreme of chicken on squash purée with toasted pine nuts and lemon and tarragon sauce come with separate bowls of beautifully cooked vegetables. Everyone applauds the massive sweet trolley, which trundles around dispensing roulades, cheesecake and mille-feuille with lashings of cream. The aspiration to offer guests an enjoyable experience is hard to fault. Readers also report the need to book well in advance for Sunday lunch. Wines from £18.50.

Chef/s: Louis Haskell. **Closed:** end Jan to end Feb. **Meals:** set D £30 (2 courses) to £38. Sun L £30. **Details:** 65 seats. Bar. Parking.

West Bexington

★ NEW ENTRY ★

The Club House

Cooking score: 2
Seafood | £40
Beach Road, West Bexington, DT2 9DG
Tel no: (01308) 898302
theclubhousewestbexington.co.uk
£5 OFF

This extended New England-style white bungalow – slap-bang on Chesil Beach and accessed via Tamarisk Farm, which supplies the organic vegetables – is a new venture from the team behind the long-established Hive Beach Café (see entry). There's an Art Deco look to the dining room, with its 1930s light fittings, old lifebelts, and a clotted cream and sea blue colour scheme. From the open kitchen come simple, no-frills dishes that major on local seafood, of course, though there are meat dishes. A starter of baked scallops served in the shell with wild garlic and hazelnut crumb butter opened a spring meal. For mains, a fresh and thick-flaked fillet of cod was roasted with a top layer of smoked anchovy butter and teamed with crushed heritage potatoes and kale from the farm next door. An individual apple and blackberry pie appeared with a dry cider and apple sorbet that 'screamed West Country'. A white-heavy wine list starts at £19.

Chef/s: Charlie Soole. **Closed:** Mon. **Meals:** main courses £17 to £40. Set L £20 (2 courses) to £25. **Details:** 56 seats. 40 seats outside. Bar. Wheelchairs. Music. Parking.

Wyke Regis

LOCAL GEM

Crab House Café

Seafood | £36
Ferryman's Way, Portland Road, Wyke Regis, DT4 9YU
Tel no: (01305) 788867
crabhousecafe.co.uk

With covetable beachside tables, wooden pergolas, fish-friendly wines and a menu of emphatically local seafood (including oysters from the owners' beds by the water's edge), the Crab House certainly makes the most of its location on the tourist-trap Jurassic Coast – brace yourself for crowds even when the weather's lousy. To eat, expect anything from curry-spiced sprats to whole plaice with anchovy butter and cider onions – although nothing beats getting messy with a Chinese-style crab, the whole complete with dissecting tools and a bib.

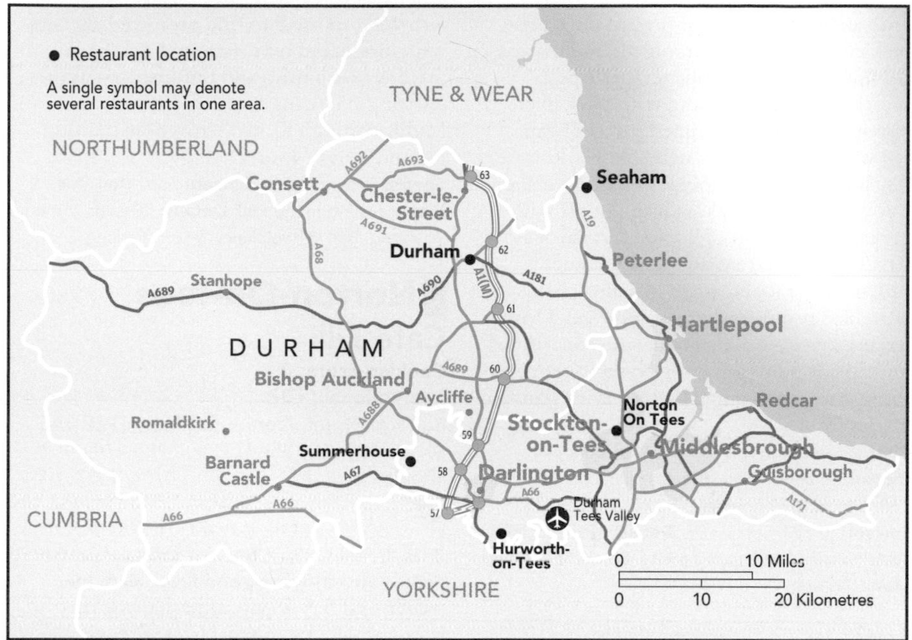

Durham

The Garden House Inn

Cooking score: 1
Modern British | £33
Framwellgate Peth, Durham, DH1 4NQ
Tel no: (0191) 386 3395
gardenhouseinn.com
£5 OFF

First off, don't expect a garden of note, just a few bench tables front and back. Much of the countrified pub interior is set aside for dining these days, with diners here for a menu that touches base with traditional comforts (fish and chips and such like) and makes something of a signature of an open lobster sandwich. Venison pasty is a cut above your average pub pie, while halibut with shellfish sauce reveals classic sensibilities. If you can stay the course, rhubarb and honeycomb parfait awaits. Drink hand-pumped ales or wines from a fashionable list starting at £18.95.

Chef/s: Ruari MacKay. **Meals:** main courses £12 to £20. Set L £20. Set D £29. Sun L £25. **Details:** 60 seats. 45 seats outside. Bar. Wheelchairs. Music. Parking.

Hurworth-on-Tees

The Bay Horse

Cooking score: 4
Modern British | £38
45 The Green, Hurworth-on-Tees, DL2 2AA
Tel no: (01325) 720663
thebayhorsehurworth.com

The old Horse has been a faithful servant to Hurworth since the 15th century, its present manifestation being a well-judged architectural compromise between its late medieval shell, complete with carriage archway, and elegantly styled interiors. Engaging paintings on sober dark grey walls make a relaxed context for James Burkhart's vigorous modern pub cooking, in which disparate elements build into dynamic combinations. Roasted king scallops arrive with an honour guard of pressed pork belly, pickled pear, celeriac rémoulade and toasted cobnuts for a bravura opener, perhaps succeeded by venison loin with duck liver boudin, a cabbage-wrapped parcel of game, red wine salsify, cavolo nero and blackberries. It's clear there's a lot going on in most dishes, but the balancing acts are brought off with great dexterity, through to desserts such as Cox's apple galette with crème pâtissière, brown butter ice cream, marinated raisins, crumbled pecans and green apple gel. Drink imaginatively, too, from the house aperitif of homemade plum gin with Prosecco topper to the stylistically arranged wines, with standard glasses from £5.50.

Chef/s: Marcus Bennett and James Burkhart. **Closed:** 25 and 26 Dec. **Meals:** main courses £20 to £30. Set L £16 (2 courses) to £20. Set D £22 (2 courses) to £27. Sun L £29. **Details:** 40 seats. 60 seats outside. V menu. Vg menu. Bar. Wheelchairs. Music. Parking.

The Orangery

Cooking score: 4
Modern European | £80
Rockliffe Hall, Hurworth-on-Tees, DL2 2DU
Tel no: (01325) 729999
rockliffehall.com

The resort grounds at luxurious Rockliffe Hall may have matured, but the restaurant overlooking them is still changing. Chef Richard Allen has steamlined the offer to just one tasting menu, while the arrival of garlanded front of house manager Jatin Parmar promises to bring personality to a room that can require a little warming up. Allen's 10 courses are built on likeable flavour matches in dishes like trout with fermented cucumber, mussel and dill, or pigeon with quince, dhal and a honey and cumin jus. The vegetarian and vegan 'Root & Branch' menus might feature smoked artichoke with beer and sour cream, or flame-grilled celeriac with chard, hazelnuts and dill respectively. Puddings get a good showing; cross the savoury-sweet bridge of Blue Monday cheese wth Waldorf salad to find preserved cherries with kirsch and pine, or a sea buckthorn macaron with miso and butterscotch. Wines start at £35, rising to prices that suit the Middlesbrough footballers whose training ground is next door.

Chef/s: Richard Allen. **Closed:** Sun, Mon, Tue. **Meals:** tasting menu £80. **Details:** 50 seats. V menu. Vg menu. Bar. Wheelchairs. Music. Parking.

Norton-On-Tees

Café Lilli

Cooking score: 2
International | £28
83 High Street, Norton-On-Tees, TS20 1AE
Tel no: (01642) 554422
lillicafe.co.uk

'Has the trademark buzz of a restaurant where people are enjoying good food,' says one reader, and he's not alone in praising this happy-go-lucky bistro-style café in the centre of Norton – a historic village that now snuggles under Stockton-on-Tees' municipal umbrella. Much depends on the efforts of ebullient host Roberto Pittalis, who not only ensures that customers have a great time but also takes care when it comes to sourcing (buffalo from Northallerton, Italian black truffles, fish from Hartlepool, locally brewed lager). The interior is an eclectic hotchpotch and so is the menu, which jogs happily from spiced panko-crusted king prawns with curried butter-bean houmous to roast venison with blue cheese and hazelnut crumble, mustard mash and port jus. Roberto has Italian roots, so pastas and risottos also figure prominently, while desserts could bring affogato with toffee ice cream. The wine list is also Italian by nature, with house selections by the carafe.

Chef/s: Phillip Wigham. **Closed:** Sun, Mon. **Meals:** main courses £11 to £20. Set D £17 (2 courses) to £22. Sun L £20 (2 courses) to £24. **Details:** 70 seats. Bar. Wheelchairs. Music. Parking.

Seaham

The Dining Room

Cooking score: 3
Modern British | £45
Seaham Hall, Lord Byron's Walk, Seaham, SR7 7AG
Tel no: (0191) 516 1400
seaham-hall.co.uk
£5 OFF

A portrait of Lord Byron holds pride of place in Seaham Hall's rebranded Dining Room (formerly Byron's) – a reminder of the poet's links with Seaham Hall (he spent his honeymoon here). With its gold-plated chandeliers, gilded artefacts and high Georgian windows, the room cuts quite a dash, although the kitchen takes a modern view of things, marrying North Country ingredients with embellishments from near and far. Small plates might bring Whitby crab with monk's beard and raw ceps, or confit Swaledale mutton on toast with pickled radish and yoghurt, while mains could span everything from rump and glazed riblet of Herdwick hogget to roast monkfish accompanied by white asparagus, sea purslane and roasted mussel sauce. Dry-aged heritage beef is sizzled on the Konro grill, and the list of desserts might include a modernist take on traditional custard tart involving salted caramel, cultured cream, apple and marigold. Wines start at a fairly pricey £25.

Chef/s: Damian Broom. **Meals:** main courses £20 to £35. Sun L £25. **Details:** 40 seats. Bar. Wheelchairs. Music. Parking.

Average price

The figure given in bold denotes the average price of a three-course dinner without wine.

Summerhouse

★ TOP 50 ★

The Raby Hunt

Cooking score: 7
Modern British | £110
Summerhouse, DL2 3UD
Tel no: (01325) 374237
rabyhuntrestaurant.co.uk
£5 OFF

It's 10 years since former pro-golfer James Close took on this remote 19th-century drovers' inn, transforming the modest 'local' into a destination restaurant with rooms with glassed-off kitchen, chef's table and kitchen garden. The self-taught Close sources locally where possible – a single Lindisfarne oyster poached at 62 degrees is an achingly beautiful overture to the 15-course menu – but refuses to be shackled by expectations of 'regional' cooking. Instead, he takes diners on a world tour with stop-offs for pristine pork tacos, tender langoustine tempura in a sansho-dusted cloud of batter, and dainty seeded buns of pastrami and black truffle. Best end of Lake District lamb with winter greens and a dab of anchovy is more conventional, while Brillat-Savarin brings a savoury edge to an artfully assembled tropical fruit tart. Close has amassed a number of 'signatures': razor clams with counterpoints of celeriac, samphire and almonds is one such, as is the seasonal 'salad' featuring myriad ingredients, raw or cooked just so. The sharp, bright flavours speak not only of fine ingredients but also of virtuosity and steely focus in the kitchen. One can't fail to notice the disparity between culinary ambitions and the small, slightly underwhelming dining room, though the front of house team – friendly but formal – pulls everything together. The wine list, like the cuisine, steers a comfortable course between classic and modern.

Chef/s: James Close. **Closed:** Sun, Mon, Tue, 2 weeks Christmas and New Year. **Meals:** tasting menu £110. **Details:** 28 seats. 4 seats outside. Wheelchairs. Parking. Children over 8 yrs.

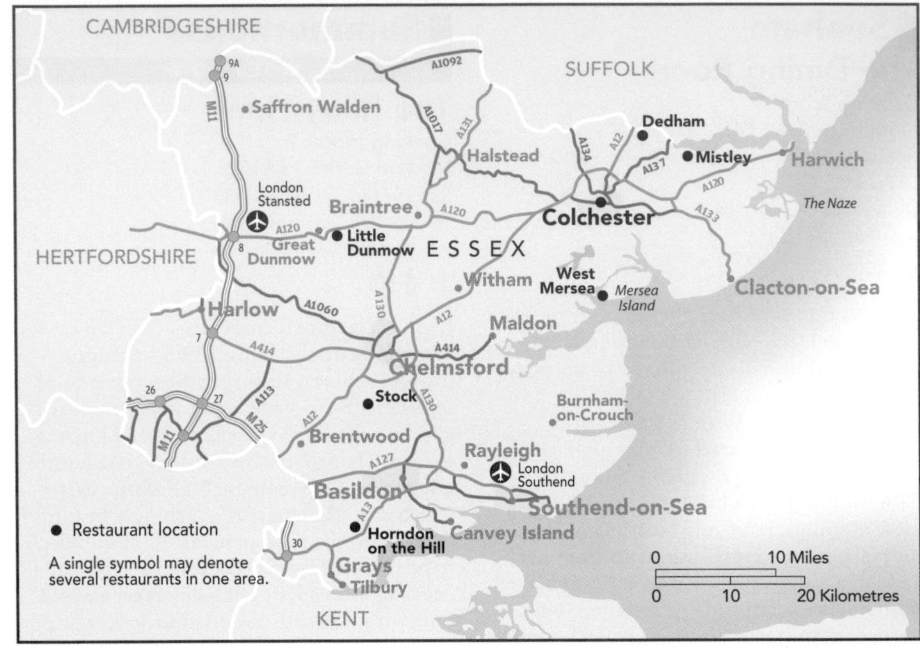

Colchester

Church Street Tavern

Cooking score: 2
Modern British | £29
3 Church Street, Colchester, CO1 1NF
Tel no: (01206) 564325
churchstreettavern.co.uk
£5 OFF 🍷 £30

A chunky piece of real estate, built as a bank back in the middle of the 19th century, provides generous spaces for eating and drinking at Piers Baker's second Essex hostelry (see also the Sun Inn, Dedham). The spacious rooms – ground-floor bar, first-floor restaurant – are decorated in fashionably muted tones. The bar is a stylish hangout for a drink or light lunch (or the main menu, if you wish), while upstairs is given over to modern British dining. Most ingredients come from the region: local favourites, Mersea rock oysters, and feel-good flavours are paramount, as seen in dishes such as roast beetroot and cauliflower tempura, a rare-breed steak or tranche of brill with preserved lemons and curried cauliflower. Sticky fig and almond tart seals the deal, and the wine list includes English fizz and well-chosen options by the glass and carafe.

Chef/s: Ewan Naylon. **Closed:** Mon, Tue, 25 and 26 Dec, first week Jan. **Meals:** main courses £13 to £25. Sun L £22 (2 courses) to £28. **Details:** 85 seats. 15 seats outside. Vg menu. Bar. Wheelchairs. Music.

Send us your review

Your feedback informs the content of the *GFG* and will be used to compile next year's reviews. To register your opinion about any restaurant listed in the Guide, or a restaurant that you wish to bring to our attention, visit: thegoodfoodguide.co.uk/feedback

LOCAL GEM

Grain

International | £25
11a North Hill, Colchester, CO1 1DZ
Tel no: (01206) 570005
grain-colchester.co.uk

£30

Set up by two energetic young chefs who went down the crowdfunding route to get things started, Grain is emphatically 'on-trend' with its busy open kitchen and menu of 'beautifully presented' small plates. Divided up into categories such as 'garden', 'water', 'land' and so on, it offers everything from charred asparagus with salsa verde and pinenut granola to cured brill with grapes, yoghurt and pumpkin seeds or beef fillet with Jersey Royals, hazelnut pesto and miso. 'Ultra-affordable' prices extend to the well-chosen wine list.

 Dedham

The Sun Inn

Cooking score: 3
Modern European | £29
High Street, Dedham, CO7 6DF
Tel no: (01206) 323351
thesuninndedham.com

£5 OFF £30

In the heart of Constable Country, at the centre of a well-preserved village, this 'proper old inn' is a hostelry for our times. It's a warm-hearted kind of place, centuries-old lineage visible in the blazing log fires and in the many oak beams and standing timbers (beautifully offset by soft colours in the dining room). Local suppliers buttress the menus while the kitchen pulls together influences from the Mediterranean in general and Italy in particular. A generous pile of oriecchiette pasta with purple sprouting broccoli, chilli, garlic, Parmesan and pangrattato or gently spiced chickpea and chard frittata with ricotta, olives and chilli might be the preludes to perfectly timed fillet of cod served with a mustard cream, monk's beard and leek and smoked haddock croquettes, or a chicken breast with crisp gnocchi, ox tongue, cauliflower and black cabbage. The wine list is full of intelligent choices, confident in both hemispheres and noted for a procession of wonderful selections by the glass at remarkably kind prices.

Chef/s: Jack Levine. **Closed:** 25 and 26 Dec. **Meals:** main courses £13 to £19. **Details:** 65 seats. 150 seats outside. Bar. Music. Parking.

Le Talbooth

Cooking score: 3
Modern British | £56
Gun Hill, Dedham, CO7 6HP
Tel no: (01206) 323150
milsomhotels.com

£5 OFF

Le Talbooth is a stunner, dressed to the elegant nines in sophisticated neutrals, and loved locally for special occasion dining. Inside, Tudor beams climb into pitched roofs, leaded windows are as luxuriantly draped as the carpet is deep; bare tables on the canopied terrace set a more informal tone, the river Stour and gorgeous gardens distracting from at times irksome road noise. Grilled mackerel with pickled samphire and spinach purée hits the starter sweet-spot, and there's praise for warm homemade sourdough. 'Beautifully tender, seriously good' Dingley Dell belly pork is a winner, terrifically crisp crackling, caramelised apple sauce, and buttery pomme purée compensating for 'lifeless and floppy' greens. A vegetarian menu tempts with three choices per course and the set lunch is worth considering, especially as most à la carte mains come in at £30 to £40. Finish with (deconstructed) strawberry and passion fruit Eton mess, or intriguing blackcurrant délice with liquorice ice cream and bourbon vanilla marshmallow. Given the cost of the food, markups on the wide-ranging wine list seem gentle with bottles starting at £21.25.

Chef/s: Andrew Hirst. **Meals:** main courses £23 to £34. Set L £30 (2 courses) to £36. Sun L £43 (3 courses). **Details:** 60 seats. 60 seats outside. V menu. Bar. Wheelchairs. Music. Parking.

Horndon on the Hill

The Bell Inn

Cooking score: 3
Modern European | £35
High Road, Horndon on the Hill, SS17 8LD
Tel no: (01375) 642463
bell-inn.co.uk

'My goodness, what a superb lunch – why did I leave it so long to return?' enthused one impressed visitor to this ancient coaching inn that has been in the Vereker family for 80 years. Low beams, flagstone floors and panelled walls contribute to the ancient feel, and it does come across as a traditional village pub, but there's nothing old-fashioned about the modern European cooking. Assertive flavours are the hallmarks of dishes such as Maldon salt-cured smoked salmon, served with beetroot and salmon roulade, which might precede Priors Hall Farm suckling pig with apple compôte, black pudding and pancetta. There's plenty of pleasure to be had, too, from milk chocolate torte with peanut butter ice cream and caramel. Arranged by country, the wine list offers plenty of good drinking from £16.95, with each bottle also available at 'take home' prices.

Chef/s: Stephen Treadwell. **Closed:** 25 and 26 Dec. **Meals:** main courses £13 to £30. **Details:** 80 seats. 50 seats outside. Bar. Wheelchairs. Parking.

Little Dunmow

Tim Allen's Flitch of Bacon

Cooking score: 3
Modern British | £49
The Street, Little Dunmow, CM6 3HT
Tel no: (01371) 821660
flitchofbacon.co.uk

In a charming British tradition that survived in Little Dunmow until the 18th century, a flitch of bacon was awarded to couples who could swear not to have regretted their marriage for a year and a day. Here's hoping this new partnership between Tim Allen and Daniel Clifford – which sees Allen taking the helm so that Clifford can focus on Midsummer House (see entry) – is a happy pairing. Allen made his mark at The Wild Rabbit at Kingham (see entry), and brings classic British dishes with occasional flourishes to this upmarket pub. The titular flitch of bacon, a terrific dish caramelised with a maple glaze and served with creamed cauliflower, Orkney scallop and compressed apple, was greedily enjoyed and followed by delicate, lightly steamed Cornish plaice with rosemary pommes Anna, chicken wing and a lustrous, deeply flavoured chicken jus. For dessert, the sticky toffee pudding – rich, treacly and moated by warm toffee sauce – is a must. In summer, the terrace is a good spot, with a Citroën van doubling as a cocktail bar. Ask the sommelier's advice on the substantial wine list, which has plenty by the glass.

Chef/s: Tim Allen. **Closed:** Mon. **Meals:** set L £21 (2 courses) to £25. Set D £49 (3 courses). **Details:** 40 seats. 30 seats outside. Bar. Wheelchairs. Music. Parking.

Mistley

The Mistley Thorn

Cooking score: 2
Modern British | £26
High Street, Mistley, CO11 1HE
Tel no: (01206) 392821
mistleythorn.co.uk

£5 OFF £30

Chef proprietor Sherri Singleton's mini empire takes in an informal restaurant with rooms plus an upmarket kitchen shop and cookery school a few doors down, all overlooking the river Stour. In the restaurant expect tongue-and-groove panelling, Farrow & Ball colours and a menu that's chock-full of fresh local seafood. Sherri's feeling for comfort food is finely tuned, and she sends out New England clam chowder, and mussels cooked in wine, garlic and herbs, served in big bowls with homemade bread for lunch. The cooking is not formulaic, however, and the starting point is great ingredients – from Mersea Island oysters via wood-fired lemon sole with

seaweed butter, to locally reared lamb and beef. Presentation is appealing, too, especially when it comes to desserts, perhaps caramel panna cotta with caramelised banana and hazelnut praline. Service is friendly and professional and the wine reflects the care taken elsewhere – house bottles from £18.
Chef/s: Sherri Singleton and Karl Burnside. **Closed:** 25 Dec. **Meals:** main courses £12 to £24. Set L and D £17 (2 courses) to £20. **Details:** 88 seats. 12 seats outside. Bar. Music. Parking.

Stock

The Oak Room at the Hoop

Cooking score: 1
Modern British | £35
21 High Street, Stock, CM4 9BD
Tel no: (01277) 841137
thehoop.co.uk

The white weatherboarded Hoop has been an alehouse for some 450 years and with its timber beams and brick fireplaces there's no shortage of character in its old bones. Bar food runs to plates of thick-cut ham with double-fried duck eggs and fat chips, but the main culinary action takes place upstairs in the reservation-only Oak Room. Whipped goat's cheese and pickled beetroot pair up in a modern starter, with Devon crab and prawn cocktail as a more retro alternative. Among main courses, belly of Shelford pork comes with black pudding Scotch egg, and fillet of cod with salt cod beignets and rarebit. Local New Hall wines figure on a list organised by style.
Chef/s: Phil Utz. **Closed:** Mon, 26 Dec, 21 May to 4 Jun. **Meals:** main courses £14 to £30. Sun L £25. Tasting menu £70. **Details:** 40 seats. Bar. Music.

Local Gem

These entries highlight a range of neighbourhood venues, delivering good, freshly cooked food at great value for money.

West Mersea

LOCAL GEM

West Mersea Oyster Bar

Seafood | £20
Coast Road, West Mersea, CO5 8LT
Tel no: (01206) 381600
westmerseaoysterbar.co.uk

The oyster business that runs this humble clapboard shack on the Blackwater Estuary knows it doesn't need sumptuous decor to pull in the crowds. Seafood lovers from near and far join the inevitable queue for unfussy, exceptionally fresh fish and shellfish. Order to take away or book a table to eat in, and go for glistening, minerally Colchester natives, harvested from Mersea Island's shallow waters (from September to May), a half pint of shell-on prawns, faultless fish and chips or an abundant seafood platter to share.

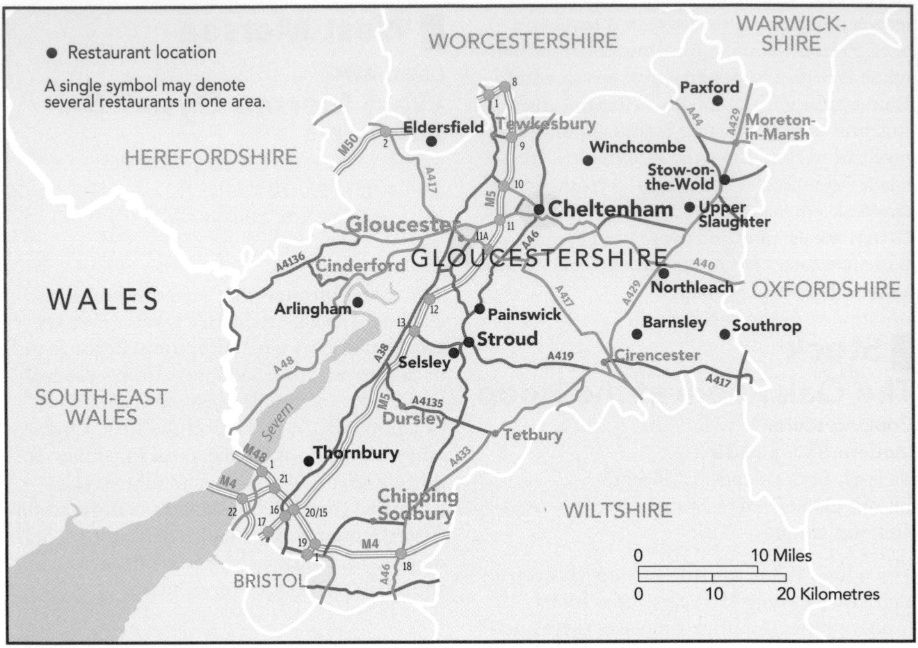

Arlingham
The Old Passage

Cooking score: 2
Seafood | £50
Passage Road, Arlingham, GL2 7JR
Tel no: (01452) 740547
theoldpassage.com

On the site of an old ford offering safe passage across the Severn to the Welsh borderlands, this converted Georgian farmhouse comes with enviable views over the water to Newnham and the Forest of Dean – an enchanting prospect for a comely restaurant-with-rooms famed for its spanking-fresh seafood. Lobster from the kitchen's seawater tanks is a highlight (perhaps grilled with garlic and parsley butter or served as part of a gargantuan fruits de mer platter), but also look for Portland Pearl rock oysters, crabs and a host of fish specials, such as a tranche of plaice with cuttlefish, rainbow chard, lemon and saffron emulsion. Meat and game aren't ignored: roast pheasant with confit leek, king oyster mushrooms and quince jam is typical. Desserts might feature dark chocolate and salt caramel délice with pink peppercorn ice cream. Enjoy it all with a refreshing white wine from nearby Three Choirs Vineyard.

Chef/s: Jon Lane. **Closed:** Mon, 25 to 27 Dec, Tue and Wed D (Jan and Feb). **Meals:** main courses £20 to £28. Set L £19 (2 courses) to £22. Tasting menu £68 (7 courses). **Details:** 44 seats. 24 seats outside. Wheelchairs. Music. Parking. Children at L only.

Barnsley
The Potager

Cooking score: 3
Modern European | £37
Barnsley House, Barnsley, GL7 5EE
Tel no: (01285) 740000
barnsleyhouse.com

Barnsley House is a romantic country house famed for its gardens designed by the late Rosemary Verey. Be sure to allow time to explore, especially the Victorian kitchen garden from which the restaurant takes its name. The dining room's interior reflects these surroundings, with plenty of greens and greenery, while the menu lists the garden produce currently featuring in the dishes – a starter of pickled home-grown beetroot with goat's cheese curds and hazelnuts, for example. Mains run from classic fillet of beef with pommes Anna, spinach and peppercorn sauce to an oriental spin on duck breast with soba noodles, stir-fried vegetables and aromatic stock. Italian options are a perennial feature, particularly the house speciality, vincisgrassi, a wild mushroom and Parma ham lasagne. This is vital, full-flavoured cooking with a penchant for crowd-pleasers, including tried-and-tested desserts such as bread-and-butter pudding or a Belgian waffle with ice cream and caramel sauce. The wine list is a charmer, divided between 'quaffable', 'classic', 'curve ball' and 'old school and serious'.

Chef/s: Francesco Volgo. **Meals:** main courses £10 to £40. Set L £26 (2 courses) to £29. **Details:** 40 seats. 24 seats outside. Bar. Parking. Children over 12 yrs at L, over 14 yrs at D.

The Village Pub

Cooking score: 2
Modern British | £35

Barnsley, GL7 5EF
Tel no: (01285) 740421
thevillagepub.co.uk

This golden-stoned inn, a sister establishment to The Potager nearby (see entry), is decorated with a similar passion for atmosphere and aesthetics: fireside chairs and heritage tones plus smooth, friendly service. In summer, the terrace comes into its own; in winter log fires blaze. Like the building, the menu flows with the seasons, plucking the best local fare and treating it with a feel for tradition and comfort. Ham hock terrine with sauce gribiche and toasted sourdough is a typical starter, while mains run from steaks with shoestring fries to roasted belly pork with fondant potato, poached garden rhubarb and sprouting broccoli. Top and tail with nibbles (maybe spiced chorizo, onion bhajis and onion rings) and comforting desserts such as apple crumble with toffee ice cream or rhubarb fool; there's also an excellent selection of British cheeses. To drink, there are real ales and ciders alongside a decent selection of wines.

Chef/s: Francesco Volgo. **Meals:** main courses £16 to £19. **Details:** 60 seats. 50 seats outside. Wheelchairs. Parking.

Cheltenham

★ TOP 50 ★

Le Champignon Sauvage

Cooking score: 8
Modern French | £68

24-26 Suffolk Road, Cheltenham, GL50 2AQ
Tel no: (01242) 573449
lechampignonsauvage.co.uk

David Everitt-Matthias has served his distinctive take on classic French food for more than 30 years, promoting seasonality and foraging decades before the current vogue. His cooking has a constant freshness and reinvention that has led many readers to consider it among the finest in the country. Though modest, Le Champignon Sauvage is certainly not dull: consider appetisers of squid ink sponge with oyster leaf and bubbles of cod roe, a blue cheese and walnut cookie sprinkled with poppy seeds, and caramelised cauliflower panna cotta with broad beans, pea shoots and fresh almonds. These segue smoothly into a starter of seared scallops partnered with a shard of salsify, dried milk crumbs, translucent leaves of cured jowl, a lightweight lardo and a jug of onion dashi for extra flavour. After that, a main course of monkfish comes with succulent baby squid and gnocchi suffused with squid ink, cleverly balanced by baby broccoli florets and tender cabbage tops. Desserts such as aerated rhubarb mousse with ginger ice cream are subtle and polite; punchier flavours come with Thai-spiced ice cream and Thai green curry sorbet to partner sliced mango with shortbread biscuit.

Generous petits fours, which might include a mini rum baba glistening with syrup, arrive with first-class coffee. The wine list is admired for its quality, range and low markups, rare for a restaurant of this calibre. Many half-bottles allow diners to experiment, and there's always excellent advice from Helen Everitt-Matthias and her team.
Chef/s: David Everitt-Matthias. **Closed:** Sun, Mon, 10 days Christmas and New Year, 3 weeks Jun. **Meals:** set L £27 (2 courses) to £34. Set D £54 (2 courses) to £68. **Details:** 38 seats.

Koj

Cooking score: 2
Japanese | £28
3 Regent Street, Cheltenham, GL50 1HE
Tel no: (01242) 580455
kojcheltenham.co.uk
£5 OFF £30

Opened with the help of a crowdfunding campaign and owned by Andrew Kojima, a former *MasterChef* finalist, Koj is very much a restaurant (and cocktail bar) for our times. It's the Japanese half of Andrew Kojima's heritage that inspires the menu, with its series of grazing plates, steamed buns, lunchtime ramen, but no sushi – this is a sushi-free zone. The food arrives in waves: Koj fried chicken with sesame mayo, tartare of sashimi with wasabi dressing, and miso roast cod. Those buns include soft-shell crab tempura with pickled fennel and yuzu mayo, and an ox heart burger with pickled shiitake and a wasabi-spiked mayo. Donburi and ramen (Tokyo-style chicken, say) are lunchtime favourites. Mini desserts include yuzu posset with raspberry and black sesame. Friendly, knowledgeable service adds to the relaxed feel in the informal space. Drink fusion cocktails, classic saké, Japanese beers or wines from £19.
Chef/s: Andrew Kojima and Robin Stock. **Closed:** Sun, Mon, Tue. **Meals:** small plates £6 to £10. Set L £16 (2 courses) to £20. Set D £23 (2 courses) to £28. **Details:** 40 seats. Bar. Music.

Lumière

Cooking score: 6
Modern British | £70
Clarence Parade, Cheltenham, GL50 3PA
Tel no: (01242) 222200
lumiere.cc

The austere front door opens into a small, calming dining room with banquettes of taupe shot silk, bold mirrors and elegant flowers. Beyond the bar, a glazed hatch peeps into the kitchen where Jon Howe, with just one young apprentice, works with great skill and imagination. Snacks include punchy taramasalata on a tapioca crisp, bright yellow with saffron, light-as-air pork scratchings with burnt apple and fennel pollen, and moreish homemade bread with two sorts of whipped local butter. Rainbow trout cured in sea salt, lightly cooked and served with torched and pickled cucumber and diced smoked eel makes a promising and well-balanced start. Or there could be quail accessorised with puffed barley, colourful beetroot and the brisk tang of fermented carrots. Every dish is the result of complex preparations and yet avoids seeming contrived: note a main course of fillet of plaice with delicate tarragon emulsion, nuggets of fresh corn and the grassy taste of wild asparagus. Local strawberries given a mild bath in green chartreuse come with apricots poached in maple syrup verjus and silky white chocolate prinked with caramel. By any standards this is dazzling cooking. A thoughtful wine list roams the globe, starting closer to home in the Cotswolds, with a handful by the glass and carafe.
Chef/s: Jon Howe. **Closed:** Sun, Mon, Tue, 2 weeks winter, 2 weeks summer. **Meals:** set L £35 (3 courses). Set D £70 (3 courses). Tasting menu L £70, D £90. **Details:** 24 seats. V menu. Music. Children over 8 yrs.

Purslane

Cooking score: 5
Modern British | £41
16 Rodney Road, Cheltenham, GL50 1JJ
Tel no: (01242) 321639
purslane-restaurant.co.uk

'From start to finish, the meal was outstanding', noted one regular who makes the trip from Birmingham to Cheltenham's Purslane. Housed in a pale yellow Georgian building in a quiet street off the main shopping area, Gareth and Helena Fulford's well-established venue offers the friendly feel of a neighbourhood restaurant. In the kitchen, Gareth oversees a regularly changing, fiercely seasonal menu that majors in seafood and foraging. Dishes are creative and technically precise, as in a starter of hand-dived Oban scallop with heritage carrots, alexanders, buttermilk and gingerbread. To follow, there might be Scottish halibut teamed with Cornish mussels, pumpkin, spinach and Cheshire saffron, or Cotswold Longhorn sirloin with barbecued brisket, purple sprouting broccoli and heritage potatoes. Intelligent flavour marriages continue through to a dessert of Comice pear, Broadway honeycomb, milk ice cream, madeleine and bee pollen. A snappy global wine list opens at £22.

Chef/s: Gareth Fulford. **Closed:** Sun, Mon, 24 to 27 Dec, 2 weeks Jan, 2 weeks Aug. **Meals:** main courses £18 to £22. Set L £15 (2 courses) to £18. Set D £31 (2 courses) to £41. Tasting menu £60. **Details:** 34 seats. 4 seats outside. Music.

Eldersfield

The Butchers Arms

Cooking score: 4
Modern British | £50
Lime Street, Eldersfield, GL19 4NX
Tel no: (01452) 840381
thebutchersarms.net

For many years Mark Block worked the stoves at various upmarket London eateries before heading west with his family in January 2018 to take on this well-known dining pub. Tucked down narrow lanes, the 16th-century rose-covered Butchers Arms looks every inch the village pub tourists dream of finding. The Blocks have maintained the simple, successful hands-on approach that kept the place in the Guide for the last 10 years. So push through the old latched door to find locals with pints in hand at the bar and a clutch of old pine tables in the three tiny, rustic rooms – booking is essential. A sensibly short carte changes daily and uses quality ingredients from trusted suppliers. There's an emphasis on balance and depth of flavour, as seen in a delicious salt cod Scotch egg with chorizo and romesco sauce, in a tender guinea fowl breast served on Moroccan-inspired chickpeas, chorizo, peppers and dukkah, and in a light lemon and almond cake with lemon curd, raspberries and vanilla ice cream that rounded off an early summer lunch. To drink, there are Wye Valley beers and a short, carefully chosen wine list (from £24).

Chef/s: Mark Block. **Closed:** Mon, 2 weeks Christmas, 2 weeks Aug. **Meals:** main courses £22 to £30. **Details:** 24 seats. Bar. Parking. No children under 10 yrs.

Northleach

The Wheatsheaf Inn

Cooking score: 2
Modern British | £35
West End, Northleach, GL54 3EZ
Tel no: (01451) 860244
cotswoldswheatsheaf.com

Quietly situated close to the square in this celebrated Cotswold wool town you'll find a smart, ivy-clad old coaching inn, thriving as the Lucky Onion group's flagship boutique pub with rooms. Hunker down in the informal bar and dining areas, all worn flagstones, big oak beams and blazing log fires, or spill out into the terraced garden when the sun decides to shine. The draw is the classy understated decor and a seasonal modern British menu that is inspired by local produce: Markham Farms asparagus and broad bean risotto with lemon and ricotta, or Old Spot pork chop with kale, apple sauce and crackling, for example. Summer berry pudding, or espresso martini cheesecake are classic desserts, with local and French cheeses making a savoury alternative. There are some impeccable choices, notably from France, on the globally inspired wine list, with bottles from £19.

Chef/s: Antony Ely and Owen Kaagman. **Meals:** main courses £15 to £25. **Details:** 70 seats. 40 seats outside. Bar. Music. Parking.

Painswick
The Painswick

Cooking score: 4
Modern British | £40
Kemps Lane, Painswick, GL6 6YB
Tel no: (01452) 813688
thepainswick.co.uk

£5 OFF

The Painswick occupies a grand 18th-century pile once known as 'Prospect House' and, indeed, diners glancing up from their plates are treated to one the finest panoramas in the county: gently contoured hills, shadowy copses and an abundance of butter-hued Cotswold stone. Interiors are correspondingly easy on the eye – done up with parquet flooring, Nordic light fittings and smatterings of modern art. And, of course, the menu offers a fine prospect, too, the kitchen guided by an ethos of country-house cool. Crisp pressed pork with romesco sauce and grilled onion was a favourite on our inspection, and ox cheek ravioli with Swiss chard not far behind. West Country accents feature among precisely constructed mains, be it Cornish cod with pommes Anna, chorizo and purple sprouting broccoli – or perfectly pink rack of Cotswold lamb, with crisp belly, roast artichoke and morels. Intense chocolate crémeux with ginger ice cream is a fine way to conclude, ahead of a refreshing stroll on the hotel's Italianate terrace. Wines from £19.

Chef/s: Jamie McCallum. **Meals:** main courses £19 to £28. Set L £25 (3 courses). Feast £35 to £40 (3 courses). **Details:** 40 seats. V menu. Bar. Music. Parking.

Paxford
The Churchill Arms

Cooking score: 2
British | £36
Paxford, GL55 6XH
Tel no: (01386) 593159
churchillarms.co

£5 OFF

The 17th-century Churchill Arms built a reputation in the 1990s, during the early days of the pub revolution, when the rustic authenticity of the public house was first mixed with a serious approach to food. Since taking over the reins in early 2015, chef patron Nick Deverell-Smith has reinvigorated the mellow stone inn, and brought his considerable experience to the table. It's still a pub, with flagstoned bar and regional ales on tap, but it's a dining destination, too, with the kitchen bringing in local produce for a menu that mixes terrific versions of pub classics with more modern British brasserie ideas. Todenham pork belly with Cornish scallops and Granny Smith apple is an opening salvo with contemporary attitude, or dive straight into chicken, mushroom and bacon pie with greens and gravy. Fish comes up from Cornwall – sole with brown crab hash, say – and dessert might be rhubarb and ginger crumble. The global wine list has interesting options by the glass.

Chef/s: Nick Deverell-Smith. **Meals:** main courses £15 to £23. Set L £15 (2 courses) to £20. Sun L £29. **Details:** Bar. Wheelchairs. Music.

Selsley
The Bell Inn

Cooking score: 1
Modern British | £27
Bell Lane, Selsley, GL5 5JY
Tel no: (01453) 753801
thebellinnselsley.com

£5 OFF £30

This listed hilltop inn, centuries old, with great views down the Woodchester Valley, has everything you might expect in a rural hostelry. The picturesque setting reinforces classy country-pub credentials and the cooking is superior. The please-all menu satisfies those with a weakness for burgers, battered fish or steak and chips, while the commitment to native seasonal produce comes across loud and clear in dishes such as potted pheasant and watercress pesto, grilled Cornish mackerel, and Barbary duck breast with parsnip purée and wild mushroom jus. To finish, there's salted caramel panna cotta. Other pluses include daily baked bread and a wide-ranging wine list that starts at £17.

Chef/s: Mark Payne. **Meals:** main courses £13 to £20. **Details:** 55 seats. 40 seats outside. Bar. Wheelchairs. Music. Parking.

Southrop

★ NEW ENTRY ★

The Swan at Southrop

Cooking score: 2
British | £30
Lechlade, Southrop, GL7 3NU
Tel no: (01367) 850174
theswanatsouthrop.co.uk

The building is 'an absolute stunner': the well-worn Cotswold stone inn wraps around a long corner site in the heart of the village, the frontage obscured by ivy with only a few ancient timber-framed windows poking through. Inside, under the mark of 'Thyme', you'll find stylish hotel rooms, a spa, cookery school, heavily beamed pub bar stocking cask ales and assorted snacks (salt cod croquettes, say), and a restaurant with a rustic interior, updated for the 21st century. The menu keeps things relatively simple – the kitchen garden provides the radishes that star in a first course of whipped ricotta on sourdough toast with a punchy wild garlic dressing, and the vegetables that pack into a spring risotto. Main courses run from hake with violet artichokes and broad beans, to Cotswold lamb rump with courgette flowers, or a pie for two to share, while a sweet hit could come from local rhubarb with meringue and lemon curd. The European-focused wine list includes some English options.

Chef/s: Matt Wardman. **Meals:** main courses £15 to £22. **Details:** 100 seats. 45 seats outside. Bar. Wheelchairs. Music.

Stow-on-the-Wold

LOCAL GEM

The Old Butchers

Modern European | £35
7 Park Street, Stow-on-the-Wold, GL54 1AQ
Tel no: (01451) 831700
theoldbutchers.com

A sign outside the Old Butchers sometimes proclaims 'Lobsters' – a reminder that this erstwhile butcher's shop is now a modern country-style restaurant catering for cosmopolitan appetites. Plates of Continental charcuterie lead the charge, ahead of fritto misto, bouillabaisse or Hinchwick venison with red cabbage, pomegranate and chocolate. Chargrilled Red Ruby steaks are a popular call, and you can round off with a Brandy Alexander dessert cocktail or a helping of custard pancakes (à la Harry's Bar). Georges Duboeuf house wine is £19.75.

Stroud

LOCAL GEM

The Woolpack Inn

British | £30
Slad Road, Stroud, GL6 7QA
Tel no: (01452) 813429
thewoolpackslad.com

Poet Laurie Lee's local is a tiny and unashamedly authentic village pub set on the side of a hill with stunning views across the Slad Valley – best enjoyed from the terrace in summer. Seek it out for the three rustic rooms, the local cider and Uley ales, and the simple daily menus that make good use of local ingredients. Typically, tuck into Wye Valley asparagus, brown butter and pecorino, or onglet, horseradish, pickled walnuts and chips, and follow with chocolate and raspberry tart with clotted cream.

Thornbury

Ronnie's of Thornbury

Cooking score: 2
Modern European | £40
11 St Mary Street, Thornbury, BS35 2AB
Tel no: (01454) 411137
ronnies-restaurant.co.uk

Sandwiched between an Aldi and a semi-abandoned shopping centre, Ronnie's has been celebrating a decade in business, during which time it has become a culinary landmark. Craggy stone walls and tall windows attest to the restaurant's former life as a schoolhouse, though big-hearted modern European fare has long been on the curriculum here. On our visit, butternut tortelloni with almond, sage and brown butter was top of the class among the starters, with scallops and cured Ibérico morcilla not far behind. Lush West Country flavours dominate the mains – Castlemead chicken with rich black truffle and Jerusalem artichoke, or delicately textured Cornish turbot deftly matched with shallot, oxtail and salsify. Apple and blackberry crumble and chocolate cheesecake set an indulgent tone for the desserts. Though there were a few minor inconsistencies among the dishes on our visit, service was faultless. Wines from £19.
Chef/s: Ron Faulkner. **Closed:** Mon, Tue, 1 to 10 Jan. **Meals:** main courses £17 to £24. Set L £18 (2 courses) to £23. Sun L £29 (3 courses). Tasting menu £55. **Details:** 32 seats. Wheelchairs. Music.

Symbols

- Accommodation is available
- £30 Three courses for less than £30
- £5 OFF £5 off voucher scheme
- Notable wine list

LOCAL GEM

Romy's Kitchen

Indian | £25
2 Castle Street, Thornbury, BS35 1HB
Tel no: (01454) 416728
romyskitchen.co.uk

Chef Romy Gill's Indian cooking – a world away from vindaloo and tikka masala clichés – has won plaudits for its imagination. Gill has her roots in the Punjab and West Bengal, and accordingly the menu spans the subcontinent. Diners in this little townhouse in Thornbury might venture north for Punjabi-style baingan bharta – spicy smoked aubergine with onions, garlic and tomatoes – strike west for the Maharashtra favourite of Malwani prawn curry, or perhaps veer east for Bengali fish curry. Look out for unusual specials – Rajasthan-style wild boar curry among them – and good value thalis at lunch.

Upper Slaughter

Lords of the Manor

Cooking score: 5
Modern British | £73
Upper Slaughter, GL54 2JD
Tel no: (01451) 820243
lordsofthemanor.com

Judging by the grandiose proportions of this one-time rectory, Georgian vicars must have lived the good life – and now visitors can too, in surroundings that blend gentrified classicism with bold contemporary strokes. Gilt-framed paintings, olive undercloths and vibrant floral displays set the tone in the dining room, where diners are pampered to the nth degree and the food exudes a certain country-house class. The kitchen sets high standards, delivering confident ingredient-led dishes with lots of fashionable detailing: a few pickled shimeji mushrooms alongside a hand-dived Orkney scallop with seaweed beurre blanc; some patatas bravas and pickled treviso adorning a plate of 55-day aged pork with romesco purée, for example. Elsewhere, a dish of fallow deer, spiced redcurrants, chard and chestnuts is as seasonally comforting as a thick winter coat, while desserts such as a chocolate and passion fruit opéra with espresso and banana ice cream are an Instagrammer's dream. The global wine list is majestic in scope, with some 20 selections by the glass, a strong biodynamic and organic contingent, excellent food-pairing suggestions and superlative choice in the upper echelons.

Chef/s: Charles Smith. **Meals:** set L £28. Set D £73. Sun L £28. Tasting menu £90 (7 courses). **Details:** 50 seats. 20 seats outside. V menu. Bar. Wheelchairs. Music. Parking.

Winchcombe

5 North Street

Cooking score: 6
Modern European | £54

5 North Street, Winchcombe, GL54 5LH
Tel no: (01242) 604566
5northstreetrestaurant.co.uk

Snuggled away in its crooked half-timbered house on Winchcombe's main street, Kate and Marcus Ashenford's pint-sized restaurant is the sort of neighbourhood eatery that's incredibly easy to befriend. Inside, it's commendably low-key, and run with warm-hearted generosity, passion and enthusiasm. Marcus cooks with real finesse and the results are sometimes delicate, sometimes decidedly robust, but always shot through with clear, forthright flavours – just consider a busy starter involving roasted Orkney scallop, smoked ham hock terrine, spiced apple chutney, creamed artichokes and violet mustard or an equally elaborate main of maple-glazed Creedy Carver duck breast and confit leg with parsley root, caramelised pineapple and five-spice sauce. A strong seasonal thread runs through the repertoire, which means plenty of local game in season (perhaps Winchcombe partridge with carrot and star anise purée), while sheer technical finesse is the hallmark of desserts such as tonka bean and thyme panna cotta with passion fruit sorbet, popcorn, fig compôte and ginger crumb. The 70-bin wine list has plenty of sound drinking for around £30.

Chef/s: Marcus Ashenford. **Closed:** Mon, 2 weeks Jan, 1 week Sept. **Meals:** set L £27 (2 courses) to £32. Set D £45 (2 courses) to £54. Sun L £36. Tasting menu £74 (7 courses). **Details:** 28 seats. V menu. Music.

Wesley House

Cooking score: 1
Modern European | £35

High Street, Winchcombe, GL54 5LJ
Tel no: (01242) 602366
wesleyhouse.co.uk

If you're looking for the essence of ye olde England, this half-timbered 15th-century merchant's house, named for its most famous guest, John Wesley, could be just the thing. There's not a right angle to be found and the welcome is as warm as the roaring fire. The dining room may be old-fashioned, but the competent cooking offers some bold, enjoyable flavours. Particularly good value can be found in the set lunch menu, which features local, seasonal ingredients in a starter of, say, chargrilled asparagus with baked ricotta and duck egg, followed by lamb rump with lyonnaise potatoes, peas and braised baby gem with a punchy red wine sauce. Desserts end the meal on a high point including, on our visit, an elderflower parfait with poached rhubarb and shortbread. The largely European wine list opens at a modest £19.

Chef/s: Cedrik Rullier. **Closed:** Mon, 26 Dec. **Meals:** main courses £16 to £38. Set L £15 (2 courses) to £20. Set D £22 (2 courses) to £28. **Details:** 50 seats. Bar. Music.

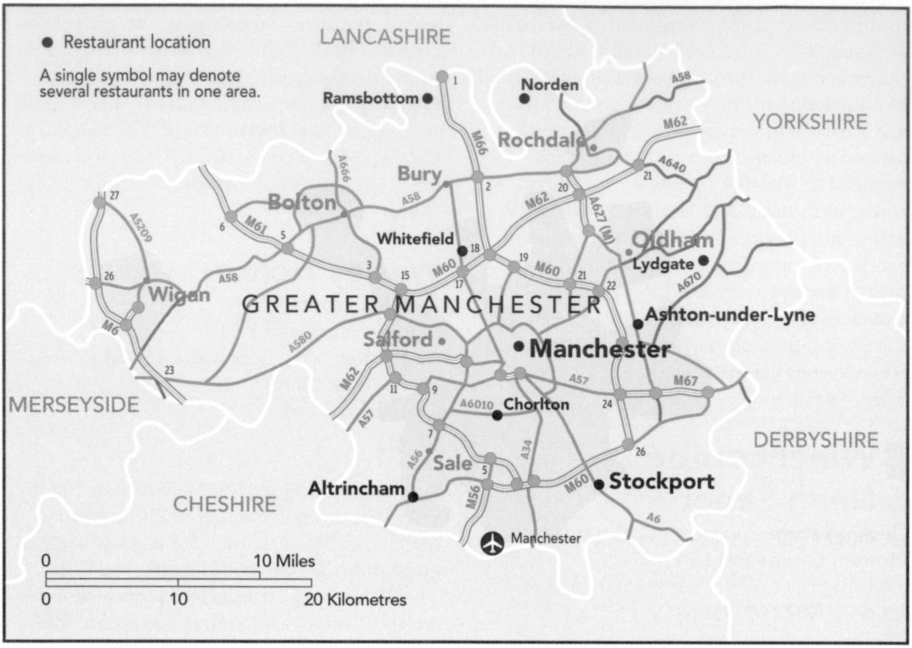

Altrincham

Porta

Cooking score: 2
Spanish | £22
50 Greenwood Street, Altrincham, WA14 1RZ
Tel no: (0161) 465 6225
portatapas.co.uk

A hit with Altrincham residents, this unpretentious tapas bar has earned a reputation for running one of the most authentic venues in town. It's related to Porta in Chester (see entry), and a rustic feel, good service and brilliant hams and charcuterie set the tone. Croquetas of ham or crab should charge up the appetite for the likes of chorizo and lentil stew, chicken wings pimentón, or slow-roast ox cheek with pickled walnuts, and there are more speculative creations on the specials board, such as a very good pork belly with chickpeas, while buffalo mozzarella with a tomato and basil salad is almost too good to share. Churros with chocolate sauce or the irresistible chocolate mousse with honeycomb fill any remaining gaps. Outside tables are at a premium when the sun shines. A short, snappy list of Spanish wines is backed up by a handful of sherries and beers.

Chef/s: Joe Wright and Joaquim Nunes. **Closed:** Mon. **Meals:** tapas £4 to £10. **Details:** 55 seats. 24 seats outside. Wheelchairs. Music.

Sugo Pasta Kitchen

Cooking score: 3
Italian | £29
22 Shaw's Road, Altrincham, WA14 1QU
Tel no: (0161) 929 7706
sugopastakitchen.co.uk

If ever a restaurant warranted the cliché 'small but perfectly formed', it's this dinky family-run pasta joint. Sugo's communal tables, hard benches and noisy hubbub aren't to everyone's taste, but doubters are soon won over by the 'spot-on service and excellent food' – especially when the kitchen can deliver

'inspired' ideas such as stracciatella di bufala with a drizzle of orange and chilli marmalade. Other hits from the refreshingly short menu have included 'foglie d'ulivo' (literally 'olive leaf') pasta with a sauce of San Marzano tomatoes, and a heart-warming dish of orecchiette with the house 'sugo' (long-cooked beef shin and pork shoulder with a hefty 'nduja kick) – 'just the sort of food you want to eat on a cold autumn night'. Away from pasta, there are 'light as a feather' beef and mortadella polpette (meatballs), while desserts might feature panna cotta with spiced apple and toasted oats. To drink? Nothing beats a carafe of the gutsy Puglian house vino.
Chef/s: Alex De Martiis, Jonathan Mulyic and Kiki Vatikiotis. **Closed:** Sun, Mon. **Meals:** main courses £10 to £17. **Details:** 25 seats. 12 seats outside.

Ashton-under-Lyne

LOCAL GEM

Lily's Vegetarian Indian Cuisine

Indian vegetarian | £12
75-83 Oldham Road, Ashton-under-Lyne, OL6 7DF
Tel no: (0161) 339 4774

Lily's has garnered huge amounts of goodwill in a district of Manchester largely untroubled by masterful cheffery. A long-planned move to more expansive local premises, due as the Guide went to press, can only enhance a reputation built on doing a proper job, fast. Lily's vegetarian Indian food is every plant-based eater's idea of a good time; fluffy idli, sada dosas (with no filling, putting the spotlight on the sambar, coconut chutney and pancake-making), chana paneer and veg makhanwala with butter and spices. For now, it's unlicensed.

Stay in the know

For the latest restaurant news, look out for the weekly *GFG Briefing*. Visit thegoodfoodguide.co.uk

Chorlton

★ NEW ENTRY ★

The Creameries

Cooking score: 2
British | £20
406 Wilbraham Road, Chorlton, M21 0UF
Tel no: (0161) 312 8328
thecreameries.co.uk

Once a dairy, this minor Chorlton landmark has been coaxed back to life by chef Mary-Ellen McTague, who headed up the kitchens at the late, great Aumbry. Lashings of greenery make a hard-edged space feel romantic – it's deliberately very casual with big communal tables and everything on blackboards – but the real love here is reserved for the baker's oven, which produces fabulous bread that's the cornerstone of the menu at lunch or dinner. McTague has cooked in fancier places, but her sure sense of flavour is very much in evidence in, say, a tomato and lovage tart with punchy anchovy dressing and a well-made green salad at lunch, or clams with cider, burnt butter, wild garlic and focaccia at dinner. All the little things, from a snack of vegetable-peeling crisps with pickled onion salt to the daily cheeses with bread, and good cakes – are done carefully, though service on our visit soon after opening was more confident than capable. In keeping with the ethos, wines are natural and cordial is homemade.
Chef/s: Mary-Ellen McTague. **Closed:** Mon. **Meals:** small dishes £4 to £18. **Details:** 40 seats. 20 seats outside. Bar. Wheelchairs. Music.

Greater Manchester's best bites

Mike Shaw of The White Hart in Lydgate shares his favourite local places to eat and drink

For **breakfast** I'm a fan of the **Albion Farm Shop** in **Delph, Oldham**. It's in a great location, with fantastic views and they use **locally sourced, seasonal ingredients**. It's nothing too complicated, they just do the simple things well.

I tend to go to **Java** in **Uppermill** for my **coffee**. They are independent and have been in the area for 20 years; they can always be relied on for a really good cup of freshly roasted coffee.

Brunch has become a lot more popular over the last few years so there's quite a lot of choice in and around Manchester. For me, **The Koffee Pot** in the **Northern Quarter** still does the job - it's been around for years and does an excellent breakfast/brunch menu, with the likes of **Manx kippers and poached eggs on toast**.

I think **Adam Reid** has done a great job at **The French** in **Manchester**. The menu has always been incredibly accomplished but Adam has implemented some positive changes and it's gone up a notch. It's easily one of the **best restaurants** in the city.

Lydgate

The White Hart

Cooking score: 4
Modern British | £33
51 Stockport Road, Lydgate, OL4 4JJ
Tel no: (01457) 872566
thewhitehart.co.uk

£5 OFF

Four family suites are the latest addition to this ever-popular inn set on the moors above Oldham, where its location by the main road ensures the place is invariably full. It is all things to all people – pub, brasserie, smart dining room, wedding venue and everything in between – with open fires and comfortable furnishings adding to the convivial atmosphere. Chef Michael Shaw works with local producers and changes his menu regularly, his modern British repertoire rolling along merrily, from beetroot tart or black pudding with mandarin and pistachio nuts to generous seasonal offerings of pot-roast pheasant or slow-cooked ox cheek with burnt onion and kale. Set lunch and early evening menus are very good value, and desserts might promise Amalfi lemon posset with poached blueberries and blueberry sorbet. Real ales add to the pubby vibe, and the affordably priced wine list has plenty of decent drinking from £22.50.

Chef/s: Michael Shaw. **Closed:** 26 Dec, 1 Jan. **Meals:** main courses £14 to £30. Set L £18 (2 courses) to £20. Sun L £28. **Details:** 50 seats. 30 seats outside. Bar. Wheelchairs. Music. Parking.

Manchester

★ TOP 50 ★

Adam Reid at The French

Cooking score: 8
Modern British | £45
The Midland, 16 Peter Street, Manchester, M60 2DS
Tel no: (0161) 235 4780
the-french.co.uk
£5 OFF

French in name only, the Midland's historic (and once oppressively chi-chi) dining room has never worked better than under local lad Adam Reid's assured stewardship. The soundtrack might be straight out of the 1990s, but the rest of the experience is bang up to date. Cooking is 'inventive, really enjoyable' and 'definitely Adam's food', presented as a choice of well-balanced tasting menus chock full of straightforwardly good ideas. Early courses include clever doings with Lancashire cheese (minuscule shavings on a multifaceted onion pie), dripping toast with grated tongue, and beef tartare reimagined as a potato hash with mushroom ketchup and a tiny, almost comedically elegant dice of souped-up stewing veg. On the side, there's beer bread with beefy butter. So far, so local. But Reid is willing to bring in the Med for a restrained dish of lobster with San Marzano tomato, or the punch of vivid green olive rising from a plate of Rhug chicken with courgettes, the thigh pressed and crisped and the breast tender and juicy. Pudding could be an excellent dish of rhubarb with a delicately spiced biscuit, malt ice cream and a shower of orange zest. It's all consistently good, and means that – factoring in a great location, well-matched wine and warm, open service – The French is unmatched for miles.

Chef/s: Adam Reid. **Closed:** Sun, Mon, 1 week Dec, 2 weeks Aug. **Meals:** set L and D £45 (4 courses) to £85. **Details:** 52 seats. V menu. Wheelchairs. Music. Children over 8 yrs.

Australasia

Cooking score: 2
Pan-Asian | £45
1 The Avenue, Spinningfields, Manchester, M3 3AP
Tel no: (0161) 831 0288
australasia.uk.com

Look for the striking glass prism rising from the pavements of Manchester's financial quarter, then head 'down under' to this subterranean hotspot dedicated to the varied cuisines of Asia and the Mediterranean. Once inside, you can expect pounding beats, oh-so-cool staff, a glassed-in kitchen and a menu of dishes with their roots in exotic climes. If grazing is your thing, pick out items such as mushroom tempura with truffle and seaweed mayonnaise, 'yum yum' squares with spicy tuna and avocado, or torched mackerel with kimchi-style fennel, burnt dill and katsuobushi mayo. You can also load up with fragrant pot-roasted lobster or crispy suckling pig belly and pineapple curry, but don't ignore the self-titled 'sharers' from the robata grill (beef fillet with braised short-rib and Asian slaw, for example). Sushi and sashimi add a Japanese note, while desserts go into fusion overdrive. To drink, premium sakés and slinky cocktails sit alongside an Aussie-dominated wine list accessed via an interactive menu.

Chef/s: Andrew Hutchinson. **Meals:** small plates £5 to £15. main courses £12 to £55. Set L £12 (2 courses) to £21. **Details:** 147 seats. Bar. Wheelchairs. Music.

El Gato Negro

Cooking score: 2
Spanish | £30
52 King Street, Manchester, M2 4LY
Tel no: (0161) 694 8585
elgatonegrotapas.com

Simon Shaw's black cat seems to be purring nicely in its high-glam, multi-storey tapas emporium bang in the centre of Manchester. El Gato Negro's new layout allows for a street-level bar, as well as a handsome rooftop cocktail lounge, although most of the action takes place in the main restaurant, sandwiched between the two drinking dens. Shaw's cooking is inspired by his Spanish travels, and his penchant for top-drawer imported provisions yields some refreshingly innovative results. Pin-sharp renditions of, say, tortilla with allioli, patatas bravas or albondigas with tomato sauce show a respect for the classics, but do seek out new-wave crossover creations such as Ostra Regal oysters with yuzu juice, tobiko wasabi and pickled cucumber. Elsewhere, don't miss Shaw's 'bikini' sandwich (Serrano ham, Manchego and truffle butter) or his mini doughnuts with chocolate sauce. Excellent sherries find favour on the all-Spanish wine list.

Chef/s: Simon Shaw. **Closed:** 25 Dec, 1 Jan. **Meals:** tapas £4 to £13. Set L £15. **Details:** 150 seats. 15 seats outside.

Hawksmoor

Cooking score: 4
British | £60
184-186 Deansgate, Manchester, M3 3WB
Tel no: (0161) 836 6980
thehawksmoor.com

This northern outpost of the Hawksmoor group was given a rapturous welcome in Manchester on its 2015 launch. It continues to impress. The setting's magnificent – a Victorian courthouse, now fitted out in vintage parquet and supple leather banquettes as far as the eye can see. The package of cool cocktails, grass-fed British beef and fine wines proves as attractive here as it does down south. Bone-in steaks and sauces (don't miss the bone-marrow gravy) are the main event, with bigger cuts to share priced per 100g. More budget-friendly options include rump and chips at lunch for £15 and the ever-popular Sunday roast. Of the seafood dishes, roasted scallops with white port and garlic and smoked haddock with kedgeree butter exemplify Hawksmoor's brand of accessible luxury well. Desserts speak to one's inner child, think salted caramel Rolos, sundaes and sticky toffee pudding. Burgers and more are served in the bar, and the global wine list runs the gamut from easy drinking to rare vintages.

Chef/s: Szymon Szymczak. **Closed:** 25 and 26 Dec, 1 Jan. **Meals:** main courses £12 to £55. Set L and early D £25 (2 courses) to £28. Sun L £21. **Details:** 137 seats. Bar. Wheelchairs. Music.

Hispi

Cooking score: 3
Modern British | £34
1C School Lane, Manchester, M20 6RD
Tel no: (0161) 445 3996
hispi.net

The third of four offerings from the uncrowned king of restaurant crowd-funding, Gary Usher's Hispi reprises many of his favourite themes, and reaffirms the chef as a champion of the modern neighbourhood bistro. Like its siblings (see entries for Sticky Walnut, Burnt Truffle and Wreckfish), this place mixes a come-as-you-please vibe with unquestionable value, upbeat cooking and a sense of fun – a formula that's guaranteed to win over the local populace. As ever, seasonal ingredients play a serious role in the kitchen: sea trout is pickled with marjoram and served with fresh peas, sorrel and yoghurt; chargrilled pork chop comes with butterhead lettuce and pickled rhubarb; roasted oyster mushrooms and goat's curd turn up in a dish of linguine. Of course, the namesake brassica also makes an appearance (perhaps steamed with blackened green pepper dressing), while desserts such as Eccles cake and custard tart doff their cloth caps to the region. Wines follow the restaurant's ethos to a T.

Chef/s: Gary Usher and Richard Sharples. **Closed:** 25 and 26 Dec. **Meals:** main courses £15 to £24. Set L and early D £16 (2 courses) to £19. Sun L £25. **Details:** 80 seats. Wheelchairs. Music.

Indian Tiffin Room

Cooking score: 3
Indian | £28
2 Isabella Banks Street, Manchester, M15 4RL
Tel no: (0161) 228 1000
indiantiffinroom.com

This 'slick operation with reliably good food' comes through whenever the need arises for city-centre spice. The big, bustling space, with siblings in Leeds and Cheadle, is thoughtfully zoned, well staffed and chock-full of colourful knick-knackery. It's possible – advisable, even – to build a meal here entirely on small plates. From snacks inspired by street food, look to chilli paneer, a grazing platter of puffed-up puri, or pav (buttered buns) with either spiced veg or goat keema; add a crisp madurai masala dosa with red chilli chutney and potato filling, and the job is pleasurably done. Among the mains, readers return to lamb dalcha ('tender, tasty lamb with a really well-flavoured gravy, thickened by lentils') and find simple comfort in dhaba-style roast chicken (inspired by Punjabi roadside eateries). Also of interest are a handful of Indo-Chinese rice and noodle dishes based on recipes from Kolkata's Chinese community. Spicy cocktails, draught beers and lassis join full-bodied wines on the well-compiled drinks list.

Chef/s: Selvan Arulmozhi. **Closed:** 25 Dec, 1 Jan. **Meals:** main courses £8 to £15. **Details:** 100 seats. V menu. Bar. Wheelchairs. Music. Parking.

★ NEW ENTRY ★

Indique

Cooking score: 2
Indian | £25
110-112 Burton Road, Manchester, M20 1LP
Tel no: (0161) 438 0241
indiquerestaurant.co.uk

In suburban restaurant terms, nothing says 'posh Indian' like crushed velvet, feature walls and slates (not plates). Indique is a fine example of the genre, attracting support for its classy poppadom trays and 'shortish menu of well-crafted food'. Street food provides inspiration for snacky puri dishes and pleasingly squidgy chicken kathi rolls; presented on a slate with vibrantly coloured squeezy-bottle mustard and green chilli-coriander sauces, they're far from their roadside roots. Lamb and smokey flavours abound, and are shown to good advantage in Rajasthani lal maas pitika, lamb chops in a gorgeously light but smokey long-cooked tomato curry, which prompted one reader to declare, 'I'll be back.' The smoke-filled cloche under which it's served might be dated, but it gives great aroma. Service is fast and competent, and the drinks list, including draught beers and aromatic white wines, has been compiled with spicy foods in mind.

Chef/s: Mamrej Khan. **Meals:** main courses £7 to £16. **Details:** 80 seats. 12 seats outside. Wheelchairs. Music.

The Lime Tree

Cooking score: 3
Modern British | £32
8 Lapwing Lane, West Didsbury, Manchester, M20 2WS
Tel no: (0161) 445 1217
thelimetree.co.uk

Putting on the style comes naturally to the team at this much-loved, long-established Didsbury restaurant and wine bar, which goes about its business against a stylish backdrop of polished wood surfaces and comfortable, high-backed chairs. A mixture of seasonality and impeccable sourcing characterises the cooking here; the kitchen is dedicated to using the very best of British produce, including Bury black pudding, Mrs Kirkham's Lancashire cheese and Goosnargh duck alongside ingredients plucked from its own Hardingland Farm at Macclesfield Forest. There are no pretensions or unnecessary garnishes – flavours are direct and enjoyable, whether in a starter of onion tarte tatin with balsamic dressing and a beetroot and goat's cheese salad, or mains of grilled plaice fillets with asparagus, new potatoes and herb butter, or roast pork fillet with chorizo, paprika and white beans. There's much praise for lunch and early evening meal deals. The wine list majors on France yet doesn't ignore equally exciting and good-value picks from elsewhere.

Chef/s: Jason Parker and David Hey. **Closed:** Mon, 25 and 26 Dec, 1 and 2 Jan. **Meals:** main courses £13 to £20. Set L £11 (2 courses) to £16. Set D £15 (2 courses) to £18. Sun L £19 (2 courses) to £22. **Details:** 70 seats. 30 seats outside. Bar. Wheelchairs. Music.

Lunya

Cooking score: 1
Spanish | £25
Barton Arcade, Deansgate, Manchester, M3 2BB
Tel no: (0161) 413 3317
lunya.co.uk

Pay homage to Catalonia at this restaurant, bar and deli in the splendid Victorian Barton Arcade, where the shelves are stocked with some 1,400 products. The bar has Spain covered, from cider to sherry, and the deli counter and kitchen offer fabulous cheeses, hams carved from the bone, and tapas old and new. On a long and eye-catching carta, pollo al moro is slow-cooked chicken with preserved lemons and Moroccan spices, dinky baby squid (chipirones) arrive with allioli, and cauliflower gets treated like royalty in a dish with yoghurt tahini and pomegranate molasses. The clued-up regional Spanish wine list opens at £18.95.

Chef/s: Patricia Salcedo Terol. **Closed:** 25 Dec, 1 Jan. **Meals:** tapas £5 to £20. Set L £10 to £14. Set D £22 to £28. Tasting menu £25 (11 courses) to £36. **Details:** 130 seats. 30 seats outside. V menu. Vg menu. Bar. Wheelchairs. Music.

Manchester House

Cooking score: 5
Modern British | £75
Tower 12, 18-22 Bridge Street, Manchester, M3 3BZ
Tel no: (0161) 835 2557
manchesterhouse.uk.com

Promoted to head chef now that Aiden Byrne has left the building (for D&D London's nearby 20 Stories, see entry), Nathaniel Tofan ably continues Manchester House's refined modern British tradition. The suspicion that the party may have moved elsewhere is as unfair as it is inevitable; the menu was already on a steady journey away from ostentation. Cooking, as in a starter of spiced quail draped with a jelly that channels mango chutney, or salmon with ricotta and a garnish-as-star salad of tomatoes with anchovies, salmon roe and chive dressing, is solid but lively. Spikes of intense flavour, like the smoked eel and green apple with crisp-carapaced pork belly, are skilfully deployed. Pudding might be chocolate pavé with lychee and rose or, more interesting, buckwheat mousse with compressed strawberries and damp pistachio micro-sponge. Some correspondents are 'not convinced' that the full works – tasting menu plus wine flight – represents value for money; lunch is slightly less painful.

Chef/s: Nathaniel Tofan. **Closed:** Sun, Mon, 2 weeks Jan, 2 weeks Aug. **Meals:** set L £24 (2 courses) to £30. Set D £50. Tasting menu £95. **Details:** 82 seats. Bar. Wheelchairs. Music.

Refuge

Cooking score: 2
International | £50
Oxford Street, Manchester, M60 7HA
Tel no: (0161) 233 5151
refugemcr.co.uk

In the afterglow of its refurb, the old Refuge Assurance Company has settled into its good looks. With the town hall closed for some serious zhuzhing, the Principal Hotel's abundantly tiled, carefully revived bar and restaurant is a great place to admire the glamour of Manchester. DJs turned restaurateurs The Unabombers remain in charge and, in dancefloor terms (there's one in the club downstairs, should you need it), the menu is all killer, no filler. Small plates like slow-cooked massaman ox cheek and scorched mackerel with cucumber and beetroot gazpacho shimmy off the page, if execution can feel a little careless. Mussels with roasted garlic and sour cream are fat, sweet and pungently salty, with chargrilled bread perfect for dunking, though burrata with orange and radicchio is rubbery and sad. Afterwards, citrus and spice Eccles cakes could do with warming through, but the pairing with Mrs Kirkham's Lancashire is a revelation every time. Cocktails, beers and easy-drinking wines play to the crowd.

Chef/s: Alex Worrall. **Meals:** small plates £4 to £11. Sun L £15 to £17. **Details:** 167 seats.

TNQ

Cooking score: 2
Modern British | £31
108 High Street, Manchester, M4 1HQ
Tel no: (0161) 832 7115
tnq.co.uk
£5 OFF

A relaxed casual place with lots of wood and little in the way of designer affectations, Jobe Ferguson's long-standing all-day eatery is the place to come for reliable, freshly cooked food. The tone is set immediately with variously coloured salt-baked beetroots – served as chunks and purées – with a very tangy goat's cheese beignet, and a ham hock and Bury black pudding terrine with apple and onion relish. Perfectly cooked Goosnargh chicken breast comes with crispy skin, gently fried chicken livers, spring onion hash browns and truffle foam, while fillet of hake is teamed with chorizo, tomatoes and mussels. The pick of desserts may well be a blackberry panna cotta with mulled fruits and meringue, and the assortment of artisanal British cheeses is also worth exploring. There's an excellent-value 'express menu', too, served from noon until 6.30pm. Wine markups are reasonable, and there's a decent by-the-glass selection.

Chef/s: Anthony Fielden. **Meals:** main courses £14 to £24. Set L £16 (2 courses) to £20. Set D £30. Sun L £20. **Details:** 55 seats. Wheelchairs. Music.

★ NEW ENTRY ★

20 Stories

Cooking score: 4
Modern European | £45
No.1 Spinningfields, 1 Hardman Square, Manchester, M3 3EB
Tel no: (0161) 204 3333
20stories.co.uk

Throw your head back, and 20 Stories' terrace is tantalisingly visible from Spinningfields, Manchester's glitzy shopping and dining district below. On a sunny evening the double-height space with glass walls, open roof and busy bar seems to be the whole point of D&D London's investment in the city. Inside, Aiden Byrne – ex of Manchester House (see entry) – is in charge of food in both grill and restaurant, and it's the latter that visitors commend. If the smartest seats arguably have the least sexy view – unless you really like the Ordsall Chord – Byrne has calibrated his cooking to stand up to a slick, glamorous room. Dishes are now less fussy than when we took a quick peek on opening, yet still look the part. To start, a simple sweetcorn velouté is poured on to purple potatoes, smoked chicken and charred corn, and silky folds of pappardelle with steamed bass, mussels and a riot of pea shoots make a winning main. Linger over coffee, rather than dessert. The wine list is predictably flash, with limited room for manoeuvre under £30.

Chef/s: Aiden Byrne. **Meals:** main courses £12 to £40. Set L £23 (2 courses) to £28. **Details:** Bar.

Manchester's best bites

Mary-Ellen McTague of The Creameries in Chorlton shares her favourite local places to eat and drink

The Koffee Pot's tagline is something like 'making and curing hangovers since 1978', and it is no lie. It's a real Manchester institution.

For food shopping I recommend **Unicorn Grocery** for the quality of the fruit and veg and lots of **local and seasonal** produce.

Siam Smiles serves lovely fresh Thai food that will cure colds, hangovers and ennui.

For **dinner, Umezushi** has been one of my favourite places for years, and they continue to offer incredibly good and interesting food and drink. I adore this place.

Spanish restaurant **Baratxuri** serves amazing **wood oven-baked fish**, whole roast chicken and baked potatoes with green sauce, plus excellent pintxos, wines and sherries. It's like being on holiday.

If I could eat only one thing around here it would have to be... the chips and anchovy hollandaise from **Hawksmoor**.

Umezushi

Cooking score: 4
Japanese | £40
4 Mirabel Street, Manchester, M3 1PJ
Tel no: (0161) 832 1852
umezushi.co.uk

Tucked under a railway arch down an alley, this tiny 14-seat sushi bar is one of Manchester's hottest tickets. It's the real deal, but earnestness doesn't play well in Manchester, so what could have been a hushed temple to authenticity is actually nicely easy-going, thanks to laid-back yet eagle-eyed service and the offer of other dishes. Taiwanese pork rice, miso congee with fish and mushrooms, and specials of miso-marinated Patagonian sea bass or chargrilled hamachi head play solid supporting roles to the headline act. Sashimi, perhaps of pickled mackerel or botan shrimp, is deftly cut and fairly priced, while sushi is the full range from slender hosomaki to chunky hand rolls, all served at room temperature – just as it should be. When it comes to tuna, four different cuts are on offer, including negitoro (minced fatty toro with spring onion); try it stuffed into a cone-shaped temaki roll or have the whole lot, greedily, over a rice bowl. A saké and wine list is bolstered by a handful of shochu options.

Chef/s: Omar Rodriguez Marrero. **Closed:** Mon, Tue, 2 to 8 July. **Meals:** sushi £4 to £12. Sushi platters £16 to £60. Donmono £18 to £48. Tasting menu £57 (6 courses). **Details:** 14 seats. Wheelchairs. Music.

Wing's

Cooking score: 3
Chinese | £45
Heron House, 1 Lincoln Square, Manchester, M2 5LN
Tel no: (0161) 834 9000
wingsrestaurant.co.uk

Readers with long memories may recall the original Wing's in Cheadle Hulme but this much-loved veteran of Manchester's dining scene continues to stand out in a city blessed with choice when it comes to Chinese restaurants. Near the central financial and business districts, weekdays see shoppers and local office workers crowding the private booths, with families flocking here at the weekend for lunchtime dim sum such as steamed beef dumplings with ginger and spring onion. With a menu of around 200 dishes, choice is never an issue – sharing platters and 'special banquets' are a good introduction – but seafood is a strong suit and you can't go wrong with dishes such as deep-fried crab claw stuffed with prawn meat. Fried sliced beef in Szechuan sauce or Shanghai hot chilli sliced lamb are reliable options too. Vegetarians are well catered for, perhaps with salt and pepper aubergine or water chestnut with sugar snaps and broccoli. The wine list is arranged by style with short descriptions to help guide your selection.

Chef/s: Mr Chi Wing Lam. **Meals:** main courses £15 to £85. Set L and D £35 to £55. **Details:** 85 seats. V menu. Bar. Wheelchairs. Music.

Yuzu

Cooking score: 3
Japanese | £20
39 Faulkner Street, Manchester, M1 4EE
Tel no: (0161) 236 4159
yuzumanchester.co.uk

Occupying the ground floor of a tall red-brick Victorian corner building on the edge of Chinatown, Yuzu is a traditional Japanese eatery that offers a simple menu of sashimi, tempura and katsu dishes at prices that are rather kinder than the norm, with seating on backless benches and stools. Appetisers run to flour-dusted fried tofu served in ginger and spring onion broth or prawn gyoza with soy and chilli oil for dipping. The sashimi options embrace an all-singing-all-dancing version comprising scallop, prawn, tuna and salmon in a donburi bowl with sushi rice, or there are udon dishes: thick noodles as the base for stir-fried strips of pork loin or chicken breast. There are no desserts – buy a Mars Bar afterwards. No wines, either, but a tempting list of sakés in 15cl jug or 72cl bottle sizes (from £8 and £35 respectively). The bone-dry seawater-based Tosatsuru is the essential Japanese tipple.

Chef/s: David Leong. **Closed:** Sun, Mon, 2 weeks Christmas, 2 weeks Aug. **Meals:** main courses £8 to £17. **Details:** 26 seats. Music.

LOCAL GEM

Albert Square Chop House

British | £29
The Memorial Hall, Albert Square, Manchester, M2 5PF
Tel no: (0161) 834 1866
albertsquarechophouse.com

Housed in a fine example of Victorian Venetian Gothic, and sporting an industrial look of brick walls, steel and oak beams, industrial ducting, booth seating and an open kitchen, this popular city-centre eatery offers patriotic food and drinks without frills. The generous, meat-packed steak and kidney pudding has a loyal fan base, as does its famed corned beef hash, but there are also chops and steaks from the grill, bacon and haddock chowder to start, and a rice pudding with honey-roasted plums and toasted Scottish oats to finish. Drink local cask ales or choose from the well-laid-out, annotated wine list.

LOCAL GEM

Mi & Pho

Vietnamese | £20
384 Palatine Road, Manchester, M22 4FZ
Tel no: (0161) 312 3290
miandpho.com

'The best Vietnamese food for miles,' thought one reader of this casual, modest and very affordable south Manchester eatery. Most of the cuisine's staples appear on the lengthy menu: lunchtime-only banh mi (stuffed baguettes); fresh, vibrant summer rolls packed with noodles, lettuce, cucumber, herbs and a filling (prawns, say) with a peanut dipping sauce; pancakes with tofu; zingy green papaya salad with mango, carrots and mixed herbs; generously filled bowls of pho (noodle soup); and versions of bun (noodles). Unlicensed, with a small corkage charge if you BYO.

LOCAL GEM

The Pasta Factory

Italian | £24

77 Shudehill Street, Manchester, M4 4AN
Tel no: (0161) 222 9250
pastafactory.co.uk

Handy for the Arndale and Manchester Arena, the compact Pasta Factory boasts a simple interior done up on a shoestring. But there's an authenticity here, a passion for simple things done well. And that passion is pasta, freshly made in-house. Ravioli is a favourite, whether a black squid ink version stuffed with salmon, soft cheese and a twist of lemon in a butter sauce, or filled with chocolate for dessert. There's also spinach gnocchi with pumpkin velouté, a simple dish of bucatini tossed with olive oil and breadcrumbs, and Italian wines from £18.

LOCAL GEM

Volta

International | £25

167 Burton Road, West Didsbury, Manchester, M20 2LN
Tel no: (0161) 448 8887
voltafoodanddrink.co.uk

Its upstart sibling Refuge may be making headlines in central Manchester (see entry), but Volta is still a strong presence on the streets of West Didsbury. Modern bistro-style surrounds set the scene for a menu of small plates 'inspired by our travels' – anything from Shanghai-style pork bao buns to chargrilled cauliflower with caraway and pomegranate or kombu-cured salmon with cucumber and wasabi ketchup. There's a busy outdoor terrace, and the soundtrack is a blast – not surprising since Volta's owners started out as DJs.

READERS RECOMMEND

No. 4 Wine and Dine

Modern British

4 Warburton Street, Manchester, M20 6WA
Tel no: (0161) 445 0448
no4dineandwine.com

'The menu is always well put together and we would have happily ordered any of the main courses. Plaice was excellent, came with rösti and spinach, but dish of the evening was brioche topped with fried mushrooms and creamy mustardy sauce.'

Marple

READERS RECOMMEND

Angkor Soul

Cambodian

12 Stockport Road, Marple, SK6 6BJ
Tel no: (0161) 222 0707
angkorsoul.co.uk

'One of only two Cambodian restaurants in the UK. We tried thin slices of rare beef with leaves, red onions, herbs, citrus, chilli and crushed peanuts for texture, and saraman, a mild beef curry, long cooked with potatoes, carrot, star anise and lemongrass.'

Norden

Nutters

Cooking score: 2
Modern British | £40

Edenfield Road, Norden, OL12 7TT
Tel no: (01706) 650167
nuttersrestaurant.com

Wolstenholme Manor, at the heart of a six-acre estate outside Rochdale, is the hub of brand Andrew Nutter, with a dining pub (the Bird at Birtle) the latest addition to the fold. Everything is on a grand scale – it's on the wedding circuit, unsurprisingly – and done with the effusive style that is Nutter to a T. French classical cooking is the bedrock of a modern British output ('it isn't as out there as you might imagine'), with a regional flavour to boot. So Goosnargh duck might appear in a first course as leg confit with butternut squash purée, 'frazzled' pancetta and pomegranate jam, while Bury black pudding gets an outing in crispy won tons. Fish figures, too (grilled cod with diver-caught scallops, truffle mash and port gel), and a surprise gourmet menu gives the kitchen free rein to impress. Among sweet courses, peach tarte tatin comes with blood orange ice cream and shards of praline. The wine list covers the globe and has the big guns at the ready for the big spenders.

Chef/s: Andrew Nutter. **Closed:** Mon, 25 to 27 Dec, 1 and 2 Jan. **Meals:** main courses £23 to £27. Set L £17 (2 courses) to £20. Sun L £25. Tasting menu £44 (6 courses). **Details:** 143 seats. V menu. Bar. Wheelchairs. Music. Parking.

Ramsbottom

Baratxuri

Cooking score: 2
Spanish | £25

1 Smithy Street, Ramsbottom, BL0 9AT
Tel no: (01706) 559090
levanterfinefoods.co.uk

Such is the success of Baratxuri – pronounced Barra-churri and related to the equally popular Levanter nearby (see entry) – that owners Joe and Fiona Botham have recently knocked through to the former shop next door to create an additional dining room. They have also installed a wood-fired oven, sourced from Spain, as further proof of their commitment to bringing an authentic taste of the Basque country to Lancashire. Small plates are the way to go, perhaps fried salt cod with chorizo fuego, rice with artichokes and smoked ewe's milk cheese, or shell-on prawns with chilli and garlic oil, before sharing a rack of Gloucester Old Spot pork ribs cooked over charcoal, or whole sea bream. And don't forget the baked cheesecake with Pedro Ximénez-soaked raisins for dessert. The Spanish wine list starts at £19 and offers plenty of good-value quality drinking under £30.

Chef/s: Rachel Stockley. **Closed:** Mon, Tue. **Meals:** pintxos from £2. Large plates £8 to £48. **Details:** 24 seats. Wheelchairs. Music. No children after 7.30pm.

Levanter

Cooking score: 3
Spanish | £30

10 Square Street, Ramsbottom, BL0 9BE
Tel no: (01706) 551530
levanterfinefoods.co.uk

'It is a couple of years since I was last here and I think they have definitely raised their game,' noted a visitor to this small, split-level tapas bar, now so popular that bookings are taken. Regulars return again and again for an ever-changing menu and for signature dishes of spicy homemade morcilla topped with a Goosnargh egg (the highlight of one meal) or Galician dairy-fed sirloin. Elsewhere, there could be chickpeas with cumin and garlic, sweet king prawns sautéed on the plancha with chilli and garlic, and hake cooked in Manzanilla, tomato and toasted breadcrumbs. And no tapas bar would be complete without hand-carved Ibérico ham; sharing platters 'look very inviting', too. They keep it simple on the dessert front, with just a couple of choices, perhaps cocoa-dusted 'bonbons' of requesón, a ricotta-like cheese, mixed with chocolate chips and biscuit crumb and served with raspberry coulis. A short, all-Spanish wine list starts at £18.50.

Chef/s: Yvonne Lumb. **Closed:** Mon, Tue. **Meals:** tapas £4 to £13. **Details:** 24 seats. Music.

Readers recommend

These entries are genuine quotes from a report sent in by one of our readers. We intend to follow up these suggestions in the year to come.

Stockport

Where The Light Gets In

Cooking score: 5
British | £75
7 Rostron Brow, Stockport, SK1 1JY
Tel no: (0161) 477 5744
wtlgi.co

It's quite possible that Where The Light Gets In is indeed 'the most exciting restaurant in the north'. It's also possibly the most divisive: the unmarked entrance, the 'no menu' menu, the vintage jazz soundtrack and prepaid ticketed reservations will not be for everyone (vegetarians, for example, aren't catered for). But WTLGI is an event. Crisps of celeriac, for example (not that crisp, alas) with homemade seasonings start proceedings by the wood stove. Pairings of either wine (£50) or soft drinks (£20) come recommended in the absence of a formal list – another WTLGI quirk. Sam Buckley is a L'Enclume alumni and cooks nimbly, as the day dictates, in a minimalist style (there's rye sourdough and whipped pork fat for ballast). The best dishes are excellent: rare venison with chicory dressed with a splash of quince vinegar; a mutton pie with clear bone broth; honeycake with saffron-like beeswax ice cream. To finish, a 'Buckfast' lozenge. In short, an experience.
Chef/s: Samuel Buckley. **Closed:** Sun, Mon, Tue, 2 weeks Apr, 2 weeks Aug, 2 weeks Dec to Jan. **Meals:** tasting menu £75 (10 courses). **Details:** 26 seats. Music. No children.

LOCAL GEM

Bombay to Mumbai

Indian | £25
10 Fir Road, Stockport, SK7 2NP
Tel no: (0161) 439 0055
bombaytomumbai.co.uk
£5 OFF £30

Readers have been quick to tell us that Sandeep Gursahani left Aamchi Mumbai in Cheadle to open this colourful, modern restaurant that 'represents old Bombay and modern Mumbai'. The menu draws heavily on Mumbai street food, perhaps perfectly crisp masala dosa stuffed with lightly spiced potato or samosa chaat. Praise, too, for 'very authentic Mumbai tasting' staff curry (lamb), chicken kolhapuri, a lamb chamku with its earthy, spiced beetroot sauce, and for breads such as chilli and onion kulcha. Service is 'top-notch'. Drink cocktails or beer.

Whitefield

One Eighty Eight

Cooking score: 2
Modern British | £30
188 Bury New Road, Whitefield, M45 6QF
Tel no: (0161) 280 0524
one88whitefield.co.uk
£5 OFF

With its alfresco tables, pale green colour scheme and attractive modern interior, this all-day bar bistro feels like a genuine local haunt, helped along by chef and co-owner David Gale's nifty take on affordable brasserie-style cooking. His feel for robust flavours and regionally sourced ingredients shows in dishes such as Lancashire hotpot, Eccles cakes and cheesy fish goujons (served with tartare sauce and pickled onions on a soft white bloomer), but he can also do colourful, eclectic food with real verve – as in 'tuna crunch' with wasabi mayo and cucumber in a toasted tortilla wrap, or a spiced lamb burger with mint yoghurt and feta. Salads include honey-roast salmon and avocado and a classic tomato and mozzarella, while puddings are mostly calorific cheesecakes, crumbles and mousses. Sunday lunch is served 'until it's gone', and there are custom-built cocktails for post-work warm-downs. House wines start at £16.95.
Chef/s: David Gale. **Closed:** 26 to 28 Dec. **Meals:** main courses £12 to £19. **Details:** 75 seats. 20 seats outside. Bar. Wheelchairs. Music. Parking.

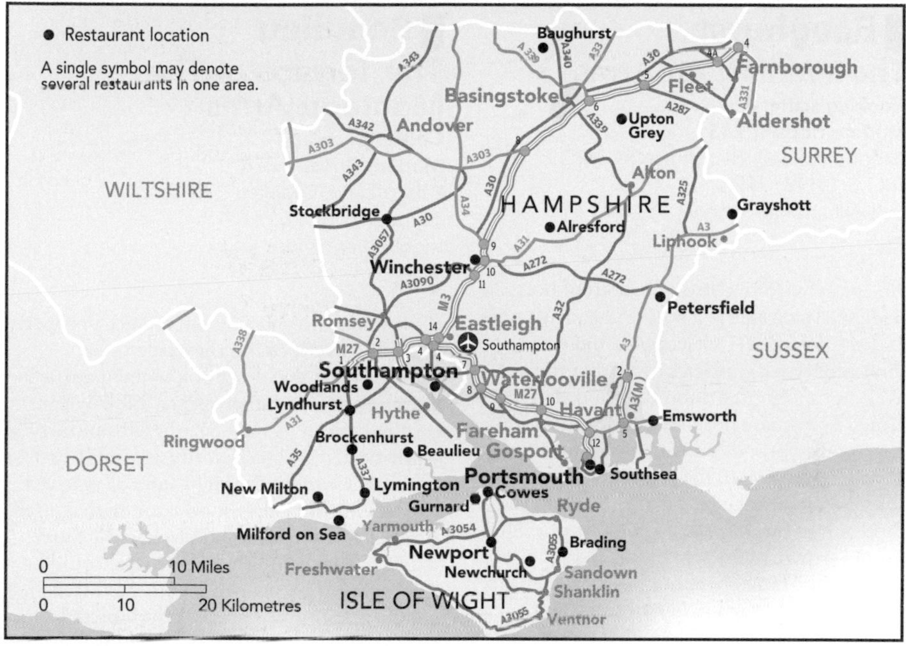

Alresford

★ LOCAL RESTAURANT AWARD ★ REGIONAL WINNER

Pulpo Negro

Cooking score: 4
Spanish | £30
28 Broad Street, Alresford, SO24 9AQ
Tel no: (01962) 732262
pulponegro.co.uk
£5 OFF

Alresford is a well-to-do town with pretty cottages, charming tearooms and, ahem, a black octopus in the shape of Pulpo Negro. And the locals are lapping it up. It has brought a bit of Latin exuberance and some easy-going contemporary style to this corner of Hampshire ('filament light bulbs, small plates, cocktails... I thought I was in Soho'). Andres Alemany buys well – like the 'melt-in-the-mouth' jamón de Jabugo that hangs above the tiled counter of the open kitchen – and adds daily specials to a tapas repertoire that covers traditional bases (crisp croquetas, classy tortillas, plump boquerones). Salads add to the mix: salt-roasted beetroots with mojo verde, or fried chickpeas with fresh, crunchy veg and Moscatel vinaigrette. Pulpo negro itself is a tender, inky delight, and do squeeze in chicken thighs with almonds and capers. Plates arrive in a joyful procession, right up to desserts such as a chocolate and peanut tart with an 'absolutely divine' cherry sorbet. The mostly Spanish and keenly priced wine list has plenty of options by the glass, including sherries.

Chef/s: Andres Alemany. **Closed:** Sun, Mon, 25 and 26 Dec, 1 Jan, bank hols. **Meals:** tapas £3 to £17. **Details:** 60 seats. 12 seats outside. Bar. Wheelchairs. Music. Children over 5 yrs.

Get social

Follow us on social media for the latest news, chef interviews and more.
Twitter: @GoodFoodGuideUK
Facebook: TheGoodFoodGuide

Baughurst

The Wellington Arms

Cooking score: 4
Modern British | £35
Baughurst Road, Baughurst, RG26 5LP
Tel no: (0118) 982 0110
thewellingtonarms.com

An apiary with five strong broods of bees, 26 pedigree Jacob sheep, a polytunnel, fruit trees and an allotment – welcome to the increasingly self-sufficient world of the Wellington Arms. Simon Page and chef Jason King's foursquare hostelry has done its local community proud, putting Baughurst on the gastronomic map in the process. Inside, all is spick and span with regional ales on tap and food rich in local favours – look for the 'HG' (home-grown) acronym beside many ingredients. Lunch is about hearty sustenance, but dinner sees the kitchen in full flight: buckwheat noodles with braised wood pigeon, brown onions and white wine might open the show, ahead of Brixham cod with a preserved lemon crust, samphire and Puy lentils or a 'pot pie' made with lamb from those Jacob sheep. Like everything else here, desserts such as 'jelly and ice cream' (elderflower and rhubarb ripple, respectively) are an absolute delight. There's a tidy wine list, too.

Chef/s: Jason King. **Meals:** main courses £14 to £24. Set L £18 (2 courses) to £20. **Details:** 30 seats. 20 seats outside. Wheelchairs. Music. Parking.

Anonymous

At *The Good Food Guide*, our inspectors dine anonymously and pay their bill in full every time.These impartial review meals, along with feedback from thousands of our readers, are what informs the content of the *GFG*. Only the best restaurants make the cut.

Beaulieu

The Terrace at The Montagu Arms

Cooking score: 4
Modern British | £70
Palace Lane, Beaulieu, SO42 7ZL
Tel no: (01590) 612324
montaguarmshotel.co.uk

If the sun is shining and you can get a 'properly laid' table overlooking the garden, the Montagu Arms' old-school, wood-panelled dining room is a rather special 'New Forest treat' enhanced by chef Matthew Tomkinson's sophisticated and technically accomplished cooking. Come at the right time of year and you might find late-season lamb with stuffed artichoke, fresh pasta and black garlic purée, while day-boat fish (hake, perhaps) could be accompanied by pressed potato and black pudding, sprouting broccoli and roasted pumpkin. More prosaic ideas such as house-made pastrami with horseradish cream and capers or roast rump of Pondhead beef with smoked creamed potato, crispy shallots and Exbury chard suggest that the 'really affordable' set lunch is something of a loss leader – although desserts including an 'utterly creamy' crème brûlée with macerated strawberries and raspberry sorbet are there to save the day. Service can sometimes seem a touch 'hapless', but the contents of the sophisticated 300-bin wine list speak of all-round professionalism, knowledge and a commitment to small producers (note the sizeable organic and biodynamic contingent).

Chef/s: Matthew Tomkinson. **Closed:** Mon, 25 Dec. **Meals:** set L £25 (2 courses) to £30. Sun L £38. Tasting menu £80 (5 courses) to £90. **Details:** 50 seats. Bar. Wheelchairs. Music. Parking. No children under 12 yrs.

Brockenhurst

LOCAL GEM

The Pig

Modern British | £38

Beaulieu Road, Brockenhurst, SO42 7QL
Tel no: (01590) 622354
thepighotel.com

The original Pig, now part of a growing empire, is an ivy-clad Georgian house turned boutique hotel that's a self-sufficient enterprise driven by a green agenda. There's an impressive vegetable garden, a plant-filled half-conservatory dining room filled with mismatched tables and chairs, and a menu that prides itself on foraged, own-grown and local produce. That might translate to wild mushrooms on toast, tomahawk pork chop (with buttered greens and creamy mash), crème brûlée or dark chocolate tart to finish.

Emsworth

36 on the Quay

Cooking score: 4
Modern European | £58

47 South Street, Emsworth, PO10 7EG
Tel no: (01243) 375592
36onthequay.co.uk

Ramon and Karen Farthing's 17-century restaurant with rooms in a listed building overlooking Emsworth's pretty harbour embodies getting away from it all. Bow windows, period charm and pristine tables set the scene and the kitchen is never short on ambition as it applies several coats of French polish to a host of seasonal ingredients. Fish is a natural choice (perhaps seared red mullet with crab, sand carrots, roasted hazelnuts, carrot purée, kale and geranium sauce), but highly worked intricacy is the norm here and it's not unusual to find countless components mingling on the plate – as in roast quail breast and Peking-style legs embellished with crispy sweetbreads, spring onion purée, sweetcorn and ceps. The same ethos also applies to desserts such as Hayling Island honey parfait with frozen yoghurt 'rocks', salted lemon curd and sumac meringue. An extensive high-end wine list starts at £21.50.

Chef/s: Gary Pearce. **Closed:** Sun, Mon, 24 to 28 Dec, 2 weeks Jan, 1 week May, 1 week Oct. **Meals:** set L £24 (2 courses) to £29. Set D £48 (2 courses) to £58. Tasting menu L £30 (5 courses), D £65 (8 courses). **Details:** 45 seats. 12 seats outside. Bar. Wheelchairs.

Grayshott

LOCAL GEM

Applegarth

International | £28

Applegarth Farm, Headley Road, Grayshott, GU26 6JL
Tel no: (01428) 712777
applegarthfarm.co.uk

The Benson family have been growing fruit and vegetables at Grayshott since 1976 but they've created something of a rural food hub since opening a farm shop, cookery school and restaurant with large decked terrace. The latter is an all-day affair, morphing from a simple café (vegetarian chilli, seasonal salads) to a dimly lit bistro in the evening where you could start with local wild rabbit rillettes with carrot jelly, gooseberry relish, black pudding and mustard toast, then move on to sea trout with beetroot, maple kohlrabi, apple gel and dill oil. Leave room for the Earl Grey panna cotta, blood orange curd and rose meringue. Book ahead at weekends.

Isle of Wight

★ NEW ENTRY ★

Heima

Cooking score: 3
Modern European | £27
46-48 High Street, Brading, Isle of Wight, PO36 0DQ
Tel no: (01983) 404090
heima-iow.co.uk
£5 OFF £30

A passion for foraging, cookbooks and Scandinavian design come together at this 'brilliant, beautiful restaurant'. The colours are neutral, surfaces natural, tables are well spaced and a fixed-price carte and tasting menus show the way. Things start very well with rye sourdough spiked with cranberries; next a wooden board piled with moss and twigs hiding beef and blue cheese croquettes. Jerusalem artichokes star in a first course with pickled hispi cabbage and a frothy truffle sauce, while pork loin is matched with curried cauliflower purée, black pudding and pink pickled apple. Not every element lives up to the ambition of the kitchen – notably a carrot and coconut sponge – but Heima is a bold and exciting address. Service is charming and informed and an Italian-led wine list (from £19) is supplemented by beers and imaginative cocktails.

Chef/s: Max Rosenberg. **Closed:** Mon, Tue, Jan. **Meals:** set L £21 (2 courses) to £26. Set D £24 (2 courses) to £29. Tasting menu £35. **Details:** 27 seats. V menu. Bar. Wheelchairs. No small children at D.

The Little Gloster

Cooking score: 4
Modern European | £35
31 Marsh Road, Gurnard, Isle of Wight, PO31 8JQ
Tel no: (01983) 298776
thelittlegloster.com
£5 OFF

Glorious views over the Solent are served up rain or shine through the ample windows of Ben and Holly Cooke's restaurant with rooms by the water's edge, a few minutes' drive west of Cowes. Within, it mixes a love of the English seaside with Scandinavia in a smörgåsbord of woody white neutrality, and in a kitchen that fires up for breakfast and lunches that extend to Danish-style open sandwiches (Isle of Wight crab, say, with avocado and soft-boiled egg) and fish and chips. In the evening, the menu ranges from chargrilled steaks to seafood bouillabaisse. Gravadlax is cured in-house, Asian flavours join the party with Vietnamese pork belly, and pasta is handmade – ravioli filled with goat's cheese, Parmesan and pesto ricotta, for example. For dessert, treacle tart is a slice of old England. The wine list focuses on organic and biodynamic producers who operate on a small scale, with bottles opening at £19.95.

Chef/s: Ben Cooke and Jay Santiago. **Closed:** Mon, 29 Oct to 27 Mar. **Meals:** main courses £10 to £25. Set L £15 (2 courses) to £20. **Details:** 70 seats. 50 seats outside. Bar. Wheelchairs. Music. Parking.

★ NEW ENTRY ★

The Oyster Store

Cooking score: 3
Seafood | £30
Sun Hill, West Cowes, Isle of Wight, PO31 7HY
Tel no: (01983) 209453
theoysterstore.co.uk

North House, a Grade II-listed, townhouse hotel in Cowes' Old Town, has been charmingly refurbished with a contemporary seaside palette of yellow, white and china blue. The pared-back nautical look extends to the hotel's Oyster Store restaurant, with its rough wood tables and vintage chairs, oars and maritime prints. It opens out on to a sunny terrace; on less temperate days, sink into the fireside sofas in the striking bar and library and try the Isle of Wight's own Mermaid gin to get things going. Colchester oysters on ice are a given, but fish and seafood make their mark too. Recommended is a classic shellfish bisque with rouille, Parmesan and croûtons or go for crab linguine, Goan seafood curry with coconut milk, or hake with leeks and pancetta.

Not a fish fan? Choose from charcoal-grilled steaks, vegetable risottos, pasta dishes and curries. Wines start at £18.
Chef/s: Matt Foster. **Meals:** main courses £16 to £21. **Details:** 40 seats. 30 seats outside. Bar. Wheelchairs. Music.

Thompson's

Cooking score: 6
Modern European | £50
11 Town Lane, Newport, Isle of Wight, PO30 1JU
Tel no: (01983) 526118
robertthompson.co.uk

£5 OFF

Behind a weathered red-brick exterior in the centre of town, Robert Thompson's place is at the heart of the island capital. He has been something of an evangelist for the Isle of Wight's gastronomic potential over the years, and if he has sometimes seemed to be ploughing a lonely furrow, it's nonetheless a richly productive one. Themed cookery tutorials are a feature, but most will be happy to leave it to our host to work his ingenious magic through dishes such as slow-cooked pig's cheeks with grilled boudin noir, the rich and engaging flavours of which are offset by apple, cauliflower and sage vinaigrette and soaked up by exemplary sourdough. Main courses look to the island catch for gratinated brill with St Austell Bay mussels in Noilly Prat velouté with Parmesan gnocchi, charred cucumber and dill, or source pedigree meats for beef sirloin in treacle and porter, or venison with a red wine pear in grand-veneur sauce. Inventive things crop up at dessert stage when pineapple is glazed in rum and barbecued, then matched with banana and walnut cake, white chocolate ganache, rum gel and pineapple sorbet. The wine list finds room for French classics, but without letting them rule the roost. Glass selections are full of varied appeal, from £4.75.

Chef/s: Robert Thompson. **Closed:** Sun, Mon, Tue, 25 Dec, 2 weeks Feb to Mar, 2 weeks Nov. **Meals:** main courses £19 to £29. Set L £24 (2 courses) to £29. Tasting menu D £65 (6 courses). **Details:** 50 seats. Bar. Wheelchairs. Music.

LOCAL GEM

The Garlic Farm Restaurant

Modern British | £20
Mersley Lane, Newchurch, Isle of Wight, PO36 0NR
Tel no: (01983) 865378
thegarlicfarm.co.uk

Between the shop, tasting room, tractor tours and education centre you could spend the best part of a day here, and the restaurant is another good reason to linger. Unsurprisingly, they put garlic in almost everything, but it's sensitively done: the whole roasted garlic bulb is lovely and mellow, while the signature garlic mushroom ravioli has an umami-laced filling of Isle of Wight oyster mushrooms, truffle oil and Parmesan. The black garlic ice cream is worth trying – but there are also (garlic-free) sundaes, brownies and cakes.

READERS RECOMMEND

Cantina

20 High Street, Ventnor, Isle of Wight, PO38 1RZ
Tel no: (01983) 855988
cantinaventnor.co.uk
'This small hidden gem is frequented by locals in the know. The menu is interesting and changes regularly. Go for the all-day brunch – shakshuka with flat bread is a favourite – or the hearty seafood stew. It's worth a visit for the homemade bread alone. Daytime only.'

Readers recommend

These entries are genuine quotes from a report sent in by one of our readers. We intend to follow up these suggestions in the year to come.

Lymington

The Elderflower

Cooking score: 4
Modern British | £44
4-5 Quay Street, Lymington, SO41 3AS
Tel no: (01590) 676908
elderflowerrestaurant.co.uk

Tucked into a cobbled quarter in the old part of town, the du Bourgs' restaurant with rooms is capably run with great warmth and an idiosyncratic culinary approach. Andrew Du Bourg has long favoured a twin-track methodology, with smaller snacking dishes – now including a section of filled buns called 'Cats & Dogs' – supplementing the main carte. People seem to appreciate the versatility, and there is undoubted intelligence at work in compositions such as 'Essence of the Sea', carpaccio-sliced scallop with pickled sea herbs, plankton emulsion and oyster ice cream. Mains might offer local lamb with wild garlic rémoulade, black olives and eucalyptus, or maybe steamed cod with hand-rolled macaroni and clementine. The signature dessert is a chocolate cigar with coffee ice cream on chocolate and whisky mousse, or look to blue cheese and white chocolate doughnuts in spiced pear consommé for something different. A clutch of wines by the glass from £6.25 opens a list that mostly steers a course through the familiar European routes.

Chef/s: Andrew du Bourg. **Meals:** main courses £23 to £30. Sun L £21. Tasting menu £55 (5 courses) to £65. **Details:** 35 seats. 6 seats outside. Wheelchairs. Music. Children over 12 yrs at Sat D.

Send us your review

Your feedback informs the content of the *GFG* and will be used to compile next year's reviews. To register your opinion about any restaurant listed in the Guide, or a restaurant that you wish to bring to our attention, visit: thegoodfoodguide.co.uk/feedback

Lyndhurst

Hartnett Holder & Co.

Cooking score: 3
Italian | £55
Lime Wood Hotel, Beaulieu Road, Lyndhurst, SO43 7FZ
Tel no: (02380) 287167
limewoodhotel.co.uk

Lime Wood is a delicious hideaway in the New Forest, a five-star escape that's a mix of designer spaces, from stylish bedrooms to luxe spa and stunning greenhouse supplying the kitchen – it's also a taste of Italy in the middle of one of England's most treasured landscapes. Hartnett (Angela) and Holder (Luke) run the food side of things – cookery school, kitchen table, and the main restaurant, with Luke responsible for the day-to-day running – so expect modern cooking of distinction to match the refined setting. Antipasti such as chalk stream trout with pickled rhubarb and ginger yoghurt could precede a pasta course of ravioli with smoked ricotta, preserved lemons, peas and pickled samphire that flies the Tricolore with gusto. Veal chop with broad beans and soused tomato is an impressive follow-on, or there's line-caught crab starring alongside Portland crab. The impressive wine list shows off English fizz alongside Italian and French classics (from £18 for a 500cl carafe).

Chef/s: Luke Holder and Angela Hartnett. **Meals:** main courses £20 to £48. Set L £20 (2 courses) to £25. Sun L £38. Sharing menu £75. **Details:** 70 seats. 40 seats outside. Bar. Wheelchairs. Music. Parking.

Milford on Sea

La Perle

Cooking score: 2
British | £37
60 High Street, Milford on Sea, SO41 0QD
Tel no: (01590) 643557
laperle.co.uk
£5 OFF

Sam Hughes' first solo venture is the sort of bijou neighbourhood restaurant that suits Milford on Sea perfectly. It projects itself as low-key and relaxed, all bare wood tables, wood floor and neutral colours and it doesn't need to flaunt its charms; a quick peek through the glass-paned frontage at the happy visitors within is usually enough to do the trick. And the menu? It's short, modern and obviously influenced by the seasons. Double-baked smoked haddock and Old Winchester cheese soufflé with spring onion cream makes a satisfying lead in to roasted hogget served with its confit shoulder and hasselback potato, purple kale and crushed minted peas. Desserts continue to delight; both bitter chocolate fondant with pistachio crumble and pistachio ice cream and the tarte tatin with vanilla ice cream have been praised. Homemade bread is 'as good as ever', and the wine list opens at £19.95.

Chef/s: Sam Hughes. **Closed:** Sun, Mon, 2 weeks Dec to Jan. **Meals:** set L and D £17 (2 courses) to £20. Tasting menu £55 (5 courses). **Details:** 30 seats. V menu. Vg menu. Music.

Verveine

Cooking score: 4
Seafood | £50
98 High Street, Milford on Sea, SO41 0QE
Tel no: (01590) 642176
verveine.co.uk

It seems that chef proprietor David Wykes is building quite a reputation at this tiny seafood restaurant that's tucked, appropriately, behind a wet fish shop. A sunny, light space by day, it has a simple, contemporary look, the focus being on the food coming out of the open-plan kitchen. It's all about big ideas and, to get the best experience, most visitors recommend choosing one of the tasting menus rather than going à la carte. Some dishes are deceptively simple but show fine complexity and flavour, say sweet-tasting prawns with a celeriac rémoulade and pickled cherries, or smoked mackerel with pickled beetroot and carrot. Eyecatching treatment is given to the likes of sea bass with 'extraordinary-looking homemade pasta' and hazelnut pesto, the highlight of one winter meal, or a just-cooked salmon accompanied by roast red pepper and pineapple and a topping of crunchy grains. Dessert might bring 'an awesome chocolate medley'. There's a serious dedication to drink, too, with fish-friendly whites grouped by style plus a handful of reds.

Chef/s: David Wykes. **Closed:** Sun, Mon, 2 weeks Christmas, bank hols. **Meals:** main courses £21 to £28. Set L £18 (2 courses) to £31. Tasting menu £45 (4 courses) to £85. **Details:** 32 seats. Wheelchairs. Children over 8 yrs.

New Milton

Chewton Glen, The Dining Room

Cooking score: 4
Modern British | £62
Chewton Glen Hotel, Christchurch Road, New Milton, BH25 6QS
Tel no: (01425) 275341
chewtonglen.com

Chewton Glen is a country house of long approach and large scale, taking in its famous spa, tree houses, croquet lawn, terrace and the like, but it's far from intimidating: 'I can honestly say that the service and attention from the staff was absolutely first class.' Simon Addison's food fits the place to a T. His style is indulgent without being too rich, taking in scallops with artichoke, truffle, verjus and apple dressing, and roast squab pigeon with boudin noir, black cabbage and pomegranate. First-class materials are well handled and while there might be Thai lobster curry with coconut rice, most dishes operate within a reassuringly classical framework. Dover sole meunière, for example, or calf's liver with Ventrèche bacon, and chateaubriand for two with béarnaise sauce. Desserts may include the likes of baked cheesecake with passion fruit and a lime leaf ice cream or a Valrhona chocolate tart with morello cherry and crème fraîche sorbet. Wines from £23.

Chef/s: Simon Addison. **Meals:** main courses £22 to £45. Set L £27. Sun L £40. Tasting menu £70. **Details:** 164 seats. 40 seats outside.

Petersfield

Annie Jones

Cooking score: 3
Modern European | £35
10 Lavant Street, Petersfield, GU32 3EW
Tel no: (01730) 262728
anniejones.co.uk

A neighbourhood asset and an eatery of several parts, Annie Jones plies its trade in chic premises at the heart of Petersfield. Pride of place goes to the restaurant, where panelled walls and wood floors provide the backdrop for cooking that veers confidently between rustic simplicity and stylish elegance. British and European themes collide in dishes such as roast cod with broccoli purée, escalivada (smokey grilled vegetables), clams, parsley and black olive dressing, or Rother Valley organic short rib and sirloin with a 'red wine crust', stuffed charred onion and port gastrique. There might be steak tartare or seafood risotto to start, while desserts could herald rhubarb and custard or banana and pecan pain perdu with banana caramel. Annie Jones' inclusive offer extends to a daytime patisserie/coffee shop and a lively tapas bar with an outside courtyard. The drinks list sees artisan beers alongside an assortment of good-value wines from the Old and New Worlds.

Chef/s: Andrew Parker. **Closed:** Mon, 25 and 26 Dec, first week Jan. **Meals:** small plates £3 to £9. Set L £25 (2 courses) to £30. Set D £30 (2 courses) to £35. Sun L £16. Tasting menu £45 (6 courses). **Details:** 35 seats. 70 seats outside. Bar. Music. No children after 9pm Fri and Sat.

JSW

Cooking score: 6
Modern British | £55
20 Dragon Street, Petersfield, GU31 4JJ
Tel no: (01730) 262030
jswrestaurant.com

'I have never been disappointed by the chef's cooking and have been going there for years,' exclaimed one grateful reader. Indeed, the strongly held values at this converted 17th-century coaching inn-with-rooms have not diminished over the 16 years it has appeared in the Guide, where the priority given to quality local and regional produce is a particular strength. Beams and standing timbers define the dining room, which is simply decorated and understated, and there is much to enjoy in a whole host of menus delivering gutsy, grown-up cooking. Deftly updated, often surprisingly flavoured dishes have included quail ravioli with dashi, cep and truffle, and a main-course sole with hot and cold crab risotto and sea herbs, or 72-hour beef cheeks with hops, marrow, dripping and chips. Honeycomb parfait with Valrhona ganache and raspberry makes a lovely finish, though southern English cheeses are worth a try. And praise pours in from readers, whether singling out the excellent bread with smoked haddock brandade or simply expressing delight with service that is as 'attentive and friendly as ever'. The wine list does justice, from its excellent by the glass and half-bottle selections to some fine drinking from reputable names and forward-looking producers worldwide.

Chef/s: Jake Saul Watkins. **Closed:** Sun, Mon, Tue, 2 weeks from 25 Dec, 2 weeks Apr, 2 weeks Aug. **Meals:** set L £35 (2 courses) to £45. Set D £45 (2 courses) to £55. Tasting menu £65 (6 courses) to £90. **Details:** 54 seats. 24 seats outside. V menu. Wheelchairs. Parking.

Portsmouth

Abarbistro

Cooking score: 2
Modern British | £29
58 White Hart Road, Portsmouth, PO1 2JA
Tel no: (023) 9281 1585
abarbistro.co.uk

There is something to be said for clarity in a name – Abarbistro is a bar and a bistro. Found on a cobbled street close to Gunwharf Quays, it has a lively, unpretentious atmosphere, a waterside terrace and is open all day for please-all dishes such as crispy whitebait, moules marinière, burgers and fish and chips. But the kitchen is just as comfortable with a risotto of fennel and lemon or Brixham lemon sole delivered in the classic manner with brown butter. Most bases are covered: pork belly with apple and bread sauce appears side by side with a vegan kofta, and Sunday roasts are as traditional as can be. Among desserts, cherry and chocolate trifle is an inspired take on an old favourite. The comprehensive wine list is arranged by grape varietal (there's a wine shop and tasting room on the premises), and cask ales man the bar.

Chef/s: Mark Andrew. **Closed:** 25 and 26 Dec. **Meals:** main courses £10 to £27. Set D £19 (2 courses) to £25. **Details:** 100 seats. 80 seats outside. Bar. Wheelchairs. Music.

Southampton

LOCAL GEM

The Dancing Man

Modern British | £25
1 Bugle Street, Southampton, SO14 2AR
Tel no: (023) 8083 6666
dancingmanbrewery.co.uk

This former wool house was built by Cistercian monks in the 14th century and is now home to the award-winning Dancing Man Brewery, maker of signature ales such as Last Waltz Black IPA and Fiddlers Jig. Although beer from the on-site micro-brewery is one side of the story, the seasonal modern British food served upstairs completes the picture with confidently cooked dishes such as grilled lamb chops and crispy spiced lamb shoulder with warm butter beans, black bean and spring vegetable succotash, watercress, pea and mint salsa. Vegans get their own menu, as do canines and kids.

Southsea

Restaurant 27

Cooking score: 4
Modern European | £50
27a South Parade, Southsea, PO5 2JF
Tel no: (023) 9287 6272
restaurant27.com

Just off the Southsea esplanade, in a whitewashed corner site, Kevin and Sophie Bingham's place has fixed its sights firmly on culinary glory. It's an understated room in modern monochrome with undressed tables and minimally adorned walls, where the focus is all on the tasting menus that come in two sizes and three regimens – omni, veggie and vegan. The dish specifications don't give a great deal away, but everything is designed with maximum flavour impact in mind, from a velouté of smoked prawns with leek and basil to maple-roasted ham hock with mash and peas. Fashionable combinations such as whipped goat's cheese with pistachios and rhubarb are present and correct, but the longer menu could climax with something as gloriously old-school as beef fillet in truffle jus. After 'a taste of cheese', the desserts arrive on a giant square platter, bringing an expansive new scale to the concept of sharing plates. There is no preselected wine option, but 10 wines by the glass, from £6, should help you mix and match with the various courses.

Chef/s: Kevin Bingham. **Closed:** Mon, Tue, 25 and 26 Dec, 1 Jan. **Meals:** tasting menu £45 (5 courses) to £55. Sun L £32 (3 courses). Sun tasting menu £45 (6 courses). **Details:** 36 seats. V menu. Vg menu. Bar. Music.

Stockbridge

The Greyhound on the Test

Cooking score: 2
Modern British | £38
31 High Street, Stockbridge, SO20 6EY
Tel no: (01264) 810833
thegreyhoundonthetest.co.uk

This smart colour-washed inn cuts a dash on the high street, drawing sportsmen (fishing and shooting) and tourists lured by stylish accommodation and ambitious modern British cooking. Chris Heather's globally influenced, seasonal menu makes good use of local produce, including Broughton buffalo – seen in a burger with bacon, Barkham Blue cheese and smoked tomato relish. Flexible and appealing to all-comers, the repertoire includes sharing and small plates, simple, delicious 'on toast' dishes (perhaps devilled duck livers) and accomplished main courses with interesting flavour combinations: tuna sashimi with avocado, soy jelly, sesame and radish, say, followed by lamb cannon with salt-baked artichoke, capers, freekeh, purple sprouting broccoli and yoghurt. Leave room for lemon curd parfait, served with raspberry sorbet, white chocolate and vanilla. The spruced-up interior retains much of its 15th-century charm and the garden backs on to the River Test. A substantial wine list opens at £25.

Chef/s: Chris Heather. **Closed:** 25 and 26 Dec. **Meals:** main courses £15 to £31. Set L £16 (2 courses) to £20. Sun L £26 (2 courses) to £32. **Details:** 68 seats. 30 seats outside. Music. Parking.

Upton Grey

The Hoddington Arms

Cooking score: 2
British | £30
Bidden Road, Upton Grey, RG25 2RL
Tel no: (01256) 862371
hoddingtonarms.co.uk

'Quintessential Hampshire', as one reader put it, the Hodd is truly a pub for all seasons – blazing wood-burners in the winter, pretty garden in the summer (check out the BBQs). It's a proper local, too, with cask ales and a cinema club. The kitchen pays its dues to pub classics and Sunday roasts, but you can also expect the likes of caramelised Roscoff onion tarte tatin with melted Yellison goat's cheese. They love a sharing board here – artisan English charcuterie, perhaps, or whole baked Tunworth cheese. Among main courses, if you're not drawn to the excellent burger or fish and chips, go for belly of Wiltshire pork with black pudding fritter, or Cornish cod with Parmesan and parsley crumb. Desserts get equal attention judging by English apple crumble with vanilla ice cream and Calvados syrup. The wine list opens at £19 and includes a Hampshire fizz by the glass or bottle.

Chef/s: Chris Barnes and Tom Wilson. **Closed:** 26 Dec, 1 Jan. **Meals:** main courses £10 to £25. Set L £22 (2 courses) to £27. Sun L £27. **Details:** 50 seats. 40 seats outside. Wheelchairs. Music. Parking.

Winchester

The Black Rat

Cooking score: 3
Modern British | £45
88 Chesil Street, Winchester, SO23 0HX
Tel no: (01962) 844465
theblackrat.co.uk

Now part of a Winchester quartet that also includes a pub, a wine bar and the B&B across the road, David Nicholson's Black Rat is a quaint and quirky restaurant residing within the shell of an 18th-century town boozer.

Symbols

 Accommodation is available
£30 Three courses for less than £30
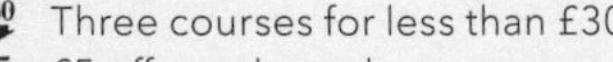
£5 OFF £5 off voucher scheme
 Notable wine list

Anatomical prints, legal tomes, candelabra and sturdy wood tables set the scene in the seriously beamed dining room, where evening meals are the main business of the week. Foraged pickings and seasonal greenstuff from the owner's garden are liberally scattered across the day's forward-thinking menu: alexanders feature in a dish of smoked eel, spätzle and Jerusalem artichoke; seaweed tapioca appears alongside pollock and brandade; Douglas Fir adds its resinous tones to a plate of pigeon breast and leg, pine nuts, celeriac and haggis. Meanwhile, modish desserts such as woodruff cheesecake with walnuts and sorrel ice cream continue the experimental theme. Fixed-price weekend lunches are a low-budget alternative, with back-up from a well-rounded 80-bin wine list.

Chef/s: Jon Marsden-Jones. **Closed:** 24 Dec to 11 Jan. **Meals:** main courses £19 to £30. Set L £26 (2 courses) to £29. **Details:** 40 seats. 16 seats outside. Bar. Music.

The Chesil Rectory

Cooking score: 4
Modern British | £35
1 Chesil Street, Winchester, SO23 0HU
Tel no: (01962) 851555
chesilrectory.co.uk

It may inhabit Winchester's oldest half-timbered house (circa 1450), but the marble-topped tables and deep blue leather upholstery in the Chesil Rectory's new Merchant's Lounge tell a very different story. By contrast, the downstairs dining room maintains its vintage good looks with creaking floorboards, crooked beams and low-slung doorways – a classy but cosy backdrop for food with Anglo-French allegiances. Chef and co-owner Damian Brown cooks with intelligence and an eye for clever detailing, as in a starter of home-cured sea bream pointed up with lime mayonnaise, shallot crisp and bacon crumb or a main course involving braised beef cheek alongside charred cabbage, cep purée, shimeji mushrooms and herb oil. Fish comes up from the South Coast and regional specialities such as Laverstoke black pudding make a significant contribution, while carefully crafted desserts such as pear tarte tatin with Poire William ice cream show off the chef's classic side. The well-spread wine list includes some big-label Coravin selections by the glass.

Chef/s: Damian Brown. **Closed:** 25 Dec, 1 Jan. **Meals:** main courses £14 to £20. Set L and D £18 (2 courses) to £22. Sun L £24 (2 courses) to £28. Tasting menu £55 (5 courses). **Details:** 75 seats. Bar. Music. No children under 10 yrs at D.

Woodlands

LOCAL GEM

Spot in the Woods

British | £15
174 Woodlands Road, Woodlands, SO40 7GL
Tel no: (023) 8029 3784
spotinthewoods.co.uk

It was a bold move for Gerard and Nina Basset to reinvent their Hotel TerraVina as a café-cum-lifestyle shop. It's been beautifully done, in a relaxed, easy way, while keeping all eyes on the ball in the kitchen. Expect generous platters of artisan-cured Italian meats, salads (heirloom tomato and onion), and a bacon and Tunworth cheese tart (a wickedly good pairing) with potato salad. Even a sandwich of homemade fish fingers with chunky tartare sauce in a soft brioche bun excels. The focus on fresh, local ingredients extends to a dessert of Eton mess made with perfect, in-season strawberries. In summer, the terrace is the place to be.

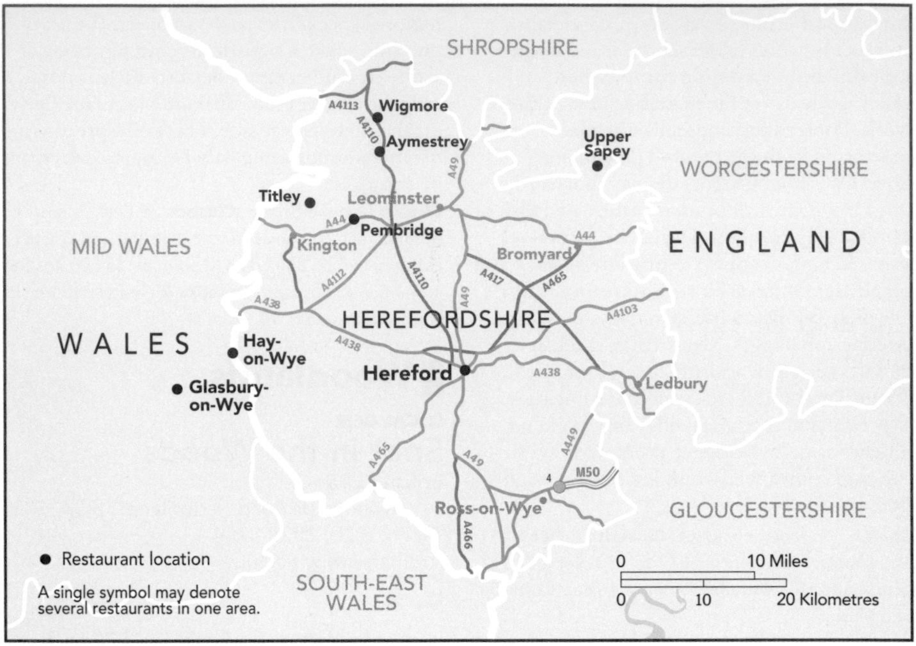

● Restaurant location

A single symbol may denote several restaurants in one area.

Aymestrey

The Riverside

Cooking score: 3
British | £30
Aymestrey, HR6 9ST
Tel no: (01568) 708440
riversideaymestrey.co.uk

The river in question is the Lugg, beside which the 16th-century part-timbered pub is positioned (by an old stone bridge on the Mortimer Trail). It's a charming place with smart en suite bedrooms and a garden that provides the kitchen with fruit, vegetables and herbs. If it's too chilly to sit outside, a wood-burning stove is likely warming the bar. Local ciders and real ales are on tap all year round and there's a serious approach to food – what isn't homegrown is sourced with rigour. Lovage, potato and apple soup features garden produce, while the river provides trout, smoked and served in a kedgeree made with barley. Among main courses, guinea fowl arrives with pickled lardo, wild mushrooms and a watercress sauce, and mutton might crop up with white beans and rosemary sauce. Finish with Herefordshire apple terrine. The wine list covers the globe, with over a dozen available by the glass.

Chef/s: Andrew Link. **Meals:** main courses £14 to £26. Sun L £22. **Details:** 70 seats. 50 seats outside. Music. Parking.

Glasbury-on-Wye

LOCAL GEM

The River Café

Anglo-European | £25
Glasbury Bridge, Glasbury-on-Wye, HR3 5NP
Tel no: (01497) 847007
wyevalleycanoes.co.uk

With canoes for hire, a posh bunkhouse and winter weddings in the converted chapel next door, this riverside café and B&B has its fingers in many pies – although the cooking remains a major draw. The café's all-day offer starts with breakfast, then lunch and dinner bring a host of nourishing dishes from home and abroad – perhaps flaked ham, pineapple and 'soft egg', ahead of Bwlch venison with red cabbage and butternut squash, steak and chips or gnocchi with celeriac and apple. Wines from £15.50.

Hay-on-Wye

LOCAL GEM

Richard Booth's Bookshop Café

Modern British | £18

44 Lion Street, Hay-on-Wye, HR3 5AA
Tel no: (01497) 820322
boothbooks.co.uk

The three-storey bookshop in bibliophilic Hay-on-Wye is not only about literature, but also embraces a cinema and a flagstoned café space with paintings of authors beadily eyeing the scene. Appealing lunchtime dishes aim to fortify you for the hours of reading ahead, with fishcakes of smoked haddock and crayfish, or slow-cooked ham hock with crushed white beans in mustard sauce, and then a cheeky wedge of banana and blueberry cake, or gooseberry and strawberry tart, to fill any gaps. Have a kirsch truffle with the coffee. Otherwise, the place serves all-day fare such as Welsh rarebit, and devilled Portobello mushrooms on sourdough.

Hereford

LOCAL GEM

Madam & Adam

Modern European | £29

23 Bridge Street, Hereford, HR4 9DG
Tel no: (01432) 639964

A couple new to the restaurant business have created a homely all-day eatery that's fast becoming a favourite with Hereford locals. The menu consists of refined small plates, carefully constructed in the kitchen by Swav, and lovingly delivered to your table by Beth. The dishes showcase faultless technical skills and imaginative flavours and textures, such as beef ribeye with crispy Shropshire Blue gnocchi, shiitake mushroom and grapes, or Parmesan ice cream with roasted figs, salted almonds and balsamic pearls. An unusual wine list starts at £20.

Pembridge

LOCAL GEM

The Cider Barn

British | £33

Dunkertons Cider Mill, Pembridge, HR6 9ED
Tel no: (01544) 388161
the-cider-barn.co.uk

'Arrived without a booking but front of house couldn't have been more helpful,' noted one winter visitor, who found the crackling log fire and complimentary mulled cider 'certainly hit the spot'. This listed 450-year-old barn is pleasantly informal, good humoured and dedicated to preparing delicious food from quality raw materials. Highlights have been squid with chorizo jam, crisp pancetta, braised chicory and onion ketchup; beef fillet and cheek with Jerusalem artichoke purée, wild mushroom gratin, chips and rosemary salt; and a show-stealing pile of doughnuts with fennel sugar and lemon curd. House wines from £18.95.

Titley

The Stagg Inn

Cooking score: 4

Modern British | £40

Titley, HR5 3RL
Tel no: (01544) 230221
thestagg.co.uk

£5 OFF

When Steve and Nicola Reynolds took over the Stagg back in 1998, it seemed like a mismatch – a chef from Le Gavroche (see entry) implanted in a foursquare drovers' pub out in the Herefordshire sticks. Fast-forward more than two decades and the place still feels like a proper country hostelry – a gregarious watering hole that just happens to serve really good food alongside its local beers and ciders. Steve Reynolds is keen-eyed when it comes to unearthing the region's seasonal produce, so expect anything from pigeon breast on pearl barley with crispy Lyonshall kale to loin and slow-cooked shoulder of venison with celeriac and chestnuts – although dry-aged Hereford beef is the undisputed headline act, especially on Sundays. It's a meaty inventory to be sure, but there's normally a fish special on Fridays (turbot and squid dressed with fennel and orange), ahead of desserts such as poached rhubarb with ginger cheesecake cream. An unmissable cheese list focuses on artisan triumphs from the 'three counties' and Wales, while Nicola Reynold's personally chosen wine selection is notable for its fair markups, eclectic grape varieties, impeccable producers and all-round excellence.

Chef/s: Steve Reynolds. **Closed:** Mon, Tue, 25 and 26 Dec, 1 week Jan/Feb, 1 week Jun/Jul, first 2 weeks Nov. **Meals:** main courses £18 to £25. Sun L £23. **Details:** 70 seats. 16 seats outside. V menu. Bar. Parking.

Upper Sapey

The Baiting House

Cooking score: 1
Modern British | £30
Upper Sapey, WR6 6XT
Tel no: (01886) 853201
baitinghouse.co.uk

High on a hill overlooking the Herefordshire/Worcestershire borderlands, this one-time drovers' inn is still in the business of feeding and watering travellers. Pub lunches and Sunday roasts do their job admirably, but drop by in the evening if you fancy generous modern dishes such as venison carpaccio with a venison bolognese fritter or beef rump with an oxtail sausage roll, charred onion and mushroom ketchup. A plate of regional cheeses plus sourdough crackers makes a fine finale, if you're not tempted by the likes of crème brûlée with marinated raspberries. To drink, good-value wines vie with local beers and ciders in the bar.

Chef/s: Charles Bradley. **Closed:** Mon, 25 Dec, last 2 weeks Jan. **Meals:** main courses £14 to £23. Set L £18 (2 courses) to £24. Sun L £20 (2 courses) to £25. **Details:** 48 seats. 60 seats outside. Bar. Wheelchairs. Music. Parking.

Wigmore

The Oak

Cooking score: 3
Modern British | £32
Ford Street, Wigmore, HR6 9UJ
Tel no: (01568) 770424
theoakwigmore.com
£5 OFF

'A work in progress', according to one reader (but none the worse for that), Lené Halliday's conversion of a half-timbered house has retained its family feel – despite some modern design flurries within the confines of the building's rough stone walls. Well-travelled local boy Rory Bunting is keen to introduce up-tempo worldly flavours to this corner of Herefordshire: whisky-cured sea trout might arrive with smoked panna cotta, while tempura cuttlefish is teamed with charred onion, red pepper and a spring-onion cottage loaf. Elsewhere, a dish of pork belly stuffed with black pudding, served alongside baked apple and burdock purée, kale, celeriac, shredded sprouts, skirlie gratin and cider jus shows that the kitchen isn't shy of intensive hard labour. Rare breed steaks and local lamb also get a look-in, while ambitious desserts could include glazed liquorice brûlée with honeycomb and rhubarb sorbet. The short wine list is ripe for development.

Chef/s: Rory Bunting. **Closed:** Mon, Tue. **Meals:** main courses £16 to £31. Sun L £24. **Details:** 50 seats. 20 seats outside. Bar. Wheelchairs. Music. Parking.

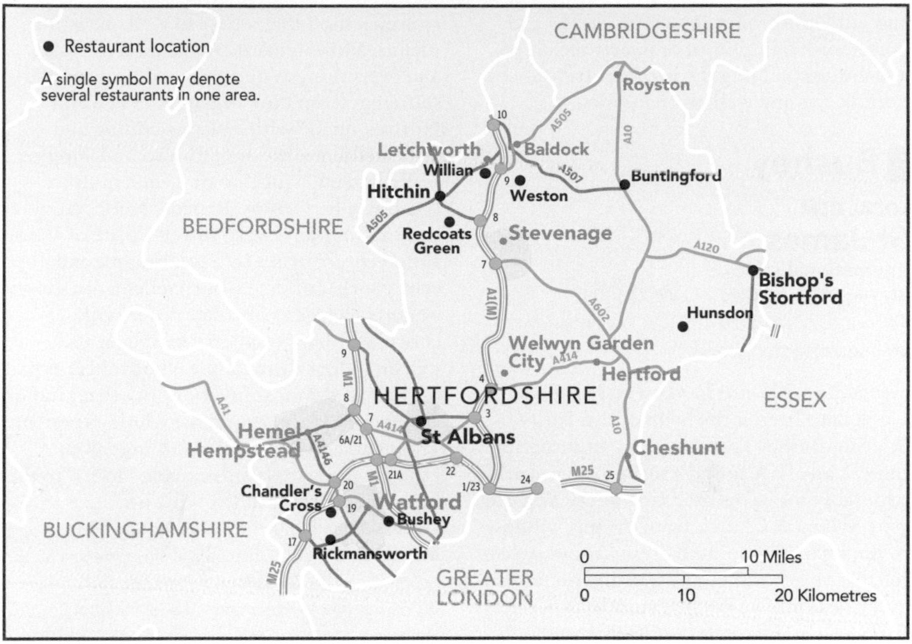

● Restaurant location

A single symbol may denote several restaurants in one area.

CAMBRIDGESHIRE
Royston
Letchworth
Baldock
Willian
Buntingford
Hitchin
Weston
BEDFORDSHIRE
Redcoats Green
Stevenage
Bishop's Stortford
Hunsdon
Welwyn Garden City
Hertford
HERTFORDSHIRE
ESSEX
Hemel Hempstead
St Albans
Cheshunt
Chandler's Cross
Watford
Bushey
BUCKINGHAMSHIRE
Rickmansworth
GREATER LONDON
0 10 Miles
0 10 20 Kilometres

Bishop's Stortford

Water Lane

Cooking score: 1
Modern British | £29
31 Water Lane, Bishop's Stortford, CM23 2JZ
Tel no: (01279) 211888
waterlane.co

One glance at this high-decibel mega conversion of Hawkes Brewery in Bishop's Stortford will tell you that it shares the same DNA as Hermitage Rd in Hitchin (see entry), all stripped-back brickwork, dramatic arches, gantries of gleaming lamps, exposed ducts and industrial staircases. The kitchen aims for a user-friendly approach, touting sharing boards, burgers and steaks alongside small plates (popcorn squid, Korean fried chicken wings), superfood salads, fish specials (from the Norfolk coast) and calorific puddings such as a wickedly rich chocolate fudge brownie sundae. Easy-drinking wines from a concise list start at £3.20 for a small glass (£18.50 a bottle). Live music sessions on Sunday evenings downstairs in the old beer vaults add to the appeal.

Chef/s: Adam O'Sullivan. **Closed:** Mon, Tue. **Meals:** small plates £5 to £8. Main courses £11 to £18. **Details:** 80 seats. Bar. Wheelchairs. Music.

Buntingford

LOCAL GEM

Pearce's Farmshop & Café

International | £25
Hamels Mead, Buntingford, SG9 9ND
Tel no: (01920) 821246
pearcesfarmshop.com

With wonderful views over the Rib Valley, this farm-shop café makes for a charming pit stop – it's easily reached from the south carriageway of the A10. In the green-oak-framed dining room, sandwiches and cakes vie for attention alongside daily specials that might include smoked haddock kedgeree with curry aïoli, boiled egg and samphire; venison and wild mushroom stew with greens and horseradish dumplings, or panettone bread-and-butter pudding. Drink local fruit juices, Suffolk ales and well-priced wines.

Bushey

LOCAL GEM

St James

International | £45

30 High Street, Bushey, WD23 3HL
Tel no: (020) 8950 2480
stjamesrestaurant.co.uk

Genial host Alfonso La Cava and chef Matt Cook have been at the helm of this hard-grafting Bushey favourite since its inception in 1997, and have found a formula that works admirably for its devoted customers. You can espy St James's Church from the big windows of the smartly appointed dining room, where reliable bistro cooking puts smiles on faces at every session. The kitchen absorbs influences from near and far, offering Moroccan lamb filo and warm tomato tatin ahead of pearl barley risotto, calf's liver and bacon or smoked haddock with wholegrain mustard sauce. To finish, the now-famous Toblerone cheesecake continues to roll back the years. Wines from £16.95.

Chandler's Cross

Colette's

Cooking score: 5
Modern European | £65

The Grove, Chandler's Cross, WD3 4TG
Tel no: (01923) 296015
thegrove.co.uk

Built for big weekends in the country back in Georgian times, the Grove now inhabits its own hospitality bubble within viewing distance of Watford's urban sprawl. Golfers and those in search of some spa pampering feel right at home here, especially amid the flamboyant accessories of Colette's – the hotel's flagship restaurant, where Russell Bateman fashions the sort of highly detailed, complex food that works so well on tasting menus. Most items also appear on the carte, and everything is underpinned by exemplary sourcing, from Norwegian skrei cod and Norfolk quail (with a black pudding and Portobello mushroom pithivier and 'Houses of Parliament' sauce) to dry-aged mutton (with swede, turnips, Roscoff onion, curry and braising juices). To finish, a plate of Baron Bigod cheese offset by a tingly apple and celery sorbet offers savoury relief from showy desserts such as a chocolate dome with chocolate foam, raspberry ice cream and marshmallow. One couple who ate here as part of their wedding anniversary (it's that kind of celebratory place) found the whole experience 'impossible to fault', from the 'ingenious canapés' and 'simply impeccable service' to the high-spec cosmopolitan wine list.

Chef/s: Russell Bateman. **Closed:** Sun, Mon. **Meals:** set D £65. Sun L £55. Tasting menu £85 (5 courses) to £95. **Details:** 45 seats. 20 seats outside. Vg menu. Bar. Wheelchairs. Music. Parking. No children.

Hitchin

Hermitage Rd

Cooking score: 2
Modern British | £30

20-21 Hermitage Road, Hitchin, SG5 1BT
Tel no: (01462) 433603
hermitagerd.co.uk

Eight years on, Hermitage Rd is still making quite a splash in Hitchin town centre. A pub for our times, the first-floor venue has a spacious, opened-up interior where drinkers are welcome, although food is top of the agenda. Indeed, the dining crowd pours in for cooking that supports local and regional suppliers and has realistic ambitions, the kitchen turning out dishes that have an instantly recognisable thumbprint. Small plates deliver crispy chickpea fries with green chilli and lime mayo or salt-baked carrots with freekeh, goat's curd and chive oil, while 18-hour braised beef short rib or cod loin with browned caper and lemon butter take their place alongside the ever popular chargrilled steaks, burgers and pork belly ribs. Sticky toffee pudding with butterscotch and salted maple ice cream is a big hit. It's all washed down with cocktails, real ales and a reasonably priced global list of wines.

Chef/s: Joe Walker. **Closed:** 25 Dec. **Meals:** main courses £13 to £24. **Details:** 150 seats. Bar. Wheelchairs. Music.

Hunsdon

The Fox & Hounds

Cooking score: 2
Modern British | £35
2 High Street, Hunsdon, SG12 8NH
Tel no: (01279) 843999
foxandhounds-hunsdon.co.uk

Cream parasols, bay trees flanking the door and a smart white and blue exterior lend an air of sophistication to James and Bianca Rix's village pub and eatery. The feel is informal with log fires, local ales and the day's newspapers (plus cookery books), but the real draw is the food, which has built a strong local following. James Rix's simple, daily changing menus draw on seasonal ingredients, his dishes a blend of British, French and rustic Italian with the emphasis on big flavours. Asparagus, pea and ricotta ravioli, or a plate of quality Bayonne ham and French melon make a good start before, perhaps, Josper-grilled whole lemon sole with spinach and spiced cockle butter, braised pig's cheeks and chorizo with white beans and aïoli, or pan-fried cod served with a rich, sweet peperonata and a piquant salsa verde. To finish, try the passion fruit and lemon pavlova. Service is 'very efficient and friendly'. Wines start at £17.50.

Chef/s: James Rix. **Closed:** Mon, 25 and 26 Dec, Tue after bank hols. **Meals:** main courses £10 to £19. Set L and D £12.50 (2 courses) to £16.50. Sun L £22.50 (2 courses) to £27.50. **Details:** 70 seats. 40 seats outside. Bar.

Redcoats Green

★ NEW ENTRY ★

The Farmhouse at Redcoats

Cooking score: 2
British | £30
Redcoats Green, SG4 7JR
Tel no: (01438) 729500
farmhouseatredcoats.co.uk

A work in progress, this ambitious rural development from Anglian Country Inns centres on The Farmhouse – a characterful country hotel of the wood panelling, ancient beams, log fires variety, with ancestral portraits of the previous owners thrown in for good measure. The conservatory dining room looks on to a trim garden and everybody seems to find the robust food delicious. In winter, for example, dinner might start with Brancaster Staithe oysters served natural or tempura-style with a roasted red pepper and chilli sauce or charcoal-roasted beetroot and heritage carrots, with goat's curd, pumpkin purée, hazelnut dukkah and Shiraz reduction, and continue with slow-cooked lamb shoulder with red wine gravy or a generous chunk of oven-roasted hake supreme ('a lovely smokey flavour from the charcoal oven'), or squid tagliatelle, basil oil and white wine beurre blanc. The keenly priced lunch remains a popular option and generous hospitality abounds. Wines from £19.50.

Chef/s: Sherwin Jacob. **Meals:** main courses £15 to £28. Set L £19 (2 courses) to £24. **Details:** 45 seats. Bar. Wheelchairs. Music. Parking.

Rickmansworth

LOCAL GEM

Café in the Park

International | £12

The Aquadrome, Frogmoor Lane, Rickmansworth, WD3 1NB
Tel no: (01923) 711131
thecafeinthepark.com

'All-day casual dining with a conscience' is the heart-on-sleeve message at this admirable eco-friendly café and one-stop shop attached to Rickmansworth Park's Aquadrome. Come here for mushrooms on toast or some meze for breakfast; otherwise drop by for a rare-breed burger, a rice bowl topped with lamb kofta or a superfood salad plus some freshly baked flatbread at lunchtime – vegetarians, vegans and kids all do well here. Expect an extended repertoire and more specials once the kitchen team is up to speed. Wines from £20.

St Albans

★ NEW ENTRY ★

Loft

Cooking score: 4
Modern British | £40

23b George Street, St Albans, AL3 4ES
Tel no: (01727) 865568
loftstalbans.com

This 'fabulous addition' to St Albans' dining scene, ensconced within the city's Cathedral Quarter, is housed in a sympathetically refurbished medieval building. Stairs from the cobbled courtyard lead up to a well-proportioned contemporary-style dining room and copper bar (600-year-old beams intact) and there's alfresco seating and a family-friendly ethos, too. Chef owner Nick Male delivers accomplished modern British food – clean flavours and creative dishes driven by seasonal produce of impeccable pedigree sum up the approach, whether in a tuna tartare, moreish confit duck with white beans, bacon and mushroom purée, or monkfish with Scottish scampi, provençale vegetables and crispy chicken skin. And to finish? Try the cherry and rose water jelly with mascarpone and honeycomb or a textbook lemon tart. Sunday's 'Family Feast' brings a roast lunch with a side order of entertainment to keep the kids happy. Global wines offer something for everyone and there's a 'black book' of special single-bottle finds.

Chef/s: Nick Male. **Closed:** Mon, 25 Dec, 1 Jan. **Meals:** main courses £16 to £26. Set L and D £20 (2 courses) to £24. Sun L £29 (3 courses). **Details:** 62 seats. 24 seats outside. Bar. Music.

Thompson St Albans

Cooking score: 5
Modern British | £55

2-8 Hatfield Road, St Albans, AL1 3RP
Tel no: (01727) 730777
thompsonstalbans.co.uk

Housed in a weatherboarded cottage conversion with a suave lounge bar, a plush but casual dining room and a quaint Victorian-style courtyard out back, Phil Thompson's self-named venture brings a touch of class to St Albans without the formality you might expect from such an outwardly smart set-up. His cooking is precise, colourful and of the moment, along the lines of cured Cornish mackerel with sorrel and a pressed beetroot and apple terrine, stuffed saddle of rabbit with caramelised turnips, or pan-roast fillet of hake in partnership with wild garlic gnocchi, steamed mussels, seaweed and smoked roe emulsion. To conclude, you can't fail to be intrigued by the toasted croissant parfait or the kaffir lime curd with blood orange sorbet and gin. Attractively priced midweek deals, kids' menus and traditional Sunday roasts add to Thompson's all-round local appeal, while the 'well-balanced' seven-course tasting menu is reckoned to be up there with the best. Fifteen wines by the glass kick off the enterprising wine list, but also note the line-up of 'carbon-neutral' Drappier Champagnes.

Chef/s: Phil Thompson. **Closed:** Mon. **Meals:** main courses £25 to £32. Set L £19 (2 courses) to £23. Set D £21 (2 courses) to £25. Tasting menu £65. **Details:** 90 seats. 18 seats outside. V menu. Bar. Wheelchairs. Music.

LOCAL GEM

The Foragers

Modern British | £24

The Verulam Arms, 41 Lower Dagnall Street, St Albans, AL3 4QE
Tel no: (01727) 836004
the-foragers.com

Team-builders looking for an away day with a difference might fancy a guided 'walk on the wild side' with the 'free food' experts from The Foragers. Alternatively, get your fill of wormwood, wood sorrel and alexanders at their enterprising back street pub not far from the cathedral. They serve muntjac 'deer spheres' with wild garlic and hedgerow sauce, while their Verulam burger is spiced up with hogweed seeds and accompanied by cherry and hawthorn ketchup. There are 'wild cocktails' too, and beers from an on-site microbrewery.

Weston

LOCAL GEM

The Cricketers

Modern British | £23

Damask Green Road, Weston, SG4 7DA
Tel no: (01462) 790273
thecricketersweston.co.uk

Thoroughly rooted in the village of Weston, this proper pub – all cricketing memorabilia, scrubbed wood tables, open fires, large garden – is a great asset to the area. The place certainly has a good buzz. The bar dispenses real ales (including the owners' Brancaster Brewery) and the cleaned-lined open kitchen, dominated by a huge wood-fired pizza oven, offers pub classics old and new. So whether you are in the mood for goat's cheese, beetroot and walnut salad, a burger, smoked haddock fishcakes, beef, mushroom and ale pot pie, or even a takeaway pizza, you won't put the kitchen off its stroke. A short global wine list starts at £18.50.

Willian

The Fox

Cooking score: 2

Modern British | £29

Willian, SG6 2AE
Tel no: (01462) 480233
foxatwillian.co.uk

In a prime spot beside the pond and parish church in a small village, yet just minutes from Letchworth and the A1, The Fox has a fresh modern feel and draws a loyal local crowd. It's still very much the village local, with a spruced-up open-plan bar, four real ales on tap, a laid-back atmosphere and an all-day bar menu that includes sandwiches (rump steak, roasted pepper, chimichurri and rocket, for example) and classic beer-battered cod and hand-cut chips. Look to the main menu for more ambitious modern British dishes, served in the bar and in the atrium-style dining room. Using local farm meats and fresh fish and seafood from the Norfolk coast, typical choices may include tempura Brancaster Staithe oysters with sweet chilli sauce, followed by lamb rump with crispy lamb belly, goat's cheese, pomme purée and salsa verde, with sticky banana cake, vanilla chantilly, toffee gel and popcorn sorbet to finish. Wines from £17.50.

Chef/s: Aron Griffiths. **Meals:** main courses £14 to £24. **Details:** 95 seats. 80 seats outside. Bar. Wheelchairs. Music. Parking.

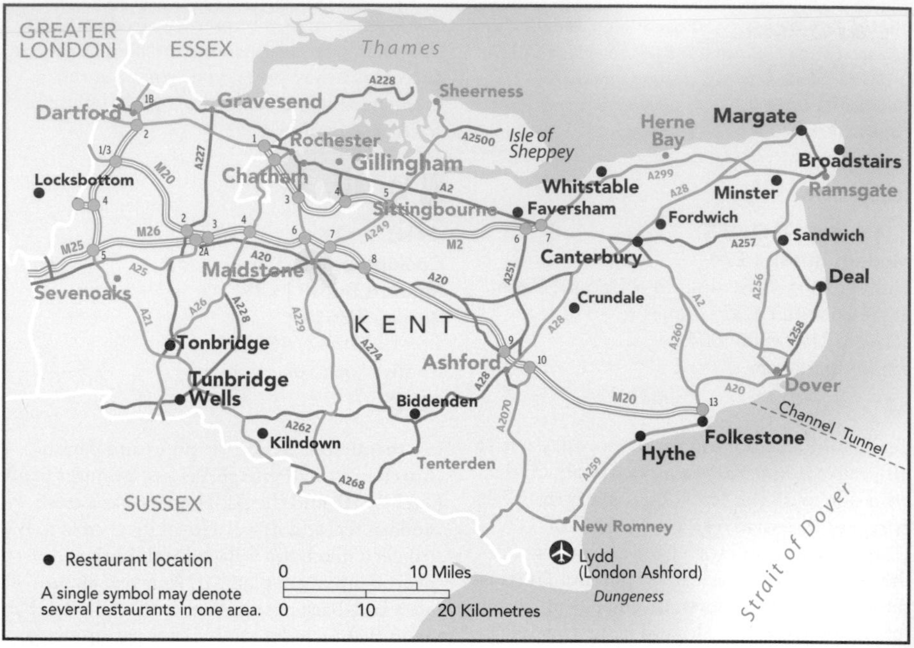

Biddenden

The West House

Cooking score: 5
Modern European | £45
28 High Street, Biddenden, TN27 8AH
Tel no: (01580) 291341
thewesthouserestaurant.co.uk

It's knocking on for 17 years since Graham Garrett took over this smart village restaurant-with-rooms (four stylish bedrooms have been introduced since the last edition of the Guide). The dining room is a mix of half timbers and contemporary styling, and makes a serene setting for Garrett's seasonal dishes. Choose between a pair of six-course tasting menus or a fixed-price list, where charcoal seared beef tartare might be teamed with onion ketchup, sourdough, Castelfranco (semi-bitter salad leaves) and pommes soufflé, or grilled fillet of mackerel with roast beetroot, rhubarb and horseradish cream. Next, an undoubted highlight: roast haunch of sika deer with a venison pasty, swede purée, kale and date ketchup, though a well-timed cod fillet with pumpkin, chilli salsa and cavolo nero comes a close second. Puddings maintain standards – especially an apple tart with custard sabayon and vanilla ice cream – as does the selection of British cheeses from Neal's Yard Dairy; and the homemade bread is sensational. The wine list does its bit with aplomb, with concise tasting notes and a strong organic and biodynamic contingent.

Chef/s: Graham Garrett and Tony Parkin. **Closed:** Mon, Tue, 24 to 26 Dec, 1 Jan. **Meals:** set L £25. Set D £45. Tasting menu £60 (6 courses). **Details:** 35 seats. V menu. Parking.

Broadstairs

Albariño

Cooking score: 2
Spanish | £22
29 Albion Street, Broadstairs, CT10 1LX
Tel no: (01843) 600991
albarinorestaurant.co.uk
£5 OFF £30

Steven Dray's restaurant is cheerful and quirky, with tightly packed tables and some 'lovely little dishes'. The ethnic guidepost is Spanish, the orientation towards modern and traditional tapas, running all the way from boards of jamón Serrano to grilled chistorra sausage (a type of chorizo) with trinxat (cabbage, potatoes, bacon) and a fried egg. In between, just about every dish begs to be ordered: from roasted cauliflower with olive and pomegranate, salt cod croquetas or gambas a la plancha, to organic sobrasada with chickpeas and spinach, and ox cheek with creamed parsnip, liquorice and wild mushrooms. Octopus with potato, red onion and pimentón has been a recent star turn, and fresh crab on toast, chickpea and fennel chips, and honey and walnut cake with kumquats and mascarpone have pleased visitors. Albariño stars on an affordable, concise wine list, which doesn't stray over Spanish borders.

Chef/s: Steven Dray. **Closed:** Sun, 2 weeks Christmas and New Year. **Meals:** tapas £3 to £14. **Details:** 24 seats. Wheelchairs. Music.

Stark

Cooking score: 5
Modern European | £55
1 Oscar Road, Broadstairs, CT10 1QJ
Tel no: (01843) 579786
starkfood.co.uk

Ben Crittenden launched his first solo venture in this tiny, wood-panelled room in 2017, with a tasting menu of beautifully crafted dishes that has caused quite a stir. Delivered at a perfect pace by Ben's partner Sophie, the six courses, which change weekly, might be dainty but all pack punch: it's a riot of textures and superb technique, delivering thoughtful – frequently innovative – assemblies. On inspection, the opening salvo, an ethereal prawn, seaweed and sesame-filled steamed bun anchored by a beautiful, clear broth was 'polished, playful and exciting'. This is food designed to thrill, with the emphasis on flavour and ingredient combinations that make sense: tender quail breast, perhaps, atop confit egg yolk and sunflower seed pesto, with toasted buckwheat and peas counteracting the softness. Sweet dishes are just as vivid and satisfying. Taking the eminently reasonable and well-matched wine flight is encouraged, though bottles are also available from £17. Loyal fans will be pleased to learn that a toilet has now been shoehorned in, but two seats were lost in the process – Stark is now smaller than ever, so book well ahead.

Chef/s: Ben Crittenden. **Closed:** Sun, Mon, Tue, 23 Dec to 2 Jan. **Meals:** tasting menu £55 (6 courses). **Details:** 10 seats. Music.

Canterbury

The Goods Shed

Cooking score: 3
Modern British | £32
Station Road West, Canterbury, CT2 8AN
Tel no: (01227) 459153
thegoodsshed.co.uk

The cavernous, raftered Victorian railway shed with a restaurant overlooking the stalls of a daily farmers' market couldn't be more charming. The casual mood and unfussy manner perfectly echo the rustic look of scrubbed tables, old kitchen chairs and blanket throws, while the kitchen applies the sparsest of preparations to produce plucked from the market. The result? Food that is leagues ahead of much of what is on offer in this chain-dominated tourist city. The short menu delivers uncomplicated starters such as a generous slab of buttery chicken liver parfait or treacle-cured trout with horseradish crème fraîche. And the straightforward approach continues to shine with mains: a generous piece of hake with asparagus, clams and samphire, say, or a hunk of pork tenderloin with lentils and mustard clotted cream. Finish with a selection of British cheeses or an old-fashioned raspberry blancmange. To drink, there are local gins and Kentish ales and ciders, as well as a short list of European wines.

Chef/s: Rafael Lopez. **Closed:** Mon, 25 to 27 Dec, 1 Jan. **Meals:** main courses £15 to £24. **Details:** 60 seats. Parking.

Crundale

The Compasses Inn

Cooking score: 5
Modern British | £35
Sole Street, Crundale, CT4 7ES
Tel no: (01227) 700300
thecompassescrundale.co.uk
£5 OFF

Dating from the 14th century, with a heavily beamed, fire-warmed bar setting the tone, Donna and Robert Taylor's rural idyll elicits delighted reactions from visitors. There's no doubt that the Compasses plays the part of a country local perfectly – with Shepherd Neame ales on tap – but these days the pub is better known for Taylor's simple yet alluring cooking. Knowledgeably sourced local and regional produce is the jumping-off point for forthright dishes such as glazed ox cheek with confit egg yolk, crisp shallot and mustard clotted cream. Elsewhere, a beautifully judged dish of citrus-cured sea trout with crème fraîche, charred radish and parsley granita might light the way for a following course of confit pork belly with a parsnip purée, morteau sausage and fermented red cabbage. Desserts have been a particular highlight for many, and rhubarb and custard tart with rhubarb sorbet garners as much praise as dark chocolate cream with honeycomb, chocolate nib granola, salted caramel ice cream and milk sorbet. Wines start at £16.

Chef/s: Robert Taylor. **Closed:** Mon, Tue, bank hols. **Meals:** main courses £19 to £22. Set L £17 (2 courses) to £20. **Details:** 50 seats. Bar. Music. Parking.

Deal

Frog and Scot

Cooking score: 2
Anglo-French | £33
86 High Street, Deal, CT14 6EG
Tel no: (01304) 379444
frogandscot.co.uk
£5 OFF

Unpretentious – that goes for both decor and food – just about sums up this high street restaurant owned by a Frenchman and a Scotswoman. People happily pack the cluttered space (think mismatched tables, chairs and blackboard menus), drawn by a kitchen turning out some nifty plates of food that reflect a dedication to localism. Seared scallops with celeriac purée and black pudding is a straightforward opener, the prelude perhaps to roast breast and confit leg of Aylesbury duck with raspberry and honey roasting juices, or a fresh, beautifully cooked piece of hake with a well-made bouillabaisse sauce. A rich, creamy lemon and lime posset with an intense raspberry and Prosecco sorbet has been praised this year. Indeed, despite a few reservations about slow service, most visitors are well pleased. Wines on a French-orientated list start at £22.

Chef/s: David Gadd. **Closed:** Mon, Tue, 25 Dec. **Meals:** main courses £16 to £25. Set L £15 (2 courses) to £18. **Details:** 52 seats. 8 seats outside. Bar. Wheelchairs. Music.

Faversham

Read's

Cooking score: 6
Modern British | £60
Macknade Manor, Canterbury Road, Faversham, ME13 8XE
Tel no: (01795) 535344
reads.com
£5 OFF

Occupying a handsome Georgian manor house, this Kent veteran has quietly evolved and matured over the years. It is regarded by regulars as a country restaurant of inestimable class, with boutique bedrooms cited as further incentive for bookmarking a visit. Muted colours and well-spaced tables create a soothing tone in the two dining rooms ('yes, they are old-fashioned, but so is the house'), and there is a real sense of locality on the food front, with produce sourced from the kitchen garden, as well as the surrounding countryside. The cooking is impressive and the combinations make sense. Glazed Whitstable Bay heritage carrots with beetroot cream, kohlrabi, goat's curd and apple, a beautifully constructed opener, might preface roast Kentish lamb with lamb-fat potatoes, courgette purée, red pepper couscous and a mint and pea dressing. Or there might be confit Gressingham duck with Asian cabbage, celeriac purée and fondant potato. The finishing line is reached with a sublimely featherlight passion fruit soufflé or a fine selection of British cheeses. Wine is taken seriously, too: reliable producers, good choices across the globe (with plenty for the French purists) and a kindly priced, wide-ranging best buys list.

Chef/s: David Pitchford. **Closed:** Sun, Mon, 25 to 27 Dec, 2 weeks Jan, 2 weeks Sept. **Meals:** set L £32. Set D £50 (2 courses) to £60. Tasting menu £40 (5 courses) to £65 (8 courses). **Details:** 60 seats. 30 seats outside. Bar. Wheelchairs. Parking.

Folkestone

★ NEW ENTRY ★

The Folkestone Wine Company

Cooking score: 4
Modern British | £28
5 Church Street, Folkestone, CT20 1SE
Tel no: (01303) 249952
folkestonewine.com

For chef Dave Hart and his partner Polly Pleasence, the Folkestone Wine Company is their proud, work-in-progress first solo venture. It's a tiny, shopfronted venue on a pretty pedestrianised street in the old town, with shoestring decor lending itself perfectly to the simplicity of the whole operation. Hart's seasonally inspired cooking forms the nerve centre, the short, daily changing blackboard giving notice that dishes are all about simple cooking techniques – roasting and braising, say – and that much is made on the premises, from superb bread and ice cream to the lovely madeleines served with coffee. What to expect? A punchily flavoured squid ink taramasalata with crudités and soft-boiled egg; a hefty slab of confit pork belly (skin deliciously crisp) atop buttery mash and cabbage, matched by an intense charcuterie sauce; or skate wing, its classic brown butter and caper accompaniment paying homage to the chef's French roots. For dessert, think along the lines of chocolate marquise with mint choc chip ice cream. The short wine list is a good match for the food.

Chef/s: David Hart. **Closed:** Mon, Tue, 22 to 27 Aug. **Meals:** main courses £12 to £15. **Details:** 24 seats. 10 seats outside.

Fordwich

★ NEW ENTRY ★

The Fordwich Arms

Cooking score: 5
Modern British | £35
King Street, Fordwich, CT2 0DB
Tel no: (01227) 710444
fordwicharms.co.uk

No one wants to hear that their local pub is getting done up, but in the case of the Fordwich Arms it's been a very good thing indeed. Dan Smith, Tash Norton and Guy Palmer-Brown are alumni of the Clove Club in London (see entry) and are doing everything they can to make the place an outstanding local food destination without alienating drinkers. Dating from 1934, with iron casement windows, solid oak floors and three open fires, the riverside pub exudes warmth. The cooking is very much in the new generation modern British mould, with some artful combinations of ingredients wedded to deft technique. Visitors wax lyrical about the splendid focaccia and soda bread, and the exquisite amuse-bouches (especially the 'dinky' Westcombe Cheddar tart). And simple starters like Stour Valley pheasant dumplings in a roasted herb broth or confit potato with pickled walnut, charred spring onion and buttermilk elicit the same degree of enthusiasm as more complex main courses, which might include various cuts of roast suckling pig (including crisp crackling), carrots, prune and sherry, and venison rump with mushroom, salsify and a braised shoulder crumble. Desserts have their followers, too, with a rich take on a Snickers bar the star of many a report. Service is full of cheer and gives good advice on the unannotated wine list; there are real ales, too.

Chef/s: Daniel Smith. **Closed:** Mon. **Meals:** main courses £18 to £26. Set L and D £35. Tasting menu £65. **Details:** 56 seats. V menu. Bar. Wheelchairs. Music. Parking.

Hythe

LOCAL GEM

La Salamandre

French | £15

30 High Street, Hythe, CT21 5AT
Tel no: (01303) 239853

This little French patisserie certainly livens up the Hythe scene – it's a class act. Regulars pop in for breakfasts of omelette or scrambled eggs, and for all manner of exquisite pastries – coffee éclairs, delicate fruit tarts, biscuits Japonais with hazelnut mousseline, passion fruit and chocolate délice – while afternoon tea is a must-book treat. There are light lunches, too, such as Stilton and spinach quiche with a properly dressed green salad or, if it's Friday or Saturday, tartiflette. Croissants and baguettes sell out quickly and, if you can't find a seat in the tiny café, you can always take away. Unlicensed. Cash only.

Kilndown

★ NEW ENTRY ★

The Small Holding

Cooking score: 2
Modern British | £30

Ranters Lane, Kilndown, TN17 2SG
Tel no: (01892) 890105
thesmallholding.restaurant

Readers have been quick to spot the opening of this homely village restaurant secreted away in glorious Kent countryside, and to praise chef proprietor William Devlin's cooking. The no-frills, brick-and-tile former pub still operates as a traditional watering hole, but the real emphasis is on things culinary – as the substantial, work-in-progress kitchen garden (and canapés) suggests. There's no choice on the six- or ten-course tasting menu, but simple, ingredient-led dishes are fiercely seasonal: spears of local asparagus teamed with a delicate mousse and pickled stems, say, or a tiny new potato atop a dab of velvety, rich purée, with wild garlic and cottage cheese adding deep notes. Triumphant standouts are the village-reared pork – served as a cube of beautifully fatty pork belly, a tiny, offaly faggot, homemade blood pudding and a slick of lovely, sticky gravy – and a dish of sweet strawberries with an intense basil ice cream and shortbread. Service is warm, the wine list short, with bottles from £23.

Chef/s: William Devlin. **Closed:** Sun, Mon, Tue, 1 week Aug, 2 weeks Christmas. **Meals:** tasting menu £30 (6 courses) to £50 (10 courses). **Details:** 26 seats. 32 seats outside. V menu. Vg menu. Bar. Music. Parking.

Locksbottom

Chapter One

Cooking score: 6
Modern European | £40
Farnborough Common, Locksbottom,
BR6 8NF
Tel no: (01689) 854848
chapteronerestaurant.co.uk

Behind the Tudoresque façade, the modern dining room of Andrew McLeish's long-standing restaurant is all starched linen and solicitous staff. McLeish is now a co-owner and keen to stamp his mark on menus that pay homage to his classical training with sophisticated, multi-textured dishes. On inspection, a cylinder of pancetta-wrapped poached and roast rabbit, served with confit leg, asparagus and Gewürztraminer sauce is an assured piece of modern European cooking, and the humble hake gets its moment of glory on an étuvée of leeks with beer-braised mussels, potatoes and delicate chive cream sauce. Game is McLeish's passion so expect great things during the season. A multifaceted pudding of Kentish strawberries with strawberry and elderflower Margarita, meringue and strawberry gel is an aromatic delight. For cooking of this pedigree the pricing is remarkably egalitarian, and there is a separate dining area that offers simpler brasserie fare. An expansive wine list, taking in Kent producers alongside top-rank Old World selections, is helpfully classified by style rather than region with 50-plus wines under £30 and an exceptional range by the glass.
Chef/s: Andrew McLeish and Dean Ferguson.
Closed: 2 to 4 Jan. **Meals:** set L £23 (3 courses). Set D £40 (3 courses). Sun L £27 (3 courses). Tasting menu £55 (6 courses). **Details:** 100 seats. 20 seats outside. V menu. Bar. Wheelchairs. Music. Parking.

Kent's best bites

Will Devlin of The Small Holding near Cranbrook shares his favourite local places to eat and drink

For **breakfast**, the legendary **Jimmy's Cafe** in Tonbridge has been the best in the area for more than 10 years.

The best place for **coffee** is **65mm Coffee** at **The Fire Station** in **Tonbridge**. Tom is like a walking coffee encyclopaedia.

Jamie Tandoh at **The Bicycle Bakery** in **Tunbridge Wells** has the best **brunch** menu and serves freshly baked croissants and sourdough every morning.

Eggs To Apples Farm Shop in **Hurst Green** literally stocks the best of everything - fruit and veg, wine, beer, cheese, meat and fish.

Fuggles Beer Cafés are always bang-on with the newest **craft beers and real ales**, served by knowledgeable staff.

The Charcoal Grill on Camden Road, **Tunbridge Wells** has the best homemade kebabs in town and the people are really friendly. You can't ask for more on the **way home from the pub**.

If I could eat only one thing around here, it would have to be... the pork belly ramen from **Kitsu** in **Tunbridge Wells** - hands down, no hesitation.

Margate

★ BEST FOR SUSTAINABILITY ★

★ NEW ENTRY ★

Angela's of Margate

Cooking score: 4
Seafood | £32
21 The Parade, Margate, CT9 1EX
Tel no: (01843) 319978
angelasofmargate.com

Occupying a plum spot just a bucket and spade's throw from Margate beach, this small seafood restaurant's formula of impeccable sourcing, minimised waste and pared-back cooking has proved a triumph. The MSC-certified fish and seafood comes direct from Hastings boats and is chalked up on two daily changing boards: set lunch and à la carte. Both comprise bold, unfussy dishes, paired with seasonal, locally grown vegetables, so kingly turbot might come with wild garlic and asparagus. Kick things off with smoked prawns and aïoli or a classic fish soup. Nothing goes to waste, and sustainability is paramount: chef Rob Cooper makes butter from sheep's milk and creates a faultless junket pudding with the leftover buttermilk; the table tops are made from recycled plastic bags; and kitchen scraps go to a local community garden project that makes them into compost, then supplies Angela's with produce. The wine list majors in native producers.

Chef/s: Rob Cooper. **Closed:** Mon, Tue. **Meals:** main courses £12 to £21. Set L £15 (2 course) to £18. **Details:** 26 seats. 2 seats outside. Music.

Send us your review

Your feedback informs the content of the *GFG* and will be used to compile next year's reviews. To register your opinion about any restaurant listed, or a restaurant that you wish to bring to our attention, visit our website.

★ NEW ENTRY ★

Bottega Caruso

Cooking score: 3
Italian | £27
2-4 Broad Street, Margate, CT9 1EW
Tel no: (01843) 297142
bottegacaruso.com

By the time your plates are cleared, you'll want to adopt Simona Di Dio's family as your own. Cooking food inspired by her Italian homeland, the fertile mountainous region of Sannio east of Naples, she and partner Harry Ryder conjure up a compelling roster of rustic, season-led dishes in Margate's Old Town. Handmade pasta dishes thrill, and the combination of imported cheeses, meats, oil and tomato sauce made by her family and friends (which you can buy at the deli) and produce from local, independent suppliers makes for transportive food. Verdure e fagioli – a frugal 'cucina povera' dish of blanched greens and slow-cooked beans – is far more than the sum of its parts, and ricotta dumplings with spicy wild black pig 'nduja will have you wiping your plate clean. Each dish speaks of a life well lived, by the ingredients themselves, as well as those who produce and consume them. A convivial and unpretentious setting, a slice of tiramisu and a glass of organic rosato from the exhilarating all-Italian list seals the deal.

Chef/s: Simona Di Dio and Harry Ryder. **Closed:** Mon, Tue, Wed. **Meals:** main courses £9 to £15. **Details:** 24 seats. Music.

LOCAL GEM

GB Pizza Co.

Italian | £17
14a Marine Drive, Margate, CT9 1DH
Tel no: (01843) 297700
greatbritishpizza.com

On the seafront with sea and sunset views, Lisa Richards' and Rachel Seed's pizzas are cooked in a wood-fired oven, topped with mostly locally sourced ingredients. Fans tuck into Kentish goat's curd with peppers and basil or lamb salami with mint and basil pesto – gluten-free bases add to the inclusivity of the place. A few nibbles or sides include houmus and flatbread; to drink there's Kentish beer and one each of red, white, rosé and fizz. A second branch has opened at 113 Lapwing Lane, Didsbury, Manchester M20 6UR, some 270 miles away.

LOCAL GEM

Greedy Cow

British | £15

3 Market Place, Old Town, Margate, CT9 1ER
Tel no: (01843) 447557
thegreedycow.com

The relaxed all-day eatery in the Old Town is a laudable independent operation, strong on local sourcing, where the casual mood, refreshing prices and unfussy manner perfectly echo the functional tables, bench seating and wood floors of the first-floor dining room, reached via a steep staircase (there are outside tables, too). Breakfast is justifiably popular, while excellent, meaty burgers served with homemade coleslaw top the billing for later in the day. Loyal fans give the grilled cheese toastie, vegan hot dog and homemade cakes the thumbs-up.

LOCAL GEM

Hantverk & Found

Seafood | £30

18 King Street, Margate, CT9 1DA
Tel no: (01843) 280454
hantverk-found.co.uk

On the edge of the Old Town, this seafooder now occupies two converted shop premises. Tables are still cramped and it's pretty short on frills, but the menu generates an enthusiastic local following. The kitchen conjures up striking flavours from fresh, seasonal ingredients: clams in harissa broth come with fregola, dressed crab with pea shoot and caper salad, and koji-marinated mackerel with Asian-style slaw. Desserts are simple confections – perhaps honeycomb ice cream with Moscatel Pasas – and wine is from a brief European list, opening at £16.50. The sometimes inflexible service needs work.

LOCAL GEM

The Kentish Pantry

British | £20

1 Duke Street, Margate, CT9 1EP
Tel no: (01843) 231150
thekentishpantry.co.uk

Venture in to bag a table at this simple, tucked-away café in the old town and you'll find yourself surrounded by shelves of chutneys, oils and vinegars, pickles and sauces, as well as candles, soaps and gels. But the kitchen shows its mettle too, with a simple repertoire of exceedingly good things to eat. Breakfast brings things on toast (oven-roasted sardines, mushrooms with garlic butter), while lunch offers leek and mustard tart, a bouillabaisse-style seafood casserole or Kentish minute steak with sautéed potatoes lyonnaise. The occasional supper club is popular, too.

Minster

The Corner House

Cooking score: 1

British | £29

42 Station Road, Minster, CT12 4BZ
Tel no: (01843) 823000
cornerhouserestaurants.co.uk

There's much to praise about Matthew Sworder's restaurant with rooms: the quiet village setting opposite an ancient church, the dedication to seasonality and local sourcing. As one visitor noted, it's 'clearly a popular local restaurant with plenty of loyal custom'. The robust cooking more than lives up to the occasion, delivering terrines of, say, chicken and chorizo or salad of confit trout with pickled fennel and cucumber, ahead of Kentish-style mussels in Biddenden cider (with triple-cooked chips) or a Stour Valley game suet pudding. Among straightforward desserts, upside-down pear and ginger cake with honeycomb ice cream and almond brittle stands out. To drink, there are Kentish ales or wines from a short list. There is a branch of the Corner House at 1 Dover Street, Canterbury, CT1 3HD.

Chef/s: Predrag Kostic. **Closed:** Mon, 2 to 14 Jan. **Meals:** main courses £17 to £22. Set L £16 (2 courses) to £20. Set D £22 (2 courses) to £28. **Details:** 40 seats. 20 seats outside. Bar. Music. Parking.

Sandwich

★ NEW ENTRY ★

The Salutation

Cooking score: 4
Modern European | £50
Knightrider Street, Sandwich, CT13 9EW
Tel no: (01304) 619919
the-salutation.com

High walls maintain an air of intrigue around this fine Lutyens house set in a deservedly famous garden and considered the smartest address in town. Shane Hughes' cooking matches the contemporary country house surroundings: modern British dishes that lean heavily on classic techniques. From the moment the trio of snacks arrive – including a crisp filo cigar filled with smoked monkfish – and some noteworthy bread with burnt leek butter, it's clear that concentrated thought, and not a little effort, has gone into everything on the plate. A virtuoso opener sees scallops, jointly teamed with salty, crisp-edged ham beignet and a Cheddar cheese espuma, followed by monkfish loin wrapped in pancetta with a lively selection of vegetables and offset by a sharp sorrel sauce. Meat might bring loin of roe deer and pork cheek cooked in cider caramel, while dessert could be a warm treacle tart served with a subtle, chilled banana parfait and walnut custard – deemed 'heavenly' by one diner. A French-leaning wine list opens at £24.

Chef/s: Shane Hughes. **Meals:** main courses £26 to £30. Set L £18 (5 small plates) to £36 (market menu). Tasting menu £70 (7 courses). Sun L £30). **Details:** 64 seats. 56 seats outside. V menu. Vg menu. Bar. Wheelchairs. Music. Parking.

Tonbridge

★ NEW ENTRY ★

The Poet at Matfield

Cooking score: 2
Modern British | £30
Maidstone Road, Matfield, Tonbridge, TN12 7JH
Tel no: (01892) 722416
thepoetatmatfield.co.uk

Named after Siegfried Sassoon, who was born in the village, this roadside brick and tile-hung dining pub feels English to a T. Both the bar and restaurant make a suitably rustic setting for food that takes due account of seasonal supplies. Readers have been delighted with the 'clean, balanced flavours' and favourites have included smoked haddock fishcake on curried tartare with a runny-yolked fried egg, and fillet of bream with cannellini beans, asparagus, mussels and Champagne sauce. Elsewhere, roast quail breast and confit quail's leg with poached plum and raspberry vinegar jus makes an impressive starter, while rum baba with spiced passion fruit consommé and coconut sorbet is a luscious finish. The welcoming service is a great draw and to drink there's a wide range of artisan gins and a wine list that opens at £19.40 with a good choice by the glass.

Chef/s: Petrus Madutlela. **Closed:** Mon. **Meals:** main courses £17 to £29. Set L and D £20 (2 courses) to £23. Sun L £27 (3 courses). Tasting menu £69. **Details:** 50 seats. 100 seats outside. Bar. Music. Parking.

Scoring explained

Local Gems, scores 1 and 2
Scoring a 1 or a 2 in *The Good Food Guide*, or being awarded Local Gem status, is a huge achievement. We list the very best restaurants in the UK; for the reader, this means that these restaurants are well worth visiting if you're in the area - and you're extremely lucky if they are on your doorstep.

Scores 3 to 6
Further up the scale, scores 3 to 6 range from up-and-coming restaurants to places to watch; there will be real talent in the kitchen. These are the places that are well worth seeking out.

Scores 7 to 9
A score of 7 and above means entering the big league, with high expectations of the chef. In other words, these are destination restaurants, the places you'll long to talk about - if you're lucky enough to get a booking.

Score 10
This score is extremely rare, with chefs expected to achieve faultless technique at every service. In total, only eight restaurants have achieved 10 out of 10 for cooking since the scoring system was introduced in 1998.

See page 13 for an in-depth breakdown of *The Good Food Guide*'s scoring system.

Tunbridge Wells

Thackeray's

Cooking score: 5
Modern European | £55
85 London Road, Tunbridge Wells, TN1 1EA
Tel no: (01892) 511921
thackerays-restaurant.co.uk

With its Japanese-style terrace garden, lavish wallpaper and twinkling lights, this ancient house (and one-time home of novelist William Makepeace Thackeray) is virtually unrecognisable these days, despite the low ceilings, lopsided staircases and cosy nooks. Chef patron Richard Phillips continues to steer the ship, although day-to-day cooking is overseen by his former sous-chef Patrick Hill. Expect elaborately crafted and highly finessed cooking, with an underpinning of French technique and an unwavering commitment to Kentish produce: cannon of aged salt marsh lamb is presented with a steamed shoulder pudding, smoked aubergine 'caviar', spiced couscous and heritage carrots, while rice-crusted local venison sits alongside red cabbage purée, a venison faggot, pearl barley and grilled pear. By contrast, fish comes from near and far – Orkney scallops with maple-glazed turnips, Cornish crab in a tartlet with 'coronation' dressing, Atlantic sea bass with lobster tortellini. On the sweet side, there are textbook renditions of the classics, often with a neat twist – as in dark chocolate marquise paired with poached clementines, kumquats and white chocolate sorbet. The food is complemented by a knowledgeably chosen global wine list.

Chef/s: Richard Phillips and Patrick Hill. **Closed:** Mon, 26 Dec, 1 Jan. **Meals:** set L £18 (2 courses) to £20. Set D Tue to Fri £25 (2 courses) to £30. Set D £39 (2 courses) to £55. Sun L £35. Tasting menu £78 (8 courses). **Details:** 68 seats. 30 seats outside. V menu. Bar. Music.

Whitstable

Harbour Street Tapas

Cooking score: 4
Spanish | £26
48 Harbour Street, Whitstable, CT5 1AQ
Tel no: (01227) 273373
harbourstreettapas.com

Locals show loyalty to this tiny tapas restaurant for good reason – and it's worth knowing about if you're in the neighbourhood. It has quite a swagger considering there's not much in the way of decor – just large windows, white walls, plain tables, an open kitchen – and you can't book. But Tim Wilson's food makes amends with its freshness, punch and flavours, kicking off simply with padron peppers and building to the gutsy full-on flavour of salt cod brandade with poached egg and piquillo, and lamb chops with escalivada. Add in grilled tiger prawns with chilli, ginger and garlic, chicken thighs with a wonderful romesco sauce and mojo verde, and a salad of baby spinach with avocado, pine nuts and Picos Blue and there's a real taste of the Mediterranean about the food. Simple desserts could include rhubarb and sherry trifle. Most of the short list of Spanish wines is available by the glass, but check out the selection of sherries, too.

Chef/s: Tim Wilson. **Closed:** Mon, Tue. **Meals:** tapas £6 to £18. **Details:** 48 seats.

JoJo's

Cooking score: 4
Tapas | £30
2 Herne Bay Road, Tankerton, Whitstable, CT5 2LQ
Tel no: (01227) 274591
jojosrestaurant.co.uk

'One of my highlights of the year,' noted a visitor to this brilliant spot on the seafront near Whitstable. Nikki Billington's light-filled and delightfully laid-back restaurant continues to impress locals and our holidaying readers – it's no surprise that booking (by telephone only) is essential, though it's worth noting that counter seats and tables in the cocktail and tapas bar are kept on a first-come, first-served basis for those who fancy only meze or nibbles. As expected, good regional and seasonal produce gets a robust workout, with the kitchen looking in the direction of the Mediterranean for sharing plates of charcuterie, thinly sliced lamb cannon, or mutton and feta koftas with a spicy tomato sauce and tzatziki. And this year reports have given good account of the lamb cutlets, chargrilled mackerel with chorizo and cherry tomatoes, a three-cheese frittata, and haddock and cod goujons with tartare mayo (a particular favourite). There's salted caramel tart for dessert and a brief wine list that opens at £19.50.

Chef/s: Nikki Billington and Buddy Rowden. **Closed:** Mon and Tues (exc school holidays). **Meals:** tapas £5 to £14. **Details:** 60 seats. 20 seats outside. Bar. Wheelchairs. Music.

Samphire

Cooking score: 2
Modern British | £35
4 High Street, Whitstable, CT5 1BQ
Tel no: (01227) 770075
samphirewhitstable.co.uk

£5 OFF

The hugely likeable Samphire is a quiet local asset, playing the role of convivial all-day bistro with great style. Everyone piles in for breakfast and brunch, perhaps 'eggs smothered in proper hollandaise', while shakshuka or avocado on sourdough keep the DFLs (down-from-Londons) happy. Come at lunch or dinner and the blackboard menu keeps things local, listing a day-boat fish of the day, as well as oysters, mussels in Biddenden cider, Stour Valley game and Kentish duck. The kitchen, however, likes to mix things up with interesting flavours. That duck, for example, comes as a cassoulet with Bath chap (cured pork cheek) and chermoula; a starter dish of pigeon is teamed with morcilla, parsnip and rainbow chard; and miso and fermented chilli hash is teamed with pak choi and fried duck egg. There's not a word to be said against sticky toffee pudding, either, or service that is 'smooth and efficient'. The brief, kindly priced wine list extends from Kent to the southern hemisphere.

Chef/s: Greig Hughes. **Closed:** 25 and 26 Dec. **Meals:** main courses £15 to £18. **Details:** 40 seats. Music.

★ TOP 50 ★

The Sportsman

Cooking score: 7
Modern British | £45

Faversham Road, Seasalter, Whitstable, CT5 4BP
Tel no: (01227) 273370
thesportsmanseasalter.co.uk

Don't let the roadside-boozer-like exterior fool you. The Sportsman's stark, spare look gives way to an interior that is a vision of comfortable rural chic with just a touch of quirkiness – blackboard menu, paper napkins, bar service – and is warmly appreciated by its faithful followers. Resources have been aimed at creating a memorable experience that's all in the detail, starting with superb, seasonal ingredients (mostly Kentish) of unimpeachable quality. The blackboard listing of Steve Harris's classic dishes is a good intro: mussel and bacon chowder, say, or seared thornback ray with brown butter, cockles and sherry vinegar dressing, followed by warm chocolate mousse with salted caramel and milk sorbet. But to gauge the sheer breadth of the cooking, we recommend the nine-course tasting menu (order when you book) which has been carefully calibrated to ensure each mouthful counts. Jumpstart the meal with a trio of impressive snacks, among them potato skin with caviar and oyster emulsion, then move on to oysters (poached and raw), crab teamed with carrot and hollandaise, an exquisite mini mushroom tart encasing a runny egg yolk and topped with celeriac foam, and the sweet-smokey notes of a slip sole simply grilled in smoked salt butter (an updated Sportsman classic). The kitchen can also play it straight and true, offering a flawless plate of 'wonderfully tasty' roast rack and neck of lamb that makes a sensational attempt to steal the show. As a finale, a fine Bramley apple soufflé with a matching salted caramel ice cream is all airborne fragility. Of course wine is no less delightful, well chosen and keenly priced.

Chef/s: Stephen Harris and Dan Flavell. **Closed:** Mon, 25 to 27 Dec, 1 Jan. **Meals:** main courses £22 to £29. Tasting menu £55 (5 courses) to £70. **Details:** 50 seats. Wheelchairs. Music. Parking. No children at D.

Wheelers Oyster Bar

Cooking score: 4
Seafood | £35

8 High Street, Whitstable, CT5 1BQ
Tel no: (01227) 273311
wheelersoysterbar.com

The original Wheelers started peddling oysters in 1856 and, as the oldest restaurant in town, is now firmly ensconced in Whitstable's heritage portfolio – photos of its distinctive candyfloss-pink and blue frontage are everywhere. Despite some renovation, it's still a tiny squeeze, with just four stools at the counter in the seafood bar and 14 covers in the famous old oyster parlour and extended back room. No matter, people keep coming back because the seafood is simply brilliant. Superb meze plates bring a host of delights, from home-smoked prawns to curried crab and beer-battered fish, and that's just the start. Depending on the catch from local day boats, you might find anything from tandoori-spiced gurnard with Indonesian seafood chowder to roast skate wing, 'fettuccine vegetables', crab bonbons and mussels in cider. Then, for pudding, how about golden syrup three ways? Wheelers is unlicensed, but you can BYO (there's an off-licence across the road); remember, it's cash only.

Chef/s: Mark Stubbs. **Closed:** Wed, 25 and 26 Dec, 1 Jan, last 2 weeks Jan. **Meals:** main courses £20 to £23. **Details:** 18 seats. Wheelchairs.

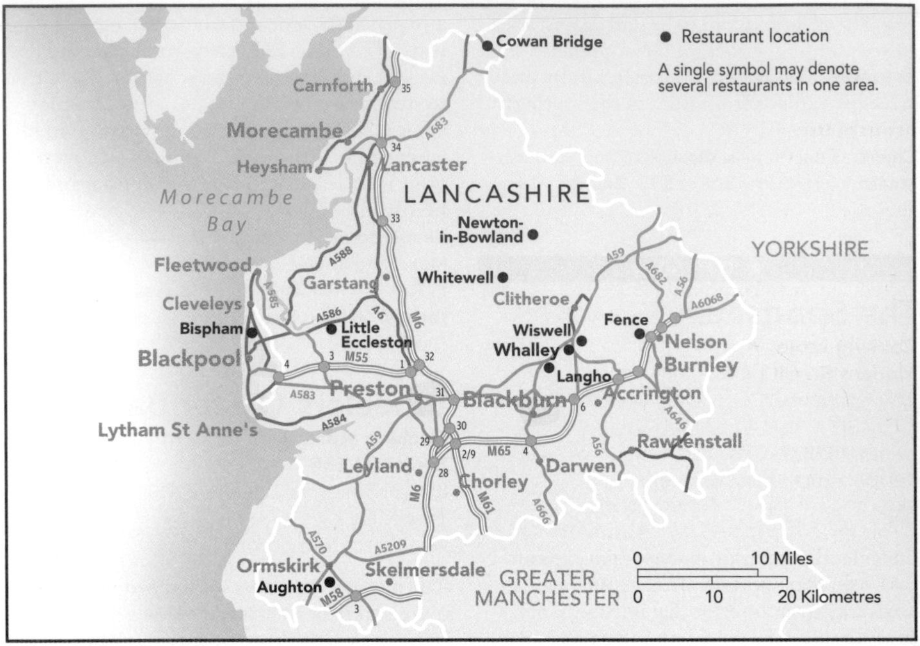

● Restaurant location

A single symbol may denote several restaurants in one area.

Aughton

★ NEW ENTRY ★

The Barn

Cooking score: 4
Modern British | £38
Moor Hall, Prescot Road, Aughton, L39 6RT
Tel no: (01695) 572511
moorhall.com

Mark Birchall has created one of Lancashire's most distinctive restaurants at Moor Hall (see entry). Now he has engineered a brilliant conversion of an adjacent barn as a casual alternative. Full of light and character, this is a spacious first-floor operation with a rustic look – massive, gnarled ceiling beams, exposed brickwork, wood floors – and is designed to appeal to all-comers. From a simple menu of easy eating dishes, readers have praised a host of things: a straightforward blob of creamy, rich chicken liver pâté served with delicious saffron-coloured brioche; a plate of Wester Ross smoked salmon, its sweetness offset by a pool of buttermilk, some fennel and beetroot; a perfectly timed chunk of cod with spinach, potato purée and a tartare butter sauce; and Goosnargh chicken with celeriac, grilled gem lettuce and grains. Desserts are good, especially 'a wobbly custard tart with perfect pastry'. To drink, there are cocktails, craft beers and a wide-reaching wine list.

Chef/s: Mark Birchall and Dom Clarke. **Closed:** Mon, Tue, first 2 weeks Jan. **Meals:** main courses from £12 to £26. **Details:** 65 seats. 30 seats outside. V menu. Bar. Wheelchairs. Music. Parking.

Send us your review

Your feedback informs the content of the *GFG* and will be used to compile next year's reviews. To register your opinion about any restaurant listed, or a restaurant that you wish to bring to our attention, visit our website.

★ TOP 50 ★

Moor Hall

Cooking score: 8
Modern British | £70
Prescot Road, Aughton, L39 6RT
Tel no: (01695) 572511
moorhall.com

£5 OFF

An ancient listed building with a 21st-century feel, Moor Hall is a singular place. The restaurant is a modernist extension with lots of glass, Scandi-style furniture and an open kitchen providing the backdrop to Mark Birchall's delicately nuanced tasting menu of five or eight courses. The food is intricate, a combination of ingeniously conceived ideas and refined treatment: for example, one satisfying and enticing dish pairs intensely flavoured baked carrots, chrysanthemum and sea buckthorn with the umami punch of Doddington cheese snow. Four snacks served in rapid succession open proceedings, among them a crisp puff of black pudding, with pickled gooseberry cutting the richness, and a single oyster magically lifted by the sweet-sour flavours of cured ham, dill and buttermilk. The skill is in how Birchall blends each flavour with the one just before and the one about to come, so they build into a crescendo. Holstein Friesian – tiny cubes of raw beef with barbecued celeriac, mustard and shallot – 'has to be the most exciting steak tartare in the country' and is a prelude to a silky sweet Isle of Mull scallop served with cauliflower, sorrel and some delicious, slightly sour grains; then comes aged Goosnargh duck breast with beetroot, beautifully cooked kale ('so hard to get right'), hen of the woods mushrooms and a rich duck ragoût. Note-perfect, too, is forced rhubarb with milk jam and blood orange, and a harmonious, understated Worcester Pearmain apple with sweet woodruff, almond and whey caramel. Service is superb, greatly contributing to the easy-going atmosphere. The knowledgeable sommelier, in particular, is a great asset, incredibly passionate about his tightly edited wine list – a diverse and up-to-date selection of interesting producers. Cocktails are unusually good, too, featuring well-made classics, as well as innovations that taste like classics in the making.

Chef/s: Mark Birchall. **Closed:** Mon, Tue, 24 to 26 Dec, first 2 weeks Jan, first 2 weeks Aug. **Meals:** set L £40 (4 courses). Tasting menu £70 (5 courses) to £105. **Details:** 50 seats. V menu. Bar. Wheelchairs. Music. Parking.

Bispham

★ NEW ENTRY ★

Mi Casa Su Casa

Cooking score: 2
Spanish | £30
117 Red Bank Road, Bispham, FY2 9HZ
Tel no: (01253) 351993

A couple of minutes along a broad shopping street off the seafront, a short tram-hop north of Blackpool, Mi Casa Su Casa – Spanish for 'my home is your home' – is a big-hearted tapas place of local repute. Spanish staff address everyone as 'my friend' and, although there are fish and chips and burgers for inveterate seasiders, it's the tapas classics and the chalked-up specials that are most appealing. Fried local shrimps on toast make an appetising prelude to the likes of floured and browned monkfish with allioli; seared tuna in a sauce of citrus juices, oregano and soy; or textbook albondigas (meatballs). If you still need sating, look to one of the painstakingly prepared desserts, such as milk chocolate and ginger cheesecake, which comes with ginger ice cream, raspberry coulis and a shot glass of pouring cream. The tiny drinks list features great Spanish house wines at £3.25 a glass.

Closed: Sun, Wed. **Meals:** tapas £3 to £8.

The North West's best bites

Stosie Madi from Parkers Arms in Lancashire shares her favourite local places to eat and drink

For **coffee**, try **The Parlour** in Clitheroe - the double espresso is smooth and almost cacao-infused.

Benedicts of Whalley is a great place for a lazy, mid-morning **brunch**.

For **lunch**, the **Bay Horse Inn** in Lancaster because Craig Wilkinson's food is timeless and classic but also relevant.

I like to shop at **Clitheroe Market**, home to **D & A Burney & Sons** - the best greengrocers ever - not only for what they buy in but for what they grow. Their potatoes are better than any others.

The best place for **pre-dinner cocktails** is **Hawksmoor Manchester**; they always get it right and serve the best G&T.

For **post-pub snacks**, try **Mughli Charcoal Pit** in Rusholme, Manchester. Have anything from the street-food menu.

If I could eat only one thing, it would have to be... Lancashire cheese from Garstang - smooth, creamy, salty, sweet, moreish and made with local milk.

Cowan Bridge

Hipping Hall

Cooking score: 5
Modern British | £60
Ingleton Road, Cowan Bridge, LA6 2JJ
Tel no: (01524) 271187
hippinghall.com
£5 OFF

The Hall came together in the late 17th and early 18th centuries, a handsome stone-built residence at the foot of Gragareth peak in the Lune Valley. It's an auspicious location for a culinary enterprise, drawing on Lancashire, Yorkshire and Cumbria for produce, so expect (among much else) Goosnargh duck, red deer and Tomlinson's rhubarb. Oli Martin's style is very much in the now, offering thrill-ride tasting menus in vegetarian and omnivore versions, and using modern techniques to confer distinctiveness on dishes such as barbecued celeriac with black garlic and lovage, then roast pheasant with hay-baked turnip and yeasted apple, perhaps followed by a pre-dessert granita of cranberries and chervil root. A diner who opted for the full eight-course deal highlighted wild halibut in squid ink with salsify, and the Goosnargh duck with elderberries and kohlrabi among the standout dishes, while the pick of the desserts was 'amazingly original' toasted artichoke mille-feuille with chestnut and caramelised pear. The wine list aims for originality, too, with a crisp Welsh sparkler, fragrant Greek Rhoditis and bunches of biodynamic bottles among the attractions. Prices open at £26.

Chef/s: Oli Martin. **Meals:** set L £30 (4 courses) to £40. Set D £60. Sun L £30 (4 courses). Sun L tasting menu £40 (6 courses). Tasting menu £80 (8 courses). **Details:** 34 seats. V menu. Bar. Music. Parking. Children over 12 yrs.

Fence
White Swan

Cooking score: 6
Modern British | £32
300 Wheatley Lane Road, Fence, BB12 9QA
Tel no: (01282) 611773
whiteswanatfence.co.uk

A village pub in east Lancashire has become one of the area's outstanding beacons of quality, with good-humoured hospitality, a decent hand-pumped pint to be had, and some stunning cooking, courtesy of the tirelessly inventive Tom Parker. The short menus change every day, according to the best that's available, but just to show that culinary fashion hasn't bypassed Fence, there is a five-course tasting menu, too. Visitors who have become loyal regulars extol a seasonal serving of grouse as a starter, a main-course presentation of different cuts of lamb with fennel, green olives and basil, and the simple opulence of a ribeye of English Wagyu in red wine with triple-cooked chips and spinach. Fish could be tender halibut in the robust armour of morels, smoked cabbage and hazelnuts, before superb chocolate soufflé with peanut butter ice cream, rhubarb tart with blood orange and mascarpone, or Courtyard Dairy cheeses and truffle honey close the show. A creditable wine list has been compiled, which just needs vintages adding in. Prices open at £18.

Chef/s: Tom Parker. **Closed:** Mon, first week Jan. **Meals:** main courses £22 to £35. Set L and D £22 (2 courses) to £28. Sun L £28. Tasting menu £50 (5 courses). **Details:** 40 seats. 12 seats outside. Music. Parking.

Langho
Northcote

Cooking score: 6
Modern British | £75
Northcote Road, Langho, BB6 8BE
Tel no: (01254) 240555
northcote.com

£5 OFF

Just off a large roundabout on the A59, in the midst of the lush Ribble Valley, Nigel Haworth's country manor retains its appeal. The verdant views from the contemporary dining room are a tonic, and the place exercises its own nostalgic charm with portrait shots of stars in the 60s – Connery, Minnelli, Sinatra – keeping watch in the lounge. Lisa Goodwin-Allen's deep understanding of Haworth's vision, which turns on creative reworkings of traditional Lancashire food in the modern idiom, produces resounding successes aplenty. Her Lancashire cheese white loaf is a perfect introduction, and heralds ingenious compositions such as the glass bowl of onion soup, retooled as a deep brown jelly topped with Parmesan-laced onion cream, with a fritter for a croûton. With the Cumbrian lamb cutlet and its glutinously sticky sweetbreads comes a cast-iron dish of braised split peas, as well as a wood-roasted baby leek and garlicky barley. Other dishes reach further afield, such as superb roast scallops on cucumber tartare with burnt lemon purée, or the glorious caramelised venison loin and shin with dried grapes, wild mushrooms and truffle. The spring dessert of the moment was a white chocolate cup filled with honey and vanilla cream (Northcote has its own beehives), shards of honey brittle and a daringly sour lemon granita. A vast, resourceful wine list has much to tempt, from carefully chosen glasses, from £7.40 a standard measure, to roll calls of the great and the gasp-inducing from around the world.

Chef/s: Lisa Goodwin-Allen and Nick Evans. **Meals:** main courses £19 to £40. Set L £35. Set D £75. Sun L £47. Tasting menu £95. **Details:** 70 seats. Bar. Wheelchairs. Music. Parking.

Little Eccleston

The Cartford Inn

Cooking score: 2
Modern British | £29
Cartford Lane, Little Eccleston, PR3 0YP
Tel no: (01995) 670166
thecartfordinn.co.uk

Found by the banks of the river Wyre, the stylishly refurbished and hugely extended Cartford Inn has morphed from a local drinking establishment to a boutique complex on a grand scale (note the on-site deli). The kitchen aims for easy satisfaction, while taking due care with the details when it comes to seasonality and local sourcing. Bury black pudding doughnuts with celeriac rémoulade stand out among the starters, while mains range from slabs of Lancashire-reared beef to fish from Fleetwood (perhaps roast cod with Puy lentils, beans, 'nduja and tarragon sauce). Otherwise, you can order deli platters and grand fruits de mer, before signing off with, say, blackberry and sourdough bread and butter pudding. There's also the opportunity for exclusive private dining (four people maximum) in the Cartford's 300-year-old cellar, while prices on the well-rounded wine list are never greedy.

Chef/s: Chris Bury. **Closed:** 25 Dec. **Meals:** main courses £13 to £25. **Details:** 80 seats. 20 seats outside. Bar. Wheelchairs. Music. Parking. No young children after 8pm.

Newton-in-Bowland

Parkers Arms

Cooking score: 2
Modern British | £28
Hallgate Hill, Newton-in-Bowland, BB7 3DY
Tel no: (01200) 446236
parkersarms.co.uk

£5 OFF £30

It's apparently the pub closest to the centre of the UK, but the Parkers Arms is far from being middle of the road. Chef Stosie Madi knows her way around the northern English canon, turning out a starter of black pudding, pork and sage roll with pork-fat pastry or a main of creamed potato and Lancashire cheese pie with buttered greens and peas, followed by co-owner Kathy's fruited wet nelly (a kind of bread pudding) and custard. But there's no shortage of flourishes, as in a starter of Argentinian red prawn estouffade or a curried mutton pie, followed by chestnut ice cream with a melting chocolate pudding. Game is a speciality, too. Readers love the glorious rural setting – you couldn't fail to – but say lunch or dinner here can sometimes be 'a mixed bag'. They note, though, that service has seen a marked improvement. Wines come from a lively list, with room for manoeuvre under £30.

Chef/s: Stosie Madi. **Closed:** Mon, Tue, 25 Dec. **Meals:** main courses £15 to £32. Set L and D £22 (2 courses) to £28. **Details:** 90 seats. 150 seats outside. Wheelchairs. Parking.

Whalley

Breda Murphy Restaurant

Cooking score: 3
Modern British | £32
41 Station Road, Whalley, BB7 9RH
Tel no: (01254) 823446
bredamurphy.co.uk

The smartly converted house hard by Whalley rail station functions as a deli and daytime venue, with the addition of two evening services on Friday and Saturday. It makes an appealing place for the kind of day that blurs the boundaries between lunchtime and afternoon tea, with snacky dishes like crab bruschetta and wasabi-dressed tomatoes, or sandwiches of Mrs Kirkham's Lancashire cheese, coleslaw and cucumber pickle, on hand to punctuate the unfolding hours. A more structured approach would be built around substantial main dishes like classic fish pie, while the dinner menu brings on smoked salmon and shrimp cannelloni in brown crab emulsion sauce, followed by duck breast with wilted pak choi, gingery leek purée and wild rice arancini. Finish with raspberry and Champagne posset and almond biscotti. The drinks list features a range of gins, including the florally aromatic Dingle from County Kerry, while wines open at £19.50 for Chilean varietals, leading off a spirited selection from around the globe.

Chef/s: Breda Murphy. **Closed:** Sun, Mon, 24 Dec to 4 Jan. **Meals:** main courses £12 to £32. **Details:** 66 seats. 12 seats outside. V menu. Vg menu. Bar. Wheelchairs. Music. Parking.

Whitewell

The Inn at Whitewell

Cooking score: 2
Modern British | £34

Forest of Bowland, Whitewell, BB7 3AT
Tel no: (01200) 448222
innatwhitewell.com

£5 OFF

Charles Bowman has imbued this ancient inn with personality and quirkiness. It stands on the banks of the river Hodder amid the beauty of the Forest of Bowland, with trees and hills all around. It's a heart-warming hostelry with all the requisite trappings, including traditional bar-lounges offering real ales, winter fires, rug-strewn flagstone floors and a summer terrace looking towards the river. While the bar menu offers a familiar run through the modern pub catalogue, say potted Cornish crab, Cumberland bangers and champ or slow-roast pork belly, the evening-only restaurant pulls out the stops with carpaccio of venison ahead of whole roast Goosnargh poussin flavoured with lemon and thyme and served with sage and onion croquette, bread sauce and roasting gravy. Sticky toffee pudding is a classic dessert, but there's also a good British and Irish cheeseboard. To cap it all, the wine list is a well-annotated labour of love, arranged by style with quality drinking all the way from France to the southern hemisphere.

Chef/s: Jamie Cadman. **Meals:** main courses £16 to £26. **Details:** 180 seats. 16 seats outside. Wheelchairs. Music. Parking.

Wiswell

Freemasons at Wiswell

Cooking score: 7
Modern British | £50

8 Vicarage Fold, Wiswell, BB7 9DF
Tel no: (01254) 822218
freemasonswiswell.co.uk

£5 OFF

It may be tucked away in a tiny Ribble Valley village, but such is the flair of Blackburn-born Steven Smith's cooking, and the relaxed informality of his no-nonsense pub setting, that people track it down, hungry to eat first-rate food without the dated encumbrance of awed silence and fawning service. For one content diner, it was simply 'impeccable food, attentive service and convivial atmosphere' and, with extension work underway as the Guide went to press, to turn the place into a restaurant with (four) rooms and a chef's table, the reasons to visit are manifold. Riches from the North West are referenced throughout the menu, but with layers of flavour that send them off in delicious culinary directions – a roasted rump of Herdwick lamb is spiced up with Middle Eastern flavours of aubergine, mint and yoghurt, while slow-cooked Goosnargh duck, its leg crispy, nods to Asia with tempura spring onion and hoisin sauce. The kitchen never loses sight of the fact that this is a pub, albeit a very fine one, so fish pie is packed with Morecambe Bay-caught seafood under a crust of nutty Lancashire cheese, and there's steak (OK, a piece of the tenderest, 60-day aged Hereford beef) with duck-fat chips, onion rings and peppercorn sauce. Finish with a sprightly dessert that infuses lemon meringue pie with the scent of pine from Wiswell Moor. A thoughtfully curated wine list includes plenty from small producers, and leads you gently to explore beyond the £20.50 opening price.

Chef/s: Steven Smith and Stephen Moore. **Closed:** Mon, Tue. **Meals:** main courses £25 to £40. Set L and D £23 (2 courses) to £28. Sun L £35. Tasting menu £80. **Details:** 74 seats. 16 seats outside. V menu. Bar. Wheelchairs. Music.

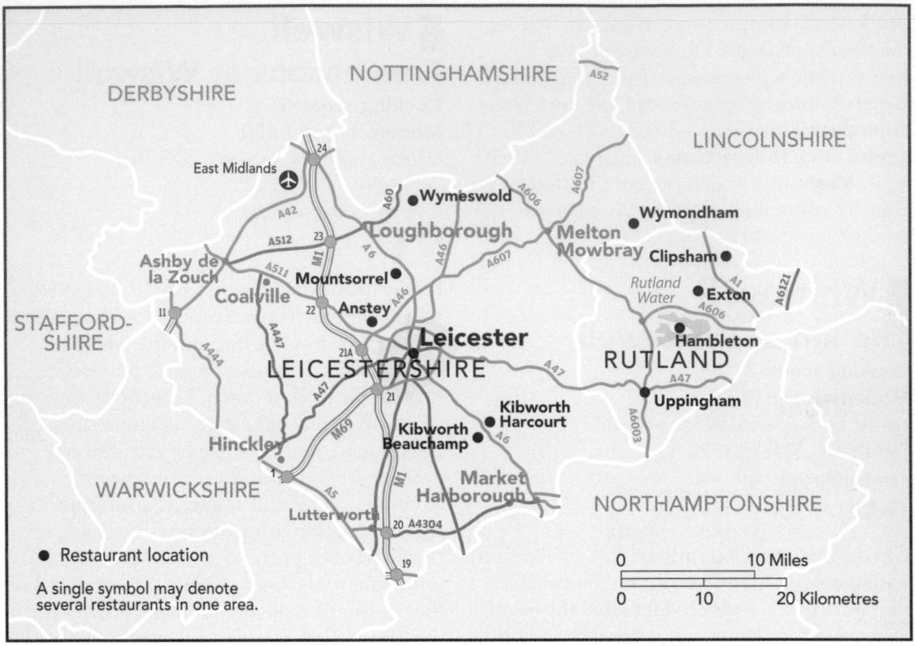

Anstey

LOCAL GEM

Sapori

Italian | £35

40 Stadon Road, Anstey, LE7 7AY
Tel no: (0116) 236 8900
sapori-restaurant.co.uk

Tucked away in a suburb of north Leicester, this busy, personally run little piece of Italy has a strong local following. If you can get past the imaginative pasta selection (perhaps candele spezzate with lamb ragù and ricotta espuma), just about every dish on the menu begs to be ordered: octopus with 'pancotto' of broccoli in olive oil, garlic and chilli, then lamb three ways (loin with mushroom purée, sweetbread Milanese-style, a tortellone of shoulder), and gianduja (hazelnut-chocolate) gelato with blood orange jelly to finish. Predominantly Italian wines start at £17.50.

Clipsham

The Olive Branch

Cooking score: 2
Modern British | £33

Main Street, Clipsham, LE15 7SH
Tel no: (01780) 410355
theolivebranchpub.com

A late-Victorian pub pulled together from three farm labourers' cottages, the Olive Branch was reborn a century on as a modern country inn with rooms. Only a couple of miles from the thrum of the A1, it remains a picture of inviting stone-built tranquillity. The newly established kitchen garden is in full production now, and there are chickens and ducks to provide the breakfast eggs, while much of the meat is sourced from local farms. Sean Hope cooks a pub menu that pleases traditionalists with devilled whitebait and ribeye steaks and onion rings, as well as enticing enquiring palates with more obviously contemporary ideas. Grilled monkfish tail with prosciutto croquettes, wild mushrooms and shallot purée might be the lead-in to guinea fowl breast with butternut squash risotto and charred leeks, before desserts such as a take on knickerbocker glory, representing the best kind of populism. Wines are taken seriously to the extent of offering a Coravin selection, with standard glasses of the everyday stuff starting at £5.75.

Chef/s: Sean Hope. **Meals:** main courses £15 to £30. Set L £18 (2 courses) to £22. Set D £33. Sun L £28 (3 courses). **Details:** 50 seats. 28 seats outside. V menu. Vg menu. Bar. Wheelchairs. Music. Parking.

Exton

Fox & Hounds

Cooking score: 2
Modern European | £37
19 The Green, Exton, LE15 8AP
Tel no: (01572) 812403
afoxinexton.co.uk

Comfort and seemingly effortless vintage chic is what this lavishly refurbished 17th-century coaching inn is all about. It's a handsome place, the creeper-clad, golden-stone frontage conspiring with the village green to make a blissfully bucolic picture, while the stylish interior combines heavy drapes, rugs, polished wood, bare stone and rich colours. The lunchtime menu is classic pub – carefully-sourced ingredients featuring in well-made burgers, four-cheese toasties and smoked trout on sourdough. In the evening, the cooking moves up a notch or two – think octopus with chorizo, cider and apple jam; or rump of local lamb with marinated romanesco, roasted salsify and artichoke purée, although you can opt for a trusty shepherd's pie or fish and chips. Sweet treats include buttermilk panna cotta with mulled spiced black figs and gingerbread matchsticks. The substantial, reasonably priced wine list is nicely annotated and divided by style.

Chef/s: David Graham. **Meals:** main courses £15 to £32. Set L and D £16 (2 courses). Sun L £16 (1 course) to £26. **Details:** 32 seats. 35 seats outside. Bar. Wheelchairs. Music. Parking.

Hambleton

★ TOP 50 ★

Hambleton Hall

Cooking score: 7
British | £73
Ketton Road, Hambleton, LE15 8TH
Tel no: (01572) 756991
hambletonhall.com

Built in 1881 on a spit of land projecting into Rutland Water, Hambleton's ornate interiors once rang to the chatter of Noël Coward and Scott Moncrieff, translator of Proust. It makes a sumptuously sited country house hotel these days, run with engaging charm by Tim and Stefa Hart, its kitchens overseen by Aaron Patterson for a good quarter-century. Time has only refined the veneer of his artfully crafted cooking, which brings seasonal ingredients into sharp focus with ingenuity and flair. Frozen accompaniments to starters are a recent theme: horseradish sorbet with seared tuna carpaccio and pickled veg, or a spiced carrot ice cream to support a matching terrine. There is a willingness to let elements of a dish work in concert so that in a main course of duck breast, mandarin provides the traditional orange note, and black beans a suggestion of east Asia, while fish, perhaps whole roast John Dory or turbot fillet, might be escorted by shellfish such as cockles and clams, and possibly sorrel-scented risotto. To conclude, expect gentle textures and indulgent richness, as in quince and honey soufflé with caramelised almond ice cream, or the house take on tiramisu. Hambleton has a wine list to write home about, with stocks of mature classics and carefully selected southern hemisphere growers at prices that come as a pleasant surprise in the opulent surroundings. Wines of the Moment offer a particularly good international shakedown, from £28.

Chef/s: Aaron Patterson. **Meals:** set L £29 (2 courses) to £38. Set D £73. Sun L £58. Tasting menu £92 (6 courses). **Details:** 60 seats. V menu. Bar. Parking. Children over 5 yrs.

Kibworth Beauchamp

The Lighthouse

Cooking score: 2
Seafood | £27

9 Station Street, Kibworth Beauchamp, LE8 0LN
Tel no: (0116) 279 6260
lighthousekibworth.co.uk

With the passions of seafood cookery running through his veins, Italian chef and co-proprietor Lino Poli has given this 'very sweet' restaurant a zesty nautical theme that feels 'charming but never ridiculous'. Plates of fish and chips fly out of the kitchen, but it pays to invest in more varied offerings such as mussels with 'nduja, tomatoes and white wine or perfectly timed, flavoursome hake fillet with Tenderstem broccoli and shrimp butter. Meat eaters and vegetarians are well catered for (think masala chicken or Moroccan-spiced houmous), while puddings might include an 'incredibly dense and rich' chocolate torte with stem ginger ice cream. Paella nights, casual 'nibbles and tipples' and early doors deals for families also earn The Lighthouse plenty of local bonus points. Lino's wife Sarah meets and greets everyone personally, while staff are effortlessly friendly and relaxed in their dealings with customers. Italian labels figure prominently on the easy-drinking wine list.

Chef/s: Lino Poli and Tom Wilde. **Closed:** Sun, Mon, 25 and 26 Dec, 1 Jan. **Meals:** main courses £8 to £21. Set D £15 (2 courses) to £18. Tasting menu £50. **Details:** 60 seats. Wheelchairs. Music.

Kibworth Harcourt

LOCAL GEM

Boboli

Italian | £29

88 Main Street, Kibworth Harcourt, LE8 0NQ
Tel no: (0116) 279 3303
bobolirestaurant.co.uk

When a classic pizza/pasta/Pinot package wrapped in friendly layers of Italian style is what you need, pull up a chair at this appealing village restaurant. Start with pear and walnut salad with Gorgonzola and mascarpone; continue with pappardelle, the fine pasta ribbons far more than just a vehicle for a rich game ragù, or pan-fried calf's liver with griddled polenta. As you finish a lively sgroppino – lemon sorbet with vodka and Prosecco – make a date to return for pizza, since diners agree that they are 'cooked to perfection'. Wine from £16.75.

Leicester

LOCAL GEM

Delilah Fine Foods

Modern European | £20

4 St Martins, Leicester, LE1 5DB
Tel no: (0116) 296 3554
delilahfinefoods.co.uk

Like its elder sibling in Nottingham (see entry), this branch of Delilah Fine Foods occupies the shell of a high-ceilinged Victorian bank, and offers the same all-day package – namely café tables surrounded by shelves of deli-style provisions. Cheeses and charcuterie share the billing with salads, sandwiches, flatbread pizzas and dishes such as sautéed potatoes with confit duck, melted Gruyère and garlic mayo, while cakes and pastries fill in the gaps. Brunch and fondues add variety, and the wine list favours bottles from family-run vineyards.

Mountsorrel

John's House

Cooking score: 6
Modern British | £47
Stonehurst Farm, 139-141 Loughborough Road, Mountsorrel, LE12 7AR
Tel no: (01509) 415569
johnshouse.co.uk

The son of a farmer, John Duffin traded wellies for whites and worked in some of the UK's hottest kitchens before opening this immensely charming restaurant right next to the family farm (now run by brother Tom). With a homely brick-walled lounge downstairs and two rough-hewn dining rooms upstairs, it's a folksy look, but that's where the rusticity ends. Influences from the chef's mentors – including Simon Rogan and Marcus Wareing – are evident as the kitchen creates a procession of finely honed dishes from seasonal ingredients and home-grown produce. Bradgate Park venison might be served tartare-style with smoked egg yolk, artichoke and truffle or as a piece of gently cooked loin, with companions including red cabbage purée, Brussels sprouts, chocolate and salsify. Farm-bred meats are dazzlingly transmuted with exotic flavourings, while fish might mean lightly salted cod with crab, cauliflower, lemon and roast chicken juices. For dessert, there's carrot sorbet with yoghurt, liquorice and mint, perhaps, or play it straight with Yorkshire rhubarb, pistachio and vanilla mousse – either way, the layers of flavour and intricacy are astonishing. A thoughtfully assembled wine list offers sound drinking at fair prices.

Chef/s: John Duffin. **Closed:** Sun, Mon, Christmas, first 2 weeks Aug. **Meals:** set L £24 (2 courses) to £28. Set D £42 (2 courses) to £47. Tasting menu £70 (7 courses). **Details:** 30 seats. V menu. Bar. Music. Parking. Children at L only.

Uppingham

★ NEW ENTRY ★

The Lake Isle

Cooking score: 1
Modern British | £37
16 High Street East, Uppingham, LE15 9PZ
Tel no: (01572) 822951
lakeisle.co.uk

Uppingham's pretty high street is chock full of attractions – not least this well-liked restaurant with rooms housed in a charming 350-year-old building. Food is served in an brightly lit room that can sometimes lack atmosphere, but the cooking is 'really competent' and the menu isn't short on invention. Ale-cured Parma ham sits well with a nicely timed egg, asparagus and dots of porcini ketchup, while rump of lamb comes with garlicky potato terrine, French-style peas and a rich jus. Considerable thought also goes into the presentation of desserts such as chocolate and stem ginger délice with burnt honey ice cream and whisky curd. Service is extremely pleasant, and wine prices are very reasonable.

Chef/s: Stuart Mead. **Closed:** 27 to 29 Dec. **Meals:** main courses £15 to £27. Sun L £28. **Details:** 35 seats. 20 seats outside. Bar. Music.

Wymeswold

The Hammer & Pincers

Cooking score: 2
Modern European | £42
5 East Road, Wymeswold, LE12 6ST
Tel no: (01509) 880735
hammerandpincers.co.uk

It's in a rural village setting and, from the outside, looks like a traditional pub, but the Hammer & Pincers has undergone some modification from its original function as a local watering hole – it's definitely a smart dining destination these days. The staff ensure the place exudes a cheery welcome, and chef proprietor Daniel Jimminson packs professional ambition into every dish, offering up contemporary menus, creative presentation and up-to-the-minute cooking techniques – which, for the most part, are pulled off. Potential abounds in the best of the dishes, perhaps a pigeon breast with a delicately made Scotch egg of black pudding and quail's egg among starters, or a main course cod fillet glazed with miso and yuzu caramel and teamed with tempura vegetables and a sriracha (hot chilli) mayonnaise. Pistachio marzipan cake with orange blossom labneh and fresh basil ice cream has been well reported, as have extras such as bread, palate-cleansing sorbets, and petits fours. An efficiently annotated wine list opens at £16.95.

Chef/s: Daniel Jimminson. **Closed:** Mon, 25 Dec. **Meals:** main courses £19 to £28. Set L and D £23 (2 courses) to £27. Tasting menu £45 (7 courses) to £60 (10 courses). **Details:** 42 seats. 30 seats outside. V menu. Vg menu. Bar. Music. Parking.

Wymondham

The Berkeley Arms

Cooking score: 3
Modern British | £35
59 Main Street, Wymondham, LE14 2AG
Tel no: (01572) 787587
theberkeleyarms.co.uk

A smart village local for a smart village, the Berkeley Arms dates from the 16th century but is geared up to satisfy the needs of savvy 21st-century customers. The local area chips in a good deal of the ingredients – locally shot game, eggs from down the road – and the staff provide the kind of welcome that makes you want to return post-haste. The opened-up interior is full of charm (and beams). The menu deals in hearty flavours, so smoked ham hock arrives in a risotto with crispy black pudding, loin of rabbit is stuffed with its own liver, and Lincolnshire sausages come with bubble and squeak. But there's also potato gnocchi with wild mushrooms, and baked cod with crab and herb crust. Desserts bring comfort and joy: a crumble, perhaps, or blackberry and apple panna cotta. The concise wine list covers the globe, opening at £18.50.

Chef/s: Neil Hitchen. **Closed:** Mon, first 2 weeks Jan, 2 weeks summer. **Meals:** main courses £13 to £25. Set L £16 (2 courses) to £20. Set D £19 (2 courses) to £23. Sun L £20 (2 courses) to £24. **Details:** 55 seats. 24 seats outside. Wheelchairs. Parking.

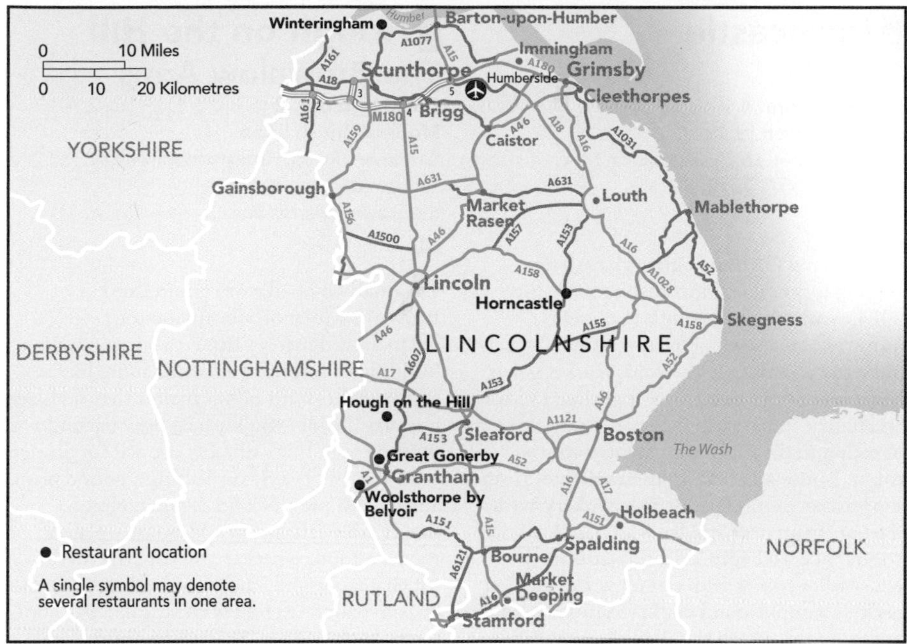

Great Gonerby

Harry's Place

Cooking score: 4
Modern French | £66
17 High Street, Great Gonerby, NG31 8JS
Tel no: (01476) 561780
£5 OFF

Celebrating their thirtieth anniversary in 2018, Harry and Caroline Hallam continue to run the Place to the same unwavering formula. It's easy to forget how innovative this once seemed, a two-handed operation with the air of a private dinner party, based on a short menu of a pair of choices at each stage. Regulars understand the drill, and appreciate the air of hospitality. Dishes often recur in the repertoire, which might include an opener of roast salmon dressed in vodka crème fraîche and caviar, with a relish of mango, avocado and lime, or main courses such as Lincoln Red beef fillet in wine and Armagnac, accompanied by spiced apricots, raisins and red onion. Dead simple desserts might be prune and Armagnac ice cream with passion fruit, or chocolate mousse with blackberries. One or two technical slip-ups marred a spring visit, but the Hallams' commitment is not in question. There is a short wine list, from £8.50 a glass.

Chef/s: Harry Hallam. **Closed:** Sun, Mon, 25 and 26 Dec, 2 weeks Aug, bank hols. **Meals:** main courses £40. **Details:** 10 seats. Parking. Children over 5 yrs.

Send us your review

Your feedback informs the content of the *GFG* and will be used to compile next year's reviews. To register your opinion about any restaurant listed in the Guide, or a restaurant that you wish to bring to our attention, visit: thegoodfoodguide.co.uk/feedback

Horncastle

Magpies

Cooking score: 4
Modern British | £49
73 East Street, Horncastle, LN9 6AA
Tel no: (01507) 527004

Andrew and Caroline Gilbert have been serving this part of Lincolnshire well since 2004, working to a formula that seems unmoved by fashion. Occupying a 200-year-old terraced cottage in a Wolds market town, Magpies puts great store by traditional virtues and honest intent, whether you're staying over or eating in the soothingly neutral dining room. Andrew's cooking mixes themes from the lexicon of modern British cookery with flavours from near and far – all handled with confidence. To begin, coconut-crumbed plaice fillet comes with tartare sauce, pickled cockles, samphire and vodka-tonic jelly, while mains might stretch to rolled ribeye with a mini steak and kidney pud, horseradish champ, calf's liver, or open wild mushroom ravioli alongside sweet potato arancini and braised fennel. For afters, plump for the assiette of hot passion fruit soufflé and triple chocolate Jaffa mousse. Around 20 house selections open the well-balanced, ever-evolving wine list – look for the new arrivals from Peru.

Chef/s: Andrew Gilbert. **Closed:** Mon, Tue, 26 to 30 Dec, first week Jan. **Meals:** set L £23 (2 courses) to £28. Set D £43 (2 courses) to £49. Sun L £28. **Details:** 34 seats. 10 seats outside. Bar. Music.

Anonymous

At *The Good Food Guide*, our inspectors dine anonymously and pay their bill in full every time.These impartial review meals, along with feedback from thousands of our readers, are what informs the content of the *GFG*. Only the best restaurants make the cut.

Hough on the Hill

The Brownlow Arms

Cooking score: 2
Modern British | £55
Grantham Road, Hough on the Hill, NG32 2AZ
Tel no: (01400) 250234
thebrownlowarms.com

Originally owned by a certain Lord Brownlow (one of a locally famous aristocratic dynasty), this 17th-century pub is a building of impressive stature, more like a sturdy stone-built Shires manor than a village hostelry. Inside, you'll find a busy bar and a dining room that's suitably dressed for dinner with Regency-style furnishings, period prints and an antique clock on the mantelpiece. Smart table settings herald smartly plated modern food, whether you're in the market for chateaubriand, cumin-spiced rack of lamb or pan-seared sea bass with steamed pak choi, crispy shrimp balls, Thai green mussels and toasted coconut. To start, the twice-baked cheese soufflé with smoked haddock is a signature dish, while desserts run the gamut from tiramisu and triple chocolate brownie to St Clement's mousse with raspberries and lemon sorbet. Chilean house wine (£20.75) starts off a list that's helpfully categorised by style.

Chef/s: Ruaraidh Bealby. **Closed:** Mon, 25 and 26 Dec, 1 Jan. **Meals:** main courses £15 to £33. Sun L £26 (2 courses). **Details:** 80 seats. 30 seats outside. Bar. Music. Parking. No children after 8pm.

Winteringham

Winteringham Fields

Cooking score: 6
Modern European | £55
1 Silver Street, Winteringham, DN15 9ND
Tel no: (01724) 733096
winteringhamfields.co.uk
£5 OFF

In the placid heart of north Lincolnshire, not far from the Humber, Winteringham Fields has nurtured a reputation for singularity over many years. With its luxurious guest rooms and smart, slate-walled restaurant, it makes statements all over the show, but none more boldly assertive than in Colin McGurran's thoroughly idiosyncratic cooking. Locally sourced raw materials and a commitment to teasing the hidden depths out of every element distinguish the eight-course 'surprise' menu that is the flagship. Presentations are witty and eye-catching, as in the cheese on toast with a coffee cup of beef consommé, or the 'unbelievably tasty and brilliantly executed' truffle linguine with mushroom foam and pickled enoki mushrooms. Elsewhere, the art of combining is given free rein in juxtapositions such as mackerel and kohlrabi, pork belly and pineapple, or a dish called 'Good Game' that combines pheasant ravioli with pork and hazelnuts. To conclude, there may well be ginger-foamed mango and vanilla ice cream, flawless apple millefeuille, or a take on Bakewell tart with raspberry sorbet. A lengthy slate of Sommelier's Selections supplements a resourceful, ambitious wine list, with small glasses from £9.50 for Hungarian rosé.

Chef/s: Colin McGurran and Gareth Bartram. **Closed:** Sun, Mon, 2 weeks Dec to Jan, 2 weeks Aug. **Meals:** main courses £28 to £31. Tasting menu £65 (6 courses) to £85. **Details:** 55 seats. Bar. Wheelchairs. Music. Parking.

Woolsthorpe by Belvoir

Chequers Inn

Cooking score: 1
Modern British | £29

Main Street, Woolsthorpe by Belvoir, NG32 1LU
Tel no: (01476) 870701
chequersinn.net

Inspiring views of Belvoir Castle are a bonus for visitors who make the effort to track down this sympathetically restored 17th-century village inn – although the Chequers also wins friends with its real ales, real fires and trusty farmhouse interiors. The kitchen pleases the old guard with simply grilled fish, suet-crusted pies and chargrilled steaks, while those with a more enquiring outlook might veer towards smoked duck breast with chicory, orange and hazelnut salad or pan-fried fillet of brill accompanied by scallop tortellini and shellfish bisque. For pudding, the four-part 'taste of coffee' and the cherry baked Alaska sound like winners. Creditable international wines from £17.50.

Chef/s: Keith Martin. **Meals:** main courses £12 to £25. Sun L £16 (2 courses). **Details:** 120 seats. 80 seats outside. Bar. Wheelchairs. Music. Parking.

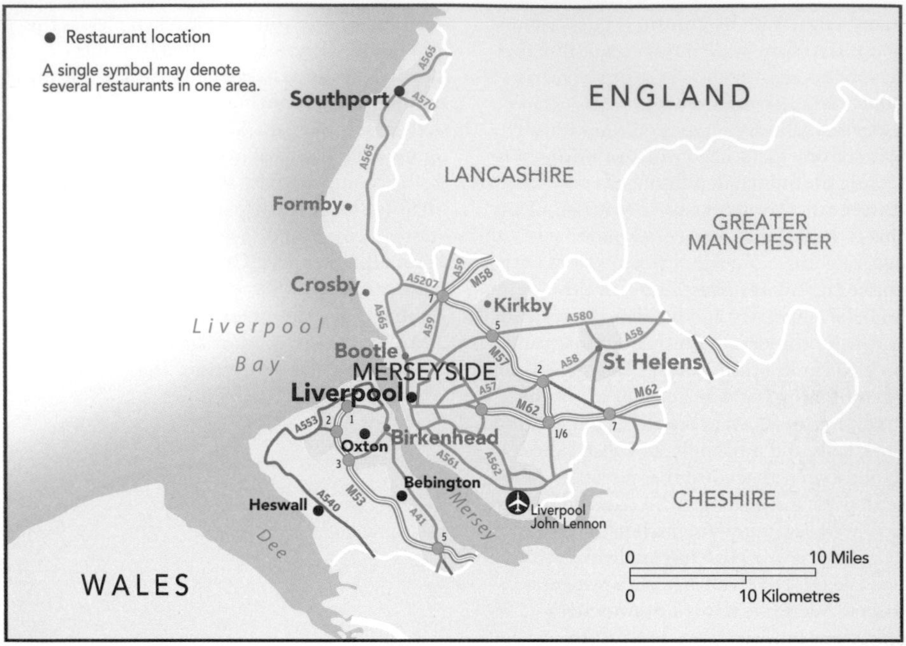

Bebington

LOCAL GEM

Claremont Farm Café

British | £22

Old Clatterbridge Road, Bebington, CH63 4JB
Tel no: (0151) 334 1133
claremontfarm.co.uk

This Wirral farm shop and café inspires devotion from its regulars – and not just during asparagus season, when the farm's own produce comes into its own. Dog-walkers, families, workshop attendees and more head this way for the lemon drizzle cake, homemade breakfasts (choose your own 'full English' or try the avocado on rye) and good lunches that run from colourful seasonal salads to beef goulash with sour cream and Welsh rarebit toasties. Afternoon teas (gluten-free, dairy-free and vegan options available) are popular.

Heswall

Burnt Truffle

Cooking score: 3

Modern European | £34

106 Telegraph Road, Heswall, CH60 0AQ
Tel no: (0151) 342 1111
burnttruffle.net

For many readers there's no doubt that Burnt Truffle defines a neighbourhood restaurant, its stripped-back look and relaxed demeanour reflecting Gary Usher's aim of providing great food and drink across his four-strong (and counting) group of North West bistros. The kitchen majors on seasonal dishes with emphatic Mediterranean overtones and a finger firmly on the pulse of today's tastes for robust combinations. Come here for celeriac risotto with salsa verde and brown-butter breadcrumbs, steamed cod fillet with salted red cabbage and dill butter, or braised featherblade steak with caramelised onion purée and truffle and Parmesan chips. Visitors consider the sourdough bread with truffle and walnut butter to be sensational and, at dessert stage, fresh doughnuts with buttermilk custard and apple granita have been a huge hit. The lunch and early evening menus are excellent value for money, the wine list an affordable tour of Old and New World vineyards.

Chef/s: Scott Griffiths. **Closed:** Mon, 25 and 26 Dec. **Meals:** main courses £14 to £32. Set L and early D Tue to Thur £16 (2 courses) to £19. Sun L £18 (2 courses) to £22. **Details:** 53 seats. 32 seats outside. Music.

Liverpool

The Art School

Cooking score: 5
Modern European | £69
1 Sugnall Street, Liverpool, L7 7EB
Tel no: (0151) 230 8600
theartschoolrestaurant.co.uk

Tucked away in a slip of a side street along one end of the Philharmonic Hall, the Art School has an austere institutional look from the outside, an impression that quickly melts to smooth, warm professionalism as soon as you set foot through the door. The dining room is a broad, inviting space beneath a large skylight, with large double-linened tables and a window on to the kitchen for the nosy neighbours among us. Paul Askew's approach could scarcely be more obliging, with vegetarian and vegan tasters alongside the regular offerings, and impeccable North West sourcing acting as solid support throughout. Some have felt Askew's style is a little old-fashioned in its fondness for appetiser soups, soufflés and creamy sauces, but everything is rendered with confident panache. Smoked haddock of superlative flavour comes with a slew of white leek in grain mustard cream with a coronet of salmon roe, while main courses at a winter meal offered full-flavoured Rhug pheasant breast with a glazed latticed pie of the leg, as well as cavolo nero, trompettes and butternut purée, while Peterhead hake turned up in neo-Spanish guise on an underlay of white beans and diced smoked pork. The sharing platters of dessert items have the look of petits fours to them, but the principal menus deal in the likes of red berry and kirsch pavlova with Turkish Delight ice cream and white chocolate soil. An excellent wine list spreads its wings confidently, opening with small glasses from £4.95.

Chef/s: Paul Askew. **Closed:** Sun, Mon, 25 and 26 Dec, 1 week Jan, 1 week Aug. **Meals:** set L and D £25 (2 courses) to £32. Set D £69 (3 courses). Tasting menu £89. **Details:** 48 seats. V menu. Vg menu. Bar. Wheelchairs. Music. Children at L and early D only.

★ NEW ENTRY ★

Belzan

Cooking score: 2
Modern British | £25
371 Smithdown Road, Liverpool, L15 3JJ
Tel no: (0151) 733 8595
belzan.co.uk

£5 OFF

Entire streets of boarded-up houses are an indicator that the once rundown Smithdown Road area is being slowly regenerated as derelict student digs are being zhuzhed up for young professionals and families. Of the new bars and restaurants opening up on the main road, Belzan is already one of the city's hottest tickets. With its whitewashed brickwork, abundant pot plants and rickety tables, it's functional and informal. In the open kitchen, Sam Grainger (ex-Maray, see entry) cooks a form of culinary fusion, but the flavours work, delivering for one delighted visitor a meal that jumped from Spain to Asia via Greece. Generous 'small' plates are the deal here and a meal might start with an Italian-style wild mushroom gnocchi, duxelles, cavolo nero and pine nuts, move on to a Korean-influenced octopus with kimchi, Jersey Royals and satay-style peanut sauce. Finish with tonka bean rice pudding teamed with vermouth spiced pear. A concise global wine list opens at £19, with carafes from £13.

Chef/s: Sam Grainger. **Closed:** 25 to 26 Dec, 31 Dec to 1 Jan. **Meals:** sharing plates £5 to £15. **Details:** 29 seats. V menu. Vg menu. Bar. Wheelchairs. Music.

Delifonseca Dockside

Cooking score: 1
Modern European | £28
Brunswick Quay, Liverpool, L3 4BN
Tel no: (0151) 255 0808
delifonseca.co.uk

Hugely popular, this sociable and informal dockside café has a please-all global menu. Open from breakfast onwards (Inverawe smoked salmon and scrambled eggs, perhaps), it's an ideal setting to share platters of charcuterie or order vibrant salads or sandwiches. Look to the blackboards for daily specials, with typical choices including beef kofta with tahini, paprika, pitta and toasted pine nuts, and confit Goosnargh duck leg served with spiced damson chutney, pomme purée, roasted squash and red wine jus. Afterwards, you can stock up in the classy deli. An interesting drinks list showcases beers from around the world and wines from £18.

Chef/s: Martin Cooper. **Closed:** 25 and 26 Dec, 1 Jan. **Meals:** main courses £12 to £21. Sun L £12 to £15. **Details:** 66 seats. 24 seats outside. Wheelchairs. Music. Parking.

The London Carriage Works

Cooking score: 2
Modern British | £44
Hope Street Hotel, 40 Hope Street, Liverpool, L1 9DA
Tel no: (0151) 705 2222
thelondoncarriageworks.co.uk

On one of the city's most famous streets, bookended by two cathedrals – Roman Catholic at the northern end, Anglican at the southern, with the Liverpool Philharmonic Hall in the middle, the grand Italian palazzo-style building that houses the London Carriage Works fits right in. It's a light, modern restaurant (the kind to dress up for), matched by a kitchen that aims for a recognisable contemporary cooking style. Hence it partners seared confit chicken thigh with celeriac rémoulade, egg yolk and puffed rice, and complements Cumbrian salt-aged fillet of beef with braised shin, smoked tongue, red cabbage, truffle mash and red wine jus. Fish, too, is given no short shrift with seared saltwater cod teamed with its tempura cheek, broccoli, smoked almonds and beluga butter emulsion. For dessert, try stewed strawberries with sesame cream, roast strawberry purée and burnt honey ice cream or a selection of regional cheeses. A global wine list opens at £19.95

Chef/s: Mike Kenyon. **Meals:** main courses £18 to £35. Set L and D £22 (2 courses) to £28. Sun L £22. **Details:** 100 seats. Bar. Wheelchairs. Music.

Lunya

Cooking score: 2
Spanish | £26
Hanover Street, Liverpool, L1 3DN
Tel no: (0151) 706 9770
lunya.co.uk

'There's a lot of great tapas in Liverpool these days,' noted one visitor, who went on to describe Lunya's move from College Lane to this converted warehouse on Hanover Street as 're-energising'. It's a huge space – a long room with a deli at the entrance and an open kitchen at the other end – with excellent service provided by chatty staff. From sharing platters of ham and cheeses to an inspired dish of morcilla rolled in cornflakes, deep fried and served with a bittersweet orange-honey syrup and pomegranate molasses, some really authentic flavours are to be had. Among the highlights are ox cheek and mushroom croquetas, crisp chipirones with good garlic mayo, and roast and pan-fried cauliflower 'steak' topped with tahini yoghurt and coriander. Desserts include the familiar tarta de Santiago, and burnt cheesecake from San Sebastián with PX-infused raisins and hazelnuts. A good selection of sherries gives heft to an all-Spanish wine list that opens at £18.95.

Chef/s: Dave Upson. **Closed:** 25 Dec, 1 Jan. **Meals:** tapas £5 to £20. Set L £10 (2 courses) to £14. Tasting menu £25 (10 dishes) to £36. **Details:** 150 seats. 25 seats outside. V menu. Vg menu. Bar. Wheelchairs. Music.

Maray

Cooking score: 1
Middle Eastern | £24
91 Bold Street, Liverpool, L1 4HF
Tel no: (0151) 709 5820
maray.co.uk

Maray strikes just the right note for an all-day eatery. The simple decor matters not a jot (plain wooden tables, hard chairs) when the kitchen belts out such flavour-packed Middle Eastern small plates, which fuse the traditional with the fashionable and/or seasonal. Layered flavours are combined deftly: aubergine with ras el hanout and salted peanuts; smoked ham with fennel and pear rémoulade, date syrup and dukkah; and octopus with kale, pistachio, chilli, grapefruit and squid ink sherbet. There's an authenticity here, a passion for simple things done well, and the cost is fair. Drink cocktails, interesting beers, or wines well chosen to go with the food.
Chef/s: Livia Alarcon. **Meals:** main courses £6 to £10. **Details:** 45 seats. V menu. Vg menu. Wheelchairs. Music.

★ NEW ENTRY ★

Röski

Cooking score: 6
Modern European | £55
16 Rodney Street, Liverpool, L1 2TE
Tel no: (0151) 708 8698
roskirestaurant.com

Packing a major punch in Liverpool's Georgian Quarter, Anton Piotrowski's high-achieving restaurant offers some exciting contemporary cooking. To get a glimpse, the five-course tasting menu is a good intro. Otherwise it's seven courses, beginning with a series of intensely flavoured bites: an umami hit in a pile of diced mushroom and mini duck-fat croûtons with cep powder and aged Parmesan, and a one-bite burst of sensuous sweet-salt in a frog's leg and wild garlic kiev lollipop. Top-notch ingredients are the kitchen's building blocks, deployed to create dishes that fully exploit contrasting flavours and textures, as seen in a finely diced Wagyu beef tartare, built up with wild garlic and tamarind paste in a tiny 'Kentucky fried' potato skin ('takes finger-licking good to another level'). Smoked haddock, creamy and full of flavour, is invigorated by kohlrabi risotto and burnt butter, and salt and pepper chicken is Piotrowski's homage to Liverpool's Chinese, the oldest Chinese community in Europe. Elsewhere, there have been good reports of the chef's take on Liverpool's famous dish, scouse; and a beautifully realised lemon slice – 'a dense sliver of pure lemon flavour' – simply dazzles. Service, led by Rose Allegra, is spot-on, and vegetarians get their own tasting menus. The wine list is a global spread with prices starting at £20 and keeping, to the most part, under £45.
Chef/s: Anton Piotrowski. **Closed:** Sun, Mon. **Meals:** set L £25. Tasting menu £55 (5 courses) to £75 (7 courses). **Details:** 30 seats. V menu. Music.

Salt House Tapas

Cooking score: 3
Spanish | £24
1 Hanover Street, Liverpool, L1 3DW
Tel no: (0151) 706 0092
salthousetapas.co.uk

Admirers of good brickwork might well spend a moment or two gazing at the curved façade of this hunk of Victorian real estate, while everyone else will likely waste no time getting stuck into the menu of compelling tapas. The pared-back semi-industrial space is usually rammed with enthusiastic diners, watched over by equally enthusiastic staff. Fried buttermilk chicken with pickled carrots, green chilli jam and tahini yoghurt is modern tapas if ever there was, but purists can always stick to Ibérico ham croquetas and tortilla with aïoli. Among many eye-catching options, prawns arrive sizzling in garlic, chilli and olive oil, cured sardines are pointed up with burnt grapefruit dressing, and sticky baby ribs come with spiced pickled cabbage. Vegans get their own menu. Expect equally creative desserts – blood orange trifle, say, with coconut cream and pistachio brittle. To drink, bottled beers from the likes of Spain, Mexico and Liverpool join Spanish wines and a dozen cocktails.

Chef/s: Matt Walsh. **Closed:** 25 Dec. **Meals:** tapas £5 to £9. Set L £13. **Details:** 80 seats. 30 seats outside. Vg menu. Bar. Wheelchairs. Music.

60 Hope Street

Cooking score: 2
Modern British | £48
60 Hope Street, Liverpool, L1 9BZ
Tel no: (0151) 707 6060
60hopestreet.com

It was 1999 when brothers Colin and Gary Manning took over a handsome corner building in the 'rebooted and suited' Georgian Quarter of the city and set about creating a dining destination. Twenty years on, this family-owned operation remains a stylish spot, with lounge and bar on the lower-ground floor, private dining room up top, and restaurant in the middle. There are menus to cover all bases, from traditional Sunday roasts to afternoon tea, early-bird dinners and cocktails. A salad of burrata, beetroot and blood orange is right on the modern money, with more zesty flavours in crab on toast with pink grapefruit, plus the comforting appeal of classic fish and chips. There's a Mediterranean spin to paprika monkfish, with octopus and chorizo, while saddle of lamb might come with its slow-cooked shoulder and a nut crust. Finish on salted caramel tart with pistachio ice cream. The descriptive wine list has a stack of options under £30.

Chef/s: Neil Devereux. **Closed:** 26 Dec. **Meals:** main courses £15 to £36. Set L and D £25 (2 courses) to £30. **Details:** 200 seats. 12 seats outside. Bar. Music.

Spire

Cooking score: 3
Modern British | £35
1 Church Road, Liverpool, L15 9EA
Tel no: (0151) 734 5040
spirerestaurant.co.uk
£5 OFF

Spire is a short hop from the city centre, a popular neighbourhood restaurant whose kitchen roams the world for inspiration and turns out well-presented contemporary dishes. It's all 'great value, especially early evening'. Readers have enjoyed some old favourites with a twist: chicken liver parfait with rhubarb and elderflower jelly; 'large, sweet' Menai mussels in a good broth with a touch of cream; and goat's cheese arancini with beetroot purée and pickled beetroot salad. Follow that with Goosnargh chicken breast, crispy leek, potato rösti and pepper sauce; sea bass with broccoli purée and crispy squid; or an excellent rump of beef with brandy, peppercorn and tarragon butter. Desserts range from a satisfyingly wobbly rhubarb and Prosecco panna cotta to hot chocolate fondant with malted milk ice cream. The short, reasonably priced wine list roams the world, with bottles starting at £17.95.

Chef/s: Matt Locke. **Closed:** Sun, first week Jan. **Meals:** main courses £16 to £23. Set L £14 (2 courses) to £19. Set D £19 (2 courses) to £22. **Details:** 70 seats. Wheelchairs. Music.

★ NEW ENTRY ★

Wreckfish

Cooking score: 2
Modern British | £30
60 Seel Street, Liverpool, L1 4BE
Tel no: (0151) 707 1960
wreckfish.co

The fourth opening from Gary Usher (see also Sticky Walnut, Chester; Burnt Truffle, Heswall; Hispi, Manchester) has quite a swagger. Big sash windows give lots of light, and those lured into the modern bistro-style dining room with its open kitchen and adjoining bar don't leave disappointed. Usher's approach to food remains consistent across the group: namely vibrant, up-to-date British dishes based on fresh, seasonal produce, with value for money a big plus. From a short, regularly changing menu (fixed price at lunch and early dinner) could come red snapper ceviche with avocado mousse – zingy blood orange brings out the fresh flavour and crispy kale adds welcome crunch. Other highlights include perfectly cooked cod with confit garlic, butter beans and sunflower seeds, or an imaginative vegetarian dish of miso-glazed parsnips with goat's yoghurt, black sesame and shichimi togarashi, a Japanese seven-spice mix. Finish with tonka bean semifreddo with warm chocolate sauce and fresh honeycomb. The wine list is reasonably priced.

Chef/s: Luke Richardson. **Closed:** 25 and 26 Dec. **Meals:** main courses £14 to £23. Set L and early D £17 (2 courses) to £20. **Details:** 90 seats. V menu. Bar. Wheelchairs. Music.

LOCAL GEM

Etsu

Japanese | £28

25 The Strand (off Brunswick Street), Liverpool, L2 0XJ
Tel no: (0151) 236 7530
etsu-restaurant.co.uk

Now comfortably into its second decade, David Abe's sleek, minimalist and compact city-centre restaurant is concealed at the bottom of Beetham Plaza, across the road from the waterfront. Staff are helpful when it comes to navigating the lengthy menu. The sushi is expertly made to order – a remarkably fresh sea bass nigiri might lead on to soft shell crab with kimchi mayonnaise and a bento box of seared tuna with ponzu sauce. For dessert try the apple gyoza dumplings with mango and yuzu sorbet. Dive into the list of Japanese sakés and gins, or stick with wine from £13.95.

Oxton

★ TOP 50 ★

Fraiche

Cooking score: 8
Modern European | £88

11 Rose Mount, Oxton, CH43 5SG
Tel no: (0151) 652 2914
restaurantfraiche.com

'There are few restaurants so small, so hard to get into, so personal,' mused one diner, who noted that since her last visit Marc Wilkinson has done everything he can to rid Fraiche of its former austerity. It's an 'eccentric fit-out and very dark', the gloaming just one of the sensory layers used to soften the dining room, along with seasonal wall projections and the chef's own, rather loud, soundtrack. It is, however, unique with none of the current chefs-at-the-table business. Balancing imagination and advanced technique with a simple appreciation of what's good to eat, a meal here unfolds easily. Highlights might be a sticky, slightly sweet egg yolk, slowly poached and served in a Jerusalem artichoke cream with hazelnuts and chives; to dip, an artichoke crisp with pinpricks of vinegar acidity. Then there's wild turbot with yuzu gel, and Balmoral venison loin with rootsy accompaniments – salsify, celeriac purée and a dense, frondy cluster of hen of the woods mushrooms. The only choice on the tasting menu is at the end, between salt (cheeses with acutely matched accompaniments and honey straight from the comb) and sweet. This might be a squat puck of banana parfait, smaller blobs of ganache with a speculoos flavour, an 'extremely good' chocolate mousse and architectural isomalt chocolate tuiles. Petits fours come in waves, service is excellent and the wine list shows dedication and enthusiasm.

Chef/s: Marc Wilkinson. **Closed:** Mon, Tue, 25 and 26 Dec, 2 weeks Aug. **Meals:** Sun L £48. Tasting menu £48 (4 courses) to £88. **Details:** 12 seats. 4 seats outside. Bar. Music. Children over 10 yrs at D.

Southport
Bistro 21

Cooking score: 3
Modern European | £29
21 Stanley Street, Southport, PR9 0BS
Tel no: (01704) 501414
bistro21.co.uk

Behind Lord Street, Southport's Victorian wrought-iron-canopied boulevard, sits this small bistro, an affable establishment with a devoted local clientele. Upmarket European fare – the starched linen gives it away – is head chef Michael Glayzer's hallmark and variously priced menus set out to satisfy all. This is 'not fine dining, but very good food', so expect to find crowd-pleasing soups, fish and chips, and fishcakes sharing the billing with more elegant dishes. There's even a teriyaki stir-fry. A remarkably good-value tasting menu (you choose three starters, which are served together, followed by two mains) combines an eclectic mix of influences and ingredients, from classic moules marinière or smoked cheese soufflé to salmon fillet with harissa paste, samphire, broad beans and lemon confit potatoes. Crème brûlée ticks the bistro box and finishes things off nicely, and a crisp unoaked Colombard opens the 'short and well-priced' wine list.

Chef/s: Michael Glayzer. **Closed:** Sun, Mon, 25 and 26 Dec, 1 Jan. **Meals:** main courses £17 to £26. Set L £13 (2 courses). Set D £17 (2 courses). Tasting menu £25. **Details:** 28 seats. V menu. Wheelchairs. Music.

Bistrot Vérité

Cooking score: 3
French | £33
7 Liverpool Road, Southport, PR8 4AR
Tel no: (01704) 564199
bistrotverite.co.uk

Eating classic French dishes outdoors on a sunny evening overlooking Birkdale Sands transported one delighted visitor to Deauville. The interior has an equally Gallic feel with low lighting, pale green wood panelling, bare tables and bentwood chairs. At inspection, nibbles of battered frogs' legs with roast garlic mayo, and starters of very good steak tartare, and smoked mackerel with horseradish potato salad and watercress, preceded a plump fillet of sea bass served with local Southport shrimps and a langoustine velouté. The 'best plate of food of the night'?: a leg of rabbit with mustard sauce served with a mélange of haricots verts, peas and roasted carrots and served with truffle-infused French fries. There's also Malaysian monkfish and tiger prawn curry and a more traditional steak-frites. Service is very good indeed – 'a well-oiled machine' – and it is clearly very popular. Finish with excellent apple tart or crème brûlee. A mainly French wine list starts at £19.

Chef/s: Marc Vérité. **Closed:** Sun, Mon, 25 and 26 Dec, 1 Jan, 1 week Feb, 1 week Aug. **Meals:** main courses £13 to £30. Set L £19 (2 courses) to £25. **Details:** 45 seats. 16 seats outside. Music.

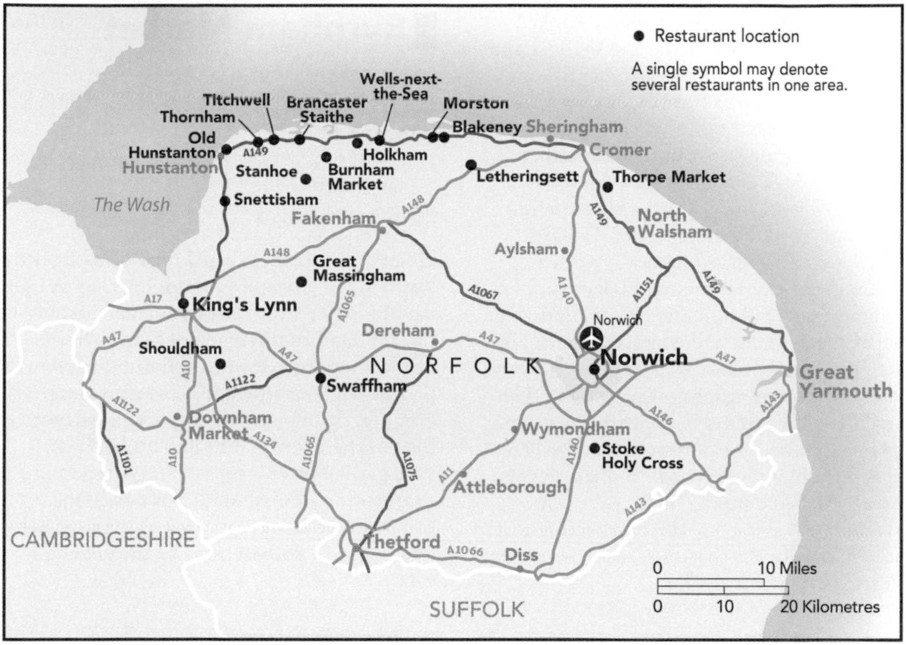

Blakeney

The Moorings

Cooking score: 2
Modern British | £32
High Street, Blakeney, NR25 7NA
Tel no: (01263) 740054
blakeney-moorings.co.uk

The sunflower-yellow walls, please-all art and chirpy welcome make this compact high-street restaurant a charming one for sandwiches and snacks at any time of day. It's useless to resist a slice of owner Angela Long's memorable cakes – there's always a tempting selection on display – but come, too, for 'proper' food, the likes of plump scallops, just-seared and butter-soft, that are served with a sweet pea purée and crisp shards of pancetta, or a satisfying French onion soup with garlicky rouille, *de rigueur* croûtons and melting cheese. There are classics elsewhere too, a nod to Spain in a much-praised dish of roasted hake with squid, braised cannellini beans and chorizo, or hearty venison with celeriac and cinnamon mash and sour cherries. To finish? Things stay reassuringly traditional with apple and rhubarb crumble or Eton mess by the generous bowlful. A short wine list has options from around £20.

Chef/s: Richard and Angela Long. **Closed:** Mon, Dec and Jan, Mon to Thur (Nov, Feb and Mar). **Meals:** main courses £16 to £20. Sun L £19 (3 courses). **Details:** 50 seats. Wheelchairs. Music.

Brancaster Staithe

The White Horse

Cooking score: 2
Modern British | £37
Main Road, Brancaster Staithe, PE31 8BY
Tel no: (01485) 210262
whitehorsebrancaster.co.uk

Mussels, harvested from the wriggle of creeks behind this roadside inn, draw aficionados from afar to this stretch of coastal north Norfolk – as do the captivating views from the vast picture windows. Brimming pans rattle with the gleaming bivalves, cooked classically with white wine and shallots, the lemongrass and chilli zing of Thai flavours, or the warming notes of Moroccan harissa and toasted almonds. Dishes where the key ingredient shines are robustly recommended: Simon Letzer's gently smoked salmon is muscular, its richness deliciously cut with segments of blood orange, and Richard Loose's oysters, served naturally with a mignonette sauce, or tempura-battered, are exemplary. A bubbling fish pie from the separate bar menu will energise you for any length of seashore walk, as will magnificent cod and chips. Engaging service more than makes up for a rhubarb sorbet that is more a grainy granita, and a summer fruit ice cream that one diner wished had been 'fruitier and creamier'. Wine from £18.50.

Chef/s: Fran Hartshorne. **Meals:** main courses £14 to £24. **Details:** 100 seats. 100 seats outside. Bar. Wheelchairs. Music. Parking.

LOCAL GEM

The Jolly Sailors

British | £23

Brancaster Staithe, PE31 8BJ
Tel no: (01485) 210314
jollysailorsbrancaster.co.uk

In an attractive Norfolk coastal village, this roadside inn with a large beer garden for summer, log fires in winter and bags of unforced charm is most people's idea of a 'real pub'. It works along comfortingly familiar lines, serving locally brewed ales and generous plates of local mussels, steak and ale pie and own smokehouse specials such as pulled pork burger or rack of ribs. And it's hard to go wrong with wood-fired pizzas, perhaps followed by a triple chocolate brownie. Children and dogs are especially welcome. Wines from £18.50.

Burnham Market

LOCAL GEM

North Street Bistro

British | £30

20 North Street, Burnham Market, PE31 8HG
Tel no: (01328) 730330
20northstreet.co.uk

Housed in a former chapel, this 'fantastic little bistro' is fast gaining a local following. A light daytime offer from chef patron and 'master of flavour' Dan Fancett includes super-fresh salads, soups (garden pea and mint, maybe) or perhaps an asparagus and feta tart. Come evening, the menu ramps up to include the likes of roast rump of Holkham lamb with wild garlic butter, or sea trout with potted shrimp sauce. Finish with a classic crème brûlée and rhubarb compôte. A short wine list opens at £19 with options by the glass and carafe.

READERS RECOMMEND

Socius

Modern British

11 Foundry Place, Burnham Market, PE31 8LG
Tel no: (01328) 738307
sociusnorfolk.co.uk

'So relaxed and modern, and I love the idea of sharing dishes – we had cured salmon with beetroot and horseradish, tandoori hake with aïoli and fennel, and pork cheek with hazelnuts.'

Great Massingham

The Dabbling Duck

Cooking score: 2

British | £26

11 Abbey Road, Great Massingham, PE32 2HN
Tel no: (01485) 520827
thedabblingduck.co.uk

Scrubbed tables, book-lined walls, hop-bedecked beams and a crackling fire in winter are the characterful backdrop for Dale Smith's muscular cooking at this popular village pub. Dexter beef burgers tower, laden with molten cheese, crisp onion and homemade sauce, while generous steaks are as tender as the dripping chips are moreishly salty, and pizzas from the outdoor oven (fired up at certain times only) generously topped. After something more refined? Start with scallops, seared not a second too long, with white pudding, black pudding crumb and flamboyantly pink beetroot and caramelised onion purée, a precursor maybe to partridge paired comfortingly with dauphinois potatoes, squash and kale. Finish with crisp-sugared custard beignets with caramelised apple in various guises, and deliciously nutty brown-butter ice cream. The global wine list has plenty of choice below £20.

Chef/s: Dale Smith. **Meals:** main courses £13 to £24. **Details:** 85 seats. 40 seats outside. Bar. Wheelchairs. Music. Parking.

Holkham

The Victoria

Cooking score: 2
British | £38
Park Road, Holkham, NR23 1RG
Tel no: (01328) 711008
holkham.co.uk

When you've had enough of wind whipping you along stunning Holkham beach, or sunshine and lapping waves caressing you, be refreshed at this perfectly formed country-celebrating pub restaurant on the edge of Holkham Estate. Ingredients on the straightforward menu are estate-sourced where possible – look out for fallow deer from the parkland herd, walled-garden produce, and pheasant or partridge from Lord and Lady Leicester's shoot. A piece of Belted Galloway sirloin from a tenant farmer's herd is perfectly pink and tender, a half-lobster from local waters is cooked sweetly and served with generously garlicky butter, and oysters with spring onion and apple cider vinaigrette are exactly as they should be. A fillet of sea bass is the star of a main course that includes a lobster bisque and enough crushed potatoes for three. Finish with a plate of his lordship's 'smelly French cheeses', or a fresh lemon syllabub with biscotti and caramelised nuts. Wine from £20.

Chef/s: Michael Chamberlain. **Meals:** main courses £14 to £26. **Details:** 86 seats. 76 seats outside. Parking.

King's Lynn

Market Bistro

Cooking score: 3
Modern British | £34
11 Saturday Market Place, King's Lynn, PE30 5DQ
Tel no: (01553) 771483
marketbistro.co.uk

'What's not to love?' sighed one happy diner; a 'real gem' chipped in another; 'a fabulous welcome... and such a talented chef', swooned a third. The affection for this welcoming neighbourhood restaurant is manifest, and the quality of the food coming out of the tiny kitchen keeps the love alive. Dangerously moreish homemade bread might precede home-smoked salmon with a cabbage velouté, the richness of the fish cut to size by horseradish cream and pickled apple. Well-chosen ingredients – many from the immediate surroundings – populate the trim menu: line-caught cod comes with a tangle of celeriac spaghetti, mussels and the umami flavours of a dashi broth and mushrooms, though you may be tempted by tender pork belly, which arrives with some of its best friends – apple, beetroot and kale. A rhubarb millefeuille evokes spring with its winning mix of crisp pastry, just-sweet fruit and rich crème pâtissière. The compact wine list doesn't stray far north of its £23 opening price.

Chef/s: Richard Golding. **Closed:** Sun, Mon, first 2 weeks Jan. **Meals:** main courses £14 to £22. Set L £16 (2 courses) to £20. Set D £35 (5 courses). **Details:** 40 seats. Wheelchairs. Music.

LOCAL GEM

Marriott's Warehouse

Modern British | £25

South Quay, King's Lynn, PE30 5DT
Tel no: (01553) 818500
marriottswarehouse.co.uk

Dipping its toes into the river Ouse as it flows through historic King's Lynn, this former corn warehouse is an understandably popular spot for an alfresco quayside meal. The menu skips across continents, so come for a Mexican prawn cocktail with nachos, teriyaki beef on toasted sourdough, or vegan balti. There's praise for slow-cooked venison stew, though a more plant-leaning diner might choose barbecued cauliflower steak with sweet potato wedges and a lively salsa. Round off with a glazed lemon tart and raspberry coulis. A compact wine list opens at £17.

Letheringsett

LOCAL GEM

The King's Head

Modern British | £28

Holt Road, Letheringsett, NR25 7AR
Tel no: (01263) 712691
kingsheadnorfolk.co.uk

Whether the king ever rested his head here or not is debatable, but what's for sure is the welcome you'll receive – royal or not – at this elegant Georgian pub. Come for familiar dishes that proclaim the glory of Norfolk produce: mushroom bruschetta is hot and crisp with runnels of Binham Blue cheese adding satisfying sweet-saltiness; meat drops deliciously from a vast lamb shank into glossy red wine gravy; and haddock, subtly smoked at Cley Smokehouse, flakes into a golden-yolked egg. Finish with a fruit crumble or sticky toffee pudding, two right royal puds. Wine from £19.50.

Morston

★ TOP 50 ★

Morston Hall

Cooking score: 7
Modern British | £80

The Street, Morston, NR25 7AA
Tel no: (01263) 741041
morstonhall.com

In a restaurant world deluged with 'concepts', it is reassuring that Morston Hall exists. Embracing the country house hotel genre with charm, this place has the picture-perfect garden, the displays of bone china and the silk drapes, and offers a seven-course dinner served by a well-drilled team. Where Morston parts company with tradition, however, is in the food. Forget fusty, tired plates; from the tartlet of confit shallots and vivacious Winchcombe cheese that opens proceedings over aperitifs, to the exquisite homemade chocolates offered as the curtain falls, dishes delight. A fluffy smoked haddock velouté gives way to a translucent raviolo, packed with local lobster. An on-point risotto, generous in its creamy truffliness (more truffle is shaved at the table), precedes a scallop with delicate Champagne sauce. Crisp-pastried, butter-soft beef wellington makes you realise that the classics – in the right hands – are to be applauded vigorously. The delicious chocolate and hazelnut bar – glossy, gold-dusted and gorgeous – is famous, and for good reason. Show-stopping names, and corresponding prices, leap out from a comprehensive wine list, but they are tempered by a welcome £30 to £40 chorus line, and £35 'wines of the month'.

Chef/s: Galton Blackiston and Greg Anderson. **Closed:** 24 to 26 Dec. **Meals:** set D £80 (7 courses). Sun L £42. **Details:** 40 seats. Wheelchairs. Parking.

Norwich

Benedicts

Cooking score: 6
Modern British | £37
9 St Benedict's Street, Norwich, NR2 4PE
Tel no: (01603) 926080
restaurantbenedicts.com

Since opening in 2015, Richard Bainbridge has attracted plaudits aplenty. His restaurant, a simple shop conversion, is pleasingly low-key, but the professional yet informal service, and especially the food, transcend the setting. Modern, innovative combinations of classic British ingredients pepper the tasting menus and carte. At inspection, textures, flavours and presentation were terrific. Amuse-bouches set the standard high, including a crisp wafer topped with apple purée and buttermilk and chive powder: a melt-in-the-mouth treat, dissolving into bursts of sweet-savoury flavours. Vegetarian options are no afterthought: note a dish of parsley-leaf porridge oats, fermented romaine lettuce, raw mushrooms and crunchy pine nuts. To follow, hake was a more conventional assembly, but equally accomplished, coming with a 'rose' of crisped potato, sea purslane and a Champagne and chive cream sauce. Pudding – Nanny Bush's trifle milk jam – was exemplary too. The short yet enticing wine list (from £22) is best sampled via the excellent-value pairing suggestions.

Chef/s: Richard Bainbridge. **Closed:** Sun, Mon, 23 Dec to 8 Jan, 31 Jul to 15 Aug. **Meals:** set L £16 (2 courses) to £20. Set D £29 (2 courses) to £36. Tasting menu £49 to £61. **Details:** 32 seats. V menu. Vg menu. Music.

Vegetarian and vegan

While many restaurants offer individual dishes suitable for non-meat eaters, those marked 'V menu' (vegetarian) and 'Vg menu' (vegan) offer separate menus.

Roger Hickman's

Cooking score: 5
Modern British | £43
79 Upper St Giles Street, Norwich, NR2 1AB
Tel no: (01603) 633522
rogerhickmansrestaurant.com

A private dining room (with its own kitchen) is the latest addition to Roger Hickman's understated restaurant, but it's business as usual on the ground floor where contemporary artworks, gentle lighting and prettily laid tables set a civilised tone. Clean-cut, sharply defined seasonal flavours are the hallmarks of Hickman's cooking, from venison tartare with pickled shallot, crispy kale and egg yolk to forced rhubarb accompanied by blood-orange jelly and cake, custard, ginger ice cream and rhubarb foam. In between, there's a robust feel to strapping meat dishes such as braised short rib with roasted Jerusalem artichoke, shallot and cashew nuts, although the kitchen shows its more sensitive side when it comes to fish – as in roast turbot with ceps, salsify and chicken wings or steamed lemon sole and mussels dressed with parsley, pearl barley and leeks. Menus are fixed price (and excellent value to boot), while the astutely collated wine list kicks off with 14 appealing selections by the glass.

Chef/s: Roger Hickman. **Closed:** Sun, Mon, 31 Dec to 12 Jan. **Meals:** set L £20 (2 courses) to £25. Set D £38 (2 courses) to £47. Tasting menu £63 (8 courses). **Details:** 45 seats. V menu.

Shiki

Cooking score: 3
Japanese | £28
6 Tombland, Norwich, NR3 1HE
Tel no: (01603) 619262
shikirestaurant.co.uk

To find yourself in a Japanese restaurant full of Japanese students is encouraging anywhere – in Norwich it's remarkable, and testament to the authenticity of Shunsuki Tomii's townhouse establishment in the city's oldest district. Sit on bare wooden benches at bare wooden tables on bare wooden flooring, the minimalism relieved by colourful Japanese textiles and paintings on the walls, and by vibrant plates of expertly presented sushi. The izakaya-style menu is an informal repertoire encompassing bento boxes and otsumami sharing plates, as well as sushi and sashimi. Try the aubergine in smokey broth, the delicately deep-fried vegetable tempura and the well-constructed California rolls. Plates of noodles and curries form part of the bargain lunchtime deals, eels and surf clams are available for more esoteric tastes, and Tuesday is the highly popular eat-all-you-can sushi night. To drink, wine (from £19) joins a list of green tea, beer and saké.

Chef/s: Shunsuki Tomii. **Closed:** Sun, Mon, 25 Dec to 8 Jan, 2 weeks Sept. **Meals:** small plates £4 to £12. **Details:** 80 seats. 24 seats outside. Wheelchairs. Music.

★ NEW ENTRY ★

Woolf & Social

Cooking score: 3
International | £20

21-23 Nelson Street, Norwich, NR2 4DW
Tel no: (01603) 443658
woolfandsocial.co.uk

Anything with 'social' in its title is striving to be on-trend, and so it is with this new sharing-plates venture. Sited opposite the famous Fat Cat pub on an otherwise residential street, this former corner shop demonstrates its fashionable credentials with makeshift decor – stackable furniture, bare floorboards and plain walls enlivened by local paintings. Personable young staff recommend up to four plates per person from the oft-changing menu, though three would satisfy all but the seriously greedy. Best at inspection was a colourful, texturally balanced dish of foraged chicken of the woods mushrooms with wild garlic pesto and fennel, but chicken strips with sriracha mayo arrived expertly cooked, as did a substantial plate of pork belly with roast squash, samphire and deeply flavoured gravy. Still hungry? Chocolate cake with peanut-butter ice cream comes highly recommended. Craft ales, naturally, provide an alternative to the well-chosen wine list (from £19) chalked on the walls.

Chef/s: Francis Woolf and Glenn Curtis. **Closed:** Mon, 25 to 31 Dec. **Meals:** small plates £5 to £12. **Details:** 36 seats. 22 seats outside. Bar. Wheelchairs. Music.

Old Hunstanton

The Neptune

Cooking score: 5
Modern British | £62

85 Old Hunstanton Road, Old Hunstanton, PE36 6HZ
Tel no: (01485) 532122
theneptune.co.uk

There's a splash of New England breeziness about Kevin and Jacki Mangeolles' perfectly chilled restaurant with rooms, although muted colours and candlelight provide a civilised backdrop for evening meals in the tasteful dining room. Kevin's cooking is not about showboating or pyrotechnics; instead, he seeks out regional produce and applies a deft touch to whatever's in season – perhaps soused mackerel dressed with fennel and beetroot mayonnaise or monkfish partnered by baked leeks, Brancaster mussels, broccoli purée and Pink Fir potato. While fish is his forte, there's also much to enjoy if you crave meat or game: dry-aged Dexter beef sirloin, for example, is adorned with a harvest festival of cavolo nero, creamed turnip and heritage carrots. Meanwhile, puddings such as tonka bean panna cotta with blood-orange jelly and Horlicks ice cream are guaranteed to raise a smile. Jacki M's substantial wine list opens with 18 recommendations by the glass.

Chef/s: Kevin Mangeolles. **Closed:** Mon, 26 Dec, 3 weeks Jan, 1 week May, 1 week Nov. **Meals:** set D £47 (2 courses) to £62. Sun L £40. Tasting menu £78 (9 courses). **Details:** 22 seats. Bar. Music. Parking. Children over 10 yrs.

Shouldham

LOCAL GEM

King's Arms

British | £27

28 The Green, Shouldham, PE33 0BY
Tel no: (01366) 347410
kingsarmsshouldham.co.uk

Highly enjoyable, hugely popular and a boon for Shouldham, west Norfolk's first co-operative pub was saved from dereliction in 2014. Overlooking the village green, the 17th-century inn is a heart-warming place with all the requisite trappings: real ales, roaring winter fires and a summer beer garden. The cooking gets straight to the point, whether you are in for lunchtime sandwiches, generous plates of venison casserole, beer-battered cod and chips or chicken and leek pie. To finish, don't miss the chocolate brownie. Wine from £16.50.

Snettisham

★ LOCAL RESTAURANT OF THE YEAR ★ OVERALL WINNER

★ NEW ENTRY ★

The Old Bank

Cooking score: 3
Modern British | £35

10 Lynn Road, Snettisham, PE31 7LP
Tel no: (01485) 544080
theoldbankbistro.co.uk

£5 OFF

'A true, true gem', insists one fan of this family-run bistro café in the pretty village of Snettisham. Pop in for good coffee and luscious brownies, or for something more substantial – either way, the food from the compact menu is skilfully prepared, beautifully presented and delivered with genuine pleasure and pride. There's praise for a starter of grilled mackerel, kohlrabi, dill mayonnaise and yoghurt, while a 'big plate' of hispi cabbage with nutty Jerusalem artichokes, pearl barley and a creamy, savoury mushroom ragù is a satisfying balance of texture, looks and taste. Try also the crisp-skinned wild bass with a potato and leek terrine, charred leeks and a crunchy scattering of hazelnuts. Avocado ice cream and cherry sorbet is a homemade winner, though others understandably fail to resist the sticky toffee pudding with caramelised walnut ice cream and butterscotch sauce. A tidy wine list offers bottles from £16, topping out at £32.

Chef/s: Lewis King. **Closed:** Mon, Tue, 26 and 27 Dec, 2 weeks Jan, 1 week Nov. **Meals:** main courses £14 to £22. Set L £15 (2 courses) to £18. **Details:** 24 seats. 16 seats outside. Wheelchairs. Music.

LOCAL GEM

The Rose & Crown

Modern British | £28

Old Church Road, Snettisham, PE31 7LX
Tel no: (01485) 541382
roseandcrownsnettisham.co.uk

Rose-covered in summer, fire-warmed in winter, the whitewashed Rose & Crown earns a big tick in the 'charming village pub' box. Applause is deserved for the pub classics – the lacy batter coating a vast piece of cod is first-rate – but praise comes, too, for the likes of quail with chicory and turnips, king prawn dhansak, or a hotpot of locally shot game. Carefully cooked sea bass fights for attention with punchy pesto gnocchi, but all is forgiven when a blood-orange tart with mandarin sorbet delights. Wine from £18.50.

Stanhoe

The Duck Inn

Cooking score: 3
Modern British | £33

Burnham Road, Stanhoe, PE31 8QD
Tel no: (01485) 518330
duckinn.co.uk

Ben and Sarah Hadley have worked wonders since moving here in 2013, transforming the Duck Inn into a showpiece Norfolk hostelry.

It just about manages to hold on to its pub status, retaining a small bar area for drinkers, but most of the space is given over to dining with food that is bang on the money. The kitchen is driven by local and regional produce, perhaps a bowl of Brancaster mussels with vanilla broth, chorizo, leeks and caviar or flavours of local heritage carrots and beetroot, served with a Norfolk-made brie-style White Lady cheese, caraway caramel and leek ash. Mains show off locally landed fish, say a thick fillet of Marmite butter-poached cod with a superb red pepper sauce, fennel and saffron potatoes or opt for a dry-aged fillet of beef pie with parsley-root purée. Puddings, too, show flair, perhaps a brown sugar sweetie pie with squash and white chocolate ganache, milk crumb and lemon mascarpone. The carefully thought-out and reasonably priced wine list is arranged by style.

Chef/s: Shaun Ireson. **Closed:** 25 Dec. **Meals:** main courses £14 to £25. **Details:** 96 seats. 70 seats outside. Bar. Wheelchairs. Music. Parking.

Stoke Holy Cross

Stoke Mill

Cooking score: 4
Modern British | £40
Mill Road, Stoke Holy Cross, NR14 8PA
Tel no: (01508) 493337
stokemill.co.uk

Once home to a certain Mr Colman's mustard-grinding machinery, this handsome, white weatherboarded mill is a gem. In pristine condition, its expansive internal space suits the modern mood by not being overly dressed up. The kitchen's output follows suit, with intelligent combinations and a good spread of regional ingredients: Binham Blue cheese, for example, appears in a salad opener with BBQ beetroots and walnuts. This is a kitchen that draws on European ideas, too, thus salt cod arrives with soft quail's egg, chorizo and roasted red pepper. Move on to fillet of beef with a wee braised beef pie and chips, or sea bass with local crab and lemon cream. Finish with a raspberry-fest of soufflé and sorbet. The wine list traverses the globe but stays at home for local Winbirri Bacchus by the glass and bottle.

Chef/s: Andrew Rudd. **Closed:** Mon, Tue, first week Jan. **Meals:** main courses £16 to £27. Set L £20 (2 courses) to £25. Set D £22 (2 courses) to £27. Sun L £28. Tasting menu £45. **Details:** 65 seats. Bar. Wheelchairs. Music. Parking.

The Wildebeest

Cooking score: 3
Modern British | £40
82-86 Norwich Road, Stoke Holy Cross, NR14 8QJ
Tel no: (01508) 492497
thewildebeest.co.uk

Wildebeest are seldom spotted in Norfolk, but it's worth taking a safari to this converted village pub to sample the accomplished seasonal cooking. Settle into a leather chair on bare-boards flooring, ideally near the kitchen hatch where young, focused chefs busy themselves. The elaborate menu changes regularly, although local ingredients are a constant and best sampled in the 'taste of Norfolk' six-courser. At inspection, this began with al dente asparagus matched with rich confit egg, puffed rice and herb oil, and proceeded with a succulent chicken and basil terrine, then crab with crème fraîche. Next came the highlight: tender smokey beef rib on buttered spinach with smoked garlic purée. Yes, each dish had an ingredient too many, but the quality of produce was top-notch, presentation superb and service knowledgeable. Only a too-sweet pre-dessert of apple sorbet topped with gin foam was forgettable. The wine list (from £21) holds much worldwide enticement, too.

Chef/s: Daniel Smith and Charlie Wilson. **Closed:** 25 and 26 Dec. **Meals:** main courses £17 to £27. Set L £18 (2 courses) to £23. Set D £24 (2 courses) to £28. Sun L £28. Tasting menu £45 (6 courses). **Details:** 65 seats. 25 seats outside. Wheelchairs. Music. Parking.

Swaffham

Strattons Hotel

Cooking score: 2
Modern British | £30
4 Ash Close, Swaffham, PE37 7NH
Tel no: (01760) 723845
strattonshotel.com

'Reuse, rationalise, recover'... just three of the 'R' words that define proceedings at this eco-minded enterprise in Norfolk's Breckland. The owners were doing 'boutique' long before it became fashionable and have transformed their Palladian-style villa into a repository for local sculptures, paintings and the like. They have also expanded their café and deli (CoCoes), although serious foodies should head to the semi-basement Rustic Room for carefully wrought, eclectic food founded on green principles and seasonal sourcing. Local flavours surface in dishes such as pan-roasted Norfolk quail with parsnip purée, wild garlic pesto and crispy capers, while cured mackerel with cucumber and lime dressing or butter-poached cod accompanied by spinach and lentil dhal, garlic and yoghurt sauce show the kitchen's fondness for global partnerships. To finish, dessert cocktails are a boozy alternative to mainstream desserts including hazelnut meringue with chunky chocolate ice cream. 'Natural' vintages figure prominently on the wine list.

Chef/s: Jules Hetherton and Dan Freear. **Closed:** 1 week Christmas. **Meals:** main courses £15 to £20. **Details:** 40 seats. 18 seats outside. Bar. Music. Parking.

Local Gem

These entries highlight a range of neighbourhood venues, delivering good, freshly cooked food at great value for money.

Thornham

LOCAL GEM

Shuck's

International | £30
Drove Orchards, Thornham Road, Thornham, PE36 6LS
Tel no: (01485) 525889
shucksattheyurt.co.uk

It may look like an unpromising tent from the outside, but Beth and Phil Milner's yurt proves to be a rustic, wood-burner-warmed den within, filled with fairy lights, chunky tables and cushion-strewn sofas. It caters for all-comers: drop by for breakfast, coffee and cake, or a full meal. The food is spot-on for the setting, and the kitchen delivers a lineup of appetising dishes spanning everything from chicken liver parfait with a loaf of Norfolk lavender bread, to tandoori buttermilk chicken, linguine vongole, ramen bowls or burgers. Sunday roasts are a winner, as is apple crumble éclair with salted caramel ice cream. Wines from £16.50.

Thorpe Market

The Gunton Arms

Cooking score: 3
British | £35
Cromer Road, Thorpe Market, NR11 8TZ
Tel no: (01263) 832010
theguntonarms.co.uk

It's easy to be swept along by the hip artiness of The Gunton Arms – an offbeat country-house hostelry plonked in the middle of an historic 1,000-acre deer park. The owners have decked out the place in quirkily eccentric style, while the main gastronomic action centres on the vast, vaulted Elk Room, where locally reared meats are cooked over a mighty open fire in what looks like a 21st-century take on a Tudor kitchen. Steaks are the big thing, although fans of all things piggy won't be disappointed by the Blythburgh pork chops, pork and leek bangers or starters of ham hock and green bean salad. Crab from the coast is a regular piscine alternative, alongside the likes of roast hake with Padrón peppers and chorizo, although the well-sourced meat is the star. After that, try elderflower jelly or apricot and almond tart with clotted cream. Service can be clunky, although a sizeable choice of decent wines by the glass offers some compensation.

Chef/s: Stuart Tattersall. **Meals:** main courses £12 to £26. **Details:** 90 seats. 100 seats outside. Bar. Wheelchairs. Music. Parking.

Titchwell

Titchwell Manor

Cooking score: 4
Modern European | £42
Titchwell, PE31 8BB
Tel no: (01485) 210221
titchwellmanor.com

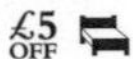

The coastline with its nature reserves and abundant bird life is just across the road from this one-time Victorian farmhouse, now a boutique hotel that celebrated its 30th anniversary in 2018. There's a genuine vibrancy to the place, reflected in bold colours, and it is run with warmth and passion by the Snaith family. The restaurant is the heart and soul of the place, with chef patron Eric Snaith and head chef Chris Mann championing the region's produce. The two menus – 'Conversation' and 'Classics' – reflect ambition and a desire to satisfy. Époisses cheese stars in a first-course quiche, with celeriac, apple and crispy shallots, or go classic with Brancaster mussels in white wine. Presentation is a strength in dishes such as fillet of gurnard with whole roast carrot and matelote sauce, and pink Gressingham duck breast with its braised leg and preserved cherry purée, while desserts like Yorkshire rhubarb with Norfolk saffron custard and tapioca have inspired flavour combinations. An extensive wine list is arranged by style.

Chef/s: Eric Snaith and Chris Mann. **Meals:** main courses £14 to £27. Set D £42. **Details:** 70 seats. Bar. Wheelchairs. Music. Parking.

Wells-next-the-Sea

LOCAL GEM

Wells Crab House

Seafood | £30
38 Freeman Street, Wells-next-the-Sea, NR23 1BA
Tel no: (01328) 710456
wellscrabhouse.co.uk

There's a bewildering variety on the menu at this no-nonsense spot in busy Wells, but here's a tip: keep it simple and choose one of the generous seafood platters (crab, lobster, smoked fish, or The Big One) to enjoy North Sea fruits at their freshest. Drawn to other options? There's praise for smoked mackerel, horseradish and beetroot salad, while plaice, baked whole and served with wild garlic butter is a triumph, and meat eaters will enjoy lamb belly with local asparagus, confit potatoes and haricot bean purée. A functional wine list opens at £18.

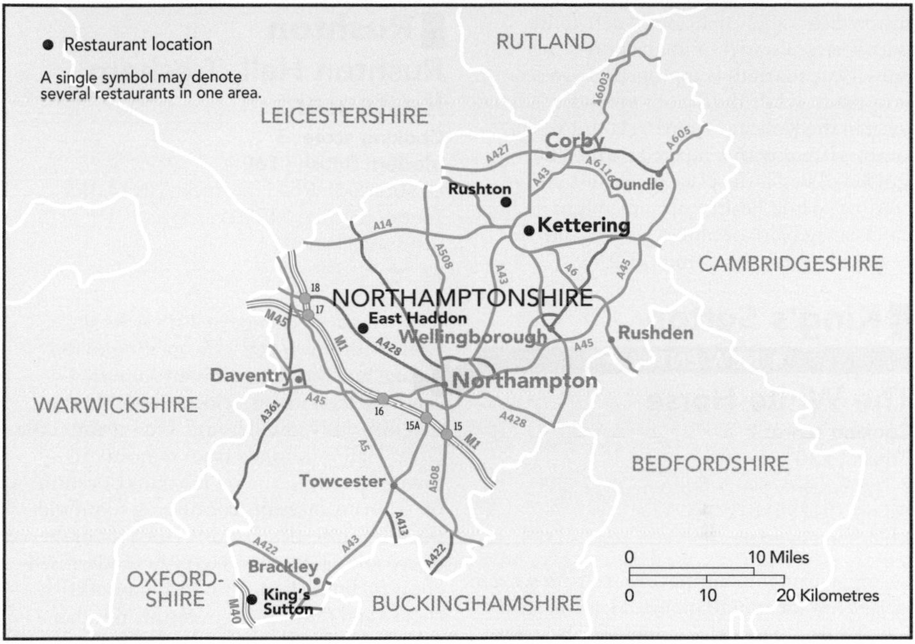

East Haddon

The Red Lion

Cooking score: 3
Modern British | £35
Main Street, East Haddon, NN6 8BU
Tel no: (01604) 770223
redlioneasthaddon.co.uk

It's a bucolic scene: from the thatched building in honey-coloured Northamptonshire ironstone, the rosemary-fringed garden looks out over fields of sheep. Inside, the menu offered in the stone-flagged bar and adjoining dining room is competent, if not overly exciting. Changing only three times a year can mean there are seasonal anomalies – no asparagus or new potatoes on a late May visit, for example, or dishes that feel overly hearty for the weather outside. That said, the food – much of which is from local suppliers – is well prepared and nicely balanced. The Scotch egg is uplifted by its caper mayo; there's a deeply flavoured beef, mushroom and Stilton pie; and the batter on the obligatory fish and chips is crisp and light. A lemon shortcrust tart, topped with a brûlée-style sugar glaze, is the standout pud, though a blowsy pavlova puts up a good fight. The short wine list includes 'fizz', 'sticky' and a focus on Warner Edwards gins, distilled just up the road.

Chef/s: Chloe Haycock. **Meals:** main courses £11 to £17. **Details:** 104 seats. 50 seats outside. Bar. Music. Parking.

Kettering

LOCAL GEM

Exotic Dining

Indian | £28
3-5 Newland Street, Kettering, NN16 8JH
Tel no: (01536) 411176
dineexotic.co.uk

Hunt out this much-loved restaurant for a lively and, as the name suggests, exotic experience – camel ribeye or grilled haunch of zebra anyone? More conventional Indian fusion dishes show deliciously deft ability with spices: a starter of jingha puri (king prawn in tamarind) is appropriately sweet-sour-spicy, while the flavour of tender sautéed meat in the Kolkata favourite, lasuni kosha lamb, is lifted with tempered garlic. The 'golden oldies' is the place for the utterly familiar, while 'healthy options' might include chicken sag balti, or bhindi gosht (lamb or beef with okra). Wine from £12.95.

King's Sutton

★ NEW ENTRY ★

The White Horse

Cooking score: 2
British | £30
2 The Square, King's Sutton, OX17 3RF
Tel no: (01295) 812440
whitehorseks.co.uk

Secure within the confines of a well-preserved village not far from Banbury, Hendrik and Julie Dutson-Steinfeld's captivating hostelry offers an agreeable blend of rusticity and easy-going vibes. The bar accommodates drinkers, while a couple of snug dining rooms cater to those with hunger pangs, delivering a very rich, cheesy mushroom and crème fraîche omelette ('about as good as it can get') or a crispy pig's head with pancetta, black pudding and brown sauce ahead of guinea fowl and morel mushroom fricassée, or fish and chips. Elsewhere, the kitchen cooks to the modern British template, deconstructing and reconstructing respectively for a Purston Manor lamb 'pie' with savoy cabbage, dauphinois potatoes, mint sauce and lamb gravy. Pick of the desserts is a sticky toffee pudding and salted caramel ice cream. An excellent-value lunch deal, well-reported Sunday roasts, real ales and a wine list that starts at £17.50 help to cement the pub's local reputation.

Chef/s: Hendrik Dutson-Steinfeld. **Meals:** main courses £15 to £38. Set L £14 (2 courses) to £17. Sun L £18 (2 courses) to £22. **Details:** Bar.

Rushton

Rushton Hall, Tresham Restaurant

Cooking score: 3
Modern British | £60
Desborough Road, Rushton, NN14 1RR
Tel no: (01536) 713001
rushtonhall.com

It was a year of change in 2018 at Rushton Hall, with a new brasserie opening in the spring, and the main dining room, the Tresham Restaurant, relocated within the magnificently grand house. One assumes the Great Hall is immune from removal, its towering ceiling and oil portraits of centuries of Tresham ancestors continuing to provide the most majestic of settings for a tot of sherry. The cooking continues to ply a modernised country-house line, with seared monkfish cheeks and cauliflower purée in an Indian-spiced dressing to start, followed perhaps by pork tenderloin with salsify, cavolo nero and burnt apple purée, as well as a little sausage roll, or a traditional take on fish with sea bass and mussels in cream sauce. British artisan cheeses with fruit loaf, or the likes of banana mousse with hazelnuts and coffee granita, close the show. The wine list picks its sedate way through the French regions before drifting obliquely into the big wide world. There's a decent selection by the glass from £7.

Chef/s: Adrian Coulthard. **Meals:** set D £60 (3 courses). Sun L £30. **Details:** 36 seats. Bar. Wheelchairs. Music. Parking. Children over 12 yrs.

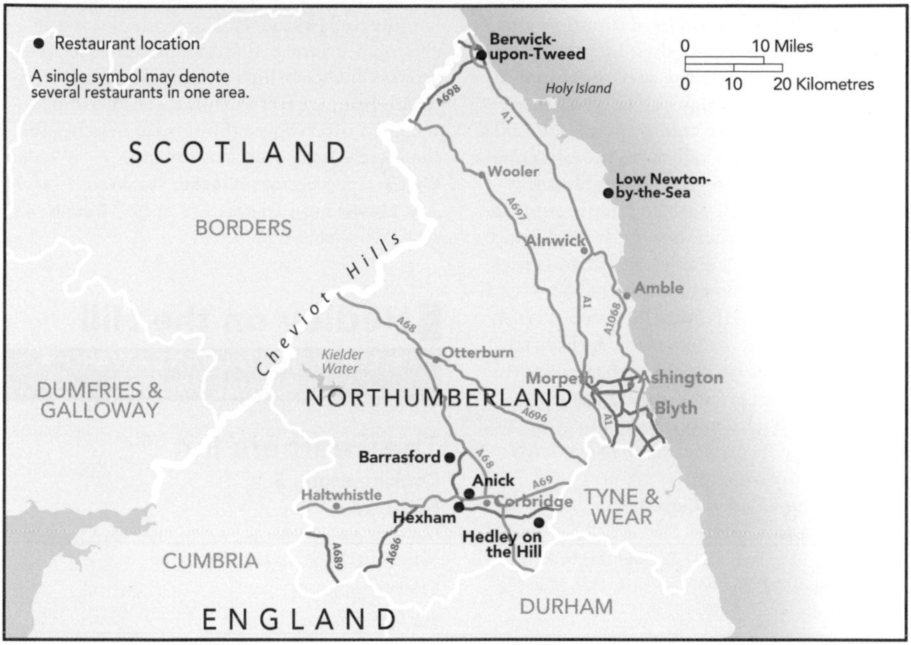

● Restaurant location
A single symbol may denote several restaurants in one area.

0 10 Miles
0 10 20 Kilometres

SCOTLAND
BORDERS
DUMFRIES & GALLOWAY
Cheviot Hills
Berwick-upon-Tweed
Holy Island
A698
A1
Wooler
A697
Low Newton-by-the-Sea
Alnwick
Amble
A1068
A68
Kielder Water
Otterburn
Morpeth
Ashington
Blyth
NORTHUMBERLAND
A696
Barrasford
Anick
A69
Haltwhistle
Corbridge
Hexham
TYNE & WEAR
Hedley on the Hill
A689
A686
CUMBRIA
ENGLAND
DURHAM

Anick

The Rat Inn

Cooking score: 2
British | £27
Anick, NE46 4LN
Tel no: (01434) 602814
theratinn.com

At the entrance to this 18th-century rural hideaway, a welcoming mosaic of plaques and awards pays testament to the Rat's long-standing success in championing great local food in a convivial atmosphere. 'One of our finds of the year,' enthused one reader after savouring perfectly cooked meat of impeccably detailed provenance that only just stops short of naming the actual animal. Sunday roasts are famous, as are the beef ribs, cooked to order, and priced by weight. The blackboard-led menu, served by friendly, knowledgeable staff, might also feature a daily handmade terrine (such as chicken and roast pepper in pancetta) or grilled hake with pecorino crust and sea vegetables. Well-executed desserts range from caramelised white chocolate mousse to the standout simplicity of a perfect custard tart. Six cask ales and a focused selection of wines complement the really good pub cooking.

Chef/s: Phil Mason and Kevin MacLean. **Closed:** 25 Dec, 1 Jan. **Meals:** main courses £12 to £22. Set L and D £18 (2 courses) to £20. **Details:** 70 seats. 70 seats outside. Bar. Music. Parking.

Barrasford

The Barrasford Arms

Cooking score: 2
Modern British | £28
Barrasford, NE48 4AA
Tel no: (01434) 681237
barrasfordarms.co.uk

This restaurant and country pub with rooms has recently been taken over by Michael and Victoria Eames, translating previous experiences in large hotels to a more homely scale with their focus on local suppliers and honest Northumbrian dishes. Lunch and dinner can be taken in the cosy restaurant by the fire or, on sunny days, alfresco on the terrace looking down across open fields and a gently wooded river valley. Menus offer a mix of delicately reinterpreted classics: black pudding Scotch egg with celeriac rémoulade, micro leaves from their own polytunnel and a pleasingly tart apple purée; or fish and chips taken up several notches using chunky North Sea hake with a well-minted fresh pea crush and punchy homemade tartare. A rhubarb panna cotta with confit rhubarb stems and a sweet purée is a perfect summer dessert to celebrate fresh garden produce. Local ales and gins as well as a compact wine list provide fitting accompaniment.

Chef/s: Michael Eames. **Closed:** Mon, 25 and 26 Dec. **Meals:** main courses £13 to £22. Set L £15 (2 courses) to £19. Sun L £17 (2 courses) to £20. **Details:** 58 seats. 20 seats outside. Bar. Music. Parking.

Berwick-upon-Tweed

Audela

Cooking score: 2
Modern British | £40

64-66 Bridge Street, Berwick-upon-Tweed, TD15 1AQ
Tel no: (01289) 308827
£5 OFF

Comments such as 'a delight on our doorstep' and 'Audela just oozes calmness and relaxed sophistication' show readers approve the move to new premises at the end of 2017. It has given Sarah Watson and Craig Pearson the scope to further develop their culinary ambitions. In elegant Georgian surroundings, with the focus on a more formal dining experience, Craig delivers an assured touch in the kitchen, while Sarah shares her passion for trusted producers and regional ingredients front of house. After a palate-tempting crumbly herbed scone, expect local fish and game conjured into rich flavour bombs such as pigeon with unctuous pig's cheek terrine on earthy celeriac, or a more delicate take on a wafer-thin crab lasagne with langoustine bisque. Passion fruit and white chocolate crème brûlée or a platter of local artisan cheeses brings a satisfying conclusion to this homage to Northumbria. A compact wine list offers some thoughtful matches for the increasingly ambitious menu.

Chef/s: Craig Pearson. **Closed:** Tue, Wed, 14 to 28 July. **Meals:** main courses £13 to £29. **Details:** 45 seats. Wheelchairs. Music.

Hedley on the Hill

★ LOCAL RESTAURANT AWARD ★
REGIONAL WINNER

The Feathers Inn

Cooking score: 3
British | £29

Main Street, Hedley on the Hill, NE43 7SW
Tel no: (01661) 843607
thefeathers.net
£5 OFF £30

In their decade at the helm, Rhian Cradock and Helen Greer's commitment to local suppliers and ethical, sustainable food has become integrated into the very fabric of this welcoming village inn that's at the heart of its community. A blackboard locates suppliers within the pub's orbit while black and white portrait photographs pay homage to these trusted partners and their produce; the seasonal menu emphasises that it's all about the ingredients. The ongoing passion for home-cured charcuterie is displayed in a sunny starter of grilled asparagus with spiced air-dried pork loin, soft polenta and a Wylam duck egg. Rustic influences are evident in a comfort-laden dish of sautéed spring lamb offal with beer balsamic and creamy mash, while roasted Whitby halibut with tarragon and Jersey Royals shows a capacity for a lighter touch. A rich marmalade Bakewell with clotted cream or homemade ices offer a satisfying close. A small but personally curated wine selection, distinctive craft and cask ales and some quirky spirits demonstrate attention to detail and prompt a wish for rooms 'so we could stay over!'.

Chef/s: Rhian Cradock. **Closed:** Mon, Tue, first 2 weeks Jan. **Meals:** main courses £12 to £16. Sun L £17 (1 course) to £25. **Details:** 39 seats. 20 seats outside. Bar. Parking.

Hexham

Bouchon Bistrot

Cooking score: 4
French | £29
4-6 Gilesgate, Hexham, NE46 3NJ
Tel no: (01434) 609943
bouchonbistrot.co.uk

With its *belle époque* Parisian music hall posters and unfussy decor, this very French bistro offers flavourful French country cuisine delivered from a kitchen abuzz with Gallic chat. Braised rabbit with tarragon and tomato is a slow-cooked sensation presented simply with a little salad for freshness and croûtons for crunch. A main course of grilled mixed fish brings together perfectly prepared morsels of sea trout, stone bass, mackerel and scallop with a clever maritime take on cassoulet, successfully pairing cockles and creamy rouille flavours with haricot beans and the faint aniseed notes of fennel. For the more traditionally minded, steak frites with duck-fat chips is a deservedly popular staple. Desserts might include such classics as tarte tatin or clafoutis, while an unctuous fondant au chocolat collapses satisfyingly into a sweet pool on the plate. A short wine list manages to embrace some lesser-known French regions with enthusiastic commentary provided by engaged staff.

Chef/s: Nicolas Kleist. **Closed:** Sun, 24 to 27 Dec, bank hols. **Meals:** main courses £13 to £20. Set L £16 (2 courses) to £17. Set D £17 (2 courses) to £18. **Details:** 100 seats. 20 seats outside. Wheelchairs.

Low Newton-by-the-Sea

LOCAL GEM

The Ship Inn

British | £25
Newton Square, Low Newton-by-the-Sea, NE66 3EL
Tel no: (01665) 576262
shipinnnewton.co.uk

Solidly moored against the waves licking this tiny cluster of seafront cottages, the Ship attracts coastal walkers with dogs, alongside less energetic visitors in smart cars. The rough-hewn interior and down-to-earth atmosphere is a great leveller, one where simple things are done brilliantly, as homage is paid to local produce. Fresh crab stotties, kipper pâté and hearty soups are enthusiastically devoured, washed down by one of the 20 unique beers from the pub's very own microbrewery. Blackboard specials increase the choice on the succinct menu at this beachside nirvana.

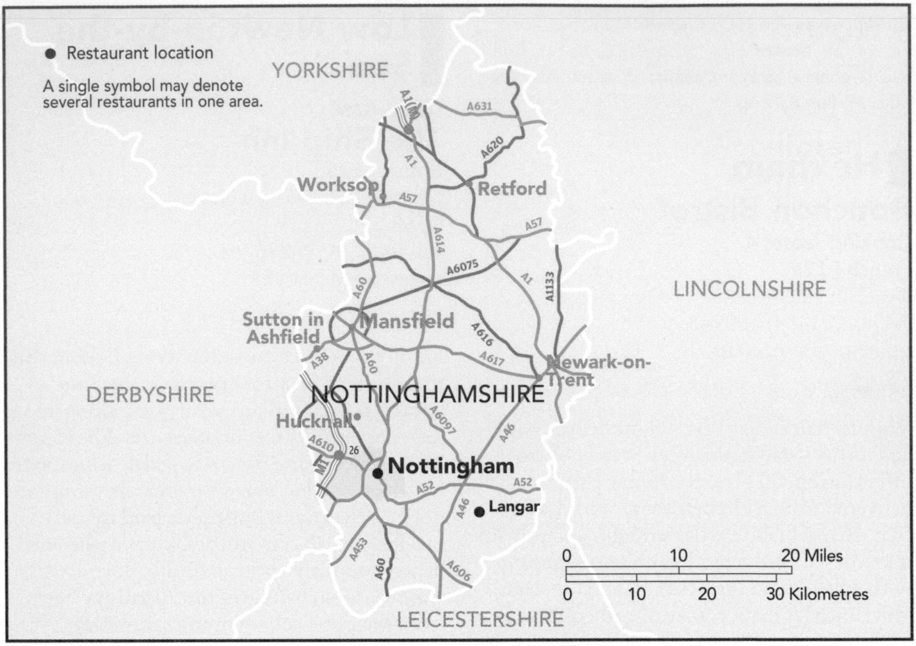

● Restaurant location

A single symbol may denote several restaurants in one area.

YORKSHIRE
LINCOLNSHIRE
DERBYSHIRE
NOTTINGHAMSHIRE
LEICESTERSHIRE
Worksop
Retford
Sutton in Ashfield
Mansfield
Newark-on-Trent
Hucknall
Nottingham
Langar
A1(M)
A631
A620
A1
A57
A614
A6075
A60
A1133
A616
A617
A38
A6097
A46
A610
M1
26
A52
A453
A606
0 10 20 Miles
0 10 20 30 Kilometres

Langar

Langar Hall

Cooking score: 4
Modern British | £43
Church Lane, Langar, NG13 9HG
Tel no: (01949) 860559
langarhall.com

A reader noted with surprise the relative paucity of good eating places in the Nottinghamshire countryside, which only goes to make this country house hotel shine all the more luminously. 'I instantly liked the style and grace of the place,' observed another, taken as much by the beautiful surroundings as by 'the hints of Merchant Ivory, eccentric favourite aunt, decadence, and days of the Raj with a modern twist.' Gary Booth has been heading the kitchen for some 20 years, building up a network of local and regional suppliers, and offering daily changing menus that feel contemporary and relevant, albeit in a classic context. Thus a typical meal could start with roasted onion broth with Tunworth cheese, move on to an assiette of Langar lamb with hay-baked carrots, goat's curd and ras el hanout, and finish with a celebration of Yorkshire rhubarb with Champagne and smoked milk ice cream. The wine list is well spread and thoughtfully chosen.

Chef/s: Gary Booth. **Meals:** set L £19 (2 courses) to £43. Set D £38 to £55. Sun L £40. **Details:** 70 seats. 20 seats outside. V menu. Vg menu. Bar. Wheelchairs. Music. Parking.

Symbols

Accommodation is available
£30 Three courses for less than £30
£5 OFF £5 off voucher scheme
Notable wine list

Nottingham

★ CHEF TO WATCH ★

★ NEW ENTRY ★

Alchemilla

Cooking score: 5
Modern British | £40
192 Derby Road, Nottingham, NG7 1NF
Tel no: (0115) 941 3515
alchemillarestaurant.uk

£5 OFF

Blink and you'll miss Alchemilla – a new restaurant set behind a rust-hued doorway in inner city Nottingham. To step inside is an almost Narnia-esque experience – diners descending into a Victorian coach house, abandoned for over a century, now rebooted with vertical moss gardens and giant skylights that cast patches of sunshine on to the tables below. It's bold, bright and rich in surprise – a mission statement echoed in the kitchen. Here, chef Alex Bond (once of Sat Bains – see entry) crafts tasting menus that work as a study in the textures and tastes of the Midlands landscape, designed to shift the spotlight from meat to vegetable-based cooking. An early summer inspection showed glimpses of magic from a restaurant gathering momentum. A course of potato cooked in seaweed with fermented garlic and smoked cream delivered a satisfying saline kick, while freshness radiated from a medley of asparagus and rhubarb resting on a silky bed of oyster. A closing dish of yoghurt, pine and lemony wood sorrel was more evidence of the kitchen deftly matchmaking unlikely ingredients. A thoughtfully curated wine list sees bottles catalogued with the aid of little maps, along with craft beers by the bottle.

Chef/s: Alex Bond. **Closed:** Sun, Mon, 2 weeks Dec, 2 weeks Aug. **Meals:** tasting menu £45 (5 courses) to £70. **Details:** 48 seats. V menu. Vg menu. Bar. Wheelchairs. Music.

Nottingham's best bites

Alex Bond of Alchemilla shares his favourite local places to eat and drink

Toast on Derby Road offers lovely filling **breakfasts** and some simple healthy options too, like **smashed avocado toasted sourdough**.

Outpost Coffee in Hockley roasts its beans on site and sources the best ones from all over the world, including **Kenya, Ethiopia, Colombia and Honduras**.

For a **pint**, try **The Sir John Borlase Warren**, a traditional old pub without the stuffy feel that you sometimes get. It has a lovely terrace, which is perfect for a summer drink.

I recommend **The Ruddington Arms** for **families**. They welcome little ones and the menu is special so you don't feel like you are compromising on taste.

The Rancliffe Arms in Bunny does a legendary **Sunday carvery** with all manner of roasted joints, an array of side dishes and the thickest, most unctuous gravy this side of the M1.

If I could eat only one thing around here, it would have to be... the cauliflower fritters at Bar Ibérico in Hockley - they are the stuff of dreams.

Hart's

Cooking score: 1
Modern British | £37
Standard Hill, Park Row, Nottingham, NG1 6GN
Tel no: (0115) 988 1900
hartsnottingham.co.uk

The hill on which Hart's stands was the peak from which Charles I raised his standard to commence the English Civil War – and though Hart's hadn't quite opened then, it is nonetheless an old monarch of the Nottingham scene, celebrating 20 years in business. The abstract paintings and polished floors of the dining room set the tone for refined modern British dining, though starters show a readiness to find inspiration beyond Blighty's shores; tuna belly with ponzu, black sesame and coriander impressed on our recent visit. Mains attest to assiduous sourcing – think tender roast lamb rump, Jersey Royals, braised fennel, tomato and red pepper ragù – while puddings don't pull punches: crowd-pleasing caramel tart with banana ice cream, for example. Though capable of stellar moments, some dishes from our visit suggested that Hart's can sometimes be a little cavalier in its cooking. A serious wine list spans continents and price ranges.
Chef/s: Daniel Burridge. **Closed:** 1 Jan. **Meals:** main courses £18 to £34. Set L £22 (2 courses) to £28. Set D £24 (2 courses) to £30. Sun L £24 (2 courses) to £30. **Details:** 80 seats. V menu. Bar. Wheelchairs. Parking.

The Larder on Goosegate

Cooking score: 2
Modern British | £28
16-22 Goosegate, Hockley, Nottingham, NG1 1FF
Tel no: (0115) 950 0111
thelarderongoosegate.co.uk

Vintage signs, medicine cabinets and salvaged apothecary bottles filled with flowers are a reminder that these high-ceilinged premises started out as the first retail venture from local lad (and pharmaceutical mogul in the making) Jesse Boot. These days, eclectic seasonal provender is the venue's common currency, with the kitchen dispensing highly palatable prescriptions, ranging from Cornish gurnard with roasted aubergine and kimchi to cod cheeks with Puy lentils and Trealy Farm chorizo. There are plenty of restorative meat and vegetarian options, too, from steaks in various guises or lamb shank with celeriac dauphinois and salsa verde to spice-roasted cauliflower with tahini, chickpeas and saffron yoghurt. To finish, custard panna cotta with Yorkshire rhubarb or a hunk of Lancashire Bomb cheese with a warm Eccles cake are just what the doctor ordered – especially when washed down with a beer from one of Nottinghamshire's indie breweries. Otherwise, dip into the helpfully annotated wine list.
Chef/s: Ewan McFarlane. **Closed:** Sun, Mon, 1 to 5 Jan. **Meals:** main courses £14 to £23. Set L and D £16 (2 courses) to £20. **Details:** 65 seats. Music.

★ TOP 10 ★

Restaurant Sat Bains

Cooking score: 9
Modern British | £95
Lenton Lane, Nottingham, NG7 2SA
Tel no: (0115) 986 6566
restaurantsatbains.com

From his chill-out spot in the flowerbeds, Junior echoes the almost tangibly laid-back vibe of Restaurant Sat Bains: Sat and his wife Amanda's pet rabbit is as comfortable in his floral surroundings as humans are made to feel at the tables inside. The incongruous location under the Clifton Boulevard (aka the relentless A52) reinforces RSB's down-to-earth feel. Dress code? Relaxed. The graciously light service is matched by exuberantly imaginative, deeply thoughtful cooking. Warm treacle bread with salty butter sets the tone for a sequence of plates (choose a seven- or ten-course tasting menu) that are vivacious with flavour and textural balance but that for all their cleverness never fall victim to gimmickry. A classic scallop and pork combination is given a makeover with braised trotter, just-seared scallops, peps of wild garlic (picked from the kitchen garden, every inch of which appears to pour forth herbs, berries, vegetables, leaves) and ponzu jelly under a cracking squid ink tapioca crisp. Anjou pigeon breasts, cooked to yielding pinkness over flame, and served with charred radicchio and carrots (roasted and puréed) make for a standout dish, the bird's offal served as a pâté on sourdough, the leg shredded and combined with Moroccan spices that caress rather than thump, and pair well with a date and olive sauce. The meal may end with a puck of baked (just) bittersweet, salt-flecked dark chocolate ganache, its punch parried by a gently tangy yoghurt sorbet with tantalising drops of Manni olive oil and 25-year-old balsamic vinegar. Macerated Gariguette strawberries hide under a snowfield of kombucha and lemon verbena granita whose sharpness is tempered by a fragrant Earl Grey crème pâtissière. To finish, a mouthful of Thai green curry ice cream, toffee-like in texture and laden with exotic kaffir lime, ginger, lemongrass and coriander, is wrapped in a playful, sticky whirl of candyfloss. It sends you home with a smile, reflecting on the brilliance of a chef (and team) who can cook with such ferocious ability without forgetting that food must essentially please, and leave you wanting more. Wines are arranged by flavour profile (the same colour-coded dots are used on the menu to indicate the relative dominance of a flavour in a dish), and with bottles at around £30 opening a lineup that tops out at £355, the list is refreshingly accessible. Do engage sommelier Laurent Richet in conversation to understand the true meaning of loving your job.

Chef/s: Sat Bains and John Freeman. **Closed:** Sun, Mon, Tue, 2 weeks Dec to Jan, 2 weeks Aug. **Meals:** tasting menu £95 (7 courses) to £110 (10 courses). **Details:** 44 seats. 16 seats outside. V menu. Bar. Wheelchairs. Music. Parking. Children over 8 yrs.

LOCAL GEM

Delilah Fine Foods

Modern European | £20

12 Victoria Street, Nottingham, NG1 2EX
Tel no: (0115) 948 4461
delilahfinefoods.co.uk

Combining the virtues of a deli and café under one (very high) roof, Delilah makes the most of its striking period setting within a converted Victorian bank. Produce from the shelves dictates the menu, a shopper-friendly lineup of charcuterie, cheeses and salads bolstered by flatbread pizzas and dishes including morcilla, pancetta and butter-bean stew. Delilah also does a splendid line in cakes and pastries to go with loose teas, artisan coffees and reasonably priced wines from family-run vineyards. There's a branch in Leicester (see entry).

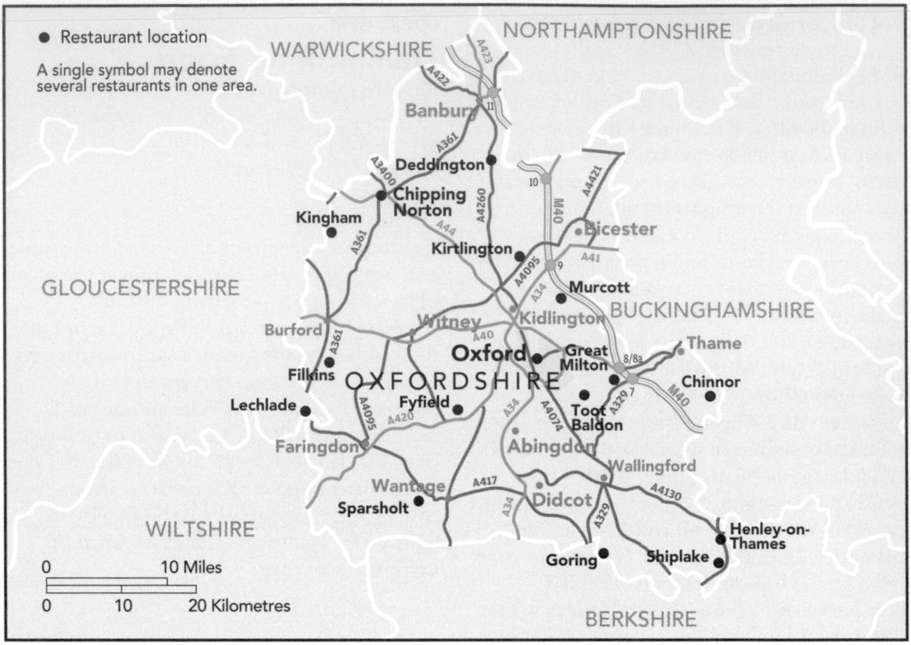

Chinnor

The Sir Charles Napier

Cooking score: 5
Modern British | £47

Sprigg's Alley, Chinnor, OX39 4BX
Tel no: (01494) 483011
sircharlesnapier.co.uk

Worth the circuitous journey around the Oxfordshire beechwoods, The Charles Napier is a country pub with personality to spare. Since mid-2018, the kitchen has been in the hands of Liam Leech (promoted from sous-chef), and he has retained the familiar robustness to many of the offerings here. A leek and potato bun is a 'stonkingly rich' combination of diced potato, leeks, spinach, Parmesan and cream en croûte, while crab salad has a layer of creamed brown meat with pickled cucumber, shredded fennel and lavosh crackers. Dishes are intensely worked, but to resonant effect, as when a boned, stuffed poussin comes filled with pork and breadcrumb forcemeat, reposing on a brace of giant morels in a mushroom-rich vin jaune sauce. Simplicity wins the day in a whole, filleted plaice, crumbed and roasted, accompanied by artichoke barigoule with thickly piped aïoli. The reference dessert is a cacao-laden bitter chocolate soufflé, with malted milk ice cream. Service is switched on and there's also an exemplary wine list, which offers value and excitement in spades, barely putting a foot wrong from Moutard's Champagnes to Rabl's Austrian eiswein. House selections start at £21.50.

Chef/s: Liam Leech. **Closed:** Mon (exc bank hols), 25 and 26 Dec. **Meals:** main courses £23 to £30. Set L and D Tue to Fri £22 (2 courses). **Details:** 70 seats. 70 seats outside. V menu. Bar. Wheelchairs. Music. Children over 6 yrs at D.

Chipping Norton

Wild Thyme

Cooking score: 2
Modern British | £40
10 New Street, Chipping Norton, OX7 5LJ
Tel no: (01608) 645060
wildthymerestaurant.co.uk
£5 OFF

The market town of Chipping Norton is as quintessentially English as it sounds, but don't go thinking the Pullens' restaurant with rooms is anyway chintzy or stuffy. Exposed stone, natural and painted wood, and colourful artworks, give a charming rusticity to the ground-floor dining room. Nick Pullen makes just about everything in-house, and has a reliable network of suppliers keeping the kitchen stocked with local cheeses, fresh veg, and seasonal game such as rabbit, venison and partridge. The fixed-price menu might take you from double-baked Gorgonzola soufflé, with sweet local honey and crunchy hazelnuts, via pan-fried stone bass with Cornish mussel ragoût and bouillabaisse sauce, to a lemon and lime combo with frozen lemon parfait, lime syllabub and limoncello granita. There's a Med spin to much of the menu – a ravioli here, an arancini there – and flavour combinations are based on sound classical principles. The well-annotated wine list opens at £19.

Chef/s: Nicholas Pullen. **Closed:** Sun, Mon, 1 week summer, 1 week winter. **Meals:** set L and midweek D £20 (2 courses) to £25. Set D £32 (2 courses) to £40. **Details:** 35 seats.

Local Gem

These entries highlight a range of neighbourhood venues, delivering good, freshly cooked food at great value for money.

Deddington

LOCAL GEM

Knife & Fork

Modern British | £50
Clifton Road, Deddington, OX15 0TP
Tel no: (01869) 336954
knifeandforkeatery.co.uk

Tanya and John Young run their Oxfordshire farmhouse primarily as a B&B, but on Friday and Saturday evenings their tasteful dining room functions as a restaurant of sorts, serving a five-course set menu of wholly gluten-free dishes (chef Tanya is a coeliac). Diners sit elbow-to-elbow at two large communal tables while the kitchen sends out the likes of carrot salad with toasted sunflower seeds and harissa, pork belly with butternut squash purée and cavolo nero, and puds such as treacle tart with blood orange curd. Unlicensed, but you can BYO.

Filkins

The Five Alls

Cooking score: 2
Modern British | £32
Filkins, GL7 3JQ
Tel no: (01367) 860875
thefiveallsfilkins.co.uk
£5 OFF

Sebastian and Lana Snow have gone for 'mass appeal' at this neatly restored Cotswold inn-with-rooms: cheap and cheerful pub classics go down well with pints of Brakspear's in the beamed and flagstoned bar, while a 'cover all bases' approach is the norm when it comes to the food served in the warren of dining rooms. Set deals, specials and so-called 'comfortable' classics (burgers, devilled kidneys, mac 'n' cheese) sit alongside the all-embracing main menu, and the sheer weight of numbers can take its toll. That said, there are plenty of satisfying successes ranging from fillet of hake with tapenade crostini, soft-boiled quail's egg and a textbook chive sauce to a nicely balanced pecan tart loaded with nuts; fans also rate the

bangers and mash very highly. Other plus points include friendly, informal and informed service and a decent selection of wines by the glass.
Chef/s: Sebastian Snow and Piotr Skoczen. **Closed:** 25 Dec. **Meals:** main courses £13 to £24. Set L and D £19 (2 courses) to £26. Sun L £26. **Details:** 80 seats. 40 seats outside. Bar. Wheelchairs. Music. Parking.

Fyfield

The White Hart

Cooking score: 3
Modern British | £37
Main Road, Fyfield, OX13 5LW
Tel no: (01865) 390585
whitehart-fyfield.com

With its soaring great hall and minstrels' gallery crowned with a high vaulted ceiling, this one-time Tudor chantry house still creaks with ecclesiastical antiquity – although current incumbents Kay and Mark Chandler have steered The White Hart into the 21st-century as a country pub with serious gastronomic aspirations. An increasingly productive vegetable garden and a trusty network of local suppliers underpin the kitchen's output, whether it's a refined assemblage of goat's curd, smoked hazelnuts, pickled kohlrabi and quinoa crisp, or a gutsier combination of home-smoked duck breast, devilled duck hearts, black pudding and pickled walnuts. While sides of miso-glazed hispi cabbage and bacon jam signal the kitchen's forward-thinking intentions, there's a cosy familiarity to slow-roast pork belly with cider jus, or a sharing board of local meats. Puddings keep things simple: rhubarb and custard, say, or sticky toffee pudding, albeit with cheffy flourishes in the presentation. Wines are several notches above the pub norm.
Chef/s: Mark Chandler and James Wilkinson. **Closed:** Mon (exc bank hols). **Meals:** main courses £16 to £27. Set L £20 (2 courses) to £23. Sun L £26 (2 courses) to £29. **Details:** 60 seats. 40 seats outside. Bar. Music. Parking.

Goring

The Miller of Mansfield

Cooking score: 4
Modern British | £45
High Street, Goring, RG8 9AW
Tel no: (01491) 872829
millerofmansfield.com

'One of the best pubs I've visited in a while,' notes one reader – although, in truth, this thoroughly modernised Georgian inn now makes most of its money from boutique accommodation and ambitious contemporary food, rather than pulling pints. Locals still drink in the bar, but the real action takes place in the stripped-back dining room. The kitchen puts down a serious marker with nibbles such as crispy pig's cheek with sauce gribiche, and a nine-course 'signature' menu. Stick with the à la carte and you'll still be rewarded with chef Nick Galer's innovative ideas: perhaps pheasant eggs 'in the nest' with black pudding, duck ham and lemon sorrel, or gravadlax of sea trout paired with cockle ketchup, treacle yoghurt and wild garlic. A dish of line-caught sea bass is cleverly aligned with smoked leeks, black garlic and pickled lemon dressing, before the final flourish – perhaps rum-soaked sponge with peanut butter mousse, lime and banana ice cream. Well-chosen wines are helpfully arranged by style.
Chef/s: Nick Galer. **Closed:** 27 and 28 Dec. **Meals:** main courses £18 to £27. Tasting menu £60 (9 courses). **Details:** 60 seats. 40 seats outside. Bar. Wheelchairs. Music.

Send us your review

Your feedback informs the content of the *GFG* and will be used to compile next year's reviews. To register your opinion about any restaurant listed in the Guide, or a restaurant that you wish to bring to our attention, visit: thegoodfoodguide.co.uk/feedback

Great Milton

Belmond Le Manoir aux Quat'Saisons

Cooking score: 7
Modern French | £170
Church Road, Great Milton, OX44 7PD
Tel no: (01844) 278881
belmond.com

£5 OFF

This 15th-century manor house in the countryside not far from Oxford has pastoral charm to spare, its sumptuous gardens a joy for wandering at almost any season. It has been the preserve of Raymond Blanc since the mid-1980s, participating in the revolutionising of British dining and the country-house movement, and still worth a place on the to-do list of modern gastronomy. The expansive, brightly decorated dining room makes a relaxing setting for menus that, as one lucky reader put it, 'could have been written just for me'. There's still a delicacy of construction to most dishes, allied to a determination to emphasise the inherent qualities of ingredients, many of which come from the extensive kitchen gardens. A risotto of spring vegetables with tomato essence and chervil cream is all vernal freshness, while the Cornish crab salad in coconut dressing with lime leaf sorbet incorporates south-east Asian elements with ease. Main courses achieve great depth, often with striking economy of means, as when veal kidneys are teamed with alliums and lovage in red wine jus, although the lamb plate that combines cutlets, rump and a croquette with white asparagus and broad beans in rosemary-scented jus pulls out all the stops. Coming across a little sorbet or ice cream at the bottom of a technically flawless soufflé is like finding the sixpence in the pudding, while the millionaire's shortbread is a bit of shameless populism. If the Gariguette strawberries are in season, do not miss. Occasionally inattentive service provokes understandable grousing, but the experience is generally reliably magical, even if the wines, from £35, are mostly an unattainable ideal.

Chef/s: Raymond Blanc OBE and Gary Jones. **Meals:** set L and D £170. Tasting menu L £140 (7 courses), D £190 (7 courses). **Details:** 80 seats. V menu. Bar. Wheelchairs. Music. Parking.

Henley-on-Thames

Shaun Dickens at the Boathouse

Cooking score: 6
Modern British | £49
Station Road, Henley-on-Thames, RG9 1AZ
Tel no: (01491) 577937
shaundickens.co.uk

Come rain or come shine (preferably the latter), Shaun and Gemma Dickens' converted boathouse by the banks of the Thames is a food lover's magnet. The vistas are at their most invigorating from the restaurant's decked terrace, although the dining room's glass frontage also promises pleasurable views. Shaun Dickens learnt his craft in some big-name kitchens, and his feel for highly detailed, precise cooking is picked up by head chef James Walshaw: the result is food prepared with real passion, full of bright notes and clever detailing. A starter of Cornish mackerel cut through with astringent carrot pickle, sweet-and-sour carrot, orzo and chervil could set the tone, while mains might see ox cheek heartily embellished with braised red cabbage and bone marrow or an equally fulsome dish of free-range duck complemented by an onion tart, baked turnip, salsify and daikon. After that, local Henley honey is teamed with polenta cake and almond and ginger anglaise. Wines from all quarters include some eye-opening sommelier's choices, plus a fair fistful by the glass.

Chef/s: Shaun Dickens and James Walshaw. **Closed:** Mon, Tue, 25 to 27 Dec. **Meals:** main courses £22 to £26. Set L £26 (2 courses) to £30. Tasting menu £59 (6 courses). **Details:** 45 seats. 20 seats outside. Bar. Wheelchairs. Music.

The Cotswolds' best bites

Emily Watkins of The Kingham Plough in Oxfordshire shares her favourite local places to eat and drink

Daylesford organic farm shop near Kingham has a wonderful **café** and a huge range of healthy **breakfasts**.

Made by Bob in Cirencester is my pick for **lunch**. Bob is a fantastic chef and cooks deliciously fresh light dishes. There is something for everyone.

For **food shopping**, there are lots of small independent farm shops between Broadway and Evesham selling all the amazing produce from the vale.

The King's Head Inn at Bledington is the epitome of a Cotswolds pub with thatched roof and a **great pint**.

The Swan Inn at Swinbrook near Burford is completely idyllic. It's very sheltered so heaven for the **children** to run around in a beautiful setting.

No. 131 hotel in **Cheltenham** has an amazing **cocktail** bar and gives a good excuse to go to town.

For **Sunday lunch**, I think our roasts at **The Kingham Plough** are legendary - luckily, we have lots of customers who agree.

Kingham

The Kingham Plough

Cooking score: 4
Modern British | £42
The Green, Kingham, OX7 6YD
Tel no: (01608) 658327
thekinghamplough.co.uk

Sitting on one side of a green that's pretty much all there is to this tiny Cotswold village, Emily Watkins' inn-with-rooms is run with warmth and intelligence. A life-sized model of a pig perches beside the fire in the flagstoned bar; settle at one of the bare tables here, or carry on to one of the two high-raftered dining rooms with their polished dressers and chunky old-fashioned chairs. Skill and dedication are part of the package, applied to well-sourced produce that might take in a starter of Salcombe brown crab, a delicately flavoured layering of sweet white meat, pea cream, courgette and crab oil. Main courses deliver some neat spins on intuitive combinations, as in grilled Cornish plaice with spears of local asparagus and a tangy tartare hollandaise or impressively tender rump of lamb teamed with a little cake of the braised belly, lightly smoked mash, broad beans and mint oil. Desserts include a textbook treacle tart, cheeses are prime local specimens, and a short list of European wines starts at £22.

Chef/s: Emily Watkins and Darren Brown. **Closed:** 25 Dec. **Meals:** main courses £17 to £24. **Details:** 69 seats. 20 seats outside. Bar. Wheelchairs. Music. Parking.

The Wild Rabbit

Cooking score: 4
Modern British | £52
Church Street, Kingham, OX7 6YA
Tel no: (01608) 658389
thewildrabbit.co.uk

The neat honey-coloured building is a vision of English pastoral loveliness that never ages, although the interiors have benefited from the most contemporary of makeovers. It's a pulled-together look, one where the old, traditional beamed bar gives way to a light-filled dining room, a towering space of bare stone mixed with pale woods. Here the open kitchen sets high standards, delivering confident cooking built around superb produce – elevating a simple Daylesford salad (a pile of roasted pumpkin, whipped goat's cheese and puréed pickled walnut) to brilliant status by virtue of the sheer quality of the mixed baby leaves. Elsewhere, excellent Wootton Estate lamb (loin, breast, faggot) comes in a glossy lamb sauce, or there's skrei cod with roasted leeks, brown shrimp, sea herbs and a seaweed sauce, deemed 'great fish, great veg, precise cooking, familiar flavours' by one diner. A wobbly, nutmeg-flecked egg custard tart could follow. Tasting menus and a lighter bar menu keep things flexible. Like the food, the wine list is pitched for affluent palates, though bottles start at £19.50.
Chef/s: Alyn Williams and Nathan Eades. **Closed:** Mon, Tue. **Meals:** main courses £23 to £30. Tasting menu £65. **Details:** 50 seats. 30 seats outside. V menu. Bar. Wheelchairs. Music. Parking.

Vegetarian and vegan

While many restaurants offer individual dishes suitable for non-meat eaters, those marked 'V menu' (vegetarian) and 'Vg menu' (vegan) offer separate menus.

Kirtlington

LOCAL GEM

The Oxford Arms

Modern British | £30
Troy Lane, Kirtlington, OX5 3HA
Tel no: (01869) 350208
oxford-arms.co.uk

A fixture in the village since 2003, Bryn Jones's characterful 19th-century pub is everything a village hostelry should be. Alongside exposed stone walls, beams, a log burner and real ales, there's a mixed bag of straightforward, accessible dishes ranging from potted shrimps and Hook Norton battered cod with triple-cooked chips and tartare sauce, to salad of game, Ramsay black pudding and blueberries, and confit of Gressingham duck leg with Toulouse sausage and butter-bean broth. There's bread-and-butter pudding should you still have room, and a short, globally minded wine list with plenty by the glass.

Lechlade

The Plough

Cooking score: 3
British | £29
Lechlade, GL7 3HG
Tel no: (01367) 253543
theploughinnkelmscott.com

This bucolic Cotswold village on the border of Gloucestershire and Oxfordshire, close to the Thames Path, was once the summer retreat of British Arts and Crafts pioneer William Morris. His home, Kelmscott Manor, is now a busy tourist destination but the attractive 17th-century pub with rooms around the corner attracts a crowd, too. Run by Sebastian and Lana Snow, who also have the nearby Five Alls at Filkins (see entry), there's a cosy bar with local ales for drinkers, and for walkers to refuel on sandwiches and burgers. There's also an appealing dining room with flagstone floors, stone walls and contemporary artwork where the straightforward cooking is seasonal. A typical meal could open with twice-baked

Double Gloucester soufflé with grain mustard, move on to game pie with rosemary gravy and caramelised vegetables and finish with Eve's pudding with brown-bread ice cream. Wines from £18.

Chef/s: George Tauchman. **Closed:** Mon. **Meals:** main courses £13 to £18. **Details:** 40 seats. 40 seats outside. Bar. Parking.

Murcott

The Nut Tree Inn

Cooking score: 5
Modern British | £50
Main Street, Murcott, OX5 2RE
Tel no: (01865) 331253
nuttreeinn.co.uk

Michael and Imogen North quickly gained acclaim after taking over this thatched, rural idyll of a pub in 2006. Enter the low-beamed interior and you'll be offered drinks in the diminutive bar, perhaps local real ale. The real action, though, happens in the little stone-walled dining area and a larger adjacent extension. Here, Michael's cooking highlights prime seasonal produce, including vegetables from the pub's garden. A flavour-packed amuse-bouche teacup of leek and potato soup with truffle oil might precede a starter of king scallop teamed with mango salsa and purée – which needed a touch more zing at inspection. Main course, though, was a triumph: torte of tender braised lamb shoulder with wild garlic and asparagus. Pudding, perfectly executed vanilla custard soufflé with apple sorbet, maintained this standard as did service, from knowledgeable, engaging staff. The wine list (from £18) contains interesting biodynamic labels, plus various house choices by the glass and carafe.

Chef/s: Mike and Mary North. **Meals:** main courses £20 to £38. Tasting menu £75 (8 courses). **Details:** 60 seats. 40 seats outside. V menu. Vg menu. Bar. Music. Parking.

Oxford

Arbequina

Cooking score: 3
Spanish | £25
74 Cowley Road, Oxford, OX4 1JB
Tel no: (01865) 792777
arbequina.co.uk

A change of tack from the team behind Oli's Thai (see entry), Arbequina turns the culinary compass from east to west with its focus on Spanish tapas and matching drinks. The interior feels just right, although it's also distinctive with rough dark-wood tables, a tile-fronted bar and high stools arranged along the stainless-steel counter. Like the menu at its Thai cousin, Arbequina's repertoire is far from formulaic: yes, there are textbook renditions of the usual suspects (salt cod croquetas, crispy chickpea salad, slow-roast pork belly with mojo verde), but you'll also find more enlightened ideas such as fried aubergine with molasses and pomegranate, ox cheek with cauliflower purée or bream with lentils and mojama (salt-cured tuna). After that, give the chocolate salami a try. Drinkers are offered Spanish sherries in proper measures, as well as Isastegi natural cider, Palax beer and a terse selection of regional wines from £18.

Chef/s: Ben Whyles and Norberto Pena Nunez. **Closed:** Sun, 22 Dec to 3 Jan. **Meals:** tapas £4 to £8. **Details:** 60 seats. 4 seats outside. Wheelchairs. Music.

Branca

Cooking score: 2
Modern European | £28
111 Walton Street, Oxford, OX2 6AJ
Tel no: (01865) 556111
branca.co.uk

It's knocking on for nearly 20 years since Branca became a mainstay of the city's eating scene, and the all-day venue epitomises everything a local restaurant should stand for.

The breadth of the clientele (from locals, tourists and business types to a fair few students) says a lot about the good eating to be had at reasonable prices. The space is huge, and building work to expand the operation still further was underway as we went to press. The beautifully lit bistro-style interior – all marble-topped tables and dark-wood floor – is matched by a please-all menu that takes in stone-baked pizzas, salads, risottos and pastas. Reports suggest the cooking has gone up a gear of late, with particular praise for king prawn bruschetta accompanied by a big dollop of punchy aïoli, crab linguine in a delicate white wine, parsley, garlic and chilli sauce, and a buttery, garlicky chicken kiev on a crisp potato pancake. Wines from £19.50.

Chef/s: Edwin Blandes. **Meals:** main courses £9 to £24. Set L £16. Set D £23 (2 courses) to £30. Sun L £17. **Details:** 100 seats. 50 seats outside. Bar. Wheelchairs. Music.

Cherwell Boathouse

Cooking score: 2
Modern British | £35
50 Bardwell Road, Oxford, OX2 6ST
Tel no: (01865) 552746
cherwellboathouse.co.uk
£5 OFF

A lunchtime or light evening on the decked terrace of this Edwardian boathouse is an Oxford delight, with white linen softening the rafters and floorboards of what is essentially a glorified hut. While the punts float by a few yards away, a repertoire of gently creative modern British food is served, perhaps beginning with a puff pastry tarte fine of truffled Jerusalem artichoke with a duck egg and cured duck ham, or langoustine raviolo in its own bisque with curly kale and celeriac. Halibut is got up in a potato coat and served with puffed rice, leek and kohlrabi in lemon sauce, or there may be slow-braised ox cheek with horseradish mash and roasted carrot. Dish design gets ahead of itself when nougat parfait arrives as a pistachio-rolled crumbed cylinder on cress-fronded chocolate soil with a brandy-soaked madeleine to one side, but tropical flavours are well handled for passion fruit and lime cheesecake with mango ice cream. Lunch is a bargain. The wine list has long been one of the city's glories, with many glamorous bottles at markups even students can cough up for. An Oxfordshire Huxelrebe makes a brave appearance among the glasses, but if you've got the cash to splash, there are French classics to conjure with. The entry point for standard glasses is £5, with bottles from £19.50.

Chef/s: Paul Bell. **Closed:** 25 to 30 Dec. **Meals:** main courses £18 to £23. Set L £15 (2 courses) to £19. Set D £24 (2 courses) to £29. **Details:** 65 seats. 45 seats outside. Bar. Wheelchairs. Music. Parking.

Gee's

Cooking score: 2
Mediterranean | £45
61a Banbury Road, Oxford, OX2 6PE
Tel no: (01865) 553540
gees-restaurant.co.uk

This sprawling, late-Victorian glasshouse was originally built as a florist and greengrocer, and as a restaurant has been an Oxford institution since the 1980s, feeding visiting parents and their student children with gusto. Everyone enjoys both the unique setting, which is smart-but-rustic with 'foliage everywhere', and the ample attention from staff. And there's much to praise, too, in the robustly seasonal Mediterranean cooking, which more than lives up to expectations. An enjoyable meal at inspection took in a terrine of rabbit served with pickled onion, cucumber and carrot, a tranche of roasted turbot ('tender flesh, juicy interior, nice and fresh') with sea urchin butter, and 'a River Café-level' chocolate nemesis with a scoop of dense pistachio ice cream. Elsewhere there could be braised octopus with lentils, wood-fired guinea fowl with salsa rossa, and pear and rhubarb crumble. The short, mainly European wine list opens with house French at £24.

Chef/s: Russell Heeley. **Meals:** main courses £15 to £28. Set L £14 (2 courses) to £17. **Details:** 80 seats. 40 seats outside. Bar. Wheelchairs. Music.

The Magdalen Arms

Cooking score: 3
Modern British | £29
243 Iffley Road, Oxford, OX4 1SJ
Tel no: (01865) 243159
magdalenarms.co.uk

A foursquare old tavern with a handsome façade, The Magdalen Arms may be some distance from the dreaming spires, but it's deservedly on the Oxford map as a dining destination. It's very much a pub indoors, with wooden floors and tables, dark brooding colours on the walls, and hand-pumped ales. The kitchen aims to match the unpretentious setting with a repertoire that takes in British classics such as game terrine with little pickles and toast, alongside European influences – a stonking Spanish sharing plate, for example, or venison goulash. In lieu of fish and chips, try beer-battered cod cheeks, while the hale and hearty rib of Hereford beef is designed for three to share. Sea bass is served up whole, and vegetarians might go for spinach and ricotta ravioli. Like the rest of the menu, desserts offer hearty refinement in the shape of rhubarb and boozy damson Bakewell tart. The wine list sticks to European soil, opening at £18.50.
Chef/s: Tony Abarno. **Closed:** 24 to 26 Dec. **Meals:** main courses £14 to £22. Set weekday L £10. Set early D £10. **Details:** 140 seats. 90 seats outside. Wheelchairs. Music.

Oli's Thai

Cooking score: 3
Thai | £25
38 Magdalen Road, Oxford, OX4 1RB
Tel no: (01865) 790223
olisthai.com

You'll need to book several weeks in advance if you want to secure a berth at this remarkable Thai eatery. There are just 28 covers in this canteen-style set-up, the seats are unforgiving, the music's blaring and the staff are as keen as mustard, but – above all – the cooking is potent, incisive and deeply flavourful. Oli's offer can be contained on a flimsy sheet of A5 (food on one side, drinks on the other), and the 12-dish menu rarely disappoints. The signature confit duck panang may top the popularity stakes, but it's closely challenged by the crispy chickpea salad, the fiery seared beef with tamarind and the 'hung lae' (literally a 'heavy curry' made with pork belly). You'll also want something on the side (perhaps cucumber with fish sauce) and you might even fancy a Portuguese-style custard tart to finish. Wines are served by the tumbler or carafe, and there's thirst-quenching Chang beer too.
Chef/s: Stacey Gledhill. **Closed:** Sun, Mon, 2 weeks Christmas. **Meals:** main courses £8 to £15. **Details:** 28 seats. 4 seats outside. Bar. Wheelchairs. Music. Children over 10 yrs.

The Oxford Kitchen

Cooking score: 5
Modern British | £50
215 Banbury Road, Oxford, OX2 7HQ
Tel no: (01865) 511149
theoxfordkitchen.co.uk

Taking its place amid the shops and salons in central Summertown, The Oxford Kitchen achieves the impressive trick of appealing to a local constituency that wants food a few clicks above the high-street bistro norm. With exposed brick walls and a lived-in look, it's a sympathetic ambience for head chef Paul Welburn's inspired take on resourceful modern cooking. A crumbed arancino of Parmesan-rich truffled risotto is offset with oat and pumpkin seed granola and a quenelle of crème fraîche, over which is poured a savoury-sweet butternut soup for a resonant opening dish. Fish might be butter-roasted halibut in sour apple dashi with chicken oysters and pickled kohlrabi, topped with salty rock samphire, while early spring brought forth expressive rump and shoulder of lamb with purple broccoli, daikon and wild garlic in the tripartite forms of pesto, bright green oil and tempura-battered leaf. The palate-cleansing pre-dessert could be a lemon thyme mousse and mandarin gel under a dense cloud of sparkling wine foam, before a homage to Yorkshire rhubarb features grenadine-pink stalks and light-textured ice cream on cream-cheese mousse with crumbled ginger biscuit. The work rate and precision of a kitchen on song have lifted this venue into Oxford's premier league. A concise wine list runs from £26 to £90, with appealing flavours all the way.

Chef/s: Paul Welburn. **Closed:** Sun, Mon, first 2 weeks Jan. **Meals:** set L £23 (2 courses) to £28. Set D £38 (2 courses) to £43. Tasting menu £55 to £65. **Details:** 70 seats. Wheelchairs. Music.

LOCAL GEM

Turl Street Kitchen

Modern British | £21

16-17 Turl Street, Oxford, OX1 3DH
Tel no: (01865) 264171
turlstreetkitchen.co.uk

Run in tandem with the Oxford Hub charity upstairs, this café and bar, drop-in and student hideaway adheres to the city's eco-friendly 'Good Food Charter', with local, seasonal, sustainable and low-waste as its watchwords. Stripped back, with scuffed wood and pictures of staff on the walls, it serves up breakfasts, wholesome one-plate lunches (braised lamb with pearl barley risotto) and proper restaurant-style dinners – think ham hock terrine followed by herb-crusted hake fillet. The chips are 'brilliant' and there's Karma Cola to drink, alongside left-field beers and a score of wines.

Anonymous

At *The Good Food Guide*, our inspectors dine anonymously and pay their bill in full. These impartial review meals, along with feedback from thousands of our readers, are what informs the content of the *GFG*.

Shiplake

★ TOP 50 ★

Orwells

Cooking score: 7
Modern British | £52

Shiplake Row, Shiplake, RG9 4DP
Tel no: (01189) 403673
orwellsatshiplake.co.uk

Betwixt Binfield Heath and Shiplake, Orwells looks very much the Georgian country inn that it is, architecturally speaking, but despite the endearingly wonky black beams inside, the emphasis is very much on contemporary design, with a clean-limbed, linened look to the dining room, and a thoroughly up-to-the-minute air to the seasonally informed tasting menus. Ryan Simpson and Liam Trotman have been the dynamic duo behind the place since the start of the decade, and have honed a style of resourceful, inimitably witty food that inspires many visitors to rhapsodies. An autumn dinner that opened with 'delightfully delicate' lobster contrasted with crunchy chicken skin, chanterelles and samphire in a superlative lobster jus gave way to exemplary sea bass with red-fleshed radish, cucumber balls and 'a dash of dashi'. Duck hearts on spongy crumpets is a winning idea, but there might also be 'one of the best vegetarian dishes we've ever had' – salt-baked pumpkin with pear, chicory, sea buckthorn, walnuts, pine nuts and a Parmesan crisp. When it comes to the heart of the menu, prime materials are stunning, perhaps sea-fresh monkfish with crispy kale and brown butter, or expressively gamey hare with sage and apple. Careful consideration of the dimensions of each dish means the avoidance of overload, so when desserts arrive, in the shape of honeycomb in heavenly chocolate cream, or vanilla panna cotta with slightly tart stewed plums, they are entirely welcome. Wines, while taking in some of the aristos of Bordeaux and Burgundy, make a genuine effort to cast the

net wide at the gentler end, with a breadth of commendable choice, and even the Coravin glasses priced more sanely than elsewhere.
Chef/s: Ryan Simpson and Liam Trotman. **Closed:** Mon, Tue, first 2 weeks Jan, 2 weeks end Aug. **Meals:** main courses £23 to £34. Set L £25 (2 courses) to £30. Set D £30 (2 courses) to £35. Sun L £40 (3 courses). Tasting menu £60 (5 courses) to £95. **Details:** 35 seats. 20 seats outside. V menu. Bar. Wheelchairs. Music. Parking.

Sparsholt

The Star Inn

Cooking score: 2
Modern British | £32
Watery Lane, Sparsholt, OX12 9PL
Tel no: (01235) 751873
thestarsparsholt.co.uk
£5 OFF

This red-brick and stone village inn wears its 300 years lightly, especially within, where there's a refreshing lack of stuffiness despite all the original beams. It's a proper country pub with real ales and treats on hand for good dogs. A quick glance at the menu will reveal a degree of ambition: Cornish mackerel with Vietnamese braised quinoa might precede lamb rump and belly with crisp sweetbreads. There are burgers, and steak and hand-cut chips, but everything is done with detail: the ham of the 'ham, egg and chips' is glazed in Kelmscott Farm honey and Coca-Cola, the egg a fried Arlington White. Fresh fish of the day arrives with caramelised cauliflower purée, and among first courses beef blade and horseradish croquette with beetroot jam is a winner. 'Sticky toffee soufflé is a must,' according to one fan. The wine list has plenty of options by the glass and carafe.
Chef/s: Matt Williams. **Meals:** main courses £13 to £26. Set L £20 (2 courses) to £23. **Details:** 50 seats. 30 seats outside. Music. Parking.

Toot Baldon

LOCAL GEM

The Mole Inn

Modern European | £34
Toot Baldon, OX44 9NG
Tel no: (01865) 340001
themoleinn.com

A stone-built country inn on the well-worn route between Oxford and Reading, The Mole has been modernised with stripped pale wood all over the show against exposed stone for contrast. Populist offerings like beer-battered fish and skinny chips, grilled ribeyes and lunchtime snacks are melded in with more venturesome excursions into territory such as shredded duck and pork belly with beansprouts, chilli, lime, coriander and rocket, roast cod with kale and parsley mash in pink grapefruit sauce, and chocolate brownie with peanut butter ice cream to finish. Factor in attentive and friendly service, well-kept ales, and an appealing wine selection from £19.50, and it's worth the drive out.

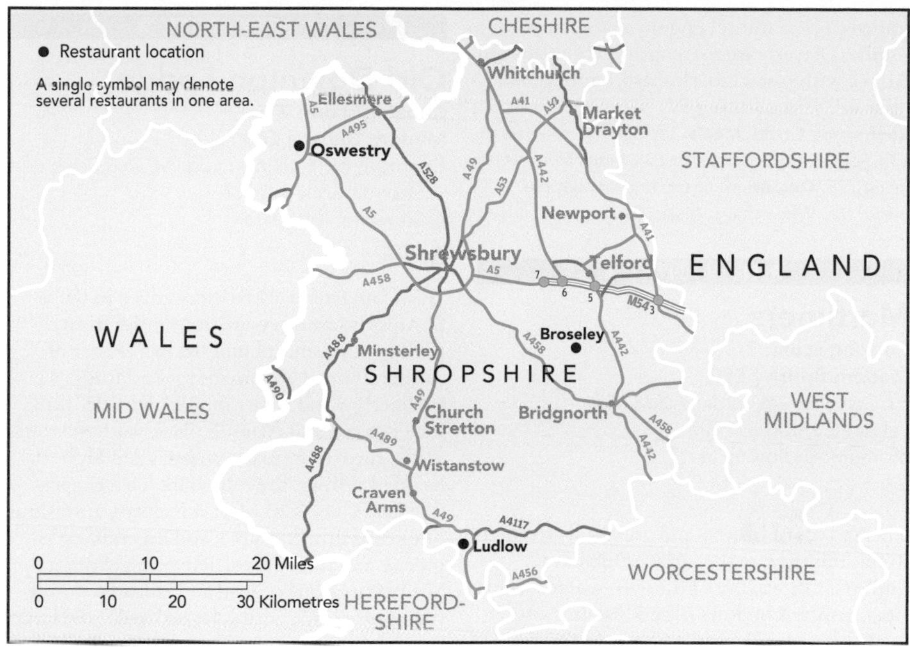

Broseley

LOCAL GEM

The King & Thai

Thai | £35

The Forester Arms, Avenue Road, Broseley, TF12 5DL
Tel no: (01952) 882004
thekingandthai.co.uk

Suree Coates' Thai restaurant is located in a one-time roadside pub and, if it still looks the part from the outside, inside it's a fully fledged dining venue, with smiling staff to greet you. The menu won't hold any surprises to those familiar with south-east Asian cuisine. Get going with a shared starter platter, fit in a soup if you can (classic tom yum, say), before red or green curries, pad thai, or sea bream with stir-fried tiger prawns. Wines open at £16.45.

Ludlow

★ NEW ENTRY ★

Forelles at Fishmore Hall

Cooking score: 1
Modern British | £55

Fishmore Road, Ludlow, SY8 3DP
Tel no: (01584) 875148
fishmorehall.co.uk

£5 OFF

This whitewashed Georgian hotel, a five-minute drive from Ludlow, is a popular wedding venue, its contemporary restaurant occupying a light-filled conservatory with views overlooking the lawn, spa and Clee Hill beyond. Young staff wearing black gloves, and tables covered with white linen add a formality to the service. Joe Gould is an ambitious chef and his food makes good use of Shropshire produce where possible: a starter of quail with butternut squash, chorizo, pomegranate, goat's curd and shallot might lead on to red mullet served with kohlrabi, tomato, pea, a mussel raviolo and saffron rouille. Desserts are a strength – try the baked Alaska with pistachio, rhubarb, vanilla and olive oil. Wines from £22.

Chef/s: Joe Gould. **Meals:** set L £29 (2 courses) to £35. Set D £43 (2 courses) to £55. Sun L £35. Tasting menu £75. **Details:** 40 seats. 12 seats outside. V menu. Bar. Wheelchairs. Music. Parking.

★ NEW ENTRY ★

Mortimers

Cooking score: 3
Modern British | £50
17 Corve Street, Ludlow, SY8 1DA
Tel no: (01584) 872325
mortimersludlow.co.uk

There's a lot of history and goodwill attached to this building in the heart of medieval Ludlow: this was once Hibiscus, where Claude Bosi, now at London's Bibendum (see entry) made his name. Wayne Smith used to work here for Bosi and now returns as chef and co-owner with Andrew Brookes, another Hibiscus alumnus. The oak-panelled walls remain (they are listed, as is the building), the carpet is thick, colours muted – it's all very elegant and formal. Whether you choose from the seven-course tasting menu or the three-course set menu, Smith's cooking is confident and restrained. An inspection meal opened with a perfectly balanced dish of quail teamed with white asparagus, snipped wild garlic, a couple of pieces of lovely, salty Ibérico and a lovely light foam bringing it all together. To follow, a perfectly cooked, meaty fillet of John Dory arrived with razor clam velouté, broad beans, crayfish, mussels and lovage. An outrageously rich chocolate marquise topped with hazelnut brittle and gold leaf with caramel ice cream made an indulgent finish. The accessible wine list opens at £25 with plenty by the glass.

Chef/s: Wayne Smith. **Closed:** Sun, Mon. **Meals:** main courses £23 to £63. Set L £23 (2 courses) to £26. Set D £50. Tasting menu £63. **Details:** 30 seats. V menu. Vg menu. Bar. Music. Parking. No children.

★ NEW ENTRY ★

Old Downton Lodge

Cooking score: 2
Modern British | £60
Downton on the Rock, Ludlow, SY8 2HU
Tel no: (01568) 771826
olddowntonlodge.com

'Well and truly tucked away', deep in the Shropshire countryside, four miles from Ludlow, this smart hotel sits in a cluster of timber-framed and medieval buildings (formerly a Tudor farmhouse and cider mill). It's a relaxed and tranquil place. With its stone walls, tiny triangular windows and high beamed ceiling, the restaurant has a chapel-like feel. Chef Karl Martin is clearly ambitious but keeps things simple, and his cooking is precise and innovative, delivering excellent Shropshire honey bread and cultured butter, then puffed rice with celeriac 'caviar' and lardo as a delicious opener. Sensational and beautifully cooked Wagyu beef teamed with beetroot, walnut and dill proved to be a stand-out dish at inspection. Impressive, too, was a piece of blowtorched cod with a disc of crunchy kohlrabi, frothy hollandaise, parsley oil and a piece of crisp fish skin like a prawn cracker, while duck served with squash, kale, grape and seeds was another winning dish. Hibiscus with white chocolate and fennel kept up the standard at dessert. Although formal, the staff are good-humoured and knowledgeable about the food and wine pairings. A wide-ranging wine list starts at £24.

Chef/s: Karl Martin. **Closed:** Sun, Mon, 24 to 27 Dec, 18 Feb to 4 Mar. **Meals:** D £50 (3 courses). Tasting menu £60 (6 courses) to £75. **Details:** 20 seats. Bar. Music. Parking. Children over 12 yrs.

LOCAL GEM

CSONS at The Green Café

Modern British | £19

Mill on the Green, Ludlow, SY8 1EG
Tel no: (01584) 879872
thegreencafe.co.uk

This converted mill, in the shadow of Ludlow Castle beside the Teme, has a riverside terrace that provides wonderful views of Dinham Bridge. It changed hands in early 2018, and while good cakes and coffee continue to keep locals and tourists happy, lunch is the main draw. Try the panko cod cheeks with aïoli, and follow with chicken shawarma served with couscous, red peppers, mint yoghurt, dukkah and kale, perhaps finishing with rhubarb and lemon tart. Staff are 'welcoming and courteous', and drinks extend to beers, ciders and wines.

Oswestry

Sebastians

Cooking score: 3
French | £45

45 Willow Street, Oswestry, SY11 1AQ
Tel no: (01691) 655444
sebastians-hotel.com

After 30 years in Oswestry, the Fishers' restaurant with rooms is still the go-to restaurant in town – one of those glorious ancient inns reinvented for the 21st century, but remaining attractively higgledy-piggledy inside. Mark Sebastian Fisher's finely honed contemporary French cuisine, offered on a five-course evening tasting menu and evidenced by an extraordinarily good concoction of mushrooms, garlic, cream, Roquefort cheese and watercress, is rich with classic combinations. Dishes are built from strong, seasonal, often unexpected flavours: a spring menu delivered warm scallops with trout tartare and lime and wasabi cream, and a plate of spring lamb loin, shoulder sausage and belly, with minted peas, potato croquettes and redcurrant jus. Dessert could be elderflower parfait with gin and elderflower choux buns and a Prosecco sorbet. The kitchen does not cut corners, so expect homemade everything, from canapés, amuse-bouches and palate-cleansing sorbets to the chocolate truffles with coffee. The French-led wine list opens at £20.

Chef/s: Richard Jones and Mark Sebastian Fisher. **Closed:** Sun, Mon, Tue, 25 and 26 Dec, 1 Jan, bank hols. **Meals:** set D £45 (5 courses). **Details:** 45 seats. 12 seats outside. V menu. Bar. Music. Parking. Children over 12 yrs.

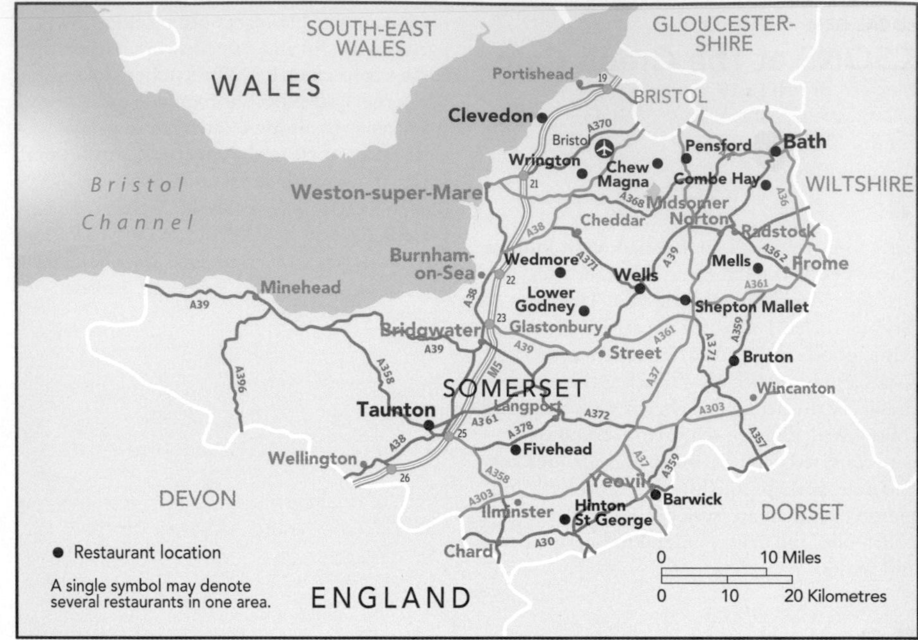

Barwick

Little Barwick House

Cooking score: 5
Modern British | £55

Rexes Hollow Lane, Barwick, BA22 9TD
Tel no: (01935) 423902
littlebarwick.co.uk

£5 OFF

A little slice of Eden, this beautiful white-painted Georgian house sits in immaculate grounds with views to nourish the soul. When it comes to physical nourishment, you're in the right place, thanks to Tim Ford's unerringly consistent classical cooking. For the past 18 years he and his wife Emma (a charming front of house presence) have been delighting guests with food that eschews foams and gimmicky showboating in favour of pristine ingredients, high-end technical skills and sensible flavour combinations. Begin with drinks in the garden or a seat by the fire in the lounge and nibble canapés of juicy venison brochettes and goat's cheese and shiitake mushroom tarts with light-as-air pastry. The dining room keeps to the classic country-house aesthetic, with smart napery and peaceful shades of cream and taupe. A warm salad of roasted duck breast, served pink, with spiced oranges and a Grand Marnier and hazelnut oil dressing delighted at inspection, while saddle of wild roe deer with braised red cabbage, wafer-thin rösti potato and beetroot purée was an equally sure-footed main course. There's a charming Englishness to the whole experience, so what better way to finish than with rhubarb posset, tart and crumble, served with perfectly creamy stem ginger ice cream. The wine list will please connoisseurs and, for those paralysed by all the choice, Emma can provide helpful suggestions.

Chef/s: Tim Ford. **Closed:** Sun, Mon, 25 Dec, first 3 weeks Jan. **Meals:** set L £29 (2 courses) to £31. Set D £49 (2 courses) to £55. **Details:** 40 seats. 12 seats outside. Bar. Parking. Children over 5 yrs.

Bath

Acorn

Cooking score: 3
Vegetarian | £39
2 North Parade Passage, Bath, BA1 1NX
Tel no: (01225) 446059
acornvegetariankitchen.co.uk
£5 OFF

This listed, golden-hued Georgian building, once the home of vegetarian restaurant Demuths, has continued the plant-based legacy under chef proprietor Richard Buckley. Set menus keep in close rhythm with the seasons, and dishes are full of contrasting textures and colours. Many of the vegetables are organic, and the amount of work involved in each dish is evident: at inspection, candy beetroots had been steamed with herbs, shaved into slices, then plated with an orange-spiked beetroot vierge and cashew purée, while what was described simply as 'one whole cauliflower' showcased various treatments: roasted florets, a truffled purée, molasses-pickled core and sautéed leaves, with an almond-milk croqueta infused with fenugreek and onion, an emulsion of spelt grain and smoked almond, and green tarragon oil. Finish with tonka bean poached pear, macadamia nut brûlée and pear. The compact wine list starts at £21, and there's a selection of local organic ciders and beers.
Chef/s: Jamie Taylor. **Closed:** 25 and 26 Dec. **Meals:** set L £18 (2 courses) to £23. Set D £27 (2 courses) to £33. Sun L £19. **Details:** 34 seats. V menu. Music.

The Bath Priory

Cooking score: 5
Modern French | £85
Weston Road, Bath, BA1 2XT
Tel no: (01225) 331922
thebathpriory.co.uk

The ivy-clad Cotswold stone manor a short amble from the city centre is just about Georgian – built when there were only two years left on the clock. It enjoys four of its own acres, which are filled with landscaped gardens and kitchen planting, as well as secluded nooks for doing whatever comes naturally. In the bright, airy dining room with its views of the lawns, Michael Nizzero's cooking balances haute cuisine flash with contemporary notes in an essentially French idiom. Glazed Cornish crab with butternut squash in lemon parsley butter feels positively classical, but the nasturtiums and caviar that garnish beef tartare tell a different story. Irreproachable sourcing of meats produces mains such as tender venison loin with wild mushrooms and potatoes amandine, as well as seasonal roast grouse and blackberries with celeriac and bacon. Seal the deal with one of the appealingly light desserts, perhaps figs roasted in red wine with caramelised walnuts. A reasonable spread of small glasses from £7.50 leads the charge on a Francocentric wine list that's also strong in Italian reds.
Chef/s: Michael Nizzero. **Meals:** set L £25 (2 courses) to £30. Set D £85 (3 courses). Sun L £35. Tasting menu £98 (7 courses). **Details:** 50 seats. V menu. Vg menu. Bar. Wheelchairs. Parking. Children over 12 yrs.

Chez Dominique

Cooking score: 2
Modern French | £32
15 Argyle Street, Bath, BA2 4BQ
Tel no: (01225) 463482
chezdominique.co.uk

Close to Pulteney Bridge and a drop kick from Bath's Recreation Ground, this homely modern bistro wrapped up in an elegant Georgian room offers much to like. Before he moved to the West Country, Chris Tabbitt worked with Simon Hopkinson when he was at Bibendum (see entry), as evidenced by his unreconstructed French dishes. From the carte, begin with peppered seared venison, celeriac rémoulade and Monégasque onions, before continuing with a fillet of sea bass, cockles, mussels, samphire and bouillabaisse sauce. For dessert there could be white

chocolate mousse with passion fruit curd and almond brittle, preceded by a plate of cheeses for an even more Gallic finale. The prix fixe menu offers really exceptional value and is a popular choice with pre-theatre diners. A conscientiously compiled wine list with a pronounced French accent starts at £19, with plenty of wallet-friendly drinking under £25.
Chef/s: Chris Tabbitt. **Closed:** 25 and 26 Dec. **Meals:** main courses £14 to £24. Set L and early D £14 (2 courses) to £17. **Details:** 40 seats. Music.

The Circus

Cooking score: 2
Modern European | £30
34 Brock Street, Bath, BA1 2LN
Tel no: (01225) 466020
thecircusrestaurant.co.uk

'We felt at home and welcome from the moment we arrived,' noted one reader following a visit to Alison Golden's popular neighbourhood restaurant in the architectural epicentre of Bath. Shades of green and grey point up the Georgian dining room with its white cornicing, original fireplaces and refurnished window seats, while 'charming staff' add to the civilised, feel-good atmosphere. Visitors also appreciate the menu's seasonal bias, its penchant for unusual meat-free ideas and the option of wine-pairing suggestions: winter vegetable fritters with verbena harissa and almond cheese alongside a glass of English wine from Sharpham Vineyards, for example. Otherwise, sturdy European flavours abound, from navarin of rabbit or flat-iron steak with Café de Paris butter, garlic mushrooms and fat chips to a Yorkshire rhubarb brûlée . A dedicated 'special diets' menu caters to vegetarians, vegans and others, and there's a roster of craft beers alongside the decently priced wine list.
Chef/s: Alison Golden. **Closed:** Sun, 3 weeks from 23 Dec. **Meals:** main courses £17 to £23. **Details:** 52 seats. 8 seats outside. V menu. Vg menu. Music. Children over 7 yrs.

Corkage

Cooking score: 2
British | £20
132a Walcot Street, Bath, BA1 5BG
Tel no: (01225) 422577
corkagebath.com

What began in 2016 as a temporary pop-up within a wine shop has grown into two permanent Bath sites (with the opening of a second Corkage on Chapel Row). Back in Walcot Street, Marty Grant and Richard Knighting's original wine bar is now well established as one of the city's must-book neighbourhood eateries. Compact and congenial, it has a genuine buzz as staff talk diners through the blackboard menus and the 50-plus wines served by the glass and bottle. Small plates are the thing here, with seasonality driving the menu – all delivered by the tiny kitchen in the corner. The crab on toast has become something of a signature starter, perhaps followed by pork belly with Asian peanut dressing. Finish with chocolate ganache and blood orange salad. Opening at £22.50 for a bottle of white, prices on the wine list can soon creep up, often resulting in an unexpectedly punchy bill.
Chef/s: Richard Knighting. **Closed:** Sun, Mon. **Meals:** main courses £8 to £14. **Details:** 38 seats. Wheelchairs.

The Dower House

Cooking score: 4
Modern European | £72
Royal Crescent Hotel, 16 Royal Crescent, Bath, BA1 2LS
Tel no: (01225) 823333
royalcrescent.co.uk

This elegant restaurant in the secluded garden of the Royal Crescent Hotel, occupies part of the former coach houses and stables of this famous Georgian crescent. Tables close to the French windows opening out on to the terrace are highly prized in summer (as is a pre-dinner drink in the garden), while the dining room's crisp linen, muted colours and silk wallpaper matches the tone of David Campbell's modern but classically rooted menu. At a May meal, a starter of roasted scallops with heritage tomatoes, smoked pepper ketchup, smoked eel, saffron and marjoram was a harmonious marriage of colours, flavours and textures. It preceded English rose veal – tender slices of fillet, creamy sweetbread and a slice of full-flavoured tongue – teamed with roasted globe artichoke, asparagus, a buttery disc of confit potato and dots of mushroom purée. To follow, caramelised pear tart was well matched by a gently spiced star anise parfait. The substantial global wine list opens at £28 (glasses from £7.50) with plenty of half-bottles.

Chef/s: David Campbell. **Meals:** set D £59 (2 courses) to £72. Tasting menu £82. **Details:** 50 seats. 100 seats outside. Vg menu. Bar. Wheelchairs. Music.

★ NEW ENTRY ★

Henry's

Cooking score: 3
Modern British | £45
4 Saville Row, Bath, BA1 2QP
Tel no: (01225) 780055
henrysrestaurantbath.com

This listed Georgian townhouse next to Bath's Assembly Rooms was previously home to Casanis (a guide regular for many years), and is now a first solo venture for an ambitious young chef. Henry Scott has worked locally at Allium and the Bath Priory (see entries), as well as in London at the late Hibiscus. With a mantra of 'honest, independent food', Henry's is a model of restraint, both in terms of the decor and the food. Stripped floorboards, unclothed tables and simple dark wood bistro chairs create a simple dining room, and the concise menu is equally understated, with three choices per course (if you aren't drawn to the four-course tasting menu). At inspection, confit duck ravioli with savoy cabbage and a tangle of sweet pickled ginger proved to be 'an arresting starter', the silky, gossamer-thin pasta brimming with tender shredded duck packed with flavour. Hereford sirloin, accompanied by kalettes, candy beetroot, radish and a tarragon emulsion, was a playful twist on the more traditional steak and béarnaise sauce, while a warm chocolate tart with spicy Szechuan custard ensured 'high quality was maintained at dessert stage'. A wide-ranging wine list opens at £17.95.

Chef/s: Henry Scott. **Closed:** Sun, Mon. **Meals:** main courses £17 to £25. Set L £19 (2 courses) to £35. Set D £40 (2 courses) to £45. Tasting menu £50 (4 courses). **Details:** 45 seats. 15 seats outside. V menu. Music.

Menu Gordon Jones

Cooking score: 5
Modern British | £55
2 Wellsway, Bath, BA2 3AQ
Tel no: (01225) 480871
menugordonjones.co.uk

On a busy corner site to the south of the city centre, Gordon Jones has established a thoroughly idiosyncratic operation that has won him a loyal following. The drill is a menu surprise as standard, utilising all the technical tricks and presentational tweaks at the modern chef's disposal, to a background of mine host's chosen mix tape. People still complain that they can't catch the servers' descriptions of dishes, which are evidently more detailed than the printed menus, but the level of excitement and intensity is sustained throughout. Breads arrive perhaps with ash butter and test tubes of various substances, and may be followed by a loose mousse presented as a soup, such as cep and geranium. Artful fish presentations include haddock with chorizo crisps and an eggshell of sauce soubise, while meat could be barbecued Middle White suckling pig, belly and kidney, with cabbage in chervil root ragù. Apple and date cake, or Muscat grape parfait with Tokaji jelly, a cinnamon bun and apple sorbet are fitting finales. The wine matches fully live up to the ethos of the cooking.

Chef/s: Gordon Jones. **Closed:** Sun, Mon, 25 to 27 Feb, 20 to 25 Apr, 28 May to 4 Jun, 1 to 17 Sept, 28 Oct to 5 Nov. **Meals:** set L £50 (5 courses). Set D £55 (6 courses). **Details:** 24 seats. Children over 12 yrs.

The Olive Tree

Cooking score: 4
Modern British | £70
The Queensberry Hotel, 4-7 Russel Street, Bath, BA1 2QF
Tel no: (01225) 447928
olivetreebath.co.uk

'On a balmy Friday night in June when most people were eating alfresco or firing up the barbecue at home, it takes a lot to entice diners into a low-lit basement dining room but this was the busiest I've seen the restaurant for a long time.' So ran the notes of one regular to this discreetly located restaurant in a palatial Georgian townhouse built for the Marquis of Queensberry. It may look elegant and formal, but cartoon prints lend an unstuffy air, as do friendly, knowledgeable staff who guide you through tasting menus of five or seven courses, or the more traditional à la carte. Chris Cleghorn's finely tuned dishes are handled with precision. Our starter of asparagus, smoked eel, spring onion and Exmoor caviar proved to be a faultless expression of seasonal cooking and regionality, and was followed by 'perfectly pink' duck breast from Woolley Park Farm teamed with earthy discs of chargrilled beetroot, briny sea beet, cherry purée and hazelnut. Lemon balm gave additional zip to a delightful summery concoction of strawberry, mascarpone, orange blossom and meringue. The smart and conscientiously curated wine list is arranged by style and starts at £24.

Chef/s: Chris Cleghorn. **Closed:** Mon, 1 week Jan, 1 week Jul to Aug, 1 week Nov. **Meals:** set L £26 (2 courses) to £33. Tasting menu £68. **Details:** 50 seats. V menu. Vg menu. Bar. Music.

Symbols

 Accommodation is available
 Three courses for less than £30
 £5 off voucher scheme
Notable wine list

LOCAL GEM

Yak Yeti Yak

Nepalese | £25
12 Pierrepont Street, Bath, BA1 1LA
Tel no: (01225) 442299
yakyetiyak.co.uk

Within striking distance of Bath station, this eminently likeable little basement restaurant is spread across three Georgian townhouses. The place wears its true Nepalese colours on its sleeve, with starters such as momos (spiced steamed dumplings) or polayko masu (strips of marinated and grilled lamb) preceding pork bhutuwa with tomato and spring onion, and chicken on the bone stir-fried with spices, tomato, onion and ginger. There are some fascinating vegetable dishes like aloo tamar (fermented bamboo shoots, potatoes, black-eyed peas and cumin), and desserts such as creamed saffron yoghurt with marinated oranges. Drink lassi, beer or house wine.

Bruton

Roth Bar & Grill

Cooking score: 3
Modern British | £28
Durslade Farm, Dropping Lane, Bruton, BA10 0NL
Tel no: (01749) 814700
rothbarandgrill.co.uk

Hauser & Wirth are contemporary art galleries in London, Zurich, New York, LA and... Bruton. Lucky Somerset. In a classy barn conversion on the Wirths' 1,000-acre farm, the kitchen makes good use of the farm's own rare-breed meats, dry-aged in the restaurant's salt room and served as classic cuts with chips and watercress salad (Hereford beef skirt, maybe); charcuterie, too, is cured in-house, perhaps their own chorizo accompanying chargrilled octopus as a starter. Main courses run to the house burger with home-cured bacon and Godminster smoked Cheddar, roast hake with white beans, lomo and aïoli, or a selection of salads from a creative selection (roasted carrots with spelt and goat's curd, say). Finish with poached pear with chocolate sauce. Classy brunches include pheasant sausages and avocado on toast. Drink regional beers, cocktails old or new, or wines from mostly small producers.

Chef/s: Steve Horrell. **Closed:** Mon, 25 to 27 Dec. **Meals:** main courses £12 to £28. **Details:** 80 seats. 80 seats outside. Bar. Wheelchairs. Music. Parking.

Chew Magna

The Pony & Trap

Cooking score: 5
Modern British | £40
Moorledge Road, Chew Magna, BS40 8TQ
Tel no: (01275) 332627
theponyandtrap.co.uk

The inviting rusticity of the interior and glorious views would make this country pub an asset to any community. Add the cooking of Josh Eggleton to the equation, and the Pony & Trap is a bright spot on the Somerset dining scene. The food is leagues ahead of your average pub offering, the kitchen showing a preference for a broadly contemporary way of doing things, with just a few culinary fireworks to impress. Food miles matter here, as home-grown produce from the kitchen garden suggests, and fiercely seasonal dishes seem to please the great majority. In March, venison faggots could precede Cornish brill 'cooked on the bone for extra flavour', while early May might bring salmon terrine with dill mayonnaise and cucumber, and dry-aged pork loin and glazed rib served with chargrilled hispi cabbage and rhubarb. Desserts such as apple cake, caramel and clotted cream ice cream or chocolate and orange mousse cake with sea buckthorn sorbet make a big impact, too. Wines from £25.

Chef/s: Josh Eggleton. **Closed:** 25 and 26 Dec. **Meals:** main courses £20 to £30. Sun L £35. Tasting menu £45 (5 courses) to £70 (10 courses). **Details:** 65 seats. 40 seats outside. Music. Parking.

Clevedon

LOCAL GEM

Murrays

Italian | £24
91 Hill Road, Clevedon, BS21 7PN
Tel no: (01275) 341222
murraysofclevedon.co.uk

Piled high with delightful edible discoveries, this long-standing Clevedon deli is ideally placed to feed its new restaurant with tiptop ingredients. The result is an Italian menu brimming with treats, from sautéed wild mushrooms in cream and parsley with sourdough crostini to Tuscan pork and fennel sausages with mashed potato, balsamic roast Tropea onions and gravy. There's also an ample pizza menu, and a selection of luxurious desserts (St Emilion au chocolat with amaretto cream, for example), plus a great selection of Italian wines to wash it all down.

Combe Hay

The Wheatsheaf

Cooking score: 3
Modern British | £36
Combe Hay, BA2 7EG
Tel no: (01225) 833504
wheatsheafcombehay.com

With sofas by the fire keeping the winter chills at bay and a glorious terrace garden for summertime pleasure, this reconfigured 18th-century watering hole is truly an inn for all seasons. It's also a heritage-style country idyll just four miles from Bath, with original stonework and flagstones holding their own alongside distressed mirrors, bucolic photographs and wicker chairs. A new wood-fired oven is the latest addition to the kitchen's armoury, so expect plenty of pizzas, and specials such as Moroccan spiced lamb with couscous and flatbread, alongside scallops with black truffle risotto or slow-cooked pork belly on grain mustard mash with rhubarb and apple purée. Elsewhere, burgers and beer-battered cod are reminders that this is still a bona fide pub – albeit one that also stages seasonal game dinners and offers glazed passion fruit curd for dessert. A serious contingent of big Bordeaux dominates the wholly European wine list.

Chef/s: Eddy Rains. **Closed:** Mon. **Meals:** main courses £15 to £26. Set L and D £18 (2 courses) to £24. Sun L £24 (2 courses) to £30. **Details:** 55 seats. 80 seats outside. V menu. Music. Parking.

Fivehead

The Langford

Cooking score: 5
Modern British | £43

Langford Fivehead, Lower Swell, Fivehead, TA3 6PH
Tel no: (01460) 282020
langfordfivehead.co.uk

'Hurrah for owner-occupied establishments,' enthused one visitor to this dashing honey-coloured manor in a lovely tranquil setting. 'Run by a charming couple and their enthusiastic staff,' the relaxed atmosphere and easy-going service work well with the comfortable interior – traditional sitting rooms, and two pretty dining rooms with well spaced white-clad tables. Olly Jackson rules the roost here with cooking that draws on the surrounding countryside and the kitchen garden for dishes such as a simple home-smoked duck breast in a tangle of beetroot, asparagus and pickled rhubarb, before a more intricate main of, say, rolled and poached Cornish sole fillets with crispy parsnip, spinach and chive beurre blanc. Dessert might be a riff on a lemon meringue pie: a square of lemon curd with some good, sweet Somerset strawberries and excellent soft Italian meringue; 'quite zingy and basically a lemon tart without the pastry,' said one reader. The short wine list is big on France.

Chef/s: Olly Jackson. **Closed:** Sun, Mon. **Meals:** set L £28 (2 courses) to £33. Set D £43 (3 courses). **Details:** 20 seats. Wheelchairs. Music. Parking. Children over 8 yrs.

Hinton St George

The Lord Poulett Arms

Cooking score: 3
Modern British | £30

High Street, Hinton St George, TA17 8SE
Tel no: (01460) 73149
lordpoulettarms.com

A proper village pub that provides the expected relaxed atmosphere and unpretentious cooking style, yet raises the bar sky-high with pinpoint attention to detail and no corner cutting. The setting is beautifully rustic: hops hang from the beams, the heritage-green walls sport everything from stuffed birds to old pub signs, and real fires set the stone fireplaces aglow. Begin in the homely, deliciously dark bar, then settle amid the happy buzz of several beautiful dining rooms – all smooth flagstones, well-worn floorboards, candles and antique furniture. The menu offers plenty of pub favourites (burgers, fish and chips) but also refined, modern dishes such as silken, creamy mushroom soup with spring truffle and mascarpone or tender confit Devon duck leg with buttery creamed potatoes, sweet-sharp marinated red cabbage, sesame pak choi and a rich, rounded star anise jus. Even simple desserts such as affogato show care and consideration. The wine list coaxes you out of your comfort zone, each classic paired with a suggested lesser-known find of a similar style. Apt recommendations are also made alongside certain dishes on the menu.

Chef/s: Phil Verden. **Closed:** 25 and 26 Dec, 1 Jan. **Meals:** main courses £15 to £27. Set L and early D £17 (2 courses, Mon to Sat) to £20. Sun L £20 (2 courses) to £25. **Details:** 65 seats. 55 seats outside. Bar. Wheelchairs. Music. Parking.

Lower Godney

The Sheppey

Cooking score: 2
International | £28
Lower Godney, BA5 1RZ
Tel no: (01458) 831594
thesheppey.co.uk

This freewheeling roadside inn won't win any prizes for external good looks, but don't be deterred by the pockmarked paint job; you are about to enter another world. Inside, it's vast and endlessly quirky, blending reclaimed late-20th-century furniture with cushion-filled grottoes, a bar strung with fairy lights, and a whitewashed, warehouse-style space. There's a permanent stage (they take their music seriously – be prepared to shout over your meal on certain nights) and a huge outdoor terrace edging the river with green fields beyond. A glance into the open kitchen shows a big team who mean business, and the service is personable and pacey. The menu takes in everything from stonking burgers to imaginative vegan options, including tamarind and coconut soup, and aquafaba meringues. The hearty fish stew with rouille and Parmesan is a deservedly regular fixture, and if you enjoy seafood, the big portions of dazzlingly plump, tender mussels are a must; we tried them cooked with a heavenly combination of cream, cider, garlic, bacon, rosemary and fenugreek. Drinks include great ciders and beers, and excellent vegan and organic wines.

Chef/s: Keiron Ash. **Meals:** main courses £14 to £24. Sun L £26 (3 courses). **Details:** 90 seats. 80 seats outside. Bar. Wheelchairs. Music.

Local Gem

These entries highlight a range of neighbourhood venues, delivering good, freshly cooked food at great value for money.

Mells

Talbot Inn

Cooking score: 3
Modern British | £35
Selwood Street, Mells, BA11 3PN
Tel no: (01373) 812254
talbotinn.com

This mellow old beauty of a country inn is made up of a cluster of honey-coloured buildings with a charming cobbled pathway leading into its heart. You enter via a pleasantly dark bar with all the beams, quarry tiles and knobbly stone walls you could wish for. Beyond this is a higgledy-piggledy sequence of dining rooms, all decked out in a relaxed heritage style. The menu breezes through a selection of native ingredients, from Wye Valley asparagus with slow-baked egg, shaved Parmesan, garlic crumbs and truffle oil to Brixham bream with potato gnocchi, rainbow chard, mussels, cucumber and ginger butter sauce, the flavours bang on, the textures interesting and the cooking exact. To round it off, try a riff on rhubarb and custard: rhubarb parfait, crème patissière, gingerbread crumb, rhubarb sorbet and a playful touch of jelly. Service is friendly and there's a delightful buzz to proceedings. Drinks include great beers and a snappy but interesting wine list that pits classics against lesser-known finds.

Chef/s: Richard Peacocke. **Closed:** 25 Dec. **Meals:** main courses £11 to £20. **Details:** 50 seats. 45 seats outside. Bar. Music. Parking.

Pensford

LOCAL GEM

The Pig

Modern British | £35
Hunstrete House, Pensford, BS39 4NS
Tel no: (01761) 490490
thepighotel.com

Part of a growing group of country hotels, this Pig brings modern sensibilities to a handsome country house. As produce from its large kitchen garden suggests, the cooking is built around local ingredients of faultless provenance. Grab a table in the rustic dining room for potted salmon on toast, freshly picked leeks in a tart of Quicke's Cheddar and pickled walnuts, or very local venison and British Lop (pork) sausages with savoy cabbage cooked in chicken stock. The wine list offers quality drinking that spans the globe.

Shepton Mallet

LOCAL GEM

Blostin's

Modern British | £35

29 Waterloo Road, Shepton Mallet, BA4 5HH
Tel no: (01749) 343648
blostins.co.uk

Restaurants don't last as long as Blostin's without doing something right, and if you enjoy highly competent, classically based cooking, you'll find something to love here. It's a local stalwart whose decor hasn't moved with the times so, instead of modern sass you get a cosily domestic look and a truly homely welcome. Typical dishes are English asparagus with hollandaise, Parma ham and a sprightly pea shoot salad, and then juicy breast of duck with clementine segments, orange sauce, dauphinois and steamed veg. The sticky toffee pudding in its glossy, rich sauce is a must. Wines are global, classic and keenly priced.

Taunton

Augustus

Cooking score: 4
Modern British | £30

3 The Courtyard, St James Street, Taunton, TA1 1JR
Tel no: (01823) 324354
augustustaunton.co.uk

Whether the sun is shining into, or rain drumming on the roof of, the glass extension of this courtyard restaurant near the river, it's a pleasant – and evidently popular – place to be. Richard Guest's gently tweaked French bistro cuisine mixes some new ideas in with the timeless classics, so a darkly winey beef rib bourguignon with buttery mash and spinach may be preceded by a baked custard of raclette and morteau, with a sharp-dressed salad of kohlrabi and tomato, or by a reef of toasted brioche topped with scrambled duck eggs bandaged in layers of smoked eel. Not everything went quite as well at inspection – overcooked halibut was a worry – but there is enough freshness and energy about the output for the kitchen to redeem itself. A slice of warm treacle tart with concentrated ginger ice cream offers the right sort of sweet indulgence. The wine list features regularly changing specials, with glass prices from £4.45.

Chef/s: Richard Guest. **Closed:** Sun, Mon, 24 Dec to 2 Jan. **Meals:** main courses £17 to £25. **Details:** 40 seats.

Brazz

Cooking score: 1
British | £30

Castle Bow, Taunton, TA1 1NF
Tel no: (01823) 252000
brazz.co.uk

'It's a classic brasserie' is one reader's appraisal of the Castle Hotel's all-day restaurant, which shares the same kitchen, chefs and dedication to localism and sustainability as the flagship Castle Bow (see entry). Sandwiches, salads, grilled steaks and burgers give weight to a confident menu that otherwise keeps to the expected classics of ham hock terrine or chicken liver parfait, and slow-cooked blade of beef with creamed potatoes and braised red cabbage or pork chop with plums, savoy cabbage, coriander, sesame and chilli dressing. There are exemplary local cheeses, desserts such as a first-class custard tart served with nutmeg ice cream, and cheerful, on-the-ball service. Wines from £17.50.

Chef/s: Liam Finnegan. **Closed:** 25 Dec. **Meals:** main courses £12 to £20. Set L and early D £12 (2 courses). **Details:** 60 seats. 8 seats outside. Bar. Wheelchairs. Music. Parking.

Castle Bow

Cooking score: 6
Modern British | £45
Castle Green, Taunton, TA1 1NF
Tel no: (01823) 328328
castlebow.com

'Wonderful food, locally sourced, classical yet with a modern touch. Delicious and at a sensible price . . . it's a must for any occasion.' It's little wonder that readers endorse the small, tastefully laid-out flagship dining room of the imposing (and genuinely ancient) Castle Hotel. Here is a smart destination that puts comfort and hospitality above grand gestures, thanks to attentive service and the inspired cooking of Liam Finnegan. He aims to impress with serious intentions and technical accomplishments, sourcing ingredients carefully and observing the seasons to produce food that is bursting with flavour. One winter diner was pleased by a rabbit and goose liver terrine, its richness cut by piccalilli and celeriac, and saluted the lemon butter sauce that accompanied a perfectly timed piece of halibut. Others have commented on dishes packed with interest, such as goat's curd with asparagus, samphire and pickled walnuts, a tasting of various cuts of Old Spot pork with bubble and squeak, spring greens, burnt apple and wholegrain mustard, and a mascarpone cheesecake with macadamia and blood orange sorbet. Care and skill has been lavished on a wine list that, though bereft of notes, teams with quality at markups that shouldn't offend.
Chef/s: Liam Finnegan. **Closed:** Sun, Mon, Tue, Jan. **Meals:** main courses £18 to £25. Tasting menu £65 (6 courses). **Details:** 36 seats. Bar. Music. Parking. Children over 5 yrs.

Wedmore

The Swan

Cooking score: 3
Modern British | £28
Cheddar Road, Wedmore, BS28 4EQ
Tel no: (01934) 710337
theswanwedmore.com

'I wish this was my local,' said one visitor to this gracious, white-painted inn in the heart of upmarket Wedmore. While food is high on the agenda, the Swan has retained the look and feel of a traditional pub, albeit a fresh, stylish one with an airy, open feel. Beyond the bar is a smart restaurant area with table service and views over the pagoda-shaded terrace – but you can eat where you choose. The menu is full of personality and interest, giving an engaging twist on great British ingredients: Brixham crab, for example, appears as crab cakes with rocket, unctuous aïoli, spiky harissa and dill, while grilled Wye asparagus is served with spring green and potato dumplings, romesco sauce and crumbled baked ricotta. Expect plenty of spicy, herby freshness, but also traditional comforts such as steak and chips or a faultless sticky toffee pudding. A 'proper' wine list delivers a good mix of classic regions and lesser-known finds, at fair prices.
Chef/s: Tom Blake and Jack Stoodley. **Meals:** main courses £14 to £24. **Details:** 74 seats. 35 seats outside. Bar. Wheelchairs. Music. Parking.

Wells

Goodfellows

Cooking score: 3
British | £36
5 Sadler Street, Wells, BA5 2RR
Tel no: (01749) 673866
goodfellowswells.co.uk

'Very good value' offering 'excellent cooking, service and presentation', this 'real gem' is especially appealing if you love fresh seafood. Adam Fellows' smart little restaurant in the heart of Wells, not far from the cathedral grounds, is classily turned out in shades of slate blue and aubergine, with a second eating area pretty much in the kitchen for a ringside view of the action. The menu sweeps through the seasonal larder, occasionally putting a few too many items in its basket, but the technical skills are unquestionable and the dishes pack a punch in terms of interest and flavour. Brixham crab layered with crispy won ton pastry atop a shredded Asian salad may deliver too much soy and brittle crunch for some, but a lovely piece of pan-fried hake with buttery potato purée, crispy Parma ham, tender asparagus and a creamy chive sauce really hits the spot, as does rhubarb and apricot frangipane tart with vanilla ice cream and a touch of crumble. In keeping with the French accents of the cooking, there's a strong Gallic flavour to the wine list.

Chef/s: Adam Fellows. **Closed:** bank hols. **Meals:** main courses £14 to £24. Set L £23 (2 courses) to £27. Set D Wed and Thur £29. Tasting menu £50 (5 courses). **Details:** 40 seats. 15 seats outside. Music.

Wrington
The Ethicurean

Cooking score: 4
Modern British | £45

Barley Wood Walled Garden, Long Lane, Wrington, BS40 5SA
Tel no: (01934) 863713
theethicurean.com

You might read the name as the 'ethical epicure', which goes some way to explaining the green ethos behind this forward-thinking, self-sufficient enterprise located within the bounds of an enchanting Victorian walled garden. From foraging to preserving, all modern trends are on show here – so don't be surprised to see pickled fennel, seaweed sherbet or primrose flowers on the daily lunchtime carte and five-course tasting 'feast'. It's all about multi-layered flavours and contrasts, from spring wild rabbit with bacon, onion ketchup and hazelnuts to a mycophile's cornucopia involving lacto-fermented wild fungus, barley, wood blewits and black truffle. Sides raid the vegetable patch to telling effect, while it's back to the orchard for desserts such as apple panna cotta with burnt apple, caramel and oats. Cider and fruit juices are produced on site, their pine-infused gin with local honey is a winning drink, and the nifty wine list is full of surprises.

Chef/s: Iain and Matthew Pennington and Simon Miller. **Closed:** Mon, 24 to 26 Dec, 2 weeks Jan. **Meals:** set L £28 (2 courses) to £35. Set D £45 (5 courses) to £50. **Details:** 60 seats. 30 seats outside. V menu. Vg menu. Wheelchairs. Music. Parking.

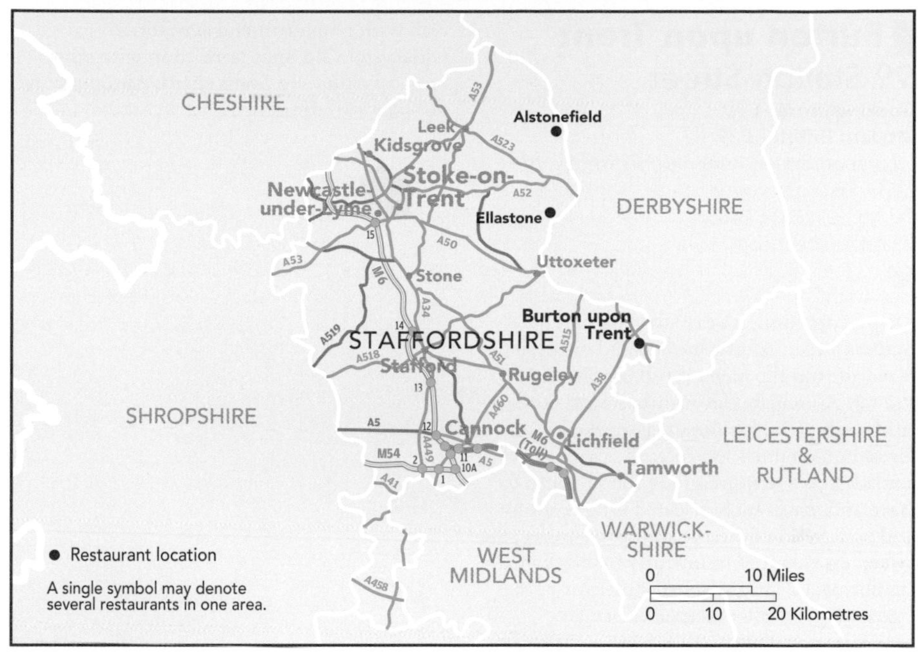

Alstonefield

The George

Cooking score: 3
Modern British | £36
Alstonefield, DE6 2FX
Tel no: (01335) 310205
thegeorgeatalstonefield.com

A picturesque Peak District village, positioned neatly between the market towns of Ashbourne and Bakewell, is the setting for this handsome stone hostelry. Scrubbed wooden tables and beamed ceilings add to its rustic charms, and while the pub is a popular lunchtime destination for ramblers, there's serious foodie intent too. Take your pick from a seasonal menu offering carefully constructed dishes such as goat's cheese custard served with savoury granola, date purée and a sweet and tart Bramley apple granita or ballotine of plaice with Jersey Royals, Cornish brown crabmeat, pickled samphire and Lichfield asparagus, and a 'proper pie' with crisp pastry and packed (on our visit) with tender steak and blue cheese. And who can resist Bakewell tart with the town so close? We loved our rhubarb version, brilliantly matched with a ball of gingery parkin ice cream, although the cheeseboard loaded with local heroes such as Hartington Blue and Bosworth Ash was tempting. There are ales on tap, and the wine list includes a good selection by the glass and carafe.

Chef/s: Kelvin Guest. **Closed:** 25 Dec. **Meals:** main courses £14 to £22. **Details:** 40 seats. 40 seats outside. Bar. Wheelchairs. Parking.

Send us your review

Your feedback informs the content of the *GFG* and will be used to compile next year's reviews. To register your opinion about any restaurant listed in the Guide, or a restaurant that you wish to bring to our attention, visit: thegoodfoodguide.co.uk/feedback

Burton upon Trent

99 Station Street

Cooking score: 1
Modern British | £29
99 Station Street, Burton upon Trent, DE14 1BT
Tel no: (01283) 516859
99stationstreet.com

Do pay attention, it's easy to walk past 99 Station Street. A little hushed and understated it may be but the menu is full of vim and vigour. Anticipate classic dishes with modern spins such as the fabulous tea-smoked Gressingham duck served with celeriac roulade and a strapping sour cherry relish to start, and mains such as seared king scallops and prawns on a buttery cauliflower purée, the sweetness balanced beautifully by blackened shallots and a sprightly tart apple compôte. Finish with a well-executed chocolate brownie served with a fudgy sauce, or baked rice pudding brûlée. Reasonably priced wines by the glass, carafe or bottle.

Chef/s: Daniel Pilkington. **Closed:** Mon, Tue. **Meals:** main courses £13 to £23. Set L £14 (2 courses) to £15. Sun L £18. **Details:** 40 seats. Bar. Wheelchairs. Music.

Ellastone

LOCAL GEM

The Duncombe Arms

Modern British | £36
Main Road, Ellastone, DE6 2GZ
Tel no: (01335) 324275
duncombearms.co.uk

The Duncombe Arms' transformation from boarded-up local boozer to sympathetically restored community hub is thanks to owners Johnny and Laura Greenall, who have given this Victorian country pub a new lease of life. Sitting bang on the Derbyshire and Staffordshire border, it matches exhilarating views with a repertoire of modern-day pub food ranging from citrus-cured salmon and crab with grapefruit and avocado to Gloucester Old Spot pork chop with white bean cassoulet and Swiss chard. Ales and wines do their job admirably.

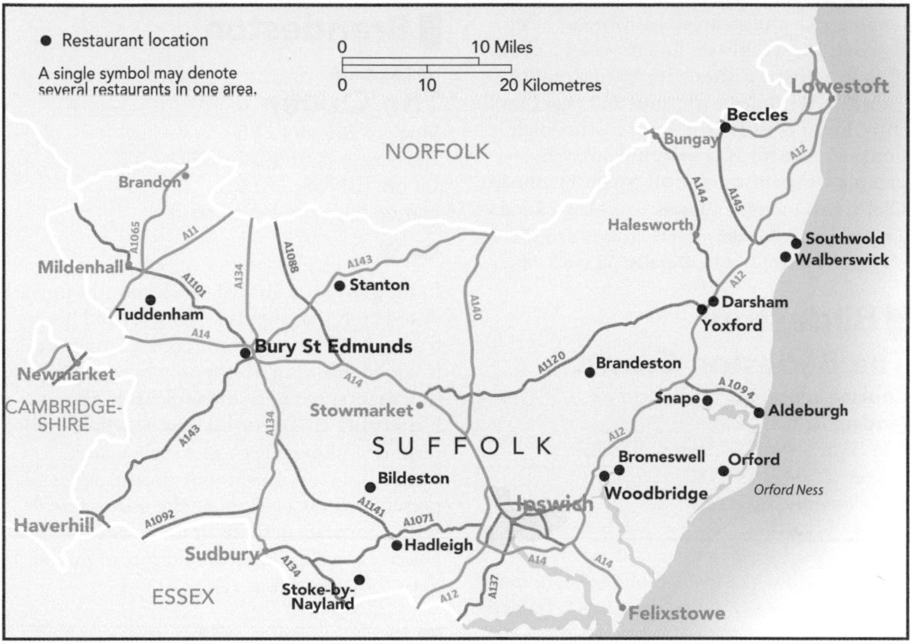

Aldeburgh

LOCAL GEM

The Aldeburgh Market

Seafood | £21

170-172 High Street, Aldeburgh, IP15 5AQ
Tel no: (01728) 452520
thealdeburghmarket.co.uk

Drop into this teeny high street spot for a taste of Suffolk's delicious coastal offerings. Freshly shucked oysters and shallot vinegar; a pot of cockles, crayfish and prawns; potted shrimps; mussels in season; or a platter of smoked fish are the dishes to choose, though there's praise, too, for a classic fish soup with Gruyère, rouille and croûtons. Kippers tempt at breakfast, and homemade cakes for elevenses or at teatime. The adjacent deli with its well-stocked fish counter is worth lingering over as you leave. Wine from £15.95.

Beccles

Upstairs at Baileys

Cooking score: 2

Spanish | £45

2 Hungate, Beccles, NR34 9TL
Tel no: (01502) 710609
upstairsatbaileys.co.uk

Baileys is Beccles' go-to deli, a delicious emporium stocked with all those desirable provisions you read about in the weekend supplements. However, that's only half the story. Upstairs is a café-cum-restaurant that fits the bill for coffee and cake yet saves its finest for supper on Fridays and Saturdays. Chef proprietor Xavier Esteve champions the rustic peasant flavours of his Spanish homeland, imbuing everything from tapas to puddings with in-the-blood authenticity. Begin with meat-packed piquillo peppers or thinly sliced octopus on potatoes with sweet paprika before tackling something more robust – perhaps sea bass stuffed with shellfish sofrito or braised beef cheeks with sweet

potato mash and steamed baby broad beans. By contrast, weekly set lunches offer a choice of more generic dishes with Spanish subtitles – think red mullet with chips and peas ('molls amb chips i pessols') followed by chocolate 'coulant'. Ask for Xavier's guidance when picking from the modest all-Spanish wine list.
Chef/s: Xavier Esteve. **Closed:** Sun, Mon, 25 and 26 Dec, bank hols. **Meals:** main courses £16 to £22. Set L £13 (2 courses) to £16. **Details:** 38 seats. Music.

Bildeston

The Bildeston Crown

Cooking score: 5
Modern British | £35
104 High Street, Bildeston, IP7 7EB
Tel no: (01449) 740510
thebildestoncrown.com

Bildeston grew prosperous on the wool trade in the 15th century, when the timber-framed house that is now the Crown was built as a look-at-me merchant's dwelling. It would be another couple of centuries before it became a coaching inn, and another 400 years before Hayley and Chris Lee turned up with big ideas. Sun-splashed courtyards and toasty corners by the brick fireplace cater for all seasons, while Chris makes his own weather with cooking that embraces classics such as fish and chips with tartare sauce, as well as more venturesome offerings. In the latter camp, expect seared scallops with cauliflower and apple, quail and duck liver with turnip boulangère, and a winning duo of Brixham sea bass and braised oxtail made vivid with rainbow chard. Artful desserts include a meringue-garnished lemon and sesame tart with lemon sorbet, or Cox's apple galette with clove ice cream. House French is £17.50.
Chef/s: Chris Lee. **Meals:** main courses £12 to £22. Set L £15 (2 courses) to £20. Tasting menu £80. **Details:** 80 seats. 30 seats outside. Bar. Wheelchairs. Music. Parking.

Brandeston

LOCAL GEM

The Queen

Modern British | £28
The Street, Brandeston, IP13 7AD
Tel no: (01728) 685307
thequeenatbrandeston.co.uk

In the garden of this red-brick country pub are raised beds that supply vegetables and herbs for the kitchen, and some cool 'glamper vans' if you're thinking of stopping over. A short pub menu runs to fashionable stuff like buttermilk chicken with slaw or whole grilled flounder, alongside classics such as beef burger, or wild mushroom risotto, and presentation is a cut above the norm. Finish with chocolate nemesis or local cheeses. The concise wine list has a decent spread by the glass (bottles start at £17).

Bromeswell

The Unruly Pig

Cooking score: 4
Modern British | £29
Orford Road, Bromeswell, IP12 2PU
Tel no: (01394) 460310
theunrulypig.co.uk

Disorderly? Disruptive? Disobedient? The dictionary definition might not fit this roadside pub restaurant, but the Unruly Pig has certainly shaken up eating out in east Suffolk. Come for a pint and a bar snack – arancini rich with chorizo and Parmesan are crisp balls of joy – or dive hungrily into Dave Wall's creative Anglo-Italian menu. Sweet seared octopus and soft burrata temper the punch of 'nduja that fills squid ink tortellini (homemade, natch), a dish you might follow with dry-aged beef cooked in the fierce heat of the charcoal oven and served with smoked celeriac purée and a delicately layered potato terrine. Finish with an extravaganza of chocolate, the richness of the dark mousse, brownie and snappy tuiles cut with Campari-soaked blood orange, or stay trad with an airily light sponge pudding in a pool of whisky custard. 'Knowledgeable but not in your face' service earns applause, as does the carefully curated wine list, which offers plenty by the glass and carafe, alongside some special vintages and two £15 wines of the month.

Chef/s: Dave Wall. **Meals:** main courses £15 to £25. Set L and D £16 (2 courses) to £19. **Details:** 90 seats. 40 seats outside. V menu. Bar. Music. Parking.

Bury St Edmunds

The Angel

Cooking score: 4
Modern British | £35
3 Angel Hill, Bury St Edmunds, IP33 1LT
Tel no: (01284) 714007
theangel.co.uk

James Carn has put the Angel right back where it belongs on Suffolk's eating-out map, dismissing with his lively, contemporary cooking any suggestion that this is just another provincial hotel restaurant. He delivers technique with dexterity, teases out the flavours of superlative ingredients, and presents plates that are a picture – witness a starter of grilled octopus curling round translucent slivers of peppery radish and a squid ink aïoli that packs just the right garlicky punch. Equally noteworthy are crisp-skinned stone bass in a pool of gently curried mussel soup finished with a tangle of monk's beard, and Ibérico pork presa, its butter-soft richness cut with fresh pomegranate and mellowed by Middle Eastern kibbeh. Pimm's jelly with basil granita, meringue and fresh strawberries is a flirty suggestion of summer, while a passion fruit pavlova with the smoothest coconut ice cream and an exhilarating smack of rum transports you in a spoonful to the Caribbean. A remarkably reasonable wine list opens at £19.

Chef/s: James Carn. **Meals:** main courses £15 to £26.

Maison Bleue

Cooking score: 5
Modern French | £50
30-31 Churchgate Street, Bury St Edmunds, IP33 1RG
Tel no: (01284) 760623
maisonbleue.co.uk

Combining Parisian chic with the kind of welcoming warmth you'd expect from a neighbourhood restaurant in a Suffolk market town, Maison Bleue's charms are many and varied. Service comes with smiles and unmistakable French accents, while the interior is cool and restful, but with striking contemporary overtones (note the abstract artworks mounted on the walls). Meanwhile, the kitchen shows its allegiance to the Gallic ways (old and new), although a few worldly-wise embellishments creep in here and there. Sustainably sourced seafood receives special attention, be it a lightly poached Jersey oyster with grilled leek, pickled cucumber, green apple and smoked eel; or line-caught Cornish sea bass accompanied by shallot butter, confit carrot and orange emulsion. Consistency and depth of flavour are also hallmarks when it comes to meat and game – perhaps roast breast and ballotine of free-range duck with braised chicory, star anise sauce and Vitelotte potato purée. To finish, desserts such as fig and olive oil bavarois or hazelnut and chestnut dacquoise with clementine, chestnut and white chocolate are testament to the kitchen's technical virtuosity. As expected, France claims pole position on the well-considered wine list.

Chef/s: Pascal Canevet. **Closed:** Sun, Mon, 23 Dec to 16 Jan, first 2 weeks Sept. **Meals:** main courses £21 to £29. Set L £20 (2 courses) to £26. Set D £37. **Details:** 55 seats. Music.

1921 Angel Hill

Cooking score: 4
Modern British | £38
19-21 Angel Hill, Bury St Edmunds, IP33 1UZ
Tel no: (01284) 704870
nineteen-twentyone.co.uk

The building may have all the topsy-turvy trappings you might expect for somewhere with medieval roots, but the food coming out of Zack Deakins' (diminutive) kitchen is bang up to date. Taking inspiration from his immediate surroundings, Zack creates food that is as extraordinary to look at as it is delicious to eat. Canapés must not be overlooked – order all eight of the inventive mouthfuls, then work it out between you – and are a perfect sharpener before, say, a starter of Denham Estate venison tartare with slivers of beetroot and pear, or Mersea crab, its gentle flavour pricked by wasabi-pickled mooli, apple and avocado. Follow with loin of cod with salt cod fishcakes and sprouting broccoli, or stuffed saddle of rabbit with confit leg, king oyster mushroom and chasseur sauce. A tonka bean parfait with textures of English strawberries, their sweetness intensified by balsamic vinegar and pepper, is a thrilling finale. An outstanding front of house team delivers notable service, particularly around the wine (bottles from £19.95).
Chef/s: Zack Deakins. **Closed:** Sun, 24 Dec to 5 Jan. **Meals:** main courses £17 to £27. Set L £18 (2 courses) to £21. Tasting menu £70. **Details:** 50 seats. Bar. Wheelchairs. Music.

Pea Porridge

Cooking score: 4
Modern British | £45
28-29 Cannon Street, Bury St Edmunds, IP33 1JR
Tel no: (01284) 700200
peaporridge.co.uk

'Continues to get better and better with each visit,' declares one fan of Justin and Jorga Sharp's highly distinctive restaurant – a converted cottage bakery in a place once known as Pea Porridge Green. The carefully preserved bread ovens are testament to the building's former life, while beams, bare brickwork and scrubbed floors reinforce the rustic mood in the 'nicely buzzy' dining room. A signature starter of lightly curried lamb's sweetbreads with celeriac and spinach is as popular as ever, although there are inspired choices across the board – from 'luscious, pink and tender' Breckland venison with beetroot and golden raisins to a multicultural marriage of Channel sea bass, cuttlefish feijoada, chorizo, chickpeas and gremolata. Elsewhere, the wood-fired Bertha oven does its sizzling work on everything from ox tongue to Ibérico presa, while desserts might include rhubarb jelly with shortbread. It's all about precise technique and freestyle flavours. Cheery staff create 'good feelings' as they go about their business, and it's worth heeding their canny recommendations when it comes to the forward-thinking, organically biased wine list: 'natural' tipples from small-scale producers are the stars of the show.
Chef/s: Justin Sharp. **Closed:** Sun, Mon, 2 weeks Christmas, 2 weeks Sept. **Meals:** main courses £15 to £23. Set L and D Tue to Thur £15 (2 courses) to £19. **Details:** 46 seats. Wheelchairs. Music. Children at L only.

LOCAL GEM

Ben's

Modern British | £31
43-45 Churchgate Street, Bury St Edmunds, IP33 1RG
Tel no: (01284) 762119
bensrestaurant.co.uk

While most restaurateurs are content with their own kitchen garden, Ben Hutton has gone a step further and rears his own livestock. Seasonal game, fish from the East Coast and fruit and veg from local farms add to the proudly local larder. The menu follows suit, favouring British classics including pork and herb terrine and venison and juniper pie – although there's the occasional curve ball such as Blythburgh pork belly with sticky rice and chilli dressing. To finish, try warm lemon pudding with berry compôte. Drinks include wines from nearby Giffords Hall vineyard, beers from Adnams, and Aspall's Suffolk cider.

Darsham

Darsham Nurseries

Cooking score: 3
Modern British | £20
Main Road (A12), Darsham, IP17 3PW
Tel no: (01728) 667022
darshamnurseries.co.uk

At Darsham, the dream of garden nursery eating is fully lived. Walk through the giftshop into the whitewashed café where single-stem flowers spring from a high wooden trough to divide the space, and glass vases of fresh blooms and mismatched furniture lend an artfully thrown-together look. The food naturally majors on plants, nuts and seeds, with a roaring house kimchi to kick the taste buds into gear. Panzanella avoids undue oiliness for a medley of lightly vinaigretted toasted sourdough with charred yellow courgette, crisp baby asparagus and mint. Grilled spring cabbage is doused in potent chilli butter and scattered with almonds, while the meat and fish section might offer a whopping cod fillet in chorizo and tomato broth, with full-throttle allioli for blending in. Desserts look as pretty as the bedding plants outside, when chilled coconut rice pudding comes with pink rhubarb granita and pistachios. Fragrant cocktails and 'posh pops' supplement a short wine selection.

Chef/s: Nicola Hordern. **Closed:** 25 and 26 Dec. **Meals:** main courses £9 to £12. **Details:** 40 seats. 20 seats outside. Wheelchairs. Music. Parking.

Hadleigh

The Hadleigh Ram

Cooking score: 2
Modern British | £31
5 Market Place, Hadleigh, IP7 5DL
Tel no: (01473) 822880
thehadleighram.co.uk

With its full contingent of beams, an ancient fireplace and bags of atmosphere throughout, you can see why the Hadleigh Ram is popular. It successfully blends traditional pub trappings with a contemporary colour scheme, and trades as a serious eatery with some appealingly soothing food that champions seasonal, often local produce. The menu combines classy renditions of pub classics (perhaps ribeye steak with béarnaise sauce, or aged beef burger and fish and chips), with an upbeat menu featuring dishes from scallops with sweetcorn purée, chargrilled baby corn, curried popcorn and bacon crumb to a trio of Suffolk pork (belly, glazed cheek, Cumberland sausage) with smoked creamed potato and hazelnut ketchup. The selection of artisan cheeses is hard to resist if you haven't been snared by the warm chocolate fondant with salted popcorn brittle and praline ice cream. There are good reports of brunch, and wines start at £20.25.

Chef/s: Oliver Macmillan. **Meals:** main courses £14 to £25. **Details:** 64 seats. 20 seats outside. Bar. Wheelchairs. Music.

Orford

The Crown & Castle

Cooking score: 3
British/Italian | £37
Market Hill, Orford, IP12 2LJ
Tel no: (01394) 450205
crownandcastle.co.uk

Escape the damply swirling North Sea mist into the comfort of the Crown & Castle, where winter is kept at bay with log fires, stylishly colourful decor, smiling welcomes and the dose of Italian sunshine administered by the food. Don't be misled by the apparent simplicity of the menu (seafood or cured meat platters, Orford-landed skate with black butter), for the authentic flavours the dishes deliver are spot-on. Ragù stirred through fresh tagliatelle is as intensely *bolognese* as you could wish, and a plump, creamy risotto is generous with its shellfish. Sprats, grilled and served with buttery, garlicky sourdough are a fine starter, one you might follow with tender veal kidneys (cooked to your pink or less-pink liking) in the glossiest Marsala and mushroom sauce. A deliciously retro jelly is a million miles from insipid childhood memories – it is deeply and darkly laden with blackcurrant, and as memorable as the accompanying oven-warm madeleine. Wine from £20.

Chef/s: Rob Walpole. **Meals:** main courses £18 to £28. **Details:** 50 seats. 25 seats outside. V menu. Vg menu. Bar. Wheelchairs. Children over 8 yrs at D.

Snape

The Plough & Sail

Cooking score: 1

Modern British | £25

Snape Maltings, Snape, IP17 1SR

Tel no: (01728) 688413

theploughandsailsnape.com

Alex and Oliver Burnside's dining pub is perfectly located for visitors to Snape Maltings or reed bed ramblers. It offers everything a good pub should: winter fires, a sheltered courtyard for when the weather co-operates and cosy, familiar cooking with a sense of place. Adnams beer is used in the fish batter, and Suffolk Baron Bigod cheese is deep fried and served with quince paste and melba toast. Otherwise there's fish soup, local sausages and mash, and a classic vanilla crème brûlée with shortbread biscuit and berry compôte to finish. The wine list offers good global coverage, including a Suffolk find.

Chef/s: Oliver Burnside. **Meals:** main courses £12 to £17. **Details:** 100 seats. 50 seats outside. Bar. Wheelchairs. Music. Parking.

GFG scoring system

Score 1: Capable cooking with simple food combinations and clear flavours.

Score 2: Decent cooking, displaying good technical skills and interesting combinations and flavours.

Score 3: Good cooking, showing sound technical skills and using quality ingredients.

Score 4: Dedicated, focused approach to cooking; good classical skills and high-quality ingredients.

Score 5: Exact cooking techniques and a degree of ambition; showing balance and depth of flavour in dishes.

Score 6: Exemplary cooking skills, innovative ideas, impeccable ingredients and an element of excitement.

Score 7: High level of ambition and individuality, attention to the smallest detail, accurate and vibrant dishes.

Score 8: A kitchen cooking close to or at the top of its game. Highly individual with impressive artistry.

Score 9: Cooking that has reached a pinnacle of achievement, making it a hugely memorable experience.

Score 10: Just perfect dishes, showing faultless technique at every service; extremely rare and the highest accolade.

Southwold

Solebay Fish Co.

Cooking score: 2
Seafood | £20
Shed 22e, Blackshore, Southwold, IP18 6ND
Tel no: (01502) 724241
solebayfishco.co.uk

The still-working harbour area, with views over the fields to Southwold, is filled with little wooden jetties, dark clapboard sheds with corrugated iron roofs and fishing boats. First-time visitors express surprise on entering this black weatherboarded restaurant (via the wet fish counter) to find a dark, atmospheric and smart beachside-style shack – all wood-clad, with discreet copper piping and filament light bulbs – and agree it is 'quite a find'. The day's specials are written up on a large fish tank, everywhere else – including the ceiling – blackboards highlight an ever-changing mix of Colchester oysters, potted shrimp or raw tiger prawns. The menu majors on generous seafood platters (from smoked fish to crab and lobster), crisp, battered fish (very fresh, served with chunky chips and mushy peas) and awesome crevettes – huge, plump, blackened on the grill and slathered in a lemon, ginger and garlic butter with a zingy lemon mayonnaise. A good wine list compensates for the lack of puddings. Note: it's open lunchtimes only, except Fridays and Saturdays in July and August.

Chef/s: Nikol Hanzalova. **Meals:** main courses £4 to £21. **Details:** Parking.

Stanton

The Leaping Hare

Cooking score: 3
Modern British | £30
Wyken Hall, Stanton, IP31 2DW
Tel no: (01359) 250287
wykenvineyards.co.uk

The giddy – but reasonable – desire to eat local and from trusted sources shows no sign of fading. Fuel it at this rural restaurant in a stylishly converted barn on the Wyken Estate where the quality of ingredients (many from the estate itself) and the light touch of a talented brigade trumps trends and technical showmanship. Plates are visually appealing, however, and composed with easy balance: a rich nugget of crispy pig's head is set against a tangy tangle of kohlrabi, slivers of peppery radish and a spoonful of tart rhubarb to lively effect. Haunch of estate-stalked venison that yields like butter to the knife is a standout main, especially when forked with some of the puréed and roasted cauliflower, sweet beetroot and shiny gravy. Puddings are notable: a passion fruit tart is sprightly in its freshness, while blood orange sorbet tempers with authority the dark, glossy promise of a chocolate marquise. There's much praise for the friendly service, and the wine list, which opens at £21 including estate-grown options.

Chef/s: Simon Woodrow. **Closed:** 25 Dec to 6 Jan. **Meals:** main courses £14 to £21. Set L £18 (2 courses) to £21. Set D £28. **Details:** 40 seats. 20 seats outside. Wheelchairs. Parking.

Anonymous

At *The Good Food Guide*, our inspectors dine anonymously and pay their bill in full every time.These impartial review meals, along with feedback from thousands of our readers, are what informs the content of the *GFG*. Only the best restaurants make the cut.

Stoke-by-Nayland

The Angel Inn

Cooking score: 2
Modern British | £28
Polstead Street, Stoke-by-Nayland, CO6 4SA
Tel no: (01206) 263245
angelinnsuffolk.co.uk
£30

Gone are the days when Constable wandered the Dedham Vale, sketchbook in hand, but a timeless quality nevertheless pervades this part of the border between Suffolk and Essex, and lingers in 16th-century village pubs like The Angel. For all the olde-worlde tropes – beams, inglenooks, wonkiness – the food on your plate dances to a contemporary tune. Start with whipped goat's cheese, pickled baby vegetables and sweetcorn in various guises, or beetroot-cured salmon whose richness is balanced prettily and tastily by curled slivers of macerated mixed beetroot and charred segments of orange. The appealing lineup of mains might include crisp-skinned hake, the flavour lifted by a playful punch from chorizo, or tender lamb rump with pea purée. A lively ginger crème brûlée could round things off sweetly, but don't rule out a platter of mainly East Anglian cheeses. There's wine from £16.95, but have a look at the Chairman's Wine Cellar list, which offers some fine bottles at remarkable prices.

Chef/s: Daniel Russell. **Meals:** main courses £12 to £28. Set L £15 (2 courses) to £17. Sun L £20. **Details:** 80 seats. 24 seats outside. Bar. Music. Parking.

Tuddenham

Tuddenham Mill

Cooking score: 6
Modern British | £42
High Street, Tuddenham, IP28 6SQ
Tel no: (01638) 713552
tuddenhammill.co.uk
£5 OFF

Maybe it's the combination of millpond, dipping willows, gliding swans and meadows, or maybe the food coming out of the talented kitchen that makes this place in an ordinary village in an unremarkable part of East Anglia feel like an effortlessly lovely oasis. Come for refined food, but don't expect fluff or fuss: Lee Bye's style is rugged, unpretentious, uncompromisingly ingredient-led. Scoop firm spears of allotment asparagus through smooth wild garlic emulsion, its richness balanced by the salty pep of feta and sea vegetables; eat butter-soft Brecks-reared lamb, served maybe with aubergine and yoghurt; or a plate of Fenland carrots finished lovingly with wild thyme and honey. Hake cooked on the bone is substantial in size, as well as taste, and is paired harmoniously with peperonata, brown shrimps and spinach. To finish? Strawberries, served simply with a clear consommé, lemon curd and the crisp fragility of crystallised elderflower, promise summer, but you could easily be tempted by a heady rum baba with demerara ice cream, Yorkshire rhubarb and candied walnuts. The burgeoning East Anglian wine scene gets a nod in a comprehensive wine list that opens at £19.95.

Chef/s: Lee Bye. **Meals:** main courses £19 to £32. Set L £21 (2 courses) to £26. Early D £20. Sun L £29. Tasting menu £65. **Details:** 60 seats. V menu. Vg menu. Bar. Wheelchairs. Music. Parking.

Walberswick

The Anchor

Cooking score: 2
Modern British | £30
The Street, Walberswick, IP18 6UA
Tel no: (01502) 722112
anchoratwalberswick.com

The Anchor, as befits its name, is got up in nautical garb, with a seaside-blue façade, white weatherboards and a white picket fence. Alfresco tables give notice of its role as focal point of this pretty Suffolk village, whose past is documented in old illustrations in the bar. At the back, the dining room is done in emerald green and grey, and makes a relaxed setting for an industrious kitchen that butchers and smokes in-house. A daily changing specials menu supplements a list of pub stalwarts and more off-piste offerings, with fish very much to the fore. A lightly grilled whole megrim sole with a spritz of lemon and a scattering of herbs is hard to argue with, while wood-roasted wild sea bass with red peppers is a fat fillet that's fully redolent of its smokey treatment. Before that, a robust approach to dressed crab comes with potato salad and saffron mayo, or there could be grilled scallops in coriander and hazelnut butter. Finish with the excellent sticky toffee pudding and salt caramel sauce. Standard glasses of wine start at £4.50.

Chef/s: Sophie Dorber. **Closed:** 25 Dec. **Meals:** main courses £15 to £21. Sun L £16 (1 course). **Details:** 75 seats. 200 seats outside. Bar. Wheelchairs. Parking.

Woodbridge

LOCAL GEM

The Table

International | £27
3 Quay Street, Woodbridge, IP12 1BX
Tel no: (01394) 382428
thetablewoodbridge.co.uk

Housed in a Grade II-listed 16th-century property, this free-spirited brasserie-style restaurant has charm in spades. The kitchen's output is unpretentious and comforting, including lunchtime salads served at the counter. Global flavours loom large: a hearty vegetarian meze or lamb pancakes to begin, perhaps, before Malaysian chicken curry or aubergine and lentil moussaka. Keep an eye out for street-food evenings in the garden in summer. Wines open at £19.

Yoxford

Main's

Cooking score: 1
Modern European | £32
High Street, Yoxford, IP17 3EU
Tel no: (01728) 668882
mainsrestaurant.co.uk

A proverbial hive of activity run by two of the busiest local bees in the business, Jason Vincent and Sally Main's converted draper's shop holds regular knitting nights and bread-making classes, as well as hosting a charity soup kitchen and feeding the crowds for café-style Saturday brunch. At other times, Jason turns out a locally inflected menu of seasonal food packed with direct, wholesome flavours: cauliflower baked custard; turnip soup with truffle oil; Dover sole with Suffolk asparagus, samphire and capers; roast pheasant with parsnip purée, white wine and lemon sauce. For afters, stay with the seasonal theme for gooseberry tart and elderflower cream. Wines from £15.

Chef/s: Jason Vincent. **Closed:** Sun to Wed. **Meals:** main courses £13 to £22. **Details:** 34 seats.

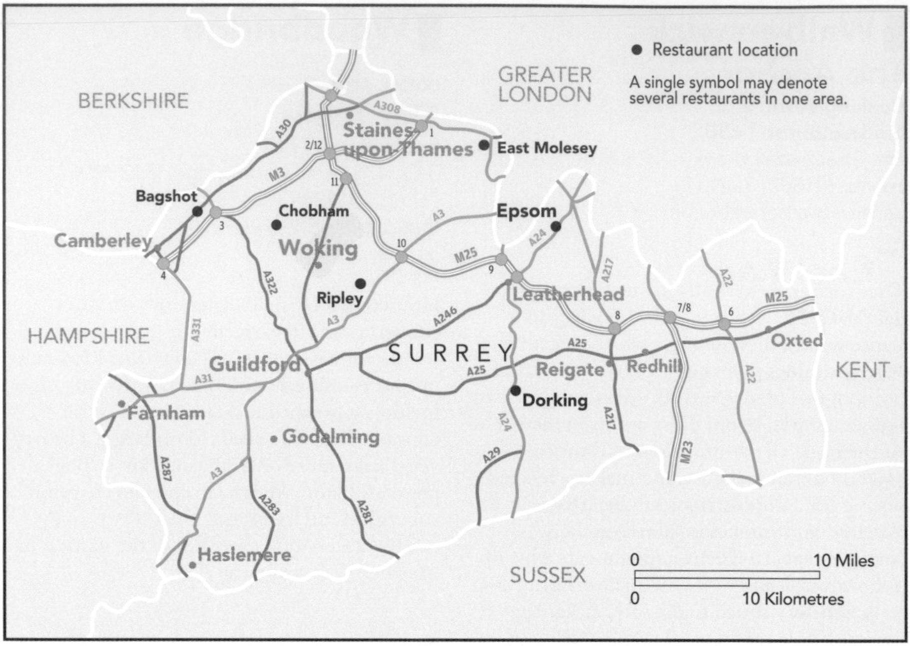

● Restaurant location

A single symbol may denote several restaurants in one area.

0 10 Miles

0 10 Kilometres

Bagshot

★ TOP 50 ★

Matt Worswick at the Latymer

Cooking score: 7

Modern European | £82

Pennyhill Park Hotel, London Road, Bagshot, GU19 5EU

Tel no: (01276) 486156

pennyhillpark.co.uk

'Finally found my way to the restaurant within the hotel complex,' noted one fraught visitor, who was promptly soothed by excellent service and Matt Worswick's food, which has a colour and life all of its own. Indeed, once cocooned inside the beautifully decorated and rather intimate restaurant, you forget you are in a massive corporate playground. The bar is set high from the get-go, a spring meal opening with delicious sourdough bread and 'fabulous' wagyu beef dripping, and a tiny, zingy diced Colchester oyster and cured sea trout combo, mixed with oyster emulsion and topped with Yorkshire rhubarb granita. And, across the board, the search for exquisitely amalgamated, dazzling flavours is a recurring theme: in the umami hit teased out of salt-baked celeriac, a dab of celeriac rémoulade, some lovage, and truffle ice cream topped with shaved black truffle; in the sweetness of an Orkney scallop, partnered not only with spiced Brixham crab, but also a vibrant sauce américaine and Attilus oscietra caviar. The sheer vitality of the ingredients shines through at every turn, notably at a Sunday lunch where the superb quality of the meat helped raise the chef's take on beef wellington to another level. The menus are laid out in tasting format (five or seven courses) and there's some theatre, which is all good fun. Desserts are a high point, judging by the amount of praise we've had for a beautifully refined chocolate délice with milk crumble and yoghurt sorbet. The wine list is easily navigable, big in France but with global forays. If your budget allows, go for the spot-on wine flight.

Chef/s: Matt Worswick. **Closed:** Mon, Tue, 2 weeks Jan. **Meals:** tasting menu L £35 (5 courses) to £49, D £69 (5 courses) to £95. Sun L £59 (5 courses). **Details:** 52 seats. V menu. Bar. Wheelchairs. Parking. Children over 12 yrs.

Chobham

Stovell's

Cooking score: 6
Modern European | £48
125 Windsor Road, Chobham, GU24 8QS
Tel no: (01276) 858000
stovells.com

'Following positive feedback from regular diners, I've continued to introduce more Mexican influences . . . which I'm really excited about, reflecting, as it does, dishes and ingredients from my childhood.' So writes Fernando Stovell, whose cooking in his mind-your-head 16th-century farmhouse continues to delight a loyal brigade of followers. You could go for it and try the 'Taste of Mexico' menu, but the ordinary fixed-price carte is enticing enough. Stovell's bold cooking doesn't deal in pastel-hued flavours and many welcome the forthrightness of a deconstructed beef wellington, the tasty chargrilled beef served atop flaky pastry with truffle mash, oxtail and brassicas, or the counterpoint of flavours in wild sea bass with pickled mushrooms, cardoons and yuzu. Otherwise, appreciate the artistry that goes into a starter of yellowfin tuna ceviche, or an osmanthus and chrysanthemum broth with crab tortellini. Top-drawer desserts have included carrot cake served in a mini garden pot with confit baby carrots and smoked sour cream. Service is pleasant, and the wine list is strong in France with shorter but still interesting finds elsewhere.

Chef/s: Fernando Stovell and Kyle Robinson. **Closed:** Sun, Mon. **Meals:** set L £22 (2 courses) to £26. Set D £42 (2 courses) to £48. Tasting menu £80 (14 courses). **Details:** 60 seats. 20 seats outside. V menu. Bar. Music. Parking.

Dorking

★ NEW ENTRY ★

Sorrel

Cooking score: 5
Modern British | £60
77 South Street, Dorking, RH4 2JU
Tel no: (01306) 889414
sorrelrestaurant.co.uk

This appealing, beautifully renovated 300-year-old building feels like just the place for a special occasion with its mix of beams and old timbers, white-clad tables and comfortably padded chairs. But Steve Drake has hit on a format that suits Dorking – delivering a restaurant that is stylish but informal, the food bang up to date. A passion for brilliant seasonal ingredients underpins the whole operation, and Drake has the confidence to treat them with panache, as evidenced by a summer set lunch starring grey mullet tartare dotted with curry meringue, sweet cicely and cucumber ketchup, and very tender rabbit with English mustard three ways (seeds, leaf, a purée with celeriac). Look to the tasting menu, and ingredients are worked into precisely timed dishes packed with accessible flavours, perhaps a stunningly presented turbot with ginger, fermented tomato, verjus, broad beans and a lovely onion dashi, with strawberries, wild marjoram ice cream, coconut sponge and pea-flavoured dots of meringue a fine finale. The wine list is a good ecelctic mix, with easy drinkers by the glass as well as serious numbers for big occasions.

Chef/s: Steve Drake and Richard Giles. **Closed:** Sun, Mon, Tue, 2 weeks Christmas, first 2 weeks Aug. **Meals:** set L £35 (3 courses). Tasting menu £60 (5 courses) to £95. **Details:** 28 seats. Parking.

East Molesey

Petriti's

Cooking score: 3
Modern European | £27
98 Walton Road, East Molesey, KT8 0DL
Tel no: (020) 8979 5577
petritisrestaurant.co.uk

'It's brilliant that we have fine-dining restaurants on hotch-potch high streets like ours,' thought one East Molesey resident, noting the adjacent pound shop, chippy, pet shop and ancient DIY store. Within, a muted-purple and pale grey colour scheme, well-spaced white-clothed tables and comfortable chairs make a nice change from the stripped down look favoured by many restaurant makeovers, while Sokol Petriti cooks classic dishes 'very well indeed'. Mushrooms on toast with 'a perfect duck egg and generous shavings of truffle', and crab on a warm, vibrant pea purée with a crisp radish and apple topping, make up a tempting preliminary roll call. Perfectly timed lemon sole could follow, accompanied by squid ink linguine, while rump of beef is teamed with ceps, bone marrow and a smooth artichoke purée. After that, a 'fabulous' blueberry and passion fruit soufflé might suffice, if you can resist the lure of dark, rich chocolate délice with a salty caramel sauce and Baileys ice cream. Wines from £19.

Chef/s: Sokol Petriti. **Closed:** 27 Dec to 14 Jan, 2 weeks Aug. **Meals:** set L £19 (2 courses) to £27. Set D £28 (2 courses) to £40. Tasting menu £60 (6 courses). **Details:** 70 seats. V menu. Wheelchairs. Music. Children over 6 yrs.

Anonymous

At *The Good Food Guide*, our inspectors dine anonymously and pay their bill in full every time.These impartial review meals, along with feedback from thousands of our readers, are what informs the content of the *GFG*. Only the best restaurants make the cut.

Epsom

Dastaan

Cooking score: 4
Indian | £25
447 Kingston Road, Epsom, KT19 0DB
Tel no: (020) 8786 8999
dastaan.co.uk

Wedged in an uninspiring row of shops on a busy main road, this contemporary Indian restaurant is no looker from the outside but ignore it at your peril. Between them, proprietor Sanjay Gour and head chef Nand Kishor previously worked for the Tamarind collection, Gymkhana, Trishna and Angela Hartnett's Murano (see entries) – it appears that this is a local curry house like no other. Paprika-coloured chairs and tandoori orange and brown walls add a vibrant but relaxed feel to the place and the cracking atmosphere and cheery service is at odds with its nondescript location. Old favourites (biryani, rogan josh, vindaloo et al) sit happily on the menu alongside innovative dishes that display careful cooking and judicious spicing. Start with duck and guinea fowl seekh kebab or tandoori broccoli with apple raita before Tellicherry Dorset crab (handpicked white and brown meat cooked with butter, garlic and pepper). Mop up any sauces with featherlight naan breads and parathas. Wines from £17.50.

Chef/s: Nand Kishor. **Closed:** Mon. **Meals:** main courses £8 to £15. **Details:** 50 seats. Wheelchairs. Music.

Ripley

The Anchor

Cooking score: 3
Modern British | £35
High Street, Ripley, GU23 6AE
Tel no: (01483) 211866
ripleyanchor.co.uk

Steve Drake made his name at the nearby Clock House before decamping to Sorrel in Dorking (see entries), and he's also behind the impressive takeover of this 16th-century hostelry on Ripley's high street – although day-to-day cooking duties are overseen by his long-time deputy Michael Wall-Palmer. One reader's 'truly excellent' lunch comprised mushroom soup with the 'very softest' chestnut gnocchi, followed by pheasant served 'beautifully' with a leg croquette, celeriac and red cabbage purée, plus ginger rice pudding sweetened with fruity rhubarb compôte ('a superior school dinner') – but that's just the beginning. Come evening, the kitchen proves that it has some more elaborate tricks up its sleeve: consider duck ravioli with smoked beetroot and Parmesan sauce followed by South Coast hake with parsnip, toasted buckwheat and citrus dressing. Value for money extends to set deals and a five-course tasting menu, while the well-spread wine list opens with a dozen selections by the glass.
Chef/s: Michael Wall-Palmer. **Closed:** 25 and 26 Dec, 1 Jan. **Meals:** main courses £16 to £24. Set L and early D £21 (2 courses) to £28. Sun L £24 (2 courses) to £28. Tasting menu £40 (5 courses). **Details:** 45 seats. 20 seats outside. Vg menu. Bar. Wheelchairs. Music. No children after 7.30pm.

The Clock House

Cooking score: 5
Modern British | £60
High Street, Ripley, GU23 6AQ
Tel no: (01483) 224777
theclockhouserestaurant.co.uk

Serina Drake's reboot of Drakes has proved a big hit. The new name works well as the landmark clock on the outside of the building 'picks it out from the crowd'. Subdued elegance reigns within, with well-spaced tables and slightly formal service and the restaurant's ambience fits well with the style of cooking: clean-cut, light, precise and innovative, showing balance and harmony and an obvious attention to detail. This is all delivered via a series of fixed-price menus, including vegetarian options, either à la carte or tasters of varying length. Pork belly with alexanders and apple is a typical opener, while mains such as turbot with cauliflower, field mushroom and truffle or beef with sweetbread, kohlrabi and trumpet chanterelles give a satisfying spin on classic flavour combinations. To finish, there are unpasteurised artisan cheeses or the likes of chocolate, orange, goat's milk and olive oil. The all-encompassing wine list opens at £28.
Chef/s: Fred Clapperton. **Closed:** Sun, Mon, Tue, 1 week after Christmas, 1 week Easter, 2 weeks Aug. **Meals:** set L £31 (2 courses) to £35. Set D £50 (2 courses) to £60. Tasting menu £75. **Details:** 40 seats. V menu. Bar. Music.

Vegetarian and vegan

While many restaurants offer individual dishes suitable for non-meat eaters, those marked 'V menu' (vegetarian) and 'Vg menu' (vegan) offer separate menus.

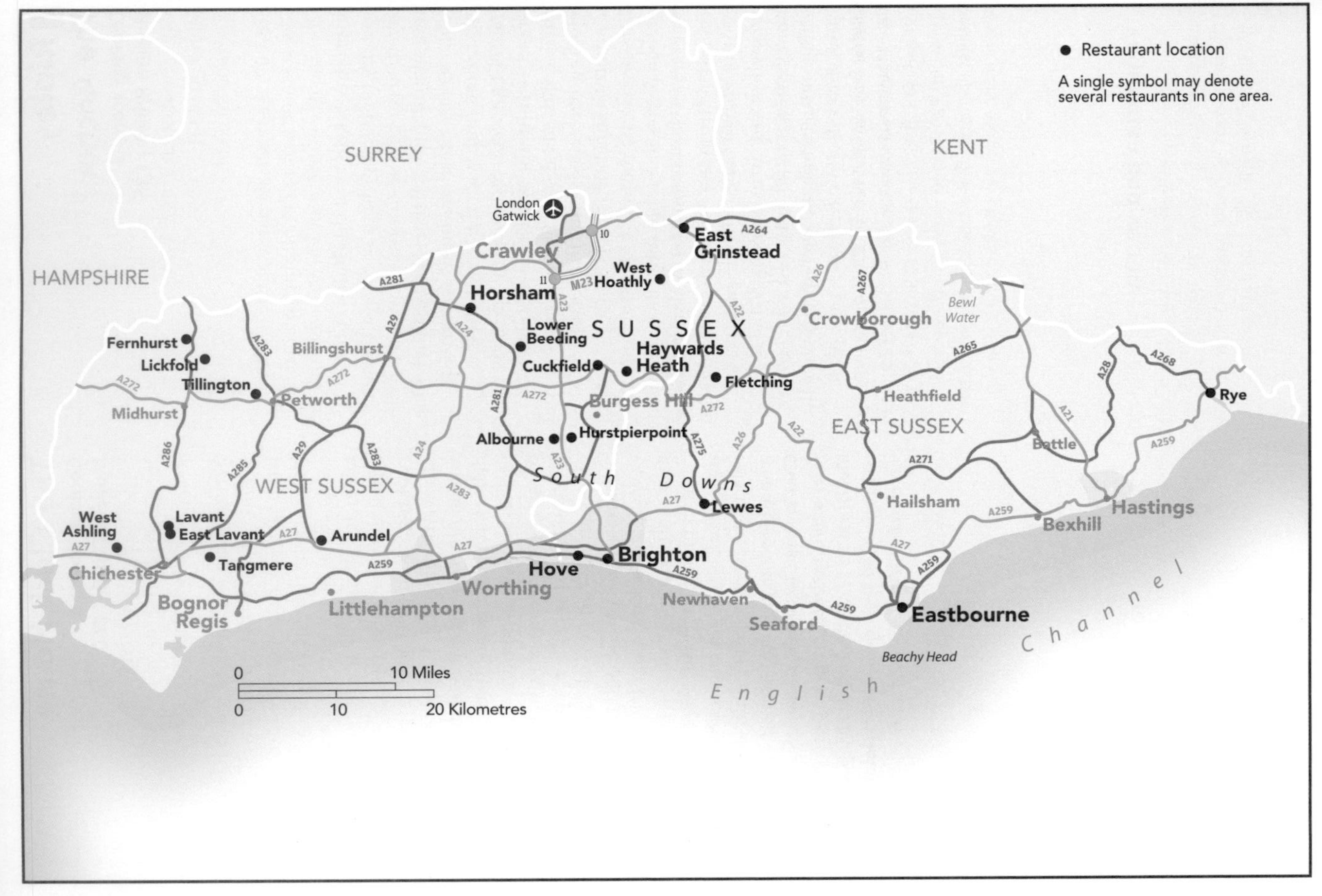
● Restaurant location
A single symbol may denote several restaurants in one area.
SURREY
KENT
HAMPSHIRE
London Gatwick
Crawley
East Grinstead
West Hoathly
Horsham
SUSSEX
Lower Beeding
Haywards Heath
Cuckfield
Fletching
Crowborough
Bewl Water
Fernhurst
Lickfold
Tillington
Billingshurst
Petworth
Midhurst
Burgess Hill
Heathfield
EAST SUSSEX
Albourne
Hurstpierpoint
Battle
Rye
WEST SUSSEX
South Downs
Lewes
Hailsham
Hastings
Bexhill
West Ashling
Lavant
East Lavant
Arundel
Tangmere
Chichester
Bognor Regis
Littlehampton
Worthing
Hove
Brighton
Newhaven
Seaford
Eastbourne
Beachy Head
English Channel
0 10 Miles
0 10 20 Kilometres

Albourne

The Ginger Fox

Cooking score: 3
Modern British | £37
Muddleswood Road, Albourne, BN6 9EA
Tel no: (01273) 857888
gingermanrestaurants.com

With its elaborate thatched roof and South Downs-facing beer garden, this country pub is brimming with bucolic charm. But don't be fooled by its olde-worlde exterior. Step inside and you'll find chic parquet flooring, rustic bistro-style furniture and all the self-confidence of a hip inner-city eatery. Executive chef Ben McKellar – the man behind the Brighton-based Gingerman restaurant group – puts Sussex ingredients centre stage, while taking a hefty dose of inspiration from the Continent. Thus, delightfully crunchy croquettes house rich and gooey Burwash Rose cheese from Stonegate; a beautifully cooked piece of locally reared beef fillet appears with Jerusalem artichoke purée, wild mushroom jus and duck-fat chips; and gnocchi is paired with spiced apple purée, candied walnuts and charred Tenderstem broccoli. To finish, an impressive desserts list features imaginative dishes like carrot cake with cream cheese crémeux and liquorice ice cream. Wines start at £20.

Chef/s: Ben McKellar and Mark Bradley. **Closed:** 25 Dec. **Meals:** main courses £15 to £25. Set L £17 (2 courses). **Details:** 62 seats. 80 seats outside. Bar. Music. Parking.

Send us your review

Your feedback informs the content of the *GFG* and will be used to compile next year's reviews. To register your opinion about any restaurant listed in the Guide, or a restaurant that you wish to bring to our attention, visit: thegoodfoodguide.co.uk/feedback

Arundel

The Parsons Table

Cooking score: 3
Modern European | £32
2 & 8 Castle Mews, Tarrant Street, Arundel, BN18 9DG
Tel no: (01903) 883477
theparsonstable.co.uk

This old flint building tucked down a little mews has a gift of a location; sitting on the front terrace with a glass of chilled white on a sunny day is very pleasant indeed. Inside it is light and modern, with blond wood floors and tables, and the whole place is run with efficient bonhomie by Lee and Liz Parsons. Classic modern European cooking is the drill, with Lee sending out some appealing dishes: starters of crispy pork and apple croquettes, say, with Bramley cider purée and pickled shallot, or cauliflower velouté with seared scallop. Mains include pan-roasted Sussex cod with potatoes, leeks, brown shrimps and chive, or breast of Barbary duck with chicory, orange and sherry vinegar sauce. Desserts defy anyone to resist them, especially treacle tart with lemon thyme and passion fruit ripple ice cream. There's enough to choose from on a wine list that is reasonably priced and has a decent selection by the glass.

Chef/s: Lee Parsons. **Closed:** Sun, Mon, 1 week Feb, 2 weeks end Aug. **Meals:** main courses £16 to £23. Set L £18 (2 courses) to £23. Tasting menu £60 (5 courses) to £80. **Details:** 34 seats. 20 seats outside. Music.

The Town House

Cooking score: 2
Modern British | £30
65 High Street, Arundel, BN18 9AJ
Tel no: (01903) 883847
thetownhouse.co.uk

It's hard not to crick your neck gawping at the original 16th-century Florentine ceiling of this Regency restaurant with rooms directly opposite the walls of Arundel's restored medieval castle. By comparison, the rest of the Grade II-listed space seems relatively understated, with tables clad in white linen, and cornflower blue walls hung with gilded mirrors and bold prints. Lee Williams cooks with regional seasonal produce: English asparagus, say, with crab ravioli and shallot cream, or local pigeon breast, smoked in-house and served cold (a little fresh from the fridge for our liking) with peas, broad beans and two dinky Stilton croquettes. Among main courses, chateaubriand arrives with old-school accoutrements (grilled tomatoes and mushrooms), while wild halibut with herb gnocchi and caponata is a well-thought-out fish option, and venison 'is always a good bet'. Meals open with 'moreish' focaccia and finish with desserts such as baked chocolate and salted caramel tart. The suitably pitched wine list opens at £25.

Chef/s: Lee Williams. **Closed:** Sun, Mon, 25 to 27 Dec, 1 to 3 Jan, 1 week Mar, 1 week Aug, 2 weeks Oct to Nov. **Meals:** set L £18 (2 courses) to £22. Set D £26 (2 courses) to £30. **Details:** 24 seats. Music.

Brighton

Bincho Yakitori

Cooking score: 2
Japanese | £25
63 Preston Street, Brighton, BN1 2HE
Tel no: (01273) 779021
binchoyakitori.com

After three years of figurative blood, sweat and tears working in Japan, learning the finer arts of formal multi-course kaiseki dining, David Biney returned to the UK and opened a place inspired by an altogether different aspect of Japanese cuisine – the casual izakaya (or pub). The charcoal grill is the hub of the operation, turning out yakitori skewers such as chicken liver, squid, charred sweet potato, chicken meatballs, and asparagus wrapped in bacon. Check out the specials board, which might include a saké or beer alongside fresh fish tempura and more. The fryer also chips in crispy chicken (karaage) or Korean-style cauliflower. Tables are tightly packed, the mood is fast and loud, and a table at the counter is either a bird's eye view of the flames or the last refuge of those who can't secure a table proper. Drink Japanese beer, or house wine, or delve into the saké selection.

Chef/s: Tomo Ishii. **Closed:** Mon, 2 weeks Christmas. **Meals:** dishes £3 to £8. **Details:** 35 seats.

The Chilli Pickle

Cooking score: 2
Indian | £27
17 Jubilee Street, Brighton, BN1 1GE
Tel no: (01273) 900383
thechillipickle.com

Some 10 years on, Alun and Dawn Sperring's sizeable Chilli Pickle continues to be 'packed out a good deal of the time' – do book (a second Guildford branch was set to open as we went to press). Head for the ground floor of the MyHotel, opposite the city's Stirling Prize-nominated library. A sacred cow marks the spot. Displays of pickles lend bright pops of colour to the largely wooden interior, while a partly open-to-view kitchen provides red-hot tandoor action (whole sea bream, lamb shank and the like). Sussex produce and distinct spicing add to the mix in a repertoire that covers India from top to tail. Start with dahi puri or crisp pakoras with habanero chutney. Goan fish curry, tandoori platter, Kashmiri mutton curry, paneer kofta kadai – each has its own bespoke accompaniments. Lunchtime thalis are irresistible. Desserts such as Valrhona dark chocolate kulfi are no afterthought, and craft ales and well-chosen wines match the food.

Chef/s: Alun Sperring. **Closed:** 25 and 26 Dec. **Meals:** main courses £14 to £19. Set D £25 (2 courses) to £29. **Details:** 115 seats. 12 seats outside. Wheelchairs. Music.

Cin Cin

Cooking score: 2
Italian | £28

13 Vine Street, Brighton, BN1 4AG
Tel no: (01273) 698813
cincin.co.uk

There's a new addition to the Cin Cin family (see entry, Hove), which is testament to the success of this, the original venue, found on a side street in the artsy North Laine district. With counter dining, a tiny open kitchen, and a concise menu of fabulous cured meats and cheeses, a few small plates and fresh pasta (handmade twice a day), it's a simple – if intimate – proposition: your waiter is right there on the other side of the counter should you want a refill or another dish. Sharing boards for two are irresistible: pancetta affumicata (rolled and smoked pork belly), or a top-drawer Gorgonzola from Milan. The mix of imported and British produce results in freshly made farfalle with cauliflower, pickled golden sultanas and rosemary crumb, plus small plates such as trout cured in Averna and dill or venison bresaola with truffled celeriac. The wine list is loyal to the motherland.

Chef/s: Jamie Halsall. **Closed:** Sun, Mon, 25 and 26 Dec. **Meals:** main courses £11 to £12. Set L and D £15 (2 courses) to £20. **Details:** 21 seats. Music.

The Gingerman

Cooking score: 3
Modern British | £40

21a Norfolk Square, Brighton, BN1 2PD
Tel no: (01273) 326688
gingermanrestaurants.com

Ben McKellar's 20 year-old Gingerman was the launching pad for a mini empire that includes Pig, Fox and Dog – Gingers all, and stalwarts of the Brighton & Hove (and surrounds) eating and drinking scene. Just up from the seafront, the Man has white walls and exposed brickwork, wooden tables, retro Danish dining chairs and button back banquettes – all very simple and unpretentious. The menu is built around regional produce and reveals a penchant for contemporary combinations; English goat's curd with beetroot and spikes of blood orange, say, or smoked South Coast mackerel in a sushi roll with wasabi yoghurt and white asparagus. At its best, the kitchen can turn out some pretty refined stuff, such as honey-roasted quail with truffled polenta, gently pickled pied bleu mushrooms and a frothy chicken velouté, or poached halibut with wild mushroom velouté. The fixed-price lunch is a steal. Local English fizz from Ridgeview is available by the glass, with house French opening at £22 a bottle.

Chef/s: Ben McKellar and Mark Charker. **Closed:** Mon, first 2 weeks Jan. **Meals:** set L £17 (2 courses) to £20. Set D £35 (2 courses) to £40. Sun L £30 (3 courses). Tasting menu £55 (5 courses). **Details:** 34 seats. Music.

Isaac At

Cooking score: 3
Modern British | £35
2 Gloucester Street, Brighton, BN1 4EW
Tel no: (07765) 934740
isaac-at.com

On a residential side street in the North Laine district, away from the madding crowds, you'll find this singular field-to-fork restaurant. Isaac Bartlett-Copeland and his team are full of youthful confidence, doing it their way with integrity, which extends to offering an exclusively British drinks list. Seasonal Sussex ingredients are the driving force of the no-choice set and tasting menus, with contemporary cooking techniques used to good effect and pin-sharp presentation adding to the impact. The high-quality produce shines, as when scallops, horseradish and apple combine in harmony; and roast carrot, coriander and caramelised onion take centre stage in a vegetarian course. Pork belly and smoked broccoli with a kohlrabi and cabbage combo works a treat, and, among sweet courses, rhubarb and almond are best friends forever. The English wine list has limited options by the glass, though beers and ciders – plus drinks pairings – are ample compensation.

Chef/s: Isaac Bartlett-Copeland. **Closed:** Sun, Mon, 23 Dec to 7 Jan, first 3 weeks Aug. **Meals:** set L and D £35 (4 courses). Tasting menu £50. Early D £29. **Details:** 20 seats. Music. Children over 12 yrs.

★ NEW ENTRY ★

Murmur

Cooking score: 4
Modern British | £29
91-96 King's Road Arches, Brighton, BN1 2FN
Tel no: (01273) 711900
murmur-restaurant.co.uk
£5 OFF £30

Around dusk in autumn and winter, the spectacular murmuration of starlings can be seen above the skeletal remains of the old West Pier opposite, while the sea view is a banker year round, with outdoor tables to up the seaside ante. This is the second Brighton & Hove address for Michael Bremner of 64 Degrees (see entry) and TV fame. Expect a utilitarian but stylish look and a menu that, although less outré than its older sister, is full of contemporary ideas and simple things done very well. Start with 'blooming lovely' lobster croquettes, or a daily special: sardines with tomato and bread salad was a ray of Mediterranean sunshine on our visit. Main courses can be as simple as steak and hand-cut chips or whole grilled brill, or as creative as pot-roast celeriac with confit yolk. Custard tart with rhubarb sorbet confirms this is a kitchen with a light touch. Cool cocktails and 'softtails', a few beers, and wines from £20 suit the all-day vibe.

Chef/s: Josh Kitson. **Closed:** 25 Dec. **Meals:** main courses £14 to £20. Set L £15 (2 courses) to £20. **Details:** 34 seats. 40 seats outside. Wheelchairs. Music.

★ NEW ENTRY ★

Pascere

Cooking score: 3
Modern British | £35
8 Duke Street, Brighton, BN1 1AH
Tel no: (01273) 917949
pascere.co.uk

This is fine dining 21st-century style, so there's an open kitchen on the first floor and not a starchy tablecloth in sight. Small plates catch the eye at lunch and early evening (two crispy cauliflower croquettes, say, with a 'divine' cauliflower and truffle purée), while the carte sticks to three-course convention. A vegetarian opener elevates the Pink Fir potato to a starring role, with warm Innes Brick goat's cheese and woodland mushrooms, and the smoking of Goosnargh duck is timed just right (served with caramelised endive, celeriac rémoulade and a sweet vinaigrette). Main course fillet of sea bream arrives with a full-flavoured nero sauce, and braised pig's cheek with a tangle of tagliatelle and a couple of pieces of 'melt-in-the-mouth' home-cured jowl bacon. Finish with an intricate dark chocolate and cherry combo. The well-chosen wine list includes biodynamic and organic options, and local Court Garden English fizz by the glass.

Chef/s: Ben Porter. **Closed:** Sun, Mon, 25 and 26 Dec, 1 Jan. **Meals:** main courses £18 to £21. Set L £16 (2 courses) to £19. **Details:** 37 seats. 16 seats outside. Bar. Music.

Pike & Pine

Cooking score: 4
Modern European | £45
1d St James's Street, Brighton, BN2 1RE
Tel no: (01273) 686668
pikeandpine.co.uk
£5 OFF

By day, this is Redroaster (an indie café/diner with its own roastery in Brighton's Kemptown); by night, the premises trade as Pike & Pine – a showcase for the considerable culinary talents of chef Matt Gillan. Readers may remember him from The Pass at Lower Beeding, but this is a less recherché set-up – albeit one defined by fashionable 'bites' and plates of various sizes. Perch at the counter for up-close views of the open kitchen, or immerse yourself amid the greenery and marble tables. Either way, expect challenges, surprises and a fair bit of creativity: crispy pork bonbons with miso mayo (that's a snack); duck leg with pineapple, chicory and peanut butter; poached trout with ox tongue, asparagus and parsley cream. Sweets such as popcorn cheesecake with rhubarb sorbet and caramel are equally modern, and British cheeses are given their full due. Cocktails chime with the clubby soundtrack, but you can also sip sherries, saké and affordably priced wines.

Chef/s: Matt Gillan. **Closed:** Mon. **Meals:** main courses £14 to £16. Tasting menu £48 (4 courses). **Details:** 45 seats. 25 seats outside. V menu. Wheelchairs. Music.

Plateau

Cooking score: 1
Modern European | £40
1 Bartholowmews, Brighton, BN1 1HG
Tel no: (01273) 733085
plateaubrighton.co.uk

'Wine, beats and bites' goes the tag line at Plateau. Wine comes first: the organic and biodynamic list (from £24) is broad, with 20 by the glass, over a dozen 'skin-contact' wines and some rare finds tipping three figures. The ingredient-driven and wine-friendly menu scales up from 'snacks' of Sardinian coppa or Sicilian olives, to a shared meat platter (of pork loin, belly, bavette and confit duck) via sides, snacks and small plates with a seasonal focus – perhaps spätzle, broad beans and ricotta salata. Finish with cheese or miso tart with ginger. Eclectic tracks on vinyl account for the buzz.

Chef/s: Will Dennard. **Meals:** main courses £14 to £19. Set L £16 (2 courses) to £20. **Details:** Bar.

The Restaurant at Drakes

Cooking score: 3
Modern European | £47
43-44 Marine Parade, Brighton, BN2 1PE
Tel no: (01273) 696934
therestaurantatdrakes.co.uk

If you do like to be beside the seaside, Drakes hotel is ideally positioned a short stroll from the pier. While some of the boutique bedrooms have sea views, the restaurant is at lower-ground floor level, a dressed-up contemporary space that's none the worse for being subterranean. It's one of the more formal dining options in the city, with a fixed-price carte and five-course tasting menu dealing in modern European fare. Among starters, tender Galician octopus ravioli in a rich tomato and olive sauce, and smoked eel and prawn mousse with quinoa and cucumber granita hit the spot. Beal's Farm in Sussex provides the morcilla that's part of an assiette of pork, with braised red lentils and quince, although one reader was disappointed to find salmon the only main-course fish, especially since 'the briny is just across the road'. To finish, caramelised mango and coconut custard enrich a soufflé that comes with a 'seriously sharp' lime granita. The helpfully annotated wine list kicks off at £22.

Chef/s: Andy Vitez. **Meals:** set L £20 (2 courses) to £25. Set D £36 (2 courses) to £47. Tasting menu £65. **Details:** 40 seats. Bar. Music. Parking.

The Salt Room

Cooking score: 3
Modern British | £40
106 King's Road, Brighton, BN1 2FN
Tel no: (01273) 929488
saltroom-restaurant.co.uk

A table on the terrace in the Brighton sun is a hot ticket at the Salt Room, with the sparkling briny and the skeletal hulk of the ruined West Pier spread out before you. Inside, domed copper lamps hover over a clean-lined modern look, and service rocks and rolls with city cool. Modern brasserie food with the emphasis on fish is the name of the game, with sharply defined flavours and on-point seasonings throughout. A salad of tender octopus with bacon, lentils and seaweed in lime dressing is a case in point, or consider a morsel of ox cheek with beetroot, watercress and mushroom ketchup. Stacked surf boards for sharing bring the sea to your table, or go for monkfish in Sauternes, got up with crosnes and truffles, or hake in devilled shrimp butter. 'Taste of the Pier' is a tribute to seaside treats, while Calvados parfait comes with ginger cake and caramelised apple. Ingenious cocktails and inspired wines from £5 a glass add to the fun. As for adding Coca-Cola to amontillado sherry – least said, soonest mended.

Chef/s: Dave Mothersill and Neil Martin. **Closed:** 25 and 26 Dec. **Meals:** main courses £13 to £28. Set L and early D £18 (2 courses) to £20. **Details:** 80 seats. 50 seats outside. Bar. Wheelchairs. Music.

Semolina

Cooking score: 1
Modern European | £27
15 Baker Street, Brighton, BN1 4JN
Tel no: (01273) 697259
semolinabrighton.co.uk

Orson Whitfield in the kitchen, Linda Whitfield front of house: Semolina is a proper family-run bistro, where consistency is provided by the ever-present owners. It's some way out from the tourist mêlée, so remains popular with locals and is well worth the trip from the centre of town. Hits of citrus and ginger fire up cured sea bream in a first course, or go for moreish goat's cheese and beetroot empanadas. The inflection is mostly European: cod and clams are teamed with parisienne gnocchi (made from choux pastry) and salsa verde, while rump of lamb arrives with the shoulder meat boulangère style. Local fizz, regional beers and imaginative cocktails join well-priced wines on the concise drinks list.

Chef/s: Orson Whitfield. **Closed:** Sun, Mon, 1 week Christmas, 2 weeks Jan, 2 weeks Aug. **Meals:** main courses £11 to £18. Set L £12 (2 courses) to £15. **Details:** 28 seats. Music.

The Set

Cooking score: 3
Modern British | £40
Artist Residence, 33 Regency Square, Brighton, BN1 2GG
Tel no: (01273) 324302
thesetrestaurant.com

It hardly counts as gentrification, but velour banquettes and padded chairs have upped the comfort levels at the Set, though the corrugated metal wall remains, lest we think it's getting all la-di-da. Dan Kenny's place is still a hipster paradise, ensconced in the Artist Residence hotel, with the front part of the ground floor now given over to creative tapas (out of the Set kitchen) while the main restaurant, with just 20 covers, has three fixed-price set menus (one vegetarian) of divertingly contemporary cooking. Things get going with three little snacks before the opener – Jerusalem artichoke cooked in liquor, say, with tahini yoghurt, pressed apple and a herby pesto. Monkfish with a fiery jerk purée and seasoning stole the show for one reader ('best dish of the night'), followed by hogget, encased in a parsley and mint 'jacket' with pommes Anna enriched with black pudding. Not every flavour hits home, but a pre-dessert lime meringue sorbet with sorrel granita is a 'classic in the making'. The drinks pairing is an enticing option, or go it alone with a bottle from £23.

Chef/s: Dan Kenny. **Closed:** 25 and 26 Dec. **Meals:** tapas £2 to £5. Tasting menu £40 to £45. **Details:** 40 seats. 8 seats outside. V menu. Bar. Music. No children.

Silo

Cooking score: 3
Modern British | £35
39 Upper Gardner Street, Brighton, BN1 4AN
Tel no: (01273) 674259
silobrighton.com

Silo's stated aims – 'reuse, reduce, share, repeat' – are not hollow words, for Douglas McMaster's restaurant is zero waste and devoted to ensuring that everything comes from an ethical and sustainable source (from food to glasses and furniture). They cure, ferment, forage and churn, but more importantly they turn out great plates of food. It all takes place in a former Victorian warehouse with a familiar utilitarian finish of zinc-topped tables, chipboard seats and dangling light bulbs. Brunch kicks off with small plates such as pig's cheek with pickled grapes, or coddled egg with kimchi and black pudding (dulse seaweed for the non-meat eaters). At dinner, choose from 'Plant' and 'Omnivore' dishes: pumpkin might shine alongside apple molasses and sunflower seeds, while pollock is paired with Tokyo turnip and crème fraîche. Among desserts, seasonal alexanders, yoghurt and walnut is a gloriously fresh finale. Organic and biodynamic wines start at £30.

Chef/s: Daniel Gibeon and Douglas McMaster. **Closed:** Mon, Tue, 25 and 26 Dec, 2 weeks Jan, 2 weeks Jun. **Meals:** set L £15 (2 courses) to £21. Set D £20 (2 courses) to £28. Sun L £25. Tasting menu £38. **Details:** 50 seats. V menu. Bar. Wheelchairs. Music.

64 Degrees

Cooking score: 4
Modern European | £35
53 Meeting House Lane, Brighton, BN1 1HB
Tel no: (01273) 770115
64degrees.co.uk

Since last year's guide there has been a change of head chef, but chef proprietor Michael Bremner continues to oversee the kitchen – he splits his time between 64 Degrees and a new restaurant, Murmur, overlooking the West Pier (see entry). With a handful of tables at the front and stools at the counter by the open kitchen, it's a sleek and intimate space hidden away in the Lanes and local spies stress that booking is a must. The deal is small plates, served in no particular order and with sharing encouraged. From the concise menu offering four choices for fish, meat or vegetables, punchy flavours are to the fore, whether it's mackerel teamed with rhubarb and chia, Roly's mutton with kidney beans and jerk, or carrot, miso and peanut. The three-ingredient rule extends to a dessert of chocolate, avocado and coffee. The short wine list starts at £22 and includes interesting bottles from Japan and Greece.

Chef/s: Michael Bremner and Michael Notman-Watt. **Meals:** small plates £8 to £15. **Details:** 20 seats. No children after 9pm.

Terre à Terre

Cooking score: 3
Vegetarian | £35
71 East Street, Brighton, BN1 1HQ
Tel no: (01273) 729051
terreaterre.co.uk

£5 OFF

Meat-free eating has become much more mainstream since this vegetarian and vegan trailblazer opened in the early 1990s, but it remains at the vanguard with its flavour-packed food. Multi-faceted, globally inspired constructions come out of the kitchen: a first course of lemony goat's cheese fritters with black sticky rice and white onion cream sauce, perhaps, or a Japanese-influenced slow-baked aubergine with sweet white miso and sesame. Dish descriptions are frequently punning – 'Aloo Sailor' (potato rösti with Indian spices, punchy pickles and tandoori halloumi), or 'Sneaky Peeking Steamers' (steamed rice buns). Finish with a citrus hit from 'More Heart than Tart'. Vegan and gluten-free options are marked on the menu, with afternoon tea and children's menus also in the mix. It's all served in a gently contemporary and surprisingly big space, with a small terrace out back. Sussex wines figure on the entirely vegetarian and organic list.

Chef/s: David Marrow. **Closed:** 25 and 26 Dec. **Meals:** main courses £16. Set L and D £35. **Details:** 110 seats. 15 seats outside. V menu. Wheelchairs. Music.

★ NEW ENTRY ★

The Urchin

Cooking score: 2
Seafood | £30
15-17 Belfast Street, Brighton, BN3 3YS
Tel no: (01273) 241 881
urchinpub.co.uk

Shellfish and craft beer are much more than a novelty double act this corner pub tucked away in residential Hove not far from the seafront. Amid a stripped-back interior with zinc-topped bar, rough and ready floorboards and lights dangling down on thick rope, local beers in keg and cask are joined by an array of bottles from near and far. The shellfish menu draws appreciative diners (booking is advisable). Keep it simple with a quarter pint of cockles, wild Cornish oysters, whole crab with garlic butter, or dive into a copper cataplana of gumbo with fat crab claws, juicy prawns and chorizo – a messy but satisfying dish. Bang-on scallops, complete with corals, come in a first course with celeriac and apple, and the daily-changing solo dessert is no afterthought. The wine list has lots of shellfish-friendly options by the glass.

Chef/s: Sean Brailsford. **Closed:** Mon. **Meals:** main courses £8 to £17. **Details:** Bar.

LOCAL GEM

The Coal Shed

Modern British | £45
8 Boyces Street, Brighton, BN1 1AN
Tel no: (01273) 322998
coalshed-restaurant.co.uk

For those whose appetite for beef cannot be tamed, the proposition of steaks cooked over charcoal in a Josper oven has ensured that this lively eatery continues to be a hit. But diners whose exploration of the menu begins and ends at the steak section are missing out: the kitchen's mastery with fish is displayed in such dishes as brill with smoked potatoes, leeks and crispy oyster and there are starters such as Orkney scallops with yuzu, chestnut satay and pickled shiitake to consider. Wines from £19. Related to The Salt Room (see entry).

LOCAL GEM

Curry Leaf Cafe

Indian | £26
60 Ship Street, Brighton, BN1 1AE
Tel no: (01273) 207070
curryleafcafe.com

The Curry Leaf brand has sprouted around the city, with another café in Kemptown and a kiosk at Brighton station. At the original, a short stroll from the sea, the riotously colourful and casual premises is rammed much of the time as diners pile in for Indian street food (fiery Chettinad chicken wings, say), full-on thalis and well-spiced curries such as Keralan chicken mappas or vegetarian kolhapuri. Drink craft beers or wines intended to cope with the often robust spicing of the food.

Cuckfield

Ockenden Manor

Cooking score: 4
Modern French | £50
Ockenden Lane, Cuckfield, RH17 5LD
Tel no: (01444) 416111
hshotels.co.uk

Set in beautiful grounds and with its roots in the 16th century, this country house hotel is traditional in style, offering a confident and classic blend of antiques, plush furnishings and rich colours – it has charm and individuality with good food at its heart. With the French doors flung open on a sunny day, the dining room feels particularly special, but reliably provides a sense of occasion whatever the weather. Stephen Crane's French-influenced cooking suits the classic surroundings and offers an opportunity to try some outstanding Sussex produce – Trenchmore Farm salt beef with crunchy spring vegetable salad, grain mustard crème fraîche, smoked tomatoes and rocket, for example, or Newhaven-landed cod with chestnut mushrooms, artichokes, sweetcorn, crispy potato and cep jus. Finish with a riff on English rhubarb featuring jam, custard, a doughnut and rhubarb ripple ice cream. The wine list is a substantial volume with picks from all over the world and especially good regional coverage of France.

Chef/s: Stephen Crane. **Meals:** set L £23 (2 courses) to £30. Set D £65 (3 courses). Sun L £40. Tasting menu £50 (6 courses) to £90. **Details:** 75 seats. V menu. Bar. Wheelchairs. Parking.

East Grinstead

Gravetye Manor

Cooking score: 4
Modern British | £75
Vowels Lane, East Grinstead, RH19 4LJ
Tel no: (01342) 810567
gravetyemanor.co.uk

A meandering approach through hundreds of acres, impressive gardens (designed by Victorian 'wild gardener' William Robinson) and a grand Elizabethan pile – Gravetye is a classic country house. The frameless glass extension of the newly refurbished dining room puts diners (almost) among the borders, while chef George Blogg uses the gardens' produce to inform his menus. Dishes look pleasingly pretty, with lightly whipped smoked cow's curd, asparagus and seasonal flowers to open proceedings, or torched mackerel and its tartare with well-seasoned brown crabmeat. Mains could include cutlet and carved breast of local hogget in a slick of demi-glace with confit potato and peas, or John Dory with umami-rich oyster dressing and caviar cream. There are odd textural lapses, though – too-thick Parmesan crisps, flaccid skin on the torched mackerel that need looking at. Rose geranium ice cream is the distilled essence of June, as are marinated strawberries and sorbet with basil mousse. When it comes to wine, all bases are covered, albeit at considerable outlay. Good glasses start at £6, gliding via Coravin to the treasures of the vaults.

Chef/s: George Blogg. **Meals:** set L £35 (2 courses) to £40. Set D £50. Seasonal menu £75. Tasting menu £90. Sunday L £50. **Details:** 60 seats. 20 seats outside. V menu. Bar. Wheelchairs. Music. Parking. Children over 7 yrs.

East Lavant

The Royal Oak Inn

Cooking score: 1
Modern British | £35
Pook Lane, East Lavant, PO18 0AX
Tel no: (01243) 527434
royaloakeastlavant.co.uk

More than 200 years old and still in fine fettle, The Royal Oak has graduated from local watering hole to dining destination – although drinkers still appreciate its winter fires, Sussex ales and cosy nooks. Breakfast is a boon for visitors to nearby Goodwood and the South Downs, while the food served in the conservatory-style dining room shows a respect for local produce. Fish from the South Coast boats and game figure on a menu that roams from Selsey crab salad and wild rabbit Scotch eggs to burgers, honey-roast chicken and tapenade-crusted lamb rump with a warm salad of mangetout. Wines are a cut above the pub norm.

Chef/s: Fran Joyce. **Meals:** main courses £12 to £21. **Details:** 55 seats. 35 seats outside. Bar. Wheelchairs. Music. Parking.

Eastbourne

The Mirabelle

Cooking score: 4
Modern European | £46
The Grand Hotel, King Edward's Parade, Eastbourne, BN21 4EQ
Tel no: (01323) 412345
grandeastbourne.com

The fact that the BBC Palm Court Orchestra used to deliver its Sunday evening radio broadcasts from the Great Hall of the Grand tells you all you need to know about this gleaming-white multi-tiered landmark on Eastbourne's seafront. Sitting in the Mirabelle restaurant, you really are whisked back to yesteryear – smart dress is expected and politeness and formality come as standard. Under the aegis of executive chef Gerald Röser, the kitchen treads carefully, ensuring that nothing shocks or disorientates the assembled company. A starter of warm asparagus with poached quails' eggs and truffled hollandaise leads on to sturdy mains such as roast rump of beef with butternut squash and girolles or seared sea trout with celeriac galette and lime butter sauce, with peach clafoutis, chocolate fondant and tiramisu to finish. The wine list is a suitably grand tome with grand prices to match.

Chef/s: Gerald Röser and Stephanie Malvoisin. **Closed:** Sun, Mon, first 2 weeks Jan. **Meals:** set L £23 (2 courses) to £28. Set D £39 (2 courses) to £46. Tasting menu £67 (7 courses). **Details:** 50 seats.

Fernhurst

The Duke of Cumberland Arms

Cooking score: 3
Modern British | £35
Henley Hill, Fernhurst, GU27 3HQ
Tel no: (01428) 652280
dukeofcumberland.com

Tricky to locate, this unspoilt 15th-century country pub, its brick walls covered with roses and wisteria in late spring, is well worth the effort to find. The tiny rustic bar 'exudes atmosphere in spades', helped by panelled walls, low beams and crackling log fires. Eat here at simple scrubbed pine tables or step up into the smart rustic dining room next door – the menu is the same. Simon Goodman is passionate about sourcing local and seasonal produce for his monthly lunch and dinner menus, which combine pub classics with more ambitious dishes: organic meat from local farms is supplemented by home-grown salads and vegetables. It is still very much a pub, so expect generous roast beef and horseradish mayonnaise sandwiches or a deliciously creamy prawn, crayfish and pea risotto at lunchtime, confit pork belly with thyme and port jus among the evening choices and Sunday roast platters. Finish with summer berry Eton mess. An impressive wine list includes half-bottles and a cellar selection.

Chef/s: Simon Goodman. **Closed:** 25 and 26 Dec. **Meals:** main courses £19 to £29. **Details:** 55 seats. 133 seats outside. Bar. Wheelchairs. Music. Parking.

Fletching

LOCAL GEM

The Griffin Inn

Modern European | £35

Fletching, TN22 3SS
Tel no: (01825) 722890
thegriffininn.co.uk

£5 OFF

Whether it's the pretty village location, the vast rear garden overlooking Sheffield Park, the blazing fires in the two bars, the wood panelling or the old world ambience, there's something about this ancient inn that hits exactly the right spot for visitors. The menu is peppered with nostalgic flavours, from honey-baked Camembert with toasted sourdough and red onion marmalade to Portland crab linguine, fish pie, wood-roast leg of lamb with basil pesto or cod and chips with minted pea purée. There are local ales for those with just a liquid appetite, and some good drinking from a wine list that's a work of passion.

Haywards Heath

Jeremy's

Cooking score: 5
Modern European | £40

Borde Hill Garden, Balcombe Road, Haywards Heath, RH16 1XP
Tel no: (01444) 441102
jeremysrestaurant.co.uk

£5 OFF

Though the light and airy interior of Jeremy's has its charms, those visiting in summer are strongly advised to bag a table in the restaurant's luscious walled gardens. Forming part of the stunning Borde Hill Estate, this could be one of the most bucolic places to eat in the UK – or is it Provence? Fortunately, the food stands up to the setting. Chef Jimmy Gray creates inventive, sprightly dishes that leave you brimming with a genuine sense of occasion. Starters, for example, might take in Wye Valley asparagus with ricotta, green olive and passion fruit, or quinoa houmous, seaweed and fermented mango. Mains, meanwhile, could see a beautifully cooked hunk of John Dory paired with lemon and fennel pollen potatoes, or South Downs lamb with chard, sea vegetables and grelot onions. As for dessert, do not under any circumstances leave without sampling the sticky toffee pudding, a dessert so good that Gray refuses to take it off the 'ever-changing' menu – and for good reason, too. The wine list starts at £19.50 and boast an impressive array of local fizz.

Chef/s: Jimmy Gray and Eliott Buchet. **Closed:** Mon, 1 to 17 Jan. **Meals:** main courses £16 to £27. Set L and D £24 (2 courses) to £29. Sun L £28 (2 courses) to £35. Tasting menu £45 to £50. **Details:** 52 seats. 35 seats outside. Bar. Wheelchairs. Music. Parking.

Horsham

Restaurant Tristan

Cooking score: 6
Modern British | £50

3 Stans Way, East Street, Horsham, RH12 1HU
Tel no: (01403) 255688
restauranttristan.co.uk

Housed in a 16th-century building in the old part of town, Tristan Mason's place works on two levels. You could begin the day with breakfast in the ground-floor coffee shop, before returning after a little light shopping to the first-floor dining room, where blue bucket seats at unclothed tables sit beneath the old beams, their gnarled unevenness lit by naked halogens. The core of the production is four-course menu formats catering to a range of regimens: vegan, vegetarian, pescatarian. A particularly happy time was had by visitors who began with a scallop accompanied by whole and puréed mushrooms, balanced by the crunchy bitterness of radicchio, went on to eloquent pork belly with beetroot, scratchings and lobster ('an odd combination that worked surprisingly well'), and then splendid autumn grouse, its richness offset with the sweetness of figs and textured by the addition of cobnuts. A perfect landing was assured by the billowy softness of mandarin soufflé with ginger granita. Wines (from £24) have evolved into a superlative roll-call of imaginatively chosen modern bottles, with Coravin glass selections and a particularly good listing of food-friendly Pinot Noirs. A slate of beers and ciders for the cheeses is encouraging.

Chef/s: Tristan Mason. **Closed:** Sun, Mon, 25 and 26 Dec, 1 Jan. **Meals:** set L £30 (3 courses) to £35. Set D £44 (3 courses) to £50. Tasting menu £70 (6 courses) to £90. **Details:** 34 seats. V menu. Vg menu. Bar. Wheelchairs. Music. Children over 10 yrs.

Hove

★ NEW ENTRY ★

Cin Cin

Cooking score: 2
Italian | £30
60 Western Road, Hove, BN3 1JD
Tel no: (01273) 726047
cincin.co.uk

This is the new sibling of the North Laine original in central Brighton (see entry), and together they have the city covered for ingredient-led, flavour-packed Italian cooking. This new version is slightly larger with some high tables and private dining, plus a grill to increase its culinary chops, but both venues are all about the easy-going counter-dining experience. Kick off with house-cured salumi and imported meats, aspargus with bagna cauda, or an arancini, like the one enriched with pistachio and mortadella. Pasta is made in-house, say tagliatelle with 'soft and tender' ox tongue, fresh peas and tapenade, and is hard to resist. That grill might offer up pollock (with herb polenta) or Calcot Farm beef (with asparagus and roast tomato pesto), and keep an eye on the blackboard for specials. Three Italian fizzes by the glass and 'moreish aperitivi' support the regional wine list.

Chef/s: Jamie Halsall. **Closed:** Sun, Mon, 25 and 26 Dec. **Meals:** main courses £9 to £14. **Details:** 35 seats. Music.

etch.

Cooking score: 5
British | £50
216 Church Road, Hove, BN3 2DJ
Tel no: (01273) 227485
etchfood.co.uk

£5 OFF

Steven Edwards' arrival at the western end of Church Road in 2016 chimed with Brighton & Hove's restaurant renaissance of recent years. Winning *MasterChef: The Professionals* was doubtless handy for marketing purposes, but as the TV series discovered back in 2013, the proof of the pudding is in the eating. And the eating is very good indeed. It's a winner in the design stakes, too, with fashionably dark tones and an open kitchen as the centrepiece; get a more intimate booth table if you can. The monthly changing tasting-menu format of five, seven or nine courses has Sussex providing its bounty of land and sea and there's a wine-pairing option. Wee snacks and Marmite brioche with seaweed butter start proceedings with an umami hit, before an array of inventive courses with clear flavours, clever technique and pretty presentation: broad bean and mint; lamb and aubergine; cod and lettuce; tomato and polenta. The kitchen delights in variations of texture and temperature, and shows a steady hand. Finish with kiwi and elderflower in perfect harmony. Sussex fizz stars on the globetrotting wine list, which starts at £25.

Chef/s: Steven Edwards. **Closed:** Sun, Mon, Tue, 25 and 26 Dec. **Meals:** tasting menu £50 (5 courses) to £60. **Details:** 32 seats. Bar. Music. Children over 8 yrs.

The Ginger Pig

Cooking score: 3
Modern British | £35
3 Hove Street, Hove, BN3 2TR
Tel no: (01273) 736123
gingermanrestaurants.com

The Ginger Pig is in fine fettle these days after some serious investment brought 11 en suite bedrooms into play upstairs and stylishly refurbished the bar and restaurant. It's more gentrified bar-cum-restaurant than boozer, but that's always been the way. The dining area, with its black leather banquettes along moody dark walls, is watched over by a cheerful team dressed in shades of grey. Daily specials such as crispy wild garlic arancini with ricotta and salsa verde support a menu that takes a wide-angle view of things, from burger and steaks, to fresh fish (lemon sole, say, with Puy lentils) and 'beautifully pink and tender' cannon of lamb. Good pastry skills are evident in a caramel custard tart. The drinks list is no slouch: local fizz by the glass (the stellar Ridgeview Bloomsbury), a host of cocktails and a goodly number of wines by the glass and carafe.

Chef/s: Robin Koehorst. **Meals:** main courses £13 to £24. **Details:** 80 seats. Bar. Music.

The Little Fish Market

Cooking score: 5
Seafood | £65
10 Upper Market Street, Hove, BN3 1AS
Tel no: (01273) 722213
thelittlefishmarket.co.uk
£5 OFF

On a quiet corner just off the main commercial drag, the Little Fish Market lives up to its name, seating just 20. Here, Duncan Ray cooks alone in his kitchen, creatively and precisely, and his cookery is of the highest order – the driving force being the freshest seafood, local and sustainable. Out front another solo effort, this time from Rob Smith, makes the whole experience seem personal and effortless. And while you may need your specs to read the blackboard menu, choosing couldn't be easier – dinner is an all-conquering five-course set. Hand-dived scallops with just-so squid risotto, a perfect piece of cod, lightly cooked, with seaweed butter, or crisp-skinned sea bream with hits of tomato and shallots, are typical of the style. Meat crops up now and again: crisp chicken skin, say, with a fine piece of halibut. It's a journey of balance and refinement, all the way to a chocolate délice and banana dessert. The wine list is Eurocentric, with Davenport Vineyards flying the flag for English fizz.

Chef/s: Duncan Ray. **Closed:** Sun, Mon, 1 week Dec to Jan, 1 week Apr, 2 weeks Sept. **Meals:** tasting menu £65. **Details:** 20 seats. Music. Children over 12 yrs.

Hurstpierpoint

LOCAL GEM

The Fig Tree

Modern British | £35
120 High Street, Hurstpierpoint, BN6 9PX
Tel no: (01273) 832183
figtreerestaurant.co.uk

Celebrating local produce in a pretty Sussex village close to the South Downs National Park, Jodie and James Dearden's elegant neighbourhood restaurant continues to please with its capably executed cooking – judging by favourable comments on dishes ranging from smoked haddock with Pink Fir potato and quail's egg to venison loin and sausage with artichokes. Elsewhere, butter-poached turbot with crab, Jersey Royals, asparagus and peas promises luxurious seasonal gratification, while dessert might bring a four-way take on rhubarb with white chocolate cheesecake and almond ice cream. Wines from £18.50.

Lavant

The Earl of March

Cooking score: 2
Modern British | £35
Lavant Road, Lavant, PO18 0BQ
Tel no: (01243) 533993
theearlofmarch.com

The views out towards Goodwood and the South Downs are just about unbeatable on a summer's day, especially if you're soaking them up from the terrace of this historic Sussex hostelry. But The Earl of March has many other attributes, not least its food. Simple dishes such as asparagus with a poached egg are 'presented with aplomb', although the kitchen is also capable of delivering more intricate compositions – as in charred octopus with chervil, cucumber, carrot and pumpkin seeds; Stansted venison with 'textures of Marmite'; or a mélange of rabbit, celeriac, wild garlic, salted grapes and wild mushrooms. Fans of briny-fresh crustacea are also well served, as are lovers of sirloin steak with triple-cooked chips, while desserts are mostly old faithfuls such as triple chocolate brownie. Readers say that the food is 'excellent', although sloppy service can sometimes rankle. A serviceable wine list opens with house selections from £20.

Chef/s: Adam Hawden. **Closed:** 25 Dec. **Meals:** main courses £18 to £30. Set L and D £25 (2 courses) to £28. **Details:** 70 seats. 60 seats outside. Bar. Wheelchairs. Music. Parking.

Lewes

★ NEW ENTRY ★

Limetree Kitchen

Cooking score: 3
Modern British | £25
14 Station Street, Lewes, BN7 2DA
Tel no: (01273) 478636
limetreekitchen.co.uk

Ask any Lewesian foodie to pick their favourite eatery in town and there's a good chance they'll name Limetree Kitchen – a pint-sized bistro with sun-bleached beach hut vibes, just seconds from the train station. The tag line here is 'farm to fork' and this means a regularly changing menu of ingredient-led small dishes designed for sharing. West Sussex tomatoes, for example, might turn up with smoked Sardinian ricotta and sherry vinegar. To follow, impossibly delicate cod cheek pakoras could be teamed with zingy tandoori yoghurt, while those wanting a meat fix might opt for a chicken cassoulet, or crispy pig's head with kimchi and bacon. For owner and head chef, Alex Von Riebech, puddings are definitely not an afterthought; a typical sweet treat might be goat's milk panna cotta with Guinness granita and crunchy honeycomb crumble, or vanilla and muscovado ice cream served with espresso and amaretto. Well-spread international wines start at £18.50, and there's an extensive list of small-batch gins.

Chef/s: Alex Von Riebech. **Closed:** Mon, Tue. **Meals:** main courses £7 to £17.

Lickfold

The Lickfold Inn

Cooking score: 5
Modern British | £48
Highstead Lane, Lickfold, GU28 9EY
Tel no: (01789) 532535
thelickfoldinn.co.uk

The 'super-cool' kitchen visible behind a glass wall next to the pub bar is a bit of a giveaway – this rural 15th-century tavern is a little out of the ordinary. Its executive chef is Tom Sellers of Restaurant Story (see entry, London), and if the Lickfold doesn't deliver quite the same level of culinary razzle-dazzle, it's still pretty 'out there' for a country pub. Head upstairs to the restaurant, where chunky beams meet contemporary neutrality. Fine British ingredients speak for themselves in an opener of aged beef tartare with 'Lickfold garnishes', including beef-fat jam and pickled wild asparagus, and in main-course halibut with pickled sloes and cauliflower purée. Modern cooking techniques are preferred, but if not every dish rises above the sum of its parts, that cannot be said of a 'triumphant' lemon cake with milk sorbet and hits of lemon verbena and honey. The well-chosen wine list includes Sussex Ridgeview fizz by the glass.

Chef/s: Graham Squire. **Closed:** Sun, Mon, Tue, 2 to 18 Jan. **Meals:** main courses £19 to £40. Set L £24 (2 courses) to £30. Sun L £30 (2 courses) to £40. Tasting menu £65 (6 courses). **Details:** 38 seats. 50 seats outside. Bar. Wheelchairs. Parking.

Lower Beeding

The Crabtree

Cooking score: 2
Modern British | £26
Brighton Road, Lower Beeding, RH13 6PT
Tel no: (01403) 892666
crabtreesussex.co.uk

This 16th-century family-run dining pub boasts a large and loyal local following, with visitors praising its 'ambitious cooking' and 'warm, welcoming atmosphere'. The selling points? Informative service and a menu of modern British dishes made with seasonal, locally sourced ingredients. Seafood, for example, is ferried in from the English Channel via Shoreham-by-Sea, while a farm just down the road supplies the top-quality meat. It's a simple formula, but it works. Starters might include grilled mackerel and beetroot with goat's cheese curd and dill oil, or chicken liver parfait with burnt apple purée and toasted brioche. Mains, on the other hand, are a heartier affair, taking in classics like pan-fried sea bass with wild garlic, beer-battered haddock and chips, and 28-day aged ribeye steak. Those with a sweet tooth are cautioned to leave room for puddings like salted caramel truffles and vanilla panna cotta with English strawberries and Earl Grey syrup. Wines from £18.

Chef/s: Dean Brackenridge. **Closed:** 25 Dec. **Meals:** main courses £14 to £22. Set L £16 (2 courses) to £23. **Details:** 70 seats. 150 seats outside. Bar. Wheelchairs. Music. Parking.

Rye

Landgate Bistro

Cooking score: 2
Modern European | £30
5-6 Landgate, Rye, TN31 7LH
Tel no: (01797) 222829
landgatebistro.co.uk

The adjoining Georgian cottages overlooking Rye's ancient Landgate have a surprisingly contemporary feel within – whitewashed brick walls and an outsized gilt-framed mirror help set the tone. A little plot not far away supplies herbs and soft fruits to Martin Peacock's kitchen, supplementing the wild and foraged materials that lend distinctiveness to the cooking. Modern European dishes with the emphasis on forthright seasonings encompass squid braised in red wine with aïoli, or herbed scallop ravioli with lemon foam, to start, and then griddled venison served with three variations of beetroot, pickled fennel and spinach, or turbot in chive velouté with Jerusalem artichoke and trompettes. To finish on a spirited note, you may well find the crème brûlée laced with prunes and Armagnac, or delve into peak chocolate with a Valrhona Manjari mousse and white chocolate ice cream, served with kirsch-lashed cherries. A gin slate includes the local Brighton brand, while the short wine list opens with house Chilean Sauvignon and Merlot at £19.80.

Chef/s: Martin Peacock. **Closed:** Mon, Tue, 25 and 26 Dec, 31 Dec to 1 Jan. **Meals:** main courses £15 to £20. Set L Sat and Sun £19 (2 courses) to £23. Set D Wed and Thur £21 (2 courses) to £25. **Details:** 32 seats. Bar. Music.

Tangmere

Cassons

Cooking score: 3
Modern British | £39
Arundel Road, Tangmere, PO18 0DU
Tel no: (01243) 773294
cassonsrestaurant.co.uk

Cassons may not serve up a pretty view – it's accessed via the westbound carriageway of the A27 and vehicles whizz past – but once you're off the road and ensconced within the 18th-century cottage, that's all a world away. Viv Casson cooks in a bright contemporary manner, while husband 'Cass' is front of house ensuring it all goes smoothly. Regional ingredients get an outing on the à la carte, and there's plenty of creativity on show. A goat's cheese and tomato opener is full of zingy fresh flavours, including an Instagram-worthy faux tomato with gazpacho filling, while the seafood platter is three flavour-packed morsels of Selsey crab, seared scallop and malt-cured salmon. Duck breast arrives 'as pink and tender as you'd hope' with crisp bonbons packed with confit leg meat, finished with a glossy duck and cherry sauce, or go for stone bass with sauce nero and then a 'heavenly' dark chocolate mousse with mango for dessert. The helpfully annotated wine list includes six house selections at £22.50.

Chef/s: Vivian Casson. **Closed:** Mon, Christmas to New Year. **Meals:** set D £31 (2 courses) to £39. Sun L £23 (2 courses) to £28. **Details:** 36 seats. 12 seats outside. Bar. Music. Parking.

Anonymous

At *The Good Food Guide*, our inspectors dine anonymously and pay their bill in full every time.These impartial review meals, along with feedback from thousands of our readers, are what informs the content of the *GFG*. Only the best restaurants make the cut.

Tillington

The Horse Guards Inn

Cooking score: 3
Modern British | £34
Upperton Road, Tillington, GU28 9AF
Tel no: (01798) 342332
thehorseguardsinn.co.uk

It's everyone's ideal country pub: 350 years old with a country-rustic interior, crackling fires and flickering candles in winter, and a lovely summer garden filled with deckchairs, roaming chickens and views towards the South Downs. Underpinning it all is good-quality, honest British cooking. All ingredients are sourced from surrounding farms and artisan producers, and the bread, ice creams and sloe gin are homemade. The result is a short, daily menu that evolves with the seasons – our enjoyable spring lunch took in local asparagus with hollandaise, a creamy smoked haddock chowder, and a perfectly cooked venison burger with dill pickle, salad and homemade chips. Alternatives could be venison, pigeon and pheasant terrine with apple chutney; a hearty bouillabaisse; or duck leg goulash with potato dumplings, peppers, sour cream and Hungarian sweet paprika. Leave room for warm chocolate and vanilla rice pudding. To drink, there are Sussex ales and an eclectic list of wines from £18.

Chef/s: Mark Robinson. **Closed:** 25 and 26 Dec, last 2 weeks Jan. **Meals:** main courses £15 to £23. **Details:** 50 seats. 50 seats outside. Bar. Music.

West Ashling

The Richmond Arms

Cooking score: 4
Modern British | £32
Mill Road, West Ashling, PO18 8EA
Tel no: (01243) 572046
therichmondarms.co.uk

An ever-so-English village on the edge of the South Downs, complete with a swan-filled pond, creates just the right impression for visitors to William and Emma Jack's charming inn. The cosy but smartly attired interior includes a rustic bar where wood-fired pizzas are dispensed from an old Citroën van parked just outside. In the restaurant, the cooking is British, executed in the modern style and tapping into a network of local producers. There are some cleverly honed ideas: crispy Moroccan-style local wood pigeon pie, say, or wild duck croquettes with watercress and chanterelles picked the previous autumn among the starters, with mains running to roast local cod with nettle and horseradish tandoori masala, or sticky, smokey slow-coked brisket of beef. Nobody can feel neglected when there's a bombe Alaska of Harvey's porter and chocolate ice cream to finish, or a homemade almond and dulce de leche 'mini Magnum'. Beer is local, the wine list full of organics, biodynamics and recherché rarity, as well as a handful of French classics.

Chef/s: William Jack and Theo Tzanis. **Closed:** Mon, Tue, 3 weeks Christmas and New Year, last week Jul, last week Oct. **Meals:** main courses £16 to £27. **Details:** 85 seats. 30 seats outside. Bar. Music.

West Hoathly

The Cat Inn

Cooking score: 2

Modern British | £29

North Lane, West Hoathly, RH19 4PP

Tel no: (01342) 810369

catinn.co.uk

£5 OFF · £30

Diners at this welcoming 16th-century bolthole are generally ushered towards a bright and airy Victorian extension. But locals – and their dogs – wisely head to the old bar, where the same menu is paired with an inviting inglenook fireplace and a low-beamed ceiling adorned with all manner of pewter and brass. Whichever space you opt for, the focus here is high-quality British comfort food that isn't afraid to doff its hat to the Continent. A typical starter, for example, could be haddock fishcakes and salsa verde or chorizo Scotch eggs with celeriac rémoulade. Mains, meanwhile, take in dishes like braised shoulder of lamb with crushed peas and red wine sauce, and pan-fried whole plaice with samphire, Jersey Royals and wild garlic pesto. For afters, a menu of proudly homemade classics (rhubarb crumble, sticky toffee pudding) is hard to resist. The wine list kicks off at £20.50, including an admirable selection from local vineyards.

Chef/s: Alex Jacquemin. **Meals:** main courses £14 to £18. **Details:** 80 seats. 40 seats outside. Wheelchairs. Parking. Children over 7 yrs.

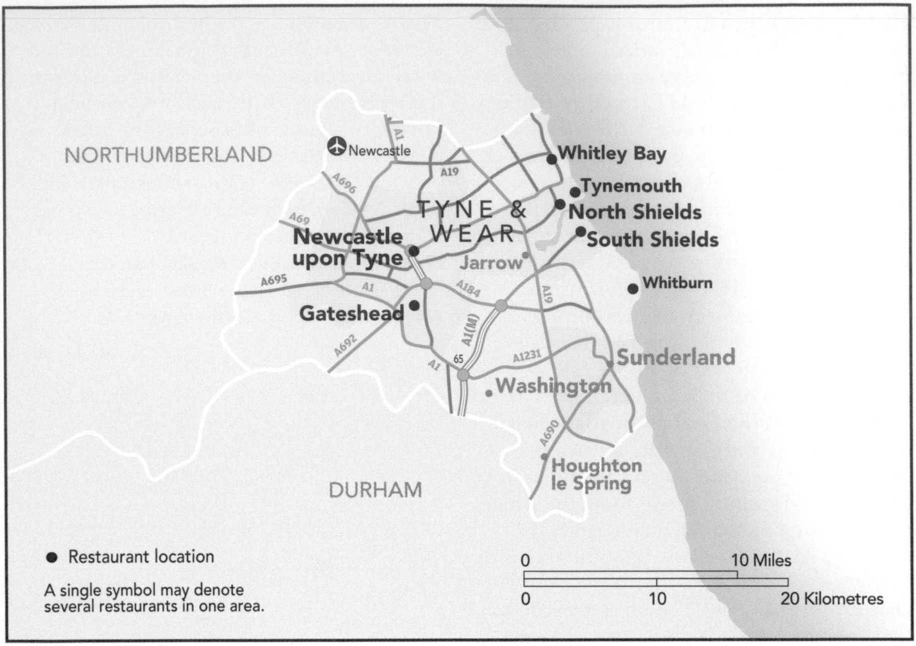

● Restaurant location

A single symbol may denote several restaurants in one area.

Gateshead

Eslington Villa

Cooking score: 2
Modern British | £30

8 Station Road, Low Fell, Gateshead, NE9 6DR
Tel no: (0191) 487 6017
eslingtonvilla.co.uk

Given the location, it's plain to see why this refashioned Victorian villa is regularly bookmarked for business bashes, birthdays and anniversaries. Built in 1880 for an industrial tycoon, it's an easy escape from the region's urban jungle, complete with views of the sprawl you've left behind – plus the added reassurance that comes from a couple of acres of landscaped grounds. Ornate candelabra, floor-to-ceiling drapes and stained glass windows provide grandeur, although the food is never excessive or overblown. Instead, regional ingredients are thoughtfully deployed for modern-sounding dishes that are guaranteed to please: seared scallops, cauliflower purée and chorizo followed by braised pork cheeks with creamed potatoes, savoy cabbage, blossom honey and grain mustard is just one option, and there are dry-aged steaks with twice-cooked chips for the diehards. To finish, take comfort from baked lemon cheesecake or apple and bread pudding. The mostly European wine list is helpfully broken down by category.

Chef/s: Jamie Walsh. **Closed:** 25 and 26 Dec, 1 Jan. **Meals:** main courses £15 to £24. Set L and early D £17 (2 courses) to £20. Sun L £21. **Details:** 80 seats. 20 seats outside. Bar. Wheelchairs. Music. Parking.

Symbols

- Accommodation is available
- £30 Three courses for less than £30
- £5 OFF £5 off voucher scheme
- Notable wine list

Newcastle upon Tyne

Artisan

Cooking score: 3
Modern British | £30
16 Stoddart Street, Newcastle upon Tyne, NE2 1AN
Tel no: (0191) 260 5411
artisannewcastle.com

Located in The Biscuit Factory, a notable independent art gallery in Newcastle's cultural quarter, Artisan is an attraction in itself, separated from the gallery by a 25-foot glass wall – through which diners can view the latest works. Chef Andrew Wilkinson's strictly seasonal, contemporary cooking lives up to its arty surroundings. Dishes are attractively presented but every element is there for a reason – namely a balance of flavours – with no room for superfluous ingredients. Begin with salt cod beignets with squid ink taramasalata, pickled cucumber, brown shrimps and lemon before daube of ox cheek, served with creamed potatoes, heritage carrots, shallot and smoked bacon, or roasted halibut with braised fennel, crab and blood orange. Finish with Yorkshire rhubarb, jelly, custard and doughnuts. The international wine list starts at £19, with plenty of good drinking under £30, plus useful tasting notes.

Chef/s: Andrew Wilkinson. **Closed:** Mon, Tue, 25 and 26 Dec, 1 and 2 Jan. **Meals:** main courses £15 to £24. Set L and early D £16 (2 courses) to £19. Sun L £25. Tasting menu £50. **Details:** 80 seats. Bar. Music. Parking.

Blackfriars

Cooking score: 1
Modern British | £40
Friars Street, Newcastle upon Tyne, NE1 4XN
Tel no: (0191) 261 5945
blackfriarsrestaurant.co.uk

Despite some recent refurbishment, there's no mistaking the antiquity of this restaurant – a Grade I-listed adjunct to a medieval priory and once the refectory for cloistered Dominican 'blackfriars'. Fast-forward eight centuries and the kitchen now deploys a full quota of regional ingredients for modern British dishes, perhaps smoked haddock brandade cakes; duck 'ham' with rhubarb marmalade and broad bean croquette; or rare-breed pork with truffle mash. For traditionalists, there's game pie or dry-aged Northumberland sirloin. After that, a slice of lemon meringue tart should fit the bill. Try it with a shot of Lindisfarne mead – you'll even find a sparkling version on a drinks list that covers everything from local ales to New World wines and 'historic' cocktails.

Chef/s: Christopher Wardale. **Closed:** 25 and 26 Dec, bank hols. **Meals:** main courses £16 to £34. Set L £15 (2 courses) to £18. Set D £18 (2 courses) to £21. Sun L £21. **Details:** 85 seats. 10 seats outside. Bar. Music.

The Broad Chare

Cooking score: 4
Modern British | £28
25 Broad Chare, Newcastle upon Tyne, NE1 3DQ
Tel no: (0191) 211 2144
thebroadchare.co.uk

'Proper pub, proper beer, proper food' is the message at this enterprising set-up from seasoned Newcastle restaurateur Terry Laybourne. With mince and dumplings on Monday, ham hock with pease pudding on Wednesday and roast beef for Sunday lunch, all washed down with pints of esoteric ale, the Broad Chare certainly lives up to its slogan. Everything fits, from the polished oak bar that takes care of boozy business downstairs to the hard-edged and often noisy first-floor dining room with its daily hotchpotch of unreformed, reinvented and off-piste pub food done to a high standard. Starters of mutton and pearl barley broth or grilled ox tongue with beetroot relish give way to calf's liver and bacon or roast hake with chickpeas, samphire and cuttlefish, but also expect things on toast, meaty sharing feasts and various homespun desserts, such as spiced apple crumble with custard. The live-wire wine list includes plenty by the glass.

Chef/s: Dan Warren. **Closed:** 25 and 26 Dec, 1 Jan. **Meals:** main courses £11 to £25. **Details:** 74 seats. Bar. Music.

Cal's Own

Cooking score: 1
Italian | £22

1-2 Holly Avenue West, Newcastle upon Tyne, NE2 2AR
Tel no: (0191) 281 5522
calsown.co.uk

From a pizza takeaway in Heaton to a restaurant in Jesmond, Cal's Own has developed into far more than just a very good pizza joint. Bruschetta of rich beef ragù and fontina is a must to start, or try the plump king prawns cooked in the imperious wood-fired Stefano Ferrara oven. The pizzas remains truly peerless – this is one of very few places outside Italy to receive Vera Pizza Napoletana accreditation – and showcase local produce, from foraged wild garlic, to locally reared meat from renowned Charlotte's Butchery. Drink beers from Wylam Brewery or Italian house wine from £16.75.

Chef/s: Calvin Kitchen. **Closed:** Mon, Tue, 25 and 26 Dec, 31 Dec and 1 Jan. **Details:** 48 seats. 12 seats outside. Wheelchairs. Parking.

Cook House

Cooking score: 2
Modern British | £17

20 Ouse Street, Newcastle upon Tyne, NE1 2PF
cookhouse.org

In what onlookers might applaud as a sign that Cook House has well and truly settled into the two shipping containers it calls home, bills here can now be paid by card. Some things haven't changed, however, at this quirky spot in the oh-so-cool and creative Ouseburn Valley: you still need to bring your own alcohol, the place is still warmed by wood-burners, and you still need a supper club ticket if you want to eat in the evening. Drop in at lunch to choose from a delightful chalkboard menu of half a dozen or so dishes that might include soused mackerel with dill, crème fraîche and shallot salad, a goat's cheese, new potato and herb frittata, or roast porchetta with chilli, fennel and orange. There's enthusiasm for a dark chocolate tart with salted pumpkin seed brittle, while a blood orange posset and a plate of local cheeses tempt similarly.

Chef/s: Anna Hedworth. **Closed:** Sun, 2 weeks Jan, 2 weeks Aug. **Meals:** main courses £5 to £10. **Details:** 22 seats. 12 seats outside. Music.

House of Tides

Cooking score: 5
Modern British | £80

28-30 The Close, Newcastle upon Tyne, NE1 3RF
Tel no: (0191) 230 3720
houseoftides.co.uk

The clatter and bustle of the Tudor merchant's life is imprinted in the DNA of Kenny Atkinson's singular historic venue on the Newcastle Quayside, close to the Tyne Bridge. A beamed and boarded dining room on the first floor retains its atmospheric period feel, yetthe cooking could hardly be more of the moment, with a multi-course tasting format and optional wine pairing on offer. The order of events is refreshingly counterintuitive, with fermented rye bread and cultured butter making an appearance only after a procession of nibbles – truffled cream cheese gougères, carrot meringues, squid ink crackers, and a single Lindisfarne oyster dressed in caviar, cucumber and ginger – has appeared. For the principal dishes, combinations sound straightforward enough, like sea bass with celeriac, or crackled pork with braised salsify and onion petals, but the modern presentations, in which the components of a dish are gathered in little heterogeneous clumps, never fail to delight. A dessert of dark chocolate ganache with caramelised hazelnuts or the puff pastry construction of Bramley apple, raisins and cinnamon seem almost trad in the circumstances. Start on the ground floor with inspired cocktails (sloe gin and melon Negroni, anyone?). Wines on a cosmopolitan list start at £30.

Chef/s: Kenny Atkinson. **Closed:** Sun, Mon, 23 Dec to 10 Jan. **Meals:** tasting menu L £65. Tasting menu D £80. **Details:** 60 seats. Bar. Wheelchairs. Music. Parking. Children over 9 yrs.

The Patricia

Cooking score: 3
Modern British | £35
139 Jesmond Road, Newcastle upon Tyne, NE2 1JY
Tel no: (0191) 281 4443
the-patricia.com
£5 OFF

First-time visitors may find themselves walking past the Patricia's anonymous frontage on a traffic-choked main road more than once before doing a final double take and stepping inside this candlelit former shop. The name was inspired by chef patron Nick Grieves' grandmother, but the look is more influenced by classic French bistros – note the dark purple walls and worn floorboards. The produce-led food is modern British with some Italian touches, courtesy of Grieves' time spent at London's River Café (see entry). A concise but carefully constructed menu may start with Brussels sprouts, onion jam and 36-month aged Parmesan, perhaps followed by Cornish pollack teamed with cannellini beans, Florence fennel and lardo di Colonnata. Meat might be confit mutton shoulder, buttermilk potatoes, braised turnip tops and salsa verde. Clever desserts include fennel and honey panna cotta with macerated Yorkshire rhubarb. The wine list is a well-rounded global selection with great glasses from £4.

Chef/s: Nick Grieves. **Closed:** Mon, Tue, 2 weeks Jan, 2 weeks Aug. **Meals:** main courses £16 to £27. Set D £20 (2 courses) to £25. **Details:** 30 seats.

The North-East's best bites

Richard Allen of The Orangery restaurant at Rockliffe Hall shares his favourite places to eat and drink

The best **breakfast** is at the **Quay Ingredient**, Newcastle. It may be small but the food rocks and my youngest loves the **boiled egg and soldiers**. For me it's **bacon and pancakes** all day long.

For **coffee**, it's **Muse** in Yarm. I can't help nipping in there whenever I'm in town for a cheeky one. There's a great buzz and the staff are wicked!

The best **brunch** I've had locally was at **Ernest** in Newcastle. It's a cosy little place where you can grab freshly made brunch on the go. The waffles are delicious, as are the flatbreads.

Jesmond Food Market on Armstrong Bridge, Newcastle, is a hive of heavenly **food stalls**. It's held every third Saturday of the month and it's a foodie haven with some serious **artisan producers**.

The best **pint** for me is at **The Bay Horse** in Hurworth-on-Tees. It's recently been refurbished; the bar is **ultra-cosy** and the staff are the friendliest you'll find. The beer garden is a secluded spot that's great for those sunny Sundays.

Peace & Loaf

Cooking score: 4
Modern British | £38
217 Jesmond Road, Newcastle upon Tyne, NE2 1LA
Tel no: (0191) 281 5222
peaceandloaf.co.uk
£5 OFF

With its punning name, a chef patron who reached the final of *MasterChef: The Professionals* and 'quirky' contemporary decor, Peace & Loaf is a restaurant for our times. Dave Coulson earned his stripes at some top venues including Le Gavroche (see entry, London), so there's refinement, creativity and ambition amid all the bonhomie. The meticulously seasonal menus reveal a penchant for modern cooking techniques and imaginative combinations: red mullet arrives with Madras flavours and crispy chicken skin, duck ham in a cassoulet with truffled white beans (and those are just for starters). Asian flavours crop up in char siu pork with pork steamed buns, while turbot with mussels and sea fennel is right out of European tradition. The three amuse-bouches put one family in a 'very happy mood', likewise the charming service. To finish, lemon, thyme and yoghurt is a holy trinity. Draught and bottled beers, a dozen or so cocktails and decent-value wines make for good drinking, too.
Chef/s: David Coulson. **Closed:** 25 to 27 Dec, 1 to 3 Jan. **Meals:** main courses £17 to £26. Set L £18 (2 courses) to £22. Set D £22 (2 courses) to £26. Sun L £26. Tasting menu £75. **Details:** 54 seats. Wheelchairs. Music.

21

Cooking score: 3
Modern British | £35
Trinity Gardens, Quayside, Newcastle upon Tyne, NE1 2HH
Tel no: (0191) 222 0755
21newcastle.co.uk

The flagship of local food hero Terry Laybourne's fleet of restaurants, this stylish Quayside brasserie, found at the back of the city's Crown Courts, remains a firm favourite with Newcastle diners. The service is well-informed and as polished as the woodwork and cutlery, while the brasserie-style menu sticks to accurately executed classics. A starter of Cheddar and spinach soufflé is a tried-and-tested winner, as is seared scallops, pork belly and spiced carrots, while mains might be a simply grilled piece of halibut with minted pea purée and tartare sauce, or roasted Northumbrian venison, candied figs, chestnut and hazelnut spätzle with sauce poivrade. After that, try the crème brûlée or Florentine doughnuts, strawberry jam and Chantilly cream. The well-chosen wine list is arranged by country and region, and divided into house selections and 'big guns'. Opening at £19.90 for a bottle, it offers plenty of class by the glass or carafe.
Chef/s: Chris Dobson. **Closed:** 25 and 26 Dec, 1 Jan. **Meals:** main courses £16 to £33. Set L £19 (2 courses) to £23. Early D £21 (2 courses) to £25. Sun L £25. **Details:** 120 seats. V menu. Bar. Wheelchairs. Music.

LOCAL GEM

Bistro Forty Six

Modern British | £30
46 Brentwood Avenue, Newcastle upon Tyne, NE2 3DH
Tel no: (0191) 281 8081
bistrofortysix.co.uk

Located in a little terrace of cafés, bars and shops in a residential backwater of Jesmond, this tiny, simple bistro continues to impress. Max Gott forages, shoots and butchers his own game and 'cooks lovely food'. The result is a fiercely seasonal and sensibly compact menu with a typical meal comprising harissa-cured mackerel, horseradish potato and blood orange, followed by pork two ways, with white beans, purple kale and mushrooms, and finishing with baked custard tart. There are posh sandwiches at lunch, and kind prices extend to a brief, mainly European wine list.

LOCAL GEM

Caffè Vivo

Italian | £32
29 Broad Chare, Newcastle upon Tyne, NE1 3DQ
Tel no: (0191) 232 1331
caffevivo.co.uk

Based on an enoteca, Terry Laybourne's homage to those Italian restaurant-cum-bars brings a touch of *la dolce vita* to the Quayside. It is casual, unpretentious, and focused on quality. This being 21st-century Britain, you can get a plank of antipasti to share – meat or vegetarian – or simply pick what you fancy: chargrilled squid with lemon and chilli, say. Among *primi* options, salsa verde works its magic on both whole grilled sea bass and chargrilled veal chop. There's a clutch of Super Tuscans on the all-Italian wine list, which starts below £18.

North Shields

The Staith House

Cooking score: 2
Modern British | £30
57 Low Lights, Fish Quay, North Shields, NE30 1JA
Tel no: (0191) 270 8441
thestaithhouse.co.uk

Right by South Shields Fish Quay, this reclaimed fishermen's boozer captures the nautical setting with charts, vintage portholes and maritime knick-knacks. Head helmsman John Calton's seasonal menu is inspired by locally landed seafood and meat from the region's farms. 'Staithy' fishcakes with Marie Rose sauce, and grilled hake with ratte potatoes, samphire, shrimp and anchovy butter share the billing with Cumberland sausage Scotch eggs, slabs of pork belly or rump of Simonburn lamb with braised pearl barley, roast carrots and sweetbreads – capably executed stuff for hale and hearty appetites. To finish, custard slice with apple and caramel is a tempter. Give Calton and his team 48 hours' notice, and they will compile a bespoke 'carte blanche' tasting menu for lunch or dinner. Wines are a cut above the local pub average.
Chef/s: John Calton. **Closed:** 25 and 26 Dec. **Meals:** main courses £15 to £26. **Details:** 45 seats. 40 seats outside. Wheelchairs. Music. Parking. No children after 7.30pm.

South Shields

LOCAL GEM

Colmans

Seafood | £20
182-186 Ocean Road, South Shields, NE33 2JQ
Tel no: (0191) 456 1202
colmansfishandchips.co.uk

One regular is happy to make a 60-mile round trip to this long-established family-run chippy (circa 1926). No wonder, because Colmans has it all: the fish is local and 'always of the best quality', the chips are second to none, and the staff are simply lovely. There are even some terrific sea views, Yorkshire beers and workaday wines to go with your fish supper. Colmans' new Seafood Temple on Sea Road, South Shields (tel: 0191 511 1349) ups the ante with a restaurant, oyster bar, cocktails and chip shop under one roof.

Tynemouth

Riley's Fish Shack

Cooking score: 1
Seafood | £18
King Edward's Bay, Tynemouth, NE30 4BY
Tel no: (0191) 257 1371
rileysfishshack.com

Small, fun and extremely popular, this glass-fronted shipping container overlooking the stunning Tynemouth coast has limited space inside and a tarpaulin-covered terrace for those braving the elements. But once you've got past the inevitable no-reservation queue, the very fresh, locally landed fish, mostly cooked in a wood-fired pizza oven, will restore your soul. Load up with Craster kippers and poached eggs for breakfast, otherwise there's a mackerel wrap with salad, crispy garlic potatoes and spicy dressing, halibut with curried shrimp butter, a chunk of pan-fried turbot, or salt cod fishcakes. It's oh-so-casual; everything comes in cardboard cartons, so you can eat down on the beach, weather permitting.

Chef/s: Adam Riley. **Meals:** main courses £7 to £24. **Details:** 12 seats. 16 seats outside.

Whitburn

LOCAL GEM

Latimers Seafood

Seafood | £25

Shell Hill, Bents Road, Whitburn, SR6 7NT
Tel no: (0191) 529 2200
latimers.com

Wonderful seafood in a simple, beachside café (with wet fish counter), pretty much sums up this all-day eatery. The decked terrace comes into its own when the sun shines and folk pile in for day boat-caught fish cooked en papillote with chunky chips or skinny fries, a smoked fish and potato pasty, or local langoustines. Start with some Lindisfarne oysters, or just order a sharing seafood platter, and finish with their famous carrot cake. No reservations, so be prepared to queue. House white is £15.

Whitley Bay

The Roxburgh

Cooking score: 2

British | £30

4 Roxburgh House, Park Avenue, Whitley Bay, NE26 1DQ
Tel no: (0191) 253 1661

'You really would walk past,' warned a reader of this modest restaurant set in a row of unprepossessing shops a couple of blocks back from the seafront. Persevere, even though the interior looks like a 'small town take-out', for this is Whitley Bay's best-kept secret. Gary Dall cooked for musicians such as Amy Winehouse in a previous life; now he's feeding lucky locals ox hearts with beetroot and wild garlic tempura. Elsewhere, there have been glowing reports for XO black pudding laced with Asian spices, confit egg yolk and togarashi crumb, and skrei cod with pistou and gnocchi. Sunday is routinely dim sum day and well worth a visit for excellent bao buns with pulled pig's trotters, prawn shumai (light dumplings), and chicken and ginger chilli won ton ('totally moreish'). There are no menus and it's not licensed, so pick up a bottle, pitch up and take pot luck.

Chef/s: Gary Dall. **Closed:** Mon, Tue, Wed, 2 to 24 Jan. **Meals:** main courses £12 to £17. **Details:** 24 seats. Wheelchairs.

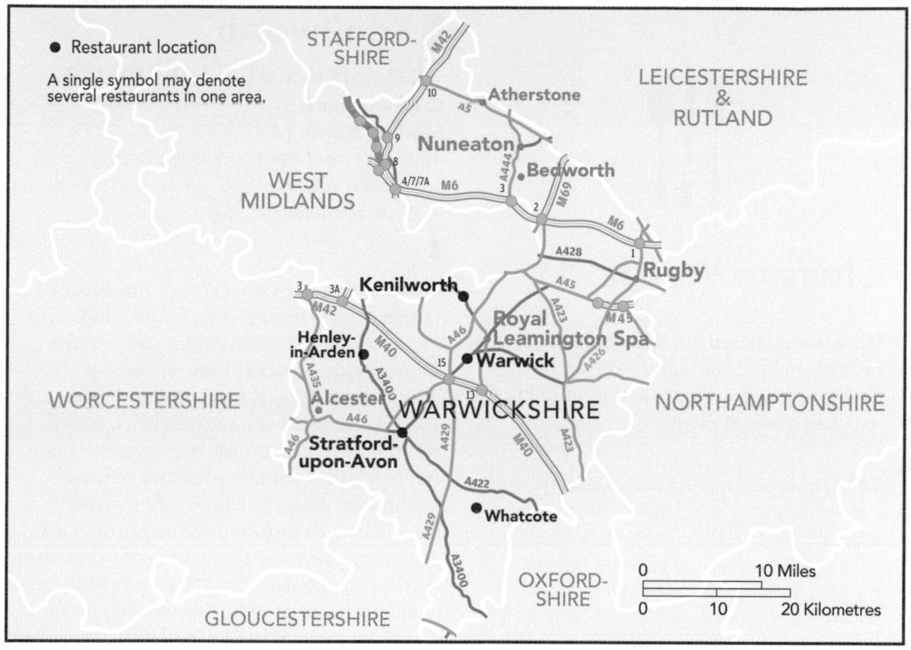

Henley-in-Arden

Cheal's of Henley

Cooking score: 5
Modern European | £40
64 High Street, Henley-in-Arden, B95 5BX
Tel no: (01564) 793856
chealsofhenley.co.uk

Marked out as a conservation area, Henley's mile-long high street is home to all manner of architectural styles, including this crooked 17th-century dwelling, now a smartly turned out restaurant. Inside, the dining room speaks of affluent 'fine dining' with its time-worn features, weathered beams, lovely terracotta floors and pristine table settings – a fittingly decorous backdrop for some ambitious and elegantly contrived seasonal cooking. Chef director Matt Cheal (ex-Simpsons in Birmingham, see entry) knows all about classic flavours and pretty plating, but isn't averse to the occasional opportunity to go off-piste – how about English asparagus with ham hock and hay hollandaise or Cornish skate with heritage carrots, Israeli couscous, onion bhajia, masala and coriander? In more orthodox mode, plates of Aberdeen Angus beef with Jersey Royals, broccoli and sauce bordelaise, or brill with braised celery, black truffle, pomme purée and apple vinegar show a mastery of all things 'haute' – as does a toasted almond panna cotta with coffee and white chocolate ice cream. The authoritative wine list opens with a dozen reputable selections by the glass.

Chef/s: Matt Cheal. **Closed:** Mon, Tue, 25 and 26 Dec, 1 to 8 Jan, 1 to 10 Apr. **Meals:** set L £22 (2 courses) to £33. Set D £33 (2 courses) to £55. Sun L £33. Tasting menu £77 (6 courses). **Details:** 40 seats. Music.

Get social

Follow us on social media for the latest news, chef interviews and more.
Twitter: @GoodFoodGuideUK
Facebook: TheGoodFoodGuide

Chefs to Watch

Since we launched our Editors' Awards in 2008, many of our *Chefs to Watch* have continued to flourish. We caught up with just a few of them

2008 Peter Sánchez-Iglesias, Casamia
Peter and Jonray Sánchez-Iglesias had just scooped the Guide's *Chef(s) of the Year* in 2015, when Jonray died. Peter moved the restaurant to central Bristol and was named *Chef of the Year* in 2018. Casamia is in this year's Top 10.

2010 Ryan Simpson, Orwells
Ryan was cooking in a smart dining pub when he first came to our attention. Since opening Orwells along with Liam Trotman, his inimitable food helped them to bag our *Readers' Restaurant of the Year* in 2012, *Restaurant of the Year* in 2017, and a Top 50 listing for the past three years.

2012 Paul Foster, Salt
We were initially wowed by Paul's 'startlingly good cooking' at Tuddenham Mill in Suffolk. In 2018, his own restaurant, Salt, won our *Best New Entry*.

2015 Gareth Ward, Ynyshir
When we tipped Gareth as one to watch, we noted that 'something extraordinary was happening here'. We were not wrong. As our current *Chef of the Year* and a Top 10 entrant, he delivers some of the most exciting food we've seen in 2018.

Kenilworth

The Cross at Kenilworth

Cooking score: 6
Modern British | £45
16 New Street, Kenilworth, CV8 2EZ
Tel no: (01926) 853840
thecrosskenilworth.co.uk

A white-fronted 19th-century inn adorned with hanging baskets, The Cross stands on a quiet road in the town centre and, despite some obvious modernisation, very much looks the traditional part inside, with red walls above buttoned banquettes, a brick fireplace and framed gastronomic mementoes. Adam Bennett offers a menu of gently refined country cooking, enhancing fine prime materials with intuitive accompaniments in dishes that have the gleam of professionalism. A crisply cooked duck egg partners beer-cured ham with salsify in truffled chicken jus for a satisfying opener, before lamb loin is matched with fashionable maritime notes in the shape of cockles and sea vegetables, or there may be smartly potato-scaled sea bream in caviar sauce. Hereford ribeye steaks with triple-fried chips are on hand for traditionalists, while desserts hit the spot by such means as orange pain d'épices soufflé and chocolate ice cream. Gargantuan efforts have been made with a varietally classified wine list that has oodles of classic claret and burgundy, in addition to products of forward-thinking global viticulture. Prices open at £24.

Chef/s: Adam Bennett. **Closed:** Mon, 25 and 26 Dec, 1 Jan, bank hols. **Meals:** main courses £28 to £42. Set L £30 (2 courses) to £33. Sun L £30. Tasting menu £75 (5 courses). **Details:** 74 seats. 30 seats outside. V menu. Vg menu. Bar. Wheelchairs. Music. Parking.

Stratford-upon-Avon

No. 9 Church St

Cooking score: 2
British | £35
9 Church Street, Stratford-upon-Avon, CV37 6HB
Tel no: (01789) 415522
no9churchst.com

The inhabitants of Stratford look kindly on Wayne Thomson's good-natured restaurant that occupies several floors of an ancient terraced cottage. With its central location, proximity to a car park and good-value food prepared from quality ingredients, it's easy to see why. And sensibly opening for dinner at 5pm so theatre-goers can eat well before curtain up at the RSC theatre (seven minutes walk away) is a boon in itself. The cooking runs with the seasons, with choice from a brief, regularly changing menu: maybe seared scallops with bacon jam and brassicas; rare-breed pork loin and confit belly served with braised haricot beans, buttered cabbage and mash; or a mixed grill of Cornish fish with brandade, sea vegetables and parsley sauce. For dessert, caramel tart with glazed banana, pecans and espresso ice cream is a particular delight. A mostly European wine list opens at £16.90.

Chef/s: Wayne Thomson. **Closed:** Sun, Mon, 25 to 27 Dec. **Meals:** main courses £15 to £23. Set L and early D £15 (2 courses) to £20. Tasting menu £43 (5 courses). **Details:** 40 seats. Bar. Music.

Salt

Cooking score: 6
Modern British | £45
8 Church Street, Stratford-upon-Avon, CV37 6HB
Tel no: (01789) 263566
salt-restaurant.co.uk
£5 OFF

'Stumbled on a gem,' noted one happy visitor, who managed to swerve the chain restaurants that dominate this tourist hot spot. The ancient building, just a hundred metres or so from the striking King Edward VI Grammar School where Shakespeare was educated, has been brought up to date with more than just a lick of paint and provides a suitably understated and comfortable setting for the contemporary cooking that is Paul Foster's forte. Foster sensibly doesn't set himself over-ambitious targets; a fixed-price à la carte offers just three choices per course, enabling him to deliver the finest materials at their seasonal best. And there are no duff ideas here. Relish in the sparkling, fresh simplicities of cured halibut layered with cucumber, grapes, almonds and dill emulsion, or a baby beetroot salad tangled with Berkswell cheese curd and chicory. A meaty piece of Cornish cod is served with English asparagus, wild garlic, sea aster and briny fresh mussels, and BBQ quail with superb peas and broad beans à la francaise. This really is delicious food, backed up by desserts such as Wye Valley rhubarb with buttermilk ice, ginger crisp and sorrel. Service is well informed, and fair prices extend to the well-considered wine list.

Chef/s: Paul Foster. **Closed:** Mon, Tue, 2 weeks Dec, 1 week spring, 2 weeks Aug. **Meals:** set L £34 (2 courses) to £37. Set D £37 (2 courses) to £45. Sun L £33. Tasting menu £65 (7 courses). **Details:** 35 seats. V menu. Music.

Warwick

Tailors

Cooking score: 3
Modern British | £40
22 Market Place, Warwick, CV34 4SL
Tel no: (01926) 410590
tailorsrestaurant.co.uk

Knives and tweezers have replaced scissors and sewing needles at this one-time gents' tailors nestled among the shops and bars of Warwick's market square. Since 2009, this bijou site has been home to Dan Cavell and Mark Fry, two chefs who are praised for their 'passionate' approach and boundless energy. Prices are reckoned to be 'incredibly reasonable' and readers say that the duo cook with 'style, panache, humour and grace'. Pan-roasted scallops with caramelised and pickled cauliflower, curry sauce and coriander is a standout starter, or you might fancy a punt on 'cornflakes and milk' (cornflake doughnuts with sheep's cheese and crumble, pickled onions and bacon jam). Elsewhere, charcoal-roasted beef fillet is cleverly paired with tomato caramel, mushroom tartare and ricotta dumplings, while 'egg and soldiers' (mango, yoghurt and shortbread) shows the chefs' cheeky side. 'Personable' service, great-value set lunches, midweek deals and wines from £18.95 help to cement Tailors' local reputation.

Chef/s: Dan Cavell and Mark Fry. **Closed:** Sun, Mon, 1 week Christmas. **Meals:** set L £17 (2 courses) to £21. Set D £30 (2 courses) to £40. Tasting menu £33 to £60. **Details:** 28 seats. V menu.

Whatcote

★ NEW ENTRY ★

The Royal Oak

Cooking score: 5
British | £50

2 Upper Farm Barn, Whatcote, CV36 5EF
Tel no: (01295) 688100
theroyaloakwhatcote.co.uk

From the outside, this thatched stone inn on the edge of the Cotswolds, not far from Shipston-on-Stour, gives off a homely feel. Step inside and the overall impression is of gnarled beams and bare brick, but step in to the modern conservatory dining room and you get the sense that this is more than a run-of-the-mill pub. Staff are refreshingly natural and the deal is sealed by Richard Craven's ambitious and ingenious cooking, in which foraged ingredients and game feature heavily. Be sure to begin with the rye loaf, part-sliced for tearing before slathering with whipped lard and pork crackling. There is technical intricacy afoot, as when a pheasant egg comes encased in a cloud of kataifi pastry on dense asparagus purée, while an extraordinary spin on lasagne features layers of braised pig's head, sliced black pudding, pasta sheets and roasted hazelnuts, its richness offset with a tart cider sauce. For main, there could be ray wing in brown butter with mussels and caramelised cauliflower, or crisply roasted quail rolled around sweetbreads on pearl barley risotto with snails. An assemblage of poached rhubarb, aerated white chocolate and rhubarb sorbet balances indulgence and refreshment with great panache. A short wine list opens at £20, and offers half of its selections by the glass, with a strong South African showing.

Chef/s: Richard Craven. **Closed:** Mon, Tue. **Meals:** main courses £19 to £23. **Details:** Bar.

Birmingham

★ TOP 50 ★

Adam's

Cooking score: 7
Modern British | £65
New Oxford House, 16 Waterloo Street, Birmingham, B2 5UG
Tel no: (0121) 643 3745
adamsrestaurant.co.uk
£5 OFF

'Just faultless – wonderful food, wine and service,' sums up one visitor, capturing the tone of this grown-up city-centre restaurant. Adam Stokes is really on song; his modern British menus – whether three-course prix fixe or eight-course tasting – are as up to date as they are seasonally influenced. While top-notch ingredients provide the building blocks, underpinning them is a keen understanding of flavour and solid technical know-how: there have been good reports of beautifully cooked veal sweetbread with mushroom ketchup and shiitake tea, as well as monkfish with mussels in Champagne sauce and sea vegetables. What gives Stokes's food its identity and character is a willingness to let elements of a dish work in concert: for example, beautifully tender duck breast is accompanied by smoked heart, with parsley root and hispi cabbage lending earthy harmony. Likewise, a disarmingly simple but dazzling masala sea trout is enhanced by butternut squash and coriander. Desserts, including a rich, dark, soft-centred chocolate fondant with Horlicks ice cream, are a particular high point, as is the whipped pork fat to be slathered on the very good bread. Service is beyond reproach, particularly when it comes to demystifying the extensive wine list, which covers the globe, with a strong French leaning. By-the-glass selections start at £5, rising to many times that for some choice Coravin options.

Chef/s: Adam Stokes and Tom Shepherd. **Closed:** Sun, Mon, 3 weeks Dec to Jan, 2 weeks summer. **Meals:** set L £30 (2 courses) to £40. Set D £53 (2 courses) to £65. Tasting menu £90. **Details:** 60 seats. V menu. Bar. Wheelchairs. Music.

The West Midlands' best bites

Paul Foster of Salt, Stratford-upon-Avon shares his favourite local places to eat and drink

Boston Tea Party in **Stratford-upon-Avon** serves good coffee, nice cakes and tasty **breakfasts**, all delivered in a lovely, friendly environment.

Box Brownie serves the best **coffee** in **Stratford-upon-Avon**, made with love and care - and **locally roasted beans**.

Steamhouse Bagels in **Leamington Spa** and **Stratford-upon-Avon** make handmade **bagels** that are crisp textured with the perfect amount of chew.

For a **pint**, **Purecraft Bar & Kitchen** in **Birmingham** has a really good range of its own beers and guest ales.

Best place for **dinner** is **Carters Of Moseley** for great tasting, seasonal food.

A wonderful place for a **post-pub snack** is **Birtelli's** in **Leamington Spa**, which makes the best **stone-baked pizza** in the area.

If I could eat only one thing around here, it would have to be... a meal at **Purnell's**. I have eaten Glynn's food for years, it's always clever, funny and tasty.

Carters of Moseley

Cooking score: 6
Modern British | £65
2c St Mary's Row, Wake Green Road, Moseley, Birmingham, B13 9EZ
Tel no: (0121) 449 8885
cartersofmoseley.co.uk
£5 OFF

The suburb of Moseley is a quiet contrast to the bustle of Birmingham's city centre and it's here, behind a respectable faux-Tudor façade, that Brad Carter works his culinary magic. There's an intensity to the place, from the menu's high-minded mission statement to the obvious passion in the team, but the mood is playful as customers enjoy highly original cooking. Appetisers include a warm, richly savoury oyster baked in the shell with a smidgen of beef fat, fine strips of cured Tamworth pork belly, and a rich chicken liver parfait topped with nuts and seeds. The six-course tasting menu at lunchtime is a masterclass of invention and 'deliciousness', especially a bowl of fragrant broth with spring vegetables or a small parcel of skate with potato and sea truffle. A mighty duck breast comes to the table 'already carved into succulent pink slices' along with white asparagus, black garlic purée and the zing of wild garlic beads. Luscious Maida Vale cheese sits atop a chunk of malt loaf and liquid beer wort – Carter collaborates with a local brewery. There is Cornish kelp ice cream with crunchy black rice, and an addictive chocolate pot that works well with saké. The wine list specialises in natural low-intervention wines, so best to sit back and enjoy the sommelier's recommendations. You won't be disappointed.
Chef/s: Brad Carter. **Closed:** Sun, Mon, first 2 weeks Jan, last week Apr, first 2 weeks Aug. **Meals:** set L £40 (4 courses) to £60. Set D £45 (4 courses) to £65. Tasting menu £85 (8 courses). **Details:** 30 seats. V menu. Bar. Wheelchairs. Music. Parking. Children over 8 yrs.

★ NEW ENTRY ★

Folium

Cooking score: 4
Modern British | £50
8 Caroline Street, Birmingham, B3 1TR
Tel no: (0121) 638 0100
restaurantfolium.com

Chef Ben Tesh has settled into his role as proprietor of this Jewellery Quarter restaurant – although he isn't about to neglect his cooking duties. It's a light-filled space; the open-to-view kitchen, bare tables and padded chairs create a suitably laid-back vibe, while the food shows just the right amount of ambition for an understated neighbourhood haunt. On offer are seasonally informed tasting menus of five or seven courses that are securely founded on bold, persuasive flavours. This ethos was demonstrated at a June meal by cured mackerel with wasabi snow and balls of pickled cucumber, golden-crusted cod in a vibrant, vivid green puddle of briny-sweet parsley broth, and Welsh lamb – nuggets of saddle, lovely fatty neck, creamy sweetbread – teamed with wild Welsh asparagus, wild garlic, sea beet, a dot of extremely rich lamb-fat hollandaise and a sticky lamb jus. Milk chocolate mousse with crumbs of sourdough and cobnuts and a caramelised ice cream made a rich finale. Lucy Hanlon's clued-up approach to service is a great asset and she gives good advice on the concise, global wine list.

Chef/s: Ben Tesh. **Closed:** 24 Dec to 9 Jan, 1 to 11 Apr, 25 Jul to 8 Aug. **Meals:** set L £28 (2 courses) to £33. Tasting menu £50 (5 courses) to £65. **Details:** 30 seats. Wheelchairs. Music.

★ LOCAL RESTAURANT AWARD ★
REGIONAL WINNER

Harborne Kitchen

Cooking score: 6
Modern British | £35
175-179 High Street, Harborne, Birmingham, B17 9QE
Tel no: (0121) 439 9150
harbornekitchen.com

'An assured, confident set-up. Well-drilled staff had just the right mix of informality and professionalism, and there was some very on-the-ball, punchy modern cooking.' So ran the thoughts of one visitor to Jamie Desogus's stylish bar-restaurant on Harborne's main thoroughfare. Those in the know make a beeline for the back dining room, which is dominated by an open kitchen (with counter seating), while a pale wood floor, simple modern furniture, and navy blue and grey walls create a relaxed but pulled-together look. Everything on the short carte and multi-course tasting menu makes the best of high quality ingredients: from an extraordinary chicken liver parfait dotted with white chocolate, strawberries, macadamia nuts and shards of crisp chicken skin, via a cod curry subtly infused with kaffir lime flavours, to a 'deeply delicious' salt marsh lamb – nuggets of the tenderest loin, a piece of confit breast with asparagus, a dab of lovage purée and a rich jus. A chocolate dome filled with passion fruit mousse alongside salted caramel ice cream is a fitting finale. Everything comes by the glass or bottle on the modern, broadly based and affordable wine list.

Chef/s: Jamie Desogus. **Closed:** Sun, Mon, 24 Dec to 8 Jan, 1 to 9 Apr, 27 May to 4 Jun, 22 to 30 Jul, 28 Oct to 5 Nov. **Meals:** set L £23. Set D £29. Tasting menu L £35, D £55 to £70. **Details:** 50 seats. V menu. Vg menu. Bar. Wheelchairs. Music.

Gareth Ward's best bites

Our *Chef of the Year* from Ynyshir in Powys shares his favourite places to eat and drink around the UK

I love **Sophie's** in **Aberystwyth** for **breakfast** - it's a proper greasy spoon, great for days off. They offer everything from a full breakfast in all sizes to hash with avocado and eggs and pancakes and milkshakes with everything on.

Machynlleth market is great for **food shopping** - one of the oldest in Wales, it takes place every Wednesday and has local farmers, butchers and fishmongers all selling what they have that week. There's a cracking **curry truck** for a bit of lunch.

Purecraft Bar & Kitchen in **Birmingham** always has a great selection of changing **beers and wines** and you can have some awesome food as well. Either that or our Uncle Trevor's club in Billy Row (my home town in **County Durham**) - you can get four of the best pints of Stone's in the country for £9!

If I could only eat one thing around here, it would have to be... local Welsh lamb. The best lamb in the world. I never get tired of it. Slow-cooked then barbecued and brushed with a mint and soy glaze.

Lasan

Cooking score: 3
Indian | £42
3-4 Dakota Buildings, James Street, St Paul's Square, Birmingham, B3 1SD
Tel no: (0121) 212 3664
lasan.co.uk
£5 OFF

Aproned waiting staff lend a rather formal Western ambience to this mirror-panelled room with caramel banquette seating. The friendliness of Lasan's approach and the lengthy menu of carefully delineated Indian food elevate it out of the ordinary. First up might be two takes on crab: fresh soft-shell in ajwain and chilli batter alongside a crab cake with tomato chutney and sour mango, garnished with pansies; or perhaps seared scallop with cauliflower pakora and nigella seed purée. The plethora of sauces and relishes adds complexity to the riot of flavours in starters, while long cooking brings depth to mains such as paya raas (braised mutton simmered with bone marrow and browned onion), or spring chicken in a South Indian curry, with roasted chickpeas, tomato, mustard seeds and curry leaves. Crossover desserts include an enjoyable mousse-textured mango and passion fruit cheesecake topped with syrupy paneer jalebi (a coil of deep-fried soft cheese), or beetroot halva with pistachio ice cream. There are wines from £19.80, and some great cocktails.

Chef/s: Khalid Khan. **Closed:** 25 Dec, 1 Jan. **Meals:** main courses £15 to £23. Banquet £40 (3 course) to £44. **Details:** 80 seats. Bar. Wheelchairs. Music. Children over 10 yrs.

Opus

Cooking score: 2
Modern British | £35
54 Cornwall Street, Birmingham, B3 2DE
Tel no: (0121) 200 2323
opusrestaurant.co.uk
£5 OFF

Since opening some 14 years ago, this modern British brasserie has firmly established itself as a huge asset in the city's business district. It's a comfortable, relaxed place flooded with light from floor-to-ceiling windows and with such top-drawer service you would be happy to linger long after finishing your coffee. Fixed-price menus please without challenging: leek and haddock fishcakes are teamed with a poached egg and butter sauce; ravioli, packed generously with slow-cooked ox cheek, arrive in a roast beef consommé with leeks and wild mushrooms; while a slow-cooked kleftiko of lamb is served with spiced sweet potato, chickpea and lentil dhal and coconut cream. There is always a steak with classic trimmings and sauces such as green peppercorn, artisanal British cheeses, and puddings such as rhubarb millefeuille with ginger, apple and poached rhubarb. More than a dozen wines by the glass feature on a well-constructed, well-annotated list.

Chef/s: Ben Ternent. **Closed:** Sun, 24 Dec to 3 Jan, bank hols. **Meals:** set L and D £30 (2 courses) to £35. Tasting menu £45 (5 courses). **Details:** 85 seats. V menu. Bar. Wheelchairs. Music.

Purnell's

Cooking score: 6
Modern British | £68
55 Cornwall Street, Birmingham, B3 2DH
Tel no: (0121) 212 9799
purnellsrestaurant.com
£5 OFF

From the moment the amuse-bouches arrive, it's clear that Glynn Purnell's flamboyant 'nicely noisy' business district restaurant is a serious operation. The colourful design makes a theatrical backdrop for inventive dishes that chart past and present triumphs (including three that featured on TV's *Great British Menu*). An inspection meal began with a Parmesan gougère filled with luscious mousse, spiced crackers with mango and cucumber, and faux charcoal of potato, breadcrumbs and squid ink to dip into punchy chorizo mayonnaise. There's sheer satisfaction to be found, too, in a starter of beef carpaccio with bresaola that comes with chunks of red-wine-braised octopus and the zing of sweet-and-sour onions, though 'Haddock and Eggs', a dish inspired by Purnell's childhood (and a GBM favourite), is 'not to be missed'. Main courses deliver beef fillet accompanied by succulent cubes of bone marrow and beef tongue, its saltiness offset by sweet carrots. A pre-dessert balances the citrus hit of blood orange sorbet with gingerbread and white chocolate, while honey caramel millefeuille with passion fruit and mango rounded off one 'impressive meal'. The service is formal but friendly and there's help on hand to navigate the daunting wine list.

Chef/s: Glynn Purnell. **Closed:** Sun, Mon, 2 weeks Christmas, 1 week Easter, 2 weeks Aug. **Meals:** set L £39 (3 courses) to £47. Tasting menu £70 (6 courses) to £90. **Details:** 45 seats. Bar. Wheelchairs. Music. Children over 10 yrs.

Purnell's Bistro

Cooking score: 2
Modern British | £35
11 Newhall Street, Birmingham, B3 3NY
Tel no: (0121) 200 1588
purnellsbistro-gingers.com

His magnum opus may be Purnell's on nearby Cornwall Street (see entry) but Glynn Purnell's unpretentious bistro is a useful place with an informal way of doing things. It is spacious, fronted by the slick, contemporary Ginger's Bar (for cocktails and bar snacks), with two expansive dining areas opening up beyond. The concise menu keeps things relatively simple and does them well: ham hock terrine with crispy pork and the house piccalilli or curried cured salmon with mango chutney; braised ox cheek with rendang sauce or 'lightly flavoured' smoked haddock with

poached egg and pomme purée. Hearty sharing plates include whole roasted free-range chicken with Moroccan spiced jewelled couscous, and a chateaubriand for two. To finish, there's dark chocolate torte with passion fruit sorbet or a well-received warm cherry clafoutis. The lunchtime and midweek early evening prix fixe is a canny deal, and the short wine list reasonably priced (from £18).
Chef/s: Glynn Purnell. **Closed:** 25 to 31 Dec, 1 Jan. **Meals:** main courses £18 to £27. Set L and D £16 (2 courses) to £20. Sun L £20 (2 courses) to £22. **Details:** 70 seats. Bar.

Simpsons

Cooking score: 7
Modern British | £70
20 Highfield Road, Edgbaston, Birmingham, B15 3DU
Tel no: (0121) 454 3434
simpsonsrestaurant.co.uk

Long established Simpsons may be, but this elegant restaurant in a Georgian mansion on the outskirts of the city centre still excites and surprises in equal measure, such is the talent of Luke Tipping and his team. Regulars will note a more modern look to the place and to the food – the set lunch and fixed-price dinner, plus tasting menus, offer a striking combination of prime ingredients and visual artistry. Look no further than an astonishing dish of carrot broth (with smoked cheese dumplings, black garlic, hen of the woods mushrooms, fennel pollen and lardo) that just bursts with savoury intensity. There's delight, too, in a starter of pig's cheek, offset by crispy onions, chicory and the umami hit of an intense smoked eel cream. Or there's spankingly fresh skrei cod, which arrives with potato purée, truffle, monk's beard and burnt leek. Aberdeenshire beef is a star dish, a happy marriage of cheek and bavette, shallot, charcoal emulsion and salsify. Desserts are clever and innovative, scaling the heights whether it's a signature soufflé (perhaps rhubarb crumble or passion fruit) or an harmonious assemblage of gingerbread, pear sorbet and almond. The picture is completed by a wine list that matches culinary aspirations, sauntering across the viticultural globe, picking out reliable producers, with plenty for the French purists as well as good southern hemisphere selections.
Chef/s: Luke Tipping. **Closed:** Mon, bank hols. **Meals:** set L £45. Set D £70. Tasting menu £110 (8 courses). **Details:** 70 seats. 20 seats outside. V menu. Bar. Wheelchairs. Music. Parking.

Dorridge

LOCAL GEM

The Forest

Modern European | £29
25 Station Approach, Dorridge, B93 8JA
Tel no: (01564) 772120
forest-hotel.com

Parking can be 'near impossible' on the roads nearby, but you can use the station car park, 'or go by train as the restaurant is in the railway hotel'. Good advice for visitors to this popular local haunt offering brasserie-style cooking without airs or graces. It's a zesty assortment of classics – duck rillettes, chicken Caesar salad, pork belly with braised pig's cheeks – alongside chipotle prawn skewers or crusted salmon fillet with Indian spiced sag potatoes, coconut and coriander sambal, with wood-fired pizzas thrown in for good measure. Wines from £19.75.

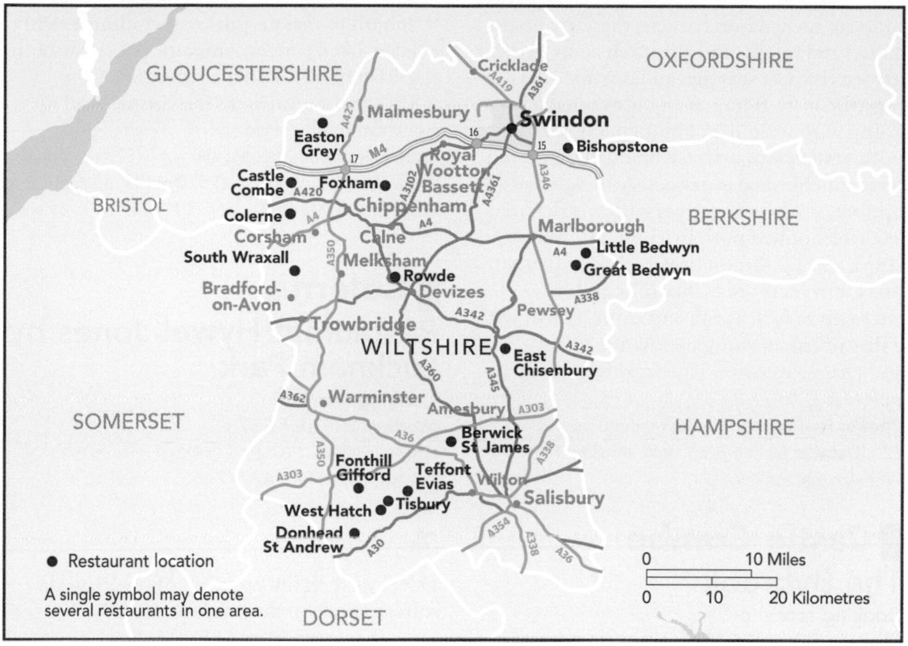

GLOUCESTERSHIRE
OXFORDSHIRE
Cricklade
Malmesbury
Swindon
Bishopstone
Easton Grey
Royal Wootton Bassett
Castle Combe
Foxham
Chippenham
BRISTOL
Colerne
Corsham
Calne
BERKSHIRE
Marlborough
Little Bedwyn
Great Bedwyn
South Wraxall
Melksham
Rowde
Devizes
Bradford-on-Avon
Pewsey
Trowbridge
WILTSHIRE
East Chisenbury
Warminster
SOMERSET
Amesbury
HAMPSHIRE
Berwick St James
Fonthill Gifford
Teffont Evias
Wilton
Salisbury
West Hatch
Tisbury
Donhead St Andrew
DORSET
A419 A361 A429 M4 A3102 A4361 A346 A420 A4 A350 A338 A342 A360 A345 A362 A303 A36 A354 A30
16 17 15
● Restaurant location
A single symbol may denote several restaurants in one area.
0 10 Miles
0 10 20 Kilometres

Berwick St James

The Boot Inn

Cooking score: 1
British | £26

High Street, Berwick St James, SP3 4TN
Tel no: (01722) 790243
theboot.pub

The Boot has been refuelling travellers to these parts since the 18th century and remains a useful pit stop, within striking distance of both Salisbury and Stonehenge. It's got a proper pub feel, with Wadworth beers at the pumps and a green lawn out back for when the sun beckons. The kitchen turns out corned beef fritters or, if the season is right, buttered Wye Valley asparagus with crispy duck egg, as well as ribeye steak with polenta chips or a warm salad of slow-roast duck leg with caramelised oranges. The homemade ice creams get the thumbs-up, while a concise wine list opens at £17.75.

Chef/s: Giles Dickinson. **Closed:** Mon, 25 Dec, first 2 weeks Feb. **Meals:** main courses £12 to £19. **Details:** 31 seats. 32 seats outside. Music. Parking.

Bishopstone

Helen Browning's Royal Oak

Cooking score: 2
British | £30

Cues Lane, Bishopstone, SN6 8PP
Tel no: (01793) 790481
helenbrowningsorganic.co.uk

Helen Browning OBE runs an organic farm, Eastbrook, and is also CEO of the Soil Association, while her interests extend to a new chop house in Swindon (see entry) and this whitewashed inn, reached down 'the narrowest two-way lanes in Britain'. The place feels pleasantly ramshackle and accidental: there are a dozen smart bedrooms, a bar stocked with the wares of Arkell's Brewery, sofas are tucked into corners, there are board games and books, and a chicken coop in the garden. Expect seasonal and organic ingredients to figure in an output that gets going with walnut and blue cheese arancini with nettle pesto, or hake brandade scattered with sun-blushed tomatoes. Among meat options, pork belly arrives with truffled mac 'n' cheese, pulled pork in a bun with 'slaw' and chips, and Eastbrook beef ragù with penne pasta, but there are plenty of populist alternatives such as fish and chips. Finish with a slice of banana upside-down cake with rum and raisin ice cream. The organic wine list opens at £20.

Chef/s: Paul Winch. **Meals:** main courses £14 to £25. **Details:** 80 seats. 50 seats outside. Bar. Wheelchairs. Parking.

Castle Combe

The Bybrook

Cooking score: 6
Modern British | £75

The Manor House Hotel, Castle Combe, SN14 7HX
Tel no: (01249) 782206
manorhouse.co.uk

Set in the heart of a pristine village on the southern fringe of the Cotswolds, the Manor House has 365 acres of Italianate park and woodland to itself. Dating back to the 14th century, its solid stone interiors and mullioned windows give the impression of being fortified against the possibility of sieges, while affording lovely views of the lawns. Rob Potter has given the cooking fresh impetus since arriving in 2016, offering dishes that are finely detailed and have plenty of culinary energy. A pairing of seared mackerel and white crab dotted with Exmoor caviar comes with the trending accoutrements of pickled mooli, charred cucumber and avocado, before local venison fillet and its braised faggot arrive with fondant parsnip and its purée, pickled red cabbage and a sauce of sloe gin; halibut is gently braised and served with hand-rolled macaroni, cockles, mussels and sea purslane. Rhubarb in various guises, including a richly concentrated jam, accompanies silky-smooth egg custard tart. Wines by the glass from £8.50, and sommelier's selections, head up a list arranged by style.

Chef/s: Robert Potter. **Meals:** set D £75 (3 courses). Sun L £35. Tasting menu £95. **Details:** 60 seats. Bar. Wheelchairs. Music. Parking. Children over 11 yrs.

Colerne

Restaurant Hywel Jones by Lucknam Park

Cooking score: 5
Modern British | £87

Colerne, SN14 8AZ
Tel no: (01225) 742777
lucknampark.co.uk

Developed on the proceeds of the Virginia tobacco trade in the late 17th century, Lucknam arose from a humble farmhouse, gradually accruing wings and porticos enough to make it into a grand country residence. Its 500 acres of grounds attest to the aspirations of its several owners. The palatial interiors, centred on a dining room accoutred with ornately framed portraits, double-clothed tables and crested chairs, set a certain tone that staff do their best to live up to. Hywel Jones offers a finely detailed version of modern British food, working with the grain of prime materials rather than constructing odd juxtapositions. There could be roast scallops and smoked eel in a resonant double act, supported by apple and horseradish purée and syrupy red wine vinaigrette, or precisely diced gribiche ingredients to accompany a pastry cylinder of fromage blanc and a single asparagus spear, with dots of sweet truffled mayonnaise. The habit of not rendering the fat on good duck breast doesn't win friends, but the endive and duck liver tart with rich dark cherry purée helps make up for that. To finish, there may be variations on a rhubarb and custard theme, with feuilletine-based crème brûlée alongside jam, gel, purée and jelly, and a warm ginger doughnut to boot. The wine list is as extensive as the grounds, with screeds of the great and the good, all at energetic markups. Bottles start at £30.

Chef/s: Hywel Jones. **Closed:** Mon, Tue. **Meals:** set D £87. Sun L £45. Tasting menu £110 (8 courses). **Details:** 87 seats. V menu. Bar. Wheelchairs. Parking. Children over 5 yrs.

Donhead St Andrew

The Forester

Cooking score: 2
Modern British | £30

Lower Street, Donhead St Andrew, SP7 9EE
Tel no: (01747) 828038
theforesterdonheadstandrew.co.uk

A well-tended 16th-century thatched pub hidden down a maze of narrow lanes on the Wiltshire/Dorset border, the Forester still looks and feels properly oldfangled with its blackened beams, cosy corners and mighty inglenook. Real ale is given the attention it deserves at the bar, while the kitchen knows how to rustle up full-blooded dishes from a cache of adroitly sourced raw materials. Seafood from West Country boats, and meat from Wiltshire farms (and beyond) are consistent standouts on an ever-changing menu that might yield anything from braised shin of Wessex Lowline beef with mash, steamed greens and wild garlic gremolata to pan-fried fillet of Brixham brill atop smoked haddock and butternut squash risotto. Start with a Dorset lamb 'scrumpet' or mackerel on toast with tomatoes and olives; finish with treacle tart or orange panna cotta with rhubarb and honeycomb. Around three dozen wines provide dependable drinking at fair prices.

Chef/s: Andy Kilburn. **Closed:** Mon, day after bank hols. **Meals:** main courses £15 to £23. **Details:** 60 seats. 30 seats outside. V menu. Bar. Music. Parking.

East Chisenbury

The Red Lion Freehouse

Cooking score: 5
Modern British | £40

East Chisenbury, SN9 6AQ
Tel no: (01980) 671124
redlionfreehouse.com
£5 OFF

A couple who have been supporting this dining pub since it opened in 2008 continue to sing its praises and enjoy its pleasant surroundings, friendly, knowledgeable service and 'consistently outstanding' food. The Red Lion is a comforting venue, a classy rural package from head to toe, with a thatched roof, beams, open fires and a menu packed with seasonal ingredients and appetising modern ideas. Guy Manning has the knack of keeping things simple while creating finely honed dishes based on locally sourced produce. Chisenbury wood pigeon breast salade paysanne with a crisp quail's egg and red wine, for example, or a main course wreckfish ('delicious fish, quite meaty but lovely') served with a crisp spring roll, pak choi, shiitakes, mussels and master stock. Or there could be a chateaubriand of Wiltshire beef for two, before British cheeses and a trio of desserts such as poached pear with caramel, candied walnuts and sage ice cream. The wine list, snappily arranged by style, offers admirable choice at prices that won't offend.

Chef/s: Guy Manning. **Closed:** Mon, Tue. **Meals:** main courses £20 to £30. Set L and D £24 (2 courses) to £28. Tasting menu £75 (7 courses). **Details:** 65 seats. 30 seats outside.

Send us your review

Your feedback informs the content of the *GFG* and will be used to compile next year's reviews. To register your opinion about any restaurant listed in the Guide, or a restaurant that you wish to bring to our attention, visit: thegoodfoodguide.co.uk/feedback

Easton Grey

Grey's Brasserie

Cooking score: 4
Modern British | £32
Whatley Manor, Easton Grey, SN16 0RB
Tel no: (01666) 822888
whatleymanor.com

£5 OFF

As you approach, this sprawling Cotswold stone manor certainly makes an impression, but the relaxed, stylish Grey's Brasserie (the hotel's second restaurant) is the surprise inside. A tasteful revamp has opened up the room, with soft blue-grey leather banquettes, polished wood tables and a terracotta floor creating a light contemporary feel. It strikes just the right note for boldly flavoured British brasserie classics, courtesy of the team responsible for Whatley's Dining Room (see entry). Ingredients are well sourced and well handled: a coastal Cheddar sausage roll bulges with meat and comes with a side of spicy tomato butter beans, Welsh rarebit packs a mighty punch, and crispy boquerones with romaine heart are pepped up by an egg yolk and Red Leicester emulsion. Mains run to tender beef brisket with Parmesan polenta and charred and crispy leeks, or sea bream with butternut squash risotto and citrus kale chimichurri. To round things off, try a light, sharp lemon tart with intense blackcurrant sorbet. Well-chosen wines by the glass include a Bacchus from Wiltshire's Maud Heath.

Chef/s: Niall Keating. **Meals:** main courses £17 to £36. Set L £20 (2 courses) to £25. Set D £35 (2 courses) to £40. Sun L £36. **Details:** 64 seats. 30 seats outside. Bar. Wheelchairs. Music. Parking.

★ TOP 50 ★

Whatley Manor, The Dining Room

Cooking score: 7
Modern British | £110
Whatley Manor, Easton Grey, SN16 0RB
Tel no: (01666) 822888
whatleymanor.com

£5 OFF

The main restaurant in this imposing hotel set in spacious grounds continues to surprise and please. Niall Keating is a talented chef, his young team full of enthusiasm, and together they have built an admiring following. Spells at Sat Bains (see entry) and Benu in San Francisco inform a tasting menu that achieves a rare degree of refinement. Descriptions are lists of ingredients 'so it's impossible to gather even a hint of what you're really about to eat'. Every ounce of Keating's accumulated skill and devotion to the craft can be witnessed in his hugely enjoyable dishes: wobbly tofu slicked with Exmoor caviar, offset by a wonderfully meaty set chicken consommé; a mini tart of delicate raw mackerel flecked with gold leaf; and a piece of halibut topped with Ibérico ham, umami-rich black truffle, yeast-flavoured hollandaise and fermented kohlrabi offset by dots of sweet medjool date purée. Then there are the fleeting, teasing contrasts in a tempura smoked eel with a sweet-and-sour citrus aigre-doux. The brown sourdough bread of 'impossible lightness' shines too, as does a beautifully rendered cylinder of honey parfait – smooth, dense, intense with honey, paired with a light custard and dotted with tapioca. Sign up for the wine flight or look to the beautifully crafted list, which has bottles around the £30 to £45 mark but quickly heads north.

Chef/s: Niall Keating. **Closed:** Mon, Tue, 6 Jan to 7 Feb. **Meals:** tasting menu £110 (12 courses). **Details:** 46 seats. V menu. Bar. Wheelchairs. Music. Parking. Children over 12 yrs.

Fonthill Gifford

The Beckford Arms

Cooking score: 3
Modern British | £30
Hindon Lane, Fonthill Gifford, SP3 6PX
Tel no: (01747) 870385
beckfordarms.com

Breathing the same country air as the rolling parkland of the Fonthill Estate, this creeper-clad 18th-century inn puts on a suitably gentrified show and comes properly attired for the changing seasons, with a summery terrace and a blazing fire when winter closes in. The cooking is founded on locally sourced seasonal ingredients – some from the inn's own kitchen garden, some from trusty Wiltshire growers – and the kitchen showcases a 'supplier of the month'. Classic pub dishes – ploughman's, battered fish, a burger – appear on the succinct menu alongside more intricately worked ideas. Start with roasted Bromham beetroots with watercress, ricotta, hazelnuts and honey, followed by chargrilled calf's liver with roasted carrots, braised chicory, kale and bacon. Local steaks, aged for 42 days, are justifiably popular. Round off with traditional cheeses, served with the inn's own digestives, or rice pudding with poached figs. Wines from £16 a carafe.

Chef/s: Harvey Spencer-Smith. **Closed:** 25 Dec. **Meals:** main courses £13 to £20. Set D £30. Sun L £17. **Details:** 75 seats. 30 seats outside. Bar. Music.

Foxham

The Foxham Inn

Cooking score: 1
Modern British | £30
Foxham, SN15 4NQ
Tel no: (01249) 740665
thefoxhaminn.co.uk

£5 OFF

A short haul from junction 17 of the M4, with a village location and rustic interior, this hostelry has few pretensions beyond providing pints of real ale in the old-fashioned bar and generous pub classics in the beamed open-plan restaurant. Chef proprietor Neil Cooper has judged to a nicety what people want from a country inn, and gives a homespun feel to the whole operation, baking his own bread, churning his own ice cream and making pretty much everything from scratch. Steak, kidney and mushroom pie and honey-roasted smoked ham hock with egg and chips have been hard to fault, while Somerset goat's curd and roasted beetroot salad, and baked egg custard tart could open and close proceedings. House French is £19.

Chef/s: Neil Cooper. **Closed:** Mon, first 2 weeks Jan. **Meals:** main courses £14 to £23. **Details:** 60 seats. 24 seats outside. Bar. Wheelchairs. Music. Parking.

Great Bedwyn

★ LOCAL RESTAURANT AWARD ★
REGIONAL WINNER

★ NEW ENTRY ★

The Three Tuns

Cooking score: 2
Modern British | £27
High Street, Great Bedwyn, SN8 3NU
Tel no: (01672) 870280
tunsfreehouse.com

James and Ashley Wilsey have been the custodians of this village free house for almost six years now, during which time they have gained a strong local following. Close to the Kennet and Avon Canal and its excellent walks, it pushes all the right village pub buttons with scrubbed pine tables, real fires, leather sofas, windowsills lined with old water jugs, and hand-pumped real ales flying the flag for independent breweries. The menu combines pub classics and more modern ideas, but is refreshingly unpretentious. We enjoyed our warm, meaty Scotch egg, the golden yolk still runny, a generous, rich wild boar ragù with orecchiette pasta, aged Parmesan and croûtons, and chalk stream trout with radishes, cucumber, fennel, white wine sauce and lobster oil. As for dessert, a traditional apple and rhubarb nut crumble with clotted cream was top-drawer comfort food. Wines (from £19.50) include sensibly priced weekly bin ends by the bottle and glass.

Chef/s: James Wilsey. **Closed:** Mon. **Meals:** main courses £13 to £19. Sun L £23 (2 courses) to £28. **Details:** 40 seats. 30 seats outside. Bar. Music. Parking.

Holt

READERS RECOMMEND

The Field Kitchen

Glove Factory Studios, Brook Lane, Holt, BA14 6RL
Tel no: (01225) 784081
thefieldkitchen.com

'Light, airy and rocking the industrial vibe, this must be the coolest place to eat for miles around. Food (all-day breakfasts and lunch only) is simple but genuinely good: perfectly dressed ham hock salad or a generous fish goujon sandwich with lively aïoli.'

Little Bedwyn

The Harrow at Little Bedwyn

Cooking score: 6
Modern British | £50

High Street, Little Bedwyn, SN8 3JP
Tel no: (01672) 870871
theharrowatlittlebedwyn.com

With very nearly 20 years here under their belts, Sue and Roger Jones have kept their country restaurant among Wiltshire's elite. A harrow is an implement for breaking up and smoothing over the land – a fair metaphor for the impact that they have had in the area, with John Brown's authoritative presence in the kitchen a constant factor. A pair of elegantly appointed dining rooms are the setting for food of rare intensity, with six- and eight-course tasting menus (plus vegetarian and vegan offerings) showcasing the style. Preparations are often disarmingly simple, such as scallop with samphire and wild garlic, or Cornish turbot with January King cabbage in ham stock, but the depth and concentration are what make them memorable. Welsh mountain mutton is one of the meat highlights, but there could also be a spin on steak and kidney, given resonance with Périgord truffle and parsnip purée. The finale might be a luxy take on bread-and-butter pudding, or classic blackberry soufflé. A cascade of expertly chosen wines is on hand to do justice to the food, including Coravin glass selections, with English sparklers, international Rieslings and Pinot Noirs among the numerous highlights.

Chef/s: Roger Jones and John Brown. **Closed:** Sun, Mon, Tue, 24 Dec to 4 Jan. **Meals:** set L £40 (5 courses). Tasting menu £50 (6 courses) to £85. **Details:** 34 seats. 28 seats outside. V menu. Vg menu. Bar. Music.

Rowde

The George & Dragon

Cooking score: 3
Modern British | £32

High Street, Rowde, SN10 2PN
Tel no: (01380) 723053
thegeorgeanddragonrowde.co.uk

£5 OFF

From the outside it looks like the archetypal roadside pub, but step inside and it's a cut above your average village watering hole. The mood is dressed down and relaxed, a familiar environment of ancient beams, polished wood and pleasant service, with the food taking centre stage. The repertoire leans heavily on fish (delivered daily from Cornwall) and treatments range from traditional – creamy baked potted crab, beer-battered whiting with chips, whole Dover sole with lemon butter – to the likes of steamed salmon teriyaki with soy sauce, ginger and spinach. Elsewhere, there are oysters, whole crabs and lobsters, and variety in the shape of favourites such as double-baked cheese soufflé, chargrilled ribeye and seasonal game, which might supplement the seafood choices. Desserts run to Eton mess, sticky toffee pudding and apple crumble. The short wine list does a good job too, with prices starting at £18.50.

Chef/s: Thomas Bryant. **Closed:** 25 Dec. **Meals:** main courses £15 to £25. Set L and D £18 (2 courses) to £23. Sun L £23. **Details:** 35 seats. 30 seats outside. Bar. Wheelchairs. Music. Parking.

Salisbury

READERS RECOMMEND

Fisherton Mill

International

108 Fisherton Street, Salisbury, SP2 7QY
Tel no: (01722) 500200
fishertonmill.co.uk

'A unique café providing tasty, interesting and unfailingly fresh food. The menu is innovative and ever changing, but there is something for everyone, including vegetarian food and our favourite pudding – the gluten-free polenta cake.'

South Wraxall

The Longs Arms

Cooking score: 3
Modern British | £32

South Wraxall, BA15 2SB
Tel no: (01225) 864450
thelongsarms.com

Rob and Liz Allcock arrived at this old stone-built village pub opposite the red phone box and church as brewery licensees in 2011, and bought the freehold in late 2017. As a free house, it has more flexibility when it comes to wine and beer, and the change has given chef Rob renewed vigour in the kitchen. Locals still pop in for a pint or to buy villager Bob's eggs on the bar, but diners travel some distance for the robust British menu, which goes to great lengths to list every local supplier. As well as pub classics – the venison faggots with buttermilk mash and swede are excellent – the daily changing menu might offer a starter of jerk kid cutlets with peanut and chilli pickle, followed by Cornish coastal lamb rump with crumbled feta or a twice-baked soufflé of Mrs Kirkham's Lancashire. A posset-like Amalfi lemon curd, meringue, blood orange sorbet and walnut brittle makes a light and zingy finale. The approachable wine list includes a decent selection by the glass.

Chef/s: Rob Allcock. **Closed:** Mon, Tue, 3 weeks Jan, 2 weeks Sept. **Meals:** main courses £14 to £20. **Details:** 46 seats. 30 seats outside. Wheelchairs. Music. Parking. 38 extra seats in private dining room.

Swindon

★ NEW ENTRY ★

Helen Browning's Chop House

Cooking score: 2
Modern European | £30

19-21 Wood Street, Swindon, SN1 4AN
Tel no: (01793) 527082
helenbrowningsorganic.co.uk

Ingredient-led cooking is an overused buzz-phrase, but it has real meaning at this no-frills, wildly popular diner in Old Swindon. Helen Browning heads up the Soil Association and is the owner of an organic farm in nearby Bishopstone produce from which is celebrated at Bishopstone's Royal Oak pub (see entry), and now here. Sit at scrubbed pine tables on mismatched chairs and tuck into a meat-based menu (burgers, chops, et al) where provenance is prized. Flavour-packed chipolatas, served gratis, might lead into a generous charcuterie board featuring locally cured meats, olives, buffalo mozzarella and more chipolatas – all good stuff. Next, Sophie's lamb (chops, steak, rib) was just the bouncy side of perfect at inspection; the faultless staff brought more terrific gravy on request, and the boiled vegetable accompaniments were comfortingly rustic. Finish, perhaps, with vanilla cheesecake matched with tangy stewed rhubarb. Wines (from £19.50) complement the selection of craft beers and ciders.

Chef/s: Helen Browning. **Meals:** main courses £12 to £25.

Wiltshire's best bites

Ben Maschler, owner of The Compasses Inn at Lower Chicksgrove shares his favourite local places to eat and drink

We live near **Tisbury** where Messums have a wonderful **art gallery**. The building is a beautiful 13th-century tithe barn - reported to be one of the largest thatched buildings in the UK. They have recently opened up a lovely **café** and there is a perfect brunch menu. I recommend the **huevos rancheros**.

My friend Charlie owns a pub about 10 minutes from where we live, **The Beckford Arms**. We used to work together at **Soho House** and he has taken some of those excellent values and applied them to this pub. The garden is beautiful and I am very happy to while away a few hours over a long **lunch** there.

About a mile from **The Compasses** there is **Kenson's Farm**. We buy most of our veg for the pub from there, but it's also open to the public. They have the very best **locally grown, seasonal veg** and it is a pleasure to shop there.

Pythouse Kitchen Garden is a restaurant and bar situated in a beautiful 18th-century walled garden. On a sunny evening I could not think of a finer place to sit and enjoy a **cocktail** or two. It is just outside **Tisbury** so only a short wobble on a bike from there to home.

Teffont Evias

Howard's House Hotel

Cooking score: 3
Modern British | £47
Teffont Evias, SP3 5RJ
Tel no: (01722) 716392
howardshousehotel.co.uk
£5 OFF

With a tiny stream meandering through its lovely gardens, and an interior that still sports original fireplaces, arched mullioned windows and a proper wine cellar, this sympathetically extended dower house glides along unhindered by fashion. Nothing much seems to change year by year, although there is a new man in the kitchen: Andrew Britton learnt his trade with the likes of Michael Caines, so expect a decent showing of local produce allied to sound culinary technique. Lunch is a light repast (Caesar salad, risotto nero, etc), while dinner is built around a well-tried format, with seasonal dishes highlighted on the carte. In summer, a mussel chowder might be zhuzzed up with garden herbs, while free-range chicken breast could be paired with artichoke purée and thyme jus come autumn. Wilted winter greens and squid ink gnocchi accompany blanquette of hake as the mercury drops. After that, blackberry and apple crumble suits the setting. House wines start at £19.

Chef/s: Andrew Britton. **Closed:** 23 to 26 Dec. **Meals:** alc £37 (2 courses) to £47. Seasonal menu £8 (2 courses) to £24. Tasting menu £80. **Details:** 30 seats. 30 seats outside. Music. Parking.

Tisbury

★ NEW ENTRY ★

The Compasses Inn

Cooking score: 2
Modern British | £27
Lower Chicksgrove, Tisbury, SP3 6NB
Tel no: (01722) 714318
thecompassesinn.com

Apart from a discreet hanging sign, this ancient pub is fairly anonymous, easy to mistake for just another lovely thatched house in a postcard-worthy hamlet. On entering, you are greeted by the alluring smell of wood smoke, head-cracking beams and, possibly, a gaggle of locals crowding around the tiny bar drinking locally brewed Three Daggers ale. Walkers, too, are drawn by a generous ploughman's platter or ciabatta filled with roast beef, Roquefort, pickled onion and watercress. Daily changing lunch and dinner menus mix a global vision with local produce – vegetables are from nearby organic growers, fish arrives daily from the South Coast. Pork terrine with a fruity, gently spiced curried apple and date chutney is one way to start, before you move on to, say, a textbook oxtail and cheek pie with buttery mashed potato and greens. To finish, a slice of almond tart 'boasting the crispiest pastry' comes with a zesty, chewy Seville orange marmalade ice cream. Wines start at £22 with plenty by the glass and carafe.

Chef/s: Patrick Davy. **Meals:** main courses £13 to £18. **Details:** Bar.

Anonymous

At *The Good Food Guide*, our inspectors dine anonymously and pay their bill in full every time.These impartial review meals, along with feedback from thousands of our readers, are what informs the content of the *GFG*. Only the best restaurants make the cut.

West Hatch

LOCAL GEM

Pythouse Kitchen Garden

British | £29
West Hatch, SP3 6PA
Tel no: (01747) 870444
pythousekitchengarden.co.uk

The south-facing 17th-century walled garden is the heart of Pythouse, where weddings, parties and events make the most of the glorious setting. The glasshouse is a lovely spot for a seasonal all-day bite (dinner Friday and Saturday only). Summer might welcome hot-smoked salmon with pea purée, garden leaves and burnt lemon, or a board of Cheddar tart with chargrilled broccoli and new potato salad, while the organic burger is made with Red Poll beef. Simple desserts of, say, treacle tart or rhubarb fool with orange and thyme shortbread make for a pleasing finale.

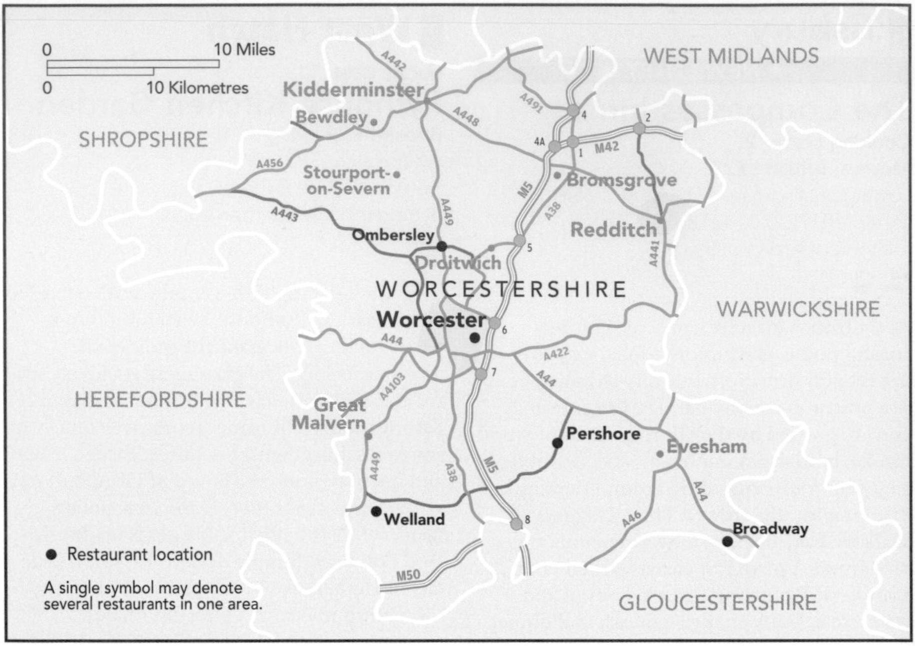

0 10 Miles
0 10 Kilometres
WEST MIDLANDS
Kidderminster
Bewdley
SHROPSHIRE
Stourport-on-Severn
Bromsgrove
Redditch
Ombersley
Droitwich
WORCESTERSHIRE
WARWICKSHIRE
Worcester
HEREFORDSHIRE
Great Malvern
Pershore
Evesham
Welland
Broadway
GLOUCESTERSHIRE
A442 A448 A491 M42 A456 A443 A449 M5 A38 A441 A44 A422 A4103 A46 M50
● Restaurant location
A single symbol may denote several restaurants in one area.

Broadway

★ NEW ENTRY ★

The Lygon Arms

Cooking score: 2
British | £40
High Street, Broadway, WR12 7DU
Tel no: (01386) 852255
lygonarmshotel.co.uk

In a prime position on the broad street that gives the village its name, this weathered stone-fronted inn has formidable staying power – it's now back in the Guide after some dozen years in the doldrums. The ancient building has benefited from lavish amounts of loving care and attention while keeping intact the uneven floorboards, rough stone walls, oak panelling, splendidly worn flagstones, carved archways and fireplaces galore. Of the many irregular-shaped spaces (arranged as bars and comfortable sitting rooms), the barrel-shaped – almost theatrical – dining room is the finest with its minstrels' gallery, massive inglenook and antique portraits. Eating here is all about comfort, familiarity, kind prices and good service, the kitchen deploying prime seasonal, often local ingredients and sound skills in dishes such as twice-baked cheese soufflé or grilled octopus with fennel and radish. From the grill comes Gower salt marsh lamb cutlets or wood pigeon with bacon, cauliflower and Bury black pudding with an exemplary, light sticky date and toffee pudding to finish. Wines from £16.

Chef/s: Ales Maurer. **Meals:** main courses £15 to £29. **Details:** Bar. Parking.

Russell's of Broadway

Cooking score: 3
Modern British | £40
20 High Street, Broadway, WR12 7DT
Tel no: (01386) 853555
russellsofbroadway.co.uk

Named after the celebrity furniture designer of yesteryear, Sir Gordon Russell, whose showroom it once was, the elegant restaurant-with-rooms makes the most of its delightful location with a terrace, while the private dining space features a splendid Russell table. Jorge Santos arrived in the kitchens at the start of 2018, with a mission to give fresh energy to the lively modern British food. The full range of textural contrasts and technical showmanship is seen in starters such as scallops and gremolata with puréed parsley roots and a Parma ham crisp, or blue cheese panna cotta with candied walnuts and roast squash, while main courses feature plenty of fish, perhaps roast monk with smoked lardon fricassée and hazelnuts in chicken jus, alongside pedigree meats. In the latter department, expect 28-day dry-aged beef fillet or herb-crusted cannon of Lighthorne lamb in caper jus with a little shepherd's pie. To finish, there are innovative compositions like pumpkin parfait with maple foam, nutmeg coral and pecans. House selections from £20 head up a compact but well-chosen list.
Chef/s: Jorge Santos. **Closed:** Mon, bank hols. **Meals:** main courses £15 to £30. Set L £20 (2 courses) to £24. Set D £23 (2 courses) to £27. Sun L £30 (3 courses). **Details:** 60 seats. 25 seats outside. Bar. Wheelchairs. Music.

Send us your review

Your feedback informs the content of the *GFG* and will be used to compile next year's reviews. To register your opinion about any restaurant listed, or a restaurant that you wish to bring to our attention, visit our website.

Ombersley

The Venture In

Cooking score: 4
Modern European | £44
Main Road, Ombersley, WR9 0EW
Tel no: (01905) 620552
theventurein.co.uk

Built in 1430, this striking black-and-white building has been owned and nurtured by Toby Fletcher for some 20 years. A comfy and traditional restaurant, it's a welcome, wonkily charming haven of warm hospitality backed up by good food; one reader appreciated 'a kitchen knocking out belting plates of food'. The menu mixes seasonal ingredients, traditional ideas and impressive techniques in gutsy starters such as seared breast of local pigeon with a creamed barley and mushroom risotto, or Brixham scallops and smoked haddock with buttered spinach, poached egg and a rich Mornay glaze. Reassuring mains include lamb saddle with a crisp lamb shoulder, haggis bonbon and neeps and tatties, or the whole lemon sole with asparagus, Jersey Royals and a well-executed beurre blanc enjoyed by one visitor at a May meal. Prune and Armagnac tart with coffee ice cream is a tempting way to finish. Wines from £19.
Chef/s: Toby Fletcher. **Closed:** Mon, 1 week Christmas, 1 week Mar, 1 week Jun, 2 weeks Aug. **Meals:** set L £30 (2 courses) to £34. Set D £44. Sun L £34. **Details:** 32 seats. Bar. Music. Parking. Children over 10 yrs.

Pershore

Belle House

Cooking score: 2
Modern British | £37
5 Bridge Street, Pershore, WR10 1AJ
Tel no: (01386) 555055
belle-house.co.uk

Belle House may have been given over to matters of hospitality since the mid-noughties (including a deli-cum-traiteur next door), but look up as you approach and you'll spot the old bell of this former fire station. Large windows look out on to the street while the decor, a mix of old and new, creates a semi-formal look. In a similar vein, the kitchen, under chef patron Steve Waites, turns out dishes with traditional and modern elements. Breast of wood pigeon is matched with spiced Puy lentils and chorizo in a first course that owes much to southern Europe, and even a classic cream of watercress and potato soup gets a smattering of salt cod flakes. Among main courses, roast brill with boulangère potatoes, rack of lamb with olive-crushed potatoes and goat's cheese choux, the lineage is clearly French. To finish, pear financier, with pear and Calvados compôte, comes topped with a biscotti and pistachio crumb. The wine list has good options by the glass, courtesy of the Verre de Vin system.

Chef/s: Steve Waites. **Closed:** Sun, Mon, Tue, 25 to 30 Dec, first 2 weeks Jan. **Meals:** set L £18 (2 courses) to £27. Set D £29 (2 courses) to £37. Tasting menu £45 (6 courses). **Details:** 70 seats.

Welland

The Inn at Welland

Cooking score: 2

Modern European | £33

Hook Bank, Drake Street, Welland, WR13 6LN
Tel no: (01684) 592317
theinnatwelland.co.uk

At the foot of the Malvern Hills in absolutely stunning countryside – 'it was a joy to drive there' – this smart country pub is clearly a hit with locals, especially when the sun shines and tables in the terraced garden are at a premium. There's something for everyone on a wide-ranging menu that features pub classics, including homemade burgers and steaks of Herefordshire beef, alongside more adventurous dishes. Begin with the likes of wood pigeon with port jus and a croquette of wild mushroom and risotto, or fat asparagus spears smothered in hollandaise and topped with a beautifully poached duck egg. Follow with a duo of woodland pork with apple tarte tatin and cider jus, and finish with custard beignets in a saffron and orange sauce, or a plate of local cheeses. A strong selection of locally brewed ales competes with an extensive list of wines by the glass.

Chef/s: Alex Boghian. **Closed:** Mon, 25 and 26 Dec, 31 Dec, 1 Jan. **Meals:** main courses £14 to £26. Sun L £23 (2 courses) to £27. **Details:** 64 seats. 36 seats outside. V menu. Vg menu. Wheelchairs. Music. Parking.

Worcester

LOCAL GEM

Saffrons Bistro

International | £32

15 New Street, Worcester, WR1 2DP
Tel no: (01905) 610505
saffronsbistro.co.uk

'Nothing is too much trouble' at this family-run 'gem' hidden among Worcester's back streets. The owners work tirelessly out front, while the kitchen serves up an assortment of big-flavoured crowd-pleasing dishes – everything from ploughman's and swordfish steaks at lunchtime to more ambitious dinnertime platefuls such as slow-braised pig's cheeks with parsnip purée, lemon and oregano chicken, or sea bass with roasted potatoes, confit baby vegetables and chive velouté. Vegans have their own mini menu, and the modest wine list does its job.

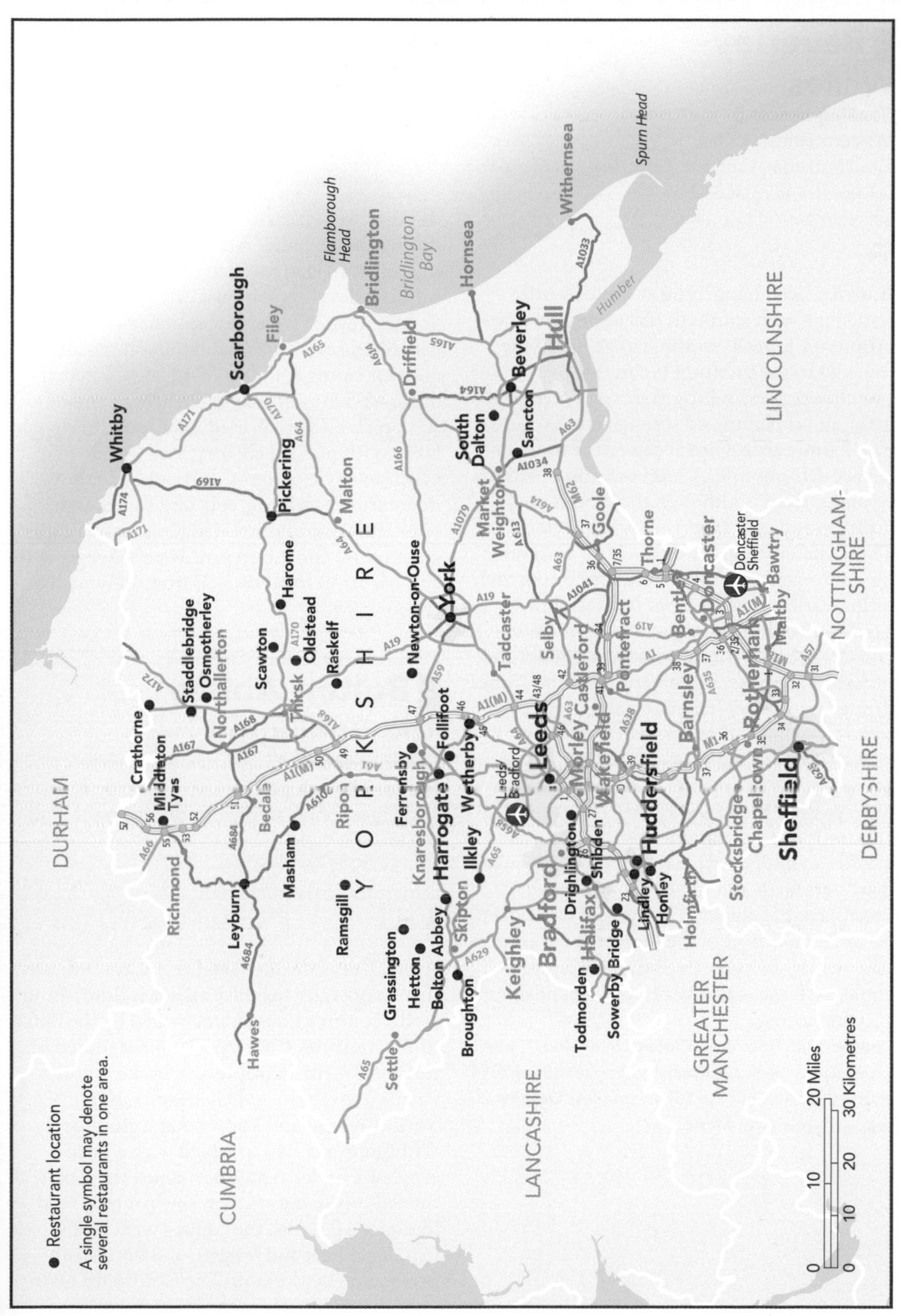

● Restaurant location
A single symbol may denote several restaurants in one area.
0 10 20 Miles
0 10 20 30 Kilometres
DURHAM
CUMBRIA
LANCASHIRE
GREATER MANCHESTER
DERBYSHIRE
NOTTINGHAM-SHIRE
LINCOLNSHIRE
Y O R K S H I R E
Whitby
Scarborough
Filey
Flamborough Head
Bridlington
Bridlington Bay
Hornsea
Withernsea
Spurn Head
Humber
Hull
Beverley
Sancton
South Dalton
Driffield
Market Weighton
Goole
Thorne
Doncaster
Doncaster Sheffield
Bawtry
Maltby
Bentley
Rotherham
Sheffield
Chapeltown
Stocksbridge
Barnsley
Pontefract
Castleford
Wakefield
Morley
Leeds
Leeds Bradford
Bradford
Drighlington
Shibden
Halifax
Huddersfield
Lindley
Honley
Holmfirth
Sowerby Bridge
Todmorden
Keighley
Ilkley
Wetherby
Harrogate
Follifoot
Knaresborough
Ferrensby
Ripon
Skipton
Bolton Abbey
Broughton
Hetton
Grassington
Settle
Ramsgill
Masham
Bedale
Leyburn
Hawes
Richmond
Middleton Tyas
Crathorne
Staddlebridge
Osmotherley
Northallerton
Thirsk
Scawton
Oldstead
Raskelf
Harome
Pickering
Malton
Newton-on-Ouse
York
Tadcaster
Selby

Beverley

Whites

Cooking score: 5
Modern British | £58
12a North Bar Without, Beverley, HU17 7AB
Tel no: (01482) 866121
whitesrestaurant.co.uk

A lot has been happening at this tidy little restaurant with rooms in recent months: chef/proprietor John Robinson has acquired the freehold to the premises (a three-storey townhouse overlooking Beverley's medieval gate), and is planning a serious refurb to add new lounge areas with access to the rooftop terrace. Meanwhile, Whites continues with its winning ways – although the food is now built around two 'surprise' tasting menus. There's no arguing with the chef's ambition, his cutting-edge Nordic-influenced approach or his fearless imagination: it takes a brave heart to match local venison with steamed 'xiao long bao' dumplings, soy, coriander and pickled cucumber. Elsewhere, skrei cod comes dressed with ras el hanout cream, pickled fennel, borage and caviar, while glazed ox cheek retains its rightful earthiness in company with Yorkshire Blue cheese, roasted pear, parsnip purée and celery. The creativity also spills over into modernist desserts such as a coffee cylinder with orange syrup, chocolate délice, rhubarb and sorrel. Home-baked breads, freshly churned butter and wickedly clever canapés add to the pleasure of dining here, while the wine list is everything you could wish for – gently priced, dependable and interesting.

Chef/s: John Robinson. **Closed:** Sun, Mon, 1 week Christmas, 1 week Jul. **Meals:** tasting menu D £30 (4 courses, Tue to Thur) to £58 (9 courses). **Details:** 20 seats. Wheelchairs. Music.

LOCAL GEM

The Pig & Whistle

Modern European | £25
5 Sow Hill Road, Beverley, HU17 8BG
Tel no: (01482) 874083
pigandwhistlebeverley.co.uk

'It's different, certainly for Beverley,' admitted one visitor to James Allcock's pint-sized bistro-cum-charcuterie, found beneath a modern development just off the Market Square. Just 25 covers are split between simply furnished bistro tables and the sought-after counter stools at the open-to-view kitchen. Tapas-style small plates take in crab tartine with pickled fennel, cold roast loin of Ryedale lamb with pickled chicory, very good Galician-style octopus, and smoked fallow deer tartare with egg yolk and sourdough toast. Pair one of the sharing boards of English charcuterie and Courtyard Dairy cheeses with a bottle from the mostly European wine list (from £19).

Bolton Abbey

The Burlington

Cooking score: 6
Modern British | £70
The Devonshire Arms, Bolton Abbey, BD23 6AJ
Tel no: (01756) 718100
burlingtonrestaurant.co.uk

A cheerful team and laid-back decor indicate that a new taste for informality is flourishing at this country house hotel owned by the Duke of Devonshire. Chef Paul Leonard joined in July 2017 with an impressive background at Pétrus (see entry) and Gleneagles, but he's a Yorkshireman and knows that technique without gimmicks, coupled with a great emphasis on local produce, is just the ticket. Indeed, his menus (six or nine courses) read like a love letter to the county with East Coast fish, local beef and hogget, and beautifully presented cheeses from The Courtyard Dairy in Settle. Canapés (in the cocktail bar) and an appetiser (at your table) lead into courses such as cured duck liver with fresh almonds, apricot, tarragon and duck-fat brioche, or a fine piece of turbot with mussels, samphire and sea purslane paddling in a rich Champagne sauce. Imaginative desserts play on the theme of peach or gooseberry with elderflower, and the vast Burlington wine list lives up to its reputation, with sommelier Spencer Brown's suggested pairings bringing many delightful surprises.

Chef/s: Paul Leonard. **Closed:** Mon, 24 to 26 Dec, 31 Dec and 1 Jan. **Meals:** set D £70 (6 courses). Tasting menu £95 (9 courses). **Details:** 70 seats. Bar. Wheelchairs. Parking.

The Devonshire Brasserie

Cooking score: 3
Modern British | £35
The Devonshire Arms, Bolton Abbey, BD23 6AJ
Tel no: (01756) 710710
devonshirebrasserie.co.uk

Can there be a prettier view than from your table in The Devonshire Brasserie? Mown pasture, sheep clustered in the shade of spreading oaks, and grassy fells sloping down to the River Wharfe – it's heavenly, and in summer the terrace tables are understandably popular. The interior is bright and cheerful, the white walls set off by jewel-bright furniture. Throw in a wood-burning stove, blackboards for specials and a cheerful, pub-style bar with local ales alongside a vast array of wines and spirits, and you've got a year-round winner. The menu offers a confident take on local produce: kitchen garden carrots with hazelnuts and carrot sorbet, or a trio of Wharfedale pig with pork belly, black pudding sausage roll and Scotch egg. There are platters of local meats, charcuterie and cheeses; Nidderdale lamb; and beef and pork from the home farm. 'Terrific' puddings include a very sophisticated take on custard tart with poached rhubarb.

Chef/s: Sean Pleasants. **Meals:** main courses £15 to £34. **Details:** 65 seats. 40 seats outside. Wheelchairs. Music. Parking.

Broughton

LOCAL GEM

The Bull

British | £28
Broughton, BD23 3AE
Tel no: (01756) 792065
thebullatbroughton.com

Craig Bancroft's Lancashire-based Ribble Valley Inns is the driving force behind this amenable old country pub. All is joyfully warm and inviting with a winter fire, a smart rustic look and summer terrace. Real ales mean drinkers are always welcome, and diners are drawn by a commitment to local produce and a repertoire of well-rendered pub food. Popular dishes include Yorkshire Blue cheese and golden beetroot on buttered crumpet; gammon, egg and chips; a tasty steak and Hetton ale pie; plus the group's famous Lancashire hotpot. Yorkshire parkin with toffee sauce and vanilla ice cream rounds things off nicely. Wines from £17.75.

Crathorne

Crathorne Arms

Cooking score: 2
British | £35
Crathorne Village, Crathorne, TS15 0BA
Tel no: (01642) 961402
thecrathornearms.co.uk

Anyone with knowledge of owner Eugene McCoy's previous association with the Cleveland Tontine might expect 'character' in abundance, and this cheery inn in a tiny village does indeed have a certain quirky charm. Filled with Eugene and wife Barbara's possessions, gathered over the years, it's very personal and colourful. It's a proper pub, too, with real ales, real fires, real dogs, and a dining area that draws diners for bistro-style dishes. You might start with smoked mussels rich with parsley and garlic butter, or pigeon faggots with prune and carrot sauce. Among main courses, there's a burger – a good one – alongside beef wellington, steaks cooked over charcoal and homemade 'luxury' fishcake with crayfish and shellfish bisque. Lunchtime sandwiches are a cut above, and roasts do the business on Sundays. Sticky toffee pudding is a populist finale. The concise wine list, opening around £24, is drawn from the major wine regions of the world.

Chef/s: David Henry. **Closed:** Mon, 25 and 26 Dec, 1 to 5 Jan. **Meals:** main courses £14 to £31. Set L and D £20 (2 courses) to £23. **Details:** 50 seats. 30 seats outside. Wheelchairs. Music. Parking.

Drighlington

Prashad

Cooking score: 2

Indian Vegetarian | £26

137 Whitehall Road, Drighlington, BD11 1AT
Tel no: (0113) 285 2037
prashad.co.uk

At Bobby and Minal Patel's family-run restaurant the compass points to India's most western state, Gujarat, but the menu touches base with the very best vegetarian dishes from the rest of the country. Flavour has always been at the forefront (they mix their own garam masala recipe from 22 herbs and spices), and presentation is always eye-catching. Opening salvos include garam masala-infused onion bhajis and the sculptural sanku (a mixed bean open samosa), but if you can't decide where to start, check out the tasting platter. Among main courses, chole is a belting chickpea curry, vegetable biryani probably needs no explanation, and renghan bataka is aubergine and potatoes with a hit of mustard seeds and ginger. Among desserts, star anise flavours bread-and-butter pudding successfully. The menu is annotated with dietary and allergy information. The wine list opens at £19 and includes organic and biodynamic options.

Chef/s: Minal Patel. **Closed:** Mon, 25 Dec. **Meals:** main courses £9 to £19. Tasting menu £46 (7 courses). **Details:** 80 seats. V menu. Vg menu. Wheelchairs. Music. Parking.

Ferrensby

The General Tarleton

Cooking score: 4

Modern British | £30

Boroughbridge Road, Ferrensby, HG5 0PZ
Tel no: (01423) 340284
generaltarleton.co.uk

'An excellent place to stop off for travellers on the A1,' noted one visitor to the Tophams' long-established pub-cum-restaurant with rooms. It ticks all the right boxes with its exposed stone and brick, beams and crackling winter fire, but is more country restaurant than pub these days, playing its role as an upmarket eatery with agility. John Topham injects vivid flavours and some bold combinations into his cooking. The quality is undeniably good, from 'excellent' Northumberland crab lasagne via a fillet of sea bass with chorizo and bean cassoulet (served with textures of shallot and smoked paprika purée), to slow-braised beef cheek with truffle whipped potatoes and bordelaise sauce. The bright, user-friendly repertoire also embraces plates of fish and chips and Sunday roasts, while desserts promise the likes of duck egg custard tart with meringue, stewed prunes and vanilla ice cream, as well as an all-Yorkshire cheeseboard. Real ales and a well-chosen, well-annotated wine list keep drinkers happy.

Chef/s: John Topham. **Meals:** main courses £14 to £27. Set L and D £15 (2 courses) to £19. **Details:** 110 seats. 50 seats outside. Bar. Music. Parking.

Follifoot

Horto

Cooking score: 5
Modern British | £40
Rudding Park Hotel, Follifoot, HG3 1JH
Tel no: (01423) 871350
ruddingpark.co.uk

The all-important symbiosis between kitchen and garden that marks so many establishments today achieves peak performance in the Rudding Park Hotel's Horto: the partnership of gardener Adrian Reeve and the restaurant's head chef Murray Wilson results in menus that have seasonal appeal in abundance. Expect adventurous explorations of pedigree produce, as in a starter of Whitby crab, pea and wasabi that appears on both the à la carte and seven-course tasting menus. Meat dishes gives a clear indication of Wilson's imaginative approach, as when Yorkshire wagyu is teamed with pickled girolle and truffle, or duck with broccoli and peanuts. The playful experimentation continues with desserts, where rhubarb and custard might be infused with a scent of woodruff, or an apple confection seasoned with five-year-old soy sauce. The short(ish) wine list opens at £36, and offers everything by the glass, from £9.50, as well as considered pairings with the tasting menu.

Chef/s: Murray Wilson. **Closed:** Mon, Tue. **Meals:** main courses £27 to £37. Tasting menu £69 (7 courses). **Details:** 46 seats. V menu. Vg menu. Bar. Wheelchairs. Music. Parking.

Grassington

Grassington House

Cooking score: 3
Modern British | £40
5 The Square, Grassington, BD23 5AQ
Tel no: (01756) 752406
grassingtonhouse.co.uk

Built to impress, this handsome Georgian residence on the corner of a cobbled square has been home to John and Sue Rudden's restaurant with rooms for 10 years. There's an elegant bar and terrace for casual dining, or continue to the main restaurant, a contemporary space with floor-to-ceiling windows. John's cooking takes a modern bistro route through Britain and Europe, so you might start with venison carpaccio with cured egg and pickled shallots, before moving on to beer-battered (and sustainable) fish of the day. Regional produce looms large: spring lamb, say, slow cooked for 24 hours, or Thirsk filet mignon with rag pudding (a suet pudding made with mincemeat and onions). The fixed price Market Menu is a cracking early-evening deal midweek (plus most lunchtimes). Poached Wakefield rhubarb with buttermilk panna cotta is a classy finish. Opening at £21.50, the wine list has a global spread.

Chef/s: John Rudden and Andrew Collop. **Closed:** 25 Dec. **Meals:** main courses £15 to £27. Set L and D (Tue to Thur) £18 (2 courses) to £20. Sun L £20 (2 courses) to £23. Tasting menu £50 (for 2 sharing). **Details:** 44 seats. 20 seats outside. Bar. Wheelchairs. Music. Parking.

Vegetarian and vegan

While many restaurants offer individual dishes suitable for non-meat eaters, those marked 'V menu' (vegetarian) and 'Vg menu' (vegan) offer separate menus.

Harome

The Pheasant Hotel

Cooking score: 4
Modern British | £45
Mill Street, Harome, YO62 5JG
Tel no: (01439) 771241
thepheasanthotel.com

A short stretch south of the A170, the Pheasant is a stone-built amalgam of what was a blacksmith's shop and barns, now repurposed as a comforting country hotel with a tirelessly creative chef on hand. Having worked under Claude Bosi (now at Bibendum in London – see entry), Peter Neville is used to pushing culinary boundaries, producing dishes that fit the village inn ethos, but with a layer of technical wizardry to add distinction. Tableside preparations confer a sense of occasion on the appearance of certain choices, as in a starter of sea trout cured in Yorkshire gin, served with beetroot purée, horseradish potato salad, dill pickles and sour cream. Mains might feature local hogget: herb-crusted loin and a spicy shepherd's pie of the shoulder, served with minted peas dotted with morteau sausage. Subtle Asian spicing adds interest to a fillet of hake, partnered with cauliflower, onion bhajia, coconut and golden raisins. Finish with the regional treasure, Yorkshire rhubarb, woven into a soufflé with ginger and crème fraîche ice cream. The exemplary wine list goes on exploring areas of the vinous globe that are worth learning about, such as the Bessa Valley, Bulgaria, the Troodos Mountains of Cyprus, and Kent, as well as providing classics for the sticklers. Prices open at £23.

Chef/s: Peter Neville. **Meals:** main courses £18 to £35. Sun L £34 (3 courses). Tasting menu £55 to £75. **Details:** 70 seats. 30 seats outside. V menu. Bar. Wheelchairs. Music. Parking.

The Star Inn

Cooking score: 6
Modern British | £45
High Street, Harome, YO62 5JE
Tel no: (01439) 770397
thestaratharome.co.uk

£5 OFF

'On our way back from Staithes we popped into the Star, just a small detour, intending to have one small plate. Ended up having the full starter and main and it was superb.' This expresses a feeling shared by many who have eaten at Andrew Pern's ancient but classy pub-with-rooms recently. Pern is a practised chef and restaurateur and, over the years, has gradually refined his version of modern British cooking, employing no tricks, trends or fiddly excess, just delivering enjoyable, generous dishes that eat superbly. The great strength here lies in the quality of regional supplies, from meat and game down to the herbs, fruit and vegetables grown in the pub's own kitchen garden. A Wensleydale Blue soufflé, for example, teamed with mulled wine onion jam, braised salsify and candied walnuts, delivers rich and powerful flavours, while an expertly cooked main course of milk-fed squab pigeon, poached in celeriac juice and served with scorched radicchio, parsnip and raw honey vinegar is simply 'magnificent'. Unwavering consistency and highly skilled executions are also the hallmarks of desserts such as baked chocolate and clementine fondant with sloe gin and gingerbread ice cream. The modern wine list is exactly right for the job, wide ranging and aiming to please, rather than impress, with excellent choice by the glass.

Chef/s: Andrew Pern and Stephen Smith.
Meals: main courses £19 to £29. Set L and D £20 (2 courses) to £25. Tasting menu L £55, D £85.
Details: 100 seats. 50 seats outside. V menu. Bar. Wheelchairs. Music. Parking.

Harrogate

Orchid

Cooking score: 2
Pan-Asian | £35
Studley Hotel, 28 Swan Road, Harrogate, HG1 2SE
Tel no: (01423) 560425
orchidrestaurant.co.uk
£5 OFF

Perhaps not the most typical location for a pan-Asian experience of real authenticity, but the traditional Studley Hotel proves that looks can often be deceiving. Something of a stalwart now in this often changing North Yorkshire town, Orchid delivers consistently bold flavours imported from Thailand, Japan, China and Indonesia. Begin with moreish Szechuan lamb pancakes that strike the perfect balance between deliciously rendered fat and tender meat, pepped up with shredded leeks and cucumber. Morning glory provides fire, crunch and punch in a notable vegetarian offering of rich red Thai curry. The rest of the considered menu continues the culinary tour and picks inspiration from lesser known Asian delights, while producing classics with plentiful authenticity and vigour. Larger dishes provide perfect grounds for groups and occasions of plenty. The wine list is as well travelled as the food, but not overly exhaustive and pairs pleasantly with the broad menu.
Chef/s: Kenneth Poon. **Closed:** 25 and 26 Dec. **Meals:** main courses £9 to £22. **Details:** 74 seats. 24 seats outside. Bar. Music. Parking.

Restaurant 92

Cooking score: 4
Modern British | £42
92-94 Station Parade, Harrogate, HG1 1HQ
Tel no: (01423) 503027
restaurant92.co.uk
£5 OFF

Occupying the first floor of a Victorian terraced townhouse, this ambitious restaurant is 'high-ceilinged and spacey'. It's a pleasant setting: grey leather banquettes curve to cup gleaming marble-top tables, the wood floor is highly polished, walls are panelled in duck-egg blue and staff 'are kitted out with formal flourish' and deliver 'good service'. Michael Carr heads the kitchen, offering a sharply contemporary, ingredient-driven British style of cooking via a short carte and various tasting menus. Seasonality is everything, prices restrained – the set lunch, in particular, is good value – and the Yorkshire beef wellington (for two) considered a triumphant main course. But there are also hand-dived scallops teamed with pea, onion and pork jelly sandwich, and butter-poached sea bass with Yorkshire mushrooms, confit potato and crispy chicken. Dessert might bring a passion fruit tart with curd, cardamom and baked white chocolate. The compact wine list is well balanced with prices from £22.
Chef/s: Michael Robert Carr. **Closed:** Mon, Tue, first 2 weeks Jan. **Meals:** main courses £18 to £26. Set L £21 (2 courses). Sun L £30. Tasting menu £70 (8 courses). **Details:** 75 seats. 10 seats outside. V menu. Bar. Music. Children over 12 yrs at D.

Sasso

Cooking score: 3
Italian | £30
8-10 Princes Square, Harrogate, HG1 1LX
Tel no: (01423) 508838
sassorestaurant.co.uk
£5 OFF

Stefano Lancellotti was born in the town of Sasso Marconi, in the Emilia-Romagna area of Italy, south of Bologna, which just happens to be the *superiore* food region in the country. The rest of Italy is far from ignored: smartly presented openers might include rich, creamy burrata from Puglia and vitello tonnato, that old favourite from Piedmont. The home region looms large though, with tortellini (homemade, naturally) filled with Parma ham, mortadella and Parmesan – 'the other holy trinity' – or lasagne with mint emulsion. While the kitchen makes much use of imported produce, local ingredients are just as valued, which is why English duck breast stars with tangerine segments and a Madeira jus, while lamb shank is slowly cooked and flavoured with mint. For dessert, semifreddo is another Italain classic done with style. The set lunch is a steal for two courses. The mostly Italian wine list opens at £17.95.

Chef/s: Stefano Lancellotti. **Closed:** 25 and 26 Dec, 1 Jan. **Meals:** main courses £13 to £42. Set L £11 (2 courses) to £15. **Details:** 110 seats. 25 seats outside. Music.

LOCAL GEM

Stuzzi

Italian | £25

46b Kings Road, Harrogate, HG1 5JW
Tel no: (01423) 705852

Run by four local lads with a passion for all things Italian, Stuzzi is an easy-going eatery that's a café by day and a restaurant come evening. Bang on target with cheery staff encouraging a sense of bonhomie, it's as good for breakfast (try the baked eggs in Neapolitan sauce with pecorino cheese) as it is for dinner, when little plates (stuzzi) are designed for sharing. Pasta is made fresh daily, say pappardelle with slow-braised game, but there's also beetroot and Negroni-cured salmon, fritto misto, Italian cheeses and a gooey dark chocolate brownie to finish. Italian wines from £19.95.

Hetton

The Angel Inn

Cooking score: 3
Modern British | £40

Hetton, BD23 6LT
Tel no: (01756) 730263
angelhetton.co.uk

Creepers cling to the old stone walls of the Angel, a country pub in the Yorkshire Dales National Park, which was considered a pretty revolutionary prospect back in the 1980s when they chucked out the chips and took cooking seriously. Pascal Watkins runs the place today (son of the founding father, Denis), and the love of good food remains. The bar brasserie menu is a cut above, while the restaurant ups the ante further. Textures of cauliflower (beignet, charred, pickled, purée) with a raisin sauce is new-wave all the way, and the Angel's seafood-filled filo pastry 'moneybag' remains as a homage to those heady radical days. Regional produce gets a good showing: ballotine of Yorkshire rabbit, say, with pancetta and apple risotto, and charred turbot as a refined fish course, with coriander citrus beurre blanc. 'Textures' appear again in a sharing dessert of strawberry and passion fruit. The formidable wine list covers the globe, though it excels in French bottles.

Chef/s: Naz Rafiq. **Closed:** 25 Dec. **Meals:** main courses £16 to £27. Sun L £24 (3 courses). Tasting menu £50 (6 courses). **Details:** 120 seats. 40 seats outside. Bar. Wheelchairs. Parking.

Holmfirth

READERS RECOMMEND

Philomena Foggs

Unit 11 Albion Mills, Miry Lane, Thongsbridge, Holmfirth, HD9 7HP
Tel no: (01484) 683444
philomenafoggs.co.uk

'It might not look like much from the outside but inside you'll find delicious, cooked-to-order café fare a cut above the norm. Vegans and special diets are catered for, and babies and dogs are welcome – indeed, nothing seems to faze the lovely staff. We go for the decadent (and very well-priced) afternoon tea.'

Honley

Mustard & Punch

Cooking score: 2
Modern British | £30

6 Westgate, Honley, HD9 6AA
Tel no: (01484) 662066
mustardandpunch.co.uk

£5 OFF

This neighbourhood bistro has stood at the heart of the attractive village of Honley since 2001. A 2018 refurbishment has brought it up to date with muted natural shades, comfy banquettes and racks of wine that suit the easy-going mood. The seasons shape a menu that is packed with good ideas and intelligent combinations in the modern British manner. Carpaccio of hay-smoked cod is a nifty contemporary opener, with cured cucumber and Parmesan custard, or how about braised pork cheek with merguez and a purée of roast onion and cloves? Local ingredients loom large – estate-shot pheasant, say, with a pastilla of leg meat and Yorkshire tea loaf – and flavours hit home. Vegans and vegetarians have imaginative options and, to finish, baked lemon meringue with mulled winter fruit sorbet invigorates the senses. The concise wine list opens at £18.95.

Chef/s: Will Orme. **Closed:** Sun, Mon, first week Jan. **Meals:** main courses £17 to £26. Set L £10 (2 courses) to £13. Set D £18 (2 courses) to £20. **Details:** 55 seats. V menu. Vg menu. Bar. Wheelchairs. Music. Parking.

Huddersfield

Epicure Bar & Kitchen

Cooking score: 2

Modern British | £30

37-39 Queensgate, Huddersfield, HD1 2RD
Tel no: (07980) 373699
epicurebarandkitchen.co.uk

£5 OFF

With a repertoire that runs from brunch to snappy lunches and indulgent weekend-only dinners, nobody can accuse this unpretentious café of having limited scope. Whether you are in for a breakfast Welsh rarebit, a lunchtime cheeseburger, salmon tagliatelle or a fish finger sandwich with twice-cooked chips, the food doesn't disappoint. Others prefer a lengthier visit and a meal from the 'after hours' evening menu (Friday and Saturday only) where the cooking takes on a distinctly modern flavour: smoked goat's cheese with beef-fat toast, pickled berries and black pudding; buttermilk-fried chicken with halloumi fritter, Emmental burger sauce and brioche; beer-battered skate wing with anchovy tartare; and milk jelly with thyme ice cream, Earl Grey raisins and honey. Coffee is considered excellent, and the well-annotated wine list, although brief, offers something for all tastes, from just £19 a bottle.

Chef/s: Lewis Myzak. **Meals:** main courses £9 to £15. **Details:** 40 seats. Bar. Music.

Ilkley

The Box Tree

Cooking score: 6

Anglo-French | £70

35-37 Church Street, Ilkley, LS29 9DR
Tel no: (01943) 608484
theboxtree.co.uk

£5 OFF

Built as a farmhouse in the first quarter of the 18th century, the Box Tree has been associated with top-end dining since 1962. Colourful flowers and those box trees mark the spot, and if it looks genteel within, rest assured the cooking is anything but. Simon and Rena Gueller took over in 2004, and Simon's cooking, with its roots in France and Britain, is a tantalising mix of classic and modern. Norfolk quail stars in a first course, its leg meat in a wee kiev and teamed with caramelised celeriac and pickled chanterelles, while Japanese flavours are deftly handled in the company of cured halibut and poached langoustine. A spiced port jus enriches loin of Richmond Park deer, and wild garlic gnocchi with soy-glazed morels is an inspired vegetarian main course. For dessert, pretty presentation brings all the senses into play, such as in a Yorkshire rhubarb and ginger parfait with calamansi lime curd and granola. Service is impeccable, as is the wine list, which is outstanding in France and pretty darn good in the rest of the world.

Chef/s: Simon Gueller and Kieran Smith. **Closed:** Mon, Tue, 26 to 30 Dec, first week Jan. **Meals:** set L £40. Set D £70. Sun L £40. Tasting menu £80 (6 courses). **Details:** 50 seats. Vg menu. Bar. Wheelchairs. Music. Children over 5 yrs at L, over 10 yrs at D.

Leeds

★ NEW ENTRY ★

Home

Cooking score: 5
Modern British | £55
16-17 Kirkgate, Leeds, LS1 6BY
Tel no: (0113) 430 0161
homeleeds.co.uk
£5 OFF

Not many restaurants hit their stride from the off but Liz Cottam, a *MasterChef* finalist, and Mark Owens, a former head chef at the Box Tree, Ilkley (see entry), have done just that with the city's most impressive opening of the year, transforming a tired old Indian restaurant into a stately yet cool bar and dining room. If their mission statement of 'reimagined familiar British flavours' sounds a touch self-conscious, the five or ten small courses amply justify the slogan. Beef tartare is one such standout, sensuously pairing beef fillet with finely sliced radish, wild mushrooms and an earthy sweetness from a slick of black garlic. Fish, chips and mushy peas come to life in the shape of cod cheek with the freshness of uncooked garden peas topped by a twirl of crisp batter, and so on through equally clever reimaginings of lamb, duck, seasonal vegetables and desserts. The menus change with the month, bolstered by superior amuse-bouches and a well-judged, well-priced wine flight, or bottles from an attractive list starting at £32 (softened by a complimentary drink on arrival), all marshalled by a smoothly drilled team.

Chef/s: Elizabeth Cottam and Mark Owens. **Closed:** Mon, Tue, 2 weeks Dec to Jan, 2 weeks Aug. **Meals:** tasting menu £55 (5 courses) to £70 (10 courses). **Details:** 42 seats. V menu. Bar. Music.

Get social

Follow us on social media for the latest news, chef interviews and more.
Twitter: @GoodFoodGuideUK
Facebook: TheGoodFoodGuide

★ NEW ENTRY ★

Issho

Cooking score: 3
Japanese | £35
Victoria Gate, Leeds, LS2 7AU
Tel no: (0113) 426 5000
issho-restaurant.com

Secreted on the rooftop of the deluxe Victoria Gate shopping mall, this contemporary Japanese-inspired restaurant boasts a handsome Kori cocktail bar, a leafy outdoor roof terrace and a 200-cover dining room, expensively kitted out in neutral shades and natural timber. The open kitchen prepares indulgent snacks like chicken karaage – superior fried chicken – with a wasabi mayonnaise, or grilled sweetcorn, basted with smoked lime butter and a dusting of furikake. Sushi, sashimi and nigiri are a given, as are the doughy bao buns stuffed with pork or cod katsu. Raw dishes include a refreshing cherry tomato salad with a whipped sesame and tofu dressing; the grill sends out duck breast with pickled nashi pear or, when you've swallowed the £34 price tag, a splendidly sweet and sticky miso black cod. Wines – part of an expansive drinks list that includes cocktails, saké and Japanese beers – rise steeply from £22.

Chef/s: Weike Zhao. **Meals:** small plates £4 to £14. Large plates £15 to £34. Set L £15 (3 courses). Set D £25 to £65. **Details:** 200 seats. Vg menu. Bar.

The Man Behind the Curtain

Cooking score: 7
Modern British | £80
68-78 Vicar Lane, Leeds, LS1 7JH
Tel no: (0113) 243 2376
themanbehindthecurtain.co.uk

Michael O'Hare is now focusing all his attention on the city where he made his name – Leeds. Although the postcode remains the same, the restaurant has moved from loft to basement, but this is no subterranean dive: polished marble stretches across a monochromatic, spacious dining area in what must be one of the more eye-catching temples to the new British cuisine in northern England. There's a constant procession of front-of-house staff delivering a 14-course tasting menu that explores contemporary techniques with such brio that the food is in a league of its own. First up might be a clear broth of kimchi and strawberry served with a poached oyster – a dish of unadorned simplicity, delicacy and balance. Indeed, familiar signatures such as the 'ackee and saltfish', 'ajo blanco, frozen tomato' and 'emancipation', a striking collision of cod loin, cod dashi and squid ink powder, made famous by *Great British Menu* have been notably simplified, revealing a new thoughtfulness in O'Hare's cooking and acting as a stark reminder of the raw talent that initially elevated his name. A headliner of squab pigeon breast with char sui crispy pigeon leg, enochi mushroom, rhubarb hoisin, prawn cracker powder and XO dried scallop is simply stunning, while a signature dessert of milk chocolate, potato and vanilla custard, honey and lavender is paired sensationally with plum saké. The wine pairing provides excellent accompaniment and value, and both the bottle and glass selection are well considered.

Chef/s: Michael O'Hare. **Closed:** Sun, Mon, 2 weeks Christmas and New Year, 2 weeks summer. **Meals:** tasting menu £60 to £95. **Details:** 43 seats. Bar. Music.

Ox Club

Cooking score: 3
Modern British | £32

Headrow House, The Headrow, Leeds, LS1 6PU
Tel no: (07470) 359961
oxclub.co.uk

£5 OFF

Headrow House, an arts and events space, is an impressive regeneration of an old textile mill with the Ox Club at its base – a concrete-floored, fairly industrial but attractive dining room with white-tiled walls and filament light bulbs. Most of executive chef Ben Davy's engaging menu comes from the imported wood-fired Grillworks – 'a hell of a thing that works on pulleys and takes up most of the kitchen . . . and capable of delivering one of the most rewarding meals I've had in a while.' There's rich, succulent Ibérico pork pluma with clams, morning glory and chicken skin crisps; red mullet, charred from the fire but perfect within and served with Tokyo fries; and roasted cauliflower in a smokey romesco sauce scattered with almonds (considered something of a signature dish). Punchy starters are equally confident, perhaps mackerel with confit horseradish and bone marrow, while smoked caramel is part of a Toffee Crisp with a difference. There's a brief, reasonably priced wine list, too.

Chef/s: Ben Davy and Ben Iley. **Closed:** Mon, 24 to 26 Dec. **Meals:** main courses £13 to £28. Early D £17 (2 courses) to £20. **Details:** 38 seats. Bar. Wheelchairs. Music.

The Reliance

Cooking score: 3
Modern British | £29

76-78 North Street, Leeds, LS2 7PN
Tel no: (0113) 295 6060
the-reliance.co.uk

A one-time cloth mill in the city's Northern Quarter is home to a 'bar & dining room' that feeds the contemporary appetite for relaxed, unpretentious surroundings and full-flavoured, unfussy food – 'it just works'. The pub-like attitude is matched by regional ales at the pumps and a quiz on Sunday nights. From the industrious, open-to-view kitchen comes house-made charcuterie – check out the blackboard for the day's choice, served on a board with bread and pickles. Game ragù and Berkswell cheese enrich spelt pappardelle in a hearty 'smaller plate', or go for the lighter slow-roasted carrots with tahini dressing. 'Bigger plates' include Erdinger-battered haddock and twice-cooked chips, and pork belly with black pudding fritter and onion purée, while a pre-theatre offering of sardines with tomato tapenade, followed by Toulouse sausages with braised lentils and herb crumb, was just the job for one early evening visitor. Finish with raspberry crème brûlée mille-feuille. The wine list has over a dozen options by the glass and carafe.

Chef/s: Tom Hunter. **Closed:** 25 and 26 Dec, 1 Jan, bank hols. **Meals:** main courses £12 to £16. **Details:** 120 seats. Bar. Wheelchairs. Music.

Salvo's

Cooking score: 2

Italian | £28

115 Otley Road, Headingley, Leeds, LS6 3PX
Tel no: (0113) 275 5017
salvos.co.uk

Family-run since 1976, Salvo's is part of the landscape hereabouts, almost as much as its near neighbour, Headingley Cricket Ground (established 1890). Both are equally rooted in tradition. Recent refurbishment has maintained the open and expansive feel of the place, with fashionable colour tones (grey is the new beige), sassy leather chairs and black and white photos focusing on the Dammone family's journey to local cult status. This is a kitchen that delivers spot-on pizzas like the 'Fresu' (smoked ricotta, roasted red peppers, spinach, black olives), alongside a hearty porcine *secondi* of belly, croquette and fennel sausage. Antipasti remain true to the motherland – sourdough bruschetta, octopus salad, and spicy pork and 'nduja polpette – and comforting pasta options impress. It's great value, too. All ends well with fig and frangipane tart. Italy rules the roost when it comes to drinks, so expect regional wines, from £18.50, craft beers, including La Bassa from Lombardy, and proper *classico* cocktails.

Chef/s: Gip Dammone and Oliver Edwards. **Closed:** 25 and 26 Dec, 1 Jan. **Meals:** main courses £11 to £29. Set L £12 (2 courses). Set D £15 (2 courses) to £19. **Details:** 88 seats. 16 seats outside. Vg menu. Bar. Wheelchairs. Music.

The Swine that Dines

Cooking score: 4

Modern British | £35

58 North Street, Leeds, LS2 7PN
Tel no: (07477) 834227

It may have started life as a moonlighting supper club by the owners of the Greedy Pig Café, but the whole operation has morphed into a restaurant, thanks to a wolfish appetite for Stuart Myers' amped-up evening cooking. Reflecting its origins, the setting is 'as unpretentious as it gets'. Food-wise, expect broadly European, informal small plate dining built on a base of classy, fresh ingredients. By day, you can take your pick, but by night it's a set menu, and the vegetarian version is available only on certain days of the month, so check before booking. Smaller dishes might include cured carrots with a seed cracker and ricotta, or rabbit terrine with fermented celeriac, caper and raisin compôte, while a typical larger course is wet garlic purée with dressed peas, charred baby gem and cured lamb. The peanut butter cheesecake has been described as 'the best ever tasted'. Friendly service is led by Jo Myers, and it's BYO, with no corkage charged.

Chef/s: Stuart Myers. **Closed:** Sun to Tue, 1 week Christmas, 2 weeks Sept. **Meals:** tasting menu £50 (for 2, sharing). **Details:** 18 seats. V menu.

Tharavadu

Cooking score: 2

Indian | £28

7-8 Mill Hill, Leeds, LS1 5DQ
Tel no: (0113) 244 0500
tharavadurestaurants.com

Tharavadu almost doubled its number of covers in 2018 – a sure sign that Leeds is getting a taste for Keralan cooking. Handily placed near the railway station, this is a colourful spot with a full-costume kathakali effigy by the door and folksy artefacts dotted around the no-frills dining room. The restaurant's name translates as 'ancestral home',

a theme reflected in the kitchen's respect for family traditions and time-honoured recipes: South Indian seafood and vegetarian specialities are the mainstays, with puris, steamed idli (rice cakes) and dosas giving way to dishes such as njandu vattichathu (whole crab cooked in a fragrant coconut sauce) or meen pollichathu (a 'toddy shop' favourite involving spiced fish wrapped in banana leaves). Alternatively, there is chicken in a punchy black pepper sauce with cashews, and Tharavadu offers plenty of interest in the vegetable department, too. Wines have been cannily selected to handle the spicy flavours.
Chef/s: Ajith Nair. **Closed:** Sun, 24 to 26 Dec. **Meals:** main courses £10 to £17. Set L £15 (2 courses) to £18. Set D £26 (2 courses) to £29. **Details:** 140 seats. Music.

Vice & Virtue

Cooking score: 2
Modern British | £50
68 New Briggate, Leeds, LS1 6NU
Tel no: (0113) 345 0202
viceandvirtueleeds.co.uk

Blink and you might just miss the entrance to this bar restaurant on the top floor of an anonymous corner building. Steep stairs lead to a dimly lit, speakeasy-style cocktail bar, then it's up again to the restaurant. In comfortable surroundings, with the kitchen on view, a monthly changing tasting menu explores the range of contemporary technique with brio. Luke Downing's modern experimental cooking isn't to everyone's taste, but for those for whom it delivers 'beautiful and innovative flavour combinations', highlights have included opening snacks of spring onion éclair stuffed with Richard III Wensleydale cheese, and Whitby crab with squid ink emulsion. There's more praise for a course of black pudding with asparagus, cured egg yolk, chicken heart in crackling, air-dried ham and pig's ear, as well as for spring hogget with mustard. Instagrammers will be delighted with the 'exquisite' presentation. There are innovative cocktails, too, and a globetrotting wine list, but do look to the complementary drinks packages that stretch 'far beyond just wine we are accustomed to'.
Chef/s: Luke Downing. **Closed:** Mon, Tue. **Meals:** tasting menu £50 (7 courses) to £65 (10 courses). **Details:** 28 seats. Bar. Music. No Children.

LOCAL GEM

Friends of Ham

Modern European | £25
4-8 New Station Street, Leeds, LS1 5DL
Tel no: (0113) 242 0275
friendsofham.com

Just metres from Leeds railway station, this little bar and charcuteria has a well-deserved reputation for impeccably sourced British and European cured meats and cheeses. It's not just cold choices – the kitchen also serves cooked brunch dishes including hot-smoked Bath chaps with poached eggs, béarnaise and toasted sourdough, You can round things off with fruit cake and Mrs Kirkham's Lancashire cheese. The wine list opens at £19, and there's a rotating choice of craft ales. A second branch is at 8 Wells Road, Ilkley LS29 9JD; tel: (01943) 604344.

LOCAL GEM

Zucco

Italian | £28
603 Meanwood Road, Leeds, LS6 4AY
Tel no: (0113) 224 9679
zucco.co.uk

This smart bacaro-style eatery sports a classic modern look, with beaten copper panel ceiling, zinc bar, dangly filament lights and tight-packed plain tables, and has built up a solid, enthusiastic fan base for its kindly priced Italian small plates – sharing, of course. The menu ranges from salt cod ravioli, fritto misto and deep-fried zucchini to smoked haddock and scallops in cream sauce, a spinach and Gorgonzola pizzetta, and ox cheek with pea and grana Padano risotto. Almond and raspberry polenta cake will fill any remaining gaps. Drink cocktails or Italian wines.

Leyburn

The Sandpiper Inn

Cooking score: 2
Modern British | £32
Market Place, Leyburn, DL8 5AT
Tel no: (01969) 622206
sandpiperinn.co.uk

A picture of stone-built Yorkshire solidity at the gateway to the Dales, this gentrified 17th-century inn overlooks Leyburn Market Place. As a hostelry, it ticks all the boxes (real ales, beams, cosy nooks), and its kitchen scores, too, delivering capable cooking with an international accent. The menu ranges widely, from fishcakes with chive sauce or local venison with crispy bacon and duck-fat potatoes via Nidderdale chicken breast on chorizo risotto to Moroccan spiced lamb with jumbo couscous. Steaks, burgers and roast cod with mushy peas and chips keep traditionalists happy, while dessert could bring bread-and-butter pud or iced lemon parfait with Yorkshire rhubarb and meringue shards. Ten house wines are available by the glass or carafe, and the Sandpiper's hospitality extends to well-reported breakfasts for residents.

Chef/s: Jonathan Harrison. **Closed:** Mon, Tue (winter only), 2 weeks Jan. **Meals:** main courses £14 to £18. Sun L £21 (2 courses) to £26. **Details:** 60 seats. 20 seats outside. Bar. Music. Parking.

Lindley

Eric's

Cooking score: 3
Modern British | £45
73-75 Lidget Street, Lindley, HD3 3JP
Tel no: (01484) 646416
ericsrestaurant.co.uk

Refurbishment in 2017 has given Eric Paxman's restaurant a dramatic and luxurious new look that sets it apart from its neighbours in this smart suburb of Huddersfield. There's also a surprise element to his cooking, which trades on colour, vibrancy and exoticism, pulling in ideas from faraway lands for a menu that aims for impact, as well as flavour. Whether your preference is for pork belly and crispy pig's head terrine with vindaloo sauce, charred corn and red onion bhaji or scorched scallops with prawn won tons, lime-spiked peanut sauce and soy coleslaw, the kitchen can oblige. Despite the emphasis on all things global, most of the core ingredients are true to the North, be it in braised daube of ox cheek with smoked potato, bacon and stout jam or a venison and Yorkshire Blue cheese pie served with black figs, kale and quince. The 50-bin wine list is invitingly peppered with lesser-known names.

Chef/s: Eric Paxman, James Thompson and Chris Kelly. **Closed:** Mon. **Meals:** main courses £24 to £30. Set L and D £20 (2 courses) to £25. Sun L £30. **Details:** 70 seats. V menu. Bar. Music.

Masham

Samuel's

Cooking score: 4
Modern British | £58
Swinton Park, Masham, HG4 4JH
Tel no: (01765) 680900
swintonestate.com

There's a touch of *Downton Abbey* about this grand ancestral pile embedded in a 20,000-acre Yorkshire estate, although Swinton Park also plays the 21st-century heritage card, with diversions ranging from a bivouac 'glamping' retreat to a cookery school. Crenellated battlements, turrets and towers set the scene, while Samuel's restaurant (overlooking the deer park) provides a suitably opulent backdrop for special-occasion dining. The estate provides seasonal game, and there are ample pickings from the four-acre walled garden to go with a storehouse of regional produce: trout from the lake is presented with dill sorbet and buttermilk; home-reared beef is given an earthy edge with truffled celeriac and morels; Middle White pork comes with young leeks, sage and caramelised apple. The kitchen also casts its net wider for skrei cod and Orkney scallops, while dessert might bring gingerbread soufflé with apple sorbet. A weighty wine list includes some inviting Coravin selections by the glass.

Chef/s: Jake Jones. **Closed:** Mon, Tue, 7 and 8 Jan. **Meals:** set D £58. Sun L £28. Tasting menu £70 (7 courses). **Details:** 70 seats. Bar. Wheelchairs. Music. Parking. Children over 8 yrs.

Middleton Tyas

The Coach House

Cooking score: 3
Modern British | £30

Middleton Lodge, Kneeton Lane, Middleton Tyas, DL10 6NJ
Tel no: (01325) 377977
middletonlodge.co.uk

£5 OFF

While wedding guests celebrate in Middleton Lodge's splendid Georgian mansion, the converted Coach House restaurant in the grounds, complete with walled kitchen gardens, peaceful terrace and a small bar, is a destination in its own right. Grey tongue-and-groove panelling, industrial lights and plush button-back banquettes make it a modern style success, though the service could do with a polish. The menu values good taste over screaming originality, but there's lots to like about an aged beef tartare dotted with sticky confit egg yolk and sourdough crisps, or a main course of skrei cod, cooked to pearly perfection, with a lightly creamy, spoonable cockle jus flecked with wild garlic oil. Puddings can be hit and miss – at inspection, pistachio baked Alaska had double the optimum meringue, while disparate rhubarb and gingerbread elements were cloaked effectively by a thick shower of white chocolate. The wine list has plenty to tempt (including half bottles) and there is a good local drinks offer including Darlington's Rocket Town brewery beer. As we went to press, a second restaurant, The Forge, was due to open.

Chef/s: Gareth Rayner. **Meals:** main courses £15 to £20. **Details:** 80 seats. 20 seats outside. V menu. Bar. Wheelchairs. Music. Parking.

Newton-on-Ouse

The Dawnay Arms

Cooking score: 3
Modern British | £35

Moor Lane, Newton-on-Ouse, YO30 2BR
Tel no: (01347) 848345
thedawnayatnewton.co.uk

It's more than 10 years since Martel Smith took over this genteel 18th-century inn with lovely gardens stretching down to the banks of the river Ouse, and it continues to delight. If the building's open fires, hop-garlanded beams and scrubbed wood tables speak of pubby honesty, there's nothing rough-hewn or provincial about Smith's cooking or his considered approach to top-notch ingredients. How about a croustade of baked goat's cheese with wild garlic pesto, pine nuts and pickled mushrooms, or honey-roast duck breast plated up with a duck leg dumpling, sweet potato fondant, lentils and griottine cherries? Steaks are salt-aged for 60 days, and chunks of Whitby cod are topped with a Yorkshire rarebit crust, while a dessert of winter-spiced caramel panna cotta with poached fruits strikes a seasonal note. Wines promise dependable drinking by the glass or bottle.

Chef/s: Martel Smith. **Closed:** Mon, 1 week Jan. **Meals:** main courses £14 to £25. Set L and D £15 (2 courses) to £19. Sun L £22. **Details:** 65 seats. 40 seats outside. Bar. Wheelchairs. Music. Parking.

Send us your review

Your feedback informs the content of the *GFG* and will be used to compile next year's reviews. To register your opinion about any restaurant listed in the Guide, or a restaurant that you wish to bring to our attention, visit: thegoodfoodguide.co.uk/feedback

Oldstead
The Black Swan

Cooking score: 6
Modern British | £98
Main Street, Oldstead, YO61 4BL
Tel no: (01347) 868387
blackswanoldstead.co.uk

Is this a country pub for modern times? Its venerable shell is visible in the beams and worn stone walls of the old bar, but the dining room above has had a subtle makeover, and polished wood floors, duck-egg blue panelling and simple, stylish furniture set the scene. Here, Tommy Banks' cooking shows a keen understanding of the art of combining disparate elements. His contemporary presentations of cool-climate food offer plenty of novelty on a 12-course tasting menu that is locally themed, farmed and foraged (you can see the restaurant's two-acre kitchen garden from the dining room windows). The sheer breadth of Banks' cooking can be gauged immediately from the terrific openers that take in langoustine with salted strawberries, chicken dumplings, and raw deer with wild garlic. Elsewhere, cod with cauliflower and parsley is a masterclass in timing and upstanding flavours: the never-off-the-menu crapaudine beetroot cooked in beef fat and topped with horseradish, goat's cheese curd and smoked cod's roe emulsion is just brilliant; and dry-aged duck with smoked damson was deemed a triumph by one diner. When it comes to desserts, the kitchen is judicious with sugar and quite comfortable with vegetables, coaxing astonishing flavour from sheep's milk with Douglas fir oil (served with an extraordinary Douglas fir cocktail) and textural contrasts from a confection of root vegetable toast. Service could hardly be more knowledgeable or more engaging. Besides home-infused cocktails, there is a diagrammatic wine list arranged by style to encourage experimentation, with every bottle offered by the (small) glass.

Chef/s: Tommy Banks and Will Lockwood. **Meals:** tasting menu £98 (12 courses) to £110. **Details:** 50 seats. Bar. Music. Parking. Children over 10 yrs.

Osmotherley
Golden Lion

Cooking score: 2
Anglo-European | £30
6 West End, Osmotherley, DL6 3AA
Tel no: (01609) 883526
goldenlionosmotherley.co.uk

'It's dark inside this 18th-century pub,' noted one lunchtime visitor, adding 'but the stove was lit and all the tables had candles . . . it looked warm and welcoming'. The Golden Lion is much loved by locals and visitors, winning everyone over with a friendly welcome and efficient service, and it makes a handsome setting for very simple pub food. The menu covers all bases, from king prawns in garlic butter or grilled halloumi with artichoke and toasted pine nut salad, and salmon fishcake with chive beurre blanc, to winter warmers such as pot-roast pheasant with sprouts, bacon and chestnut stuffing or calf's liver with crispy onions, mashed potato and red cabbage. After that, consider cranachan trifle with honey, whisky and cranberries or keep it traditional with steamed treacle sponge with vanilla custard. There's a choice of four real ales and the wine list promises dependable drinking from £18.95.

Chef/s: Nick Georgiou and Christopher Wright. **Closed:** 25 Dec. **Meals:** main courses £11 to £23. **Details:** 67 seats. 16 seats outside. Wheelchairs. Music.

Pickering

The White Swan Inn

Cooking score: 1
British | £36
Market Place, Pickering, YO18 7AA
Tel no: (01751) 472288
white-swan.co.uk
£5 OFF

This grand coaching inn has been in the Buchanan family for nearly four decades and is run with great warmth. It's the genuine article, centuries old with open fires, beams, flagstone floors, nooks and crannies, and an agreeable menu that makes much of local and regional produce. Homemade black pudding with charcoal-roasted cauliflower purée, Granny Smith and cider dressing, or beetroot-cured salmon gravadlax with heritage potato salad might precede satisfying and generously proportioned plates of Yorkshire lamb rump, served with charred carrot, caper, pressed potato and black olive, or beer-battered Whitby cod and chips. Wines from £18.75.

Chef/s: Darren Clemmitt. **Meals:** main courses £14 to £30. Sun L £20 (2 courses) to £25. **Details:** 50 seats. 20 seats outside. Bar. Wheelchairs. Parking.

Ramsgill

The Yorke Arms

Cooking score: 6
Modern British | £65
Ramsgill, HG3 5RL
Tel no: (01423) 755243
yorke-arms.co.uk

'Stunning early summer evening in the Dales, with birdsong, sunshine, the Yorke Arms immaculate outside . . . inside, I was surprised to find it looking exactly the same, despite the major refurb.' So ran one reader's reassuring notes, for uncertainty gripped the Yorke Arms' very loyal fans when chef Frances Atkins sold the business in November 2017. Fears were allayed when a deal was struck with the buyer – as a result, Atkins remains at the pass with her crew. The style is much the same, though some tweaks signal a fresh eye on a menu that features produce from the kitchen garden, local meat and game, and fish from both coasts 'with breathtaking effect'. At inspection, 'great textures and hues' came through in the lightest lovage mousse with pea and oregano and a scattering of bacon crumb, while perfectly cooked, gently spiced turbot in a vivid puddle of turmeric reduction dotted with black squid ink croûtons was equally impressive. Truffled cauliflower with artichoke and asparagus was another stunner – a perfect pile of dinky shaved vegetables, a sliver of truffle atop, set on a mild Parmesan foam, likewise chin and cheek of veal with broad beans, earthy mushrooms, a disc of deeply flavoured veal stuffing and sauce was 'rich, dark, immensely satisfying'. A pretty-as-a-picture tower of rhubarb and strawberry mousse, jelly, biscuit and meringue made 'a fabulous finish'. The largely French wine list opens at £35.

Chef/s: Frances Atkins. **Meals:** main courses £25 to £35. Set L £45. Tasting menu £85 (8 courses). **Details:** 40 seats. 20 seats outside. Bar. Music. Parking.

Raskelf

Rascills

Cooking score: 4
Modern British | £50
Village Farm, Howker Lane, Raskelf, YO61 3LF
Tel no: (01347) 822031
rascillsrestaurant.co.uk

'A wonderful meal... good and consistent... food, drinks, service and ambience were all superb and memorable.' Readers have been unstinting in their praise for this smart husband-and-wife operation just off the A19 between York and Thirsk. Although they only landed here in 2016, Richard and Lindsey Johns have form. They first appeared in the Guide with the charming Artisan, near Hull, then a dining pub in East Yorkshire, and now they're here doing what they do best: enhancing quality ingredients with a sensibility that is both modern and classic. Three set courses (plus cheese) at dinner proffers a Thai-inspired broth, redolent with lemongrass, served with homemade focaccia. A beautifully butter-poached fillet of halibut comes with pea and mint risotto, and beef rump is topped with sweet onions served with a red wine sauce and a slick of carrot purée. Wind up with a choice of rich chocolate and orange délice or a model vanilla crème brûlée. The wine list starts at £22.95 with Portuguese Prunus Dao, or good-value choices by the glass and some intriguing pairings.

Chef/s: Richard Johns. **Closed:** Mon, Tue, every other Sun, early Jan, bank hols. **Meals:** set L £20 (2 courses) to £23. Set D £45 (4 courses). **Details:** 20 seats. 8 seats outside. Bar. Wheelchairs.

Sancton

The Star Inn

Cooking score: 4
Modern British | £50

King Street, Sancton, YO43 4QP
Tel no: (01430) 827269
thestaratsancton.co.uk

The Star shines like a beacon in the Yorkshire Wolds under the guidance of Ben and Lindsey Cox. Ben's innovative modern British cooking has put the place firmly on Yorkshire's culinary map, the once grubby roadside boozer drawing visitors from afar, but it thrives as a community hub, too, with local ales on tap in the traditional bar. The dining rooms beyond are smart with high-backed leather chairs and tables that gleam with glasses and cutlery, but the vibe remains comfortable and laid-back. Exciting menus embrace the best Yorkshire produce available, with delicious pies and the famous filled Yorkshire pudding on the bar menu. Ben shows a deft touch in reinventing classics and delivering sound flavours, as seen in braised sticky pig's cheek with rosemary beignets, homemade black pudding and sage aïoli; and a beautifully cooked cod loin with coconut curry sauce, bhaji scraps, mini crab cake and Ellerker spinach. Puddings may include vanilla pod crème brûlée with rhubarb jammy dodger. The fascinating global wine list favours smaller producers and offers variety, value and good tasting notes.

Chef/s: Ben Cox. **Closed:** Mon, 1 week Jan, bank hols. **Meals:** main courses £17 to £30. Set L £18 (2 courses) to £20. Set D £30 (2 courses) to £38. **Details:** 80 seats. 30 seats outside. Vg menu. Bar. Wheelchairs. Music. Parking.

Scarborough

★ NEW ENTRY ★

Courtyard at Ox Pasture Hall

Cooking score: 3
Modern British | £30

Lady Edith's Drive, Scarborough, YO12 5TD
Tel no: (01723) 365295
oxpasturehallhotel.com

Ollie Moore made his name and reputation at the Black Rat in Winchester (see entry). Now, after a year abroad, he has resurfaced at this demure country hotel three miles inland from Scarborough. From a remarkably good-value three-course lunch (with a discount for seniors) and a serviceable wine list starting at £18, Moore has put together a promising menu: wild garlic soup with a poached egg and fried potato strings; cod with poppy seed spätzle; and pork tenderloin elevated by accompaniments of celeriac and lovage purée, bubble and squeak and crispy pig's ears. If intricate desserts like Granny Smith parfait and chocolate délice with cherryade sorbet didn't quite wow at inspection, then the squid ink and Parmesan bread rolls served with burnt and whipped butter (Black Rat favourites) certainly did. The slightly longer dinner menu is more ambitious again. With a reputation for wild foods and foraging, clean flavours and seasonal ingredients, Moore may have yet more to offer as the Ox Pasture continues its transition from more conservative Yorkshire fare.

Chef/s: Ollie Moore. **Meals:** main courses £14 to £20. Set L £18 (2 courses) to £23. Set D £28 (3 courses). **Details:** 64 seats. 24 seats outside. Bar. Wheelchairs. Music. Parking.

Lanterna

Cooking score: 3
Italian | £40
33 Queen Street, Scarborough, YO11 1HQ
Tel no: (01723) 363616
lanterna-ristorante.co.uk

Trends come and go but Lanterna continues much as it has done for the past 40 years. It's had a lick of paint but the napkins still stand like pixie hats, breadsticks sit beside the table-top food warmer, and the hallmark café curtains signal that all is well in Queen Street's treasured Italian stronghold. Giorgio Alessio has cooked here single-handedly throughout, producing a roster of classics: Parma ham with melon, minestrone, veal with Marsala and cream, and – famously – Italian white truffles when in season. There are numerous 'specials' reeled off tableside, which, if you can remember, might be hare ragù; halibut in white wine sauce; a rich hake stew with tomatoes and anchovies; or a shamelessly creamy velvet crab linguine, most reflecting Alessio's devotion to the town's fish market. To see him at work at first hand, order the zabaglione, a confection whipped up beside you with a copper pan, a spirit stove and lashings of Marsala. Pure theatre.

Chef/s: Giorgio Alessio. **Closed:** Sun, Mon, 25 and 26 Dec, 1 Jan, last 3 weeks Oct. **Meals:** main courses £16 to £49. **Details:** 30 seats. Music.

Local Gem

These entries highlight a range of neighbourhood venues, delivering good, freshly cooked food at great value for money.

LOCAL GEM

Eat Me Café and Social

Modern British | £18
2 Hanover Road, Scarborough, YO11 1LS
Tel no: (07445) 475328
eatmecafe.com

Handy for the Stephen Joseph Theatre, this buzzing café has bags of contemporary style, and a menu that runs from breakfast to grilled sandwiches and globally inspired lunches (chicken satay, maybe). After 4pm, it becomes 'Social': tables can be booked, and you can order a cocktail with your bowl of ramen, homemade burger or choose-your-own meatball combo. Ingredients are sourced with care, and vegetarians and vegans fair very well indeed. Asian beers, well-chosen spirits and a few wines add to the social mix.

Scawton

The Hare Inn

Cooking score: 6
Modern British | £60
Scawton, YO7 2HG
Tel no: (01845) 597769
thehare-inn.com

Abandoning conventional courses in favour of a multiplicity of small dishes is not something you would expect from a chef in an ancient off-the-beaten-track country inn deep in walking and cycling country. But Paul Jackson is sticking to his guns and doing it very well. The six- or eight-course tasting menus (with vegetarian versions) elicit delight from readers – at the ambitious yet accessible cooking, and the first-class ingredients. Both can be witnessed in the beetroot with goat's cheese ice cream that kicks off our evening, just one of the extra little treats that punctuate the meal. What dazzles is the razor clam, served finely chopped in its shell with a subtle dressing; mackerel two ways (hot and cold); and duck with cauliflower, truffle and Tunworth cheese. It all works because the precision and care in every dish shines through. Desserts are no less impressive, the kitchen delivering a mini 'milk and honey' that's 'worthy of its own award', and a combination of chocolate, salted caramel and hazelnut that is simply delightful. Accommodating service adds to the air of geniality. 'I wish I didn't live over 200 miles away,' complained one reader, who may be pleased to learn that bedrooms have been added this year. If you don't fancy the wine pairing, a short list of well-chosen bottles opens at £20.

Chef/s: Paul Jackson. **Closed:** Sun, Mon, Tue, 26 Dec to 18 Jan, 1 week Jun, 2 weeks Nov. **Meals:** set L £55 (6 courses). Set D £70 (8 courses). **Details:** 22 seats. V menu. Bar. Music. Parking. No children.

Sheffield

Jöro

Cooking score: 5
Modern European | £45
Krynkl, 294 Shalesmoor, Sheffield, S3 8US
Tel no: (0114) 299 1539
jororestaurant.co.uk
£5 OFF

Despite being constructed from reclaimed shipping containers, with rough-textured walls painted forbidding steel grey, this compact restaurant still feels 'very hygge' according to one reader. Jöro (meaning 'earth' in old Norse) delivers a new interpretation of modern British cooking, embracing contemporary techniques with gusto, either via a series of small plates or through an eight- or ten-course tasting menu. Dishes 'bring out the very best of local, seasonal produce', as in a fat finger of celeriac slow-cooked in beef fat and teamed with Lincolnshire Poacher cheese sauce, gherkin ketchup and crispy shallots, or charred brassicas (kale, purple sprouting broccoli and savoy cabbage) with a pungent, umami-rich black mustard emulsion spiked with Chinese XO sauce. Dashi and seaweed give extraordinary depth of flavour to a sweet, succulent barbecued langoustine tail served in a bowl of wild garlic cream. To finish, a palate cleanser of lemon pie and lemon thyme espuma on the daintiest brik pastry paves the way for jasmine tea ice cream with a compôte of forced rhubarb and a light, crisp ginger biscuit. Staff are both passionate and knowledgeable, and the intelligent wine list offers plenty of pleasant surprises, not least some excellent organic Austrian reds.

Chef/s: Luke French. **Closed:** Sun, Mon, Tue, first 2 weeks Jan, 1 week Apr, 1 week Jul, 1 week Sept. **Meals:** small plates £6 to £20. Set L £22 (2 courses) to £28. Tasting menu £45 (8 courses) to £55. **Details:** 50 seats. Wheelchairs. Music.

★ NEW ENTRY ★

No Name

Cooking score: 2
Modern British | £35
253 Crookes, Sheffield, S10 1TF
Tel no: (0114) 266 1520

'This is quite a find, a genuinely exciting new opening for Sheffield,' thought one visitor to Thomas Samworth's modestly named restaurant located in a former shop in the Crookes district. The chef, however, is making quite a name for himself, working solo behind a curtain in a tiny kitchen with two basic induction hobs and two sittings a night. In a room illuminated by strings of bulbs and fairy lights and filled with mismatched vintage furniture, diners sit cheek-by-jowl next to shelves of bric-à-brac that wouldn't look out of place in a charity shop. None of this detracts from the concise, seasonal menu handwritten on a large wall-mounted roll of brown paper. At a February dinner, a starter of pheasant boudin was teamed with parsnip purée and lentils. Confit duck leg followed, accompanied by potato rösti, green beans and a zesty blood orange sauce with rhubarb jelly, white chocolate and vanilla custard to finish. Bookings are pretty much essential and the cash-only, BYO wine policy adds a pop-up feel to proceedings.

Chef/s: Thomas Samworth. **Closed:** Sun, Mon, Tue, 1 week Christmas. **Meals:** main courses £14 to £18. **Details:** 21 seats. Music.

Rafters

Cooking score: 4
Modern British | £55
220 Oakbrook Road, Nether Green, Sheffield, S11 7ED
Tel no: (0114) 230 4819
raftersrestaurant.co.uk
£5 OFF

'Excellent food and attentive service' was the verdict of one visitor to this neighbourhood gem in Nether Green. With its discreet entrance and location above a row of shops, it's not the easiest place to spot, but that doesn't hinder the restaurant's popularity. Patrolling an airy, high-ceilinged room with beams and exposed brickwork, well-drilled staff are efficient, knowledgeable and good-humoured. Centred around fixed-price and tasting menus, the cooking is equally assured and ambitious. A meal might start with aged soy-cured mackerel with radish, cucumber and yuzu before moving on to spiced hogget rump served with carrots cooked in lamb fat, creamy garlic purée and a rich jus. To conclude, dark Peruvian single-origin chocolate, miso caramel, yuzu sorbet and banana has been described as 'a winning combination'. Arranged by style, and with helpful pairings listed on the menu, the global wine list starts at £20.

Chef/s: Thomas Lawson. **Closed:** Sun, Mon. **Meals:** set D £35 (3 courses). Tasting menu £55 to £75. **Details:** 38 seats. V menu. Music.

LOCAL GEM

Ashoka

Indian | £22
307 Ecclesall Road, Sheffield, S11 8NX
Tel no: (0114) 268 3029
ashoka1967.com

A Sheffield institution since it opened in 1967, this Ecclesall Road stalwart has certainly moved with the times. The design is fresh, yet faithful to the look of colonial Indian railway waiting rooms, with hand-painted Sanskrit, mahogany mirrors and family photos. A nod to its Yorkshire location comes in a starter of spiced potato mixed with Sheffield-made Henderson's Relish and fresh coriander in a featherlight puri bread. Follow it with a chicken- and lamb-based taxi driver curry or Mr Singh's saag karai. Wines from £15.50.

Shibden

Shibden Mill Inn

Cooking score: 2
Modern British | £35
Shibden Mill Fold, Shibden, HX3 7UL
Tel no: (01422) 365840
shibdenmillinn.com

The vertiginous cobbled lane gets narrower the further down the deep folds of the valley you drop, but the dramatic descent is rewarded as this smartly whitewashed, wisteria-covered 17th-century inn heaves into view. On a warm day take lunch on the handsome stone-flagged terrace and enjoy the brook and birdsong; inside, it's awash with low beams, wonky walls, open fires and antique oak sideboards – a 'great winter pub'. But there's nothing dated about the menu. Adam Harvey specialises in Yorkshire steaks grilled over charcoal on the Kopa but there's much more besides: seared mackerel fillet comes with cucumber purée, sauce vierge and a 'stunning horseradish sorbet'; curried monkfish tail with peas and lobster sauce; and sumac pork fillet with turnip and peach. The menu bristles with seasonal diversity, and good use is made of the herb and vegetable garden, as well as local produce. A comprehensive wine list traverses the world, but do try the bespoke Shibden Special bitter – it's a belter.

Chef/s: Adam Harvey. **Closed:** 25 and 26 Dec (evening), 1 Jan (evening). **Meals:** main courses £14 to £30. **Details:** 100 seats. 60 seats outside. Bar. Music. Parking.

South Dalton

The Pipe & Glass

Cooking score: 5
Modern British | £46
West End, South Dalton, HU17 7PN
Tel no: (01430) 810246
pipeandglass.co.uk

For over a decade now, fans have been beating a path along the narrow lanes of the Yorkshire Wolds to James and Kate Mackenzie's 17th-century pub with rooms beside the gates to Dalton Park. The spick-and-span building is a shining example of a traditional country inn run with modern style and great attention to detail. Arrive early if you wish to eat by the fire in the rustic, beamed bar (no bookings), or go through to the conservatory overlooking the garden. Commendably, it's still very much a pub, so feel free to order a seared steak and onion sandwich or a classic fish pie to accompany a pint of Wold Top, but there are more unusual ingredient combinations on James's seasonal menus (packed full of local, regional and home-grown produce), too. Try asparagus, crispy hen's egg, chorizo jam and lovage mayonnaise, followed by well-executed lamb rump and braised crispy lamb belly served with Fine Fettle cheese and nettle croquette, anise carrots and nettle and mint sauce, and sticky toffee pudding with stout ice cream and walnut brittle to finish. The carefully selected wine list offers great value (half of the 100-strong list is under £30) and exceptional choice by the glass.

Chef/s: James Mackenzie. **Closed:** Mon (exc bank hols), 2 weeks Jan. **Meals:** main courses £14 to £32. **Details:** 80 seats. 60 seats outside. V menu. Bar. Wheelchairs. Music. Parking.

Sowerby Bridge

Gimbals

Cooking score: 4
International | £32
76 Wharf Street, Sowerby Bridge, HX6 2AF
Tel no: (01422) 839329
gimbals.co.uk

An exhibit salvaged from Blackpool Illuminations is just one of the collectibles on show in this idiosyncratically designed restaurant. Janet Baker went for a highly personal, 'seductively decadent' look when she filled Gimbals' close-packed dining areas with mosaic mirrors, frilly lampshades and other ephemera, and Simon Baker matches the setting with his equally eclectic food. Whether you're in the market for sticky barbecue pork belly with garlicky green beans and spiced apple salsa or a three-part assemblage involving pan-fried cod steak, tempura cod cheek and brandade with sautéed artichokes, 'this guy cooks consistently'. To start, the signature smoked fish platter takes some beating with its 'truly memorable' array of cured delicacies ranging from BBQ octopus to hot-smoked Lincolnshire eel with caraway air-dried tomatoes, while desserts have included an outstanding blackberry, apple and almond crumble. Service is invariably seamless, and the short wine list is matched by cocktails in the upstairs lounge.

Chef/s: Simon Baker. **Closed:** Sun, Mon. **Meals:** main courses £16 to £29. Set D £19 (2 courses) to £23. Tasting menu £29 (5 courses). **Details:** 55 seats. V menu. Vg menu. Bar. Music.

Anonymous

At *The Good Food Guide*, our inspectors dine anonymously and pay their bill in full. These impartial review meals, along with feedback from thousands of our readers, are what informs the content of the *GFG*.

★ BEST NEW ENTRY, UK ★

The Moorcock

Modern British | £35
Moorbottom Lane, Sowerby Bridge, HX6 3RP
Tel no: (01422) 832103
themoorcock.co.uk

Alisdair Brooke-Taylor's period in Belgium at the late In de Wulf shines forth from every last foraged leaf and berry at this top-of-the-moor pub overlooking the Ryburn Valley. On offer, a masterclass in the new British cuisine with the focus on brilliant seasonal ingredients and in-vogue preservation techniques: smokehouse cooking, pickling, fermenting and curing. There's a delight in the reckless approach to pushing boundaries, with fried herring bones 'a glorious skeleton of a thing'. This sterling opener is followed by a smokey chunk of dry-aged Hebridean mutton with jew's ear mushroom relish and paper-thin slices of pickled lamb's heart and a satisfyingly rich homemade blood pudding served with beetroot and pickled walnut. Elsewhere, barbecued squid in an antioxidant rich velouté of kale, basil and sunflower seed, dry-aged duck with fresh raspberries, cucumber and samphire, a cooling tea of sorrel and meadowsweet, and pineapple weed ice cream topped with foraged bilberries reveal carefully considered flavour combinations. In addition, the wood-fired sourdough bread and hand-churned butter is exemplary. Consider the small-plates bar menu if the restaurant is full. The interior is unpolished, bordering on basic, the staff genuinely committed, and there are interesting cocktails, real ales and Belgian beers, and a wide-ranging wine list arranged by style.

Chef/s: Alisdair Brooke-Taylor. **Closed:** Mon, Tue, 13 to 24 Aug. **Meals:** small plates (in the bar) £3 to £9. Tasting menu £35 (7 courses). **Details:** 28 seats. 30 seats outside. Bar. Music. Parking.

Staddlebridge

The Cleveland Tontine

Cooking score: 4
Modern British | £32
Staddlebridge, DL6 3JB
Tel no: (01609) 882671
theclevelandtontine.com
£5 OFF

This 19th-century coaching inn was run for some 35 bohemian years by the three McCoy brothers, who created a destination restaurant before we knew the meaning of the phrase. Under new ownership (Provenance Inns), the public rooms and bedrooms have been given a contemporary redesign, but the basement restaurant remains largely and delightfully unchanged with its decorative plasterwork ceiling, dark panelling and agreeable glow cast from lamps, candles and firelight. There's an attractive, please-all menu, too, expertly prepared from a list that could feature a salad of Whitby crab or a guinea fowl terrine with brioche and leeks served with ewe's curd, roast hazelnuts and wild mushrooms. At mains, a satisfying, tender chicken breast comes with barley, caramelised shallot and Madeira sauce, and there's rump steak with all the trimmings, including peppercorn sauce and triple-cooked chips. Wines are from a comprehensive list starting at £20.95, with many by the glass.

Chef/s: Luke Taylor. **Meals:** main courses £15 to £33. Set L and D £22 (2 courses) to £25. Sun L £22 (2 courses) to £27. **Details:** 120 seats. 20 seats outside. Bar. Wheelchairs. Music. Parking.

Todmorden

The White Rabbit

Cooking score: 2
Modern British | £35
1 White Hart Fold, Todmorden, OL14 7BD
Tel no: (01706) 817828
whiterabbittodmorden.com
£5 OFF

The Pennine town of Todmorden is becoming quite the gastronomic redoubt, with an award-winning market and enthusiastic local participation in the Incredible Edible local food movement. David and Robyn Gledhill play their part, too, at the White Rabbit, where references to Lewis Carroll are never far away. In 2017, the kitchen went to tasting menus as standard, at five or eight courses. These change monthly, but might offer goat's brie with roast butternut and date crumb, ahead of chicken and ham hock risotto with pea cream and chicken-skin crisps, and desserts such as white chocolate and passion fruit gâteau. Reports suggest the longer menu, perhaps including seared scallop with smoked haddock cream and samphire potatoes, or beef fillet in Choron sauce – has the more convincing balance overall. There are vegetarian versions, too. A short wine list opens at £17.50.

Chef/s: David and Robyn Gledhill. **Closed:** Sun, Mon, Tue. **Meals:** tasting menu £25 (5 courses) to £55. **Details:** 22 seats. V menu. Music.

Wetherby

LOCAL GEM

Mango

Indian Vegetarian | £25

12-14 Bank Street, Wetherby, LS22 6NQ
Tel no: (01937) 585755
mangovegetarian.com

Hidden down a side street off Wetherby's main drag, and originally two stone cottages, this modern vegetarian restaurant focuses on the aromatic cooking of southern India. As well as being meat-free, it has a wide range of vegan and gluten-free dishes to set it apart from your average local curry house. Start, perhaps, with cassava spheres of coconut, sesame seeds and green chilli, then move on to a main course of palak ringhan (spinach and aubergine in light tomato curry sauce). Finish with chocolate pistachio cake. Wines from £18.

Whitby

Bridge Cottage Bistro

Cooking score: 3
Modern British | £30

East Row, Sandsend, Whitby, YO21 3SU
Tel no: (01947) 893438
bridgecottagebistro.com

Alex Perkins' likeable cottage eatery close to Sandsend beach has steadily upped its game, morphing from a café-style refuelling point for the nearby B&B to a full-blown daytime bistro, with dinner three nights a week. Inside, it's a cheery blend of Verner Panton chairs, mirrors and white tiles, with blackboards spelling out the day's menu. Expect a roster of creative, confident dishes underpinned by bold seasonal flavours, from Yellison goat's cheese in familiar company with heritage beetroot and walnuts to whole roast partridge with chanterelles, thyme and nut-brown butter. Steaks and pheasant pie satisfy larger appetites, although fish from the Whitby boats is the real standout – perhaps torched mackerel with forced Yorkshire rhubarb or roast monkfish with Tenderstem broccoli, tartare hollandaise and bacon crumb. Brunch and afternoon tea fill in the gaps, while 'slow-cooked Sunday' deals might bring roast pork belly with salt-baked celeriac followed by sticky toffee pudding. Wines from £17.95.

Chef/s: Alexander Perkins. **Closed:** Mon. **Meals:** main courses £10 to £18. Sun L £16 (2 courses). Tasting menu £38 (8 courses). **Details:** 26 seats. 20 seats outside. Music. Parking.

LOCAL GEM

Magpie Cafe

Seafood | £25

14 Pier Road, Whitby, YO21 3PU
Tel no: (01947) 602058
magpiecafe.co.uk

Form an orderly queue! Following a devastating fire in 2017, this harbourfront legend is back in business, much to the delight of its many fans. The Magpie was always a bit old-fashioned (in a good way) and despite a complete refurbishment nothing seems to have changed, right down to finding the same sort of swirly carpet. Come for fresh fish and seafood: 'rich, deeply flavoured' sea bass with tomato and bean cassoulet, 'flawless' scallops with beetroot, goat's curd and honeycomb, crayfish and lobster fettucine and, of course, classic, beautifully battered fish and chips. Is the wait worth it? Yes it is.

York

The Bistro at Walmgate Ale House

Cooking score: 2
International | £26
25 Walmgate, York, YO1 9TX
Tel no: (01904) 629222
walmgateale.co.uk

Michael Hjort's reinvention of Melton's Too as a thoroughly traditional alehouse-cum-bistro continues to evolve, with a new bar billiards table added to the games room at the back of the pub. If you're not interested in (Yorkshire) beer and skittles, head upstairs for some capably rendered European food backed by a modest selection of eminently drinkable wines. Blackboard specials play a big part here, although the regular menu is full of good things – from wild mushroom tart or coronation guinea fowl in filo pastry to twice-baked cheese soufflé, bowls of bouillabaisse or slow-cooked confit duck served on an old-style bean and sausage cassoulet topped with breadcrumbs. Desserts are also a sturdy bunch, from spiced apple sponge with custard to sticky toffee pudding or chocolate sundae with a chocolate brownie on the side. Set menus are outstanding value, and the bistro also does a good line in Sunday roasts.

Chef/s: Michael Hjort. **Closed:** Mon, 25 and 26 Dec, 31 Dec and 1 Jan. **Meals:** main courses £14 to £20. Set L and D £16 (2 courses) to £18. Sun L £18. **Details:** 110 seats. Bar. Wheelchairs. Music.

Le Cochon Aveugle

Cooking score: 4
French | £60
37 Walmgate, York, YO1 9TX
Tel no: (01904) 640222
lecochonaveugleyork.com

One reader who was taken on a birthday 'mystery tour' through his native Yorkshire was pleasantly surprised to end up at this idiosyncratic eatery in York. With its bare tables, high ambitions and come-as-you-please demeanour, Le Cochon Aveugle ('the blind pig') embraces the spirit of the Parisian bistronomy movement, gives it a spin and pulls out a no-choice, eight-course tasting menu in the modern French mode. Joshua Overington is full of surprises, offering boudin noir macarons as nibbles, matching smoked eel with Jerusalem artichoke and hispi cabbage, adding some 'tasty paste relish' to a plate of local duck breast with heritage beetroots, and even embellishing Yorkshire's sacred rhubarb with yoghurt whey sorbet and lovage granita. There's a resourceful lineup for vegetarians (think nasturtium ice cream with onion squash velouté), and each dish comes with an appropriate wine pairing. A new private dining room now occupies Le Cochon's first floor, and the owners also run the Cave du Cochon wine bar at 19 Walmgate.

Chef/s: Joshua Overington. **Closed:** Sun, Mon, 23 Dec to 8 Jan. **Meals:** set D £60 (8 courses). **Details:** 30 seats. V menu. Bar. Music. Children over 10 yrs.

Melton's

Cooking score: 5
Modern British | £42
7 Scarcroft Road, York, YO23 1ND
Tel no: (01904) 634341
meltonsrestaurant.co.uk
£5 OFF

Michael and Lucy Hjort's bistro would be an asset to many high streets, but it belongs happily to Bishy Road, the street recently rendered as a mural in the upstairs dining room. Readers rate Melton's as a 'fantastic local restaurant with something different at every visit'. As the owners approach 30 years in business, the confident hospitality of the place is paired with a menu that cherry-picks from current trends: pickled daikon and apple served with celery and Gruyère rarebit; yeasted cauliflower starring alongside rump and short rib of rare-breed beef. Local produce is subtly evident throughout. The kitchen can't go wrong with Whitby crab, East Coast cod or, in season, Yorkshire rhubarb. Soufflés are a mainstay of the dessert menu, which aims to please with flourishes such as cumin caramel garnishing a chocolate parfait. Service is every bit as capable as you'd hope, with warmth to spare, and the French-leaning wine list has good-value selections from the South West.

Chef/s: Michael Hjort and Calvin Miller. **Closed:** Sun, Mon, 2 weeks from 24 Dec. **Meals:** set L and early D £28 (2 courses) to £32. Set D £34 (2 courses) to £42. Tasting menu £55 (5 courses) to £60. **Details:** 40 seats. Music. No children after 8pm.

The Park

Cooking score: 3
Modern British | £60

Marmadukes Town House Hotel, 4-5 St Peter's Grove, York, YO30 6AQ
Tel no: (01904) 540903
marmadukestownhousehotelyork.com

The Victorian townhouse hotel Marmadukes, a little way outside York's medieval city walls, utters 'boutique' in the most tasteful way possible, and is home to The Park, housed in a softly hued conservatory. Here, Adam Jackson's principal offering is a seven-course evening taster, supplemented by a four-course-plus-wines deal for midweek evenings. Modern British dishes presented with panache offer plenty of neatly counterpointing flavours, from balsamic-dressed burrata with beetroot, through mackerel with sour cream and caviar, on to Indian-spiced scallop with carrot and coriander. Main courses might offer succulent beef with ham and mushrooms, ahead of a pair of desserts, perhaps chocolate, yuzu and honey, and then – what else? – Yorkshire rhubarb with blood orange and smoked almonds. The shorter menu might turn on a main dish of poussin with leeks and hen of the woods. There's Yorkshire rhubarb gin, too, made in Harrogate, as well as a short list of well-chosen wines.

Chef/s: Adam Jackson. **Closed:** Sun, Mon, 26 to 28 Dec, first 2 weeks Jan. **Meals:** set D Tue to Thur and set L Wed and Sat £45 (4 courses). Tasting menu £65 (7 courses). **Details:** 28 seats. V menu. Bar. Music. Parking. Children over 12 yrs.

★ NEW ENTRY ★

Partisan

Cooking score: 4
Modern British | £35

112 Micklegate, York, YO1 6JX
Tel no: (01904) 629866
partisanuk.com

This distinctive arrival on blossoming Micklegate is principally a daytime café with a rustic ambience, serving imaginative brunches and lunches featuring Persian eggs, deliciously scrambled with spinach, dates, yoghurt and spices, or eggs Benedict, the latter according to one visitor 'the best poached eggs I've ever eaten'. Another comes every day for their Korean bibimbap. In the evenings (Thursday to Saturday) chef James Gilroy puts together a more ambitious menu of globally inspired dishes that might include sea bream ceviche or mallard with fried plantain. Vegetables are given proper respect, as in roast carrots with yoghurt, dill and za'atar, or a salad of raw Jerusalem artichokes and orange. Desserts come from a tempting display of cakes made in-house, and the drinks list includes non-alcoholic Seedlip and a brightly edited wine list with a respectable Merlot at £5 a glass. The brains behind this imaginative enterprise are owners Hugo Hildyard and Florencia Clifford, who cook, as they say, 'with attention, compassion and awareness'. We're inclined to agree.

Chef/s: James Gilroy. **Closed:** 25 and 26 Dec, 1 Jan. **Meals:** main courses £16 to £18. **Details:** 48 seats. 20 seats outside. Wheelchairs. Music.

The Rattle Owl

Cooking score: 3
Modern British | £35
104 Micklegate, York, YO1 6JX
Tel no: (01904) 658658
rattleowl.co.uk

There's no doubt that Clarrie O' Callaghan's 'very attractive' restaurant is an asset to lovely, cobbled Micklegate. The listed building dates from the 17th century, though it stands on Roman remains, found during renovation, which have been incorporated into the wine cellar. Chef Jamie Hall has created something special with his contemporary, ingredient-driven British style. Seasonality is everything, as seen in dishes from buttered mussels and clams with Jerusalem artichoke, almonds and samphire to fillet of sea trout with beetroot, orange and celery. Hall knows how to pack in flavour, teaming East Coast crab with avocado and razor clam salad, or slow-cooked beef featherblade and smoked fillet with salt-baked turnip, cavolo nero, roast garlic and shallot. Puddings, too, show flair: a chocolate tart with clementine, orange ice cream, poached pear and passion fruit provides a luscious finish. Service is pitched so that no customer feels unloved. As for drinks, there are cocktails and mostly organic wines, which suit the food admirably.

Chef/s: Jamie Hall. **Closed:** Mon, Tue, 1 week after New Year. **Meals:** main courses £17 to £22. Set L £20. Set early D £16 (2 courses) to £21. Sun L £20. **Details:** 42 seats. Bar. Wheelchairs. Music.

Skosh

Cooking score: 4
Modern British | £25
98 Micklegate, York, YO1 6JX
Tel no: (01904) 634849
skoshyork.co.uk

Since it opened in 2016, Skosh (meaning 'small' in Japanese) has quickly established itself as one of the hottest tickets in York. Neil Bentinck's punchy menu of small plates may have an Asian influence, but the raw materials are predominantly local. Dishes are listed in order of size and price, kicking off with an appetiser of beetroots, rhubarb, basil ricotta and green tea, before moving on to Goosnargh duck liver mousse with passion fruit and apple chutney and miso baguette. Further down the list, more main-sized dishes include chargrilled Galician octopus with peanut and watermelon, and crisp pork belly with vindaloo sauce, pickled carrots and yoghurt rice. End with a rum-spiced milk and quince jam doughnut, or a savoury finale of Gorgonzola dolce, burnt apple, celery and walnuts. To drink, a concise wine list (from £20), seasonal cocktails and a range of international craft ales and ciders.

Chef/s: Neil Bentinck. **Closed:** Mon, Tue, 25 and 26 Dec, 1 week Jan, 1 week May, 2 weeks Sept. **Meals:** small plates £4 to £16. **Details:** 38 seats. Music.

The Star Inn the City

Cooking score: 1
Modern British | £40
Lendal Engine House, Museum Street, York, YO1 7DR
Tel no: (01904) 619208
starinnthecity.co.uk

In a 'tourist honeypot' between Lendal Bridge and the Museum Gardens, this city offshoot of the Star Inn at Harome (see entry) makes the most of its location – especially in fine weather, when terrace tables overlooking the river are in high demand. Proceedings open with breakfast before the all-day repertoire

delivers its take on reinvented Yorkshire heritage food. Rhubarb gets its own celebratory menu when in season, and you can also expect Whitby crab cocktail, Beverley-reared duck hash or Rievaulx gamekeeper's toad-in-the-hole with braised red cabbage. To drink, there's unpasteurised Pilsner Urquell straight from the tank, plus gins galore and around 20 commendable wines by the glass.
Chef/s: Matt Hunter. **Closed:** 25 and 26 Dec, 1 Jan. **Meals:** main courses £14 to £32. Set L and D Mon to Fri £17 (2 courses) to £22. **Details:** 125 seats. 52 seats outside. Bar. Wheelchairs. Music.

LOCAL GEM

The Greenhouse Tearoom

Modern British | £15

Vertigrow, Lawnswood House, Malton Rd, York, YO32 9TL
Tel no: (01904) 400082
vertigrow.co.uk

Amid the foliage and greenery of a garden centre on the outskirts of the city, this simple tea room could easily be mistaken for an unassuming domestic conservatory. But there's skill in the kitchen, as can be seen in lunches of Yorkshire rarebit, hot filled sandwiches, well-sourced ploughman's platter, and salads – say garlic and chilli tiger prawns with avocado purée and pink grapefruit. There's moreish homemade bread and a good selection of fresh baked cakes for afternoon tea. Unlicensed.

LOCAL GEM

Mannion & Co

Modern European | £20

1 Blake Street, York, YO1 8QJ
Tel no: (01904) 631030
mannionandco.co.uk

With cheese and charcuterie displayed on the deli counter, plus a table loaded with home-baked breads, pies and pastries, this no-bookings café-cum-bakery is a veritable cornucopia of artisan provisions. However, Mannion & Co's prowess also extends to a daily blackboard menu of rustic dishes ranging from duck liver parfait with red onion and apple to a ragù of spiced lamb and white beans with dukkah. After that, try the spiced orange cake with blood orange and cardamom. Wines from £19.50. There's an offshoot at 5 Castlegate, Helmsley, YO62 5AB.

SCOTLAND

Borders, Dumfries & Galloway,
Lothians (inc. Edinburgh),
Strathclyde (inc. Glasgow), Central, Fife,
Tayside, Grampian, Highlands & Islands

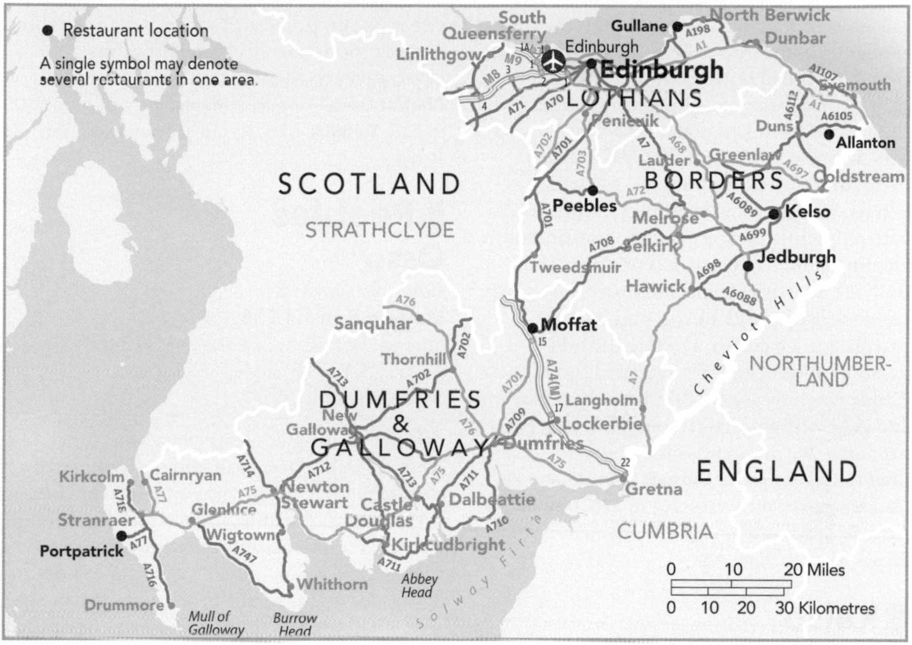

Allanton

Allanton Inn

Cooking score: 2

Modern British | £28

Main Street, Allanton, TD11 3JZ
Tel no: (01890) 818260
allantoninn.co.uk

Any traditional village pub that delivers a little something extra will attract travellers and delight locals. The Allanton Inn's restaurant-style layout boasts an open fire and fresh flowers, and its rightly popular Sunday lunch draws regular family gatherings. A starter sharing platter gives a taster of the chef's eclectic influences – five-spiced duck breast, local hot-smoked salmon and Serrano ham croquettes all marry well with a punchy tomato relish. Main courses take a more traditional approach with a 'well-prepared and generously portioned' rare lamb rump and haggis bonbon atop caramelised cauliflower, redolent with the roasting pan juices. Indulgently rich desserts might see a witty transformation of lemon meringue pie into cheesecake guise. Service is 'informal and perfectly pleasant'. Local beers and a short wine list offer adequate accompaniments.

Chef/s: Katrina Reynolds. **Closed:** 25 to 27 Dec. **Meals:** main courses £13 to £25. **Details:** 40 seats. 50 seats outside. Bar. Music.

Jedburgh

The Caddy Mann

Cooking score: 2

Modern British | £25

Mounthooly, Jedburgh, TD8 6TJ
Tel no: (01835) 850787
caddymann.com

Run as a lunchtime bistro (with suppers two evenings a week), Lynne and Ross Horrocks' neighbourhood restaurant feels decidedly retro with its paper napkins stuffed into wine glasses and random knick-knacks dotted around the dining room. Ross packs his daily menus with local and seasonal ingredients and applies well-tutored technique to everything from rare-breed pork to Borders beef and game: consider breast of pigeon with poached rhubarb and smoked pheasant croquette or a dish of pan-roast hare fillet with roe deer meatballs, braised shallots and red wine jus. Elsewhere, East Coast haddock comes boozily battered, while burgers and wraps suit those wanting something quick. For afters, stay with the Scottish theme and order the Selkirk bannock bread-and-butter pud with marmalade ice cream. Despite the odd grumble about clumsily executed food, The Caddy Mann is personable, homely, appealing and generous with its flavours. Local beers support a decent, gently priced wine list.

Chef/s: Ross Horrocks. **Closed:** Mon, 25 and 26 Dec. **Meals:** main courses £14 to £26. **Details:** 40 seats. 30 seats outside. V menu. Vg menu. Wheelchairs. Parking.

Kelso

The Cobbles

Cooking score: 2

Modern British | £27

7 Bowmont Street, Kelso, TD5 7JH
Tel no: (01573) 223548
thecobbleskelso.co.uk

'Freehouse & Dining' sums up this tap house of the Tempest Brewing Co to a tee. Found just off the town's main square, there could be six or so of those beers at the pumps (Elemental Dark Ale, maybe), as well as a gently contemporary interior with real fires and plenty of tables for dining – the food here is modern pub classics done well. Prime steaks get their own menu – Aberdeen Angus 7oz thick rib from Hardiesmill, say – while prime Scottish ingredients play their part in daytime sandwiches, in classic burgers and in fish and chips. Daily specials raise the bar, with the likes of tempura samphire with garlic aïoli, or curried roast cauliflower with caper and raisin purée, and pan-seared Scottish salmon with miso and mirin noodles. Desserts bring joy in the shape of dark chocolate fondant with sweet potato purée and stracciatella ice cream. A short food-friendly wine list offers alternatives to those local ales.

Chef/s: Daniel Norcliffe. **Meals:** main courses £10 to £30. **Details:** 60 seats. 16 seats outside. Bar. Music.

Peebles

Osso

Cooking score: 2

Modern British | £35

Innerleithen Road, Peebles, EH45 8BA
Tel no: (01721) 724477
ossorestaurant.com

An unassuming-looking place near the church, Osso covers just about every base in the hospitality repertoire, opening for late breakfasts and brunches, then gliding through a lunch session, with dinner following up five nights a week, and outside catering to boot. The place opens up in surprisingly expansive style inside, with laminate floor and unclothed tables, to make a relaxed setting for appealing modern bistro cooking. The evening might offer scallops with chicken risotto in brown butter with capers and lemon, and then local pork with pickled kohlrabi, carrot purée and spruce oil, perhaps with a side of truffly chips draped in Parmesan. Finish with dark chocolate crémeux, poached pear and tonka ice cream. Appealing lunchtime propositions include a fishcake with creamed leeks and dulse, while early birds start the day with the house take on a bacon sandwich that incorporates Monterey Jack and hot chilli jam. House Chileans are £19.

Chef/s: Ally McGrath. **Closed:** 25 Dec, 1 Jan. **Meals:** main courses £17 to £24. Set D £22 (2 courses) to £28. **Details:** 37 seats. 4 seats outside. Wheelchairs. Music.

Moffat

The Limetree

Cooking score: 1

Modern British | £29

Hartfell House, Hartfell Crescent, Moffat, DG10 9AL
Tel no: (01683) 220153
hartfellhouse.co.uk

The dining room of this rather dour Victorian mansion is plain verging on austere with wooden tables, wood floor, bright lights and little in the way of warmth. Thankfully, compensation comes from Matt Seddon's assured cooking and his short menu of solid British dishes. A risotto of smoked haddock with asparagus and dill to start was delicate and flavourful, while a pork terrine was enlivened with an excellent celeriac coleslaw. Simply grilled lemon sole followed with nicely matched Jersey potatoes, mint and pea purée, chargrilled courgette and beautifully cooked fennel with flavours of lemon. Local Annanwater hogget rump had seriously deep flavour served alongside a sharply flavoured shepherd's pie giving a hint of spice. From desserts that included lemon and ginger sponge, pear and honey parfait we chose a pleasing warm chocolate pot with brazil nut shortbread. In all, reliable, conscientious cooking. Wines from £17.

Chef/s: Matt Seddon. **Closed:** Sun, Mon, 24 to 26 Dec, 10 days Jan, 10 days Oct. **Meals:** set D £25 to 29 (3 courses). **Details:** 24 seats. Wheelchairs. Music. Parking.

Portpatrick

Knockinaam Lodge

Cooking score: 4

Modern British | £70

Portpatrick, DG9 9AD
Tel no: (01776) 810471
knockinaamlodge.com

This former hunting lodge three miles south of Portpatrick is hard to beat for traditional comfort and off-grid seclusion, situated at the end of a winding lane and surrounded by neat lawns, a charming boathouse and its own private beach. With luck you could find yourself with a table in the bay window with mesmerising views of the sea and diving terns. Tony Pierce offers a set menu at lunch and dinner of four or five elegant courses which, on inspection, brought asparagus and chervil soup elevated with a splash of white truffle oil; accurately poached local brill with samphire and a red pepper emulsion; then a generous rump of Galloway lamb with rosemary jus; and dessert of white, milk and dark chocolate terrine with lime sorbet. A comprehensive wine list with helpful tasting notes starts at £23 and the sense of Scottish heritage is exemplified by the panelled whisky bar with its range of 120 single malts.

Chef/s: Tony Pierce. **Meals:** set L £40 (4 courses). Set D £70 (5 courses). Sun L £40 (5 courses). **Details:** 20 seats. Bar. Wheelchairs. Music. Parking. Children over 12 yrs at D.

Send us your review

Your feedback informs the content of the *GFG* and will be used to compile next year's reviews. To register your opinion about any restaurant listed in the Guide, or a restaurant that you wish to bring to our attention, visit: thegoodfoodguide.co.uk/feedback

Edinburgh

Aizle

Cooking score: 4

Modern British | £55

107-109 St Leonard's Street, Edinburgh, EH8 9QY
Tel no: (0131) 662 9349
aizle.co.uk

'This is what eating out should be about,' mused one reader, thrilled by the 'outstanding' cooking at this minimal bistro. Aizle, which means glowing ember or spark in old Scots, has a no-choice blackboard menu of six courses, and what arrives on the plate is a superb mix of natural produce and modern cooking techniques. Start with an array of snacks, tiny mouthfuls such as potato dauphine with seaweed, or sourdough brioche with crab butter. Everything is made in-house, so expect the likes of beetroot and venison, fired up with Aizle's own yuzu kosho (a fermented Japanese chilli paste), or short rib of Borders beef with coffee and maple. Handsome bowls, plates and slates serve to enhance the delightful presentation. Fermentation works its magic again on koji-cured veal, with parsley root and cherry mustard, while desserts are fresh-tasting and full of zing. A few cocktails and Scottish beers back up the well-judged wine list.

Chef/s: Stuart Ralston. **Closed:** Sun, Mon, Tue, 25 Dec to 23 Jan, 4 to 18 Jul. **Meals:** set D £55 (6 courses). **Details:** 36 seats. V menu. Wheelchairs. Music. No children after 10pm.

Angels with Bagpipes

Cooking score: 4

Modern British | £40

343 High Street, Royal Mile, Edinburgh, EH1 1PW
Tel no: (0131) 220 1111
angelswithbagpipes.co.uk

Edinburgh's famously roisterous Royal Mile is an unlikely spot for a refined, modern restaurant, but Angels continues to be a tasteful retreat. The discreet entrance buried among the souvenir shops reveals two long narrow dining rooms divided by the pass – in fashionable grey and copper with a fetching statue of a bagpipe-playing angel above the staircase. The menu matches the interior for elegance and prices are pleasantly modest. At inspection, starters of smoked salmon garnished with cucumber, avocado, dill and buckwheat, and a fresh young goat's cheese with beetroot, verjus, crushed walnuts and poppy seeds impressed. A well-judged lemon sole was served on the bone with brown butter, capers and a squeeze of lemon. An imaginative dish of grilled polenta with ricotta, grilled cauliflower, Swiss chard and pumpkin seed also stood out, while desserts maintained the quality and substance of the rest of the menu. A thoughtful wine list starts at £23 for organic Verdejo.

Chef/s: Alister Munro. **Closed:** 24 to 26 Dec, 2 weeks Jan. **Meals:** main courses £16 to £32. Set L £18 (2 courses) to £22. Set D £32 (2 courses) to £40. Tasting menu £40. **Details:** 75 seats. 11 seats outside. V menu. Vg menu. Wheelchairs. Music.

Cafe St Honoré

Cooking score: 4

Modern European | £40

34 North West Thistle Street Lane, Edinburgh, EH2 1EA
Tel no: (0131) 226 2211
cafesthonore.com

£5 OFF

'We like the *fin de siècle* feel of this place,' noted one reader with a soft spot for Neil Forbes' long-serving Edinburgh bistro, which could be straight out of a Parisian arrondissement, right down to its liqueur-stocked bar, chequerboard floors, distressed mirrors and quirky cartoons. The cooking also has a pronounced French accent, although there are plenty of name-checked Scottish ingredients (many of them organic). An 'absolutely spot-on' dish of Perthshire pigeon accompanied by Waldorf salad is typical, although the kitchen's repertoire takes it all the way from blade of beef with beer-braised onions, Arran mustard mash and savoy cabbage to Scrabster cod and Shetland blue-shell mussels in leek and fennel chowder. Cheeses are local heroes, while desserts could feature warm almond and orange cake alongside peaty Benromach whisky ice cream. To drink, crusading Scottish beers mingle with a healthy contingent of organic wines.

Chef/s: Neil Forbes and Joe Simpson. **Closed:** 24 to 26 Dec, 1 Jan. **Meals:** main courses £17 to £23. Set L £15 (2 courses) to £19. Set D £20 (2 courses) to £26. **Details:** 45 seats. Music.

Cannonball

Cooking score: 2

Modern British | £34

Cannonball House, 356 Castlehill, Edinburgh, EH1 2NE

Tel no: (0131) 225 1550

contini.com

Taking its lead from the Contini family's self-named flagship on George Street (see entry), this upmarket offshoot comes with the added bonus of a luxe whisky bar. The name references an old cannonball lodged in the outer wall of the premises, but there's nothing archaic or touristy about the style or indeed the culinary focus here – despite the location right by Edinburgh Castle. Native oysters, lobsters and dry-aged beef get top billing, but you might also encounter a gratin of Isle of Mull scallops topped with seaweed and citrus crumb, pigeon (cooked rare) with crème fraîche, mint, pomegranate and lime, or braised and pressed beef cheeks with confit red onions. Haggis 'cannonballs', venison sausages and battered fish strike a more traditional note, while puds could feature chocolate and orange mousse with hazelnut praline and lime cream. Wines from £23.

Chef/s: Marcin Medrygal. **Closed:** Sun, Mon, 25 and 26 Dec, 2 weeks Jan. **Meals:** main courses £14 to £32. Set L £15 (2 courses) to £19. Tasting menu £45 (5 courses). **Details:** 70 seats. 6 seats outside. V menu. Bar. Wheelchairs. Music.

★ TOP 50 ★

Castle Terrace

Cooking score: 7

Modern French | £70

33-35 Castle Terrace, Edinburgh, EH1 2EL

Tel no: (0131) 229 1222

castleterracerestaurant.com

'Big, contemporary, spacious, smart', Dominic Jack's restaurant in the shadows of Edinburgh Castle comes from the same stable as The Kitchin (see entry) and draws an appreciative crowd with an appealing modern menu. Prime ingredients lay a secure foundation, evident in a starter of tartare of Shetland salmon served sushi-style with wasabi ice cream. Clear flavours and attractive presentation form part of the deal, as in another opener of first-class scallops in a creamy curry sauce. Dishes can be complex, requiring serious skill in the kitchen, but what is promised is delivered: Jack's famous take on paella – exquisite seafood served on a risotto of spelt – or a pillow of perfectly timed cod with a brown crab bisque and minestrone of vegetables are both note-perfect renditions. Assured and considered meat dishes might include tender, tasty roasted rump of Inverurie lamb served with exemplary smoked aubergine, fennel and basil gnocchi. Desserts, meanwhile, run to a benchmark coffee soufflé with mascarpone ice cream, and a flawless dark chocolate and orange délice, its richness offset by an orange sorbet. Extras are on a par, from excellent bread to fine petits fours, while staff are knowledgeable and professional. There's serious dedication to drink too. The wine list is a roll call of fine vintages, with its roots in France, all handled with great insight by the sommelier.

Chef/s: Dominic Jack. **Closed:** Sun, Mon, 25 Dec to 14 Jan, 3 to 7 Apr, 24 to 28 Jul, 9 to 13 Oct. **Meals:** set L £33. Set D £70 (3 courses). Tasting menu £80 (7 courses). **Details:** 75 seats. V menu. Bar. Wheelchairs. Music. Children over 5 yrs.

Contini

Cooking score: 2

Italian | £35

103 George Street, Edinburgh, EH2 3ES
Tel no: (0131) 225 1550
contini.com

Carina and Victor Contini's flagship Italian – they also have Cannonball (see entry) and the Scottish restaurant at the National Gallery – has always had glamour, having inherited the soaring columns and decorative ceilings of this former banking hall. Now with an expensive refurbishment it's looking even more flamboyant with chandeliers, cherubs and a feature wall of Renaissance-style frescoes. But there's no need to whisper in church, it remains a fun, accessible, family-friendly trattoria. The new menu is familiar, too, with an à la carte that includes top arancini, beef carpaccio, pasta dishes – like the perennial favourite of orecchiette pasta with sausage, porcini and fresh cream – and mains of Isle of Mull scallops with peas or, new this year, a selection of smaller, lighter dishes to share. A refreshed wine list offers some 50 plus Italian wines.

Chef/s: Carina Contini. **Closed:** 25 and 26 Dec. **Meals:** main courses £15 to £32. Set L and early D £16. Set D £35. **Details:** 120 seats. 30 seats outside. Bar. Wheelchairs. Music.

Dishoom

Cooking score: 2

Indian | £30

3 St Andrew Square, Edinburgh, EH2 2BD
Tel no: (0131) 202 6406
dishoom.com

Facing on to the city's grand old St Andrew Square, and spread across three floors of a handsome period building, this is the first branch of this independent-minded chain to open outside London (see entries). The artwork on the walls references Scottish botanist Sir Patrick Geddes whose links to Bombay in the early 20th century chime with Dishoom's culinary inspiration – the Irani cafés of old Mumbai. The first-floor restaurant and ground floor with open-to-view kitchen are open all day for Anglo-Indian tucker – perhaps bacon naan roll for breakfast, an afternoon snack of prawn koliwada, or the full menu of chargrilled meats and slow-cooked biryanis. Expect spot-on spicing throughout, whether you start with keema pau (spiced mince and peas on a toasted bun) or crispy coated calamari, before salli boti, a tender dish of lamb that's exclusive to this branch. Cocktails, cooling lassis and house IPA keep the drinks list on-message and the basement bar, The Permit Room, is open from 5pm.

Chef/s: Naved Nasir. **Closed:** 25 and 26 Dec, 1 and 2 Jan. **Meals:** main courses £8 to £13. **Details:** 156 seats. Vg menu. Bar. Wheelchairs. Music.

Field

Cooking score: 2

Modern British | £28

41 West Nicolson Street, Edinburgh, EH8 9DB
Tel no: (0131) 667 7010
fieldrestaurant.co.uk

'Definitely an old favourite,' says a reader who loves the 'candlelit intimacy' of this tiny one-room restaurant in the heart of Edinburgh's student quarter. In the kitchen, Scottish ingredients are treated with a degree of contemporary verve that yields some impressively satisfying results – note a 'gutsy' duck ballotine with spiced apple chutney and onion seed lavash, a 'deconstructed stir-fry' involving braised pork belly, pak choi, wild rice 'crispies' and soba noodles, or sourdough-crusted cod on chorizo and bean cassoulet. Game dishes are also worth serious consideration in season (venison haunch with Jerusalem artichoke purée, purple kale and red berry jus, for example), while carrot cheesecake with carrot purée and walnut brittle takes pride of place as the signature dessert. Lunch and pre-theatre menus are deemed 'very good value', and the thoughtfully curated global wine list spells out the owners' philosophy with its bias towards small indie growers, terroir and organic production.

Chef/s: David Louwrens. **Closed:** Sun, Mon, 25 and 26 Dec, 1 week Jan, 2 weeks Sept. **Meals:** main courses £13 to £19. Set L and early D £14 (2 courses) to £17. **Details:** 22 seats. Music.

Fishers Leith

Cooking score: 1

Seafood | £30

1 The Shore, Leith, Edinburgh, EH6 6QW
Tel no: (0131) 554 5666
fishersrestaurantgroup.co.uk

The original of three Fishers restaurants is housed in a 17th-century watchtower on Leith's waterfront. Kitted out in full maritime regalia, it retains a loyal clientele for its aesthetically pleasing plates of seafood. Expect confidently cooked bistro-style dishes, perhaps Arbroath smokie with cod and herb fritters and green pea tartare to start, followed by Peterhead coley fillet with polenta chips, clack pudding and wild garlic pesto or a chilled seafood platter. The set menu is superb value for money and puddings are of a homely persuasion. Score a nook in the wood-panelled Shore Bar next door where you can expect live jazz and heartier plates of food.
Chef/s: Andrew Bird. **Meals:** main courses £14 to £27. Set L £15 (2 courses) to £18. **Details.** 40 seats. 12 seats outside. Bar.

★ LOCAL RESTAURANT AWARD ★
REGIONAL WINNER

Forage & Chatter

Cooking score: 4

Modern British | £30

1a Alva Street, Edinburgh, EH2 4PH
Tel no: (0131) 225 4599
forageandchatter.com

Rough wooden tables, pot plants and a touch of contemporary tartan delivers just the right amount of rustic charm to this modern Scottish restaurant tucked away in a West End basement. We can confirm the consistently good reports from readers of 'excellent value for money' and 'an absolute delight' based on a generous plate of cured salmon served with oyster mayonnaise, dill and seaweed with added explosions of flavour from salmon roe. An original combination of chargrilled cauliflower with dates and capers also impressed at inspection. Loin of lamb was accurately cooked and, together with a slow-cooked patty of lamb shoulder, was doubly successful. It came with fried sweetbreads, wild garlic and a pleasing smokiness from chargrilled baby gem lettuce. Chocolate mousse with malt ice cream and a plate of Scottish cheeses completed an excellent meal. Wines start at a reasonable £19.50.
Chef/s: Liam Massie. **Closed:** Sun, Mon, 25 and 26 Dec. **Meals:** main courses £15 to £22. Set L £16 (2 courses) to £19. **Details:** 44 seats. Music.

Galvin Brasserie de Luxe

Cooking score: 3

French | £40

Waldorf Astoria Edinburgh – The Caledonian, Princes Street, Edinburgh, EH1 2AB
Tel no: (0131) 222 8988
galvinbrasseriedeluxe.com

Located in the flamboyantly restored Caledonian Hotel, this brasserie from Chris and Jeff Galvin has all the Gallic swagger we've come to expect from the brothers although the dining room's Parisian-style fixtures and fittings are almost eclipsed by a dramatic central counter piled high with crustacea. Enjoy a plate of seafood preceded by a 'well-herbed salad' or cherry-pick from the carte – perhaps duck and fig terrine with pineapple chutney followed by some Scottish beef or Spey Valley venison with beetroot, celeriac, chanterelles and chocolate. After that, the apple crumble soufflé with apple sorbet is reckoned to be an 'interesting' possibility. Everyone is as helpful as can be, judging by one diner's appreciative comments: 'the lobster eaters didn't feel strong enough to do the work with picks and shovels, so the chef kindly removed the shell for us'. French wines 'on tap' kick off a comprehensive global list.
Chef/s: Jamie Knox. **Meals:** main courses £16 to £33. Set L and D £19 (2 courses) to £25. Sun L £24. **Details:** 160 seats. Wheelchairs. Music. Parking.

The Gardener's Cottage

Cooking score: 2

Modern British | £40

1 Royal Terrace Gardens, London Road, Edinburgh, EH7 5DX
Tel no: (0131) 558 1221
thegardenerscottage.co

True to its name, this rustic Georgian cottage was once home to the gardener for the surrounding Royal Terrace Gardens. Under its low roof sits a schoolroom-style space with long communal tables – a simple, pared-back look befitting the uncluttered feel of the menu, which majors on beautiful heritage ingredients prepared with minimal intervention. Lunch is a regular à la carte while dinner brings five or seven courses. Typical of the style is a nibble of crispy Perthshire organic chicken skin with North Sea Stout mayonnaise, then local mackerel tartare with pepper dulse, fennel cracker and gooseberry. Nettle soup with local bacon might be followed by organic lamb loin with neck terrine, Pink Fir Apples, yoghurt and groats. This is honest, heartfelt cooking with a strong sense of place, right through to a thoroughly Scottish dessert of strawberry, custard, sweet cicely and oats. There's a decent selection of wines by the carafe or glass.

Chef/s: Dale Mailley and Edward Murray. **Meals:** main courses £12 to £25. Set D £40 (5 courses) to £60. **Details:** 30 seats. Music.

★ TOP 50 ★

The Kitchin

Cooking score: 7

Modern British | £75

78 Commercial Quay, Leith, Edinburgh, EH6 6LX
Tel no: (0131) 555 1755
thekitchin.com

'Clearly, Tom Kitchin is doing lots of things very well indeed,' noted one satisfied visitor to this former whisky warehouse on Leith's re-energised waterfront. Graciously appointed, with striking stone walls, pillars and girders, the dining room makes a suitable backdrop for menus that change punctiliously with the seasons. Thankfully, the chef's near-obsessive dedication to sourcing is never at the expense of flavour or creativity, especially when it comes to fish: his 'rockpool' of local seafood and sea vegetables in a shellfish consommé has acquired near-legendary status, while other ideas roll with the catch – perhaps poached Scrabster monkfish with squid ink pasta, capers and saffron sauce. Meat and game are also handled with awe-inspiring dexterity as the kitchen extracts every last drop of flavour and goodness from the finest raw materials: crispy veal sweetbreads, given full-blooded treatment with Jerusalem artichoke risotto, crispy tongue and bone-marrow marmalade, while game might include glorious woodcock from the Isle of Lewis served with two variations on pumpkin and salmis sauce. To finish, Kitchin reverts to the classic French mode (coffee soufflé with chocolate sauce), but matches set yoghurt, orange meringue and apple sorbet with sea buckthorn consommé. Service has been described as 'impeccable'. Prices, however, still raise a few eyebrows, especially as regards the wine list – an otherwise unimpeachable catalogue distilling the best of modern viticulture, with thoroughbred producers and daring young contenders on every page.

Chef/s: Tom Kitchin. **Closed:** Sun, Mon, 25 Dec to 12 Jan, 10 to 14 Apr, 31 Jul to 4 Aug, 16 to 20 Oct. **Meals:** set L £33. Set D £75. Tasting menu £85 (6 courses) to £130. **Details:** 80 seats. V menu. Bar. Wheelchairs. Music. Parking. Children over 5 yrs.

Number One

Cooking score: 6

Modern European | £85

The Balmoral, 1 Princes Street, Edinburgh, EH2 2EQ
Tel no: (0131) 557 6727
roccofortehotels.com

Originally a railway hotel, now a city landmark, the grand old Balmoral sports a vibrantly decorated and lavishly designed basement restaurant dominated by a triptych of an oak tree and supported by a veritable gallery of black-framed prints from the Royal College of Art. Exec chef Jeff Bland continues to mastermind the kitchen, although day-to-day cooking duties are in the hands of Brian Grigor. Sound technique is a given as Grigor's team fashions eye-catching, flavour-rich compositions from shrewdly sourced, mostly Scottish, produce: new season's garlic and potato velouté is embellished with Loch Etive sea trout and caviar, while East Lothian lobster is complemented by charred watermelon, watercress and Jersey Royals. Scottish-reared beef and moorland game receive luxurious treatment (squab pigeon with summer truffle and hay oil, say), although the kitchen's virtuosity reaches its peak with desserts such as a chocolate crémeux with caramel ice cream and cocoa nib brittle. The mighty wine list is stuffed with aristocratic vintages and big-name labels with a noticeable French bias.

Chef/s: Jeff Bland and Brian Grigor. **Meals:** set D £85 (3 courses). Tasting menu £95. **Details:** 65 seats. Bar. Wheelchairs. Music.

Ondine

Cooking score: 4

Seafood | £45

2 George IV Bridge, Edinburgh, EH1 1AD
Tel no: (0131) 226 1888
ondinerestaurant.co.uk

Since the turn of the millennium, Roy Brett's suave monochrome dining room has been pleasing Edinburgh's diners with a telling combination of wraparound views and 'proper seafood' (his words). Perched above the Royal Mile, Ondine is an eye-catching prospect complete with baroque mirrors, pieces of abstract art and a crustacea bar holding centre stage (grand platters of fruits de mer are a speciality). Sustainable seafood is the chef's passion, and his menu promises high-end sophistication as well as haddock and chips – so expect a haul of ambitious, elegantly assembled dishes ranging from masala-spiced mussels mouclade to brown crab risotto or roast cod with mash and braised lentils. Meat eaters might prefer duck and chicken liver parfait followed by rib of Orkney beef, while desserts keep faith with perennial favourites such as treacle tart or apple crumble. Wines include plenty of fish-friendly whites, and there's a tartan army of single malts too.

Chef/s: Roy Brett. **Closed:** Sun, 25 and 26 Dec. **Meals:** main courses £16 to £48. Set L and D £21 (2 courses) to £25. **Details:** 85 seats. Wheelchairs. Music. No children under 5 yrs after 8pm.

The Pompadour by Galvin

Cooking score: 5

French | £60

Waldorf Astoria Edinburgh, The Caledonian, Princes Street, Edinburgh, EH1 2AB
Tel no: (0131) 222 8975
thepompadourbygalvin.com

The Galvin brothers continue to bring their reliable take on French culinary style to the Scottish capital. There's still an aesthetic nod to Versailles in the recently refreshed dining room on the first floor of the Waldorf Astoria with its pastel wedding-cake decor and floral walls lined with mirrors. An international clientele looks outwards over Edinburgh's architectural heritage and inwards across a contemporary interpretation of Gallic-inspired classics. Humble roots are given the star treatment in a flavour-packed dish of barbecued celeriac, Jerusalem artichoke and truffled crème fraîche, while a tender assiette of Pyrenean goat with ras el hanout and apricot blends French ingredients with North African inspiration. The regional bounty on the doorstep isn't overlooked, though, as in a dish of Gigha halibut and fennel with a chervil velouté, while a signature Valrhona chocolate-laden mousse, toasted hay ice cream and almond is patisserie paradise. The wine list is well balanced in both range and pricing, while the Coravin system allows an unusually extensive choice by the glass.

Chef/s: Dan Ashmore. **Closed:** Mon, Tue, first 2 weeks Jan. **Meals:** set D £35 to £65. Sun L £30 (3 courses). Tasting menu £55 (5 courses) to £75. **Details:** 68 seats. V menu. Wheelchairs. Parking.

Purslane

Cooking score: 2

Modern British | £35

33a St Stephen Street, Stockbridge, Edinburgh, EH3 5AH
Tel no: (0131) 226 3500
purslanerestaurant.co.uk

Space may be at a premium, but the enjoyment factor remains sky-high at this diminutive basement restaurant in Edinburgh's Stockbridge district. The look may be informal, with dark wooden tables, and walls clad in reclaimed timber boards, but the kitchen shows plenty of ambition when it comes to fashioning modern dishes from top-drawer ingredients. To start, there might be crab and courgette cannelloni with chilli, coriander and shellfish reduction, while mains could take in everything from roast breast of guinea fowl with sprout fricassée, artichoke purée, roast salsify and turnip to sea bream alongside sautéed leeks, button onions, cucumber and Champagne velouté. Elsewhere, pavé of beef with fondant potato and red wine jus steps up as the traditionalist's choice, while tried-and-true desserts are often given a refreshing uplift – rice pudding with cardamom ice cream or chocolate parfait with cherry compôte and cherry sorbet, say. The wide-ranging wine list is generously loaded with by-the-glass selections.

Chef/s: Paul Gunning. **Closed:** Mon. **Meals:** set L £15 (2 courses) to £18. Set D £30 (2 courses) to £35. Tasting menus £50 (5 courses) to £60. **Details:** 20 seats. Music. Children over 5 yrs.

Anonymous

At *The Good Food Guide*, our inspectors dine anonymously and pay their bill in full every time.These impartial review meals, along with feedback from thousands of our readers, are what informs the content of the *GFG*. Only the best restaurants make the cut.

★ TOP 50 ★

Restaurant Martin Wishart

Cooking score: 7

Modern French | £85

54 The Shore, Leith, Edinburgh, EH6 6RA
Tel no: (0131) 553 3557
martin-wishart.co.uk

The flagship of Martin Wishart's three-pronged restaurant group is his place in Leith, opened nearly 20 years ago and maintaining a standard of enviable consistency ever since. In an understated room, where neutral wood tones predominate, the focus is on finely detailed Anglo-French cooking that displays obvious roots in tradition, as one would expect of a Roux-trained chef, but which is also assured in bringing modern technique into play to maximise impact. A six-course tasting menu drawn from the carte is typically a trio of seafood dishes, a main meat and a pair of desserts, but before all that, the canapés are little miracles of savoury intensity, not least the beetroot macaron with its horseradish cream filling. The Shetland squid with Puy lentils, bellota ham and rouille is singled out for particular plaudits by readers, while the vigorous treatment of an Orkney scallop with parsnip, pear and Comté in a sauce of vin jaune is a demonstration dish of inventive boldness. Roe deer from the Borders is a main-course standby, or there may be roast breast and pastilla of Goosnargh duck in a crimson livery of red cabbage, beetroot and redcurrants, with macadamias for good measure. If you're after something lighter to finish, look no further than satin-soft buttermilk mousse with fennel sorbet, sorrel parfait and a garnish of Granny Smith, but the lure of Valrhona chocolate and caramel will prove too strong for many. An enterprising wine list leaves no stone unturned in its hunt for original accompaniments, with three Lebanese and six Uruguayan bottles muscling their way behind the several battalions of the French regions. Prices open at £20.

Chef/s: Martin Wishart. **Closed:** Sun, Mon, 25 and 26 Dec, 12 days Jan, 2 days Apr, 1 week Aug, 2 days Oct. **Meals:** set L £32 (3 courses). Set D £90 (4 courses). Tasting menu £85 (6 courses) to £110. **Details:** 50 seats. V menu. Wheelchairs. Children over 7 yrs.

Rhubarb at Prestonfield

Cooking score: 4

Modern British | £55

Prestonfield House, Priestfield Road, Edinburgh, EH16 5UT

Tel no: (0131) 225 1333

prestonfield.com

Looking as ravishing as Versailles, James Thomson's gloriously extravagant hotel flaunts its splendid baroque excess behind a fine 17th-century façade. The restaurant is a riot of ancestral portraits, gold-trimmed drapes, gilded antiques and exotic fabrics. The interiors may be pure ostentation, but the kitchen eschews such unbridled extravagance in favour of contemporary dishes inspired by top-quality Scottish produce: Isle of Mull scallops are crusted with lemon and pine nuts; brown crabmeat appears in a panna cotta alongside wasabi and pepper dulse (seaweed); venison is given the wellington treatment – wrapped in cocoa and hazelnut pastry, with accompaniments including roast parsnip, medjool dates, pickled garlic and orange grand-veneur sauce. To finish, Prestonfield's Pink Lady apples go into a tarte tatin – or you might fancy a Balvenie whisky parfait with black plums. Also expect an epically proportioned global wine list that includes some rarities, but starts at a modest £23.

Chef/s: John McMahon. **Meals:** main courses £17 to £40. Set L £27. Set D £38. **Details:** 88 seats. 100 seats outside. Bar. Music. Parking.

★ NEW ENTRY ★

Le Roi Fou

Cooking score: 4

French | £50

1 Forth Street, Edinburgh, EH1 3JX

Tel no: (0131) 557 9346

leroifou.com

Jérôme Henry, formerly of Belgravia's Mosimann's and Les Trois Garçons in Shoreditch, settled on Edinburgh to open his first restaurant in the spring of 2017 and is making his mark on the city with this smart, modern – if rather cramped – restaurant in New Town. His comprehensive menu has a welcome focus on vegetables at least among the dozen starters, which included Isle of Wight tomato salad with fennel, cucumber and basil; white asparagus; saffron pappardelle with leeks, asparagus and mushroom broth; and a very pleasing asparagus salad with marinated anchovies. Courses are unusually generous for this level of cooking, illustrated by a substantial steak tartare starter and a rack of three juicy lamb chops with a slice of lamb breast on the plate, too. The à la carte prices are top end, though the two-course lunch offers good value and wines begin with a manageable £24 for a French Chardonnay. Expect crisp service and well-informed sommelier recommendations.

Chef/s: Jérôme Henry. **Closed:** Sun, Mon, 25 Dec, 10 Jan. **Meals:** main courses £16 to £32. Set L £18 (2 courses). Set D £20 (2 courses) to £23. Tasting menu £50 (6 courses). **Details:** 50 seats. Music.

The Scran & Scallie

Cooking score: 2

British | £30

1 Comely Bank Road, Edinburgh, EH4 1DT

Tel no: (0131) 332 6281

scranandscallie.com

A relaxed operation from top-drawer chefs, Tom Kitchin of The Kitchin in Leith and Dominic Jack of Castle Terrace (see entries), resulting in 'a public house with dining'. While the bar offers whisky and gin flights and plenty of draught and bottled beers, dining dominates. The menu steadfastly promotes pub classics like fish pie, sausage and mash, and fish and chips (the scran) in generous servings, albeit at restaurant prices – on our visit a crab and avocado starter was £12.50. A beetroot and lentil burger given a thick slab of goat's cheese needs some refining but the 'specials' menu trades up with a pleasing dish of Orkney scallops, peas and pancetta and an equally good portion of plaice wrapped in pancetta with mussels and wild garlic. The main room has a Nordic meets Highlands vibe, and a European-focused wine list, helpfully broken down by category, offers plenty by the glass and carafe.

Chef/s: James Chapman. **Closed:** 25 Dec. **Meals:** main courses £12 to £20. Set L Mon to Fri £18. Sun L £20. **Details:** 75 seats. Bar. Wheelchairs. Music.

Taisteal

Cooking score: 2

International | £30

1-3 Raeburn Place, Edinburgh, EH4 1HU
Tel no: (0131) 332 9977
taisteal.co.uk

£5 OFF

Scottish ingredients, global flavours, that's the thing at Gordon Craig's Stockbridge restaurant. It's all in the name if your Gaelic is up to snuff (Taisteal means 'journey' or 'travel'). The inspiration might come from Europe – a first-course Jerusalem artichoke panna cotta, say, in the company of vegetarian haggis and Scotch egg – or the air miles might build up with a mackerel number (charred, cured and tartare), with guacamole and pickled grapes in citrussy ponzu. Among main courses, roast cod and crab arrive in green curry sauce with rice noodles, while those European flavours crop up again with fillet and pork belly with Toulouse sausages. The lunchtime and early-evening set menu is really good value. For dessert, hot chocolate mousse with passion fruit sorbet, and chocolate and yuzu crémeux with star anise ice cream, fit the brief to a T. A concise global wine list gets support from a few world beers and feisty cocktails.

Chef/s: Gordon Craig. **Closed:** Sun, Mon, 25 and 26 Dec, 1 and 2 Jan. **Meals:** main courses £14 to £19. Set L and early D £12 (2 courses) to £15. Tasting menu £35 (5 courses). **Details:** 44 seats. Music.

Timberyard

Cooking score: 5

Modern British | £50

10 Lady Lawson Street, Edinburgh, EH3 9DS
Tel no: (0131) 221 1222
timberyard.co

A huge warehouse space transformed some five years ago into a voguish restaurant, where, among the iron pillars and naked light bulbs, natural materials dominate: distressed wooden beams, worn timber floors, hand-thrown plates – all softened with rugs, sofas and candlelight. There have been numerous imitators of its innovative Caledonian Nordic vibe since it opened, though happily Timberyard has not lost its distinctive edge, typified by a modish cocktail list featuring, say, pine sap Negroni – and a select range of natural wines from small producers. If dinner is less experimental than in its early days – fewer foraged leaves and berries – Ben Radford has a mature and confident hand on the tiller and Timberyard is all the better for it. Standout dishes from the four, six-and eight-course menus were a soothing veal tartare with turnip, mustard, sorrel and duck yolk, and sea bass partnered by sweet and savoury accompaniments of celery, wild leek, apple and potato. Sharp service from a well-drilled team underscores the engaging ambience.

Chef/s: Ben Radford. **Closed:** Sun, Mon, 24 to 26 Dec, first week Jan, 1 week mid Apr, 1 week mid Oct. **Meals:** main courses Tue to Thur £13. Set L and D £18 (2 courses) to £25. Tasting menu £55 (4 courses) to £75. **Details:** 65 seats. 20 seats outside. V menu. Vg menu. Bar. Wheelchairs. Music. Children over 12 yrs at D.

Valvona & Crolla

Cooking score: 2

Italian | £26

19 Elm Row, Edinburgh, EH7 4AA
Tel no: (0131) 556 6066
valvonacrolla.co.uk

The bountifully stocked Italian deli is the first step on a visit to this Edinburgh institution established in 1934. Rows of shelves stocked with every Italian ingredient – meats, cheeses, olives – and a superb wine store line the passage to a dining room that opens behind the shop with a wide-ranging menu of tried-and-trusted dishes from pastries and full Scottish breakfast to the all-day menu of arancini, caprese salad, pasta dishes such as tomato and Tuscan pork sausage and a regular list of pizzas. Specials are worth considering with pleasing fried courgette flowers stuffed with ricotta and anchovies or calf's liver with red onions and mash. Wines start at a bargain £12.90 and any bottle from the shop is offered with just £4 corkage on the retail price.

Chef/s: Mary Contini. **Closed:** 25 and 26 Dec, 1 and 2 Jan. **Meals:** main courses £10 to £14. Set L £16 (2 courses) to £19. Set D £25 (2 courses) to £35. **Details:** 60 seats. V menu. Music. Parking.

The Wee Restaurant

Cooking score: 3

Modern British | £36

61 Frederick Street, Edinburgh, EH2 1LH
Tel no: (0131) 225 7983
theweerestaurant.co.uk

Craig and Vikki Wood opened their first Wee Restaurant in 2006 across the Forth Bridge in North Queensferry (see entry); the second opened a decade later in a Georgian terrace in Edinburgh's New Town. Craig earned his spurs at some top Scottish addresses and, along with head chef Michael Innes, has taken the principles of working upwards from a foundation of quality ingredients to a more brasserie style of operation. Seared king scallops with squid ink risotto fits the bill, as does another starter of Shetland mussels in a sauce enriched with bacon. A chargrill does the business on beef from the Black Isle (served with chips or gratin dauphinois), while roasted cod is matched with crab linguine, or Ibérico pork with roasted Padrón peppers. To finish, try the rich chocolate and honey tart with raspberry sorbet. The lunchtime and midweek evening menu is a banker, and the wine list, starting at £19.75, isn't all that wee.

Chef/s: Michael Innes. **Closed:** Mon, 25 and 26 Dec, 1 and 2 Jan. **Meals:** set L (Tue to Sat) and D (Tue to Thur) £16 (2 courses) to £20. Set D £29 (2 courses) to £36. Sun L £23. **Details:** 38 seats. Music.

Gullane

La Potinière

Cooking score: 4

Modern British | £39

34 Main Street, Gullane, EH31 2AA
Tel no: (01620) 843214
lapotiniere.co.uk

With its high-backed leather chairs, deep red curtains, cream wallpaper and white-clothed tables, La Potinière seems to live in its own respectful and reassuring little world – a culinary cocoon immune to the vagaries and fashions of 21st-century gastronomy. The cooking here is gently pleasurable, accurate and sympathetic when it comes to handling decent seasonal ingredients, whether Mary Runciman and Keith Marley are serving up a duck pithivier with preserved cherry sauce or a warm beetroot panna cotta alongside beetroot and Roquefort salad. Bowls of Thai coconut soup with scallops may jolt the palate and interrupt the flow, but it's back to reassuring normality when the main courses arrive – perhaps poached and seared fillet of Scotch beef with dauphinois, morels and beef jus. Whether you're here for lunch or dinner, meals always conclude with cheese and a choice of two desserts such as raspberry and Drambuie mousse. Attractively priced house wines start at £19.

Chef/s: Mary Runciman and Keith Marley. **Closed:** Mon, Tue, 24 to 26 Dec, Jan, bank hols. **Meals:** set L £22 (2 courses) to £27. Set D £39 (3 courses) to £47. **Details:** 24 seats. Wheelchairs. Parking.

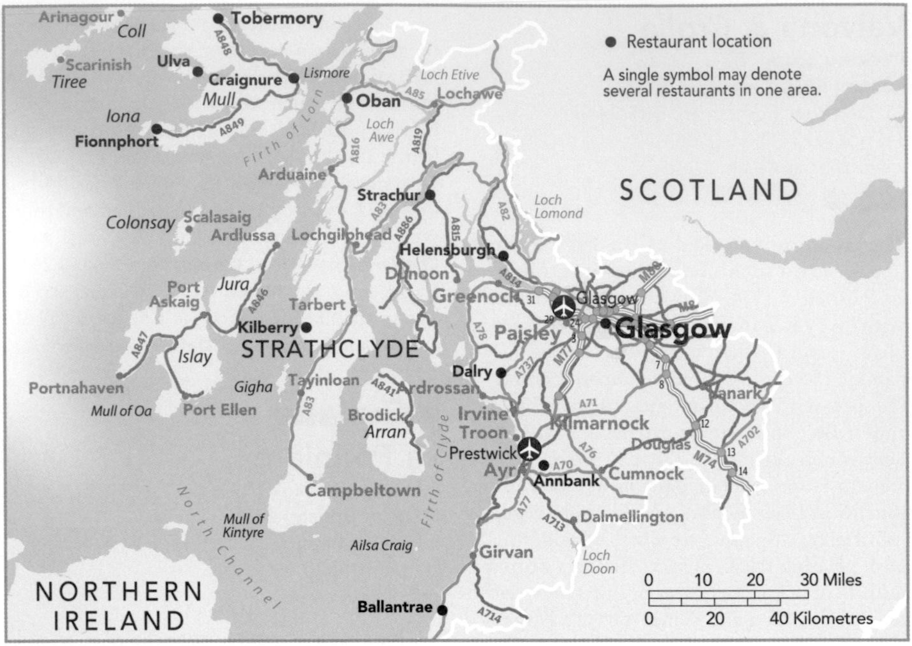

Annbank

Browne's

Cooking score: 4

Modern British | £42

Enterkine House Hotel, Annbank, KA6 5AL
Tel no: (01292) 520580
enterkine.com

The unexpected Art Deco feel of Enterkine House dates from a major rebuild in the 1930s, and the genteel dining room of Browne's restaurant overlooks the tangled romanticism of an overgrown formal garden. Chef Paul Moffat has been a steady fixture in the kitchen since 2004, catering for predominantly resident diners and lively weddings and events. His approach is grounded in sound classical techniques but the dishes remain fresh and contemporary. The set dinner may start with canapés and amuse-bouches including a rich mouthful of mushroom velouté. A Ticklemore goat's cheese soufflé with braised ceps, spinach and truffle is a perfectly balanced precursor to fragrant olive-oil-poached halibut complemented by clams, saffron and a squid ink tuile. Desserts offer delicacy or comfort – a choice of iced pumpkin seed parfait with early rhubarb and limoncello custard or warm sticky ginger pudding with salted caramel sauce. A selection of whiskies in the library underscores the country-house ambience but the wine list, though kindly priced, is a disappointing partner to quality cooking.

Chef/s: Paul Moffat. **Meals:** main courses L £9 to £16. Set D £42. **Details:** 40 seats. Wheelchairs. Parking.

Send us your review

Your feedback informs the content of the *GFG* and will be used to compile next year's reviews. To register your opinion about any restaurant listed in the Guide, or a restaurant that you wish to bring to our attention, visit: thegoodfoodguide.co.uk/feedback

Ballantrae

Glenapp Castle

Cooking score: 5

Modern British | £49

Ballantrae, KA26 0NZ

Tel no: (01465) 831212

glenappcastle.com

£5 OFF

Glenapp is a masterstroke of Scots baronial, a turreted Gothic castle built at the behest of the industrialist James Hunter in 1870. It has been jealously preserved through the generations, making it a perfect candidate for the country-house experience, and its location in the UNESCO biosphere of Ayrshire is a regional feather in its cap. In a dining room of surpassing splendour, a daily changing, three-course table d'hôte menu is served, drawing on the produce of the South West and on Glenapp's own kitchen plots for a conservative, but eloquently honed version of Scottish modernity. First up might be seared Skye scallops in sauce nero with crispy fennel, dressed in cardamom and dill oil, as an entrée to loin and shank of Girvan lamb, accompanied by roasted cabbage, a potato and spring onion bonbon and puréed swede, in rich lamb jus. A finish might be tarte fine of rhubarb and blood orange, with a crumble and custard garnish and crème fraîche sorbet. Expect some serious, and costly, drinking as standard, with French classics to the fore.

Chef/s: David Alexander. **Closed:** 2 to 19 Jan. **Meals:** set L £40. Set D £49. Tasting menu £69 (6 courses). **Details:** 34 seats. Wheelchairs. Parking.

Dalry

Braidwoods

Cooking score: 5

Modern British | £50

Drumastle Mill Cottage, Dalry, KA24 4LN

Tel no: (01294) 833544

braidwoods.co.uk

The isolated whitewashed Ayrshire mill cottages that were turned, a generation ago, into the Braidwoods' country restaurant remain an entrancing prospect. While Nicola runs the show out front with inspiring bonhomie, Keith is busy behind the scenes producing a classically based version of Scottish cooking that mobilises an understated richness for much of its appeal. The four-course evening format might open with Arran Blue cheese panna cotta on a salad of roast baby beetroot, apple, crisp Parma ham and hazelnuts, prior to an intervening course of pea and watercress soup. After that, it could be halibut on crushed potato and artichoke in lobster sauce, or perhaps the mainstay beef fillet from Cairnhill Farm, a long-running fixture. Indulgences to beat the band are the order of a dessert menu that might take in Valrhona chocolate truffle cake with salt caramel ice cream, or rhubarb and ginger crème brûlée. Value is the watchword of an enterprising wine list that opens at £24.95 for South Africa's De Wetshof Chardonnay or a Rioja Crianza.

Chef/s: Keith Braidwood. **Closed:** Mon, 25 Dec to 31 Jan, first 2 weeks Sept. **Meals:** set L £28 (2 courses) to £32. Set D £50 (3 courses) to £55. Sun L £35. **Details:** 24 seats. Parking. Children over 5 yrs at L, over 12 yrs at D.

Glasgow

Alchemilla

Cooking score: 3

Middle Eastern | £35

1126 Argyle Street, Glasgow, G3 8TD

Tel no: (0141) 337 6060

thisisalchemilla.com

Alchemilla manages to squeeze lots of character and charm into a very small space, as the modish customers searching for foodie experiences on the Finnieston strip will tell you. Perching at the tiny tables or directly at the bar, this is inspired small plate food for informal sharing rather than a place that adheres to traditional meal structures or seating. Simple ingredients innovatively combined might lead you to graze from a selection that includes shaved kohlrabi with fennel and herbs, octopus, clementine and capers, salted onglet with pickled clams and spinach or sea bass carpaccio. A few options for a sweet finish include the well-judged panna cotta with burnt caramel and pine nut biscuit. Natural and organic wines along with imaginative house cocktails complement the food.

Chef/s: Rosie Healey. **Meals:** small plates £4 to £12. Set L £10.

Brian Maule at Chardon d'Or

Cooking score: 4

French | £51

176 West Regent Street, Glasgow, G2 4RL
Tel no: (0141) 248 3801
brianmaule.com

As chef patron, Brian Maule continues to bring a personal touch and oversight to his self-named restaurant on a daily basis. The genteel environment provides an elegant backdrop to the quiet murmur of celebratory couples, business gatherings and the occasionally more lively participants in the regular tutored gin or cocktail lunches. The food here is a meticulous interpretation of classic French with some subtle twists that inject broader Mediterranean or Asian influence: seared tuna loin is aromatic with pickled mouli, sweet chilli and toasted sesame, while a more hearty main of rare Scotch lamb is accompanied by rich truffled polenta and an aubergine caviar. Afterwards, it's hard to move past the tarte tatin, but other desserts are equally well executed. Lunch and pre-theatre options offer good value for this level of hospitality and the wine list ensures a safe range of classic quality.

Chef/s: Brian Maule. **Closed:** Sun, Mon, bank hols. **Meals:** main courses £29 to £33. Set L £22 (2 courses) to £25. Tasting menu £60. **Details:** 150 seats. V menu. No children after 6pm.

Cail Bruich

Cooking score: 6

Modern British | £45

725 Great Western Road, Glasgow, G12 8QX
Tel no: (0141) 334 6265
cailbruich.co.uk

'This is my nearest restaurant and I consider myself fortunate,' declared one reader; 'blown away with the food and service,' enthused another. It's easy to see why. Behind a modest frontage, steampunk copper light fittings add edge to soothing neutral tones and the open kitchen brings dynamism to Cail Bruich's small-ish space. But it's the food that counts. In an ambitious series of market, à la carte and tasting menus, seasonal ingredients are drawn together in a distinctive Scottish style that is both light and satisfying. Sea bream, brown crab, cucumber, celery and seaweed sees a verdant emerald broth bathing a tian of fish in a perfect balance of sweetness, acidity and richness. A main of pork, artichoke, celeriac and green olive is exceptionally tender while a deconstructed carrot cake featuring the punchy flavours of sea buckthorn and caramelised whey is a quirky interpretation of a classic. Service is engaging and well informed, with the enthusiastic sommelier's focus on boutique producers and imaginative food and wine pairings injecting contemporary vigour into an Old World list.

Chef/s: Chris Charalambous. **Closed:** 25 and 26 Dec, 2 weeks Jan. **Meals:** set L £22 (2 courses) to £28. Set D £35 (2 courses) to £45. Tasting menu £55 (6 courses). **Details:** 42 seats. Music. Children over 5 yrs.

Crabshakk

Cooking score: 2

Seafood | £40

1114 Argyle Street, Glasgow, G3 8TD
Tel no: (0141) 334 6127
crabshakk.com

£5 OFF

A huge favourite among lovers of Scottish seafood, Crabshakk also has a claim to having kickstarted Finnieston's now-lauded food scene. The promise of a cracking good time – there are a lot of shells to get through – is irresistible to those who cram themselves into the confines of the Shakk to get knee-deep in lemon mayonnaise and fish suppers. The titular seafood comes whole, as claws or as cakes, there are oysters on ice and scallops seared with anchovies, langoustines 'chilled or grilled' and as much pasta vongole as you can throw a clam at. Most of the riches are simply, Scottishly prepared, but squid is turned into tempura with soy and coriander dipping sauce, or added to gurnard to be salted, peppered and fried. Wines match the menu, Irn Bru does not – and it is, of course, no place for either the vegetarian or the defiant carnivore.

Chef/s: David Scott. **Closed:** 25 and 26 Dec, 1 and 2 Jan. **Meals:** main courses £11 to £30. **Details:** 50 seats. 8 seats outside. Bar. Wheelchairs. Music.

Eusebi Deli

Cooking score: 2

Italian | £24

152 Park Road, Glasgow, G4 9HB
Tel no: (0141) 648 9999
eusebideli.com

Giovanna Eusebi and family have been at the heart of Glasgow's Italian scene for more than 40 years, first at their deli in Shettleston and latterly at this ambitious set-up on Park Road. Combining a ground-floor emporium and café with a trattoria-style basement dining room, their West End venue is all about provenance and provisions – whether you're here for a quick espresso, breakfast or a more leisurely evening repast. Pasta is made on site in the family's 'laboratory' and you can taste the results in anything from 'yesterday's lasagne' to meat tortellini in brodo. The owners are champions of the Slow Food Movement, so also expect long-cooked 'kitchen specials' such as confit corn-fed chicken with pearl barley risotto or 12-hour braised ox cheek partnered by potato purée, horseradish gremolata and shallots. Small plates, antipasti and cured meats (from an artisan specialist in Umbria) are other highlights, while wines represent the home country with a vengeance.

Chef/s: Sebastian Wereski. **Closed:** 25 to 27 Dec, 1 to 3 Jan. **Meals:** main courses £11 to £16. Set L £15 (2 courses) to £18. **Details:** 65 seats. 18 seats outside. Bar. Wheelchairs. Music.

Gamba

Cooking score: 3

Seafood | £35

225a West George Street, Glasgow, G2 2ND
Tel no: (0141) 572 0899
gamba.co.uk

'It has a certain timelessness and authenticity,' notes a visitor to this vintage seafooder, now in its 20th year. With its simple, clean-lined good looks and gentle lighting, Derek Marshall's basement restaurant is a little haven of tranquility in the busy streets of Glasgow's West End. There's no gimmickry here, just top-class fish and shellfish prepared with natural acumen and a feel for vibrant flavours. Typically, you might begin with the popular fish soup – a wonderful concoction of crabmeat, stem ginger, coriander and prawn dumplings – or a plate of yellowfin tuna and scallop sashimi, then move on to a meaty whole-roast sea bream with a delicious aged balsamic sauce or a half lobster thermidor with thick-cut rooster chips. If you're determined to order meat, there's usually fillet of Scotch beef, while warm cherry Bakewell with vanilla ice cream makes a perfect finish – that's if the all-Scottish cheese plate hasn't taken your fancy. A well-annotated, wide-ranging wine list has been chosen with the food in mind.

Chef/s: Derek Marshall. **Closed:** 25 and 26 Dec, 1 week Jan. **Meals:** main courses £21 to £35. Set L and pre-theatre D £20 (2 courses) to £22. Market menu £35 (3 courses). **Details:** 60 seats. Bar. Music. No children after 10pm

The Gannet

Cooking score: 3

Modern British | £40

1155 Argyle Street, Glasgow, G3 8TB
Tel no: (0141) 204 2081
thegannetgla.com

£5 OFF

The Gannet's continuing popularity with Glasgow's foodie hipsters makes accessibility to its closely packed, pared-back premises in Finnieston challenging. Whether the general hubbub, proximity to fellow diners and bar prominence adds to the upbeat vibe or reduces serenity is personal preference. Luckily, the food draws your attention: 'with an ethos of field to plate, it's simply delightful'. This is technically tidy cooking that delivers both subtlety and 'oomph'. Rabbit shoulder, haggis and loin present three distinctive takes on this delicate meat and wry additions of baby carrots and quail's egg evoke a miniature smallholding. Gartmorn Farm duck, perfectly cooked, oozes flavour even before its accompaniments of confit leg, prune and hazelnut pastilla and five-spice pack their respective punches. Salt caramel fondant with tonka bean ice cream offers a closing sugar hit. Portions are small, though with wine and cocktails the bill can quickly end up less so. A kindly priced six-course tasting lunch offers an affordable entry.

Chef/s: Ivan Stein and Peter McKenna. **Closed:** Mon, 25 and 26 Dec, 1 and 2 Jan. **Meals:** main courses £16 to £24. Tasting menu £39. **Details:** 55 seats. V menu. Bar. Wheelchairs. Music.

Number 16

Cooking score: 1

Modern British | £30

16 Byres Road, Glasgow, G11 5JY
Tel no: (0141) 339 2544
number16.co.uk

£5 OFF

Situated at the bottom of Byres Road, and well established over many years, Number 16 is, as its name suggests, a diminutive but much-loved neighbourhood fixture with a bijou kitchen. Owners Joel Pomfret and Gerry Mulholland ensure the decor and the feel of the place remain fresh and relevant, and the cooking comes with enough of a twist to keep it contemporary. Cosying up with the neighbouring tables, diners can enjoy quality local ingredients: plump, well-caramelised scallop with confit chicken, a corn purée and bacon popcorn, say, and ox cheek enriched by a bone-marrow crumb and smoked heritage potatoes – the ultimate comfort crumble. Informal service and quirky bespoke tableware reflect the owners' humour and originality.

Chef/s: Sean Currie. **Closed:** 25 and 26 Dec, 1 to 4 Jan. **Meals:** main courses £14 to £20. Set L £16 (2 courses) to £20. **Details:** 35 seats. Music.

111 by Nico

Cooking score: 2

Modern European | £22

111 Cleveden Road, Glasgow, G12 0JU
Tel no: (0141) 334 0111
111bynico.co.uk

A five-course tasting menu for just £30 that showcases fresh Scottish ingredients while supporting disadvantaged young people is worth a punt, and, when the menu changes weekly, a return trip is not uncommon for customers of Nico Simeone's neighbourhood restaurant. Granted, it's a little off the beaten track in the West End suburb of Kelvindale, but the welcome is warm, the close tables convivial and the venue normally buzzing. Vivid, imaginative and generally well-presented plates offer up delights such as smoked ham hock with honey and ginger or pig's cheek with a rich cassoulet and a tart seasoning of leek ash. Desserts might include a sweet beetroot and apple semifreddo with meringue. A regularly changing selection of house cocktails are offered as a prelude, along with a short but adequate wine list.

Chef/s: Nico Simeone and Modou Diagme. **Closed:** Mon. **Meals:** set L and D £19 (2 courses) to £22. Tasting menu £30 (5 courses). **Details:** 44 seats. No children.

Stravaigin

Cooking score: 1

International | £32

28 Gibson Street, Glasgow, G12 8NX
Tel no: (0141) 334 2665
stravaigin.co.uk

Stravaigin is a neighbourhood institution catering companionably to generations of students as well as longer-established locals. Whether lazy Sunday brunch, cocktails or craft beers in the bustling bar or a more adventurous meal in the restaurant, this is a place of wide appeal and informal charm. Dishes such as homemade 'haggis, neeps 'n' tatties' reflect their Scottish essence, but the menu could just as easily embrace the street food of south-east Asia or feature ras el hanout lamb neck with aubergine, labneh and pomegranate, redolent of North African souks. The common factor is a commitment to fresh local ingredients and punchy flavours. Regular themed events offer deep dives into quirky culinary corners for the exploratory diner.

Chef/s: Doug Lindsay. **Closed:** 25 Dec, 1 Jan. **Meals:** main courses £13 to £28. Set D £30 to £35. **Details:** 70 seats. 12 seats outside. Bar. Wheelchairs. Music. No children after 10pm.

Ubiquitous Chip

Cooking score: 5

Modern British | £40

12 Ashton Lane, Glasgow, G12 8SJ
Tel no: (0141) 334 5007
ubiquitouschip.co.uk

Run by the Clydesdale family since 1971 and considered an iconic venue, the Chip is housed in the courtyard of a former undertakers' stable block, now alive with greenery. There's no resting on laurels here: the kitchen has moved with the times, and while it's still rooted in classic Scottish ingredients, the output feels zippy and modern. Yes, you can get haggis, neeps and tatties (in 'wee' or 'big' portions) or good old Aberdeen Angus with hand-cut chips on the brasserie menu, but equally there might be roasted beets with caraway yoghurt, caramelised walnut and rosemary oil, or West Coast hake with Pink Fir potatoes, mussel and leek fricassée and smoked almond sauce. The restaurant menu takes things up a notch while still singing a Scottish tune: think Barra scallops with pork belly, carrot and sesame consommé and pickled grapes, and then Galloway red deer haunch with salt-baked celeriac, game bolognese and red cabbage purée. To finish, try baked goat's cheesecake with rhubarb sorbet, bitter orange gel and hazelnuts. Wine and whisky lovers take note: there is plenty to love here.

Chef/s: Andrew Mitchell. **Closed:** 25 Dec, 1 Jan. **Meals:** main courses £20 to £35. Set L and early D £20 (2 courses) to £24. Sun L £24 (3 courses). **Details:** 115 seats. 20 seats outside. V menu. Bar. Wheelchairs.

LOCAL GEM

The Finnieston

Seafood | £32

1125 Argyle Street, Glasgow, G3 8ND
Tel no: (0141) 222 2884
thefinniestonbar.com

There's plenty of metropolitan buzz at this cocktail-bar-cum-restaurant with its contemporary flavours and lively clientele. However, the low-ceilinged, wood-panelled interior of this former pub gives a solid, almost nautical air, underscoring the fishy focus of the menu. Regulars squeeze into the closely packed booths for classic fish and chips or oysters served with Bloody Mary or gin and cucumber gel. There are more complex dishes on the menu, say braised rabbit, white balsamic carrots, basil and lime aïoli or halibut with Puy lentils, celeriac purée, cockles and Morello cherry.

Local Gem

These entries highlight a range of neighbourhood venues, delivering good, freshly cooked food at great value for money.

LOCAL GEM

Ox and Finch

International | £30
920 Sauchiehall Street, Glasgow, G3 7TF
Tel no: (0141) 339 8627
oxandfinch.com

The industrial-chic decor and small sharing plates continue to attract a stylish and mixed crowd to this bustling social hub. Plates come out as the kitchen determines so it's not a place to expect a structured three-course meal. Kitchen inspirations range both global and local with fusions between the two and might include venison, juniper and peppercorn carpaccio with crowdie or confit duck leg with yellow curry and Thai basil. The peanut butter, apple and sesame millefeuille is a crowd-pleasing pud.

LOCAL GEM

Porter & Rye

British | £45
1131 Argyle Street, Glasgow, G8 8ND
Tel no: (0141) 572 1212
porterandrye.com

Porter & Rye's up-front proposition is dry-aged beef from Gaindykehead Farm in Airdrie with 'molecular plate' accompaniments featuring wild and foraged food. In practice this might translate into pheasant rillettes with pear jelly and olive oil wafer followed by sharing cuts for two (perhaps porterhouse or tomahawk), or a choice of six carnivorous indulgences for one. Prices include sauces and sides, of which bone-marrow mac and cheese is a guilty pleasure. Late opening sees a cocktail vibe prevail, supported by a more limited snack menu.

LOCAL GEM

Saramago

International | £20
Centre for Contemporary Arts, 350 Sauchiehall Street, Glasgow, G2 3JD
Tel no: (0141) 352 4920
cca-glasgow.com

In an airy atrium courtyard in Glasgow's bustling Centre for Contemporary Arts (CCA), the all-day flexibility and cultural vibe of this café and bar draws an eclectic mix. No one is out of place, whether in for a quick bite, dinner for two, group drinks or simply solo with a laptop. The vegetarian, mostly vegan menu features seasonal ingredients in a range of small plates, sharing dishes or hearty mains. Mediterranean sunshine flows from a summer heirloom tomato panzanella, while the rich golden broth of Malaysian laksa brims with smoked tofu, crisp beans, pak choi and coconut. Chai-spiced waffles with chocolate mousse and toasted nuts reflects a toothsome selection of comfort puds.

Helensburgh

Sugar Boat

Cooking score: 2
Modern European | £28
30 Colquhoun Square, Helensburgh, G84 8AQ
Tel no: (01436) 647522
sugarboat.co.uk

A few miles downstream from Glasgow, Helensburgh on the Clyde is home to the latest venture from Will Smith – the restaurateur of Arbutus and Wild Honey (see entry) fame. A move from London has resulted in a dapper makeover for the Colquhoun Square premises: an all-day affair, part café, bar and bistro (and wine shop), with Scottish produce given first dibs and a broadly European feel to the (open) kitchen's output. Gurnard, white bean and chorizo cassoulet is a typical starter, being both rustic and sophisticated, while crisp ox tongue with pickled mushrooms and green sauce is another example of hearty refinement. A touch of appley sharpness works wonders with loin and cheek of pork among main courses, while the house bouillabaisse includes a donation to the local RNLI. For dessert, almond and prune tart fits the bill. The set lunch is a good shout, or simply pop in for a croque-madame. The wisely put-together wine list opens at £15.

Chef/s: Scott Smith. **Closed:** 25 and 26 Dec, 1 and 2 Jan. **Meals:** main courses £11 to £17. Set L and early D Mon to Fri £14 (2 courses) to £17, Sat £17 (3 courses). Sun L £16 (3 courses). **Details:** 65 seats. Bar. Wheelchairs. Music.

Isle of Mull

Café Fish

Cooking score: 3

Seafood | £33

The Pier, Main Street, Tobermory, Isle of Mull, PA75 6NU
Tel no: (01688) 301 253
thecafefish.com

Proof, if it were needed, of the timeless pleasures of fish and seafood, simply prepared, can be found at this highly popular café restaurant on Tobermory's picturesque harbour. Always busy – be sure to book at dinner – the speedy front of house team works flat out opening oysters, cracking crab claws and taking orders, while chef cooks the likes of seafood linguine, turbot with brown shrimps and sauce vierge, all in the tiniest of kitchens. It's no-nonsense, fresh and satisfying. The various shellfish options, landed by their own boat (the *Highlander*) constitute a roll call of the local bounty: a dozen oysters on ice, creel-caught langoustine, squat lobster tails, West Coast scallops, Mull lobster, velvet crab or the whole lot on a platter for two. There's Champagne to go with the oysters and Albarino at £30 a bottle. They do have steak and a few non-fish starters – but that's not what you're here for.

Chef/s: Liz McGougan. **Closed:** 1 Nov to 17 Mar. **Meals:** main courses £12 to £35. **Details:** 32 seats. 50 seats outside. Music. No children under 5 yrs at D.

Ninth Wave

Cooking score: 5

Modern British | £56

Bruach Mhor, Fionnphort, Isle of Mull, PA66 6BL
Tel no: (01681) 700757
ninthwaverestaurant.co.uk

John Lamont spends his day fishing the abundant waters of the Sound of Mull on his little boat, the *Sconsie*, then, after exchanging his oilskins for a kilt, he takes over front of house at this remote croft at the south-western tip of Mull. In the kitchen is his Canadian born wife, Carla, who has created a menu that majors on John's catch along with ingredients fastidiously sourced from local seashore, hedgerow and garden. Dinner can be three, four or five exemplary courses beginning, perhaps, with crisp fried Mull oysters with pickled beetroot and Strathdon Blue cheese or Mull scallops with wild garlic, sea lettuce and pea sauce. John's lobster is served with smoked lobster kedgeree and asparagus. Add to that elaborate desserts, a distinctive wine list, exceptional cocktails and mocktails, a loaf of own-baked bread at every table served with seaweed butter and their own chocolates to complete a standout meal.

Chef/s: Carla Lamont. **Closed:** Mon, Tue, winter. **Meals:** set D £48 (3 courses) to £68. **Details:** 18 seats. Wheelchairs. Parking. Children over 12 yrs.

Anonymous

At *The Good Food Guide*, our inspectors dine anonymously and pay their bill in full every time.These impartial review meals, along with feedback from thousands of our readers, are what informs the content of the *GFG*. Only the best restaurants make the cut.

★ NEW ENTRY ★

Pennygate Lodge

Cooking score: 3

British | £37

Craignure, Isle of Mull, PA65 6AY
Tel no: (01680) 812333
pennygatelodge.scot

This handsome Georgian manse, a short stroll from the Craignure ferry, is well placed not just for an arrival from Oban, but also for long-distance views across the Sound of Mull and, with luck, magnificent sunsets and mackerel skies. Fiona Langton and Tony McGill opened this immaculate operation with six stylish bedrooms and have recently extended it to serve an equally stylish dinner for guests and non-residents. Three well-cooked courses of refined home cooking defines the style that may begin with a small plate of Isle of Mull haggis and mash, or hot- and cold-smoked trout with cucumber granita. They have a non-meat dish at every course; we enjoyed the beetroot tartare and walnut. Mains may be cod on crushed new potatoes and a smoked haddock velouté, or pork with sweet potato and black pudding. A delicate carrot cake and cinnamon mousse makes a rewarding finish, as does a choice from their select collection of island malts, to be enjoyed in the delightful picture-window sitting room. Wines start at £18.50.

Chef/s: Jordan Clark. **Meals:** main courses £19 to £22. **Details:** Bar. Parking.

Isle of Ulva

LOCAL GEM

The Boathouse

Seafood | £15

Isle of Ulva
Tel no: (01688) 500241
theboathouseulva.co.uk

The Isle of Ulva, a sparsely inhabited Scottish island – four adults, two children – is reached by hailing the little ferry boat from a remote quay on the Isle of Mull and making the five-minute crossing to The Boathouse, a delightful whitewashed bistro where cousins Emma Mackie and Rebecca Munro have built up this romantic enterprise. Inside it amounts to no more than a few pine tables, a fridge for bottled beers and wine and a short menu of soup, sandwiches and its true attraction: the shellfish caught in the family creels. The daily harvest of Soriby Bay oysters and langoustines served with homemade bread is best taken outdoors on one of the picnic tables overlooking the sound, Loch Na Keal, and Mull's highest mountain, Ben More. Don't miss the specials, either – maybe potted crab or smoked haddock risotto, with chocolate fudge cake to finish.

Kilberry

The Kilberry Inn

Cooking score: 3

Modern British | £34

Kilberry Road, Kilberry, PA29 6YD
Tel no: (01880) 770223
kilberryinn.com

Follow the long and winding B8024 and you'll eventually arrive at this former croft – a testament to the old Scottish way of life, with rough-hewn stone walls, low beamed ceilings and a red tin roof. The Kilberry Inn also promises log-burning warmth, genuine personable hospitality and plenty of good food courtesy of chef owner Clare Johnson and her team. The kitchen eschews highly worked culinary pyrotechnics in favour of well-sourced seasonal ingredients and simply fashioned dishes along the lines of beef bourguignon or roast pheasant with root vegetable mash. Prime Scottish seafood such as fresh, perfectly cooked Gigha halibut is well matched by its accompaniments (carrot purée, pickled carrot and crispy quinoa, for instance), while dry-aged ribeye steaks appear with just some mustard butter and Parmentier potatoes for company. After that, look no further than plum and frangipane tart. The wine list is a labour of love from co-owner David Wilson.

Chef/s: Clare Johnson. **Closed:** Mon, 1 Jan to mid Mar. **Meals:** main courses £14 to £24. **Details:** 26 seats. 12 seats outside. Music. Parking.

Oban

Ee-Usk

Cooking score: 1

Seafood | £28

North Pier, Oban, PA34 5QD
Tel no: (01631) 565666
eeusk.com

This modern seafood bistro is right on the harbour, so the magnificent fish and shellfish landed at Oban doesn't have far to travel. Its expansive glass frontage affords unadulterated views of fishing boats, the bay and the islands and hills beyond. Keep it simple with Loch Creran oysters or local mussels in wine and garlic, or seek out the more exotic delights of Thai fishcakes or the Med-influenced scallops with chorizo and lemon butter. If your appetite allows, move on to a glorious seafood platter – or the grand platter for two to share. Drinks matching is easy with more than a dozen whites by the glass, plus a serious range of whiskies.

Chef/s: David Kariuki. **Closed:** 25 and 26 Dec, 3 weeks Jan. **Meals:** main courses £12 to £50. Set L and D £16. **Details:** 94 seats. 20 seats outside. Wheelchairs. Music. Children over 12 yrs at D.

Strachur

Inver

Cooking score: 6

Modern British | £40

Strathlachlan, Strachur, PA27 8BU
Tel no: (01369) 860537
inverrestaurant.co.uk

From their remote converted cottage in its idyllic loch-front location, Pamela Brunton and Rob Latimer have quickly built a reputation and enthusiastic following for their authentic, innovative approach to Scottish food. Mini masterpieces are conjured from humble elements, flavours are bold, traditional techniques of foraging, pickling and fermenting abound and 'individually diverting items marry together into unexpectedly imaginative and welcome flavour experiences'. Under Rob's careful eye front of house, it all comes together seamlessly in an atmosphere of warmth and familiarity, sound-tracked by eclectic vinyl choices on the gramophone. The four-course set menu or à la carte might open with purple sprouting broccoli with dried blackberries, anchovy and buckwheat to be followed by plump Gigha halibut with smokey mussel notes and coastal greens. Desserts plunder surrounding hedgerows and might feature sorrel sorbet with damson vodka or hatted kit – a buttermilk curd with flavourings of rhubarb and caraway topped with a creamy milk crumb. The addition of five self-contained luxury bothies offers welcome accommodation in this secluded spot.

Chef/s: Pamela Brunton. **Closed:** Mon, Tue, 3 Jan to mid Mar. **Meals:** main courses £7 to £23. Set D £49 (4 courses). **Details:** 40 seats. 20 seats outside. Bar. Wheelchairs. Parking.

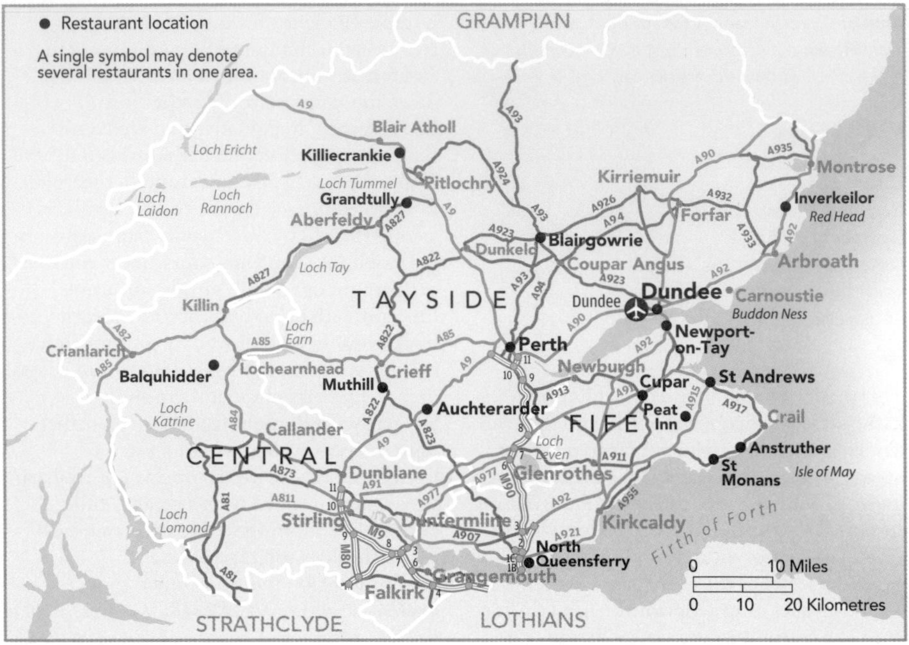

● Restaurant location

A single symbol may denote several restaurants in one area.

Balquhidder

Monachyle Mhor

Cooking score: 5

Modern British | £65

Balquhidder, FK19 8PQ
Tel no: (01877) 384622
mhor.net

This laid-back country house and working farm at the end of a long single-track road, and surrounded by picture postcard Scottish lochs and glens, is the former home of the Lewis family. Over two generations, they have created a field-to-fork food empire in the Trossachs but remain laudably close to their roots – Tom Lewis still lives on site. The tiny bar might welcome local workers off the neighbouring hills but the restaurant achieves greater refinement. Set lunch and dinner menus are unashamedly local in their conception: wild wood pigeon is complemented by earthy notes of beetroot and kohlrabi but lifted by fresh thyme and aromatic mustard; Blackface lamb from the farm is sweetly paired with chorizo, confit tomato, olives and capers. Creative desserts might see a thyme crème fraîche parfait enriched with macerated quince and cherry gel. The wine list contains some gems and guests can enjoy coffee and petits fours in the cosy lounge complete with gramophone.

Chef/s: Marysia Paszkowska and Graham Kerr.
Meals: set L £24 (2 courses) to £30. Set D £65.
Details: 42 seats. 16 seats outside. V menu.

LOCAL GEM

Mhor 84

Modern British | £30

Balquhidder, FK19 8NY
Tel no: (01877) 384646
mhor.net

This younger sibling of the Lewis family's fine-dining Monachyle Mhor (see entry) does a roaring trade with savvy locals, residents, passing motorists and walkers, all delighted with the all-day welcome. Whether you start at 8am with a veggie breakfast featuring halloumi, spinach and vegetarian haggis, are looking for a lunchtime sandwich, or want smoked paprika squid followed by cod with artichoke risotto for dinner, you will enjoy hearty food often produced by the Lewises' own farm and bakery. All-day cakes and a well-stocked bar meet most additional needs.

Grandtully

★ NEW ENTRY ★

Ballintaggart Farm

Cooking score: 4

Modern British | £35

Grandtully, PH9 0PX

Tel no: (01796) 482738

ballintaggart.com

£5 OFF

'I cannot recall two more enjoyable evenings spent dining out in the UK,' noted an enthusiastic reader, one of many who have praised this elegant restaurant with rooms amid the rolling pastures of rural Perthshire. Chris Rowley, a former banker, moved here with his wife Rachel in 2016 and together they've created an impressive concern that, besides two stylish bedrooms, puts prime Scottish produce at its heart. A sharing board taken on a sunny terrace brought locally produced venison salami, gravadlax with samphire and goat's cheese crostini. The beautiful dining room is where guests eat together at the long mahogany table dressed with flowers and candles. We enjoyed nettle soup with Skye langoustines followed by tender hay-smoked lamb with rocket, wild garlic and capers and on the side an indulgent shepherd's pie. Gorse flower crème brûlée and coconut macaroon followed. Rowley's sourdough bread was outstanding. Wines come from a short but thoughtful list. After coffee and Scottish tablet came a farewell of locally made marshmallows to toast on the fire pit. 'It's simply sublime,' enthused an early visitor, and we concur.

Chef/s: Chris Rowley. **Closed:** 24 Dec to 7 Jan. **Meals:** set L £18 (2 courses) to £25. Set D £45. Sun L £25. Tasting menu £65. **Details:** 40 seats. 8 seats outside. V menu. Vg menu. Bar. Music. Parking. Children at L only.

Anstruther

The Cellar

Cooking score: 6

Modern British | £60

24 East Green, Anstruther, KY10 3AA
Tel no: (01333) 310378
thecellaranstruther.co.uk

Billy Boyter has been at The Cellar for some four years now and continues to expand his skill and ambition. Contemporary rustic decor – hewn stone, ancient timbers, warm plaids and delicate silver birch – offers a subtle backdrop to the vibrant palette of colour and texture in the highly seasonal fixed menus (five courses at lunch, seven at dinner). Miniaturist culinary masterpieces of true complexity and depth, sometimes crafted from humble ingredients, suit the informal atmosphere. A standout appetiser of caramelised ox tongue in a creamy Parmesan velouté with pickled baby onions and chive oil sets the scene for what follows. Local crab is served with crisped wild rice, and squid tartare is innovatively cocooned in soft kelp jelly – an evocative reflection of the Fife coast. Mains might include tender pink hogget with a zingy mint and lemon balm relish and wild garlic purée. Finish perhaps with a stellar interpretation of simple blackberry and apple – offering a surprise in every mouthful. Wines from £24.

Chef/s: Billy Boyter. **Closed:** Mon, Tue, 24 to 26 Dec, 2 weeks Jan, 1 week May, 2 weeks Sept. **Meals:** set L £35 (5 courses). Set D £60 (7 courses). **Details:** 26 seats. Bar. Music. Children over 12 yrs.

Stay in the know

For the latest restaurant news, look out for the weekly *GFG Briefing*. Visit thegoodfoodguide.co.uk

Cupar

Ostlers Close

Cooking score: 4

Modern British | £45

25 Bonnygate, Cupar, KY15 4BU
Tel no: (01334) 655574
ostlersclose.co.uk

The Grahams have run their tiny restaurant off Cupar's main street for nearly four decades, building up a strong and cherished local reputation along the way. It's a tiny space 'where you are close to your neighbour', the decor 'simple with rich colours but not over fussy', with the marvellously hospitable Amanda Graham firmly in charge. In the kitchen, Jimmy Graham's cooking is exact and generous, solid technique allowing him to pull off dishes that still manage to feel contemporary and relevant – albeit in a classic context. Seasonal produce is everything, supplied by the restaurant's own kitchen garden, foraging trips and a network of local producers. Thus a winter meal could open with partridge breast on creamed celeriac with wild mushroom sauce, go on to roast fillet of cod with confit vegetables and a langoustine sauce, and finish with a steamed marmalade sponge. The wine list is carefully considered, well annotated and reasonably priced.

Chef/s: Jimmy Graham. **Closed:** Sun, Mon, 25 and 26 Dec, 1 and 2 Jan, 2 weeks Jan, 2 weeks Apr. **Meals:** main courses £25 to £29. **Details:** 28 seats. Children over 6 yrs.

Newport-on-Tay

The Newport

Cooking score: 4

Modern British | £50

1 High Street, Newport-on-Tay, DD6 8AB
Tel no: (01382) 541449
thenewportrestaurant.co.uk

This former pub offers a stunning panoramic view of the north Fife coast and across to Dundee but it is the cooking that is the star. Make no mistake, Jamie Scott (the 2014

winner of *MasterChef: The Professionals*) can deliver the goods and he has made his restaurant with rooms a serious contender on the local food scene since his arrival some three years ago. Scott's strength lies in the quality of his suppliers – he is dedicated to sourcing the finest seasonal ingredients, whether foraged or grown nearby – and his style is very much of the moment, offering a selection of small plates and tasting menus – the latter in vegetarian, pescatarian and omnivore versions – using modern techniques to confer distinctiveness on dishes such as tempura of East Neuk squid with lemongrass and chilli dressing or pigeon with beetroot and malted grains. Desserts confidently push the right buttons and wines start at £18.

Chef/s: Jamie Scott. **Closed:** Mon, 24 to 26 Dec, 1 to 7 Jan. **Meals:** small plates £6 to £14. Sun L £35. Tasting menu £55 (6 courses). **Details:** 40 seats. 12 seats outside. V menu. Bar. Wheelchairs. Music. Parking.

North Queensferry

The Wee Restaurant

Cooking score: 3

Modern British | £36

17 Main Street, North Queensferry, KY11 1JG
Tel no: (01383) 616263
theweerestaurant.co.uk

The Wee Restaurant is right by *the* bridge across the Forth, the mighty cantilevered railway bridge designed by a couple of Englishmen at the end of the 19th century. The stone-clad house, once a jail by all accounts, has been home to Craig and Vikki Wood's restaurant since the mid noughties, and has built a solid reputation for good food and good times. It's lively, informal and serious where it counts – fine Scottish ingredients cooked with care. A brasserie-style output runs to classic moules marinière and 28-day aged steaks cooked on the char-grill, to the more contemporary spiced Strathspey pork belly salad with an Asian dressing, and herby gnocchi with Gorgonzola and salsa verde. A lunchtime and midweek evening daily menu ensures a steady footfall. To finish, pear tarte tatin competes for your attention with cheeses from Iain Mellis, or you could have both. The globetrotting wine list opens at £19.75.

Chef/s: Craig Wood and Sam Dorey. **Closed:** Mon, 25 and 26 Dec, 1 and 2 Jan. **Meals:** set L (Tue to Sat) and D (Tue to Thurs) £16 (2 courses) to £20. Set D £29 (2 courses) to £36. Sun L £23. **Details:** 36 seats. Music.

Peat Inn

★ TOP 50 ★

The Peat Inn

Cooking score: 8

Modern British | £55

Peat Inn, KY15 5LH
Tel no: (01334) 840206
thepeatinn.co.uk

An 18th-century staging post of stature and significance, the Peat Inn is now a premier-league destination renowned for its matchless hospitality and precisely honed modern gastronomy. The interior is blessed with tweed fabrics, fresh flowers, log fires and other cosy touches and the whole place is a model of seamless organisation: Katherine Smeddle emanates genuine warmth out front, while husband Geoffrey creates culinary miracles, weaving his artistry around a larder full of seasonal Scottish ingredients. His take on kedgeree involves not only smoked haddock and pearl barley but also warm langoustines and poached Baldinnie quail's eggs, while wild halibut might appear in company with wilted spinach, salt-baked celeriac, cockles, poached white beans, sea kale and mushroom velouté. Regular visitors have also been impressed by the kitchen's sublime game dishes – from an 'exquisite' pairing of East Neuk wood pigeon breast and roast veal sweetbread with pickled peach, smooth liver parfait and smoked almond dressing to roast grouse accompanied by cocotte potatoes, spinach, oyster mushrooms, brambles and roasting juices. This is masterful, complex cooking to be sure, but it never feels contrived or overworked. There's also something almost

effortless about multi-layered, multi-part desserts such as a croustillant of rhubarb and custard with stem ginger ice cream. The global wine list has impressive breadth and depth, with fine wines offered by the glass (thanks to a Coravin system) and a helpful assortment of half bottles for those who want to explore.
Chef/s: Geoffrey Smeddle. **Closed:** Sun, Mon, 24 to 27 Dec, 1 week Jan. **Meals:** main courses £17 to £32. Set L £25. Set D £55. Tasting menu £75 (6 courses). **Details:** 53 seats. V menu. Vg menu. Bar. Wheelchairs. Music. Parking.

St Andrews
The Seafood Ristorante
Cooking score: 3
Seafood | £55
The Scores, Bruce Embankment, St Andrews, KY16 9AB
Tel no: (01334) 479475
theseafoodristorante.com

The striking glass cube right on the shoreline is deservedly popular with everyone who enjoys the local fish; it's considered quite an asset in the town. The culinary doings are essentially modern, with the menu looking in the direction of Italy for dishes such as hand-rolled pappardelle with crab, chilli, coriander and seafood bisque, hand-dived scallops with San Daniele ham, chicory and orange, and monkfish wrapped in prosciutto and teamed with slow-cooked beef, porcini mushrooms, onion and carrots. But smoked haddock rarebit with braised leeks, Arran mustard and crushed potatoes, and Anstruther lobster simply grilled with garlic butter are attractive propositions, too. The sophisticated way to finish is with lemon Amalfi tart with raspberry sorbet. Perhaps due to a regular influx of wealthy golfers and a well-heeled student population with generous parents, the wine list is really very good, with choice by the glass and an extensive range of quality classics by the bottle.
Chef/s: David Aspin. **Closed:** 25 and 26 Dec, first 10 days Jan. **Meals:** main courses £19 to £32. Set L £19 (2 courses) to £24. **Details:** 80 seats. 40 seats outside. Wheelchairs. Music.

St Monans
Craig Millar at 16 West End
Cooking score: 3
Modern British | £45
16 West End, St Monans, KY10 2BX
Tel no: (01333) 730327
16westend.com
£5 OFF

On sunny days, you might abandon the calm atmosphere of the dining room in favour of a seat outside, all the better to savour the harbour location and sea views. The location of this Fife stalwart means that fish is inevitably a feature of Craig Millar's menus, but the bounty of Scotland's fields is also well represented. Set-price lunch and dinner menus are collated into 'Land' and 'Sea' and might open with the ever-popular savoury hit of the twice-baked Mull Cheddar soufflé, or a lighter Jerusalem artichoke panna cotta with pickled mushrooms giving an intriguing balance of sweet and savoury. Halibut is served with a tomato and shallot crust with scallop, sea vegetables and chive sauce as worthy accents. Toothsome desserts such as chocolate crémeux with malt ice cream and salted caramel, or fresh bramble parfait, provide a satisfying conclusion. A thoughtful wine list covers the main New and Old World bases.
Chef/s: Craig Millar. **Closed:** Mon, Tue, 24 to 26 Dec, 2 weeks Jan. **Meals:** set L £22 (2 courses) to £28. Set D £45. Tasting menu £65. **Details:** 40 seats. 20 seats outside. Bar. Wheelchairs. Music. Parking. Children over 12 yrs at D.

Auchterarder

★ TOP 50 ★

Restaurant Andrew Fairlie

Cooking score: 8

Modern European | £110

Gleneagles Hotel, Auchterarder, PH3 1NF
Tel no: (01764) 694267
andrewfairlie.co.uk

The ambition of being luxurious but not stuffy is well met by the locale and team at Restaurant Andrew Fairlie. In the heart of Gleneagles Hotel, away from views and distractions, diners are cocooned in a gilded cave of dark chocolate, cappuccino and whipped-cream tones accented with sparkling crystal, subtle leaf motifs and muted lighting. The world outside and indeed time itself is left behind as engaging staff glide through a seemingly effortless choreography with the diner at the centre. The food is as polished as the performance. A sequence of opening morsels: hot fondue gougère, mushroom tart, confit duck encased in butternut and panko, all set the scene for delights to follow. Technical excellence and French savoir-faire combined with premium Scottish ingredients results in near-faultless interpretations of classic combinations. A starter of delicate boudin blanc with pistachios, spinach and wild mushrooms in truffle and Madeira sauce achieves just the right balance of finesse and rusticity. A generous portion of firm, flaking turbot stands proud amid razor clams and sweet samphire bathed in a shellfish bisque of depth and complexity. Desserts expand the classical flavour repertoire with variations on milk and dark chocolate introducing yuzu, basil, raspberries and smoked salt to the four complementary mini desserts on the plate. An expansive wine list offers some interesting, affordable options as well as plenty for oligarchs' wallets.

Chef/s: Andrew Fairlie and Stephen McLaughlin. **Closed:** Sun, 25 and 26 Dec, 3 weeks Jan. **Meals:** alc £110 (3 courses). Tasting menu £155 (8 courses). **Details:** 50 seats. V menu. Wheelchairs. Music. Parking. Children over 5 yrs.

Blairgowrie

Kinloch House

Cooking score: 5

Modern British | £55

Dunkeld Road, Blairgowrie, PH10 6SG
Tel no: (01250) 884237
kinlochhouse.com

Members of the Allen family have been conscientious custodians of this creeper-clad Victorian manor since 2002, shoring up its reputation for proper country-house hospitality and promoting the hotel as a showcase for Steve MacCallum's technically adept cooking. Luckily, the chef also knows his way around Scotland's food networks and treats seasonal produce with the respect it deserves, be it a salad of Stornoway black pudding and Ayrshire bacon or roast loin of Perthshire lamb. That said, dishes are often more elaborately conceived and fancifully presented than the menu suggests: a starter of red mullet with aubergine purée and vegetable relish, for example, might arrive embellished with roast langoustine tails, while a plate of Scotch beef rump, smoked butter potatoes, roast carrots and peppercorn sauce could also feature an oxtail croquette. To conclude, waiting 15 minutes for the hot chocolate fondant with milk ice cream is no hardship in the civilised surroundings of the pleasantly airy dining room. Vintage Bordeaux and Burgundies form the backbone of the heavy-duty wine list, although there's plenty from the New World too.

Chef/s: Steve MacCallum. **Closed:** 12 to 30 Dec. **Meals:** set L £20 (2 courses) to £26. Set D £45 (2 courses) to £55. Sun L £30. **Details:** 34 seats. Bar. Wheelchairs. Parking. Children over 6 yrs at D.

Little's

Cooking score: 2

Seafood | £30

4 Wellmeadow, Blairgowrie, PH10 6ND
Tel no: (01250) 875358
littlesrestaurant.co.uk

Still in the centre of Blairgowrie, Little's restaurant has moved across the river Ericht to magnificent new surroundings in a converted church, bathed in light from the stained-glass windows. While capitalising on the more spacious and accessible environment, chef patron Willie Little nonetheless stays true to his popular and honest focus on serving fresh fish, simply prepared. Alongside classics such as plump mussels with garlic, bacon and white wine or roast monkfish in Parma ham, the old-school blackboard offers regular specials ranging from John Dory to velvet crab. Classic steaks and an unexpected house speciality of pizzas meet the needs of those not drawn by seafood, and the desserts will please the sweet-toothed.

Chef/s: Willie Little. **Closed:** Sun, Mon. **Meals:** main courses £8 to £26. Set L and D £22 (2 courses). **Details:** 38 seats.

Dundee

Castlehill

Cooking score: 6

Modern British | £38

22 Exchange Street, Dundee, DD1 3DL
Tel no: (01382) 220008
castlehillrestaurant.co.uk

£5 OFF

Head chef Graham Campbell took over the ownership of Castlehill at the beginning of 2018, a logical move for an operation that had his personality already stamped indelibly on it. Behind an aubergine façade a little way back from the waterfront, it's a pleasantly spacious place, with a striking wall feature listing some of Scotland's wildlife. Two lunches and four dinners a week allow Campbell room to spread his wings, and from the homemade breads and appetisers onwards it's clear this is a classy show. Presentations are intriguing, turning a dish such as seafood ravioli of salmon, lobster and lemongrass into a thing of wonder, or productively reinventing a Parmesan- and anchovy-rich Caesar salad with croquettes rather than croûtons. A reader won't soon forget her opulent main course of partridge with chestnuts and truffle custard, or there may be Atlantic cod in a butter of lapsang tea with mussels and artichokes. At dessert there could be blood orange soufflé with 70 per cent chocolate, or a lemon study in which fennel gives an aromatic lift to parfait and meringue. A concise wine list ticks the fashionable boxes, from Picpoul to Malbec, starting at £19.50.

Chef/s: Graham Campbell. **Closed:** Sun, Mon, Tue, 24 to 26 Dec, 31 Dec to 4 Jan. **Meals:** set L £18 (2 courses) to £22. Set D £32 (2 courses) to £38. **Details:** 40 seats. Wheelchairs. Music. No children after 8pm.

Inverkeilor

Gordon's

Cooking score: 5

Modern British | £65

Main Street, Inverkeilor, DD11 5RN
Tel no: (01241) 830364
gordonsrestaurant.co.uk

Gordon's comes as something of a surprise in the little village of Inverkeilor, not an obvious location perhaps for fine dining. The converted house is elegant and tasteful, inside and out, and is a tight family business, owned and run for 32 years by Maria Watson, with her son Garry now at the helm in the kitchen. Passion and commitment to detail is evident from the crisp linen and sparkling Riedel glasses in the dining room, through to the regularly changing fixed-price five-course menu. A perfectly judged venison tartare with pickled shimeji, hazelnut aïoli and tart apple is umami-rich yet delicate, while the signature Tobermory cheese soufflé is 'genuinely a comfort blanket, perfectly presented, unctuous and rich with immense depth of flavour'. Mains showcase Scotland's rich larder, perhaps duck with earthy root vegetable purée, or cod with brown shrimp, piperade and saffron mussel velouté, while desserts often pay homage to Valrhona chocolate. The personal touch front of house and in the kitchen is well appreciated.

Chef/s: Garry Watson. **Closed:** Sun (winter only), Mon, Jan. **Meals:** set L £35. Set D £65 (5 courses). **Details:** 24 seats. Bar. Wheelchairs. Music. Parking. Children over 5 yrs at L, over 12 yrs at D.

Killiecrankie

Killiecrankie Hotel

Cooking score: 2

Modern British | £45

Killiecrankie, PH16 5LG
Tel no: (01796) 473220
killiecrankiehotel.co.uk

Just to the north of Pitlochry, with commanding views over the Pass, Killiecrankie stands in sparkling-white splendour amid four acres of wooded grounds, herbaceous borders and rose gardens, having been built in the early Victorian era for a discerning man of the cloth. As we go to press, it's on the market, so watch this space, but if there are no sudden changes, expect a delightful Tayside rural retreat with carefully considered country-house cooking. That could mean seared king scallops with crispy Parma ham, cauliflower purée and parsley oil or sautéed fillet of Perthshire venison with pommes Anna, fondant celeriac, braised red cabbage and stem broccoli in crab apple jus. A choice of Scottish cheeses and oatcakes, or perhaps Catalan tart with blood orange jelly and lemon sorbet complete the meal. The usefully annotated wine list opens at £22.50, with a nice spread by the glass in three sizes, from £6.10 for the medium measure.

Chef/s: Mark Easton. **Closed:** 3 Jan to 22 Mar. **Meals:** set D £45 (4 courses). **Details:** 30 seats. Bar. Parking.

Muthill

Barley Bree

Cooking score: 3

Anglo-French | £45

6 Willoughby Street, Muthill, PH5 2AB
Tel no: (01764) 681451
barleybree.com

There's a marriage of France and Scotland at this restaurant with rooms occupying the bones of an old coaching inn. Quite literally, in the case of owners Fabrice and Alison Bouteloup – and figuratively when it comes to the output from Fabrice's kitchen. Fine Scottish ingredients star on menus that combine classic French techniques with modern presentation and occasional fusion flourishes. Seared hand-dived scallops arrive with crispy anchovy and a soy dressing, while main courses run to saddle of Perthshire venison with pancetta and chestnuts, or hake fillet with a delicate lemon jelly. Finish with tarte tatin for two, or dark chocolate and hazelnut délice with blackcurrant sorbet. Antlers adorn the mantelpiece of the traditional dining areas with their dark beams and welcoming wood-burning stove, while upstairs are six comfortable bedrooms. Alison has put together an engaging wine list opening at £20.

Chef/s: Fabrice Bouteloup. **Closed:** Mon, Tue, 24 to 26 Dec, 1 week Jul. **Meals:** main courses £12 to £24. Set L £17 (2 courses) to £21. **Details:** 48 seats. 12 seats outside. Bar. Music. Parking.

Perth

Deans

Cooking score: 3

Modern British | £33

77-79 Kinnoull Street, Perth, PH3 1LU
Tel no: (01738) 643377
letseatperth.co.uk

Occupying what was Perth's old Theatre Royal (circa 1822), William and Margo Deans' long-running neighbourhood restaurant continues to play to a packed house and still operates as a genuine family-run enterprise, with one son working as manager and another now installed as head chef. Done out in silvery tones with lots of varnished wood and crimson upholstery, the dining room provides an elegant backdrop for food that gives Scottish ingredients a thoughtful and professional workout. Smoked Shetland scallops might be imaginatively paired with roe emulsion, BBQ chicken, sea herbs and sweetcorn shoots, while rump of spring lamb (cooked pink) could appear alongside glazed sweetbreads, tarragon gnocchi, asparagus and a fricassée of peas and broad beans. Slabs of Orkney beef are sizzled on the grill, while desserts could include anything from sticky gingerbread pudding to piña colada panna cotta with saffron-poached pineapple. Cocktails and wee drams are served in the bar, and the 80-bin wine list features house selections from £18.95.

Chef/s: Jamie Deans. **Closed:** Mon, Tue, 1 Jan, 2 weeks Jan, 1 week Nov. **Meals:** main courses £16 to £29. Set L £14 (2 courses) to £19. Set D £18 (2 courses) to £22. Sun L £23. **Details:** 60 seats. Bar. Wheelchairs. Music.

The North Port

Cooking score: 3

British | £32

8 North Port, Perth, PH1 5LU

Tel no: (01738) 580867

thenorthport.co.uk

'What a find,' exclaimed one visitor, suggesting we ignore the unglamorous back-street location behind Perth Concert Hall and concentrate on the 'assured and vibrant cooking'. Andrew Moss and Karen Milne's small, darkly panelled restaurant occupies an 18th-century building and is a comfortable, atmospheric and sociable place with prices that keep locals returning. Menus are constantly updated to reflect availability and seasonality, in winter delivering beautifully cooked Scrabster gurnard with broccoli, bacon, lemon purée and almonds, ahead of North Sea cod served with celeriac, spinach and clam and parsley sauce, and Portmahomack pork belly with Jerusalem artichoke, apple, hazelnut and savoy cabbage. Expect virtuoso desserts such as caramelised carrot with walnut meringue, Knockraich yoghurt ice cream and carrot crisps. This is unaffected cooking where incidentals charm too: excellent bread, wonderful butter and a fantastic regional Scottish cheese selection, all backed up by a wine list that offers good drinking from £17.95.

Chef/s: Andrew Moss. **Closed:** Sun, Mon, 24 Dec to 3 Jan. **Meals:** main courses £13 to £25. Set L £14 (2 courses) to £17. Early D £17 (2 courses) to £20. **Details:** 32 seats. V menu. Vg menu. Music.

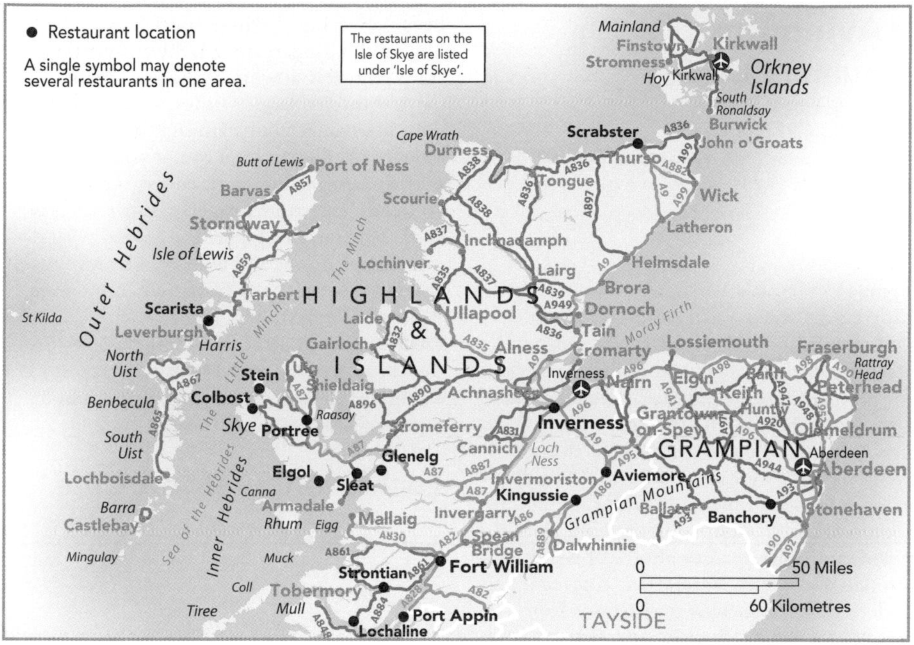

● Restaurant location

A single symbol may denote several restaurants in one area.

The restaurants on the Isle of Skye are listed under 'Isle of Skye'.

Banchory

LOCAL GEM

The Cowshed

Modern British | £26

Raemoir Road, Banchory, AB31 5QB
Tel no: (01330) 820813
cowshedrestaurant.co.uk

An on-site chippy, light lunches of toasted panini and open sandwiches, plus great Sunday roasts are just some of the reasons why locals and visitors continue to pack the Buchans' welcoming restaurant. Set in a spacious, clean-lined modern building with a conservatory and terrace offering restful views over farmland to the flat-topped Hill of Fare, it promises great value and a menu of comforting food ranging from fishcakes and langoustine tails with a sweet chilli dip to chicken breast with oatmeal stuffing or caramelised pork belly with white bean, potato and bacon cassoulet.

Send us your review

Your feedback informs the content of the *GFG* and will be used to compile next year's reviews. To register your opinion about any restaurant listed in the Guide, or a restaurant that you wish to bring to our attention, visit: thegoodfoodguide.co.uk/feedback

Aviemore

Mountain Café

Cooking score: 2

International | £23

111 Grampian Road, Aviemore, PH22 1RH
Tel no: (01479) 812473
mountaincafe-aviemore.co.uk

Some 15 years after Kirsten Gilmour set up shop here, she remains a hands-on presence and a key part of the friendly, welcoming atmosphere that keeps visitors coming back for more. Indeed, so popular is the Mountain Café that 'at 12.15 we had to queue for 15 minutes, but when we got into the dining room the staff were super efficient'. The decor is mountain-hut pine with 'bits of mountaineering equipment hanging from the beams' and 'some quality photos of wildlife, animals and nature'. Vegetarians and vegans are well catered for on a menu that runs from breakfast (granola, French toast, filled breakfast rolls) to lunch of carrot, ginger, almond and basil soup with a chunk of homemade bread. Sweetcorn fritters are layered with sour cream and bacon and topped with avocado smash and chipotle dipping sauce, while the lavish cake display comes into its own in the late afternoon. To drink, there's a brief wine list and Cairngorm Brewery beers.

Chef/s: Kirsten Gilmour. **Closed:** 25 and 26 Dec, 1 Jan. **Meals:** main courses £11 to £15. **Details:** 43 seats. 12 seats outside. Music. Parking.

Fort William

Crannog

Cooking score: 1

Seafood | £35

Town Pier, Fort William, PH33 6DB
Tel no: (01397) 705589
crannog.net

Jolly fairy lights adorning the entrance, and a sense of being all but cantilevered out over Loch Linnhe from the town pier, bestow regional distinctiveness on Crannog. It has been delivering classic seafood dishes to Highland voyagers since 1989, with cullen skink, mussels in white wine and cream, garlic-buttered langoustines, and peppered salmon in sauce vierge among the mainstream attractions. There's meat too, if you will, perhaps lamb saddle with aubergine and couscous, and some properly lavish desserts, such as cranachan cheesecake loaded with raspberries, honey and whisky. Always consult the daily specials board first: when it's gone, it's gone. Wines start at £19.75.

Chef/s: Stewart MacLachlan. **Closed:** 25 and 26 Dec, 1 Jan, 1 week winter. **Meals:** main courses £16 to £24. Set L £16 (2 courses) to £19. **Details:** 55 seats. Wheelchairs. Music. Parking.

Lochleven Seafood Café

Cooking score: 2

Seafood | £43

Onich, Fort William, PH33 6SA
Tel no: (01855) 821048
lochlevenseafoodcafe.co.uk

Views from this seasonal café across Loch Leven to the peak of the Pap of Glencoe are 'breathtaking', but if the shellfish served here doesn't come out of the waters of this loch, then be assured, it won't have travelled very far – perhaps from Lochs Linnhe and Creran. Water tanks ensure the shellfish are perfectly fresh and the kitchen treats them with respect and simplicity: Loch Linnhe langoustines with lemon and mayonnaise, or Loch Leven mussels cooked in cider. Hot or cold seafood platters are hard to resist. You might start with razor clams or shellfish soup with aïoli, move on to fillet of cod with patatas bravas, and finish with cherry cake and Calvados ice cream. Keep an eye on the specials blackboard and note there are meat and vegetarian options such as slow-cooked shoulder of lamb or baked ricotta gnudi. The Europe-focused wine list opens at £18.10.

Chef/s: Katie MacFarlane Slack. **Closed:** 31 Oct to 16 Mar. **Meals:** main courses £12 to £43. **Details:** 40 seats. 20 seats outside. Bar. Wheelchairs. Parking.

Glenelg

The Glenelg Inn

Cooking score: 1

British | £35

Glenelg, IV40 8JR

Tel no: (01599) 522273

glenelg-inn.com

'No meat, no milk, no bread, no eggs, no wine.' So ran the report of James Boswell and Dr Johnson's visit to Glenelg in 1773. Happily, things have changed in the intervening years and there are now all these things and more in this moody old inn overlooking the Sleat of Skye and the little car ferry to Kylerhea. There's nothing elaborate about the blackboard menu chalked up daily with no-fuss dishes such as smoked mackerel pâté, beer-battered haddock and chips, smoked haddock risotto and, on lucky days, crab claws, Skye langoustines, squat lobster and hand-dived scallops. You can eat in the dining room but it's the bar that really matches the ideal of a traditional Scottish inn with its dark, panelled walls, worn leather armchairs by the log fire and fading sepia photographs.

Chef/s: Verity Hurding. **Closed:** mid Nov to 1 Mar. **Meals:** main courses £9 to £14. **Details:** 50 seats. 30 seats outside. Wheelchairs. Music. Parking.

Inverness

Chez Roux at Rocpool Reserve

Cooking score: 3

French | £40

Rocpool Reserve Hotel, 14 Culduthel Road, Inverness, IV2 4AG

Tel no: (01463) 240089

rocpool.com

A grand stone-pillared portico marks the entrance to Rocpool Reserve, although the main talking point at this boutique hotel is its classically styled restaurant, where the mood is often hushed and guests sit at pale leather chairs surrounded by cheffy cartoons. However, if the Roux nametag conjures up visions of rarefied ultra-expensive haute cuisine, think again: the food here is refined but approachable, and prices never overstep the mark. There's respect for Scotland's seasonal larder too, from a Highland game pâté en croûte partnered by salt-baked beetroot, pickles and Sauternes jelly, to a Scottish seafood zarzuela with roast butternut squash, fermented cabbage and langoustine velouté. Albert Roux's shadow also hangs over the menu in the shape of studiously replicated signature dishes such as his celebrated tarte au citron with coconut meringue, blackberry sorbet, sea salt and hazelnut crumble. Meanwhile, an impressively collated French-led wine list lends a certain lustre to proceedings.

Chef/s: Lee Pattie. **Closed:** Mon and Tue (Nov, Jan and Feb only). **Meals:** main courses £19 to £28. Set L £35. Set D £38. **Details:** 40 seats. Bar. Wheelchairs. Music. Parking.

Rocpool

Cooking score: 2

Modern European | £40

1 Ness Walk, Inverness, IV3 5NE

Tel no: (01463) 717274

rocpoolrestaurant.com

With its leather-trimmed booths, dramatic green lampshades, contemporary wallpaper and big windows, Rocpool brings a degree of swagger to Inverness. The kitchen also plays its part, tempering its larder of seasonal Scottish ingredients with influences from far and wide: hand-dived West Coast scallops are perked up with baby chorizo and spring onion crème fraîche, Speyside venison is roasted with Parma ham, haggis, glazed baby turnips and shallots, while tempura turbot with jasmine rice and shaved cucumber salad adds an oriental note to proceedings. There's generally something lively for vegetarians (perhaps gnocchi with fried duck egg, wild mushrooms and samphire), and desserts sit squarely in the comforting world of crème brûlée, mango pavlova and warm pecan pie. Set lunches and early-evening deals are worth noting, and there's plenty of good-value drinking on the helpfully annotated wine list. Not to be confused with Chez Roux at Rocpool Reserve (see entry).

Chef/s: Steven Devlin and George Sleet. **Closed:** Sun, 24 to 26 Dec, 1 to 4 Jan. **Meals:** main courses £14 to £26. Set L £17 (2 courses). Early set D £20 (2 courses). **Details:** 55 seats. Wheelchairs. Music.

Isle of Harris

Scarista House

Cooking score: 2

Modern British | £48

Scarista, Isle of Harris, HS3 3HX
Tel no: (01859) 550238
scaristahouse.com

Tim and Patricia Martin are due to celebrate 20 years at this converted Hebridean manse in 2019, and during their tenure they have turned Scarista House into a fixture of the Scottish scene, famed for its homespun hospitality. Geographically speaking, this is the back of beyond, so it's only fitting that the owners should bake their own bread, grow what they can, and look to the island's resources when it comes to putting food on the plate. Dinner might begin with a bisque of Harris Minch langoustines and smoked scallop mayonnaise, while mains could range from Stornoway turbot in boozy lovage sauce to loin of venison accompanied by Puy lentils, spiced red cabbage and thyme jus (beefed up with a slug of Harris-distilled gin). Menus change daily, but meals always end with a homely dessert (orange marmalade tart, for example) and a slate of Scottish cheeses. Wines include some inviting possibilities by the glass.

Chef/s: Scott McKenzie. **Closed:** 1 Dec to 28 Feb. **Meals:** set D £38 (2 courses) to £48. **Details:** 20 seats. Parking. Children over 8 yrs.

Isle of Skye

★ NEW ENTRY ★

Coruisk House

Cooking score: 2

Modern European | £45

26 Elgol, Isle of Skye, IV49 9BL
Tel no: (01471) 866330
coruiskhouse.com

Elgol, where a single-lane road ends on the far west coast, is about as remote as it gets. From a little harbour, there are boat trips to Loch Coruisk at the foot of the daunting Black Cuillin mountains and it's this spectacular scenery that persuaded Clare Winskill and Iain Roden to give up careers as London lawyers to open beautiful Coruisk House. With just three bedrooms and six tables at dinner they provide stylish accommodation and superior home-cooked food that might begin with a shellfish bisque and Clare's own bread rolls, or scallops in a barley and coral risotto. At inspection a generous piece of halibut with mussels and crab ravioli worked well, though its pairing of cauliflower 'couscous' and mussel consommé less so. Desserts were back on form with a delicate ginger sponge and cardamom ice cream. The regular wine list starts at £20 but Clare and Iain spend the winter visiting vineyards, creating a superior offering starting at £33 and rising.

Chef/s: Iain Roden. **Closed:** 1 Nov to mid March. **Meals:** set D £38 (2 courses) to £45. Tasting menu £65. **Details:** 14 seats. V menu. Vg menu. Bar. Music. Parking.

Vegetarian and vegan

While many restaurants offer individual dishes suitable for non-meat eaters, those marked 'V menu' (vegetarian) and 'Vg menu' (vegan) offer separate menus.

Dulse & Brose

Cooking score: 3

Modern British | £35

9-11 Bosville Terrace, Portree, Isle of Skye, IV51 9DG
Tel no: (01478) 612846
bosvillehotel.co.uk

Dulse & Brose (aka seaweed and oatmeal porridge) sounds like the title of a Scottish cookbook, and there's certainly an emphatic Caledonian bent to this comfortable restaurant within Portree's Bosville Hotel, from the dining room's heritage decor and Hebridean tweeds to a repertoire that makes much of pure-bred provenance. Venison Scotch eggs with celeriac rémoulade and pickled vegetables, hake fillet on Lochaber smoked haddock risotto, or pan-roasted duck breast partnered by confit leg, haggis bonbons and Puy lentils are typical examples. House-smoked halloumi with warm chickpea salad and pesto caters to the vegetarians among us, while desserts such as sticky toffee pudding with date sponge, butterscotch sauce and popcorn ice cream please all-comers. Incidentally, dulse and brose come together in the restaurant's offer of oaty bread with seaweed butter, while Scottish-brewed Thistly Cross cider and beers from the Isle of Skye Brewing Co. line up alongside some attractively priced wines.

Chef/s: Peter Cullen. **Meals:** main courses £17 to £23. **Details:** 48 seats. Bar. Music.

Kinloch Lodge

Cooking score: 4

Modern British | £80

Sleat, Isle of Skye, IV43 8QY
Tel no: (01471) 833214
kinloch-lodge.co.uk

'Over a three-night stay we ate wonderfully,' noted one reader, of this former hunting lodge idyllically situated on the shores of Loch na Dal. It was run for decades by Claire and Godfrey Macdonald, he the 34th chief of the Macdonald clan and she a talented cook, but now daughter Isabella maintains the same formula of elegant dining in this sumptuous hotel with prices to match. Drinks are taken in a drawing room with log fires, deep sofas and family photographs. The splendid, panelled, portrait-lined dining room is the setting for Marcello Tully's exacting dishes: a delicate sweetcorn panna cotta and white crabmeat worked especially well, followed by a delightful foamy parsnip and Pernod soup, progressing through seared pigeon breast; scallops; lamb with a cashew nut and black olive crust; and finishing with an orange cream. Service is precise and the wine list biblical, beginning modestly at £18.50 and rising well into the hundreds for some famous labels.

Chef/s: Marcello Tully. **Meals:** set L £40 (2 courses) to £45. Set D £80. Sun L £40 (2 courses) to £45. Tasting menu £90. **Details:** 40 seats. Bar. Wheelchairs. Music. Parking.

Loch Bay

Cooking score: 4

Seafood | £44

1-2 Macleod's Terrace, Stein, Isle of Skye, IV55 8GA
Tel no: (01470) 592235
lochbay-restaurant.co.uk

Marooned out on the Waternish peninsula in the north west of Skye, Loch Bay, once a simple traditional fish restaurant, is playing its full part in the emergence of a distinctive island cuisine. In an atmosphere of antique mirrors and exposed brickwork, Michael Smith cooks a contemporary Scottish menu overlaid with touches of the classical French kitchen. Roast hake Rockefeller or saddle of Highland venison with chanterelles in brambly gravy are typical of main-course offerings, while the more homespun note is sounded in a starter broth of cockles, mussels and squid, and the covetable pudding, a clootie dumpling in whisky cream and custard. A five-course seafood menu recalls something of the original focus of the place, centring on Sconser scallops with squash purée and hazelnuts in claret, followed by monkfish with an oyster in shrimp and fennel sauce. The French-led wine list opens with small glasses from £4. Need we say the views of shingle and water and spits of land are sublime?

Chef/s: Michael Smith. **Closed:** Mon, Jan. **Meals:** set L £30 (2 courses) to £34. Set D £44. Sun L £44. Tasting menu £70 (5 courses). **Details:** 22 seats. V menu. Music. Parking.

Scorrybreac

Cooking score: 3

British | £42

7 Bosville Terrace, Portree, Isle of Skye, IV51 9DG
Tel no: (01478) 612069
scorrybreac.com

Scorrybreac describes itself as simple, elegant, cosy, intimate. This tiny, mid-terrace restaurant is little more than a front room but if you snag a booking at one of their eight tables, you can enjoy cuisine that reflects its island influences while surveying Portree harbour. Dishes follow the modern trend of simply listing ingredients but there's usually a little twist along the way, starting with the umami-rich mushroom butter accompanying the homemade bread. A starter of salmon, dulse, fennel and horseradish cleverly marries the salty seaweed and earthy root components, while parsnip, wild garlic and carrot offers a delicate sweetness alongside a dish of venison. A dessert of peanut butter and jam is a (slightly) sophisticated take on nursery comforts. A short drinks menu offers some interesting wines and Scottish malts and gins for the full island experience.

Chef/s: Matt Kidd and Calum Munro. **Closed:** Mon, Tue, Nov to Dec. **Meals:** Tasting menu £42. **Details:** 20 seats.

★ TOP 50 ★

The Three Chimneys

Cooking score: 7

Modern British | £65

Colbost, Isle of Skye, IV55 8ZT
Tel no: (01470) 511258
threechimneys.co.uk

The Three Chimneys scooped our *Restaurant of the Year* accolade in last year's guide and we are delighted to report that Scott Davies is still hitting the heights at the understated whitewashed 'cottage', breathtakingly positioned on the shores of Loch Dunvegan. The pared-back decor of exposed stone walls, tweedily upholstered chairs and a pot of garden flowers on every table allows the food to take centre stage – and to take a bow. While Davies pays ample respect to the abundance of ingredients that make up Skye's local larder, with native breed Soay lamb, Skye red deer, Orbost beef and locally grown vegetables and herbs, when you're surrounded by sea and loch, inevitably it's fish and seafood that star – in both the à la carte or the 'Skye, Land and Sea' tasting menu. From the latter comes a delicate plate of the sweetest langoustines, both raw and scorched with pickled carrots and a dash of smoked cod's roe. Dishes then build with Dunvegan crab combining fresh white crabmeat with a soothing oyster emulsion; miniature ravioli of peat-smoked haddock with confit egg yolk and buttered leeks is given a crumble of black pudding and a pouring of full-flavoured dashi for an umami explosion of flavour and texture. A cheering apple dessert places baked apple alongside cider cream and a mini doughnut to complete a balanced, artfully composed menu of superb quality. A well-judged wine list delivers by glass, carafe, bottle or pairing though the bill can soon mount.

Chef/s: Scott Davies. **Closed:** 16 Dec to 18 Jan. **Meals:** set L £40 (3 courses). Set D £68 (3 courses). Tasting menu L £65 (6 courses), D £95 (8 courses). **Details:** 40 seats. V menu. Vg menu. Bar. Wheelchairs. Music. Parking. Children over 8 yrs at D.

Kingussie

The Cross

Cooking score: 4

Modern British | £55

Tweed Mill Brae, Ardbroilach Road, Kingussie, PH21 1LB
Tel no: (01540) 661166
thecross.co.uk

Nature looms large at this one-time mill in an idyllic setting: the babbling waters of Gynack Burn, birds chirping high in the surrounding trees, and four acres of abundant gardens waiting to be explored. The dining room with its stone walls and wooden beams is seemingly immune to passing fashion but the kitchen does not shy away from engaging with some modern culinary fascinations. Thus roast quail arrives with a confit leg bonbon, and salmon is also given the confit treatment (and matched with baby beets and horseradish cream). Main courses are similarly refined and on point, with regional ingredients making an impression; loin of local venison, say, with beetroot tarte tatin, or halibut with Parmesan gnocchi and wild mushrooms. The same can be said of blackcurrant crémeux with apple (compressed, sorbet and crisp). The fabulous choice of wines and whiskies offers great reward for those willing to explore.

Chef/s: David Skiggs. **Closed:** Sun, Mon, Christmas, Jan (exc Hogmanay). **Meals:** set L £30. Set D £55. Sun L £30. Tasting menu £65 (7 courses). **Details:** 26 seats. 10 seats outside. V menu. Bar. Wheelchairs. Parking.

Lochaline

The Whitehouse

Cooking score: 5

Modern British | £45

Lochaline, PA80 5XT
Tel no: (01967) 421777
thewhitehouserestaurant.co.uk

From the CalMac Ferry, it's a five-minute walk up a 'modest' hill to this unprepossessing family-run restaurant overlooking the Sound of Mull. Remoteness means that all resources are carefully nurtured, so the owners grow their own greenstuff, rear chickens and generally maintain strong links with the local food network. You can sample the results in their chunkily furnished, white-walled dining room, where tasting menus rule the roost. Pick anything from two to six courses from a line-up that's couched in deliberately archaic language: 'Hoof' is 12-hour braised Western Isle 'hough' (shin), with duck liver, pickled Lochaline quail's egg and cabbage, while 'Morven traigh' sees a Hebridean kippered 'finnie' with Tobermory smoked haddie, seawater, saffron crema, blood orange and seashore 'botanics'. Despite the florid descriptions, the cooking is very fine indeed, sharply executed and precise while ensuring that flavour is always paramount. To conclude, there's always a 'tour' of Scottish cheeses, alongside desserts such as a festive Morven tart – roast nuts and cake fruits soaked in 12-year-old Jura whisky in caramel pastry with baked Caledonian cream. Wines start at £21.50.

Chef/s: Mike Burgoyne. **Closed:** Sun, Mon, Nov to end Mar. **Meals:** tasting menu L £25 (2 courses) to £65, D £45 (4 courses) to £65. **Details:** 24 seats. 8 seats outside. V menu. Wheelchairs. Parking.

Port Appin

Airds Hotel

Cooking score: 3

Modern British | £58

Port Appin, PA38 4DF
Tel no: (01631) 730236
airds-hotel.com

'A complete experience with superb food, excellent, friendly and professional service and a beautiful, romantic setting,' says one of many happy customers who regularly beat a retreat to this old-school hotel on the shores of Loch Linnhe. Evenings run to a classic country-house format, starting with drinks and canapés in one of several lounges before heading to the restaurant where 'you are met with incredible views' to the Isle of Lismore. Memorable dishes this year have included

Inverawe smoked salmon and poached salmon teamed with crispy avocado and red pepper, a velouté of pumpkin with Parmesan and smoked mussel 'which combined admirably', 'tender and succulent' roast venison loin accompanied by pear, beetroot, elderberry and pommes dauphine, and baked lemon sole with scallops, peppers, spinach and shellfish mayonnaise. As a finale, dessert has yielded an excellent apple pie soufflé served with caramel crème anglaise and vanilla ice cream. The global wine list starts at £27.50.

Chef/s: Chris Stanley. **Closed:** first 2 weeks Dec. **Meals:** set L £19 (2 courses). Set D £58 (5 courses). Sun L £25. Tasting menu £78 (7 courses). **Details:** 32 seats. 20 seats outside. V menu. Bar. Parking. Children over 8 yrs at D.

Scrabster

The Captain's Galley

Cooking score: 4

Seafood | £54

The Harbour, Scrabster, KW14 7UJ
Tel no: (01847) 894999
captainsgalley.co.uk

West of John o'Groats, on the northernmost tip of the Scottish mainland, the Captain's Galley proudly flies the flag for 'simplicity, integrity, traceability, seasonality and sustainability', thanks to the sterling efforts of one-time fish trader Jim Cowie and his wife Mary. Appropriately set in an old salmon store and barrel-vaulted ice house, this remarkable little place is a Scottish treasure defined by the pure essence of its food – in this case fresh seafood from the local boats, served without compromise. On a typical day, that might mean Shetland mussels and cockles infused with ginger, chilli, lemongrass and coconut juice followed by grilled hake atop paella, parsley-crusted cod or Asian-style steamed pollock with shiitake mushrooms and rice noodles. There's often some seasonal game, too, ahead of desserts such as a nutty crumble of rhubarb, apple and brambles. Twenty workaday wines do their job in the drinks department. Simpler, cheaper food is available in the Cowie's Scrabster Seafood Bar next door.

Chef/s: Jim Cowie. **Closed:** Sun, Mon, Tue, 25 and 26 Dec, 1 and 2 Jan. **Meals:** set L £18 (2 courses) to £25. Set D £41 (2 courses) to £54. Tasting menu £72 (7 courses). **Details:** 30 seats. 25 seats outside. Bar. Music. Parking.

Strontian

Kilcamb Lodge

Cooking score: 3

Modern British | £55

Strontian, PH36 4HY
Tel no: (01967) 402257
kilcamblodge.co.uk

£5 OFF

Reputedly one of the oldest stone houses in Scotland, this stately Georgian hunting lodge makes much of its setting right by the shores of Loch Sunart – and there's no shortage of handsome, soothing trappings indoors. You can eat in the cosy little Driftwood Brasserie or the more formally attired restaurant from a menu that gives prominence to Scottish seafood – perhaps salt and pepper calamari and crispy whitebait pepped up with a sweet chilli and coriander dressing, or pan-fried sea bass with Parmesan gnocchi, Ardtornish vegetable stew and buttered samphire. Elsewhere seafood burgers and beer-battered haddock suit the traditionalists, although it's not all about fish. The kitchen is equally adept at transforming Caledonian meat and game into precise, clear-flavoured dishes (seared fillet of Highland beef with ox cheek suet pudding, wild mushroom ragù and bourguignon sauce, for example), while desserts include an unmissable Drambuie and raspberry bavarois with a tongue-tingling raspberry and Champagne sorbet. The wine list favours reliability over innovation.

Chef/s: Gary Phillips. **Closed:** 1 to 12 Dec, 2 to 30 Jan. **Meals:** main courses £18 to £25. Set D £55. Sun L £25. Tasting menu £69 (7 courses). **Details:** 40 seats. 12 seats outside. V menu. Bar. Music. Parking.

WALES

Mid-Wales, North-East Wales,
North-West Wales, South-East Wales,
South-West Wales

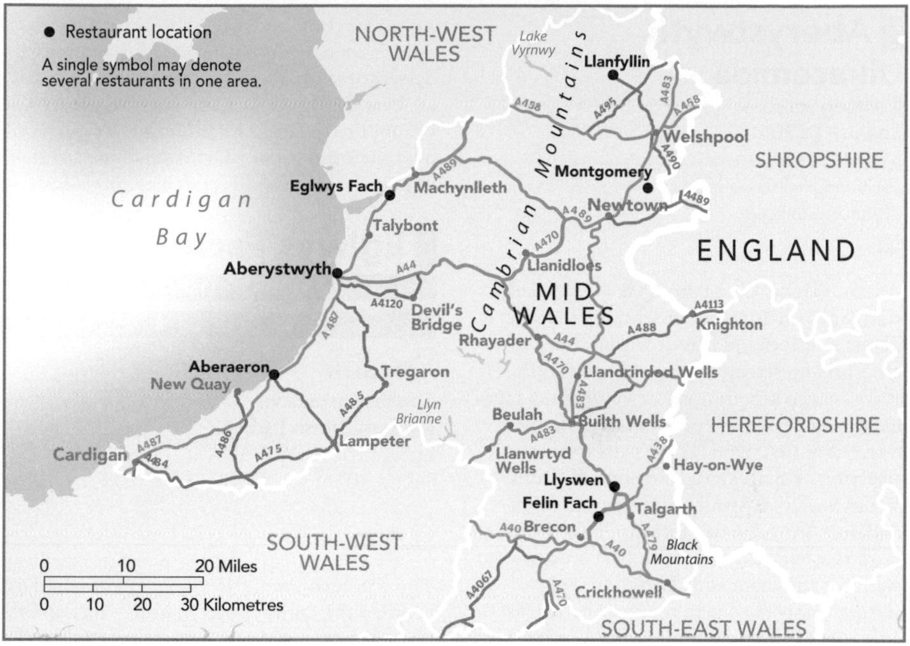

Aberaeron

Harbourmaster

Cooking score: 2
Modern British | £35
Pen Cei, Aberaeron, SA46 0BT
Tel no: (01545) 570755
harbour-master.com

A minute up from the beach, the Harbourmaster isn't difficult to spot. In the evening, its spotlit shimmering violet frontage could almost serve as a warning to shipping. Inside has a laid-back ambience, with a marine blue colour scheme backing the unclothed tables and bare-boarded floor of the dining room. The cooking takes a vigorous approach to the modern brasserie repertoire, devilling lamb's kidneys or cramming crab into ravioli with a fricassée of shallots, garlic and parsley for starters, before slow-roasting pork belly, and teaming it robustly with black pudding, roast squash and a sauce of wholegrain mustard and cider. Vegetarian mains include a lentil pie with cauliflower mash and glazed carrots, and the dessert list is a comprehensive roll-call of temptation, from date and cinnamon pudding with salt caramel sauce and pecan cream to proper tatin dolloped with crème fraîche. A straightforward double-sided wine card offers exemplary value, opening with Australian Chardonnay, Italian rosé and Chilean Merlot at £16.

Chef/s: Ludo Dieumegard. **Closed:** 25 Dec. **Meals:** main courses £11 to £22. Set D £28 (2 courses) to £35. Sun L £19 (2 courses) to £25. **Details:** 100 seats. 15 seats outside. Bar. Wheelchairs. Music. Parking.

Send us your review

Your feedback informs the content of the *GFG* and will be used to compile next year's reviews. To register your opinion about any restaurant listed, or a restaurant that you wish to bring to our attention, visit our website.

Aberystwyth

Ultracomida

Cooking score: 2
Spanish | £20
31 Pier Street, Aberystwyth, SY23 2LN
Tel no: (01970) 630686
ultracomida.co.uk

At first glance, Ultracomida is a deli filled with Spanish 'cupboard essentials', massive bowls of olives and legs of jamón, but this enterprising set-up close to Aberystwyth seafront also accommodates a congenial tapas bar where you can explore all those faraway flavours at first hand. There's always a big selection of charcuterie and cheeses (from Wales as well as Spain), but it pays to pick-and-mix from the full line-up: baked salt cod with roasted fennel and allioli; lentils cooked with Serrano ham and chorizo; or spicy Basque peppers fried in tempura batter, for example. If sweet cravings strike, move on to a classic tarta de Santiago or deep-fried churros with thick chocolate 'a la taza' for dipping. Drinks are on-message too, with a decent choice of Spanish beer, cider and sherry alongside big G&Ts and a gently priced all-Spanish wine list. There's a second branch at 7 High Street, Narberth; tel: (01834) 861491.
Chef/s: Cheryl Price. **Closed:** 25 and 26 Dec, 1 Jan. **Meals:** tapas £4 to £8. **Details:** 32 seats. Wheelchairs. Music.

LOCAL GEM

Pysgoty

Seafood | £32
The Harbour, South Promenade, Aberystwyth, SY23 1JY
Tel no: (01970) 624611
pysgoty.co.uk

'We only come on holiday to the area to eat here,' said one visitor, which says a lot about this 'lovely little restaurant' specialising in fish and seafood. The menu is built on the daily catch from Cardigan Bay, the local grilled lobster with laverbread and lime butter being a popular choice. Other options include a sailor's Scotch egg with curried mayo, and a dessert of rhubarb and custard choux buns. It's all 'beautifully cooked and elegantly served', brought to the table by 'attentive yet not overwhelming staff'. Drinks include a clutch of popular wines, plus craft ales and ciders.

Eglwys Fach

★ CHEF OF THE YEAR ★

★ TOP 10 ★

Ynyshir

Cooking score: 9
Modern British | £110
Eglwys Fach, SY20 8TA
Tel no: (01654) 781209
ynyshir.co.uk

£5 OFF

The winner of our 2015 *Chef to Watch* award has justified the faith we had in him – he comes through as a passionate, enthusiastic talent, cooking to a level that demands to be considered among the very best. Gareth Ward doesn't just ape trends, but is that rare chef who genuinely creates his own inimitable style with an 19-course extravaganza, which may last four hours (there is a truncated version at lunch). Working with fantastic Welsh produce, Ward delivers flavour in punchy small bites. His industrious kitchen bakes, pickles, ferments, cures and bottles, although a magpie creativity draws as much on Far Eastern flavours as European. This is modern British cooking at its most deliberate, delivering touches of sheer brilliance in, for example, a sharp, umami-laden 'not French onion soup', described as 'an absolute blast of freshness'. Or in an Aylesbury duck leg that's 'like a superior Peking duck', and in a sensational mini burger of wagyu beef topped with pickled lettuce and a dab of sourdough mayo. Other highlights from our spring meal included a spoonful of intense duck liver mousse with birch syrup, topped with a delicate spelt biscuit and a grating of smoked eel; and the two dinky servings of exquisite lamb riding high on minty, salty sweetness. And the dishes keep coming: a nugget of voluptuous Manjari chocolate and tofu mousse with a crisp shiitake wafer and shiitake oil; and a glorious take on sticky toffee pudding – compressed mejdool dates, a tiny blob of vanilla ice cream and sticky toffee sauce poured over. Completing the picture, the bar and dining room have a wonderful simplicity into which furnishings and the open kitchen slot sympathetically, while staff are young and enthusiastic yet thoroughly professional and add to the impression that this is very much a serious, unique restaurant. The wine list does the place justice, pulling together fine drinking from reputable names and forward-looking producers, with most available by the glass.

Chef/s: Gareth Ward. **Closed:** Sun, Mon, Tue, Christmas and New Year, 1 week Apr, 2 weeks late summer. **Meals:** tasting menu L £75 (12 courses) to £140, D £140 (19 courses). Chef's Table D £180. **Details:** 24 seats. Bar. Wheelchairs. Music. Parking. Children over 12 years.

Felin Fach
The Felin Fach Griffin

Cooking score: 4
Modern British | £38
Felin Fach, LD3 0UD
Tel no: (01874) 620111
felinfachgriffin.co.uk
£5 OFF

A pioneer in its day, this is one of those classily rustic, seriously foodie pubs-with-rooms that have transformed the UK dining landscape over the past couple of decades. It remains as lovely as ever, with an interior straight out of a glossy country lifestyle magazine (real fires, big leather sofas, interesting artwork) complete with organically certified kitchen garden. Family- and dog-friendly, it's unpretentious and forward-thinking, with a menu that skips happily between Scandi, Middle Eastern and Western European influences. Try mackerel fillet with cured onion, knäckebröd and buttermilk labneh, then Welsh lamb loin with crispy breast, beetroot, curd and wild garlic, and lemon and rapeseed oil cake with sherbert and lemon curd to finish. Its motto is 'simple things done well' and that's exactly what you get, backed by great ales and a proper selection of wines.

Chef/s: Ben Ogden. **Closed:** 25 Dec, 4 days early Jan. **Meals:** main courses £17 to £21. Set L £19 (2 courses) to £24. Set D £24 (2 courses) to £29. Sun L £28 (3 courses). **Details:** 60 seats. 30 seats outside. V menu. Vg menu. Bar. Wheelchairs. Music. Parking.

Llanfyllin
Seeds

Cooking score: 1
Modern British | £29
5 Penybryn Cottages, High Street, Llanfyllin, SY22 5AP
Tel no: (01691) 648604

Paintings line the walls, books and puzzles are scattered across the tables, and the wood-burning stove is often called into action at this slate-floored, oak-beamed cottage bistro. Mark and Felicity Seager have been in residence here since 1991 (he cooks, she serves) and have established a rock-solid reputation for their simply executed honest-to-goodness food over the years – think asparagus and pea risotto, sautéed chicken breast with port and cream sauce, treacle tart with ice cream and suchlike. More surprising is the owners' personally curated 160-bin wine list, which goes well beyond the bistro call of duty.

Chef/s: Mark Seager. **Closed:** Sun, Mon, Tue. Limited opening in winter (telephone in advance). **Meals:** main courses L £12 to £22. Set D £26 (2 courses) to £29. **Details:** 20 seats. 6 seats outside.

Llyswen

Llangoed Hall

Cooking score: 5
Modern British | £55
Llyswen, LD3 0YP
Tel no: (01874) 754525
llangoedhall.co.uk

Formerly owned by Sir Bernard Ashley, whose more famous wife inspired much of the florally themed interior design, Llangoed was remodelled by Clough Williams-Ellis of Portmeirion repute, just before the Great War. It sits amid the undulating splendour of the Wye Valley, a mere nine miles from the bookworm's paradise of Hay, and makes a striking impression as a classic country house hotel, complete with linened and posied dining room and cooking of impeccable modernistic bent. Nick Brodie is responsible for that last, and takes a resourceful global approach for dishes such as crab with barbecued sweetcorn, cultured buttermilk and togarashi chilli, followed perhaps in the game season by mature grouse with mushroom fricassée, damson toast and chestnuts in a jus boosted with 100 per cent cocoa chocolate. The Japanese theme returns for a dessert that incorporates plum, saké and shiso leaf as accompaniments to a white chocolate sphere and hazelnuts. A wine list compiled by Tanners opens at £28.

Chef/s: Nick Brodie. **Meals:** set L £25. Set D £55. Sun L £25. Tasting menu £70 (7 courses). **Details:** 40 seats. V menu. Bar. Wheelchairs. Parking.

Montgomery

The Checkers

Cooking score: 6
French | £65
Broad Street, Montgomery, SY15 6PN
Tel no: (01686) 669822
checkerswales.co.uk

To taste contemporary, classic French cooking that's as carefully crafted as any you'd find in a flash city setting, trip over the border between England and Wales into handsome Montgomery. There, in a 17th-century coaching inn (its interior fits the pale-painted, inglenooked, beamed trope to a T), you'll find Stéphane Borie at work on his six-course tasting menu. He might be preparing cannelloni of crab and langoustine with cauliflower purée and creamy, crayfish-laden sauce Nantua, or an assiette of pork from nearby Neuadd Fach farm with chantenay carrots and pomme mousseline. In season, a venison wellington with Jerusalem artichoke purée, oyster mushroom and Madeira jus balances perfectly on the line between hearty and refined, while the whole meal could happily be completed with a damson crumble soufflé with stem ginger ice cream, or nougatine cannelloni filled with white chocolate and passion fruit mousse. Praise is heaped on the tempting array of breads, and the France-dominated wine list that offers bottles from £16.

Chef/s: Stéphane Borie. **Closed:** Sun, Mon, 25 and 26 Dec, 2 weeks Jan, 1 week summer, 1 week autumn. **Meals:** tasting menu D £65 (6 courses). **Details:** 30 seats. Bar. Children over 8 yrs.

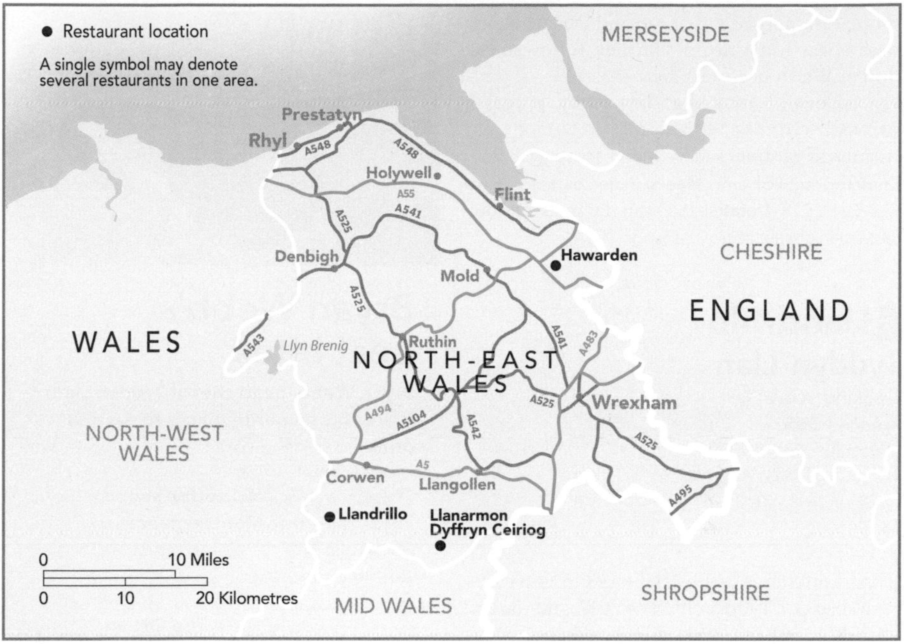

● Restaurant location

A single symbol may denote several restaurants in one area.

MERSEYSIDE

Prestatyn
Rhyl
A548
Holywell
A55
A541
Flint
A525
Denbigh
Hawarden
CHESHIRE
Mold
ENGLAND
WALES
A543
Llyn Brenig
Ruthin
NORTH-EAST WALES
A541
A483
A525
Wrexham
A494
A5104
A542
NORTH-WEST WALES
A525
A5
Corwen
Llangollen
A495
Llandrillo
Llanarmon Dyffryn Ceiriog
0 10 Miles
0 10 20 Kilometres
MID WALES
SHROPSHIRE

Hawarden

The Glynne Arms

Cooking score: 1

International | £28

3 Glynne Way, Hawarden, CH5 3NS
Tel no: (01244) 569988
theglynnearms.co.uk

Run by Caroline and Charlie Gladstone, this Welsh border pub is part of an extended family that includes the Hawarden Estate Farm Shop and an online vintage homeware business. The pub is a mix of old and new, with a menu that has broad reach – shredded duck bao buns alongside cod cheek bhajis and black pudding fritters. There are steaks with all the usual trimmings, and a burger served in a pretzel bun. Finish with hazelnut knickerbocker glory or three local cheeses. A concise global wine list gets support from six local ales on draught.

Chef/s: Adam Stanley. **Meals:** main courses £12 to £25. Set L £13 (2 courses) to £17. Sun L £12. **Details:** 76 seats. 40 seats outside. Bar. Wheelchairs. Music. Parking.

Llanarmon Dyffryn Ceiriog

The West Arms

Cooking score: 1

Modern British | £39

Llanarmon Dyffryn Ceiriog, LL20 7LD
Tel no: (01691) 600665
thewestarms.co.uk

You'll feel instantly at home in this ancient stone inn-with-rooms found in the foothills of the Berwyn Mountains. With whitewashed stonework on the outside, low beams and numerous rooms warmed by real fires within, it has the kind of relaxed feel that lifts the spirits. On the food front, expect honest cooking of quality ingredients in the dining

room: caramelised red onion and Perl Wen tart with a pear and pine nut chutney, followed by shin of Welsh beef with herb-roasted vegetables and smoked garlic pomme purée, and apple crumble with clotted cream ice cream and caramel sauce. Wines from £18.95.
Chef/s: Grant Williams. **Meals:** main courses £16 to £22. Sun L £13. **Details:** 150 seats. 80 seats outside. Bar. Wheelchairs. Music. Parking.

Llandrillo

Tyddyn Llan

Cooking score: 6
French | £65
Llandrillo, LL21 0ST
Tel no: (01490) 440264
tyddynllan.co.uk

Bryan and Susan Webb celebrated 15 years as custodians of Tyddyn Llan in 2017, and they remain an impressive double act when it comes to warm-hearted hospitality – he cooks, while she takes care of front of house. The setting is a converted shooting lodge in the tranquil expanses of the Dee Valley – a civilised backdrop for some civilised dining. Bryan's cooking acknowledges his Welsh roots, although the traditions of mainstream European cuisine provide a sturdy backbone for his gentle culinary talents. Expect clear flavours and thoughtful pairings across the board, from starters of dressed langoustine with avocado, fennel and radish to desserts such as pecan tart or baked Alaska. In between, there's wild sea bass with laverbread beurre blanc, prized Welsh Black beef au poivre, roast turbot with leek risotto, and venison with goat's cheese gnocchi, port and elderberry sauce. The Webbs' thoughtfully curated wine list is also the subject of much attention, with its ungreedy markups, helpful notes and 16-strong selection by the glass or carafe.
Chef/s: Bryan Webb. **Closed:** Mon, Tue, last 2 weeks Jan. **Meals:** set L £30 (2 courses) to £38. Set D £55 (2 courses) to £65. Sun L £30 (2 courses). Tasting menu £75 (6 courses) to £90. **Details:** 40 seats. Bar. Wheelchairs. Parking.

Bryan Webb's best bites

Bryan Webb, head chef at Tyddyn Llan, shares his favourite places to eat and drink

There is a delightful **coffee shop** in the Royal Exchange **Manchester** called **Michaels**. The coffee is perfect and the **sandwiches** are delicious.

I recently had lunch at **The Ritz** and for the first time in a very long time it blew me away. It's **classic cooking** with nothing on the plate that does not need to be there, plus perfect service.

There is a **pub** just over the mountain from us called **The Hand At Llanarmon**, run by Jonathan and Jackie Greatorex. The **beers** are well kept and the **steak pie** is perfect pub food.

Bryn Williams at Porth Eirias is right on the beach with **amazing views** and great food: try the homemade fish fingers, tasty burgers, plus delicious grown-up options including fish pie, local mussels and a warm lamb breast salad. It's an ideal spot for **families**.

The **Chester Grosvenor** has a great bar and an amazing choice of **cocktails**, but it's nearly an hour's drive home, so we always have to stay the night!

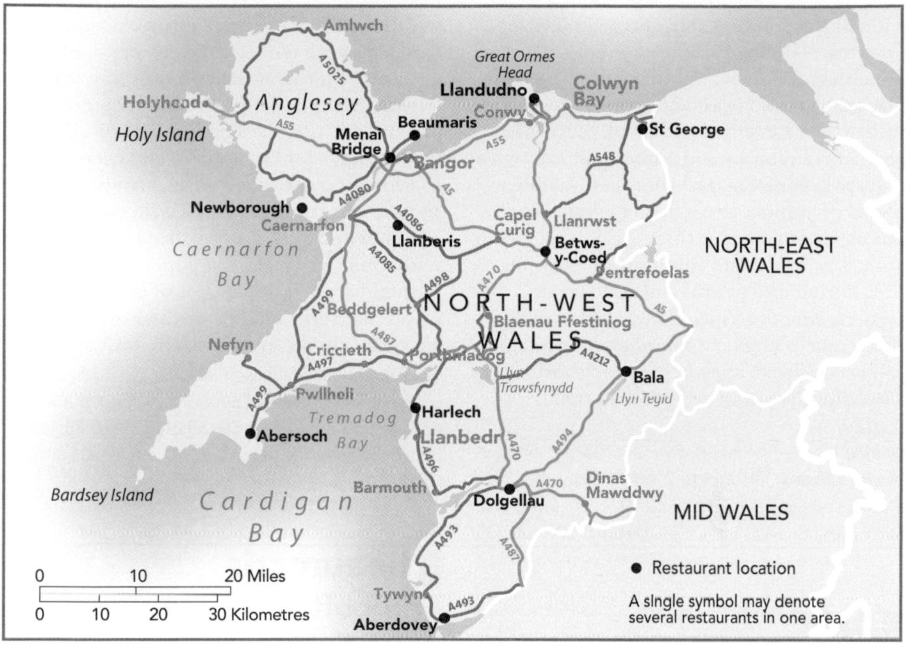

Amlwch
Anglesey
Holyhead
Holy Island
Menai Bridge
Beaumaris
Llandudno
Great Ormes Head
Colwyn Bay
Conwy
St George
Bangor
Newborough
Caernarfon
Caernarfon Bay
Llanberis
Capel Curig
Llanrwst
Betws-y-Coed
Pentrefoelas
NORTH-EAST WALES
NORTH-WEST WALES
Beddgelert
Blaenau Ffestiniog
Nefyn
Criccieth
Porthmadog
Pwllheli
Tremadog Bay
Abersoch
Harlech
Llanbedr
Llyn Trawsfynydd
Bala
Llyn Tegid
Bardsey Island
Cardigan Bay
Barmouth
Dolgellau
Dinas Mawddwy
MID WALES
Tywyn
Aberdovey
0 10 20 Miles
0 10 20 30 Kilometres
● Restaurant location
A single symbol may denote several restaurants in one area.

Aberdovey

Seabreeze

Cooking score: 1

Modern British | £30

6 Bodfor Terrace, Aberdovey, LL35 0EA
Tel no: (01654) 767449
seabreeze-aberdovey.co.uk

'We had a really good experience here,' confirmed one reader who also applauded the service at this appealing stone-walled restaurant on Aberdovey's seafront. Staff show 'just the right blend of friendliness and professionalism' as they serve up a concise daily menu of robust dishes inspired by locally sourced ingredients: mussels are steamed with leeks and Welsh cider, dressed Aberdovey lobster is slathered in garlicky chive butter, and red mullet appears with bouillabaisse. Elsewhere, melting lamb shank braised in balsamic and rosemary receives a vote of confidence, likewise the chocolate and praline tart with orange purée. Keenly priced wines offer value as well as quality.

Chef/s: Henry Severn. **Closed:** 25 and 26 Dec, 2 weeks Jan. **Meals:** main courses £12 to £25. **Details:** 40 seats. 8 seats outside. Music.

Abersoch

Porth Tocyn Hotel

Cooking score: 2

Modern British | £49

Bwlch Tocyn, Abersoch, LL53 7BU
Tel no: (01758) 713303
porthtocynhotel.co.uk

Porth Tocyn is in a dream location for walkers, glampers and gazers of all sorts, with the Wales Coast Path running right by the grounds, which embrace a shepherd's hut for the more enterprising guest, and views over Cardigan Bay to the mountains of Snowdonia. The stone-walled dining room enjoys those views to the full, and Louise Fletcher-Brewer, latest scion of the family that has owned the place since the 1940s, oversees the cooking of a modern Welsh menu of broad range. First up might be pressed seafood terrine with a sweet chilli glaze, garnished with apple, cucumber, pickled red cabbage and white crabmeat, with perhaps bacon-wrapped venison to follow, served on juniper berry mash in caramelised onion jus, or perhaps a three-bird convocation of duck, chicken and confit guinea fowl in Thai-influenced peanut and chilli cream. Dessert seductions include white chocolate cheesecake with berry compôte, or vanilla panna cotta with strawberries and shortbread. The helpfully annotated wine list opens at £20.

Chef/s: Louise Fletcher-Brewer and Darren Henton-Morris. **Closed:** late Oct to 2 weeks before Easter. **Meals:** main courses £12 to £27 (L only). Set D £42 (2 courses) to £49. Sun L £27. **Details:** 50 seats. 30 seats outside. Bar. Parking. Children over 5 yrs at D.

Bala

★ NEW ENTRY ★

Palé Hall

Cooking score: 5

Modern European | £60

Palé Estate, Llandderfel, Bala, LL23 7PS
Tel no: (01678) 530285
palehall.co.uk

Built for a Scottish industrialist in the 1870s, Palé Hall is on the palatial side of bijou, an imposing pile set amid undulating countryside just outside Bala. The sumptuous lounges make a suave initial impression, and then it's on to one of the dining rooms, either the Venetian or an amber-hued room named after the first resident, Henry Robertson. Chinese drawings and paintings of bowls of fruit make a backdrop to some delicately constructed modern cooking that is securely founded on rumbustious, persuasive flavours. Roast scallops with smoked tomato purée in an old-school beurre blanc makes a perfectly balanced opener, before sliced monkfish tail with Moroccan and Indian manifestations of cauliflower and a gingery raisin chutney competes with tenderly roasted breast of lamb with a medallion of the loin, served with stewed chickpeas and a sensational purée of preserved lemon. Desserts are technically fascinating, a pink grapefruit and coconut combination garnished with coconut snow and a sesame tuile roll filled with coconut ice cream, while miso-laced banana cake comes with tonka ice cream and popcorn. A well-wrought wine list takes care of business at prices that verge on the breathtakingly reasonable in the grandiose circumstances.

Chef/s: Gareth Stevenson. **Meals:** set L 30 (2 courses) to £37. Set D £60. Sun L £25 (2 courses) to £32. Tasting menu £85. **Details:** 40 seats. 20 seats outside. V menu. Vg menu. Bar. Wheelchairs. Music. Parking. No children after 8pm.

Beaumaris

The Loft

Cooking score: 3

Modern British | £50

The Bull, Castle Street, Beaumaris, LL58 8AP
Tel no: (01248) 810329
bullsheadinn.co.uk

The Bull is all things to all people – an old-school pub, informal brasserie and aspirational restaurant, depending on your business. That last, The Loft, is on the first floor and is a slope-ceilinged space with swirling wall design and low-lit ambience. Here, the cooking aims to offer something of the modern British style, while keeping one foot planted on terra firma. The butter, churned in-house, is decadently creamy and garnished with shaved truffle and sea salt. Fish is well handled, whether for a rosette of citrus-cured halibut, a ceviche-like preparation with fennel and pink grapefruit, or a delightful main of sea bream with asparagus and samphire in sumptuous tarragon cream. Duck fared less well at inspection, the so-so meat let down by dull accompaniments, including some rather strident pickled blackberries, but the rump of Welsh hogget with mint and liquorice is more

finely honed. Finish with a take on rum baba incorporating pineapple and ginger. A conservative wine selection majors on France.
Chef/s: Andrew Tabberner. **Closed:** Sun, Mon, Tue, 25 and 26 Dec. **Meals:** set D Wed to Fri £35. Set D £50. **Details:** 45 seats. Music. Children over 7 yrs.

Betws-y-Coed

LOCAL GEM

Bistro Betws-y-Coed

British | £29
Holyhead Road, Betws-y-Coed, LL24 0AY
Tel no: (01690) 710328
bistrobetws-y-coed.co.uk

£5 OFF £30

Betws-y-Coed is a popular gateway to Snowdonia National Park and, as such, this stone-built bistro is a tourist honeypot, especially in summer. But a respect for high-quality Welsh produce ensures the food is good year round. Sautéed breast of wild wood pigeon with blueberry pancakes, crispy bacon and a rich red wine and chocolate sauce, and rump of local Welsh lamb marinated in Snowdonia honey and balsamic vinegar served with buttered cabbage, butternut squash purée, sautéed potatoes and laverbread in leek sauce have garnered particular praise. Wines from £15.50.

Dolgellau

Mawddach

Cooking score: 2
Modern European | £33
Llanelltyd, Dolgellau, LL40 2TA
Tel no: (01341) 421752
mawddach.com

It is over a decade since Ifan Dunn returned to the family farm to open a restaurant in a converted barn, and it's very much part of the landscape these days. The barn still looks the business, with its natural surfaces and sharp contemporary finish, and the view across the Cader Idris mountain range is as timeless as ever. The cooking focuses on the region's produce, as you might well expect, with plenty of modern thinking going on. A risotto is enriched with smoked haddock, whey and curry oil in a full-flavoured opener, or go for a hearty taste of Tuscany in the form of ribollita. Local sirloin is slow poached at 55° and served pink with mash and roast Jerusalem artichokes, finished with a red wine sauce. There's more of that Med feeling in roast cod with Puy lentils and salsa verde, and a panna cotta dessert with spicy poached pear and almond praline. Cheeses are Welsh all the way. The canny wine list opens at £16.50.
Chef/s: Ifan Dunn. **Closed:** Mon, Tue, Wed, 26 Dec, 2 weeks Jan, 2 weeks Apr, Nov. **Meals:** main courses £15 to £22. Sun L £25. **Details:** 50 seats. 30 seats outside. Bar. Wheelchairs. Music. Parking. Children over 5 yrs.

Harlech

Castle Cottage

Cooking score: 2
Modern British | £42
Y Llech, Harlech, LL46 2YL
Tel no: (01766) 780479
castlecottageharlech.co.uk

£5 OFF

Glyn and Jacqueline Roberts became custodians of this listed 16th-century cottage in 1989 – it's one of the Guide's longest-serving restaurants, and comes with low beams, oak tables and a glorious view of Snowdon. The Robertses deliver generous helpings of seasonal cooking that befit the location next door to Harlech Castle and with the Dwyryd river valley, Llyn Peninsula, sand dunes, beaches and of course the wide open sea nearby. The fixed-price menu offers a choice of two or three courses with generous canapés and rustic homemade bread 'setting the scene beautifully', before a full-flavoured shellfish and king prawn soup with croûtons, rouille and Gruyère (the highlight of an inspection meal). Aberdaron lobster thermidor with Wye Valley asparagus and ratte potatoes impressed too, as did grilled brochette of monkfish and a comforting warm treacle tart with raspberries and vanilla ice cream. A reasonably priced wine list arranged by New or Old World starts at £18.50.

Chef/s: Glyn Roberts. **Closed:** Sun, Mon, Tue, Christmas and New Year, 3 weeks Nov. **Meals:** set D £40 (2 courses) to £42. Tasting menu £45. **Details:** 35 seats. Bar. Music.

Llanberis

LOCAL GEM

The Peak

Modern British | £29

86 High Street, Llanberis, LL55 4SU
Tel no: (01286) 872777
peakrestaurant.co.uk

The wide picture window looks aslant at towering Snowdonia from Julia Roberts' simply furnished venue that seems permanently busy. Carefully composed bistro food aims to please: to start, perhaps houmous and grilled aubergine bruschetta, or smoked trout on beetroot salad with a sour cream dressing. Follow with a generously loaded bowl of bouillabaisse (featuring cod, sea bass and red mullet) or Welsh ribeye and chips with peppercorn sauce before, say, apple and rhubarb crumble with clotted cream or a plate of regional cheeses. A generous spread of wines below £20 adds to the good cheer.

Llandudno

Jaya

Cooking score: 2

Indian | £32

36 Church Walks, Llandudno, LL30 2HN
Tel no: (01492) 818198
jayarestaurant.co.uk

Housed within Space – a boutique B&B occupying one of Llandudno's townhouses – Jaya is the enterprising brainchild of Bobby and Sunita Katosh, who have created a surprising local hit here. Three evenings a week, the chandeliers in their breakfast room are switched on and the glass tables are neatly laid up in anticipation of accurately spiced food with punchy Punjabi and East African overtones on a menu that ranges from lamb samosas, tandoori prawns and karahi chicken to pan-fried chilli-spiked mogo (cassava) or salmon (locally sourced) in a spicy Kenyan masala sauce. Vegetarians also do well here – note wok-fried paneer with peppers, deep-fried vegetable bhajias or aloo anday (a North Indian curry of hard-boiled eggs and potatoes). To drink, there are fruity cocktails, virgin mojitos and some everyday wines, although masala chai and mugs of hot chocolate also find favour as soothing nightcaps – especially with those who are staying over.

Chef/s: Steve Bloor. **Closed:** Sun to Wed, 23 Dec to 18 Jan. **Meals:** main courses £11 to £14. **Details:** 20 seats. V menu. Bar. Music. Parking.

Menai Bridge

Freckled Angel

Cooking score: 3

Modern British | £27

49 High Street, Menai Bridge, LL59 5EF
Tel no: (01248) 209952
freckled-angel-fine-catering.co.uk

Lucky little Menai Bridge boasts two gastronomic stars, positioned mere yards apart on the through-road. The Freckled Angel, with its sober grey frontage and pair of intimate rooms, is run with personable charm and efficiency, and takes a small-plate approach, representing especially good value at lunch. Portions are just big enough for respectable sharing and offer plenty of punchy, sharply defined flavour. Twice-baked Perl Las blue cheese soufflé is full of mustardy pungency, offset with balsamic grapes; a bowl of creamy chowder combines smoked haddock and chorizo to great smokey effect; cod cheeks on pea purée with puffed potato and capers is a neat textural essay; another cheek, this time pig's, is braised and bedded on spiced lentils with celeriac and apple. Dessert ideas maintain the pace, with lime tart, toasted

coconut parfait and roasted pineapple all finding their way on to one seductive plate. A short drinks list just about keeps up.
Chef/s: Michael Jones. **Closed:** Sun, Mon, Christmas to New Year. **Meals:** small plates £6 to £13. Set L £13. **Details:** 28 seats. Music.

Sosban and the Old Butcher's

Cooking score: 6
Modern British | £80
Trinity House, 1 High Street, Menai Bridge, LL59 5EE
Tel no: (01248) 208131
sosbanandtheoldbutchers.com

The decor is a study in retro cool with traces of the old butcher shop's interior offset by simple modern furnishings. It's understated yet cosy, and deservedly popular so book well ahead. Stephen Stevens works wonders in the kitchen, and wife Bethan is warmly welcoming front of house. Quite how two people manage to keep this restaurant not just steady, but running smoothly, may give pause for thought, especially as everything is so perfect. The no-choice menu changes daily, rummaging through Britain's heritage larder and emerging with such beauties as Welsh laverbread – served with lamb cheek and beetroot marshmallow; Wiltshire truffle – teamed with artichoke and ewe's cheese; and a triumphantly Welsh dish of salt-aged lamb rump with wild garlic, yoghurt and leek. This is supremely sophisticated cooking, but it still has a sense of fun; expect playful presentation and unpredictable but effective pairings such as cod skin with banana, bitter cress and peanut or cod with yeast purée, crisp potato, pickled onion and ox heart. Two contrasting desserts – rhubarb and custard, and lemon with olive and chocolate – perfectly sum up Stevens' ability to skip between beloved familiarity and surprising tangents. In a similar vein, the global wine list eschews predictability for interest.
Chef/s: Stephen Owen Stevens. **Closed:** Sun to Wed, Christmas, New Year, Jan. **Meals:** set L £40. Tasting menu D £80. **Details:** 16 seats. Children over 12 yrs.

Newborough

The Marram Grass

Cooking score: 4
Modern British | £35
White Lodge, Penlon, Newborough, LL61 6RS
Tel no: (01248) 440077
themarramgrass.com
£5 OFF

What was once a greasy-spoon campsite caff serving under-canvas staples has been transformed by brothers Liam and Ellis Barrie into a destination restaurant. Thankfully, it has retained its quirky charm, with a weather-beaten corrugated iron roof, vine-covered pergola and an abundance of exposed wood. The interior may look homespun but there's nothing modest about the Barries' ambition in the kitchen, which goes that extra mile in terms of local sourcing, right down to rearing their own animals. The regularly changing menus are concise, seasonal and written around what produce is available on the day. Start with Anglesey crab risotto, apple, garlic and white truffle before continuing with pan-roasted Conwy Valley lamb with minted lamb ragù and Wirral watercress purée, and Anglesey sheep's yoghurt. Equally indulgent is a dessert of black treacle tart with rhubarb and a sesame ice cream. Arranged by style, the short wine list opens at £16.50 (£4.50 for a glass).
Chef/s: Ellis Barrie. **Closed:** Mon, Tue, Wed, 1 to 18 Jan. **Meals:** main courses £11 to £28. Set L £35. Tasting menu L £55, D £85. **Details:** 40 seats. 10 seats outside. Music. Parking.

North-west Wales's best bites

Stephen Stevens of Sosban & The Old Butcher's in Menai Bridge shares his favourite places to eat and drink

Monday mornings wouldn't be the same without our visit to **Bangor**'s best asset, **Blue Sky**, for **breakfast**. Try the organic scrambled eggs and smashed avocado on locally baked Becws Alun toast.

We travel to **Providero** at **Llandudno Junction** for our **coffee** fix. Providero started life as an old Citroën van, working the Colwyn Bay seafront and they serve coffee from local roasters, **Heartland Coffi** that's like no other.

For the best selection of **local artisan produce** visit the compact **Hooton's Homegrown Farm Shop & Café** in **Llanfairpwllgwyngyll**, which has everything you could possibly need. On a Saturday morning, once a month, there is a **local farmers' market** offering a taste of the best Anglesey has to offer.

Situated in the village of **Porthdinllaen** on the north coast of the Llyn peninsula, **Ty Coch Inn** at **Morfa Nefyn** has views across the Irish Sea to the Yr Eifl mountains and a sandy beach. What better way to while away the hours than with a cool **pint of craft ale**?

St George

The Kinmel Arms

Cooking score: 2

Modern British | £35

The Village, St George, LL22 9BP
Tel no: (01745) 832207
thekinmelarms.co.uk

Set on a wooded slope overlooking the Irish Sea, just outside the magnificent gates to Kinmel Hall (an amazing-looking but sadly abandoned Victorian mansion), this pub is quite some package. Yes, it still has a traditional bar, but locals and holidaymakers are more interested in its deli, tearoom and conservatory-style restaurant – an airy space emblazoned with the owner's colourful artworks. The menu offers everything from pub 'classics' (steaks, fish and chips, burgers) to modern dishes loaded with Welsh ingredients – as in a tart of richly smoked lamb and peas with cubes of mint jelly or an 'intriguing' combination of griddled asparagus, sorrel panna cotta, crumbled baked ricotta and egg yolk purée, and desserts such as dark chocolate tart with banana ice cream. The venue has a reputation for afternoon tea; although service is friendly and swift, it can seem out of step with the style of cooking. Wines include a generous selection by the glass.

Chef/s: Paul-Anthony Smith. **Closed:** Mon, 25 Dec, 1 Jan. **Meals:** main courses £15 to £26. **Details:** 70 seats. 30 seats outside. Bar. Wheelchairs. Music. Parking.

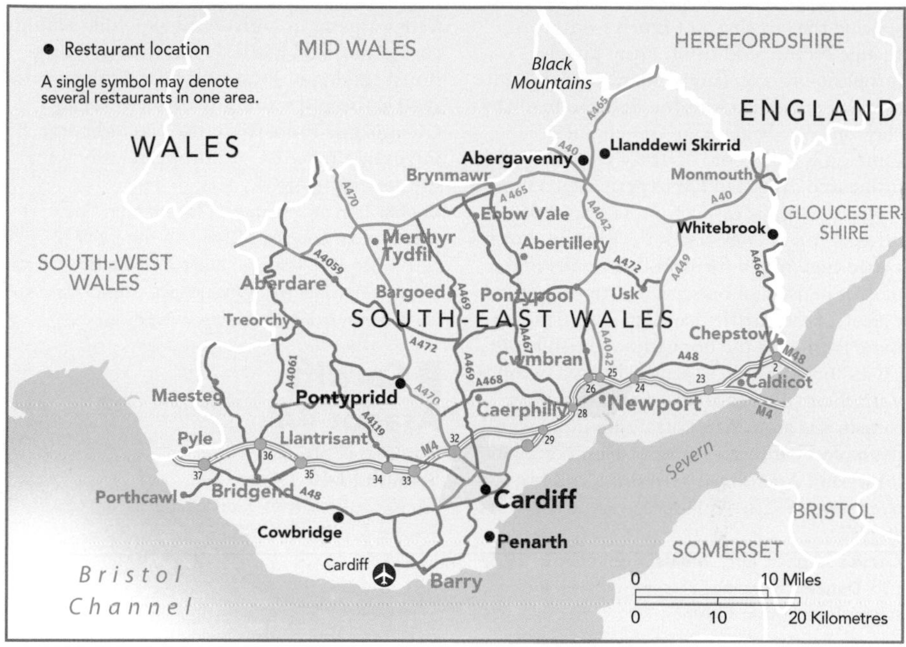

Abergavenny

1861

Cooking score: 4
Modern British | £40
Cross Ash, Abergavenny, NP7 8PB
Tel no: (01873) 821297
18-61.co.uk

£5 OFF

Simon and Kate King have been in residence at this foursquare mid-Victorian black-and-white fronted house for more than a decade and have made the place very much their own – thanks to a blend of exposed beams, original fireplaces, genuine family hospitality and aspirational modern cooking. Simon tops up his supplies of regional Monmouthshire produce with vegetables from his father-in-law's nursery, although the emphasis is on intricately worked dishes, often with a classical lineage (fricassée of pheasant with grain mustard sauce or pork belly braised in apple juice, for example). There's also an appetite for trying new things, as in a starter of scallop cannelloni or a dessert combining acorn panna cotta with iced pumpkin parfait. Set lunches and 'prestige' tasting menus offer value and variety, while the thoughtfully chosen well-spread wine list opens with 10 house selections by the glass.

Chef/s: Simon King. **Closed:** Mon, Tue, 26 to 31 Dec, first 2 weeks Jan. **Meals:** main courses £22 to £26. Set L £25 (2 courses) to £30. Set D £38. Sun L £30. Tasting menu £68 (7 courses). **Details:** 35 seats. Bar. Music. Parking.

The Hardwick

Cooking score: 3
Modern British | £35
Old Raglan Road, Abergavenny, NP7 9AA
Tel no: (01873) 854220
thehardwick.co.uk

Set against the backdrop of the Black Mountains, this roadside pub with rooms continues to attract admirers after 12 years with chef Stephen Terry at the helm. Regulars applaud the fact that 'not much seems to change' on the food front. From purple sprouting broccoli (supplied by 'Joyce Watkins down the road') to sourdough bread made by Hay-on-Wye baker Alex Gooch, local sourcing is at the core of Terry's Italian-influenced dishes. In less experienced hands, the vast menu (at inspection, 14 starters were offered) might overstretch the kitchen, but it's a tried-and-tested formula that results in the likes of braised rabbit served with deep-fried polenta, peas, soffritto and grana Padano, the meat 'falling off the bone into the rich broth'. Or an 'incredibly rich', tender braised octopus with chargrilled chorizo, gnocchetti, peas, tomato and aïoli. After that, a 'faultless' vanilla panna cotta with segments of blood orange in honey and Aperol was 'refreshing and not overly sweet'. The well-spread wine list starts at £22.

Chef/s: Stephen Terry. **Meals:** main courses £9 to £30. **Details:** 100 seats. 25 seats outside. Bar. Wheelchairs. Music. Parking.

Aberthin

★ LOCAL RESTAURANT AWARD ★
REGIONAL WINNER

Hare & Hounds

Cooking score: 3

British | £30

Maendy Road, Aberthin, CF71 7LG
Tel no: (01446) 774892
hareandhoundsaberthin.com

After working in London at St John and the Anchor & Hope (see entries), chef Tom Watts-Jones returned home to run the village pub where he had his first pint as a young man. This homely inn retains a proper bar festooned with dried hops, low beams and local real ales, but walk through to the restaurant and it's a different story. Warmed by a wood-burner, the dining room's bare floorboards, whitewashed brickwork and farmhouse tables provide a relaxed setting in which to watch chefs toiling in the open kitchen. As befits a chef who worked under Fergus Henderson, Tom's food is strictly seasonal and simple. An early spring meal produced a confident starter of Wye Valley asparagus with confit egg yolk, Hafod cheese and wild garlic. It was followed by a breast and leg of Picketson duck with bacon, wild garlic and morels, whiles a towering Champagne rhubarb soufflé was light and intensely flavoured. A European-only wine list opens at £16.95.

Chef/s: Tom Watts-Jones. **Closed:** Mon, Tue. **Meals:** main courses £12 to £19. Set L £17 (2 courses) to £20. Tasting menu £55. **Details:** 44 seats. 30 seats outside. Bar. Wheelchairs. Music. Parking. No children in bar area after 7.30pm

Cardiff

Asador 44

Cooking score: 2

Spanish | £40

14-15 Quay Street, Cardiff, CF10 1EA
Tel no: (029) 2002 0039
asador44.co.uk

£5 OFF

In the shadow of the imposing Principality Stadium, Asador 44 is fast becoming the mothership of the growing Bar 44 group (see entry, Cowbridge). The model might be Spanish grill restaurants, but owners Tom and Owen Morgan wear their Welsh roots with pride, so 40-day aged local steaks jostle for attention alongside rare-breed 'old cow' beef from Galicia and Asturia, and Castilian milk-fed lamb. Settled at your marble-topped table, you can admire the output from the custom-made wood-fired grill – perhaps octopus with criollo sausage (and served with pisto and beetroot), or Segovian suckling pig belly (which is teamed with smoked morcilla and caramelised heritage carrots). If you can resist the walk-in cheese room with its dozen cheeses, the almond and lemon curd Santiago tart with Moscatel cream and glazed quince is worth a try. Arranged by regions of Spain, the wine list starts at £21.

Chef/s: Ian Wood. **Closed:** Sun, Mon, 25 and 26 Dec, 1 Jan. **Meals:** main courses £11 to £41. Set L £15 (2 courses) to £20. **Details:** 80 seats. V menu. Wheelchairs. Music.

Bully's

Cooking score: 2
Modern French | £31
5 Romilly Crescent, Cardiff, CF11 9NP
Tel no: (029) 2022 1905
bullysrestaurant.co.uk

'We are a French restaurant, not American' says the tongue-in-cheek sign outside Bully's – a fixture of Cardiff's neighbourhood scene. Inside, Parisian chic meets strictly personal English jumble, with wall-to-wall paintings and prints, retro memorabilia, curios of every description and French music in the background. There's no doubting where the kitchen's allegiances lie, either, judging by a menu that offers such pure-bred Gallic conceits as confit rabbit leg and black pudding cassoulet, beef fillet with potato and celeriac dauphinois or chicken breast and leg croquette partnered by chicory, onion purée, bacon crumb and Madeira sauce. Occasionally the kitchen goes off-piste (curried poached egg with sultana and almond couscous, for example), but it's back to the French heartlands for tarte tatin with rhubarb ice cream or Valrhona chocolate mousse with vanilla sponge and hazelnut crumb. The wine list is international, but with a strong French regional bias.
Chef/s: Christie Matthews. **Closed:** Mon, Tue, 24 to 27 Dec, 1 Jan. **Meals:** main courses £15 to £26. **Details:** 40 seats. Bar. Music.

Casanova

Cooking score: 1
Italian | £30
13 Quay Street, Cardiff, CF10 1EA
Tel no: (029) 2034 4044
casanovacardiff.com
£5 OFF

It may not be as rakish as its namesake, but there's a mood of spirited independence about this Italian restaurant – in contrast to the myriad chains that dominate the area around Cardiff's Principality Stadium. Chef proprietor Antonio Cersosimo has been at the helm since 2005, and continues to deliver generous regional cooking with a modern accent in warm-hearted, low-key surroundings. Tuscany contributes farro e fagioli (a soup of borlotti beans and spelt), there's scialatielli pasta with seafood from the Amalfi coast, and a raft of desserts including hazelnut panna cotta to finish. An all-Italian wine list also scours the regions in search of bargains.
Chef/s: Antonio Cersosimo. **Closed:** Sun, 24 to 26 Dec, bank hols. **Meals:** set L £14 (2 courses) to £18. Set D £25 (2 courses) to £32. **Details:** 35 seats. Music.

Mint and Mustard

Cooking score: 2
Indian | £35
134 Whitchurch Road, Cardiff, CF14 3LZ
Tel no: (029) 2062 0333
mintandmustard.com

An unassuming suburb of Cardiff might not be the first place you expect to find authentic Keralan dishes but Mint and Mustard flies the flag for modern cooking from South India and beyond. One of four branches (there are others in Taunton, Chepstow and Penarth) owned by two Keralan doctors, the emphasis here is on light and healthy dishes with clearly defined flavours. That's not to say staples like chicken tikka masala don't make an appearance, but lesser-known dishes such as Pondicherry lamb and Kochi prawn mango curry catch the eye of the more adventurous. A more familiar starter of spice-crusted lamb tikka straight from the tandoor might lead on to chicken dhaba murgh, heady with garlic and ginger, the sauce mopped up with a fig and coriander naan bread. Desserts are no afterthought, as proven by a honey and saffron-marinated tandoori pineapple with pistachio ice cream. A global wine list of fragrant whites and robust reds opens at £18.50.
Chef/s: Santhosh Kumar Nair. **Closed:** 25 and 26 Dec. **Meals:** main courses £9 to £17. Set L £10. Tasting menus £37 to £47. **Details:** 90 seats.

Purple Poppadom

Cooking score: 3
Indian | £29
Upper Floor, 185a Cowbridge Road East, Cardiff, CF11 9AJ
Tel no: (029) 2022 0026
purplepoppadom.com
£5 OFF £30

The name sums up the purple-hued decor of this first-floor Indian restaurant in Canton, a primarily residential area just west of the city centre. There are quite a few favourites on the menu, among them tandoori king prawns, Kashmiri rogan josh or a Kerala-style biryani, but the kitchen thrives on innovation, too. Inventive dishes offer astonishing layering of fresh, vibrant flavours, seen in a bright pan-seared sea bass, served on curry-leaf-infused mashed potato with a raw mango, ginger and coconut sauce and beetroot pachadi, or raan akbari, a slow-braised, spice-marinated lamb shank, finished in the tandoor and served with a butternut squash mash, an intense sauce reduction and mint sorbet. If you make it as far as dessert, consider the signature chocomosa – a samosa-style pastry filled with runny Belgian chocolate. Set lunches seem good value, and there's a helpfully annotated, decently priced wine list.

Chef/s: Anand George. **Closed:** Mon, 25 and 26 Dec, 1 Jan. **Meals:** main courses £14 to £20. Set L £15 (2 courses) to £22. Set D £15 (2 courses) to £25. Sun L £20. Tasting menu £50 (6 courses). **Details:** 70 seats. Bar. Music.

LOCAL GEM

Canna Deli

British | £35
2 Pontcanna Mews, 200 Kings Road, Cardiff, CF11 9DF
Tel no: (07767) 726902

Tucked away in a quiet courtyard in the Cardiff suburb of Pontcanna, this is the sort of buzzy neighbourhood food hub we would all like to have on our doorstep.This deli café is a proud champion of Welsh produce, which is hardly surprising as it's owned by a family of cheesemakers. Their award-winning Anglesey Blue might make an appearance in sandwiches and platters but specials like Welsh beef cawl and Wye Valley asparagus with poached eggs and coppa are just as enticing.

Cowbridge

LOCAL GEM

Bar 44

Spanish | £25
44c High Street, Cowbridge, CF71 7AG
Tel no: (0333) 344 4049
bar44.co.uk
£5 OFF £30

This friendly first-floor tapas joint has spawned other Bar 44 sites since opening in 2002 but locals still flock to the Cowbridge original. The tiled floor is more Med than Vale of Glamorgan and the menus are resolutely Spanish, whether you order the charcuterie and cheese plates or hot dishes like Duroc pork belly with smoked morcilla and beans or seared chicken livers with pancetta and Pedro Ximénez. The Iberian theme continues with the all-Spanish wine list, which includes 20 sherries with helpful notes on food matching.

Llanddewi Skirrid

The Walnut Tree

Cooking score: 5
Modern British | £60
Llanddewi Skirrid, NP7 8AW
Tel no: (01873) 852797
thewalnuttreeinn.com

Readers remain firm in their enthusiasm for Wales's most famous restaurant – a sturdy whitewashed and low-ceilinged building beneath Skirrid mountain – testament to the diligence of Shaun Hill. He has forged dependable links with producers and takes trouble over quality raw materials, and his appetite for simple, seasonal food is as keen as ever, be it a plate of cured sea bass with blood orange, avocado and fennel or skate with octopus and roast hispi cabbage. Hill can summon up muscular, meaty flavours, too – think loin of venison and hash with lingonberries or a very good dish of wild duck embellished with its own faggot and morel gravy. Elsewhere, the mushroom Scotch egg is an object lesson in flavour, or there might be an equally tasty artichoke and barba di frate pappardelle. Irresistible desserts take in a classic caramel fondant with tonka ice cream and a vanilla cheesecake with blood orange and popcorn. The set lunch is 'superb' and 'a snip at £30'. The authoritative wine list takes a broad-minded approach, so expect small, artisan producers at markups that shouldn't offend among the lordly Old World classics.

Chef/s: Shaun Hill. **Closed:** Sun, Mon, 1 week Christmas. **Meals:** main courses £16 to £32. Set L £25 (2 courses) to £30. **Details:** 50 seats. 20 seats outside. Bar. Wheelchairs. Parking.

Penarth

★ TOP 50 ★

Restaurant James Sommerin

Cooking score: 7

Modern British | £50

The Esplanade, Penarth, CF64 3AU
Tel no: (029) 2070 6559
jamessommerinrestaurant.co.uk

Surveying the shingle and the Bristol Channel from its prime position on the Esplanade at Penarth, James Sommerin's destination venue is designed to be as soothing as the maritime views. The main room has the feel of an executive lounge, with restful tones of light green and blue, and the air of professionalism to the front of house inspires confidence, particularly when one of the kitchen team brings the dish for which they are responsible to the table, with a voluble explanation to accompany it. There is skill and originality in abundance on the carte, which can be turned into six or nine tasting courses, and the hits keep on coming. A dark-toned study in deep, earthy flavours involves adding black pudding, raspberries and beetroot to a preliminary dish of wood pigeon, while a tranche of cod is lifted with herbal notes from rosemary and parsley and pointedly garnished with caviar. Main dishes work with the grain of their prime materials, so that monkfish arrives in its now customary guise of Indian spices, with salsify and kale, while the superlative Welsh lamb and butternut squash gain lift from the North African tones of cumin and mint. Nor is there any undue elaboration in a serving of premium 32-day-aged sirloin with oxtail and shallots in red wine jus. The longer tasting menu extends to three desserts, the perfect way of obviating a difficult choice among lemon and blueberry sablé, variations on tarte tatin, or raspberry and violet granola. A sheet of sommelier's selections is a good way into a voluminous and resourceful wine list that makes appreciable efforts at the affordable end, from £26.

Chef/s: James Sommerin. **Closed:** Mon. **Meals:** main courses £18 to £30. Tasting menu £65 (6 courses) to £85. Surprise menu £75 (6 courses) to £95. **Details:** 60 seats. Vg menu. Wheelchairs. Music.

Pontypridd

Bunch of Grapes

Cooking score: 2

Modern British | £30

Ynysangharad Road, Pontypridd, CF37 4DA
Tel no: (01443) 402934
bunchofgrapes.org.uk

This community pub was built in the 1860s for the workers of the nearby Glamorganshire canal and the Brown Lenox Chainworks, which made chains and anchors for the British Navy and for the *Titanic*. It's on a road that goes nowhere, one lined with traditional terraced houses, and is owned by the Otley Brewing Company, whose range of beers dominates the handpumps in the traditionally attired bar. A seasonal menu is offered in the vine-covered conservatory restaurant. Starters might include wild mushroom and pearl barley risotto with wilted spinach and truffle oil. For mains, you could opt for brisket of beef braised in Otley 06 Porter, roasted heritage carrots and kale mash. Despite some exotic-sounding dishes, such as pear cheesecake, star anise jelly and pear crisps, this remains a proper pub: lunchtime choices include fish and chips, Breconshire steaks, homemade curries and a bar menu of sandwiches. A keenly priced wine list arranged by style starts at £16.90.

Chef/s: Nicholas Otley and Mathew Traylor. **Meals:** main courses £14 to £25. Sun L £18 (3 courses). **Details:** 70 seats. 24 seats outside.

Whitebrook

★ TOP 50 ★

The Whitebrook

Cooking score: 7

British | £52

Whitebrook, NP25 4TX
Tel no: (01600) 860254
thewhitebrook.co.uk

£5 OFF

About four miles out of Monmouth in the paradisiacal Wye Valley, The Whitebrook is the creation of Chris and Kirsty Harrod, its eight guest rooms a stylish adjunct to the bright, smartly linened restaurant. Chris is a confirmed gleaner and forager, gathering wild ingredients that find their way into the kitchen's daily production, from resident breakfasts to the seven-course evening tasting menu. A reader who buys meat at the same Ross-on-Wye supplier confirms the outstanding quality of the Huntsham Court Farm suckling pig, served here with caramelised celeriac, pear and lamb's sorrel. Prior to that, there could be deliciously intense duck liver parfait with a croquette, quince, hazelnuts and bittercress, as well as a seafood medley of Cornish cod and clams in buttermilk with kohlrabi, rainbow chard and radish. It's unmistakably contemporary cooking, but with its roots firmly bedded in the local soil, and thus with a hawkish eye on the turning of the seasons. A pre-dessert delivers welcome piquancy via blackberries, chamomile and blackcurrant sage, before poached pear with maritime pine and yoghurt crumble brings down the curtain. One visitor wondered what exactly you had to do to get more of the wonderful bread, but otherwise service is intent on charming. As indeed is the wine list, which has natural and biodynamic producers scattered through the authoritative roll call of younger and forward-thinking growers. Glasses alone include Chavy's Puligny-Montrachet and a Monmouth Pinot Noir, with bottles from £25.

Chef/s: Chris Harrod. **Closed:** Mon, Tue, first 2 weeks Jan. **Meals:** set L £39. Sun L £39. Tasting menu £52 (5 courses) to £82. **Details:** 26 seats. V menu. Bar. Music. Parking. Children over 12 yrs at D.

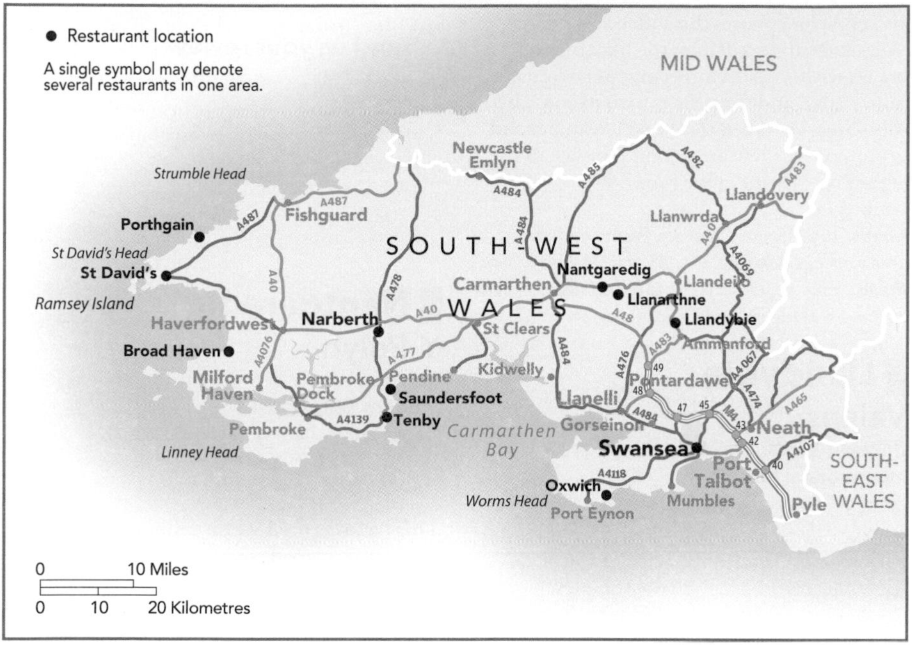

Broad Haven

LOCAL GEM

The Druidstone

International | £35

Druidstone Haven, Broad Haven, SA62 3NE
Tel no: (01437) 781221
druidstone.co.uk

Run by successive members of the Bell family for more than 40 years, this idiosyncratic hotel is a veteran of Pembrokeshire's holiday scene renowned for its live music, dramatic views over St Brides Bay and enterprising international food. On a typical day, you might cruise from salmon gravadlax with almond skordalia via hake with curried mung bean dhal or organic chicken breast stuffed with chorizo and Monterey Jack cheese to chocolate terrine or coconut rice pudding with caramelised pineapple. Well-priced wines also straddle the globe.

Llanarthne

Wright's Food Emporium

Cooking score: 2

Modern British | £22

Golden Grove Arms, Llanarthne, SA32 8JU
Tel no: (01558) 668929
wrightsfood.co.uk

Handy for the National Botanical Gardens, and a beacon of hospitality in an area not generally noted for good places to eat, the Wrights' utilitarian but convivial set-up (now with bedrooms) is valued for its honest, no-frills cooking. The dedication to local, regional and seasonal produce is refreshing, and hearty, uncomplicated flavours prevail. It's as good for breakfasts of bubble and squeak with poached egg and salumi, as it is for lunches of, say, a generously filled rare steak sandwich with Hafod Cheddar and caremelised onions, or the pork belly cubano that is such a hit with visitors. Chorizo and white bean stew is another sure-fire winner, and everyone praises the coffee and cakes. Weekend suppers deliver the likes of red bream with soy and mirin greens and green onion salsa, and if a table is hard to come by (bookings are taken for weekend supper and groups only) there are goodies for sale in the adjoining deli and wine room. Wines from £15.

Chef/s: Aled Evans, Charlotte Pasetti and Stefan Emamboccus. **Closed:** Tue, 25 and 26 Dec, 1 Jan. **Meals:** main courses £10 to £16. **Details:** 80 seats. 20 seats outside. Wheelchairs. Music. Parking.

Llandybie

Valans

Cooking score: 1

International | £25

29 High Street, Llandybie, SA18 3HX
Tel no: (01269) 851288
valans.co.uk

Don't be put off by the unassuming frontage, this family-run restaurant is very much a part of the community and has been going about its business since 2005. Welsh ingredients play their part on a fixed-price menu that takes a sweep through a broader European landscape. That means toasted brioche gets a topping of Perl Wen cheese and garlic mushrooms, and cockles and laverbread partner sautéed gnocchi and crispy Carmarthen ham. Carmarthenshire beef is a signature, slow-cooked for six hours, and daily fish specials are chalked up on the blackboard. End on a sweet note with chocolate truffle torte. The concise, good-value wine list opens at £14.50.

Chef/s: Dave Vale. **Closed:** Mon, 2 weeks Jan. **Meals:** main courses £17. Set L £14 (2 courses) to £18. Set D £21 to £25. Sun L £16. **Details:** 35 seats. Wheelchairs. Music.

Send us your review

Your feedback informs the content of the *GFG* and will be used to compile next year's reviews. To register your opinion about any restaurant listed, or a restaurant that you wish to bring to our attention, visit our website.

Nantgaredig

Y Polyn

Cooking score: 3

Modern British | £40

Capel Dewi, Nantgaredig, SA32 7LH
Tel no: (01267) 290000
ypolyn.co.uk

This reconfigured Welsh tollhouse sits at a country crossroads so you definitely need to drive. Once inside, Y Polyn proves its worth as a rustic destination for dining rather than drinking – despite the presence of three reputable Welsh ales. The kitchen makes a good fist of things, transforming native produce into dishes with bags of personality: deeply flavoured fish soup comes with a Pernod kick and textbook accompaniments, while pig's head is wrapped in Carmarthen ham, timed to 'tender perfection' and served with a 'ridiculously good' cauliflower purée. Elsewhere, guinea fowl was 'slightly tough' but accompanied by a 'first-class' pithivier and shredded savoy cabbage, and chocolate délice was teamed with excellent espresso ice cream. From the 'fabulous' home-baked breads to the provision of proper kids' meals, there's much to enjoy here. Y Polyn also wins friends with its genuinely offbeat wine selection.

Chef/s: Susan Manson. **Closed:** Mon. **Meals:** main courses £16 to £20. Set L £16 (2 courses) to £20. Set D £30 (2 courses) to £40. Sun L £24 (2 courses) to £29. **Details:** 100 seats. 15 seats outside. Bar. Wheelchairs. Music. Parking.

Narberth

The Grove

Cooking score: 6

Modern British | £64

Molleston, Narberth, SA67 8BX
Tel no: (01834) 860915
thegrove-narberth.co.uk

Owners Neil Kedward and Zoe Agar have given the ground floor of their eminently desirable Pembrokeshire retreat a complete makeover, although the views out towards the Preseli Mountains and the warm intimacy of the aptly named Fernery dining room are unchanged – as is the highly complex food masterminded by head chef Allister Barsby. While his cooking is utterly dependent on regional produce, foraged snippets and the seasonal harvest from the kitchen garden, Barsby is not immune to the esoteric possibilities of, say, marinated daikon, lemongrass foam or candied pecans. A signature starter of sweetbread raviolo paired with celeriac purée, pickled pear, confit egg yolk and winter truffle demonstrates the style, while mains embrace everything from stone bass roasted with star anise, saffron onions and tapenade in bouillabaisse sauce to fillet of Welsh beef conventionally sauced with Madeira, alongside Jerusalem artichoke, pickled onions and oyster mushrooms. To finish, explore the warm Golden Cenarth cheese with cauliflower, apple and cider vinegar or try the pear fritters offset by green-tea ice cream. Back-up comes from an intelligently annotated 200-bin wine list replete with prestigious bottles from across the globe; make a beeline for the thoughtful 'sommelier's recommendations'.

Chef/s: Allister Barsby. **Meals:** set L £29 (2 courses) to £38. Set D £47 (2 courses) to £64. Sun L £38. Tasting menu £94 (8 courses). **Details:** 34 seats. Bar. Wheelchairs. Music. Parking. No children after 7pm.

Wales's best bites

Nick Brodie of Llangoed Hall in Powys shares his favourite places to eat and drink across Wales

The Cock Hotel at **Bronllys** serves a hearty **breakfast**, with welcoming and very accommodating staff.

For food shopping, **Swansea market** has superb **fish, meat and veg** at good prices.

The Wheelwright Arms at **Erwood, Builth Wells**, is the place to go after work for a **pint**, and they also do great **pub food**.

My favourite place to go with my **family** is **Seoul House** at **St Mellons in Cardiff**. They serve great **Korean food** - my son has always liked going, especially for the open-table barbecues.

The best **Sunday lunch** is at **The Felin Fach Griffin**. It's a favourite in the area with well cooked **meat and fish** and a good atmosphere.

If I could eat only one thing around here, it would have to be... the local lamb - it's melt in the mouth with good fat coverage. Barbecued would be the best way as it's sweet in the summer but it has a fuller flavour towards the autumn.

Oxwich

Beach House

Cooking score: 5

Modern British | £48

Oxwich Beach, Oxwich, SA3 1LS
Tel no: (01792) 390965
beachhouseoxwich.co.uk

£5 OFF

'Is there a finer view than the one from the window tables of the Beach House?', asks one visitor to this modern stone-built restaurant looking across Oxwich Bay to the Three Cliffs and beyond. This is a stunning part of the Gower Peninsula and the location – like that of its sister, Coast at Saundersfoot (see entry) – is reflected in the bright, breezy interior and in the short, focused menu. Of course, local seafood plays a starring role, but so too does crab from England's south coast, Gloucestershire venison and Norfolk quail – if it's top quality, then chef Hywel Griffith (ex-Ynyshir and the Freemasons at Wiswell, see entries) will use it. Atlantic prawn ravioli, lemongrass, ginger and pork noodles is a light and fragrant opener that might lead on to tandoori roasted hand-dived scallops teamed with crispy pork shoulder, roasted onion, yoghurt and coriander (although the £32 price tag makes the £28 three-course lunch menu look a bargain). Round things off with duck egg custard tart, rhubarb, lemon and nutmeg. An interesting wine list starts at £25 and features bottles from Thailand, India and Croatia.

Chef/s: Hywel Griffith. **Closed:** Mon, Tue, 2 weeks Jan. **Meals:** main courses £22 to £32. Set L £28 (3 courses). Tasting menu £55 (5 courses) to £75. **Details:** 46 seats. 30 seats outside. V menu. Bar. Wheelchairs. Music. Parking.

Porthgain

The Shed

Cooking score: 1

Seafood | £35

Porthgain, SA62 5BN
Tel no: (01348) 831518
theshedporthgain.co.uk

When it comes to harbourside seafood eateries, there aren't many quite like The Shed. It's loyally supported, the kind of place that's full in midweek, no matter what the weather. Most come for fish and chips, the menu taking in not only haddock and cod, but also monkfish and John Dory, with praise for sides of mushy peas and cucumber and fennel slaw. Generous portions of moules marinière, and monkfish, mussel and chorizo stew have gone down well too, and beef shin stew with root vegetables is a tasty alternative for those not in the mood for fish. There's a good, kindly priced selection by the glass on the global wine list.

Chef/s: Brian Mullins. **Closed:** 25 and 26 Dec. **Meals:** main courses £11 to £19. **Details:** 51 seats. 50 seats outside. Wheelchairs. Music.

St David's

LOCAL GEM

Cwtch

Modern British | £34

22 High Street, St David's, SA62 6SD
Tel no: (01437) 720491
cwtchrestaurant.co.uk

£5 OFF

Jackie and John Hatton-Bell's long-established restaurant on St David's main street is run with a warmth that is much appreciated by readers. The stripped-back rustic charm of the dining room is in step with the restrained, respectful seasonal cooking, which showcases prime local ingredients. Typical offerings might include a starter of beetroot-pickled salmon, cucumber ribbons, blood orange and vinaigrette, say, followed by pan-fried duck breast and confit leg with creamy dauphinois. The wine list opens at £20.

Saundersfoot

Coast

Cooking score: 4

Seafood | £42

Coppet Hall Beach, Saundersfoot, SA69 9AJ
Tel no: (01834) 810800
coastsaundersfoot.co.uk

£5 OFF

'You could be in the South of France,' mused one couple with blue sky and shimmering sea stretched out before them, but this is South Wales and Coast is a dining destination come rain or shine. The curved structure and split-level interior of the striking cedar-clad building give everyone a crack at the spectacular views over Coppet Hall Beach. Head chef Tom Hine may well deliver the opener himself – an array of snacks that might include steamed scallops in ponzu dressing. Local crab is layered with compelling flavours and textures – smoked haddock, pink grapefruit, radish and charred lettuce – or go for belly and cheek of Middle White pork, balanced by compressed watermelon and chilli jam. Main courses are no less contemporary: skate with saffron couscous and a caper and raisin vinaigrette, say, bring back those thoughts of the Mediterranean. The fixed-price lunch might offer up flat-iron steak with pomme purée, and kids have their own menu, too. The global wine list includes interesting options by the glass.

Chef/s: Thomas Hine. **Closed:** Mon, Tue, second and third week Jan, 9 Sept. **Meals:** main courses £16 to £32. Set L £28 (3 courses). **Details:** 54 seats 30 seats outside. Bar. Wheelchairs. Music. Parking.

Get social

Follow us on social media for the latest news, chef interviews and more.
Twitter: @GoodFoodGuideUK
Facebook: TheGoodFoodGuide

Swansea

Hanson at the Chelsea

Cooking score: 3

Modern European | £38

17 St Mary Street, Swansea, SA1 3LH
Tel no: (01792) 464068
hansonatthechelsea.co.uk

£5 OFF

Wind Street around the corner may still be as lively as when Dylan Thomas frequented the bars there, but slip down a quiet pedestrianised side street to this long-established little restaurant and it feels like another, much calmer world. Andrew Hanson's cheery, yellow-painted bistro has an old-school air to it but the food stays the right side of retro thanks to his intelligent and confident cooking of locally sourced seafood and meats. At inspection, precisely cooked scallops teemed with freshness added by tuna sashimi, ginger, soy and lime, but the accompanying risotto was clumsily cooked. Honey-roast Gower rack of lamb (cooked pink) with a ramekin of crisp-topped shepherd's pie, fondant carrot, soft butter leeks and rosemary jus was a well-handled main, and was followed by treacle tart and custard. Elsewhere, a grilled fillet of halibut with linguine, smoked pancetta and Parmesan was keeping fish fans happy. Wines from £15.95.

Chef/s: Andrew Hanson. **Closed:** Sun. **Meals:** main courses £14 to £29. Set L £16 (2 courses) to £20. Tasting menu £40 (7 courses). **Details:** 40 seats. Music.

Slice

Cooking score: 4

Modern British | £42

73-75 Eversley Road, Swansea, SA2 9DE
Tel no: (01792) 290929
sliceswansea.co.uk

Five years since they took over what was already a long-established star of Swansea's dining scene, chefs Adam Bannister and Chris Harris have well and truly made Slice their own – it's still 'the hottest ticket in Swansea'.

The ground-floor kitchen grabs your attention, entirely visible through the large former shop window on the pavement. The wedge-shaped, six-table dining room with its chunky wooden furniture and twinkling spotlit ceiling is above, and the chefs take it in turns to bring dishes up from the kitchen. The modern Welsh cooking blends classical techniques with modern presentation and a starter of poached salmon, crispy potatoes and watercress sauce impresses with or without the indulgent supplement of Exmoor caviar. Lamb wellington with roast artichoke, artichoke purée and a punchy wild garlic salsa verde is equally pleasing, as is a finale of rum baba, mojito gel, pineapple carpaccio, roast pineapple and rice pudding ice cream. Wines from £17.

Chef/s: Chris Harris and Adam Bannister. **Closed:** Mon, Tue, Wed, 1 week Apr, 1 week Jul, 2 weeks Oct, 1 week Dec. **Meals:** set L £29 (2 courses) to £32. Set D £42. Tasting menu £55. **Details:** 16 seats. Music.

Tenby

The Salt Cellar

Cooking score: 3

Modern British | £39

The Esplanade, Tenby, SA70 7DU
Tel no: (01834) 844005
thesaltcellartenby.com

£5 OFF

Inhabiting a world of its own on the lower ground floor of the Atlantic Hotel, this stand-alone restaurant, bar and terrace proves to be quite a catch. It's an unpretentious, friendly place with deep leather sofas in the bar, a lighter crisper feel to the dining room, and inventive cooking showcasing fashionable flavours. Fish is a strength: gin-cured sewin (Welsh sea trout) beautifully presented on shavings of fennel and vibrant green oyster leaf with cucumber and tonic dressing, and sautéed brill teamed with orzo in a rich, foaming crab bisque, were hits on our visit. As indeed was a chunky piece of local pork collar in a dark, sticky, malty glaze and served with pig's cheek, parsnips, cabbage, apple sauce and crackling. Straightforward desserts, such as a 'deeply fragrant' chamomile panna cotta, are well liked, too. 'It's hard not to wolf down the homemade bread', and there is an excellent range of local, bottled beers alongside the wide-ranging wine list.

Chef/s: Duncan Barham and Matt Flowers. **Closed:** Mon and Tue (Dec and Jan), 24 to 26 Dec, 2 to 6 Jan. **Meals:** main courses £18 to £26. Set L £15 (2 courses) to £19. Sun L £20 to £25. **Details:** 45 seats. 20 seats outside. V menu. Vg menu. Bar. Wheelchairs. Music.

CHANNEL ISLANDS

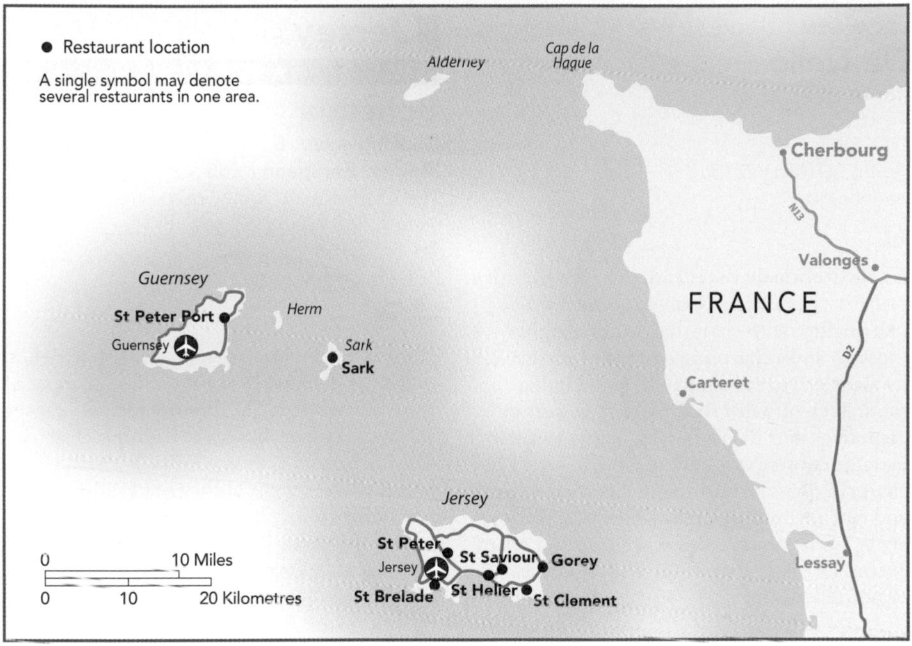

Restaurant location
A single symbol may denote several restaurants in one area.
Alderney
Cap de la Hague
Cherbourg
N13
Valognes
FRANCE
D2
Guernsey
St Peter Port
Guernsey
Herm
Sark
Sark
Carteret
Jersey
St Peter
Jersey
St Saviour
Gorey
St Brelade
St Helier
St Clement
Lessay
0 10 Miles
0 10 20 Kilometres

Guernsey

La Frégate

Cooking score: 3
Modern British | £43
Beauregard Lane, Les Cotils, St Peter Port, Guernsey, GY1 1UT
Tel no: (01481) 724624
lafregatehotel.com

Perched on a hill overlooking St Peter Port harbour, this is one of those out-of-the-way hotel restaurants where, after years spent serving a captive clientele, the food could be forgiven for slipping into anachronism. The reality is quite the opposite (though the dining room, albeit with an impressive panorama, would admittedly benefit from a refurb). The extensive menu focuses mainly on classic preparations, generously plated, with a restrained smattering of modernism here and there, perhaps chicken and duck liver terrine with translucent, pyramidal jellies of Sauternes, followed by risotto nero topped with two fat, lightly grilled Guernsey scallops complete with roe. Crêpes Suzette, flambéed at table, makes for a theatrical finish. Lunchtime is arguably the best time to visit both for value and that view. Service is more formal than it needs to be but the sommelier knows his stuff: wine is a triumph – some serious bargains pepper the moderately chunky list.

Chef/s: Tony Leck. **Meals:** main courses £21 to £28. Set L £20 (2 courses) to £25. Set D £40. Sun L £25. Tasting menu £65. **Details:** 65 seats. Bar. Parking.

Send us your review

Your feedback informs the content of the *GFG* and will be used to compile next year's reviews. To register your opinion about any restaurant listed in the Guide, or a restaurant that you wish to bring to our attention, visit: thegoodfoodguide.co.uk/feedback

LOCAL GEM

Da Nello

Italian | £35

46 Lower Pollet, St Peter Port, Guernsey, GY1 1WF
Tel no: (01481) 721552
danello.gg

£5 OFF

An institution on the island, this 15th-century property has a larger-than-it-seems Tardis-like quality, with character running right through and a charming courtyard out back. It's the place to eat unreconstructed Italian food. Kick off with six Guernsey oysters or carpaccio done the right way, before a classic pasta or risotto (spaghetti marinara, say). The chargrill does the business on Scottish steaks and rack of English lamb, while local scallops arrive with balsamic syrup, spinach and crispy bacon. Drink Italian wines by the glass, carafe or bottle.

LOCAL GEM

Octopus

Seafood | £35

Havelet Bay, St Peter Port, Guernsey, GY1 1AX
Tel no: (01481) 722400
octopusgsy.co.uk

With its impressive glass frontage and wooden decking right down to the sea wall, it's hard to beat this modern seafood joint for location. The pared-back nautical interior belies the runaway variety of the menu that, though it makes a feature of fish, also takes in steaks, street food, salads and more. On the seafood side, there are oysters, scallops with chilli butter, bouillabaisse-style fish stew, and sole with beurre blanc. To finish, homely favourites include apple tart, tiramisu and rice pudding. With a host of cocktails, beers and well-priced wines, it's the best place for a drink in this pretty harbour town.

Jersey

★ TOP 50 ★

Bohemia

Cooking score: 8
Modern European | £65

The Club Hotel & Spa, Green Street, St Helier, Jersey, JE2 4UH
Tel no: (01534) 880500
bohemiajersey.com

£5 OFF

There is an embarrassment of elaborate riches at this much-fêted Jersey restaurant. Part of a luxury hotel it may be, but the identity carved out by executive chef Steve Smith is clear: to take the best ingredients, from the island if possible, and use the ability of his talented brigade to create plates of food where invention, looks, seasonality and taste meld with a sense of generosity – this is a kitchen that first and foremost wants to feed you. Tasting menus include full pescatarian, vegetarian and prestige options, there's a conventional à la carte, and even a one-course midweek offer that might include turbot with sea buckthorn, mussels and pennywort, or lamb loin and braised neck with mild Cevennes onion and melting Vacherin cheese. A local crab tart with mango and coriander receives effusive praise, as does bass with onion, smoked eel and rock samphire, and the nutty, smooth celeriac velouté poured round a slow-cooked bantam egg. The sweetness of a playful popcorn dessert (parfait and caramelised pieces with dots of salted caramel sauce) is countered by a sharp lime sorbet, though you may prefer the moodier tones of sour cherry, kirsch and dark chocolate. Some feel the lighting could be cranked up a notch (and the music down), but for a whizz-bang meal round these parts, this place is hard to beat. The world-class wine list has heft and variety though you'll find nothing below £29.

Chef/s: Steve Smith. **Closed:** Sun, 24 to 30 Dec, bank hols. **Meals:** main courses £19 to £28 (L only). Set L £25 (2 courses) to £30. Set D £55 (2 courses) to

£65. Tasting menu £79. Surprise menu £45 to £49. **Details:** 62 seats. V menu. Bar. Wheelchairs. Music. Parking.

Green Island Restaurant

Cooking score: 1
Mediterranean | £40
Green Island, St Clement, Jersey, JE2 6LS
Tel no: (01534) 857787
greenisland.je

Right by the beach, overlooking the grassy islet from which it takes its name, Green Island looks like a seaside café but pitches its food considerably higher. A long list of specials, recited at table, covers crab, lobster, tuna, scallops, oysters, sole, skate, mullet and more, all with a choice of cooking methods and sauces. A thermidor-style mix of crab, spring onion and a little cream sauce impressed one diner, while sole fillets with scallops, crab-laced mash, grilled Parmesan and beurre blanc proved a fresh and satisfying main course. There's plenty to love here, including desserts such as a classic crème brûlée with sablé biscuits. Wines start at £21.95.
Chef/s: Paul Insley. **Closed:** Mon, Christmas, Jan. **Meals:** main courses £18 to £29. Set L £19 (2 courses) to £22. Sun L £28 (3 courses). **Details:** 40 seats. 20 seats outside. Music. Parking.

The Green Olive

Cooking score: 3
Mediterranean | £30
1 Anley Street, St Helier, Jersey, JE2 3QE
Tel no: (01534) 728198
greenoliverestaurant.co.uk
£5 OFF

Tall windows and high ceilings help to create a feeling of light and space in this appealing first-floor dining room overlooking St Helier's business district, while chef proprietor Paul Le Brocq gets everything absolutely right when it comes to food and service, openly eschewing red meat in favour of fish, white meats, poultry and vegetarian dishes, and conjuring up vibrant Mediterranean fusion riffs such as pan-fried sea bass with chorizo and mussel risotto, salsa verde, tempura king prawns and herb dust. Jersey produce always figures prominently, although it's generally embellished, as hand-dived scallops with peanut, pineapple and lime or a jumbo pork chop ('white meat') served with burnt aubergine, a pulled pork fritter, pea, mint and puffed skin. To conclude, there might be frozen vanilla parfait with strawberry and basil compôte. One-dish 'express canteen lunches' are tremendous value and the 20-bin wine list keeps its prices pegged back too.
Chef/s: Paul Le Brocq. **Closed:** Sun, Mon, 23 Dec to end Jan. **Meals:** main courses £16 to £23. **Details:** 45 seats. Music.

Longueville Manor

Cooking score: 6
Modern French | £65
Longueville Road, St Saviour, Jersey, JE2 7WF
Tel no: (01534) 725501
longuevillemanor.com

The finest hotel on Jersey, Longueville Manor may have Norman ancestry but age is no barrier when it comes to doling out creature comforts. In the two low-ceilinged dining rooms, huge mirrors and glass doors add some light relief to the deep-pile carpets and comfortable upholstery and, best of all, staff 'never seem remotely robotic'. Long-serving Andrew Baird guarantees stability and consistency in the kitchen, although diners say that the cooking has been 'turned up a notch' of late. Consider a hugely generous celebration of Jersey seafood in the shape of a concassé-topped tower of white crabmeat, a tempura crab claw and a beignet of dark meat; or a fabulous piece of beef fillet accompanied by a crisp oxtail bonbon, some béarnaise-glazed braised shin and a super-beefy red wine sauce. Pre-desserts are pure fun, while dessert itself might be a milk chocolate délice and feuillantine 'sandwich' with a filling of fragrant geranium crémeux. The two-tiered cheese trolley is unmissable, and Longueville also boasts a 'genuinely passionate' sommelier with immense knowledge of the monumental 400-bin wine list.

Chef/s: Andrew Baird. **Meals:** set L £25 (2 courses) to £30. Set D £53 (2 courses) to £65. Sun L £45. Tasting menu £85 (7 courses). **Details:** 90 seats. 35 seats outside. V menu. Vg menu. Bar. Music. Parking.

Mark Jordan at the Beach

Cooking score: 3
Modern British | £36
La Plage, La Route de la Haule, St Peter, Jersey, JE3 7YD
Tel no: (01534) 780180
markjordanatthebeach.com

Mark Jordan initially conceived this modern seaside brasserie as an informal counterpoint to his cooking at The Atlantic Hotel, and has maintained his stake here since departing the hotel in 2017. The menu sports a handsome fish and seafood selection, plus Jordan's signature burgers and a host of competently cooked, classic combinations with the emphasis on Jersey produce. A paper cone of whitebait – crisp-fried, cayenne-spiked, with silky mustard mayo – sets the tone, followed by Jersey scallops, cooked golden in butter, with bacon, chargrilled cucumber and a lick of light, sharp chive and cucumber beurre blanc, and a fine fillet of brill with crab tortellini, a light fish mousse, fish goujon, juicy asparagus and a thick lobster bisque sauce. We preferred the petits fours (a huge chocolate macaron and four chocolates on lollipop sticks) to dessert at inspection. The wine list spans affordable favourites and fine wines, with a strong focus on Europe.

Chef/s: Mark Jordan and Alex Zotter. **Meals:** main courses £16 to £26. Set L £20 (2 courses) to £25. Early set D £25. Sun L £28. **Details:** 50 seats. 30 seats outside.

Oyster Box

Cooking score: 3
International | £40
Route de la Baie, St Brelade, Jersey, JE3 8EF
Tel no: (01534) 850888
oysterbox.co.uk

This 'beach bar and restaurant' makes the most of its seaside setting with a covetable alfresco terrace and gallery windows overlooking the briny expanses of St Brelade's Bay. Inside it's sleek, contemporary and gleaming white, with blue mosaic tiles and a globally diverse menu that includes a galley full of Jersey seafood. Rock oysters from the Royal Bay of Grouville get top billing, ahead of tempura king prawns with Asian slaw, Thai monkfish curry or battered haddock and chips, but there's much else besides. Well-hung steaks, burgers and even roast pigeon with wild mushroom tortellini are manna for the carnivorous brigade, while vegetarians can satisfy themselves with beetroot carpaccio and goat's cheese fritters followed by asparagus and courgette risotto. Sides naturally include Jersey Royals in season, and pud could mean lemon tart with poached rhubarb. There are rich pickings from nearby France and faraway South Africa on the well-chosen wine list.

Chef/s: Tony Dorris. **Closed:** 25 and 26 Dec, 1 Jan. **Meals:** main courses £12 to £28. Set L and D £28 (2 courses). **Details:** 90 seats. 50 seats outside. Bar. Wheelchairs. Music.

Samphire

Cooking score: 5
Modern European | £50
7-11 Don Street, St Helier, Jersey, JE2 4TQ
Tel no: (01534) 725100
samphire.je
£5 OFF

Situated in St Helier's financial district, Samphire was born in spring 2018 from what was Ormer, one of Jersey's reference venues for modern European cooking. A refurbishment has resulted in a stylish room with buttoned banquettes and diverting photographic prints, and a range of eating options, from a 'Casual Dining' menu of lobster thermidor, fish and chips and so forth, leading up to a seven-course tasting menu. From the latter there are highlights aplenty, including a pair of golden scallops with roasted asparagus in truffled hollandaise, and a buttery rendition of brill with pancetta, broad beans, pea purée and a single morel. The centrepiece might be a rolled piece of immaculate sirloin with purées of artichoke and watercress in a resonant beef jus. After a strawberry sorbet interlude, dessert could comprise duck-egg custard topped with rhubarb ice cream and nutmeg crumble. The vegetarian tasting menu turns on pea risotto with goat's cheese and wild garlic, ahead of cauliflower with romesco dressing and hazelnuts. Wines from a carefully chosen list inspire confidence, with bottles from £25.

Chef/s: Lee Smith. **Closed:** Sun. **Meals:** main courses £10 to £45. Set L and D £29 (3 courses) to £35. Tasting menu £80 (7 courses). **Details:** 70 seats. 24 seats outside. V menu. Bar. Wheelchairs. Music.

Sumas

Cooking score: 2
International | £40

Gorey Hill, St Martin, Gorey, Jersey, JE3 6ET
Tel no: (01534) 853291
sumasrestaurant.com

£5 OFF

When the mercury is up, 20 lucky souls get to sit outside on the first-floor terrace of this seafood-focused restaurant and take in the views over the harbour and Mont Orgueil castle. No matter if you're indoors, though, for white brick walls, blond wood floors and shimmering blue chairs make for a soothing setting. The kitchen matches the room when it comes to contemporary good taste, with an output that extends to charred mackerel with burnt apple and cooling labneh, or pork kromeski with new-season pickles and a hit of curry spice. Whole plaice with beurre noisette is old-school classicism at its best, while pot-roast guinea fowl arrives with morteau cassoulet and a hit of Cognac. Meadowsweet parfait is a creative finale, with honey, cultured yoghurt, caramelised lemon and spikes of meringue. The wine list embraces New and Old Worlds with equal enthusiasm, and weekend breakfasts might kick off with a Bloody Mary or buck's fizz.

Chef/s: Dany Lancaster. **Closed:** 21 Dec to 18 Jan. **Meals:** main courses £16 to £27. Set L and D £21 (2 courses) to £26. **Details:** 35 seats. 20 seats outside. Vg menu. Bar.

Tassili

Cooking score: 5
Modern European | £45

Grand Jersey Hotel, The Esplanade, St Helier, Jersey, JE2 3QA
Tel no: (01534) 722301
handpickedhotels.co.uk

£5 OFF

The views from the terrace overlooking St Helier's esplanade may not have changed much since this grand old spa hotel was built in 1890, but the food served in its soothing, split-level restaurant moves with the times. Nicolas Valmagna is steeped in French cuisine, but he's happy to fuse haute technique with global flavours and a barrow load of Jersey produce – all reinterpreted and refashioned via a series of menus. Given the location, the 'land and sea' tasting option is a good bet with its promise of fastidiously assembled and finely judged dishes such as turbot with saffron risotto and sea purslane or Anjou pigeon with a duxelle spring roll, artichoke, pied bleu mushrooms and black garlic purée. There's also value to be had from the three-course 'grazing' carte, which offers everything from langoustine with parsley root purée, bisque sauce and pennywort to Granny Smith apple with pecans, Calvados and apple sorbet or artisan cheeses with accompaniments aplenty (including watermelon and rosemary chutney). Back-up comes from a knowledgeably curated wine list.

Chef/s: Nicolas Valmagna. **Closed:** Sun, Mon, Jan. **Meals:** set D £45. Tasting menu £62 to £75 (7 courses). **Details:** 24 seats. V menu. Bar. Wheelchairs. Music. Parking. Children over 12 yrs.

Sark

★ NEW ENTRY ★

La Sablonnerie

Cooking score: 2
Modern French | £35
Little Sark, Sark, GY10 1SD
Tel no: (01481) 832061
sablonneriesark.com

A roadside gem at the southern end of Sark, this old white farmhouse is festooned with hanging baskets, the surrounding gardens combining subtropical flora and pressed-sand paths with precisely manicured lawns. Tables are scattered beneath the trees and climbing foliage. Inside is more prosaic, and the time-warp feeling extends to unpriced menus that offer melodies and montages, as well as a mid-meal 'water ice'. Service is engagingly eccentric, but the food is serious. Dressed crab in a sea urchin shell, delicately spiced tuna, roast salmon with lemon mayo and tender lobster; all turn up on a fine chef's seafood platter, while carefully timed sliced turbot with shredded ginger in lemon thyme cream sauce is equally pleasing. Meat could be pork belly confit with celeriac and sweet potato purée in lie de vin sauce. Duck liver parfait with red onion jam and orange and watercress salad might start the show, and chocolate tart with dark rum sauce brings down the curtain. The retro theme continues with horses and carriages for hire, and wines from £14.80 that include a Liebfraumilch.

Chef/s: Colin Day. **Closed:** end Oct to late Apr. **Meals:** main courses £20 to £35. **Details:** 39 seats. 36 seats outside. Bar. Music.

Anonymous

At *The Good Food Guide*, our inspectors dine anonymously and pay their bill in full. These impartial review meals, along with feedback from thousands of our readers, are what informs the content of the *GFG*.

LOCAL GEM

Stocks

British | £40
Le Grand Dixcart, Sark, GY10 1SD
Tel no: (01481) 832001
stockshotel.com

There is a lot to like about this tiny island close to Guernsey, which famously bans cars, is reached by a limited ferry service and is super-seasonal – everything shuts down in the winter. Stocks is the island's main hotel, with a lovely stone terrace where one reader enjoyed a lunch of fresh crab salad overlooking the manicured grounds complete with swimming pool. Dinner is served in the smart but plainly adorned dining room. Expect locally caught fish – lobster tail, turbot, fillet of crisp-skinned bream – or lamb rump before, say, rhubarb soufflé with vanilla sandwich. Wines from £19.95.

NORTHERN IRELAND

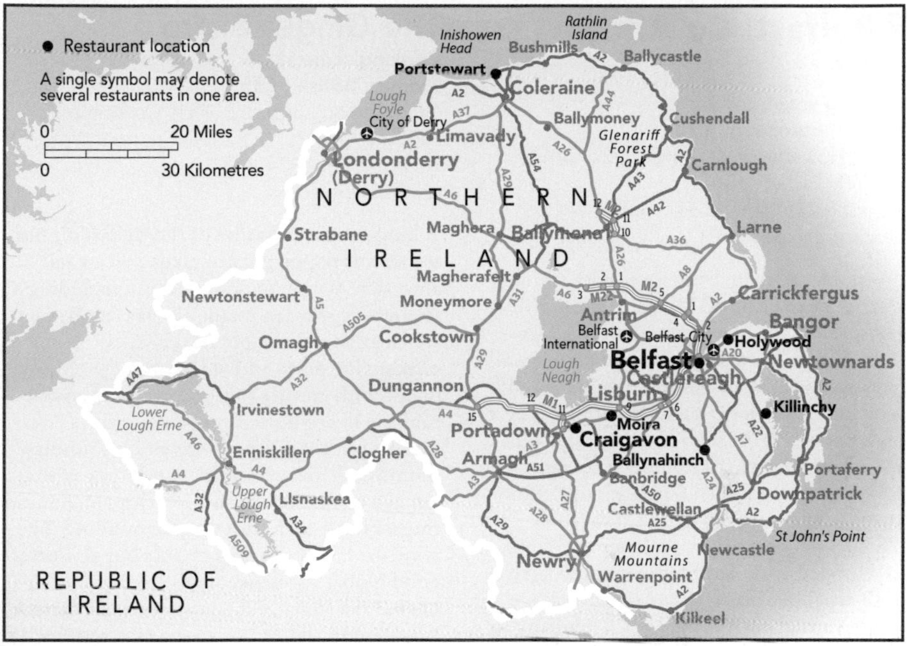

Ballynahinch, Co Down

The Bull & Ram

Cooking score: 2
Modern British | £28

1 Dromore Street, Ballynahinch, Co Down, BT24 8AG
Tel no: (028) 9756 0908
bullandram.com

Appropriately housed in a Grade I-listed Edwardian butcher's shop, the Bull & Ram is all about meat – more specifically beef from Northern Ireland, aged for a minimum of 30 days in Himalayan salt and served against a backdrop that makes the most of some sympathetic restoration work (note the emerald and white tiles, the herringbone oak ceiling and the original butcher's block). Steaks and burgers are obviously the main contenders on the menu, but you can also ring the changes with venison wellington, the day's fish special or, say, fried chicken and waffles with guacamole and chargrilled corn salsa on the side. Starters and sweets are mostly well-tried bistro favourites, from smoked black pudding Scotch eggs or goat's cheese fritters with pear chutney to crème brûlée or sticky toffee pudding with rum and raisin ice cream. Just about everything on the short, bare-bones wine list is offered by the glass or carafe.

Chef/s: Kelan McMichael. **Closed:** Mon, Tue, 25 and 26 Dec. **Meals:** main courses £12 to £17. Set L £14 (2 courses) to £18. Sun L £18 (1 course). **Details:** 75 seats. Wheelchairs. Music. Parking.

Send us your review

Your feedback informs the content of the *GFG* and will be used to compile next year's reviews. To register your opinion about any restaurant listed in the Guide, or a restaurant that you wish to bring to our attention, visit: thegoodfoodguide.co.uk/feedback

Belfast, Co Antrim

Eipic

Cooking score: 5
Modern European | £70
28-40 Howard Street, Belfast, Co Antrim, BT1 6PF
Tel no: (028) 9033 1134
deaneseipic.com

Overlook the shared entrance (with siblings Deanes Love Fish and Michael Deane's Meat Locker) and the decor that, with its silver-framed mirrors, white leather, and grey walls, remains stuck in the 90s, and you'll find the food here is as modern and ambitious as ever under new chef Alex Greene. An asparagus and lobster starter combines lobster tail, lardo, asparagus gel, poached asparagus tips, white asparagus velouté and endive. Two thick tranches of 'beautifully pink, tender' lamb loin topped with a soft lovage crumb, arrive with artichoke hearts, Jerusalem artichoke purée, turned potatoes and a rich demi-glace – a dish that typifies the classical bent of Greene's cooking. To finish, the Guanaja 70 per cent chocolate dessert combines milk chocolate ganache, a quenelle of 'superb, smooth' banana ice cream, another of dark chocolate mousse, a chocolate tuile sprinkled with chopped peanuts, and frothy 'peanut tea bubbles'. There's no doubting the creativity and flair on show here, and the overall experience is memorable for all the right reasons. The wine list offers plenty of familiar favourites, with global reach.
Chef/s: Alex Greene. **Closed:** Sun, Mon, Tue, 26 Dec to 3 Jan, 28 to 31 Mar, 11 to 21 Jul. **Meals:** tasting menu £70. **Details:** 26 seats. V menu. Bar. Wheelchairs. Music.

The Ginger Bistro

Cooking score: 1
Modern British | £35
Great Victoria Street, Belfast, Co Antrim, BT2 7AF
Tel no: (028) 9024 4421
gingerbistro.com

A long-running fixture of the Belfast dining scene, this popular bistro takes a please-all approach, with plenty of options, including a separate vegetarian menu. Dishes run from a warm salad of baby potato, chorizo, mozzarella, pesto and red peppers, to chicken breast with creamy mushroom pureé, savoy cabbage in cep butter, pine nuts and mushroom cottage pie – given a resounding thumbs-up by one reader – and steak with sauteéd spinach, garlic butter, chips and onion rings. Finish with sticky toffee pudding. The wine list favours French classics but also offers good global coverage.
Chef/s: Tim Moffet and Conor Mcgreeve. **Closed:** Sun, Mon, 25 and 26 Dec, Easter Mon and Tue, 12 and 13 Jul. **Meals:** main courses £16 to £27. **Details:** 100 seats. V menu. Bar. Wheelchairs. Music. No children after 9pm

★ LOCAL RESTAURANT AWARD ★
REGIONAL WINNER

Hadskis

Cooking score: 3
Modern European | £30
33 Donegall Street, Belfast, Co Antrim, BT1 2NB
Tel no: (028) 9032 5444
hadskis.co.uk

Amid the tattoo parlours and coffee bars of the Cathedral Quarter, down a cobbled alleyway, Hadskis is a cool, modern strip of a place, with bar seating for ringside views of the cheffing, and booth and windowside tables for convivial dining. Cathal Duncan, ex-Ox (see entry), furnishes a modern menu structure with permutations of small dishes, backed by fish and meat options from the charcoal grill. Crisply battered squid with a decent dollop of sweet, nutty romesco and herb leaves, and dressed Portavogie crab topped with sliced pear and fennel shavings, are full of bracing freshness. The much-prized Hannan's beef, seen in sirloins and burgers, also stars in a Mediterranean fusion affair of harissa-spiced meatballs along with chunks of chorizo, al dente orecchiette and a shower of potent Parmesan. Finish with seriously good rhubarb and pistachio pavlova, its pleasingly chewy meringue napped with rhubarb syrup and finished with yoghurt ice cream. The concise wine list opens at a wallet-friendly £18.

Chef/s: Cathal Duncan. **Closed:** 25 and 26 Dec, 1 Jan, Easter Sun, 12 Jul. **Meals:** main courses £13 to £31. **Details:** 75 seats. 16 seats outside. Bar. Wheelchairs. Music.

Il Pirata

Cooking score: 3
Italian | £20
279-281 Upper Newtownards Road, Ballyhackamore, Belfast, Co Antrim, BT4 3JF
Tel no: (028) 9067 3421
ilpiratabelfast.com

'The Pirate' is a cool, high-ceilinged warehouse-style space with tiled walls and chunky tables beneath myriad filament bulbs. It's the kind of place where views of the kitchen add to the sense of animation, and the vigorous Italian repertoire is presented as a mixture of small-plate cicchetti, pizzetti, pasta and sides for mixing and matching to taste. Dig in where you will, and be prepared for everything arriving at once. Burrata on a bed of pickled radicchio and pistachios is offset with luscious truffle honey, and Taleggio fritters with olive salsa are as sure-fire a winner as deep-fried cheese can't help but be. Pork and fennel meatballs in tomato and almond sauce with a chilli kick offer a world of umami satisfaction, while the tagliatelle carbonara brings whole new resonance to a home-cooked favourite, with pancetta, garlic and Parmesan adding depth to the creamy sauce. Finish with the densely rich take on tiramisu, which combines boozy sponge and ganache with opulent coffee mousse. The short international wine list opens at 18½ (pounds, that is).

Chef/s: Marc Heron. **Closed:** 25 and 26 Dec. **Meals:** main courses £9 to £19. **Details:** 80 seats. V menu. Wheelchairs. Music. Parking.

James Street South

Cooking score: 4
Modern European | £40
21 James Street South, Belfast, Co Antrim, BT2 7GA
Tel no: (028) 9043 4310
jamesstreetsouth.co.uk

The flagship of Niall McKenna's city-centre restaurant group (see also Hadskis), this bustling, white-columned space motors along on a flow of adrenaline, supplying contemporary brasserie cooking to a youthful urban crowd. There is a fine streak of inventive brio in dishes that dare to step outside the mainstream in which they could so easily paddle along. Grilled scallops are energised with liquorice and squid ink, while air-dried ham from Connemara is partnered by a tartlet of pickled onions and Gruyère. Main courses are similarly intent on making an impression, as when a stonking hunk of monkfish is served on the bone with burnt leek salsa verde, or when the beef fillet arrives in a shellfish reduction with coffee-scented carrots and cauliflower. Inevitably, not everything quite works out, but with sides of champ and smoked-butter hispi cabbage, and an éclair of Valrhona Dulcey to accompany the Yorkshire rhubarb, there's still plenty to cheer. A trim wine list focuses on the classic regions, with bottles from £19.

Chef/s: David Gillmore. **Closed:** Sun, 24 to 26 Dec, 1 Jan, Easter Mon to Wed, 12 and 13 Jul. **Meals:** main courses £16 to £28. Tasting menu £50 (4 courses) to £55. **Details:** 68 seats. Bar. Wheelchairs. Music.

Mourne Seafood Bar

Cooking score: 2
Seafood | £30
34-36 Bank Street, Belfast, Co Antrim, BT1 1HL
Tel no: (028) 9024 8544
mourneseafood.com
£5 OFF

This younger city sibling of the Seafood Bar in Dundrum Bay is usually crammed with diners who push past the wet fish counter to hunker down over enamel pots of steamed mussels, salt and chilli squid, fish and chips, and seafood casserole. Weekend lunchers queue for a table – at other times, you can (and should) book. The main space is all bare brick, metro tiles and blackboard walls, with corresponding noise levels. Soak up the atmosphere while tucking into Japanese-style oysters with shredded cucumber, pickled ginger and spiced soy dressing, or look to daily specials such as langoustines with homemade mayonnaise. Buttermilk panna cotta with lemon-scented strawberries and shortbread, or sticky toffee pudding with toffee sauce and vanilla bourbon ice cream are typical desserts. Beers and wines are all chosen for their affinity with seafood: Hop House 13, a crisp lager with notes of apricot and peach, for example, or a flinty Picpoul Sauvignon.
Chef/s: Gerrard Lynott. **Closed:** 24 to 26 Dec, 12 Jul. **Meals:** main courses £12 to £25. **Details:** 80 seats. Wheelchairs. Music. Parking. No children after 9pm.

The Muddlers Club

Cooking score: 3
Modern European | £50
Warehouse Lane, Belfast, Co Antrim, BT1 2DX
Tel no: (028) 9031 3199
themuddlersclubbelfast.com
£5 OFF

Named after a group of 18th-century rebels who used to meet secretly in the area around Warehouse Lane (now part of Belfast's Cathedral Quarter), The Muddlers Club certainly has all the trappings of a modern-day hangout – industrial ducts, bare filament bulbs, tattooed staff, Guinness in cans and even a vegan tasting menu. However, the skilfully fashioned contemporary food emanating from the obligatory open kitchen shows plenty of substance as well as style: trout with miso, broccoli and almonds; salt-aged beef with girolles and Jerusalem artichokes; Wicklow venison with mustard and quince; cauliflower with onion and porcini. Sides of new potatoes come dressed with dulse seaweed, while dessert might bring an intriguing combo of chocolate, espresso and milk or the boozy exoticism of banana, caramel, rum and pineapple. Cleverly muddled cocktails reference the revolutionary Muddlers of yore, and almost everything on the concise wine list is available by the glass.
Chef/s: Gareth McCaughey. **Closed:** Sun, Mon, 24 to 26 Dec, 1 to 10 Jan, 1 week after Easter, 2 weeks Jul. **Meals:** main courses £16 to £28. Set L £18 (2 courses) to £24. Tasting menu £50 (5 courses). **Details:** 50 seats. V menu. Vg menu. Bar. Wheelchairs. Music. No children after 9pm.

Ox

Cooking score: 6
Modern European | £28
1 Oxford Street, Belfast, Co Antrim, BT1 3LA
Tel no: (028) 9031 4121
oxbelfast.com

Despite the hard-edged surrounds, where half-boarded walls meet whitewashed brick, Ox is a gentle beast, its ambience softening in the evenings into a sympathetic tone helped along greatly by the chatty warmth of staff. The menus printed on brown card list what's in season week by week, much of which you can expect to find on the single tasting menu. Dishes are composed with a keen appreciation of their successive impact, beginning perhaps with a scallop in bisque with salsify, as a prelude to salt-cured halibut with its silkening elements of buttermilk, almonds and dill. Principal meats are one of the outstanding aspects of dinner here, perhaps Wicklow venison with red cabbage, bone marrow and chestnuts, and the intermission for Irish cheeses sets up the palate efficiently for the pair of dessert offerings, which might conclude triumphantly with a rich chocolate and clementine creation, served with Jerusalem artichoke ice cream. The lively and imaginative wine matches, for an extra £30, are well worth considering.

Chef/s: Stephen Toman. **Closed:** Sun, Mon, 1 week Dec, 1 week Apr, 2 weeks Jul. **Meals:** set L £22 (2 courses) to £28. Tasting menu £55 (5 courses). **Details:** 40 seats. Bar. Wheelchairs. Music.

Shu

Cooking score: 4
Modern European | £32
253 Lisburn Road, Belfast, Co Antrim, BT9 7EN
Tel no: (028) 9038 1655
shu-restaurant.com

Named after the ancient Egyptian god of the atmosphere, Shu delivers both buzz and good looks, its interior a blend of dark woods and soothing neutrals. A long-established fixture, it's equally praised for a 'fabulous value' fixed-price lunch or a leisurely evening meal. Brian McCann's cooking has its roots firmly in classical France, but that doesn't stop him adding a touch of miso (in a hollandaise, with a pork cromesquis and pickled kohlrabi), while Italian influences come through in a snack portion of pork meatballs or a risotto of leeks and Parmesan with corn-fed chicken. A salad of broccoli, peas and radish with tahini dressing impressed at inspection, as did a blade of beef, 'so tender you could probably eat it with a spoon', served with a glossy jus – the side of buttery champ an absolute must. To finish, a warm tart of almond-rich frangipane and just-sharp-enough blueberry. The substantial wine list offers value and interest, and a decent selection by the glass.

Chef/s: Brian McCann. **Closed:** Sun, 24 to 26 Dec, 1 Jan, 12 and 13 Jul. **Meals:** main courses £13 to £27. Set L £11 (2 courses) to £14. Set D £15 (2 courses) to £20. **Details:** 80 seats. Bar. Wheelchairs. Music. No children in bar area after 9pm.

★ NEW ENTRY ★

Yügo

Cooking score: 4
Pan-Asian | £30
3 Wellington Street, Belfast, Co Antrim, BT1 6HT
Tel no: (028) 9031 9715
yugobelfast.com

'I simply cannot wait to go back again', enthused one visitor to this cool and vibrant little restaurant whose interior blends the softness of greenery and lanterns with hard industrial lines. The open kitchen is the focal point and the care with which the chefs work is mesmerising, sending out dishes that are a glorious magpie mix of snacks, and small and large plates. Crispy pork dumplings with hot crispy chilli, soy sauce and garlic delighted one diner, and the sushi roll with wagyu, teriyaki and truffle was 'heaven' to another. A bao filled with Korean fried chicken, kimchi, chilli sambal and cucumber is also a winner, while the son-in-law egg – crisp on the outside, molten in the middle – served with charred asparagus, crab and chilli, is not to be missed. For dessert, look out for the hot barbecue pineapple with miso butterscotch and white chocolate snow. Drinks-wise, the house Yügo Sour cocktail is a good call – or opt for Japanese and Chinese beers, or wines from the short, global, pocket-friendly list.

Chef/s: Gerard Mcfarlane **Closed:** Sun. **Meals:** small plates £5 to £9. Large plates £14 to £19. **Details:** V menu. Vg menu.

Vegetarian and vegan

While many restaurants offer individual dishes suitable for non-meat eaters, those marked 'V menu' (vegetarian) and 'Vg menu' (vegan) offer separate menus.

Craigavon, Co Armagh

★ NEW ENTRY ★

Clenaghans

Cooking score: 2
Modern British | £33
48 Soldierstown Road, Craigavon, Co Armagh, BT67 0ES
Tel no: (028) 9265 2952
clenaghansrestaurant.com

A far cry from Danni Barry's last gig at Eipic (see entry), Clenaghans is a proper pub equipped with the requisite stonework, exposed beams, stone floors and real fire. It's darkly atmospheric – you can have candlelight by day here without it seeming odd, and Barry has relaxed into a style of pubby, homely cooking that suits the traditional surroundings. Opening bites of Scotch quail's eggs with mustard point the way, while roast chicken with smoked bacon, chestnut mushrooms and truffle macaroni typifies the luxurious touches added to otherwise simple dishes. This is honest, hearty cooking done with flair and attention to detail – and while the main menu might favour pub stalwarts such as gammon, egg and chips or fish pie, there's also an appealing vegetarian menu – sample dishes include Cheddar and onion tart with pickled walnuts and leaves; and miso-glazed aubergine with spiced chickpeas and fried greens. To finish, try a chocolate pot with miso caramel and peanut butter ice cream. A short wine list opens at a kindly £19.

Chef/s: Danni Barry. **Closed:** Mon, 25 and 26 Dec, 1 Jan, Easter Mon and Tue, 12 and 13 Jul.
Meals: main courses £17 to £29. Set D £20 (2 courses) to £25. **Details:** 60 seats. 20 seats outside. Wheelchairs. Music. Parking.

Holywood, Co Down

LOCAL GEM

The Bay Tree

Modern British | £24
118 High Street, Holywood, Co Down, BT18 9HW
Tel no: (028) 9042 1419
baytreeholywood.co.uk

The Bay Tree's customers are a loyal bunch, drawn back time and time again to this popular all-day café found in the courtyard of a listed building; they're understandably taken by the neighbourly vibe, flexible menus and the café's famed cinnamon scones. Breakfast brings bacon and banana toasted sandwich with maple syrup, and lunch runs to chowders, super salads, burgers, chicken casserole and the like. Friday dinner promises lemon and pine-nut-stuffed suprême of chicken, served with romesco sauce, sautéed kale and crunchy polenta. Wines from £16.50.

Killinchy, Co Down

Balloo House

Cooking score: 2
Modern British | £27
1 Comber Road, Killinchy, Co Down, BT23 6PA
Tel no: (028) 9754 1210
balloohouse.com

First licensed back in the 1600s, this farmhouse inn flaunts its history with rugged stone walls, heavy panelling, a warming fire in the grate and a maze of interconnecting rooms. The downstairs bar now doubles as a cheery all-day bistro serving up assorted 'pub classics' (Caesar salad, burgers, goat's cheese tart) alongside a compendium of more elaborate modern dishes with a bias towards seafood: mussels from nearby Strangford Lough served with nuggets of chorizo in a chilli-laced dish of orzo pasta, while roast fillet of hake could arrive with guanciale and leek risotto. To start, there might be crispy smoked chicken dumplings; to finish, perhaps rhubarb cheesecake with gingerbread ice cream. Balloo House may be out of the way, but it's not out of touch – note its splendid home-baked Guinness bread, 35-day salt-aged steaks and dedicated menus for vegetarians and vegans. Ten by-the-glass selections top the modestly priced wine list.

Chef/s: Danny Millar and Grainne Donnelly. **Closed:** 25 Dec. **Meals:** main courses £9 to £27. Set L and weekday D £15 (2 courses) to £20. Sun L £24. **Details:** 80 seats. 20 seats outside. V menu. Vg menu. Bar. Wheelchairs. Music. Parking.

Moira, Co Armagh

Wine & Brine

Cooking score: 4
Modern British | £35
59 Main Street, Moira, Co Armagh, BT67 0LQ
Tel no: (028) 9261 0500
wineandbrine.co.uk

Chris and Davina McGowan's labour of love is a great local restaurant. A clean modern look and open kitchen give a sharp urban feel and there's an unpretentious confidence about the place – the service, in particular, is appreciated for its unshowy civility. And praise comes thick and fast for snacks such as homemade black pudding sausage rolls with house ketchup, and for the wheaten bread served with caramelised butter and a lovely thick goat's curd sprinkled with crispy bacon. Starters such as game terrine served with crubeens, and mains of rump of roast Mourne lamb with crispy shoulder, smoked yoghurt and harissa, make the most of the region's rich larder. Comforting desserts include 'the best sticky toffee pudding I have ever tried in my life', and a clementine-flavoured buttermilk cream topped with granola, clementine pieces and a blob of Italian meringue, a warm doughnut on the side filled with a citrussy curd. The mood is relaxed and there are some pleasing wines to match the gutsy food.

Chef/s: Chris McGowan. **Closed:** Mon, Tue, first 2 weeks Jan, 2 weeks Jul. **Meals:** main courses £17 to £30. Set L £14 (2 courses) to £18. Sun L £25. Tasting menu £48. **Details:** 80 seats. V menu. Bar. Wheelchairs. Music.

Portstewart, Londonderry

Harry's Shack

Cooking score: 3
Seafood | £28
116 Strand Road, Portstewart, Londonderry, BT55 7PG
Tel no: (028) 7083 1783

Portstewart Strand on the north coast can feel like another world, especially in winter when vast Atlantic breakers roar towards the shoreline, so it's a real boon to find that this shed-like shack on the beach is as warm and welcoming as you would hope. The concise menu 'of simple homely pleasures' focuses on fresh fish plucked from the ocean in front of you: Mulroy Bay mussels with sourdough; whole megrim sole; fresh, light, crisp, breaded squid streaked with saffron aïoli with a pickled chorizo salad on the side; a satisfying, rich seafood chowder piled high with fish, plump mussels and new potatoes ('a comforting, warming bowlful to have on a cold day'); and a lovely flaky fillet of haddock in a buttermilk batter with chips and homemade tartare. There are a few meaty classics, perhaps a burger with bacon jam, and don't leave without trying the sticky toffee pudding. Local beers and a short wine list complete the picture.

Chef/s: Ian Malcolm. **Meals:** main courses £13 to £32. **Details:** 65 seats. 30 seats outside.

ATLAS MAPS

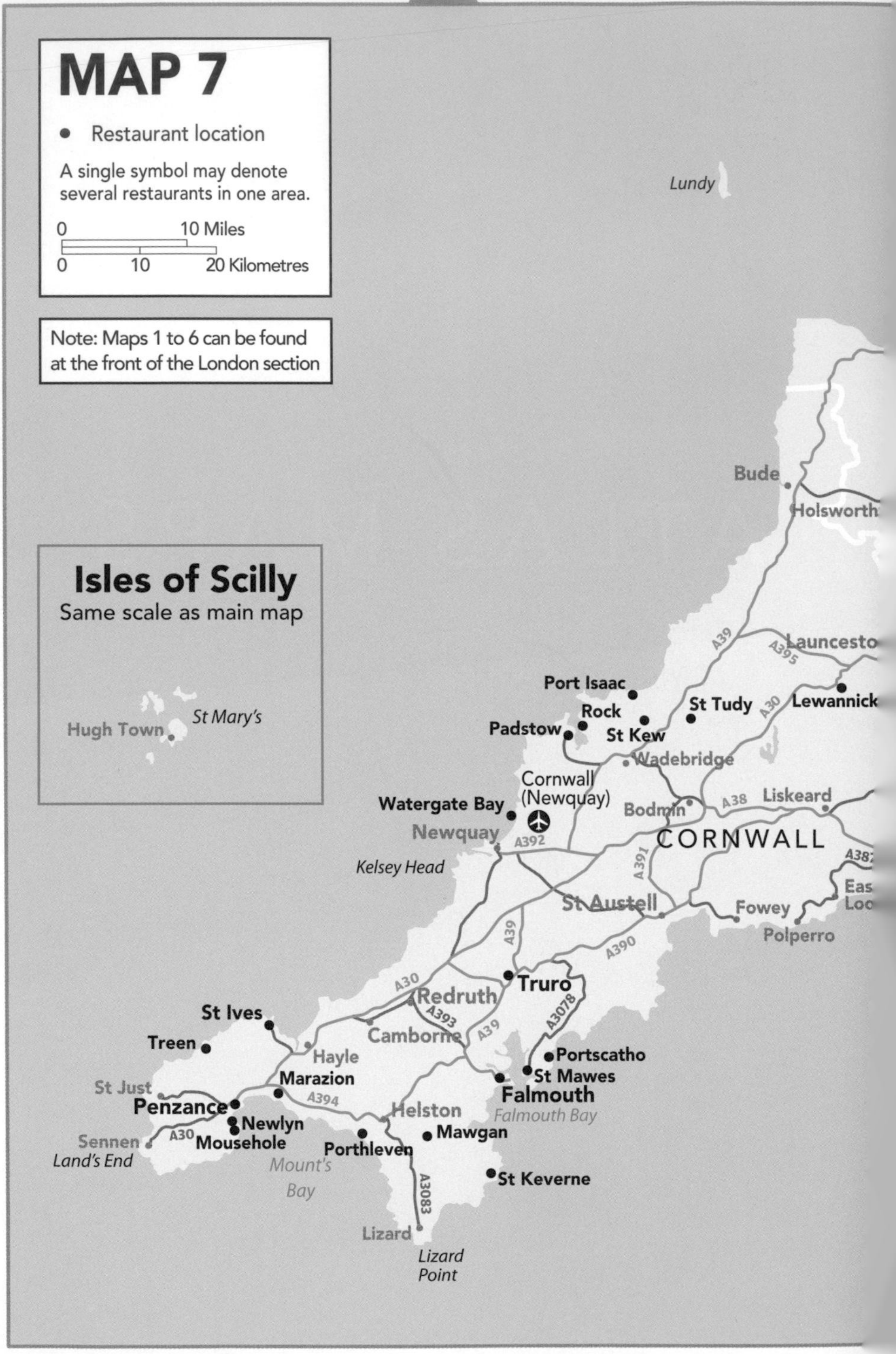

MAP 7

• Restaurant location

A single symbol may denote several restaurants in one area.

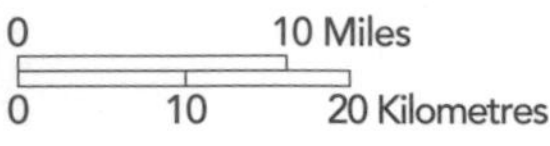

Note: Maps 1 to 6 can be found at the front of the London section

Isles of Scilly

Same scale as main map

Hugh Town
St Mary's

Lundy
Bude
Holsworth
A39
A395
Launcesto
Port Isaac
Rock
St Tudy
A30
Lewannick
Padstow
St Kew
Wadebridge
Cornwall (Newquay)
Watergate Bay
Bodmin
A38
Liskeard
Newquay
A392
CORNWALL
Kelsey Head
A391
A387
East Looe
St Austell
Fowey
Polperro
A39
A390
A30
Truro
Redruth
A3078
St Ives
A393
Treen
Camborne
A39
Hayle
Portscatho
St Mawes
Marazion
St Just
Falmouth
Penzance
A394
Falmouth Bay
Helston
Newlyn
Sennen
A30
Mousehole
Mawgan
Land's End
Porthleven
Mount's Bay
A3083
St Keverne
Lizard
Lizard Point

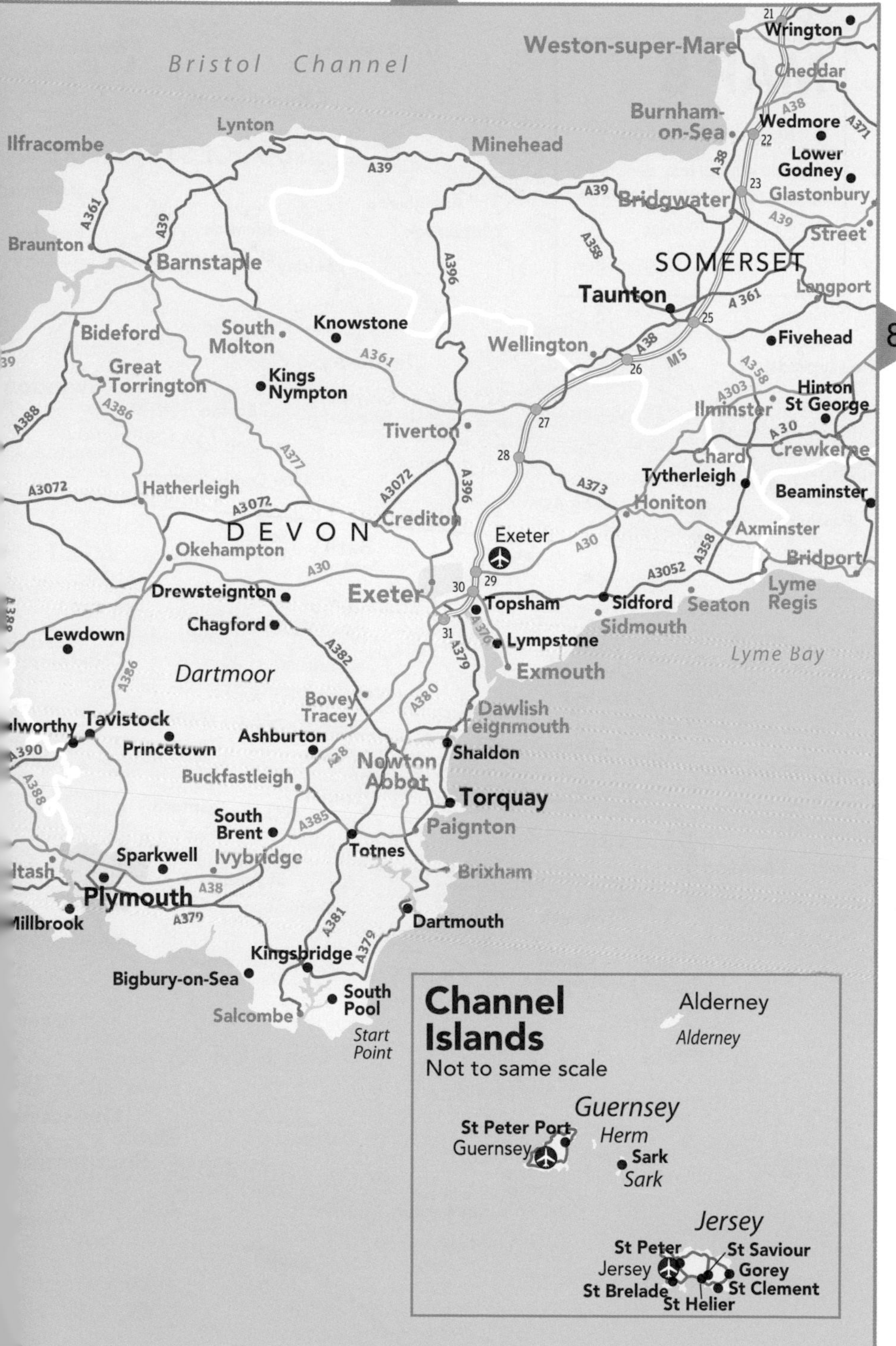
10
8
Bristol Channel
Weston-super-Mare
Wrington
Cheddar
Burnham-on-Sea
Wedmore
Lower Godney
Glastonbury
Lynton
Ilfracombe
Minehead
Bridgwater
Street
Braunton
Barnstaple
SOMERSET
Taunton
Langport
Bideford
South Molton
Knowstone
Wellington
Fivehead
Great Torrington
Kings Nympton
Ilminster
Hinton St George
Tiverton
Chard
Crewkerne
Tytherleigh
Beaminster
Hatherleigh
Honiton
DEVON
Crediton
Exeter
Axminster
Okehampton
Bridport
Drewsteignton
Exeter
Topsham
Sidford
Seaton
Lyme Regis
Chagford
Sidmouth
Lewdown
Lympstone
Lyme Bay
Dartmoor
Exmouth
Bovey Tracey
Dawlish
Teignmouth
Tavistock
Princetown
Ashburton
Shaldon
Newton Abbot
Buckfastleigh
Torquay
South Brent
Paignton
Sparkwell
Ivybridge
Totnes
Plymouth
Brixham
Millbrook
Dartmouth
Kingsbridge
Bigbury-on-Sea
South Pool
Salcombe
Start Point
A39
A361
A396
A358
A38
A371
M5
A303
A30
A386
A377
A388
A3072
A373
A3052
A376
A379
A382
A380
A385
A381
A390
Channel Islands
Not to same scale
Alderney
Alderney
Guernsey
St Peter Port
Guernsey
Herm
Sark
Sark
Jersey
St Peter
St Saviour
Jersey
Gorey
St Brelade
St Clement
St Helier

MAP 8
Restaurant location
A single symbol may denote several restaurants in one area.
0
10 Miles
0
10
20 Kilometres
11
10
7
Felin Fach
Eldersfield
Tewkesbury
Winchcombe
Stow-on-the-Wold
Hills
Cheltenham
Upper Slaughter
Ross-on-Wye
Gloucester
GLOUCESTERSHIRE
Cinderford
Monmouth
Arlingham
Northleach
Cotswold
Painswick
Barnsley
Whitebrook
Stroud
Selsley
Cirencester
Severn
Bargoed
Usk
Cwmbran
Chepstow
Dursley
Tetbury
Cricklade
Pontypridd
Thornbury
Swindon
Caldicot
Chipping Sodbury
Easton Grey
Malmesbury
Caerphilly
Newport
Royal Wootton Bassett
Avonmouth
Cardiff
Portishead
Castle Combe
Foxham
Chippenham
Long Ashton
Penarth
Clevedon
Bristol
Colerne
Calne
Bath
South Wraxall
Corsham
Melksham
WILTSH
Barry
Pensford
Rowde
Cardiff
Chew Magna
Wrington
Combe Hay
Bradford-on-Avon
Devizes
Pewse
Weston-super-Mare
Midsomer Norton
Trowbridge
East Chisenbury
Cheddar
Radstock
Burnham-on-Sea
Mells
Frome
Wedmore
Wells
Warminster
Amesbury
Lower Godney
Shepton Mallet
Glastonbury
Berwick St James
Bridgwater
Street
Bruton
Fonthill Gifford
Teffont Evias
Wilto
SOMERSET
Tisbury
Wincanton
Salisbury
Taunton
Langport
Donhead St Andrew
West Hatch
Fivehead
Wellington
Shaftesbury
Yeovil
Sherborne
Sturminster Newton
Hinton St George
Barwick
Ilminster
Chard
Crewkerne
Blandford Forum
Ringwoo
Tytherleigh
Wimborne Minster
DORSET
Honiton
Beaminster
Bournemouth
Axminster
Christchur
Dorchester
Poole
Sidford
Bridport
Lyme Regis
Seaton
Wareham
Bournemou
Burton Bradstock
West Bexington
Poole Bay
Sidmouth
Lyme Bay
Studla
Weymouth
Wyke Regis
Swana
Fortuneswell
St Alban's Head
Easton
Bill of Portland

12

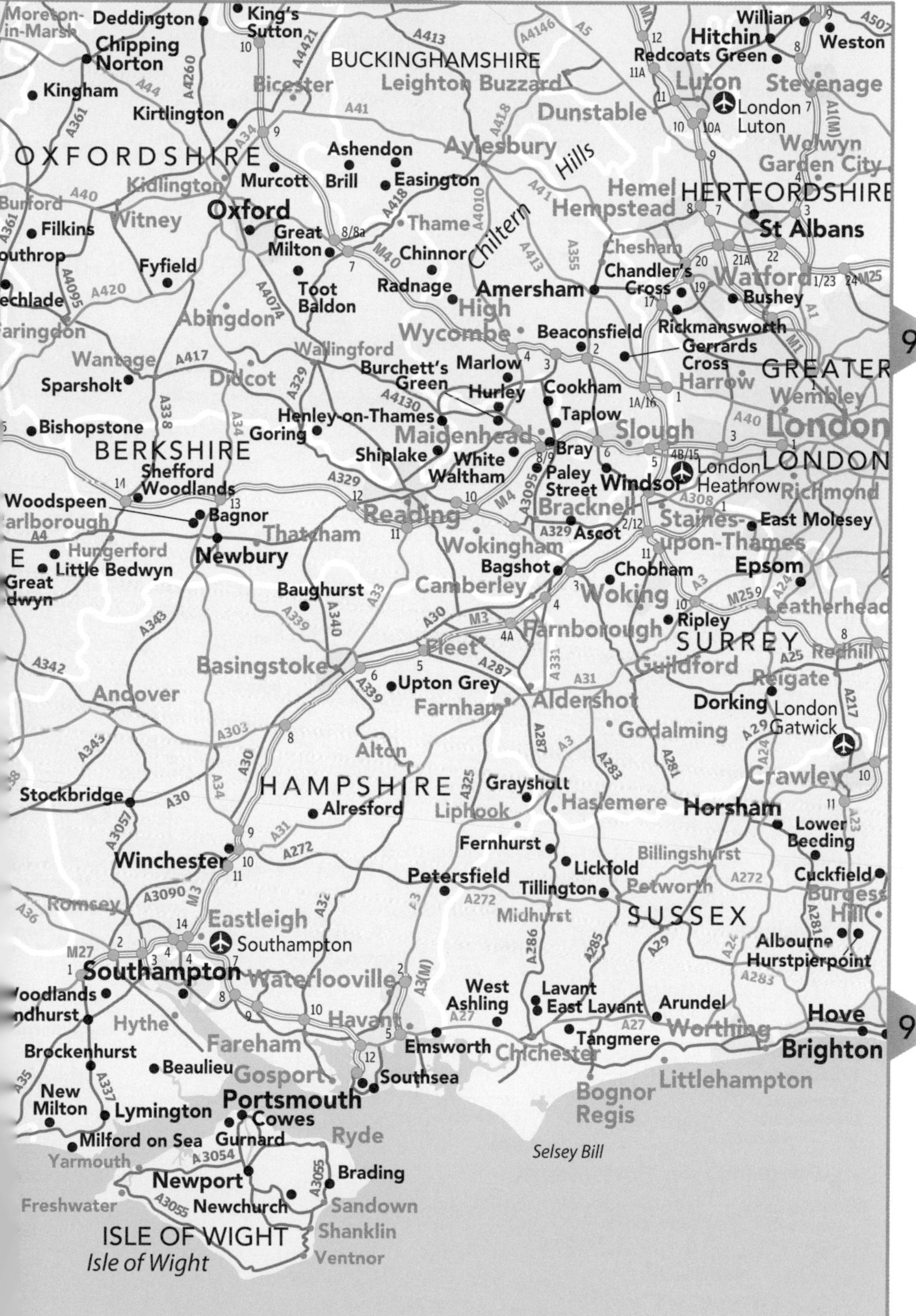

Moreton-in-Marsh
Deddington
King's Sutton
Chipping Norton
Kingham
Kirtlington
BUCKINGHAMSHIRE
Bicester
Leighton Buzzard
Dunstable
Willian
Hitchin
Weston
Redcoats Green
Luton
Stevenage
London Luton
Welwyn Garden City
OXFORDSHIRE
Ashendon
Aylesbury
Murcott
Brill
Easington
Kidlington
Chiltern Hills
Hemel Hempstead
HERTFORDSHIRE
Burford
Witney
Oxford
Great Milton
Thame
St Albans
Filkins
Southrop
Fyfield
Chinnor
Chesham
Chandler's Cross
Watford
Bushey
Lechlade
Toot Baldon
Radnage
Amersham
High Wycombe
Faringdon
Abingdon
Rickmansworth
Wallingford
Beaconsfield
Gerrards Cross
Wantage
Sparsholt
Didcot
Burchett's Green
Marlow
Harrow
GREATER
Hurley
Cookham
Wembley
Henley-on-Thames
Taplow
Bishopstone
Goring
Maidenhead
Slough
London
BERKSHIRE
Shiplake
White Waltham
Bray
Paley Street
Windsor
London Heathrow
LONDON
Shefford Woodlands
Richmond
Woodspeen
Bagnor
Reading
Bracknell
Staines-upon-Thames
East Molesey
Marlborough
Hungerford
Thatcham
Newbury
Little Bedwyn
Great Bedwyn
Wokingham
Ascot
Bagshot
Chobham
Epsom
Baughurst
Camberley
Woking
Leatherhead
Ripley
Farnborough
SURREY
Fleet
Redhill
Basingstoke
Upton Grey
Guildford
Reigate
Andover
Farnham
Aldershot
Dorking
London Gatwick
Godalming
Alton
Crawley
Stockbridge
HAMPSHIRE
Grayshott
Haslemere
Horsham
Alresford
Liphook
Lower Beeding
Fernhurst
Winchester
Lickfold
Billingshurst
Petersfield
Tillington
Petworth
Cuckfield
Romsey
Midhurst
SUSSEX
Burgess Hill
Eastleigh
Southampton
Albourne
Hurstpierpoint
Southampton
Waterlooville
Woodlands
Lyndhurst
West Ashling
Lavant
East Lavant
Arundel
Hythe
Havant
Worthing
Hove
Fareham
Emsworth
Tangmere
Chichester
Brighton
Brockenhurst
Beaulieu
Gosport
Southsea
Littlehampton
New Milton
Lymington
Portsmouth
Cowes
Bognor Regis
Milford on Sea
Gurnard
Ryde
Selsey Bill
Yarmouth
Newport
Brading
Freshwater
Newchurch
Sandown
ISLE OF WIGHT
Shanklin
Isle of Wight
Ventnor

9
9

12

8

Banbury
Brackley
Milton Keynes
Royston
BEDFORDSHIRE
Baldock
King's Sutton
Woburn
Letchworth
Deddington
Buckingham
Bletchley
William
Weston
Hitchin
Buntingford
Chipping Norton
Leighton Buzzard
Redcoats Green
Stevenage
BUCKINGHAMSHIRE
Luton
London Luton
Bicester
Dunstable
Kirtlington
Welwyn Garden City
Hertford
Ashendon
Aylesbury
Chiltern Hills
OXFORDSHIRE
Murcott
Brill
Easington
Hemel Hempstead
HERTFORDSHIRE
Kidlington
Witney
Great Milton
Thame
St Albans
Oxford
Chesham
Fyfield
Chinnor
Amersham
Chandler's Cross
Watford
Enfield
Toot Baldon
Radnage
Bushey
Faringdon
Abingdon
High Wycombe
Beaconsfield
Rickmansworth
Wallingford
Marlow
Gerrards Cross
Wantage
Didcot
Burchett's Green
Harrow
GREATER
Sparsholt
Cookham
Hurley
Wembley
London
Henley-on-Thames
Taplow
Goring
Maidenhead
Slough
BERKSHIRE
Shiplake
White Waltham
Bray
London Heathrow
LONDON
Shefford Woodlands
Paley Street
Windsor
Richmond
Bromley
Reading
Bracknell
Woodspeen
Bagnor
Staines
East Molesey
Hungerford
Thatcham
Ascot
upon Thames
Croydon
Newbury
Wokingham
Bagshot
Chobham
Epsom
Baughurst
Camberley
Woking
Ripley
Leatherhead
Farnborough
SURREY
Fleet
Guildford
Reigate
Redhill
Basingstoke
Upton Grey
Andover
Farnham
Aldershot
Dorking
Godalming
London Gatwick
Alton
Crawley
Stockbridge
HAMPSHIRE
Grayshott
Haslemere
Horsham
West Hoathly
Alresford
Liphook
Fernhurst
Billingshurst
Lower Beeding
Winchester
Lickfold
Petersfield
Cuckfield
Tillington
Burgess Hill
Romsey
Midhurst
Petworth
Eastleigh
Southampton
Albourne
Hurstpierpoint
Southampton
Waterlooville
West Ashling
Lavant
East Lavant
Arundel
Woodlands
Hythe
Havant
Lyndhurst
Emsworth
Tangmere
Worthing
Hove
Brockenhurst
Fareham
Chichester
Beaulieu
Southsea
Gosport
Littlehampton
Bognor Regis
Lymington
Cowes
Portsmouth
Milford on Sea
Gurnard
Ryde
Yarmouth
Newport
Brading
Freshwater
Newchurch
Sandown
Shanklin
ISLE OF WIGHT
Isle of Wight
Ventnor
English

8

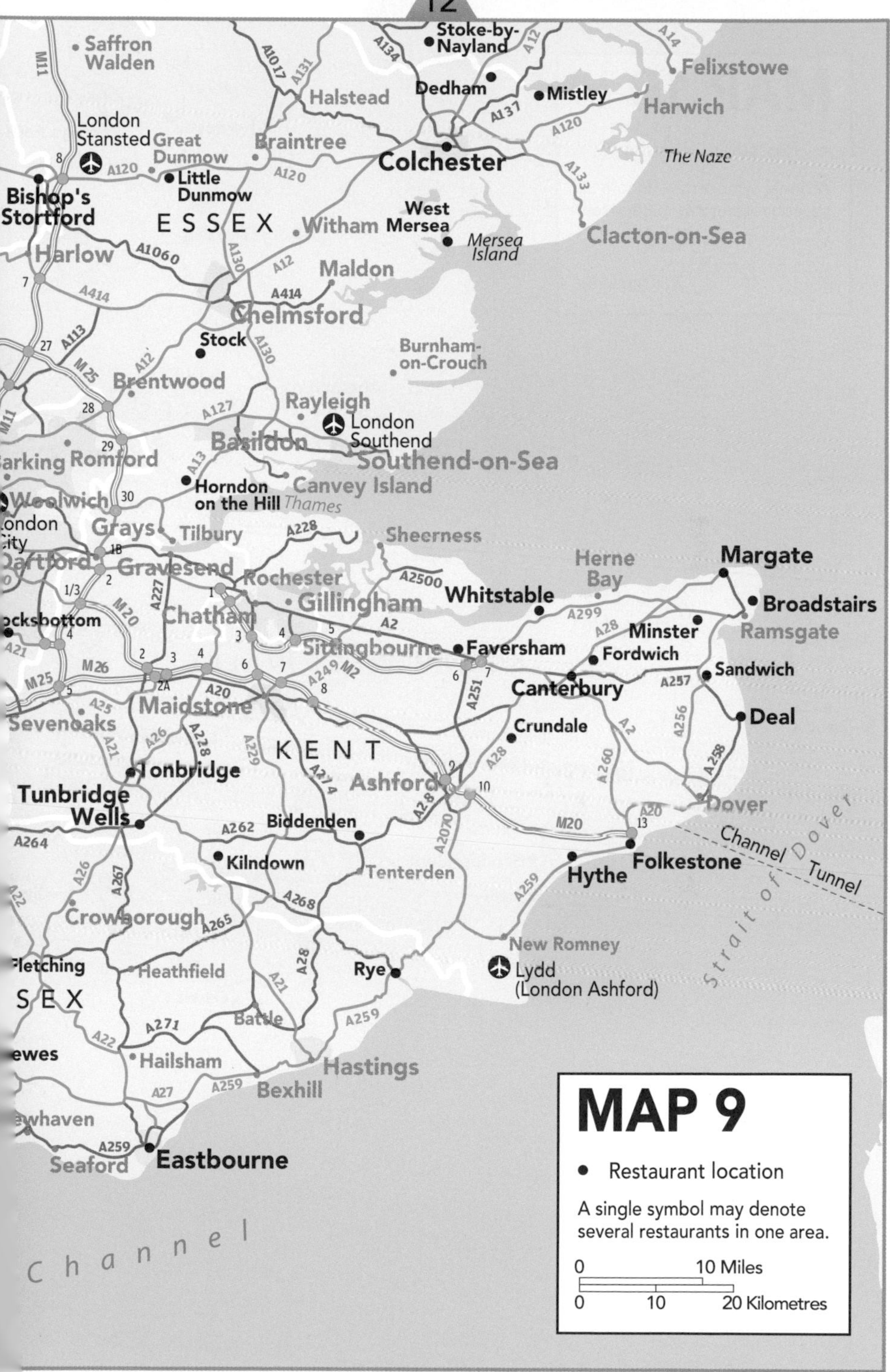

12
Stoke-by-Nayland
Saffron Walden
Felixstowe
Dedham
Mistley
Halstead
Harwich
London Stansted
Great Dunmow
Braintree
Colchester
The Naze
Little Dunmow
Bishop's Stortford
ESSEX
West Mersea
Witham
Mersea Island
Clacton-on-Sea
Harlow
Maldon
Chelmsford
Stock
Burnham-on-Crouch
Brentwood
Rayleigh
London Southend
Basildon
Southend-on-Sea
arking
Romford
Horndon on the Hill
Canvey Island
Thames
Woolwich
ondon
ity
Grays
Tilbury
Sheerness
Dartford
Gravesend
Rochester
Herne Bay
Margate
Gillingham
Whitstable
Broadstairs
ocksbottom
Chatham
Minster
Ramsgate
Sittingbourne
Faversham
Fordwich
Sandwich
Canterbury
Maidstone
Sevenoaks
Crundale
Deal
KENT
Tonbridge
Ashford
Tunbridge Wells
Dover
Biddenden
Channel Tunnel
Kilndown
Folkestone
Hythe
Tenterden
Strait of Dover
Crowborough
New Romney
Fletching
Heathfield
Rye
Lydd (London Ashford)
SEX
Battle
ewes
Hailsham
Hastings
Bexhill
ewhaven
Eastbourne
Seaford
Channel
MAP 9
• Restaurant location
A single symbol may denote several restaurants in one area.
0 10 Miles
0 10 20 Kilometres

11

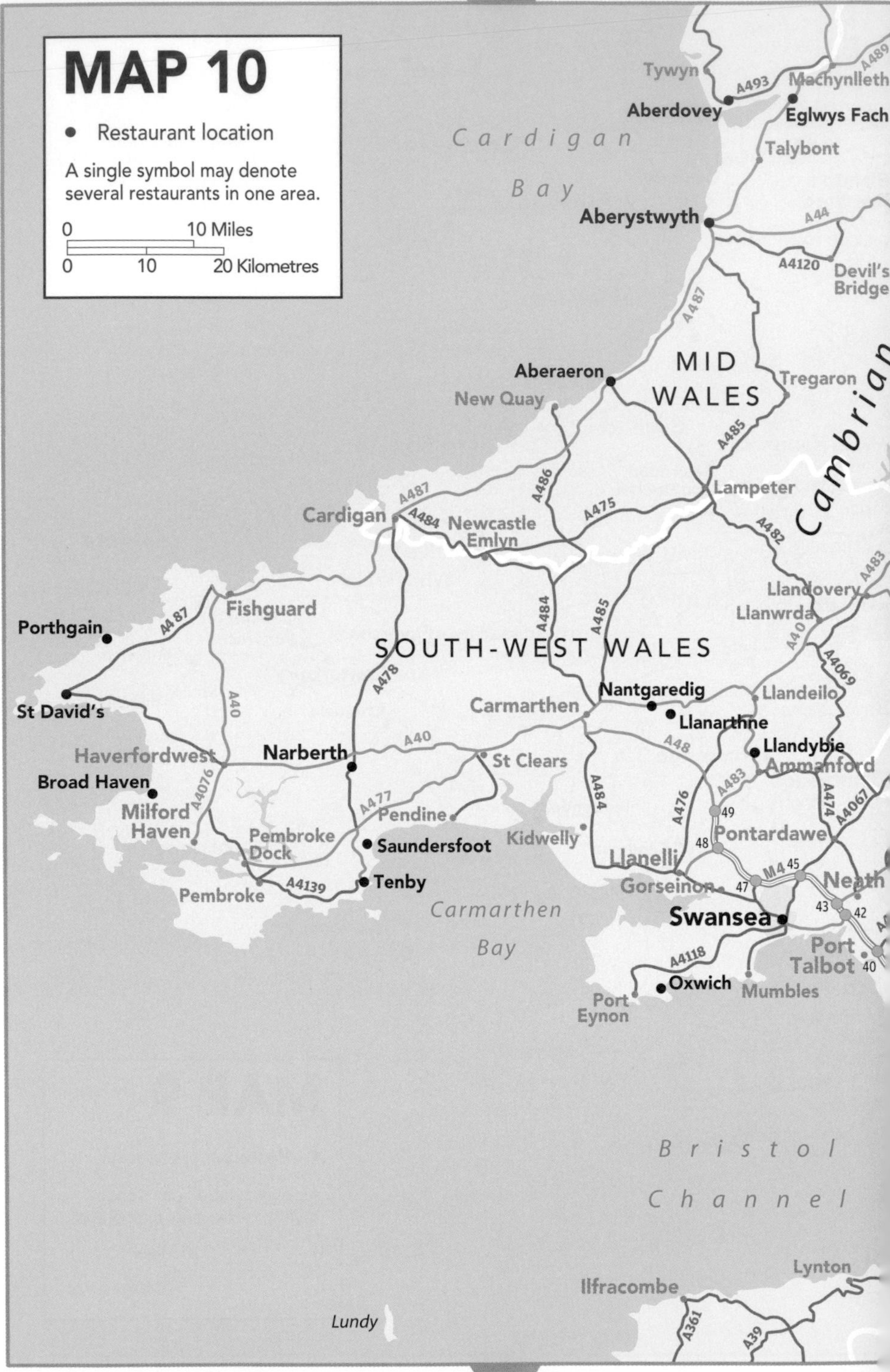
MAP 10
Restaurant location
A single symbol may denote several restaurants in one area.
0 10 Miles
0 10 20 Kilometres
Cardigan Bay
Tywyn
Machynlleth
Aberdovey
Eglwys Fach
Talybont
Aberystwyth
Devil's Bridge
MID WALES
Aberaeron
New Quay
Tregaron
Cambrian
Lampeter
Cardigan
Newcastle Emlyn
Fishguard
Porthgain
St David's
SOUTH-WEST WALES
Llandovery
Llanwrda
Llandeilo
Nantgaredig
Llanarthne
Carmarthen
Llandybie
Ammanford
Haverfordwest
Narberth
St Clears
Broad Haven
Milford Haven
Pendine
Pembroke Dock
Saundersfoot
Kidwelly
Pontardawe
Llanelli
Tenby
Pembroke
Gorseinon
Neath
Carmarthen Bay
Swansea
Port Talbot
Oxwich
Mumbles
Port Eynon
Bristol Channel
Lynton
Ilfracombe
Lundy
A493
A489
A44
A4120
A487
A485
A486
A475
A484
A482
A483
A40
A4069
A478
A48
A4076
A477
A476
A474
A4067
A4139
M4
A4118
A361
A39
49
48
47
45
43
42
40

7

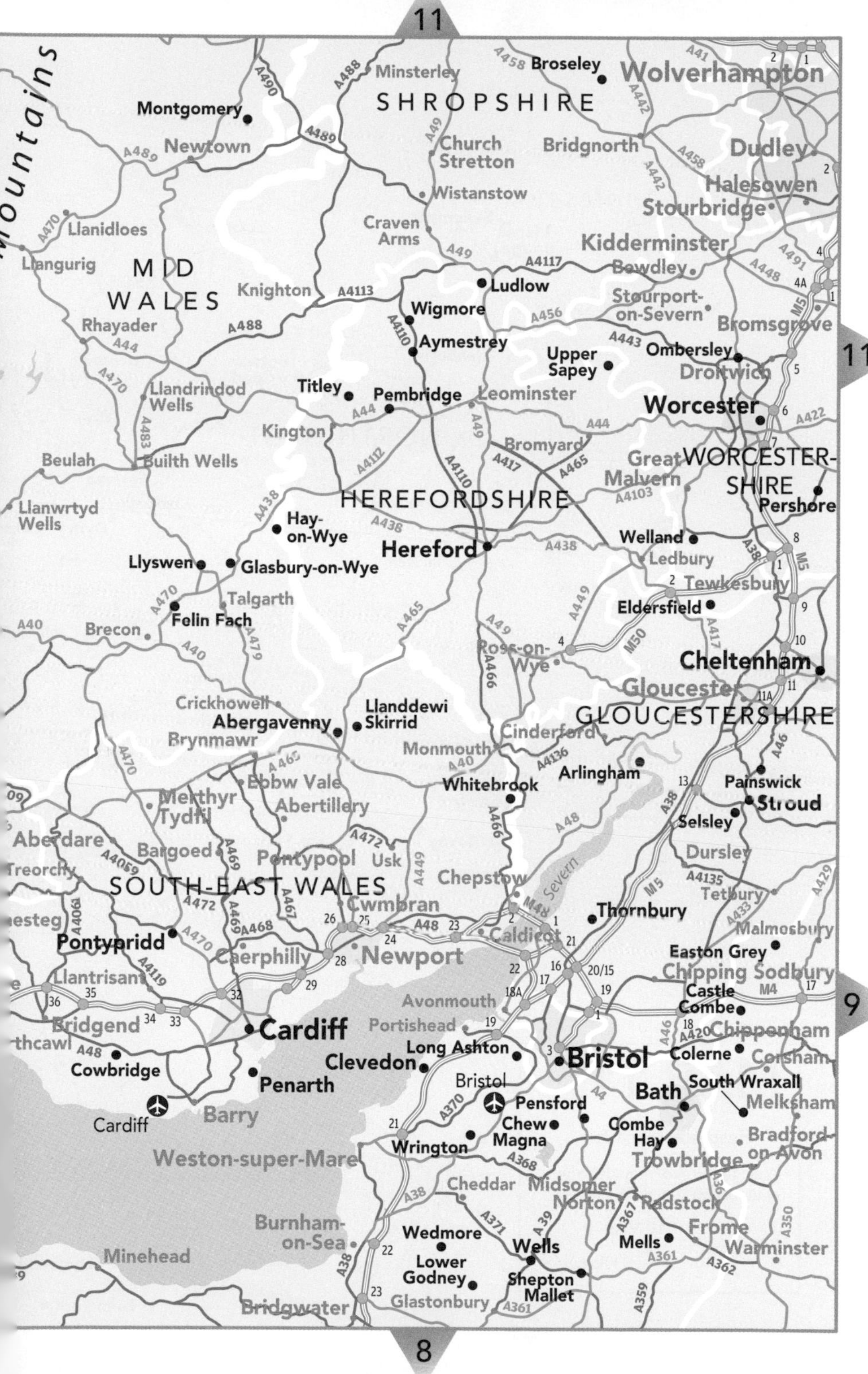
11
11
9
8
Mountains
SHROPSHIRE
MID WALES
HEREFORDSHIRE
WORCESTERSHIRE
GLOUCESTERSHIRE
SOUTH-EAST WALES
Minsterley
Broseley
Wolverhampton
Montgomery
Newtown
Church Stretton
Bridgnorth
Dudley
Halesowen
Wistanstow
Stourbridge
Llanidloes
Craven Arms
Kidderminster
Llangurig
Bewdley
Knighton
Ludlow
Stourport-on-Severn
Wigmore
Rhayader
Aymestrey
Bromsgrove
Upper Sapey
Ombersley
Droitwich
Titley
Llandrindod Wells
Pembridge
Leominster
Worcester
Kington
Bromyard
Beulah
Builth Wells
Great Malvern
Pershore
Llanwrtyd Wells
Hay-on-Wye
Hereford
Welland
Llyswen
Glasbury-on-Wye
Ledbury
Tewkesbury
Talgarth
Eldersfield
Felin Fach
Brecon
Ross-on-Wye
Cheltenham
Gloucester
Crickhowell
Llanddewi Skirrid
Abergavenny
Brynmawr
Cinderford
Monmouth
Arlingham
Whitebrook
Painswick
Ebbw Vale
Stroud
Merthyr Tydfil
Abertillery
Selsley
Aberdare
Bargoed
Pontypool
Usk
Dursley
Treorchy
Chepstow
Severn
Tetbury
Cwmbran
Thornbury
Pontypridd
Caldicot
Malmesbury
Newport
Easton Grey
Caerphilly
Chipping Sodbury
Llantrisant
Castle Combe
Avonmouth
Bridgend
Chippenham
Portishead
Cardiff
Long Ashton
Colerne
Cowbridge
Clevedon
Bristol
Corsham
Penarth
Bath
South Wraxall
Bristol
Melksham
Barry
Pensford
Cardiff
Chew Magna
Combe Hay
Bradford-on-Avon
Weston-super-Mare
Wrington
Trowbridge
Cheddar
Midsomer Norton
Radstock
Burnham-on-Sea
Wedmore
Frome
Mells
Minehead
Wells
Warminster
Lower Godney
Shepton Mallet
Bridgwater
Glastonbury

13

MAP 11
Restaurant location
A single symbol may denote several restaurants in one area.
0 10 Miles
0 10 20 Kilometres
Anglesey
Amlwch
Holyhead
Holy Island
Beaumaris
Menai Bridge
Bangor
Newborough
Caernarfon
Caernarfon Bay
Great Ormes Head
Llandudno
Conwy
Colwyn Bay
Prestatyn
Rhyl
Holywell
St George
Denbigh
Llanrwst
Capel Curig
Betws-y-Coed
Llanberis
Llyn Brenig
Pentrefoelas
NORTH-WEST WALES
Beddgelert
Blaenau Ffestiniog
Corwen
Llandrillo
Nefyn
Criccieth
Porthmadog
Pwllheli
Bala
Dyffryn Ceiriog
Llyn Trawsfynydd
Llyn Tegid
Harlech
Abersoch
Tremadog Bay
Llanbedr
Lake Vyrnwy
Bardsey Island
Barmouth
Dolgellau
Dinas Mawddwy
Cambrian Mountains
Tywyn
Machynlleth
Aberdovey
Eglwys Fach
Montgomery
Talybont
Cardigan Bay
Llanidloes
Aberystwyth
Llangurig
Devil's Bridge
MID WALES
Rhayader
Llandrindod Wells
Tregaron
Llyn Brianne
Beulah
Builth Wells
Lampeter
Llanwrtyd Wells
Llyswen
Llandovery
Felin Fach
Llanwrda

10

13
Bootle
Liverpool
St Helens
Warrington
Sale
Chorlton
Stockport
Glossop
Chapeltown
Sheffield
Oxton
Birkenhead
Widnes
Lymm
Altrincham
Manchester
Bebington
Runcorn
Wilmslow
Castleton
Bradwell
Dronfield
Heswall
Liverpool John Lennon
Bollington
Chapel-en-le-Frith
Knutsford
Alderley Edge
Macclesfield
Buxton
Baslow
Ellesmere Port
Northwich
CHESHIRE
Marton
Bakewell
Flint
Hawarden
Chester
Winsford
DERBYSHIRE
Congleton
Matlock
Leek
Alstonefield
12
Crewe
Kidsgrove
Nantwich
Wrexham
Stoke-on-Trent
Newcastle-under-Lyme
Ashbourne
Belper
Ellastone
Whitchurch
Uttoxeter
Boylestone
Stone
Ellesmere
Market Drayton
Oswestry
Burton upon Trent
STAFFORDSHIRE
Stafford
Newport
Rugeley
Swadlincote
Shrewsbury
Telford
Cannock
Lichfield
Welshpool
Tamworth
Minsterley
Broseley
Wolverhampton
Walsall
Brownhills
SHROPSHIRE
Sutton Coldfield
West Bromwich
WEST
Church Stretton
Bridgnorth
Dudley
Birmingham
MIDLANDS
Stourbridge
Wistanstow
Craven Arms
Halesowen
Solihull
Kidderminster
Bewdley
Dorridge
Kenilworth
Ludlow
Bromsgrove
Wigmore
Stourport-on-Severn
Royal Leamington Spa
12
Redditch
Henley-in-Arden
Warwick
Aymestrey
Upper Sapey
Ombersley
Droitwich
Titley
WARWICKSHIRE
Leominster
Alcester
Pembridge
Kington
Worcester
Bromyard
Stratford-upon-Avon
Great Malvern
WORCESTERSHIRE
HEREFORDSHIRE
Pershore
Evesham
Whatcote
Hay-on-Wye
Hereford
Welland
Ledbury
Broadway
Paxford
Tewkesbury
Moreton-in-Marsh
Eldersfield
Winchcombe
10

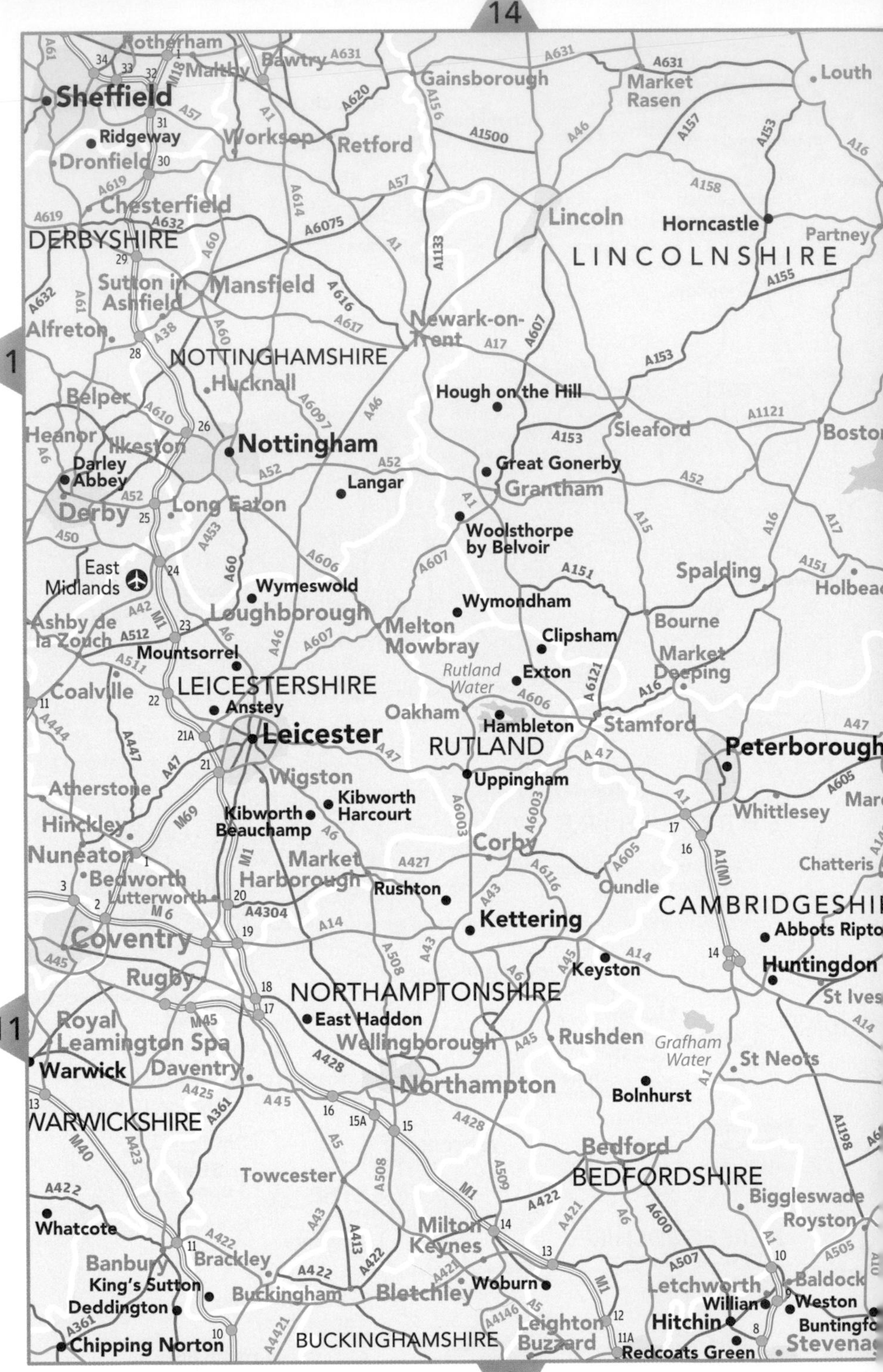
14
11
11
9
Sheffield
Rotherham
Maltby
Bawtry
Gainsborough
Market Rasen
Louth
Ridgeway
Worksop
Retford
Dronfield
Chesterfield
Lincoln
Horncastle
Partney
DERBYSHIRE
LINCOLNSHIRE
Sutton in Ashfield
Mansfield
Newark-on-Trent
Alfreton
NOTTINGHAMSHIRE
Hucknall
Hough on the Hill
Belper
Heanor
Ilkeston
Nottingham
Sleaford
Boston
Darley Abbey
Great Gonerby
Langar
Grantham
Derby
Long Eaton
Woolsthorpe by Belvoir
East Midlands
Spalding
Holbeac
Wymeswold
Wymondham
Loughborough
Melton Mowbray
Bourne
Ashby de la Zouch
Clipsham
Mountsorrel
Market Deeping
Rutland Water
Exton
LEICESTERSHIRE
Coalville
Anstey
Oakham
Hambleton
Stamford
Leicester
RUTLAND
Peterborough
Wigston
Uppingham
Atherstone
Kibworth Harcourt
Kibworth Beauchamp
Whittlesey
Hinckley
Nuneaton
Corby
Bedworth
Market Harborough
Chatteris
Rushton
Oundle
Lutterworth
CAMBRIDGESHI
Kettering
Abbots Ripto
Coventry
Keyston
Huntingdon
Rugby
NORTHAMPTONSHIRE
St Ives
Royal Leamington Spa
East Haddon
Wellingborough
Rushden
Grafham Water
Warwick
Daventry
St Neots
Northampton
Bolnhurst
WARWICKSHIRE
Bedford
Towcester
BEDFORDSHIRE
Biggleswade
Whatcote
Royston
Milton Keynes
Banbury
Brackley
King's Sutton
Woburn
Letchworth
Baldock
Deddington
Buckingham
Bletchley
William
Weston
Hitchin
Leighton Buzzard
Chipping Norton
BUCKINGHAMSHIRE
Redcoats Green
Stevenag

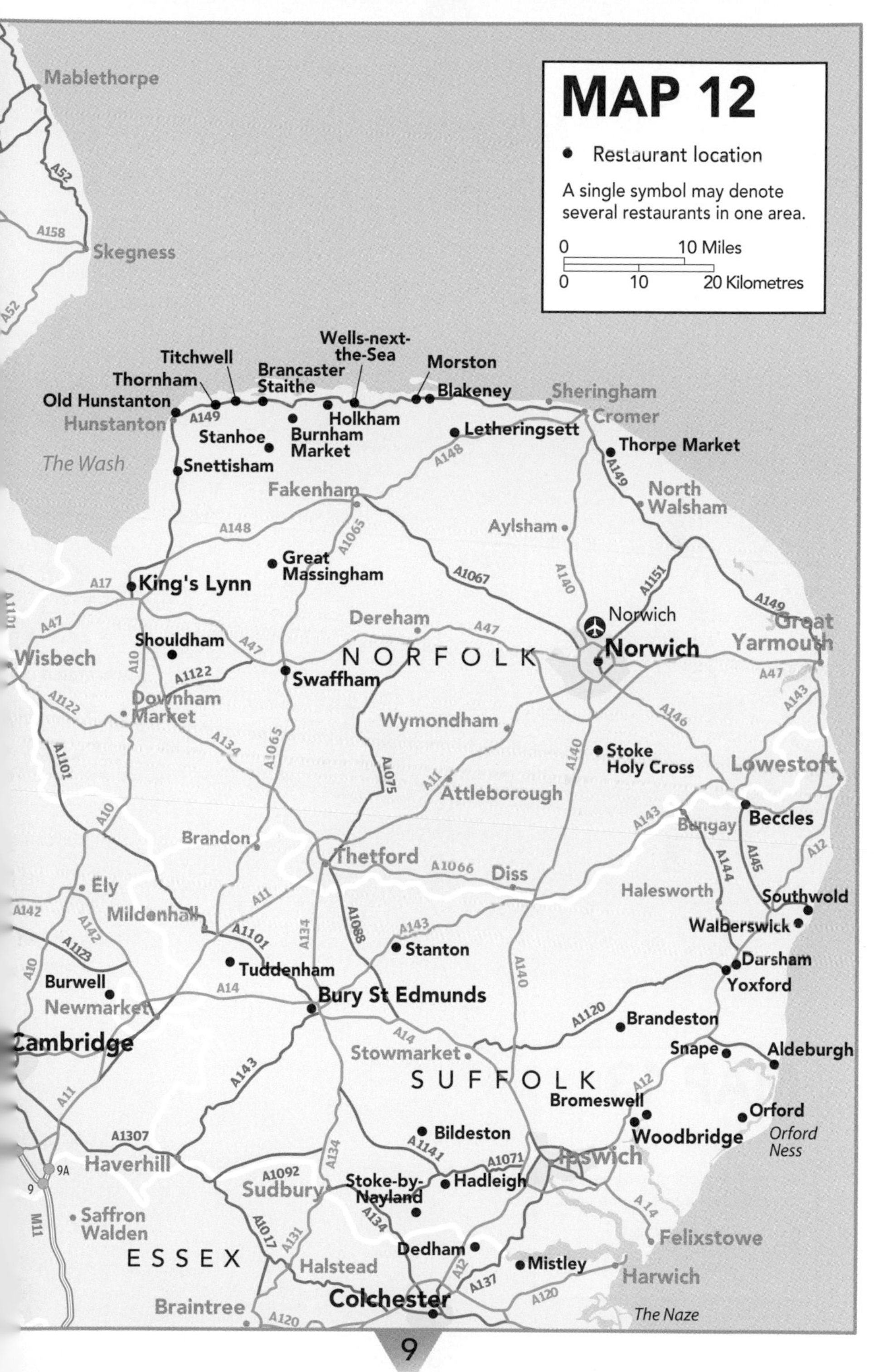

MAP 12
Restaurant location
A single symbol may denote several restaurants in one area.
0 10 Miles
0 10 20 Kilometres
Mablethorpe
A52
A158
Skegness
A52
Wells-next-the-Sea
Titchwell
Brancaster Staithe
Morston
Thornham
Blakeney
Sheringham
Old Hunstanton
Hunstanton
A149
Holkham
Cromer
Stanhoe
Burnham Market
Letheringsett
Thorpe Market
The Wash
Snettisham
A148
A149
Fakenham
North Walsham
A148
A1065
Aylsham
Great Massingham
A1067
A140
A1151
A17
King's Lynn
A149
Norwich
Great Yarmouth
A1101
A47
Dereham
A47
Shouldham
Wisbech
A47
NORFOLK
Norwich
A10
A1122
Swaffham
A47
A1122
Downham Market
Wymondham
A146
A143
A134
A1065
Stoke Holy Cross
Lowestoft
A1101
A1075
A140
A11
Attleborough
A10
A143
Beccles
Bungay
Brandon
A144
A145
A12
Thetford
A1066
Diss
Ely
Halesworth
Southwold
A142
A142
Mildenhall
A11
A1101
A143
Walberswick
A1123
A134
A1088
Stanton
A140
Darsham
A10
Tuddenham
Yoxford
Burwell
A14
Bury St Edmunds
Newmarket
A1120
Brandeston
Cambridge
A14
Snape
Aldeburgh
Stowmarket
A143
SUFFOLK
A12
Bromeswell
A11
Orford
Bildeston
Woodbridge
Orford Ness
A1307
A1141
A134
A1071
Haverhill
9A
9
A1092
Ipswich
Sudbury
Stoke-by-Nayland
Hadleigh
M11
A134
A14
Saffron Walden
A1017
A131
Felixstowe
Dedham
ESSEX
Halstead
A12
Mistley
A137
Harwich
Colchester
A120
Braintree
A120
The Naze
9

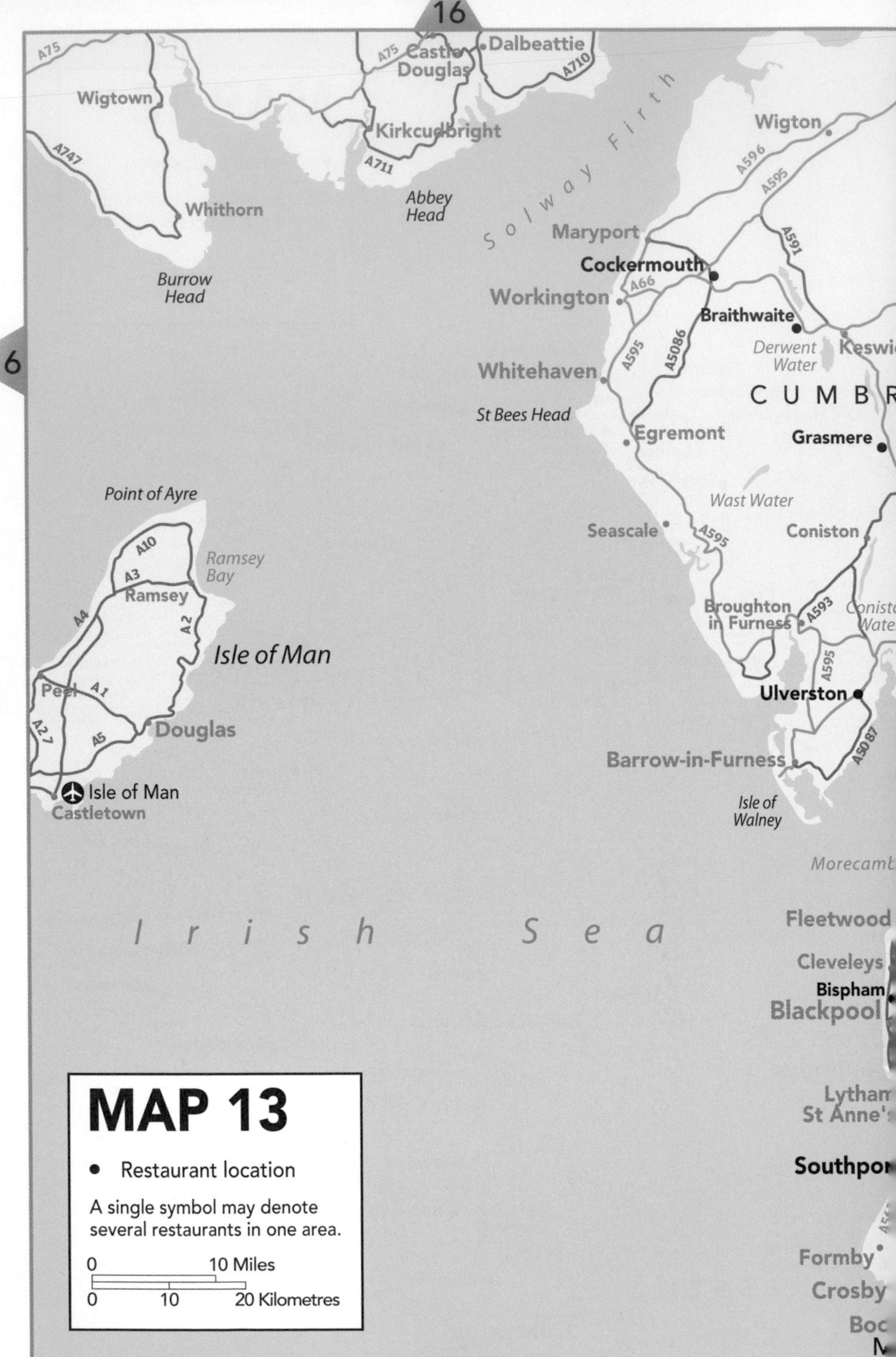
16
16
11
A75
Wigtown
A747
Whithorn
Burrow Head
A75
Castle Douglas
Dalbeattie
A710
Kirkcudbright
A711
Abbey Head
Solway Firth
Wigton
A596
A595
A591
Maryport
Cockermouth
A66
Workington
Braithwaite
Derwent Water
A595
A5086
Whitehaven
St Bees Head
Egremont
Grasmere
Wast Water
Seascale
A595
Coniston
Broughton in Furness
A593
A595
Ulverston
A5087
Barrow-in-Furness
Isle of Walney
Point of Ayre
A10
A3
Ramsey Bay
Ramsey
A4
A2
Isle of Man
Peel
A1
A27
A5
Douglas
Isle of Man
Castletown
Irish Sea
Fleetwood
Cleveleys
Bispham
Blackpool
Formby
Crosby
MAP 13
Restaurant location
A single symbol may denote several restaurants in one area.
0
10 Miles
0
10
20 Kilometres

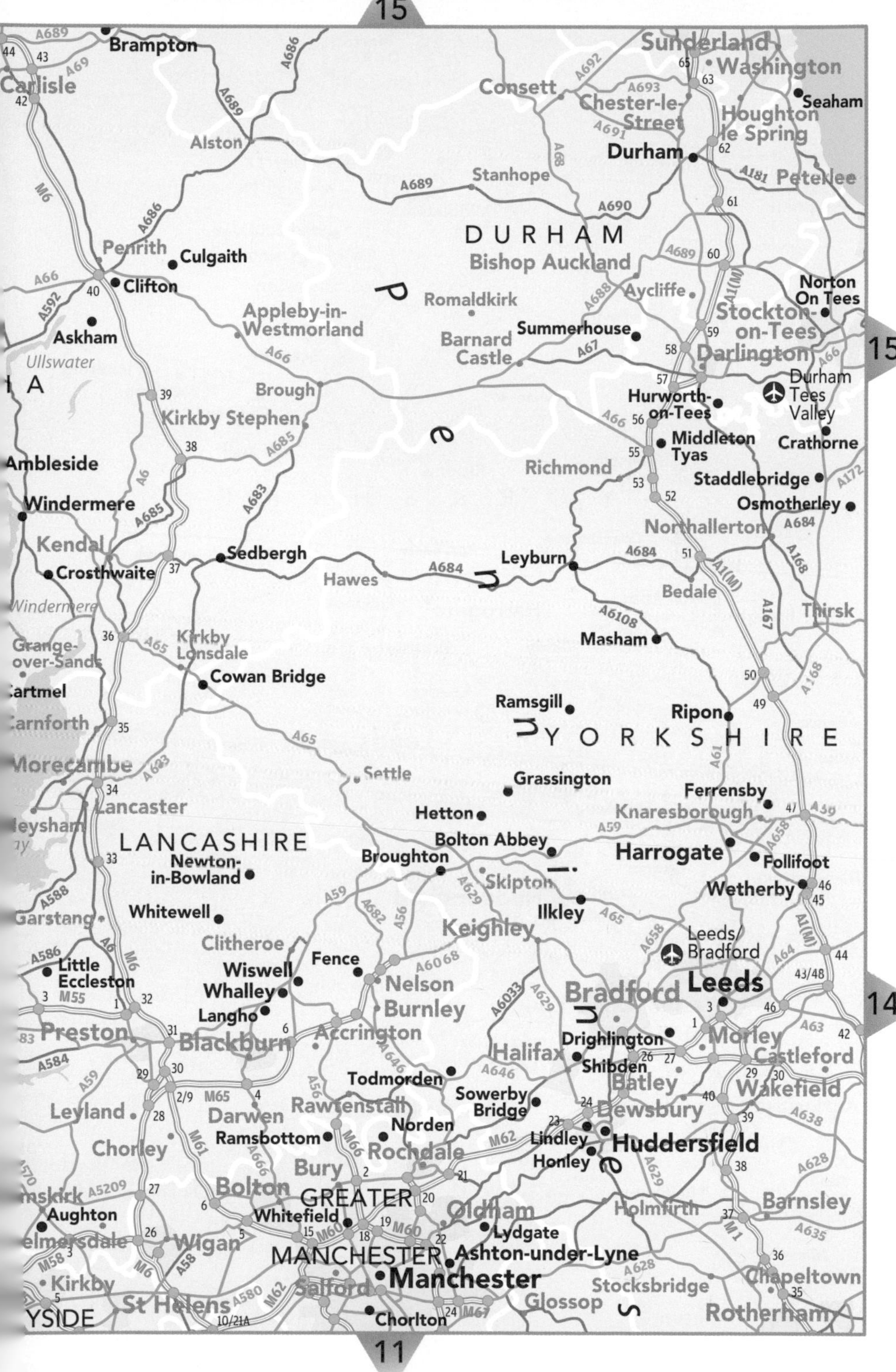
15
15
14
11
Brampton
Carlisle
Sunderland
Washington
Seaham
Consett
Chester-le-Street
Houghton le Spring
Alston
Durham
Peterlee
Stanhope
DURHAM
Bishop Auckland
Penrith
Culgaith
Clifton
Askham
Ullswater
Appleby-in-Westmorland
Romaldkirk
Aycliffe
Norton On Tees
Stockton-on-Tees
Summerhouse
Barnard Castle
Darlington
Durham Tees Valley
Brough
Hurworth-on-Tees
Kirkby Stephen
Middleton Tyas
Crathorne
Ambleside
Richmond
Staddlebridge
Windermere
Osmotherley
Northallerton
Kendal
Sedbergh
Leyburn
Crosthwaite
Hawes
Bedale
Windermere
Thirsk
Grange-over-Sands
Kirkby Lonsdale
Masham
Cartmel
Cowan Bridge
Ramsgill
Ripon
Carnforth
YORKSHIRE
Morecambe
Settle
Grassington
Ferrensby
Lancaster
Hetton
Knaresborough
Heysham
LANCASHIRE
Bolton Abbey
Harrogate
Newton-in-Bowland
Broughton
Follifoot
Skipton
Wetherby
Whitewell
Ilkley
Garstang
Keighley
Clitheroe
Leeds/Bradford
Little Eccleston
Fence
Wiswell
Nelson
Whalley
Burnley
Bradford
Leeds
Langho
Preston
Blackburn
Accrington
Drighlington
Morley
Halifax
Shibden
Castleford
Todmorden
Batley
Wakefield
Leyland
Sowerby Bridge
Darwen
Rawtenstall
Dewsbury
Norden
Lindley
Huddersfield
Chorley
Ramsbottom
Rochdale
Honley
Bury
Bolton
GREATER
Holmfirth
Barnsley
Aughton
Whitefield
Oldham
Lydgate
Wigan
MANCHESTER
Ashton-under-Lyne
Kirkby
Manchester
Stocksbridge
Chapeltown
St Helens
Salford
Glossop
Chorlton
Rotherham
Pennines
M6
M61
M65
M66
M62
M60
M58
M55
M67
M1
A1(M)
A66
A689
A686
A69
A692
A693
A691
A68
A181
A690
A688
A67
A685
A683
A6
A592
A684
A6108
A167
A168
A172
A65
A61
A59
A658
A629
A682
A56
A6068
A6033
A646
A64
A63
A638
A628
A635
A666
A588
A586
A584
A5209
A570
A58
A580
A6
A683

15
13
13
11
P
e
n
n
i
n
e
s
YORKSHIRE
DERBYSHIRE
NOTTINGHAMSHIRE
Bishop Auckland
Aycliffe
Norton On Tees
Redcar
Stockton-on-Tees
Middlesbrough
Summerhouse
Barnard Castle
Darlington
Guisborough
Durham Tees Valley
Brough
Kirkby Stephen
Hurworth-on-Tees
Crathorne
Middleton Tyas
Richmond
Staddlebridge
Osmotherley
Northallerton
Leyburn
Hawes
Bedale
Scawton
Thirsk
Pickering
Harome
Masham
Oldstead
Raskelf
Ramsgill
Ripon
Malton
Settle
Grassington
Ferrensby
Newton-on-Ouse
Hetton
Knaresborough
Bolton Abbey
Follifoot
Harrogate
Broughton
Skipton
Ilkley
Wetherby
York
Keighley
Leeds/Bradford
Tadcaster
Fence
Nelson
Wiswell
Burnley
Bradford
Leeds
Selby
Accrington
Drighlington
Morley
Goole
Todmorden
Shibden
Castleford
Rawtenstall
Halifax
Batley
Wakefield
Sowerby Bridge
Pontefract
Dewsbury
Ramsbottom
Norden
Lindley
Huddersfield
Thorne
Honley
Bury
Rochdale
Bentley
Oldham
Holmfirth
Barnsley
Lydgate
Doncaster
Ashton-under-Lyne
Salford
Manchester
Doncaster Sheffield
Stocksbridge
Glossop
Chapeltown
Rotherham
Bawtry
Sale
Chorlton
Maltby
Gainsborough
Altrincham
Stockport
Sheffield
Cheadle
Manchester
Castleton
Wilmslow
Ridgeway
Bradwell
Worksop
Retford
Alderley Edge
Chapel-en-le-Frith
Bollington
Knutsford
Dronfield
Macclesfield
Buxton
Chesterfield
Baslow
Marton
Bakewell
Congleton
Matlock
Mansfield
A1(M)
A688
A67
A66
A171
A174
A172
A167
A684
A168
A6108
A170
A61
A19
A64
A65
A59
A166
A661
A1079
A629
A682
A56
A6068
A658
A613
A6033
A614
A63
M62
A646
A1041
A638
A628
A635
A1
M1
A57
M18
A631
A620
A161
A18
M66
M60
M67
A6
A625
A623
M56
A619
A632
A60
A6075
A616
A537
A536
A34
A54
A515
A53

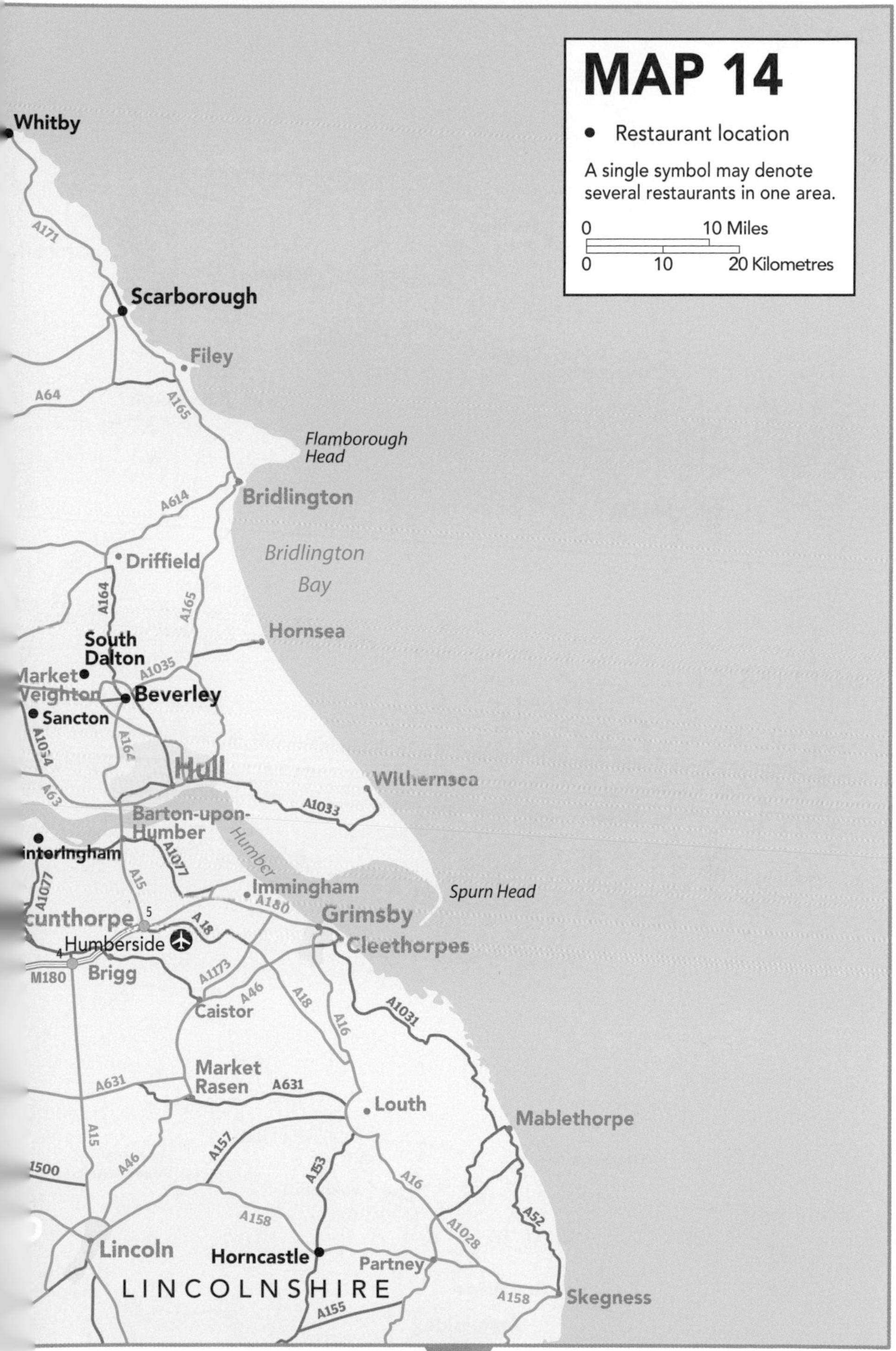

MAP 14
Restaurant location
A single symbol may denote several restaurants in one area.
0 10 Miles
0 10 20 Kilometres
Whitby
A171
Scarborough
Filey
A64
A165
Flamborough Head
Bridlington
A614
Driffield
Bridlington Bay
A164
A165
Hornsea
South Dalton
A1035
Market Weighton
Beverley
Sancton
A1034
A164
Hull
A63
Withernsea
A1033
Barton-upon-Humber
Humber
Winteringham
A1077
A15
A1077
Immingham
A180
Spurn Head
Grimsby
Scunthorpe
5
A18
Humberside
Cleethorpes
4
M180
Brigg
A1173
A46
A18
A16
A1031
Caistor
Market Rasen
A631
A631
Louth
Mablethorpe
A15
A1500
A46
A157
A153
A16
A52
A158
A1028
Lincoln
Horncastle
Partney
LINCOLNSHIRE
A158
A155
Skegness

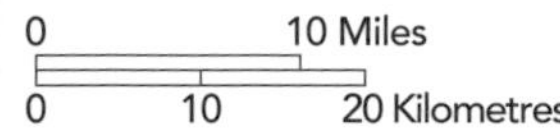

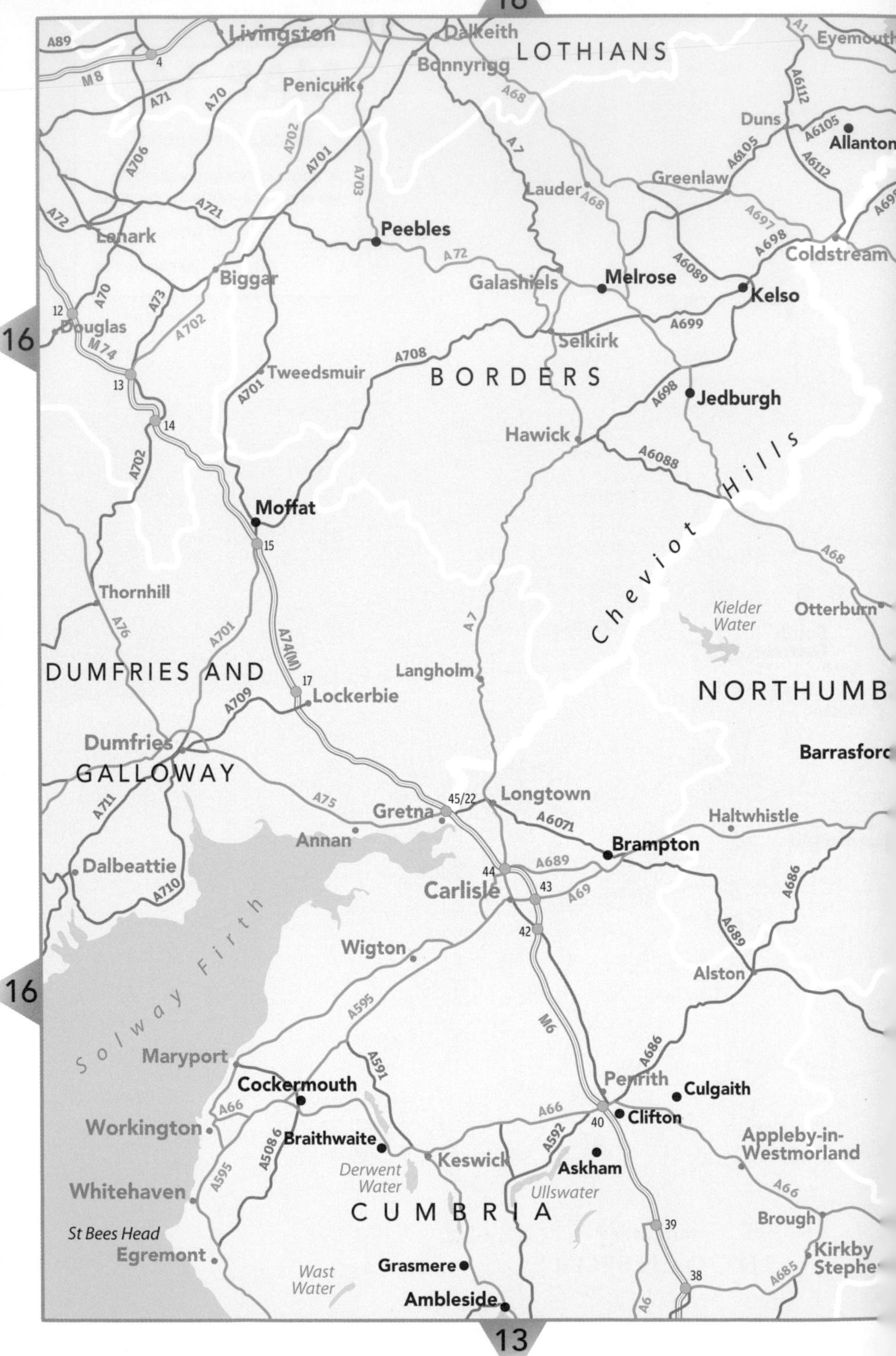

16
LOTHIANS
Livingston
Dalkeith
A1
Eyemouth
A89
M8
4
Bonnyrigg
Penicuik
A68
A6112
A71
A70
Duns
A6105
Allanton
A706
A702
A701
A703
A7
A6105
A6112
Greenlaw
Lauder
A68
A698
A72
A721
A697
Lanark
Peebles
A698
Coldstream
A72
A6089
Biggar
Galashiels
Melrose
Kelso
12
A70
A73
Douglas
A702
A699
16
M74
Selkirk
A708
Tweedsmuir
13
BORDERS
A701
A698
Jedburgh
14
Hawick
A6088
A702
Cheviot Hills
Moffat
15
A68
Thornhill
Kielder Water
Otterburn
A76
A7
A701
A74(M)
DUMFRIES AND
Langholm
17
Lockerbie
NORTHUMB
A709
Dumfries
Barrasford
GALLOWAY
Longtown
45/22
A75
Gretna
A6071
Haltwhistle
A711
Annan
Brampton
A689
A686
Dalbeattie
44
A710
43
Carlisle
A69
Solway Firth
42
A689
Wigton
Alston
16
A595
M6
A591
A686
Maryport
Penrith
Cockermouth
Culgaith
A66
A66
Clifton
40
Workington
A5086
Braithwaite
A592
Appleby-in-Westmorland
Derwent Water
Keswick
Askham
A595
Ullswater
Whitehaven
A66
CUMBRIA
Brough
39
St Bees Head
Kirkby Stephe
Egremont
Grasmere
38
Wast Water
A685
Ambleside
A6
13

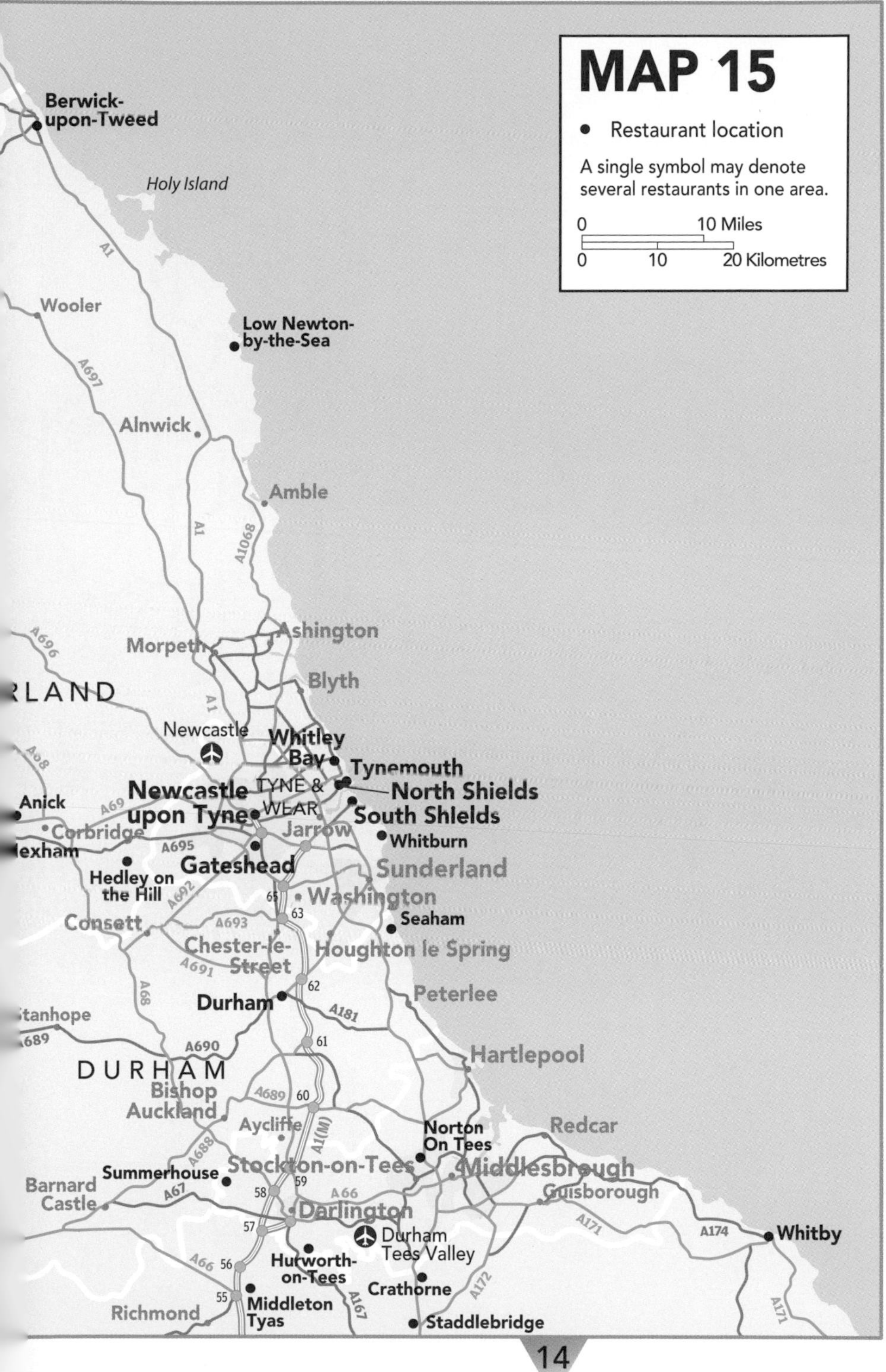
MAP 15
Restaurant location
A single symbol may denote several restaurants in one area.
0
10 Miles
0
10
20 Kilometres
Berwick-upon-Tweed
Holy Island
Wooler
Low Newton-by-the-Sea
Alnwick
Amble
Morpeth
Ashington
Blyth
RLAND
Newcastle
Whitley Bay
Tynemouth
North Shields
Anick
Newcastle upon Tyne
TYNE & WEAR
South Shields
Corbridge
Hexham
Jarrow
Whitburn
Hedley on the Hill
Gateshead
Sunderland
Washington
Consett
Seaham
Chester-le-Street
Houghton le Spring
Durham
Peterlee
Stanhope
Hartlepool
DURHAM
Bishop Auckland
Aycliffe
Norton On Tees
Redcar
Summerhouse
Stockton-on-Tees
Middlesbrough
Barnard Castle
Guisborough
Darlington
Durham Tees Valley
Whitby
Hurworth-on-Tees
Crathorne
Richmond
Middleton Tyas
Staddlebridge

Orkney Islands
Mainland
Stronsay
Shapinsay
Finstown
Kirkwall
Stromness
Scapa Flow
Hoy
South Ronaldsay
Burwick
Pentland Firth
Island of Stroma
Duncansby Head
Dunnet Head
Scrabster
Thurso
John o'Groats
Noss Head
Wick
Shetland Islands
Not to same scale
Herma Ness
Haroldswick
Unst
Gutcher
Belmont
Fetlar
North Roe
Yell
Ulsta
Esha Ness
Hillswick
St Magnus Bay
Papa Stour
Whalsay
Mainland
Sandness
Lerwick
Bressay
Scalloway
Sumburgh Head
Sumburgh
Cape Wrath
Whiten Head
Durness
Melvich
Loch Hope
Tongue
Loch Naver
Altnaharra
Kinbrace
Latheron
Helmsdale
Brora
Scourie
Point of Stoer
Lochinver
Rubha Coigeach
Inchnadamph
Loch Shin
Lairg
Elphin
Ullapool
Cailleach Head
Bonar Bridge
Dornoch
Tain
HIGHLANDS AND ISLANDS
Moray Firth
Laide
Gairloch
Loch Maree
Kinlochewe
Shieldaig
Achnasheen
Garve
Dingwall
Alness
Invergordon
Cromarty
Fortrose
Nairn
Inverness
Tore
Beauly
Loch Monar
Cannich
Drumnadrochit
Loch Ness
Stromeferry
Kyle of Lochalsh
Glenelg
Loch Affric
Invermoriston
Fort Augustus
Grantown-on-Spey
Carrbridge
Aviemore
Kingussie
Newtonmore
Invergarry
Loch Quoich
Loch Arkaig
Loch Lochy
Spean Bridge
Dalwhinnie
Loch Ericht
Mallaig
Glenfinnan
Fort William
Blackwater Reservoir
Loch Rannoch
Loch Tummel
Loch Laidon
Galmisdale
Loch Shiel
Strontian
Ballachulish
Kilchoan
Tobermory
Lossiemouth
Buckie
Portknockie
Banff
Macduff
Fraserburgh
Rattray Head
Mintlaw
Peterhead
Elgin
Forres
Aberchirder
Turriff
Keith
Craigellachie
Huntly
Dufftown
Ellon
Oldmeldrum
Rhynie
GRAMPIAN
Alford
Inverurie
Dyce
Aberdeen
Stonehaven
Banchory
Ballater
Braemar
Grampian Mountains
Blair Atholl
Killiecrankie
Pitlochry
TAYSIDE
Kirriemuir
Forfar
Brechin
Montrose
Inverbervie
Inverkeilor
Red Head
Outer Hebrides
Butt of Lewis
Port of Ness
Barvas
Tolsta Head
Callanish
Stornoway
Isle of Lewis
Kebock Head
The Minch
Tarbert
Scarista
Harris
Leverburgh
The Little Minch
Lochmaddy
North Uist
Benbecula
South Uist
Lochboisdale
Eriskay
Barra
Castlebay
Mingulay
Sea of the Hebrides
Hebrides
Stein
Colbost
Uig
Dunvegan
Portree
Raasay
Sconser
Scalpay
Skye
Sleat
Elgol
Armadale
Canna
Kinloch
Rhum
Eigg
Muck

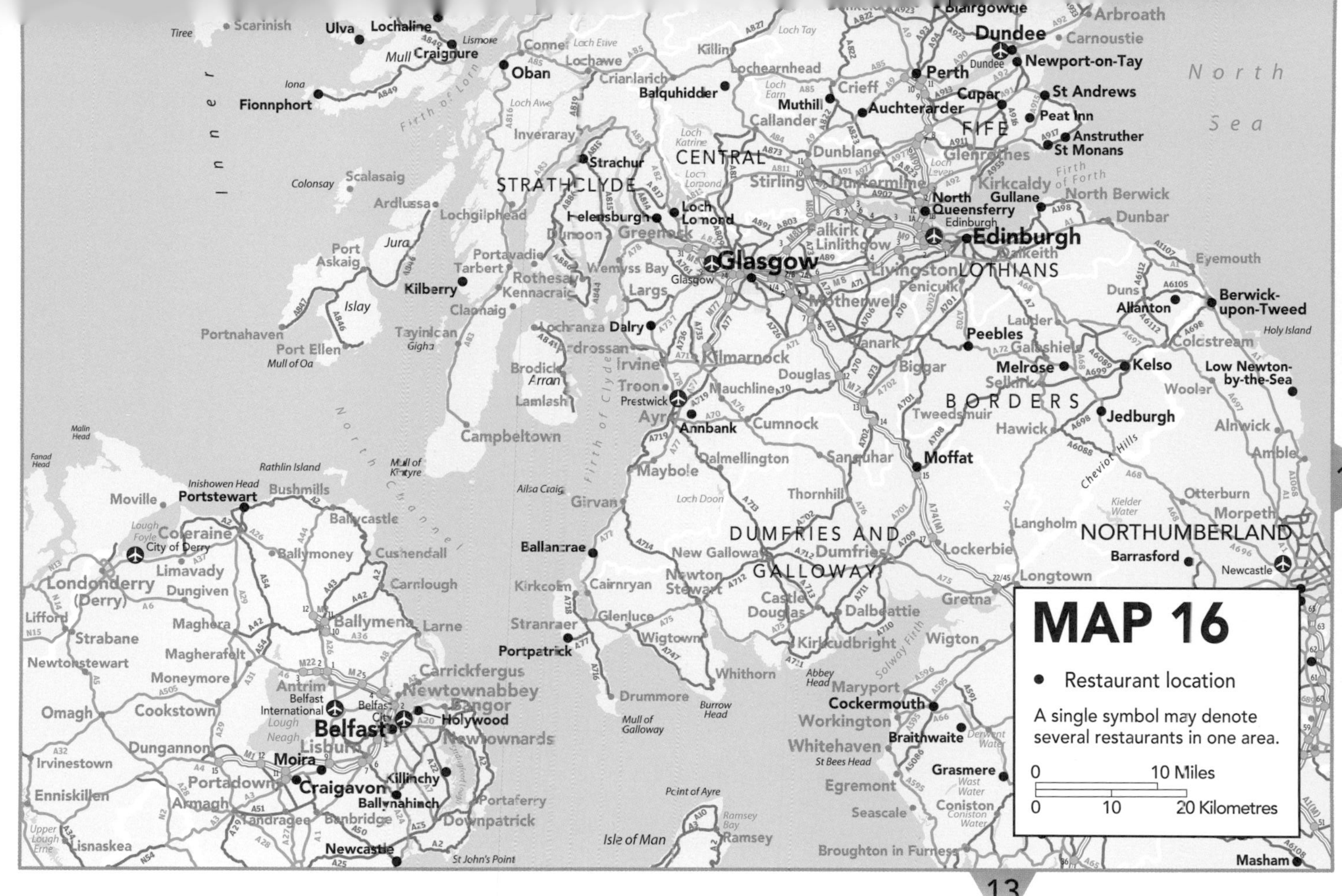
MAP 16
Restaurant location
A single symbol may denote several restaurants in one area.
0 10 Miles
0 10 20 Kilometres
15
13
Dundee
Perth
St Andrews
Edinburgh
Glasgow
Belfast
Berwick-upon-Tweed
Newcastle
STRATHCLYDE
CENTRAL
FIFE
LOTHIANS
BORDERS
DUMFRIES AND GALLOWAY
NORTHUMBERLAND
North Sea
Isle of Man

Note: The INDEX BY TOWN does not include London entries.

A

B

I

J

K

L

T

Thank you

This book couldn't have happened without a cast of thousands.
This is just a sample of the many contributors to whom thanks are due.

Rebecca Abbott
Anthony Abrahams
Alasdair Adam
Judith Adam
Dorothy Adams
Ken Adams
Maxine Adamson
Rachel Ainsworth
Eddy Aiossa
John Aird
Christopher Airey
Tanya Aitken
Simona Aiuto
Judy Alexander
Gillian Alexander-Davis
Richard Allan
Gillian Allen
Paul Allen
Tessa Allingham
June Allinson
Sheila Allison
Luci Allison
Mariam Alloo
Steve Almond
Simon Amey
Margaret Anderson
Lynda Anderson
Victoria Andersons
Liz Andersson
Danielle Andrews
Nicki Andrews
Tjobbe Andrews
Sarah Ankerson
Sebastian Anstey
Helene Apelgren
Angela Armstrong
Hilary Armstrong
Alison Arrowsell
Janie Ash
Kenneth Ashken
Rose Aspinall
Viv Astling
Margaret Atherton
Andrew Atkin
Paul Atkins
Frank Attwood
Alan Aubert
Laura Aucott
Richard August
Wendy Austin
Catalin Avramescu
Joanne Ayris
Jennie Azizi
Fiona Back
Liz Backhouse
Alexander Badeni
Carey Baff
Joy Bailey
Peter Baker
Robyn Baker
Angela Ball
Ashwath Bandi
Peter Banks
Melanie Barber
Larry Barcas
Charlotte Barder
Paul Barker
Anne Barons
Penelope Barr
John Barrett
Thomas Barrett
Phil Barron
Jane Barry
Diane Bartle
Emily Bartle
Celia Bartlett
Grace Bartolazo-Tuttle
Tracy Bass
Ryan Bassinder
Alan Batcheldor
Tim Battle
Eddie Bayfield
Vicky Baylis
Frances Beardwell
Liz Beattie
Christine Beatty
Bev Beavan
Val Beetham
John Belchem
Maria Benassi
John Bence
Alex Benn
Eliza Bennett
Elizabeth Bennett
Hannah Bentham
Sarah Bertram
W J Best
John Bester
Nigel Bettinson
Vas Beve
Stephen Beynon
Fiona Bianco
Gareth Bickerton
Andrew Bickle
Gill Biershenk
Levent Bilgic
Vida Bingham
Jonathon Binns
Graham Bishop
Lynne Bishop
Diana Blackburn
Hazel Blackburn
Jane Blackledge
Natalie Blackman
Helen Blackwell
Benjamin Blake
Pam Blay
Judi Bloede
Dianne Blundell
Andy Boase
Jennifer Bodey
Caroline Boggust
Saskia Boissevain
Peter Bolton
Brenden Bongani Manyathela
Clare Botterman
Gemma Bottomley
David Bourne
Mimi Bow
Sarah Bowers
Rachel Boylan
Richard Bradburn
Anthony Bradbury
Tessa Bradley
Nicola Bradshaw
Sarah Bradshaw
Julie Braithwaite
Tracey Brambleby
Lauren Bransby
Charles Brasted-Pike
Anne Breese
Victoria Brenha
Mark Brennan
Alan Brett
Geoffrey Bridge
John Bridge
Ron Bridgeman
Jenny Briggs
Helen Brigham
Mike Brightman
Linda Brimfield
Christina Brion
Julian Britton
Maggie Broad
Donald Brodie
Ruth Bromley
Karen Brookes
Bronwen Brookes-Johnson
Duncan Brooksbank
Marion Brooksbank
Andrea Broomfield
Gillian Broster
Peter Broster
Adrian Brown
Carole Brown
Colin Brown
Debra Brown
Janice Brown
Lisa Brown
Nina Brown
Oliver Brown
Patricia Brown
Tony Brown
Toni Brungberg
John Bryant
Michelle Bryant
John Buchanan
Michelle Buchanan
Gabriele Buchhierl
Susan Buckett
Kath Bulmer
Graham Burden
Heather Burgess
Tristan Burgess-Ovenden
Jennifer Burner
Annie Burton
Annishia Buss
Gill Butcher
Katrina Butler
Poyann Butterfield-Tracey
Mark Butterworth
Leigh Byas
Brendan Byrne
Barnabas Calder
Helen Calder
James Calderston
Tim Caley
David Callaghan
Emma Jane Callaghan
Hamish Cameron
Iain Campbell
Margaret Campbell
Thomas Campbell
Philippa Camps
Jeff Cansdale
Senay Caplan
Tony Capon
John Carr
David Carruthers
Louise Carruthers
Kay Carslaw
Joy Carson
David Carter
Jane Carter
Julian Carter
Rob Carter
Timothy Carter
Robert Carty
Phillip Case
Sandy Case
Geoff Cash
Melanie Casling
Pardeep Cassells
Phoebe Cassels
Sue Catlin
Mary Caws
Diane Cayless
Amy Challis
Jane Chamberlain
Dennis Chan
Nicola Chan
Elizabeth Chapman
Gill Chapman
James Chapman
Kingman Cheng
Sue Chesterman
Alex Cheung
Rebecca Child
Natalie Chillcott
Alex Choi
Richard Christopher
Mary Christou
Yvonne Chung
Patience Churcher
Anna Cinotti
Frank Cinotti
Pasquale Cinotti
Margaret Clancy
Elizabeth Clapton
Mark Claremont
Joanne Clark
Lucy Clark
Rachael Clark
Fiona Clarke
Francesca Clarke
Colin Clarkson
Jeremy Clarkson
David Clasper
Pauline Clasper
Lucy Clayphan
Viv Clayton
Ruth Clement
Mark Clifton
Tom Cobbledick
Michael Coe
Annabelle Coelho
Sonia Cole
Alan Coleman
Helen Coleman
Paul Coleman
Sarah Coles
Mark Collen
James Collett
Kate Colling
Ben Collins
Duncan Collins
Emily Collins
Harry Collins
Jade Collins
Lorna Collins
Martha Collins
Barbara Collinson
Duncan Colvin
Steph Colvin
John Comyn
Noreen Connole
Holly Cook
John Cooke
Jemima Cookson
Giséle Cooney
John Cooney
Chrissa Cooper
Maddy Cooper
Claudia Coory
Stephen Coram
Nigel Corbett
Susan Corfield
Selina Coton
Suzanne Cotterell

John Counter
Gary Cove
Jack Cox
Jackie Cox
Maxine Cox
Steven Cox
Pauline Crawshaw
Sally Cripps
Judith Cro
Jocelyn Crook
Jennifer Crosbie
Abigail Crowther
Michelle Crowther
Rachel Crowther
David Cubey
Brendan Cummins
Ian Currie
Alex Cursley
Annie Curtis
Howard Curtis
Tracy Curtis
Debbie Cutler
Alan Dacey
Andy Daniels
Olivia Dann
Susan Dannatt
Sam Darby
Patrick D'Arcy
Matthew Davenport
Alun Davies
Ann Davies
Bethan Davies
Debra Davies
Howard Davies
Jerry Davies
Judith Davies
Naomi Davies
Rhys Davies
Terry Davies
Brian Davis
Jenny Davis
Anna Davison
Lorraine Davy
Anne Dawson
Natalie Dawson
Surajit De
Paul Deakin
Rosemary Deakin
Anne Dean
Rosie Dean
Nele Debolster
Helen De'Courcy
Nicholas Dee
Maralyn Delmedico
Sophie Dening
Lindsey Denton
Andy Detheridge
Carol Detheridge
Gill Devalve Otty
Rebecca Devaney
Gilpatrick Devlin
Moira Dickson
Ash Dimelow
Andy Diss
Colin Divall
Amy Divers
Martin Dodd
Jane Don
Kay Douglas
Mike Doupe
Fiona Downs
Jackie Doxey
Jessica Doyle
Richard Doyle
Tony Doyle
Dudley Drayson
Iana Dreyer
Paul Dring
Jessica Drury
John Dudfield
Patrick Dunaway
Chris Duncan
Claire Dunn
Tom Dunn
Susannah Durant
Emily Dyer
Leanne Earnden
Kevin East
Lindsay Easton
Paul Easton
Alice Eastwood
Richard Eastwood
Sarah Eaves
Tracey Edges
Tracy Edgington
Janet Edmunds
Lorrayne Edwards
Rachel Edwards
Andrew Edwards
Matthew Eglise
Yvonne Elderbrant
Emilie Elliot
Grace Ellis
Jane Ellis
Stephen Ellis
Joshua Emery
Matthew Emms
Sandra England
Emma Enos
Michelle Erdmann
Albert Evans
Carol Evans
Clare Evans
Lyndon Evans
Margaret Evans
Rachel Evans
Richard Evans
Sue Evans
Ian Everett
Suzanne Everingham
Karen Ewington
Mel Eyers
Seb Fadian
Tom Fahey
Hayley Fairbank
Michelle Fairweather
Virginia Falconer
Jacqueline Faller
Sam Fallowfield
Andrew Farkas
Alastair Farquhar
Samantha Farrar
Danielle Fear
Annemarie Fell
Gordon Fen
Elizabeth Ferguson
Tara Ferguson
Max Fernando
Ellicia Ferrerio
Alexander Few
Jamie Fidler
Neville Filar
Tina Finbow
Joshua Finbow
David Finch
Kelly Fisher
Paul Fisher
Libby Fitter
Carrie Fitzgerald
Linda Fitzgerald
Michelle Flanagann
Martina Flavin
Claire Fleck
Morgan Fleet
Hannah Flippance
Sandra Flower
Stephen Flynn
Elizabeth Foley
Andrew Ford
Tom Ford
Christina Forster
Neal Foster
Alison Fountain
David Fowler
Anna Fox
Catherine Fox
Tina Fox-Edwards
Katie Francesca
Claire Francis
Silvana Franco
Gwenno Francon
Antje Franke
Nick Frankgate
Diane Franks
John Fraser
Merlin Fraser
Russ Freeman
Inika French
Rosemary French
Mairi Friesen-Escandell
Peter Frost
Annice Fry
Rita Fulcher
Pamela Gadsby
Roger Gadsby
Curtis Galbraith
Vanda Galer
Danielle Gallagher
Sandra Gannon
Dijon Gardiner
Lliani Gardiner
Michael Garrison
Miles Gasston
Doreen Gauntlett
Amy Gavin
Derek Gennard
Anne George
Steve Gerrard
John Gibbon
Cleo Gibbons
Geoff Gibbs
Sebastian Gibbs
Angela Gibson
Margaret Gibson
Margaret Gilhooley
Amanda Gill
Shirley Gillbe
Joseph Gilles
Martyn Gilroy
Warren Ginn
Sandra Glazer
Sally Glover
Richard Glynne-Jones
Carolina Godinho
Pauline Godley
Kenneth Goodall
Barrie Goode
Natasha Goodfellow
Trevor Goodfellow
Kay Goodridge
Georgina Goodwin
David Gore
William Gosling
Janet Govey
Pauline Grainger
David Grant
Gloria Gray
Norman Gray
Hannah Grealish
Lawrence Greasley
Kim Greaves
Van Greaves
Debra Green
Katie Green
Margaret Green
Peter Green
Susan Green
Timothy Green
Karina Greenan
Glenice Greenwood
Roberto Gregoratti
Sarah Griffeth
Megan Griffeths
Ray Griffin
John Griffiths
Rhiannon Griffiths
Janet Griffiths
Don Grigg
Martin Grimes
Debbie Grobbelaar
Laszlo Grof
Deana Grondona
Carole Grove
Jill Guest
Roopa Gulati
Sarah Gun
David Gunn
Chris Gunningham
Wei Guo
Kim Hadden
Anthony Hainsworth
Dominic Halfpenny
Danny Hall
Donna Hall
Elle Hall
June Hall
Netta Hallam
Nicola Hamblin
Barbara Hamilton
Jennifer Hammond
Stephen Hammond
David Hancock
Chantal Hannah
Nisha Haque
Jane Harber
Martin Hardman
Richard Hardman
Linda Hardy
Susan Hargreaves
Ginny Harland
Jan Harley
Dean Harnwell
Shona Harper
Heidi Harris
Josh Harris
Vicky Harris
Dean Harrison
Phil Harriss
Anna Harrisson
Ross Harrisson
Chris Harrold
Carol Hart
Madeleine Hart
Micheal Hartles
John Hartley
Roger Harvey
Susan Hassett
G Hatfield-Chetter
Emma Hawkins
James Hayes
Leanne Hayes
Stanley Haywood
Tyler Head
Louise Healey
Samantha Healey
Philip Healing
William J Heard
Alan Heason
Anne Heason
Judith Heffernan
Mandy Henderson
Ben Henry
Lindsey Henry
Juliet Herd
Geoff Herring
Katia Hervy
Michael Hession
Sheila Hesson
Clive Hewgill
Spencer Hewitt
Mark Heydon
Gregory Hicks
Tim Hickson
Karen Higgins
Paul Hill
Caireen Hill
Melanie Hill
Pauline Hill
Sylvia Hilton
Gillian Hinton
Louise Hirst
James Hirth
Andrew Hjort
John Hoare
Guy Hobbs
Martin Hobbs
Christine Hodgkin
Marilyn Hodgson
Mark Hodgson
Philip Hodgson
Margaret Hogarth
Jenny Holden
Peter Holden
Barry Holgate
John Holland
Tim Holland
Mike Holley
Aileen Holloway
Gary Holloway
Simon Holmes
Jacquie Holmes
Colin Honey
David Horder
Julia Hornaday
Andrew Horner
Rosemary Horsnell
Gail Horton
Katy Horton
Tracy Hostler
Lachlan Houghton
Cheryl Houston
Anne Howard
Gavin Howard
Sandra Howarth
Andy Howell
David Howell
Lawrence Hoy
Amy Hudson
Ben Hughes
Lara Hughes
Sue Hughes
Tracy Hughes
Sam Hughes
Steve Hulse
Amanda Humphreys
Martin Hunt
Bev Hurst
Michael Hutchin
Laurence Hybs
Roger Hyslop
Jan Hytch
Claire Iford
Donald Innes
Joanne Irving
Kazi Islam
Leslie Iversen
Simon Iveson
Annabel Jackson
Karen James
Melanie James
Sara James
Robert Jamieson
Chris Jarman
Ellen Jarrett
Alison Jarvis
Ian Jarvis
Sally Jay
Martin Jeeves
Sue Jefferson
Craig Jeffery
Bethan Jenkins
Liz Jenkins
Simon Jenkins
Tony Jenkins
Philippa Jenner
Vanessa Jennifer
Matthew John
Ron Johns
Hayley Johnson
Ian Johnson

Louise Johnson
Pat Johnson
Gillian Jolley
Ailsa Jones
Anne Jones
Bradley Jones
Carla Jones
Chelsea Jones
Chloe Jones
Chris Jones
Corey Jones
Deb Jones
Deborah Jones
Helen Jones
Ian Jones
John Jones
Leeann Jones
Llinos Jones
Matthew Jones
Melanie Jones
Nicholas Jones
Paula Jones
Pauline Jones
Peter Jones
Phillip Jones
Rebecca Jones
Richard Jones
Tom Jones
Maxine Joseph
Michael Joyner
Safiya Juma
Ralf Kabelitz
Linda Kahan
Norman Kaphan
Sanjeev Kapur
Bec Karp
Lyn Keane
Jonathan Keddie-Dixon
Brian Keel
Phil Keen
Jane Keith
Hannah Kelly
Ilse Kelly
Jenny Kennedy
Bradley Kent
Tim Kent
Lynn Kenworthy
Annabel Kershaw
Peter Kettell
David Key
Liz Keys
Colin Keyworth
Sofia Khlynovskaya
Tim Killen
Adam King
Jennifer King
Jo King
Malcolm King
Beckie Kingsnorth
Clare Kingston
Christopher Kirby
Ray Kirby
Barbara Kirkwood
Colin Kirkwood
Anett Kis
Sheila Kissane
Jeremy Knott
Peter Koch
Roger Kohn
Penny Kokkali
Barbara Koscia
Bella Koth
Piers Krause
Natallia Kunets
Kim Lacey
Julie Lahiffe
Ian Laidlaw-Dickson
Brian Lake
Trudy Lamb
Michelle Lambert
Paul Lambert
Sophie Langford

Nikki Langley
Sandra Lanigan
Lesley Larkins
George Lavery
Courtney Lawler
Patrick Lawrence
Chloe Lay
George Lazarus
John Leach
Kathy Leahy
Alan Leaman
Geoffrey Lear
Samantha Ledbury
David Lee
Jane Lee
Rebecca Lee
Rhona Leighton
Richard Leighton
Alexander Leiper
Alison Leister
Martin Le Jeune
Eileen Leonard
Katie Leonard
Simon Levy
David Lewis
Emily Lewis
Peggy Ley
Jay Li
Mervyn Lickfold
David Lipsey
Chanin Lloyd
Chris Lloyd
Fiona Lloyd
Lesley Lloyd
Daniel Lloyds
Adrian Lockyer
Richard Lockyer
Gwyneth Lodge
Lorraine Lonergan
Chris Long
Katie Long
Rhys Long
Jacqui Lord
William James Lorimer
Theresa Louis
Andrew Lozanski
Grant Lucas
Victoria Lundie
Georgie Lydon
Nicki Lygo
David Mabey
Jacob Macaskill
Casey Machen
Susan Macinnes
John Mackay
Peter Mackenzie-Williams
Clare Mackie
Hugh Mackintosh
Jemma Maclean
Naraindra Maharaj
Jan Maish
Katie Malcolm
Karen Manning
Michelle Mansell
Harry Manson
Adrian Markley
Darryl Marks
Richard Marks
Charles Markus
Gavin Markwick
Andrew Marrian
Ian Marris
StJohn Marston
Basil Martin
Graham Martin
Ian Martin
Lily Martin
Mark Martin
Nigel Martin
Valerie Martin
Stuart Martinson
Daisy Massingham

Simon Mather
Jason Mathews
Roy Mathias
Ann Mathie
Michael Matthews
Michelle Matthews
Ray Matthews
Jonathan Maxfield
Claudette Maxted
Gemma Mayer
Emily Mayy
Claudia Mazareanu
William McAllister
David McBrien
Louise McCallum
Ross McClean
Anita McCullough
David McDonald
Kate McDougall
Karen McFarlane
Dale McGleenon
Patrick McGuire
Gordon McInnes
Charlotte McIntyre
James McJames
Elizabeth McKenna
Colin McKenzie
Gordon McKenzie
Tom McKenzie
Patrick McKeown
Vanessa McKeown
Carla McLachlan
Debra McNair
Shelagh McNeil
Neal McTier
Melissa Meadwell
Ron Mealyou
Garry Mearns
Stephen Meester
Laura Melville-Brown
David Melzack
Alexandra Mercieca
Robin Middleton
Leanne Milburn-Turner
Simon Miller
Elaine Millington
Glaucia Minei
Alice Minson
Liz Mitchell
Vivien Mitchell
Simon Mitchell
Joanna Moffatt
Hassan Mohammed
Kevin Molineux
Adam Moliver
John Molyneux
Andy Monk
Victoria Monsellato
Alan Montgomery
Stephen Montgomery
Julie Moon
Arabella Mooney
Samantha Moore
Steve Moore
David Morgan
Liam Morgan
Marc Morgan
Peter Morgan
Richard Morgan
Colin Morison
Doreen Morris
Joshua Morris
Dominic Morrison
Elaine Morrison
Mari Morriss
Tim Morton
Craig Moss
Grace Moss
Tony Mottram
Alan Mould
Annabelle Moult
David Mountford

Liz Mountstephen
Toni Mudge
Lizzie Muir
Stewart Muir
A Muirhead
Jeet Mukerji
Matthew Murfitt
Ed Murphy
Andrew Murray
Lindsay Murray
Sarah Murray
Jillian Musson
Margaret Myszor
Frances Nade
Judith Nash
Barry Natton
Jeremy Naunton
Jennifer Nealon
Jill Neesham
David Neeson
Stefan Negura
Aaron Neill
Elaine Nelson
David Nevett
Philippa Neville
Abi Newell
Alex Newland
Charlotte Newlands
Melanie Newman
Andrea Newton
Andy Newton
Jeffrey Ng
Carol Nichol
Laura Nickoll
Peter Nightingale
Peter Nissen
Alistair Niven
Daniel Nixon
Hilary Nock
Diane Noel
Amelia Norris
Gillian Nowell
Rebecca Nugent
Deborah O'Brien
Linda O'Brien
Rebekah O'Connell
Tony O'Connor
Tim Odgeler
Peggy O'Donoghue
Elaine Ogg
Sharon O'Keefe
Abigail O'Leary
Mike O'Leary
Paula O'Leary
Lorraine Olivehouse
Mark Olivehouse
E Oliveira
Ruth Oliver
Susan Oliver
Brendan O'Neill
Steve Ongeri
Justin Orde
Graeme Osborn
Joe Osborn
Hannah Osborne
Jenna Osborne
Mark Osborne
Richard Osborne
Victoria Osgood
Lisa Osman
Jodie Oswald
Denise Outen
Thomas Overton
Conrad Owen
Janis Owen
Mari Owen
Caroline Owens
Michael Owers
Naomi Ozanne
Amanda Page
Colin Page
Tracey Page

Valerie Page
Darcy Palmer
Gerald Palmer
Ulick Palmer
Chris Pannell
Kelly Parker
Helen Parkins
Martyn Parrott
Heather Parry
Katie Parsonson
Jamie Paterson
Laura Paterson-Groen
Margot Paton
Henry Pavlovich
Charlotte Peacock
Victoria Pearce
Peter Pears
Claire Pearse
Debbie Pearson
Gabriela Pearson
Tony Peel Cross
Pam Peers
Angela Pennington
Robert Penny
Robin Peters
Kathy Peterson
Jacqueline Petherick
Brian Pettifer
Lion Philips
Amy Phillips
David Pickup
Helen Pine
Michael Pini
Louise Pinnington
Pamela Plows
Nathan Plummer
Michael Pointon
Colin Poke
Preslava Polendakova
Louisa Pool
Caroline Poole
Nina Poole
Joanne Pope
Ben Popplewell
Nick Portalski
David Porter
Jan Portlock-Barker
Anna Poston
Russell Poston
Tim Potter
Rebecca Powell
Mike Power
Jeannie Prescott
Lyn Presence
Daphne Price
Francesca Price
Nigel Price
Noel Price
Simon Priestly
Chloe Prigmore
Maura Prior
Julian Procter
Stacey Proctor
Paul Pronini-Fisher
Pauline Protheroe
Sara Protheroe
Paula Purslow
Grace Pyne
Mark Quinney
David Quint
Emily Rabbatts
Arlene Rabin
Clive Radley
Belinda Raitt
Diane Ramsden
Mike Ramsey
Sarah Rankin
Ronald Rankine
Moira Rathbone
Adriano Raucci
Duncan Read
Simon Redwood

Wendy Reed
Alison Reid
Clare Reid
Eileen Reid
Margaret Renucci
Janice Rotto
Claire Reuben
Sonia Reynolds
Beth Rhian
Katherine Riach
Carl Richardos
Alison Richards
Carolyn Richards
Helen Richards
Rebecca Richards
Kevin Richardson
Joanne Riding
Christopher Ridley
Karen Rigby
Carl Riley
Florence Riley
Martin Riley
Sarah Riley
Zach Riley
Arianna Rinaldi
Jonathan Ripley
Steve Rist
James Robbins
Glyn Roberts
Jade Roberts
Marion Roberts
Mark Roberts
Michelle Roberts
Andrea Robinson
Gary Robinson
Geoff Robinson
Hayley Robinson
Lydia Robinson
Nicole Robinson
Polly Robinson
Steve Robson
Richard Rodway
Christopher Rogers
Katie Rogers
Paul Rogers
Elisabeth Rohmer
Elton Rohrer
Peter Romaniuk
Emma Rose
Kim Rose
Donald Ross
Kathryn Ross
Colin Roth
Fliss Rothery
Maggie Routledge
Diana Rowlands
Michael Rowley
Rachel Rowley
Simon Rowntree
Bethany Rowsel
Angela Royle
John Rozier
Clare Rucastle
Emma Rudman
Betty Rumney
Willie Runte
Jonathan Rushworth
Barry Russell
Jeremy Russell
Margaret Russell
Nicola Rust
Mark Rutherford
Helen Rutherford-Gregory
William Rutter
Lucy Rycroft
Sue Saines
Robin Sainty
Francine Salles
Patricia Salmon
Christopher Salter
Keith Salway

Oliver Samuel
Richard Sands
Leila Sangar
Karen Sargant
Philip Saunders
Isikia Savua
Eleanor Sawbridge Burton
Fyrne Sawyer
Ges Sawyer
Laura Sayles
David Scally
David Scarrett
Simon Scarrott
Gillan Schlangen
Theo Schofield
Pete Schreiber
Kim Scott
Sean Scott
Tom Scott
Hugh Scorgie
Alun Scourfield
Sue Scrivener
Gaynor Scrivenger
Rosalind Seal-Coon
Elizabeth Searls
Lisa Seddon
Paula Seddon
David Sefton
Jackie Sellars
Robert Selley
Andrew Selmer
Geoffrey Senior
Gary Shacklady
Jennifer Shail
Joanne Shannon
Margaret Shannon
Anne Sharp
Jennifer Sharp
Darren Shaw
Robert Shaw
Janet Sheridan
Kathryn Shipman
Laura Shipton
Naj Shipu
Tom Shirm
Gilbert Short
Daioni Shuter
Josh Siddle
Kerry Sidney
Lin Silcock
Jennifer Sime
Alison Simmons
Eva Simmons
Kathy Simmons
Margaret Simmons
David Simpkin
Olivia Singh
Vincenzo Siragusa
Jenny Slater
Nicholas Slater
Isabelle Slee
Gary Sloan
Lorna Sloan
Michelle Sloan
Vicki Sloan
Gillian Smale
Kate Smart
Amanda Smith
Brian Smith
Claire Smith
Deborah Smith
David Smith
Edward Smith
Jill Smith
John Smith
Keith Smith
Louise Smith
Marie Smith
Oliver Smith
Pat Smith
Trev Smith
Lisa Smiths

Caroline Snape
Darius Sobczynski
Hayley Soper
Hilary Southgate
Antony Spear
John Speller
Kimberley Spence
Catherine Spencer
Natalie Spencer
Alison Spencer Condon
Hannah Springham
Beth Squires
Pamela Stanier
Denis Stanley
Tiffany Starkey
Julie Steele
Carrie-Ann Stein
Frances Stephens
Anne Stephenson
Joanna Steven
Danielle Stevens
Lloyd Stevens
Matthew Stevens
AJ Stewart
Blair Stewart
Chris Stinchcombe
Mark Stinchcombe
Kate Stone
Jennifer Stratford
Melissa Strevens
Victor Strum
Naomi Stuart-Smith
Tracy Stubbs
Emma Sturgess
Meagan Sturgess
Sathees Sun
Emma Sundvall
Charlie Sutton
Susan Sutton
Peter Swift
Ridhi Tank
Tracy Tann
Ian Tanner
Dan Tapper
Amanda Tarrant
Gareth Tartt
Andreas Tatt
George Taylor
Gerald Taylor
Jean Taylor
Joanna Taylor
Lucy Taylor
Mark Taylor
Michelle Taylor
Nicola Taylor
Peter Taylor
Serena Taylor
Andy Taylor
Caroline Taylor
Joshua Taylor
Chris Terry
Nigel Theorchard
Phoebe Thirlwall
John Thomas
Kara Thomas
Ben Thompson
Gail Thompson
Nicholas Thompson
Robert Thompson
Simon Thompson
Tina Thompson
Nicola Thompson
David Thomson
Sophie Thornley
Adam Thorpe
Georgina Thorpe
Kirsty Thos
Emma Threadgold
Robert Thurlow
Janet Tillotson
Shella Tilston
Bernadette Tingle

Lorraine Tingle
Anne Toomer
Ian Townsend
Jo Townsend
John Townsend
Susan Treloar
Julia Trinder
Samantha Trinder
Maddie Trobridge
Anthony Tropeano
Paul Trott
Charlotte Tuffim
Alistair Turk
Antony Turner
Derek Turner
Karen Turner
Tinna Turner
Rob Turney
Jill Turton
Andrew Turvil
Rachael Tutton
Andrew Tye
Karen Tyler
Ian Tysh
Nicholas Underwood
Anita Unsworth
Robert Upton
Ross Urquhart
Louise Van Dyke
Clare Vardon
Jonathan Varey
David Varley
Deborah Velay
Mary Vernon
Michael Wace
Anna Wadolowska
Jean Wagstaff
Sarah Wales
Adrian Walker
Dominique Walker
Jenny Walker
Timothy Walker
Richard Wall
Sarah Wallace
Jen Walmsley
Adrian Walsh
Lee Walsh
Susan Walsh
Robert Walt
Stuart Walton
Gary Wannan
Cliff Want
Constance Ward
Robert Wardle
Lynda Warne
Emily Warner
Ronnie Warner
Sarah Warner
Christopher Warren
Nicola Wates
Anne Watkin
Ian Watkins
Angharad Watson
Georgina Watt
Sarah Watt
Lloyd Watts
Gayle Waywell
Carole Weatherspoom
Susan Weaver
Annie Webb
Michael Webber
Mandy Webster
Jeanette Wedge
Gill Weeks
Maria Welch
Keith Wells
Lyndsey Wells
Pauline West
Sarah Westbrooke
Christian Western
Stacey Whalling
Debbie White

Jenny White
Roger White
Tracy White
Jane Whiteman-Turl
Karen Whitfield
Richard Whitley
Stephanie Whitlow
Mark Whittington
Lindsay Whittle
Sharon Whittle
Kate Wicks
Carl Wiggin
Emma Wilcox
Harriet Wilcox
Rosie Wild
Martin Wilkes
David Wilkie
Carla Wilkinson
Nadine Wilkinson
Alan Williams
Alison Williams
Anthony Williams
Carys Williams
Darren Williams
Helen Williams
Natalie Williams
Owain Williams
Roy Williams
Sarah Williams
Chris Williamson
Debbie Williamson
Emily Williamson
Lucy Williamson
April Willmott
Elizabeth Wilsey
Jane Wilson
Jean Wilson
Lin Wilson
Margaret Wilson
Paul Wilson
Peter Wilson
Ralph Wilson
Denise Winks
Gabriel Winn
Dawn Wise
Rob Wise
Brian Witting
Milena Wobbe
Diana Woo
Gillian Wood
Stephen Wood
Clare Woodall
Kirstie Woodcock
Dave Woodruff
Linda Woods
Rachel Woodward
Ruth Woodward
Selina Woodward
Jack Woolgar
Ian Woolverton
Nicola Wordsworth
Robert Worgan
Amanda Wragg
Jane Wren
Lottie Wride
Graham Wright
Juliett Wright
Kelly Wright
Natasha Wright
Tony Wright
Chris Wyatts
David Wyllie
James Wyse
Francis Yang
Cathy Yates
Kevin Yates
Lynne Yates
Chris Young
Tanya Young
Emma Yufera
Klaudia Zaluszniewska
Carmelo Zappulla

Longest serving

The Good Food Guide was founded in 1951. The following restaurants have appeared consistently since their first entry in the guide.

The Connaught, London, 66 years
Gravetye Manor, West Sussex, 62 years
Porth Tocyn Hotel, Gwynedd, 62 years
Le Gavroche, London, 49 years
Ubiquitous Chip, Glasgow, 47 years
Plumber Manor, Dorset, 46 years
The Druidstone, Pembrokeshire, 46 years
The Waterside Inn, Berkshire, 46 years
Airds Hotel, Argyll & Bute, 43 years
Farlam Hall, Cumbria, 42 years
Hambleton Hall, Rutland, 40 years
The Seafood Restaurant, Padstow, Cornwall, 38 years
The Sir Charles Napier, Oxfordshire, 38 years
Little Barwick House, Somerset, 37 years
Paris House, Bedfordshire, 36 years
Ostlers Close, Fife, 36 years
The Angel Inn, Hetton, 35 years
Brilliant, London, 34 years
Clarke's, London, 34 years
Le Manoir aux Quat'Saisons, Oxfordshire, 34 years
Blostin's, Somerset, 33 years
Read's, Kent, 33 years
The Castle at Taunton, Somerset, 33 years
The Three Chimneys, Isle of Skye, 33 years
Tyddyn Llan, Llandrillo, 33 years
Wilton's, London, 33 years
Launceston Place, London, 33 years
Northcote, Lancashire, 32 years
The Lime Tree, Manchester, 32 years
The Old Vicarage, Ridgeway, 31 years
Cherwell Boathouse, Oxford, 31 years
Le Champignon Sauvage, Glos, 30 years
Quince & Medlar, Cumbria, 30 years
Harry's Place, Lincolnshire, 29 years
Bibendum, London, 29 years
Ynyshir, Powys, 29 years
Crannog, Fort William, 29 years
The Chester Grosvenor, Cheshire, 29 years
Eslington Villa, Tyne & Wear, 28 years
Melton's, York, 28 years
Horn of Plenty, Devon, 28 years
Castle Cottage, Gwynedd, 27 years
Kilcamb Lodge, Highlands, 26 years

History of the guide

The Good Food Guide was first compiled by Raymond Postgate in 1951. Appalled by the British post-war dining experience, Postgate formed The Good Food Club, recruiting an army of volunteers to inspect restaurants anonymously and report back. His aim was simple: 'to raise the standard of cooking in Britain' and 'to do ourselves all a bit of good by making our holidays, travels and evenings-out in due course more enjoyable'. Following the success of The Good Food Club, the volunteers' reports were compiled and *The Good Food Guide* was published.

Although much has changed since the very first edition of *The Good Food Guide*, including the addition of expert restaurant inspectors, the ethos of the original book remains. *The Good Food Guide* is about empowering diners, helping them to find the very best places to eat and encouraging restaurants to offer the best possible food, service and experience.

THE GOOD
FOOD GUIDE
2019
£5 VOUCHER

THE GOOD
FOOD GUIDE
2019
£5 VOUCHER

THE GOOD
FOOD GUIDE
2019
£5 VOUCHER

THE GOOD
FOOD GUIDE
2019
£5 VOUCHER

THE GOOD
FOOD GUIDE
2019
£5 VOUCHER

THE GOOD
FOOD GUIDE
2019
£5 VOUCHER

THE GOOD
FOOD GUIDE
2019
£5 VOUCHER

THE GOOD
FOOD GUIDE
2019
£5 VOUCHER

THE GOOD
FOOD GUIDE
2019
£5 VOUCHER

THE GOOD
FOOD GUIDE
2019
£5 VOUCHER

WAITROSE
& PARTNERS

AND CONDITIONS

ucher can only be used in participating restaurants, nted by the £5 OFF symbol. It is redeemable against a ooked meal for a minimum of two people, provided customer highlights the intention to use the voucher ne time of booking. Only one voucher may be used per ole booked. This voucher may not be used in conjunction ith any other scheme.

Offer valid from 01/09/2018 – 01/09/2019
For additional terms and conditions, see below.

TERMS AND CONDITIONS

This voucher can only be used in participating restaurants, highlighted by the £5 OFF symbol. It is redeemable against a pre-booked meal for a minimum of two people, provided the customer highlights the intention to use the voucher at the time of booking. Only one voucher may be used per table booked. This voucher may not be used in conjunction with any other scheme.

Offer valid from 01/09/2018 – 01/09/2019
For additional terms and conditions, see below.

TERMS AND CONDITIONS

This voucher can only be used in participating restaurants, highlighted by the £5 OFF symbol. It is redeemable against a pre-booked meal for a minimum of two people, provided the customer highlights the intention to use the voucher at the time of booking. Only one voucher may be used per table booked. This voucher may not be used in conjunction with any other scheme.

Offer valid from 01/09/2018 – 01/09/2019
For additional terms and conditions, see below.

TERMS AND CONDITIONS

This voucher can only be used in participating restaurants, highlighted by the £5 OFF symbol. It is redeemable against a pre-booked meal for a minimum of two people, provided the customer highlights the intention to use the voucher at the time of booking. Only one voucher may be used per table booked. This voucher may not be used in conjunction with any other scheme.

Offer valid from 01/09/2018 – 01/09/2019
For additional terms and conditions, see below.

TERMS AND CONDITIONS

This voucher can only be used in participating restaurants, highlighted by the £5 OFF symbol. It is redeemable against a pre-booked meal for a minimum of two people, provided the customer highlights the intention to use the voucher at the time of booking. Only one voucher may be used per table booked. This voucher may not be used in conjunction with any other scheme.

Offer valid from 01/09/2018 – 01/09/2019
For additional terms and conditions, see below.

TERMS AND CONDITIONS

This voucher can only be used in participating restaurants, highlighted by the £5 OFF symbol. It is redeemable against a pre-booked meal for a minimum of two people, provided the customer highlights the intention to use the voucher at the time of booking. Only one voucher may be used per table booked. This voucher may not be used in conjunction with any other scheme.

Offer valid from 01/09/2018 – 01/09/2019
For additional terms and conditions, see below.

TERMS AND CONDITIONS

This voucher can only be used in participating restaurants, highlighted by the £5 OFF symbol. It is redeemable against a pre-booked meal for a minimum of two people, provided the customer highlights the intention to use the voucher at the time of booking. Only one voucher may be used per table booked. This voucher may not be used in conjunction with any other scheme.

Offer valid from 01/09/2018 – 01/09/2019
For additional terms and conditions, see below.

TERMS AND CONDITIONS

This voucher can only be used in participating restaurants, highlighted by the £5 OFF symbol. It is redeemable against a pre-booked meal for a minimum of two people, provided the customer highlights the intention to use the voucher at the time of booking. Only one voucher may be used per table booked. This voucher may not be used in conjunction with any other scheme.

Offer valid from 01/09/2018 – 01/09/2019
For additional terms and conditions, see below.

TERMS AND CONDITIONS

This voucher can only be used in participating restaurants, highlighted by the £5 OFF symbol. It is redeemable against a pre-booked meal for a minimum of two people, provided the customer highlights the intention to use the voucher at the time of booking. Only one voucher may be used per table booked. This voucher may not be used in conjunction with any other scheme.

Offer valid from 01/09/2018 – 01/09/2019
For additional terms and conditions, see below.

TERMS AND CONDITIONS

This voucher can only be used in participating restaurants, highlighted by the £5 OFF symbol. It is redeemable against a pre-booked meal for a minimum of two people, provided the customer highlights the intention to use the voucher at the time of booking. Only one voucher may be used per table booked. This voucher may not be used in conjunction with any other scheme.

Offer valid from 01/09/2018 – 01/09/2019
For additional terms and conditions, see below.

Vouchers are valid from 01/09/2018 – 01/09/2019. Only one £5 voucher can be used per table booked (for a minimum of 2 people). No photocopies or any other kind of reproduction of vouchers will be accepted. Some participating establishments may exclude certain times, days or menus from the scheme so long as they a) advise customers of the restrictions at the time of booking and b) accept the vouchers at a minimum of 70% of sessions when the restaurant is open. Please note that the number of participating restaurants may vary from time to time.